T0226988

30ᵀᴴ EUROPEAN SYMPOSIUM ON COMPUTER AIDED PROCESS ENGINEERING

PART A

30TH EUROPEAN SYMPOSIUM ON COMPUTER AIDED PROCESS ENGINEERING

PART A

Edited by

Sauro Pierucci
AIDIC Servizi s.r.l.,
Milano, Italy,
sauro.pierucci@polimi.it

Flavio Manenti
SuPER Team, Sustainable Process Engineering Research
Dipartimento di Chimica, Materiali e Ingegneria Chimica,
Politecnico di Milano, Milano, Italy,
flavio.manenti@polimi.it

Giulia Luisa Bozzano
SuPER Team, Sustainable Process Engineering Research
Dipartimento di Chimica, Materiali e Ingegneria Chimica,
Politecnico di Milano, Milano, Italy,
giulia.bozzano@polimi.it

Davide Manca
PSE-Lab - Process Systems Engineering Laboratory,
Dipartimento di Chimica, Materiali e Ingegneria Chimica,
Politecnico di Milano, Italy,
davide.manca@polimi.it

ELSEVIER

Amsterdam – Boston – Heidelberg – London – New York – Oxford
Paris – San Diego – San Francisco – Singapore – Sydney – Tokyo

Elsevier
Radarweg 29, PO Box 211, 1000 AE Amsterdam, Netherlands
The Boulevard, Langford Lane, Kidlington, Oxford OX5 1GB, UK
50 Hampshire Street, 5th Floor, Cambridge, MA 02139, USA

Notices
Knowledge and best practice in this field are constantly changing. As new research and experience
broaden our understanding, changes in research methods, professional practices, or medical treatment
may become necessary.

Practitioners and researchers must always rely on their own experience and knowledge in evaluating
and using any information, methods, compounds, or experiments described herein. In using such
information or methods they should be mindful of their own safety and the safety of others, including
parties for whom they have a professional responsibility.

To the fullest extent of the law, neither the Publisher nor the authors, contributors, or editors, assume
any liability for any injury and/or damage to persons or property as a matter of products liability,
negligence or otherwise, or from any use or operation of any methods, products, instructions, or ideas
contained in the material herein.

British Library Cataloguing in Publication Data
A catalogue record for this book is available from the British Library

Library of Congress Cataloging-in-Publication Data
A catalog record for this book is available from the Library of Congress

ISBN (Part A): 978-0-12-823511-9
ISBN (Set) :   978-0-12-823377-1
ISSN: 1570-7946

For information on all Elsevier publications visit our
website at https://www.elsevier.com/

Working together
to grow libraries in
developing countries

www.elsevier.com • www.bookaid.org

Publisher: Susan Dennis
Acquisition Editor: Kostas Marinakis
Editorial Project Manager: Lena Sparks
Production Project Manager: Paul Prasad Chandramohan
Designer: Greg Harris

Typeset by SPi Global, India

Contents

Preface

This volume of the Computer-Aided Chemical Engineering series puts together a selection of the contributions presented at the 30th European Symposium on Computer-Aided Process Engineering (ESCAPE), originally scheduled in Milano, Italy, from May 24th to 27th, 2020. Due to Covid-19 contingency, ESCAPE30 has been presented as Virtual Symposium from August 30th to September 2nd, 2020.

This 30th event of the ESCAPE series is a continuation of the conferences under the auspices of the CAPE Working Party of the European Federation of Chemical Engineering (EFCE).

The conference has been organized since 1992, starting with two meetings in 1992 in Denmark and France, and since then having one event annually. Hosting countries to the conference have been Austria (1993, 2018), Ireland (1994), Slovenia (1995, 2016), Greece (1996, 2011), Norway (1997), Belgium (1998), Hungary (1999, 2014), Italy (2000, 2010), Denmark (1992, 2001, 2015), The Netherlands (2002, 2019), Finland (2003, 2013), Portugal (2004), Spain (2005, 2017), Germany (2006), Romania (2007), France (1992, 2008), Poland (2009), and the United Kingdom (2012).

The themes of ESCAPE-30 have been selected after a comprehensive discussion with the CAPE Working Party members and the scientific community. The particular topics within these overarching themes have been formulated to allow researchers from CAPE-related sciences to present their results and exchange valuable knowledge and experience. The themes and topics include:

Theme 1: Modelling and Simulation
Theme Coordinators: Ana Barbosa-Povoa (Spain), David Bogle (UK)
New modelling approaches, Metamodeling, Multi-scale New industrial applications

Theme 2: Synthesis and Design
Theme Coordinators: Antonio Espuna (Spain), Zdravko Kravanja (Slovenia)
Process/Supply chain, Synthesis and design, Advanced materials, Products design, Process intensification, Micro and nano applications. Design for reliability and safety

Theme 3: Process control and operations
Theme Coordinators: Sebastian Engell (Germany), Sigurd Skogestad (Sweden)
Scheduling, operability, Flexibility and optimization under uncertainty, Supply-chains optimization and logistics, Off- and on-line control, Real-time optimization, Nonlinear model predictive control

Theme 4: CAPE in Sustainable Energy Applications
Theme Coordinators: Fabrizio Bezzo (Italy), Francois Marechal (Switzerland)
Heat and power integration, Waste-to-energy applications, Renewable resources in total-site integration, Integration of energy sources & sinks, Reliable dynamic supply & demand

Theme 5: Bioresources, Bioprocesses and Biomedical Systems
Theme Coordinators: Antonis Kokossis (Greece), Stefan Radl (Austria)
Biorefineries, Biomolecular and genetic engineering, Bioreactors applications

Theme 6: Digitalization
Theme Coordinators: Filip Logist (Belgium), Flavio Manenti (Italy)
Cloud application, Digitalization of chemical processes, Industry 4.0

Theme 7: Concepts, Methods and Tools
Theme Coordinators: Xavier Joulia (France), Heinz A. Preisig (Norway)
Advances in numerical methods, Global mixed-integer optimization, Multiobjective optimization, Decision making under uncertainty and risk management, Big data management, methods and tools

Theme 8: Education in CAPE and Knowledge Transfer
   Theme Coordinators: Patrizia Perego (Italy), Eric Shaer (France)
   Best practices in academia, Continued training in a changing professional practice, Effective selling of high quality CAPE solutions to industry, Knowledge transfer hurdles, Effective exploitation of CAPE tools

ESCAPE-30 attracted 572 contributions from five continents (Europe, Americas, Africa, Asia and Australia). The papers have been reviewed and 345 selected for publication by the International Scientific Committee together with the help of 16 Theme Coordinators. We are deeply thankful for timely and careful reviews by these Scientists, as well as their invaluable help in suggesting lecture speakers..

As Editors of this special volume, we hope that the contributions in this edition of Computer Aided Process Engineering are excellent illustrations of the current state of the art in their respective field.

Sauro Pierucci
AIDIC Servizi srl, Milano

Flavio Manenti
Politecnico di Milano

Giulia Bozzano
Politecnico di Milano

Davide Manca
Politecnico di Milano

Organizing & Scientific Committee

Local National Organizers

Chairboard: Giorgio VERONESI (Techint, AIDIC)
Giulia BOZZANO (Politecnico di Milano)
Davide MANCA (Politecnico di Milano)
Members: Raffaella DAMERIO (AIDIC Accounting)
Manuela LICCIARDELLO (AIDIC Events)
Sauro PIERUCCI (AIDIC Servizi srl)
Gaia TORNONE (AIDIC Events)

International Scientific Committee

Chairboard

Sauro Pierucci (Past CAPE Chairman), AIDIC, Italy
David Bogle (EFCE Sc. Vice-President), University College London, United Kingdom
Flavio Manenti (CAPE Chairman), Politecnico di Milano, Italy

Members

Cristhian P. Almeida-Rivera, OPCW, The Netherlands
Olga Arsenyeva, Kharkov Polytechnical Inst., Ukraine
Norbert Asprion, BASF SE, Germany
Roberto Baratti, University of Cagliari, Italy
Ana Paula Barbosa Povoa, Instituto Superior Tecnico, Portugal
Andre Bardow, RWTH Aachen University, Germany
Fabrizio Bezzo, University of Padua, Italy
Lorenz Biegler, Carnegie Mellon University, USA
Giulia Bozzano (CAPE Secretary), Politecnico di Milano, Italy
Xi Chen, Zhejiang University, China
Selen Cremaschi, Auburn University, USA
Vasile Mircea Cristea, Babes-Bolyai University, Romania
Giorgia De Guido, Politecnico di Milano, Italy
Mario Eden, Auburn University, USA
Sebastian Engell, TU Dortmund, Germany
Antonio Espuna, Universitat Politecnica de Catalunya, Spain
Michael Fairweather, University of Leeds, United Kingdom
Miroslav Fikar, Slovak University of Technolog, Slovakia
Rubens Maciel Filho, Unicamp University, Brazil
Ferenc Friedler (EFCE Charity Trustee), Pazmany Peter Catholic University, Hungary
Rafiqul Gani (Past EFCE President), PSE for SPEED, Denmark
Ignacio Grossmann, Carnegie Mellon University, USA
Rene' Hofmann, TU Wien, Austria
Xavier Joulia, University of Toulouse, France
Petro Kapustenko, National Technical University, Ukraine
Anton Kiss, University of Manchester, United Kingdom
Antonis Kokossis, National Technical University of Athens, Greece
Emilia Kondili, University of West Attica, Greece
Andrzej Kraslawski (Past CAPE Chairman), Lappeenranta University of Technology, Finland

Editor Biography

PIERUCCI SAURO

Sauro Pierucci was Full Professor in Chemical Engineering at CMIC Politecnico di Milano, where he graduated in Chemical Engineering in 1969. He retired in 2016.

He was responsible of the course "Chemical Plant" in the faculty of Chemical Engineering at Politecnico di Milano.

His research interests focused on Process System Engineering, Modelling, Online Control and Optimisation of chemical plants (experiences c/o Oxychem (Houston), PolimeriEuropa (France), Erg (Priolo)).
He was Vice President of AIDIC (Italian Association of Chemical Engineering) until 2007 and today covers the office of member of the executive board.
He is responsible of the events organized by AIDIC Servizi srl, held by AIDIC.

He was member of EFCE (European Federation of Chemical Engineering) executive board until 2010.
He has been editor of several international issues as: "Computer Aided Chemical Engineering", Vol. 8, Elsevier Science, Amsterdam, 2000; "Computers & Chemical Engineering", Vol. 25, Issue 4-6, Pergamon.2010.
He is editor in chief of Chemical Engineering Transactions Journal, published by AIDIC.
He is author of more than 200 scientific publications.
He was awarded by "the Dieter Behrens Medal" from EFCE, in 2017
Today is President of AIDIC Servizi Srl, a limited company owned by AIDIC.

Sauro Pierucci, Flavio Manenti, Giulia Bozzano, Davide Manca (Eds.)
Proceedings of the 30th European Symposium on Computer Aided Process Engineering
(ESCAPE30), May 24-27, 2020, Milano, Italy. © 2020 Elsevier B.V. All rights reserved.
http://dx.doi.org/10.1016/B978-0-12-823377-1.50001-X

Computer-aided Semi-empirical Model of Interphase Mass and Enthalpy Transfer in a Packed Column Distillation Process

Goro Nishimura,[a*] Kunio Kataoka,[a] Hideo Noda,[a] Naoto Ohmura[b]

[a]*Kansai Chemical Engineering Co., Ltd, Minami-nanamatsu-cho, Amagasaki, 660-0053, Japan*
[b]*Dept. Of Chemical Science and Engineering, Kobe University, Rokkodai-cho, Nada, Kobe, 657-8501, Japan*
Nishimura@kce.co.jp

Abstract

The objective of this study is to model the transport phenomena in packed column distillation with the aid of experiment and computer-aided process simulation. The main concept is in that local distillation efficiency *HETP* is considered as the height of control volume for shell balance of mass and enthalpy, so that it becomes possible to bridge between the ideal and real processes. Distillation experiment was conducted under the total-reflux condition. Determination of local *HETP*s was performed by comparing the vertical temperature distribution experimentally observed with the stage-by-stage temperature distribution calculated by computer process simulation. In a manner similar to the analogy analysis of a single-phase boundary layer flow over a flat plate, a semi-empirical model of local similarity between simultaneous interphase mass and enthalpy transfer was successfully built by experiment collaborating with a computer-aided process simulation.

Keywords: mass and enthalpy transfer model, distillation, packed column, similarity

1. Introduction

A packed column distillation proceeds with non-isothermal and counter-diffusional interphase mass transfer accompanied with phase transformation. This complicated mechanism of mass and enthalpy transfer makes not only theoretical but also experimental approaches difficult. Except for the mass transfer model by Bravo *et al.* (1985), there are few investigations analyzing from a viewpoint of transport phenomena. Especially there is no investigation dealing with local variation of mass and enthalpy transfer in packed column distillation. This research deals with a semi-empirical model by making up the mutual defects between the experiment in a real column and the theoretical process simulation based on the equilibrium stage model.

2. Modeling Concept --- Shell Balance and Definition

The concept of modeling is in how to combine the continuous distillation behavior observed in a real packed column with the theoretical stage-by-stage distillation behavior calculated by an equilibrium-stage model in an ideal trayed column. As shown in Figure 1, a cylindrical control volume for shell balance is defined in a packed column. A local *HETP* (Height Equivalent to a Theoretical Plate) obtained at *j*th theoretical stage of process simulation is considered as the *j*th shell height h_{etp} (*m*) of the real

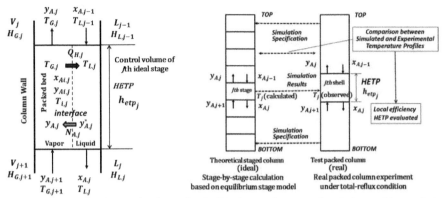

Figure 1 Definition of control volume for shell balance of mass and enthalpy and interrelation of ideal-state stage-by-stage data by computer process simulation with actual experimental data obtained in a real packed column.

differential contacting column. This implies that local distillation efficiency is taken into account in modeling of the real column distillation.

The volumetric mass transfer coefficients $k_{yA}a$, $k_{xA}a$, $K_{yA}a$ $(kmol/m^3s)$ are defined by the molar-flux N_A in the jth control volume (y_A, x_A,: vapor- and liquid-phase mole fractions, subscript A: component A, i: interface, $l.m.$: logarithmic mean):

$$N_{Aj} = V_j y_{Aj} - V_{j+1} y_{Aj\ 1} = \left(k_{yA}a\right)_j \left(y_{Aj,i} - y_{Aj}\right) h_{etp,j}$$
$$= \left(k_{xA}a\right)_j \left(x_{Aj} - x_{Aj,i}\right) h_{etp,j} = \left(K_{yA}a\right)_j \left(y_A^* - y_A\right)_{l.m.} h_{etp,j} \tag{1}$$

Here y_A^* is the bulk concentration of the liquid phase expressed with the units of the gas-phase concentration. Similarly the volumetric enthalpy transfer coefficients $h_G a$, $h_L a$, Ua (W/m^3K) are defined by the enthalpy-flux Q_H equation (T_G, T_L :vapor- and liquid-phase temperature (K), H_G, H_L : enthalpy $(J/kmol)$, V, L : superficial molar velocity $(kmol/m^2s)$, subscript G, L: vapor- and liquid-phase)

$$Q_{Hj} = V_{j\ 1} H_{Gj+1} - V_j H_{Gj} = \left(h_G a\right)_j \left(T_{Gj} - T_{ij}\right) h_{etp,j}$$
$$= \left(h_L a\right)_j \left(T_{ij} - T_{Lj}\right) h_{etp,j} = \left(U\ a\right)\left(T_G - T_L\right)_{l.m.} h_{etp\ j} \tag{2}$$

The interrelation between the ideal-state process simulation and the real column experiment is also shown in Fig.1, where jth stage of process simulation corresponds to the jth shell of a real column.

3. Process Simulation

A convenient process simulator package (PRO/II by Invensys.) serves as a McCabe-Thiele stage-by-stage calculation tool with an assumption of ideal equilibrium stage. The stage-by-stage process simulation is conducted by the following equations:

(Mass and enthalpy balance set up around jth stage under total-reflux distillation)

$$M_{jk} = V_j y_{j,k} + L_j x_{j,k} - V_{j+1} y_{j+1,k} - L_{j-1} x_{j-1,k} = 0 \tag{3}$$

$$E_j = V_j H_{Gj} + L_j H_{Lj} - V_{j+1} H_{Gj+1} - L_{j-1} H_{Lj-1} = 0 \tag{4}$$

(Mass balance and cooling duty of overhead condenser)

$$M_{1k} = L_1 x_{1,k} - V_2 y_{2,k} = 0 \tag{5}$$

$$Q_1 = L_1 H_1 - V_2 H_{G2} = 0 \tag{6}$$

(Mass balance and heating duty of bottom reboiler)

$$M_{Nk} = V_{Nk} y_{N,k} - L_{N-1} x_{N-1,k} = 0 \tag{7}$$

$$Q_N = V_N H_{GN} - L_{N-1} H_{LN} = 0 \tag{8}$$

(Equilibrium coefficient and vapor-liquid equilibrium condition)

$$K_{jk} = p_{k,sat}\left(T_j\right)/P \tag{9}$$

$$S_{j,k} = K_{j,k} x_{j,k} - y_{j,k} = 0 \tag{10}$$

(Mole fraction requirement)

$$_{xj} = \sum_{k=1}^{m} x_{j,k} - 1 = 0 \tag{11}$$

$$_{yj} = \sum_{k=1}^{m} y_{j,k} - 1 = 0 \tag{12}$$

where the NRTL model is used to evaluate activity coefficients and physical properties of vapor and liquid of a binary mixture.

4. Experiment

4.1. Experimental apparatus and operating condition

Figure 2 shows an experimental packed column equipped with three structured packing beds stacked up in series. Those top, central and bottom beds have 1.90 m, 1.90 m, and 1.52 m in height, respectively. The inside diameter of the column is $D_T = 0.1532$ m.

The wire-mesh corrugated structured packing employed has the hydraulic equivalent diameter $d_{eq} = 0.018$ m and the specific surface area $a_p = 490$ m^2/m. In each empty space between the respective packing beds, a funnel-type liquid collector and a channel-type liquid distributor are installed in order to avoid maldistribution of liquid stream. Usually the *HETP* test (Lockett 1998) for practical design of packed columns is conducted under a total-reflux condition.

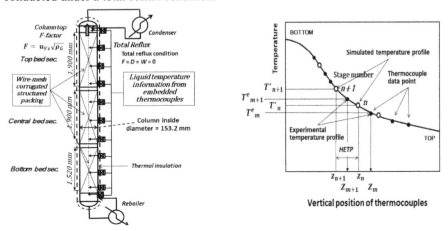

Figure 2 Structured packing column for total-reflux distillation experiment and graphic method for determining local *HETP*s.

In this study, the only total-reflux distillation experiment was conducted to obtain necessary information of performance parameters for a real packed column, which can be used for the specification of computer process simulation. In order to observe a vertical distribution of liquid temperature, 12 sheathed thermocouples were embedded on the centerline of the respective packed beds.

The F-factor $F = u_{Vs}\rho_G^{0.5}$ $(m/s)(kg/m^3)^{0.5}$ based on the superficial vapor velocity u_{Vs} (m/s) is defined at the column top as the control parameter of distillation experiment. Two kinds of binary solutions were tested: methanol-ethanol and methanol-n-butanol. However owing to the page limitation, the only experimental result of methanol-ethanol binary system is reported in this article since the methanol-n-butanol system shows almost the similar tendency of mass and enthalpy transfer. The purpose of this study is to analyze local transfer of mass and enthalpy for future process intensification by a semi-empirical model built with the mutual aid of the computer-aided process simulation and the total-reflux distillation experiment.

4.2. Determination of local HETPs

By using the experimental data and condition as the specification of process simulation, the stage-by-stage process simulation based on equilibrium-stage model was performed with a commercial simulator package (`PRO/II by Invensys Systems, Inc.). Assuming the total number of theoretical stages, the process simulation was conducted by a trial-and-error method to obtain a proper required number of theoretical stages until the calculated data became equal to the experimental data within an error limit.

As shown in Fig.2 (right), comparing the calculated liquid temperature T_n^{th} obtained at theoretical stage n with the experimental liquid temperature T_m^{ex} measured by the thermocouple embedded at a vertical position Z_m, a local value of *HETP* can be determined by the following equation:

$$HETP = h_{etp,j} = \frac{T_n^{th} - T_{n+1}^{th}}{T_m^{ex} - T_{m+1}^{ex}} \times \left(Z_m - Z_{m+1} \right) \tag{13}$$

4.3. Evaluation of local volumetric coefficient of mass and enthalpy transfer

The following simultaneous equation is obtained applying a mass transfer resistance equation based on two-film theory at arbitrary two positions j and $j+n$, where $1/k_{yA}a$ and $1/k_{xA}a$ are two unknowns to be solved.

$$\frac{1}{\left(K_{yA}a \right)_j} = \frac{1}{k_{yA}a} + \frac{m_j}{k_{xA}a} \tag{14}$$

$$\frac{1}{\left(K_{yA}a \right)_{j+n}} = \frac{1}{k_{yA}a} + \frac{m_{j+n}}{k_{xA}a} \tag{15}$$

where m is local slope of equilibrium curve and $K_{yA}a$ is local overall volumetric mass transfer coefficient experimentally obtained. Therefore the $k_{yA}a$, $k_{xA}a$ can be obtained as an approximate solution averaged between j and $j+n$. Figure 3 shows local distribution of the molar flux and volumetric mass transfer coefficients $k_{yA}a$, $k_{xA}a$. plotted against the vertical height of packing sections (L_B: total height of packing section). The right side figure suggests the possibility of similarity between the vapor bulk flow in a packed column and the boundary layer flow over a flat plate.

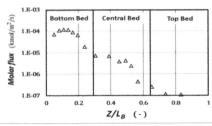 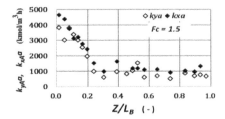

Figure 3 Vertical variation of molar-flux and vapor- and liquid-phase mass transfer coefficients when the column-top F-factor is 1.5 for methanol-ethanol system.

An unavoidable problem has arisen that in the column-top and column-bottom regions, the above elementary equations cannot become consistent to each other owing to almost linear variation of equilibrium curve. In those regions, the film coefficients $k_{yA}a$, $k_{xA}a$ were determined from the slope of the Tie-line $-k_{xA}/k_{yA}$ by assuming that the Tie-line at each stage has a perpendicular intersection with the equilibrium curve.

5. Experimental Results and Similarity Analysis

5.1. Definition of j-factors for volumetric film coefficients
Local variation of mass transfer in Fig.3 (right) resembles the streamwise variation of mass transfer in a boundary layer flow over a flat plate. The superficial vapor velocity is certainly kept almost constant in a packed distillation column. However the only big difference is in that the concentration or temperature changes downstream in the vapor bulk, as distinct from uniform concentration or temperature in the free stream of boundary layer flow. In order to discuss the existence of local similarity between mass and enthalpy transfer, the following j-factors can be defined using local *HETP* h_{etp} :

(vapor-phase)   (liquid-phase)

$$i_{DG} = \frac{k_{yA}ah_{etp}}{V} Sc_G^{2/3} \qquad\qquad i_{DL} = \frac{k_{xA}ah_{etp}}{L} Sc_L^{2/3} \qquad (16)$$

$$i_{HG} = \frac{h_G ah_{etp}}{Cp_G V} Pr_G^{2/3} \qquad\qquad i_{HL} = \frac{h_L ah_{etp}}{Cp_L L} Pr_L^{2/3} \qquad (17)$$

Therefore in a manner similar to the analogy analysis of single-phase boundary layer flow over a flat plate, the following local length Reynolds numbers are defined based on the superficial relative velocity $u_s = u_{Vs} - u_{Ls}$:

(vapor-phase)   (liquid-phase)

$$Re_{zG} = \frac{u_s \rho_G c_G \left(Z/d_{eq}\right)}{a_p \mu_G} \qquad\qquad Re_{zL} = \frac{u_s \rho_L c_L \left(Z/d_{eq}\right)}{a_p \mu_L} \qquad (18)$$

where Z/d_{eq} indicates local distance from the lowest edge of the bottom bed. The developing-rate parameters c_G and c_L (-) are determined by a trial-and-error method changing them as the control parameter in correlation analysis.

5.2. Similarity analysis between simultaneous interphase transfer of mass and enthalpy
Figures 4 and 5 show the boundary-layer-like plot of j-factors against local length Reynolds numbers. Here F is the F-factor defined at the column top. It has been found that both the j-factors i_{DG}, i_{HG} for mass and enthalpy transfer indicate the same dependency of local length Reynolds numbers. This implies that local similarity exists between mass and enthalpy transfer in the vapor-phase film.

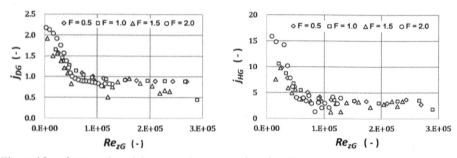

Figure 4 Local vapor-phase j-factors against vapor-phase length Reynolds number.
(c_G = 8.5 when F = 0.5, 6.0 when F = 1.0, 2.3 when F = 1.5, and 1.0 when F = 2.0)

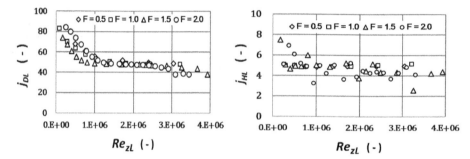

Figure 5 Local liquid-phase j-factors against liquid-phase length Reynolds number.
(c_L = 12.0 when F = 0.5, 6.3 when F = 1.0, 2.0 when F = 1.5, and 1.3 when F = 2.0)

The liquid-phase j-factors also indicate similar dependency, but the data points are slightly scattered. At any rate, it has for the first time been demonstrated that the transport phenomena in packed column distillation have local similarity between mass and enthalpy transfer and that the mass and enthalpy transport proceeds accompanied with the streamwise development similar to a boundary layer flow over a flat plate.

6. Conclusions

The local behavior of mass and enthalpy transfer in a structured-packing distillation column has been made clear by proposing a semi-empirical model of transport phenomena. It has been emphasized that the model based on total-reflux distillation experiment cannot be completed without the aid of computer-aided process simulation. It has for the first time been confirmed that the streamwise development of interphase transfer of mass and enthalpy can be correlated by length Reynolds number and that its packed column distillation proceeds downstream with local similarity in a manner similar to the development of a single-phase boundary layer flow over a flat plate.

References

J.L. Bravo, J.A. Rocha, and J.R. Fair, 1985, Mass Transfer in Gauze Packings, *Hydrocarb. Proc.*, 64(1), 91-95

M.J. Lockett, 1998, Easily Predict Structured-Packing HETP, *Chem. Eng. Prog.*, January, 60-66

Sauro Pierucci, Flavio Manenti, Giulia Bozzano, Davide Manca (Eds.)
Proceedings of the 30th European Symposium on Computer Aided Process Engineering
(ESCAPE30), May 24-27, 2020, Milano, Italy. © 2020 Elsevier B.V. All rights reserved.
http://dx.doi.org/10.1016/B978-0-12-823377-1.50002-1

Methanol Kinetics from Optimal Dynamic Experiments

Carsten Seidel[a], Achim Kienle[a,b]

[a]*Otto von Guericke University Magdeburg, Universitätsplatz 2, 39106 Magdeburg, Germany*
[b]*Max Planck Institute for Dynamics of Complex Technical Systems, Sandtorstraße 1, 39106 Magdeburg, Germany*
carsten.seidel@ovgu.de

Abstract

Methanol is an essential primary chemical in the chemical industry. Further, there is a growing interest in using methanol also for chemical energy storage. Excess electrical wind or solar energy can be converted to hydrogen and react with CO and CO_2 from bio-gas or waste streams to methanol. Suitable kinetic models are required for designing such processes. Established kinetics need to be extended to account for strongly varying input ratios of H_2, CO, and CO_2 in such applications leading to the need for dynamic process operation. Kinetic models for methanol synthesis accounting for dynamic changes of the catalyst morphology were proposed recently (Seidel et al., 2017). These comprise: a detailed model which relies on elementary reaction steps based on the work of (Vollbrecht, 2007) and a simplified kinetic model where elementary reaction steps are lumped together. Most of the kinetic parameters were determined from steady-state experiments reported by Vollbrecht. As a consequence identifiability was limited. In this contribution, we explore how parameter sensitivity and identifiability can be improved with dynamic experiments using optimal experimental design (OED), i.e., we determine suitable input variations by solving a dynamic optimal control problem. It is shown that for the lumped model, parameter sensitivity and identifiability can be improved. Identifiability is checked quantitatively by bootstrapping (Joshi et al., 2006). Although the sensitivity of the detailed model is also improved, the identifiability of this model has not improved significantly. Hence, it is concluded that additional measurement information is required for the full identifiability of the detailed model.

Keywords: methanol synthesis, optimal experimental design, kinetics

1. Introduction

$$CO + 2H_2 \rightleftharpoons CH_3OH \tag{1}$$

$$CO_2 + 3H_2 \rightleftharpoons CH_3OH + H_2O \tag{2}$$

$$CO_2 + H_2 \rightleftharpoons CO + H_2O \tag{3}$$

Methanol is essential for the chemical industry. It can be used as fuel and starting material for paraffin, olefins, or various organic chemicals like acetic anhydride. It is produced continuously in large amounts from synthesis gas using $Cu/ZnO/Al_2O_3$ catalysts. The reaction network involves three main reactions, i.e. hydrogenation of CO and CO_2 as well as the reverse water-gas shift reaction (RWGS) according to Eq. 1-3. With the upcoming focus on renewable resources as a basis for energy supply, methanol also becomes a serious option as an energy carrier. Excess wind or solar energy can supply electrolysis for hydrogen, which reacts with CO/CO_2 to methanol for chemical energy storage. In the case of an energy shortfall, methanol can be transformed back into electrical energy. This option results in a more flexible grid and efficient usage of renewable resources. In this case, the methanol reactor will face strongly varying ratios in the feed. The most established kinetics are designed for steady-state operation and are therefore insufficient for these scenarios (Raeuchle et al., 2016). When the dynamic operation of methanol reactors is considered, forced periodic operation becomes an option to improve the process using asymmetrical transient effects (Petkovska et al., 2018). Therefore a detailed and a simplified kinetic model suitable for the dynamic operation were introduced. While the simplified model was identifiable using deterministic global optimization and showed good results for steady-state and dynamic operation, the detailed model was not fully identifiable with the existing data. In this paper, we are using optimal experimental design strategies to improve the identifiability of the detailed model. This approach gives an optimal dynamic control input for the feed for a dynamic experiment that is maximizing the information content and thereby improves the identifiability. As proof of concept, the strategy is also applied to the simplified model.

2. Kinetic Models

2.1. Model Equations

The reaction takes place in an isothermal micro-berty reactor (CSTR). For dynamic operation, accumulation on the catalyst (solid phase) has to be considered. Therefore a set of dynamic equations is formulated, where the left-hand side (LHS) describes the transfer between fluid and solid phase and the right-hand side (RHS) describes the reaction on the catalyst.

$$\left[n^G \cdot I + \mathrm{m}_{kat} q_{sat} P(I - Y) \frac{\partial \Theta}{\partial p} \right] \frac{dy}{dt} = \dot{n}_0 \left(y_0 - y \right) + m_{kat} (I - Y) v r \tag{4}$$

2.2. Simplified Model

The recently developed kinetics describe the reactions Eq. (1-3) using lumped reactions (Seidel et al., 2017). Three different surface centers are assumed and will be denoted by $\theta^\square$ for oxidized centers, θ^* for reduced centers, and $\theta^\circledast$ for hydrogen. All equations are summarized in Table 1.

The Arrhenius-equation describes the temperature dependence of the rate constants with six additional parameters (k_i & E_A). The equilibrium constants K_{P1}-K_{P3} are taken from (Vollbrecht, 2007). The unknown parameters were estimated by using deterministic global optimization and steady-state experimental data (Seidel et al., 2017). To explain transient effects, as seen in (Choi et al., 2001; Muhler et al., 1994; Nakamura et al., 2003; Peter et al., 2012) after feed changes, we considered a conversion of reduced to oxidized centers and vice versa which is described by the following dynamic equation:

$$\frac{d\phi}{dt} = k_1^+ \left(y_{H_2} (1-\phi) - \frac{1}{K_1} y_{H_2O} \phi \right) + k_2^+ \left(y_{CO} (1-\phi) - \frac{1}{K_2} y_{CO_2} \phi \right) \tag{5}$$

The two unknown parameters k_1^+ and k_2^+ are fitted to dynamic experiments.

2.3. Detailed Model

The model is based on the elementary reaction steps behind Eq. 1-3 with one rate determining step each (Seidel et al., 2017; Vollbrecht, 2007). The temperature dependence and the equilibrium constants are the same as for the lumped model. The corresponding equations are summarized in Table 1. Parameter estimation for this model was done by Bert Vollbrecht with gradient-based methods with non-satisfying results, which is probably caused by a non-convex problem with multiple minima. Even a deterministic global optimization did not converge for the steady-state experiments. This indicates that different parameters were not structurally identifiable for the existing experimental data.

Table 1: Reaction rates and surface coverage equations of both kinetic models

Eq.	Simplified model	Detailed model
r_{CO}	$(1-\phi)k_1 p_{CO}p_{H_2}^2\left(1-\frac{1}{K_{P1}}\frac{p_{CH_3OH}}{p_{CO}p_{H_2}}\right)\theta^O\theta^\otimes$	$(1-\phi)k_1\left(p_{CO}p_{H_2}^2-\frac{p_{CH_3OH}}{K_{P1}}\right)\theta^O\theta^\otimes$
r_{CO_2}	$\phi^2 k_2 p_{CO_2}p_{H_2}^2\left(1-\frac{1}{K_{P2}}\frac{p_{CH_3OH}p_{H_2O}}{p_{CO_2}p_{H_2}^3}\right)\theta^{*2}\theta^{\otimes 4}$	$\phi^2 k_2\left(p_{CO_2}p_{H_2}-\frac{1}{K_{P2}}\frac{p_{CH_3OH}p_{H_2O}}{p_{H_2}^2}\right)\theta^{*2}\theta^O$
r_{RWGS}	$\phi(1-\phi)^{-1}k_3 p_{CO_2}\left(1-\frac{1}{K_{P3}}\frac{p_{CO}p_{H_2O}}{p_{CO_2}p_{H_2}}\right)\theta^*\theta^O$	$\phi(1-\phi)^{-1}k_3\left(p_{CO_2}-\frac{1}{K_{P3}}\frac{p_{CO}p_{H_2O}}{p_{CO_2}p_{H_2}}\right)\theta^*\theta^O$
$\theta^\otimes$	$\left(1+\sqrt{K_{H_2}p_{H_2}}\right)^{-1}$	$\left(1+\beta_7\sqrt{p_{H_2}}\right)^{-1}$
θ^O	$\left(1+K_{CO}p_{CO}+K_{CH_3OH}^O p_{CH_3OH}+K_{CO}^O p_{CO}\right)^{-1}$	$\left(1+\beta_8 p_{CO}+\beta_9 p_{H_2}^{3/2}p_{CO}+\beta_{10}p_{CH_3OH}+\beta_{11}p_{CO_2}\right)^{-1}$
θ^*	$\left(1+\frac{K_{H_2O}K_O}{K_{H_2}}\frac{p_{H_2O}}{p_{H_2}}+K_{CO_2}p_{CO_2}+K_{CH_3OH}^* p_{CH_3OH}+K_{H_2O}p_{H_2O}\right)^{-1}$	$\left(1+\beta_{13}\frac{p_{H_2O}}{p_{H_2}}+\beta_{16}\frac{p_{CH_3OH}}{p_{H_2}^{1/2}}+\beta_{14}p_{CH_3OH}+\beta_{15}\frac{p_{H_2O}}{p_{H_2}^{1/2}}+\beta_{12}p_{H_2O}\right)^{-1}$

3. Optimal Experimental Design

To design an optimal experiment, we consider an objective which maximizes the information content and also minimizes the correlation between the parameters. In the present paper, we choose the E^*-criterion that minimizes the ratio of biggest and smallest eigenvalue of the Fisher-Information-Matrix (FIM) (Pronzalo and Walter, 1997).

$$obj = \min\left(\frac{\lambda_{max}}{\lambda_{min}}\right) \tag{6}$$

By minimizing this objective, we find an optimal control input that maximizes the sensitivity S for unknown parameters p of the functions f (Eq. (4-5)). For dynamic experiments, the sensitivity function is also time-dependent and has to be evaluated at every time point.

$$\dot{S} = \frac{df}{dx}S + \frac{df}{dp} \qquad (7)$$

The overall sensitivity is calculated by evaluating the sensitivity of every time-point and is then used to calculate the FIM or respectively, the inverse, which is the covariance matrix. An experiment with high sensitivities raises the information content and therefore minimizes the correlation between the unknown parameters, resulting in more precise parameter estimation.

Available inputs for the optimal control are steps in concentration of CO, CO_2, H_2, temperature, and variable time between each step. The number of steps for the experiment is fixed because, after a certain amount of steps, repetitions occur. The following outputs can be measured: methanol, CO, CO_2, and H_2. They are therefore considered for the sensitivities. Additionally, we are assuming that ϕ from Eq. 5 is also measurable. For each model, the parameter estimation can be divided into three sub-problems that reduce the number of simultaneously estimated parameters (Seidel et al., 2017). For the optimization problem, we used a genetic algorithm (MATLAB) with a population size of 1000 and 30 generations. The result of this optimization is applied as the starting point for a second optimization with *fmincon* to check for nearby optima.

$$FIM = \begin{bmatrix} S(t_k) \\ S(t_{k+1}) \\ \vdots \\ S(t_{k+n}) \end{bmatrix}^T C_{y_t}^{-1} \begin{bmatrix} S(t_k) \\ S(t_{k+1}) \\ \vdots \\ S(t_{k+n}) \end{bmatrix} \qquad (8)$$

4. Parameter Estimation

To evaluate the optimal experimental design, bootstrapping (1000 runs) is applied (Joshi et al., 2006). The standard approach relies on steady state experiments from (Vollbrecht, 2007), which are perturbed with some normal distributed measurement noise ($\sigma = 0.01$) After identification the noisy measurements translate in parameter distributions as indicated in the blue bars in Figure 1 & 2.

For the optimal experimental design, artifical experimental data were generated with the optimal controls from Section 3 and the same measurement noise as above. Parameter distributions obtained after identification are illustrated in red in Figure 1 & 2. The given values for the artificial dynamic experiments are marked as black lines in both figures. We are minimizing the residuals of CH_3OH, CO, CO_2, H_2 at the output, and additionally ϕ by using a Maximum-log-Likelihood estimator (Myung, 2003).

$$\min L = -\left(\log \sigma + \frac{1}{2}\log 2\pi - \frac{1}{2N\sigma^2}\sum_{i=1}^{N_k}\sum_{k=1}^{N}\left(y_i^M(t_k) - y_i^{EXP}(t_k)\right)^2 \right) \qquad (9)$$

For the simplified and the detailed model, the parameter estimation is divided into three sub-problems. The first sub-problem takes all parameters for the CO-hydrogenation into account. These results are used for the other sub-problems, considering the parameters for the CO_2-hydrogenation and the RWGS. In the case of the simplified model, the first sub-problem contains five unknown parameters, the second seven, and for the third four with a total number of 16 unknown parameters. The detailed model is also separated in three sub-problems considering six, nine and three unknown parameters for the first, second, and third sub-problem with a total number of 18 unknown parameters.

5. Results

For the simplified model, the standard design results in parameter distributions that are giving rise to different locally optimal parameter sets, as can be seen in Figure 1. Additionally, E_{A,CO_2}, K_{H_2}, $K_{CH_3OH}^{\square}$, and k_2 seem to be not identifiable using the standard design. Applying the OED, the parameter sets are showing definite improvement. The parameter distribution corresponds, as shown in Figure 1, with the used reference

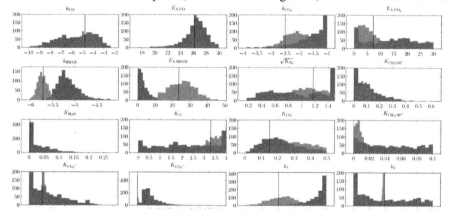

Figure 1: Parameter distribution simple model with OED (red), Standard design (blue) and reference value (black).

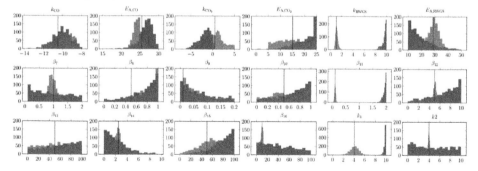

Figure 2: Parameter distribution detailed model with OED (red), Standard design (blue) and reference value (black).

parameter set, and the confidence intervals are 42.6% smaller compared to the standard design. The detailed kinetic model is, however, not completely identifiable with the standard design, which is pictured in the corresponding parameter distributions. For the majority of the parameters, the standard design results in distributions on the upper or lower bounds or in a uniform distribution of the allowed parameter region, as shown in Figure 2. When applying the OED, an apparent enhancement of the parameter distribution is noticeable. Ten parameters become identifiable with distinct distribution around the reference parameter set. The parameters β_4, β_8, β_{10}, and β_{13} are still not identifiable with given measurement information. Nevertheless, the average confidence intervals for the detailed model is 21.2% smaller than the standard design.

6. Conclusion

The proposed optimal experimental design strategy was implemented, and the effectiveness is shown for the simplified model. The parameter sensitivity can be increased and confidence intervals decreased. Various parameters of the detailed model are, however, not identifiable. Additional measurement information like intermediates on the catalyst or adsorption constants under reaction conditions may improve the identifiability of the model. Besides, the shown method only uses local sensitivities and the linear approximation of the nonlinear model. So global sensitivity strategies (McRae et al., 1982) and derivation of the covariance matrix directly from the nonlinear model, like the sigma point method (Mangold et al., 2009), could improve the results and will be the object of future work.

Acknowledgements

Gefördert durch die Deutsche Forschungsgemeinschaft (DFG) – SPP2080 "Katalysatoren und Reaktoren unter dynamischen Betriebsbedingungen für die Energiespeicherung und -wandlung" - KL 417/6-1. Financial support by the German Research Foundation (DFG) is gratefully acknowledged through the priorty program SPP 2080 under the grant KL 417/6-1.

References

Y. Choi, K. Futagami, T. Fujitani, J. Nakamura, 2001. The difference in the active sites for CO2 and CO hydrogenations on Cu/ZnO-based methanol synthesis catalysts. Catal. Letters 73, 27–31.

M. Joshi, A. Seidel-Morgenstern, A. Kremling, 2006. Exploiting the bootstrap method for quantifying parameter confidence intervals in dynamical systems. Metab. Eng.

M. Mangold, R. Schenkendorf, A. Kremling, 2009. Optimal experimental design with the sigma point method. IET Syst. Biol. 3, 10–23.

G.J., McRae, J.W. Tilden, J.H. Seinfeld, 1982. Global sensitivity analysis-a computational implementation of the Fourier Amplitude Sensitivity Test (FAST). Comput. Chem. Eng.

M. Muhler, E. Törnqvist, L.P. Nielsen, B.S. Clausen, H. Topsøe, 1994. On the role of adsorbed atomic oxygen and CO2 in copper based methanol synthesis catalysts. Catal. Letters 25, 1–10.

I.J. Myung, 2003. Tutorial on maximum likelihood estimation. J. Math. Psychol.

J. Nakamura, Y. Choi, T. Fujitani, 2003. On the issue of the active site and the role of ZnO in Cu/ZnO methanol synthesis catalysts. Top. Catal. 22, 277–285.

M. Peter, M.B. Fichtl, H. Ruland, S. Kaluza, M. Muhler, O. Hinrichsen, 2012. Detailed kinetic modeling of methanol synthesis over a ternary copper catalyst. Chem. Eng. J. 203, 480–491.

M. Petkovska, D. Nikolić, A. Seidel-Morgenstern, 2018. Nonlinear Frequency Response Method for Evaluating Forced Periodic Operations of Chemical Reactors. Isr. J. Chem.

L. Pronzalo, E. Walter, 1997. Identification of parametric models from experimental data, Springer, Berlin

K. Raeuchle, L. Plass, H.-J. Wernicke, M. Bertau, M., 2016. Methanol for Renewable Energy Storage and Utilization. Energy Technol. 4, 193–200.

C. Seidel, A. Jörke, B. Vollbrecht, A. Seidel-Morgenstern, A. Kienle, 2017. Kinetic Modeling of Methanol Synthesis from Renewable Resources. Chem. Eng. Sci. 175, 130–138.

B. Vollbrecht, 2007. Zur Kinetik der Methanolsynthese an einem technischen Cu/ZnO/Al2O3-Katalysator. Otto-von-Guericke-Universität Magdeburg.

Sauro Pierucci, Flavio Manenti, Giulia Bozzano, Davide Manca (Eds.)
Proceedings of the 30th European Symposium on Computer Aided Process Engineering
(ESCAPE30), May 24-27, 2020, Milano, Italy. © 2020 Elsevier B.V. All rights reserved.
http://dx.doi.org/10.1016/B978-0-12-823377-1.50003-3

Rigorous Modelling and Simulation of the Mass transfer on the Trays of a Pilot Scale Distillation column

Mayra Margarita May-Vázquez, [a] Fernando Israel Gómez-Castro, [a,*] Mario Alberto Rodríguez-Ángeles [b]

[a] *Departamento de Ingeniería Química, División de Ciencias Naturales y Exactas, Campus Guanajuato, Universidad de Guanajuato, Noria Alta S/N, Col. Noria Alta, Guanajuato, Guanajuato, 36050, México, fgomez@ugto.mx*
[b] *Departamento de Ingeniería en Plásticos, Universidad Politécnica de Juventino Rosas, Calle Hidalgo 102, Comunidad de Valencia, Santa Cruz de Juventino Rosas, Guanajuato, 38253, México.*

Abstract

Distillation is a well-known separation process, which takes advantage on the differences on the relative volatilities of the components of a given mixture. Separation occurs on either trayed or packed towers, where simultaneous mass and heat transfer occurs. One of the mathematical models used to represent the phenomena occurring in distillation is the rate-based model. Opposite to the equilibrium model, the rate-based model avoids the use of efficiencies and computes mass and heat transfer rates. One of the most important requirements of the rate-based model is an adequate mass transfer model, whose structure depends on the kind of mixture and the trays/packing geometry. In this work, a mass transfer model is proposed for the sieve trays on a pilot scale batch distillation column. In this column, a mixture of 50 mol% methanol and 50 mol% ethanol is separated. The column used in this work has four trays, a total condenser and a pot. The operation regime of the column is bubbling. The whole rate-based model of the column is solved using Matlab R2013a, and the composition and temperature profiles are obtained. The results indicate that rate-based model with the proposed mass transfer model has a mean decrease of 7% in the error for the compositions, in comparison with previously reported approaches.
Keywords: batch distillation, rate-based modelling, mass transfer model.

1. Introduction

Distillation is among the most important operations for the separation and purification of multicomponent mixtures in the chemical industry. This process is based on the differences on relative volatilities and boiling points between the components. Distillation can be done either in a continuous operational regime or a discontinuous regime (batch distillation). Batch processes are commonly used in pharmaceutical, food, and specialized products as alcoholic beverages, essential oils, perfume, pharmaceutic and petroleum products (Lucet et al., 1992). The advantages of batch distillation over a continuous distillation relies on its capacity to produce many different products.

Two models are commonly used to represent the phenomena occurring during distillation: the equilibrium model and nonequilibrium (rate-based) model. The first one assumes that phase equilibrium occurs in all the stages of the column, making use of efficiencies to predict the deviation from the actual performance of the column; the second one avoids the use of efficiencies, instead, it involves calculations for the mass transfer rates between the phases. Rate-based model consist of material and energy balances for each phase, models for mass and energy transfer rates across the interface, and equilibrium relations for the interface compositions. An important requirement of the rate-based model is an adequate mass transfer model, which is related with the kind of mixture and the trays/packing geometry. Trays are used to contact the liquid and vapor phase and through these the mass transfer takes place. Trays are widely used in distillation columns because they are easy to design and have a relatively low cost. Correlations of mass transfer coefficients for a wide variety of contacting devices have been published in the literature. The mass transfer coefficients depend on properties such as viscosity and diffusivity, as well as on operating and design parameters such as flowrates and column diameter, tray or packing type and so on. Khrishnamurthy and Taylor (1985) published a mathematical model for nonequilibrium stages in multicomponent separation processes. The model includes the mass balance of each component in each phase, the heat balances, the mass transfer rate, energy transfer equations and the equilibrium equations at the interface. Gorak et al. (1991) found that the compositions predicted by the nonequilibrium model are closer to the experimental data than those predicted by an equilibrium model. Kooijman and Taylor (1995) presented a nonequilibrium model for the dynamic simulation of distillation columns. Nada et al. (2009) presented two models (equilibrium and nonequilibrium) to study the dynamic behavior of multicomponent azeotropic system in a batch column with bubble-cap trays. Taylor y Krishna (1993) used a model in which they consider the bubbling and jet regime for a sieve tray in a distillation column.

The batch column involves a time-dependent process, therefore requires differential equations for the molar and energy balances and algebraic equations for all other relationships; i.e. a differential-algebraic (DAE) system. There are methods for solve the DAE system: solver than employ backwards differentiation formulas (BDF) and one-step implicit methods (such as Runge-Kutta methods). In this work, a pilot-scale batch distillation column is modelled through a rate-based approach. A mass transfer model is proposed for the sieve trays on the column. The mass transfer model is incorporated to the rate-based model, and the whole set of equations is solved using a specialized software (Matlab R2013a).

2. Methodology

The present work concerns on the rigorous modelling and simulation of the mass transfer on the trays of a pilot scale distillation column using the rate-based model. The methodology can be divided in four stages: (i) experimental, (ii) simulation in Aspen Plus V8.8, (iii) development of the mass transfer model, and (iv) solution of the obtained system of equations (DAE), using Matlab R2013a.

The experimental work was performed in a batch distillation column with four sieve trays, a pot and a total condenser. Figure 1 shows a diagram of the column. The batch system separates a methanol/ethanol, mixture, with an initial composition of 50% mol of methanol. Initial charge of the mixture is 0.172 kmol. The operation is stopped at 80 minutes, with constant thermal duty of 500 W. Samples were taken in each stage and analyzed in a gas chromatographer.

The simulation in Aspen Plus V8.8 was performed to obtain preliminary values of the mass and heat transfer rates. Methodology for this simulation has been already reported in a previous work (May-Vázquez et al., 2019). These constant mass transfer rates are included in a first version of the rate-based model, which will be labeled as Model 1.

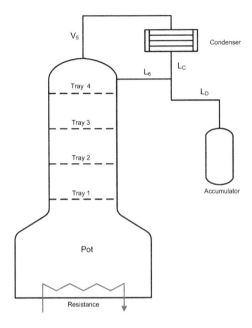

Figure 1.- Simplified representation of the batch column.

The proposed mass transfer model is based on the one reported by Locket (Taylor and Krishna, 1993), which considers a free bubbling regime and a spray regime. The first one is divided in jetting zone and free bubbling zone. In the second zone a distribution of bubble size is usually obtained. This model assumes a bimodal bubble size distribution (large and small bubbles). During the experimental work it was observed that the column operates in bubbling regime, with only one size of bubble. The Locket model is thus adapted for the system under study. The mass transfer model for the batch column is presented next.

The average molar fluxes:

$$N = c_t^V \beta^V K_{OV} \left(\Omega^V \right)^{-1} Q_I \left(y_{1E} - y_1^* \right) \tag{1}$$

Where c_t^V is mixture molar density of the vapor [mol/m³], β^V is the bootstrap coefficient for the vapor, y_{iE} is the mol fraction on the component i in the vapor entering the tray and y_1^* is the mole fraction of the vapor in equilibrium with the bulk liquid.

The function Ω^V is defined as:

$$\Omega^V = \left(-N_{OV} \right) / \left(\exp\left(-N_{OV} \right) - 1 \right) \tag{2}$$

The departure from equilibrium in the bubbles is given by:

$$Q_I = \exp\left(-N_{OV} \right) \tag{3}$$

The overall number of transfer units is:

$$N_{OV} = K_{OV} a' t \tag{4}$$

Overall mass transfer coefficient:

$$\frac{1}{K_{OV}} = \frac{1}{k^V} + \frac{c_t^V}{c_t^L} \frac{K_1}{k^L} \tag{5}$$

The mass transfer coefficient for the liquid phase:

$$k^L = 2 \left(\frac{D^L}{\left(\pi d / U \right)} \right)^{1/2} \tag{6}$$

The vapor phase mass transfer coefficient

$$k^V = -\ln\left(1 - F\right) / \left(a' t\right) \tag{7}$$

The fractional approach to equilibrium in the bubbles

$$F = 1 - \frac{6}{\pi^2} \sum_{n=1}^{\infty} \frac{1}{n^2} \exp\left\{ -n^2 \pi^2 Fo \right\} \tag{8}$$

The Fourier number for the bubbles

$$Fo = \frac{4 D^V t}{d^2} \tag{9}$$

Where d is the bubble diameter [m], a' is the interfacial area per unit of volume of vapor in the bubbles, t is the residence time, K_1 is the equilibrium ratio, D^V is the vapor-phase Maxwell-Stefan diffusivity, D^L is the liquid-phase Maxwell-Stefan diffusivity and c_t^L is mixture molar density of the liquid. Hereby, the rate-based model including equations (1)-(9) for the calculation of the mass transfer rates will be labeled as Model 2.

The whole rate-based model of the pilot scale distillation column was reported by May-Vazquez et al. (2019). The solution of the model for the batch column requires initial values for all the time-dependent variables. The initial values required for the solution were computed by solving the model under total reflux for 10 minutes. With the initial values obtained, the simulation of the distillation column with the rate-based model was carried out. The rate-based model is codified and solved in Matlab R2013a, aiming to obtain the composition and temperature profiles. The simulation time was 80 minutes.

3. Results

In this section, the obtained experimental data is compared with the data predicted by the developed rate-based model. Table 1 shows the component mass transfer rates, the positive sign indicates that the transfer is from vapor to liquid. In the case of Model 2, the reported mass transfer rates are for t = 80 min.

The mass transfer rate equations were included in the rate-based model, the numerical method used to solve the system of differential and algebraic equations was Runge-Kutta with constant step size of 0.001.

Table 2.-Mass transfer rates (kmol/s)

	Mass transfer rate – Model 1		**Mass transfer rate – Model 2**	
Tray	Methanol	Ethanol	Methanol	Ethanol
4	-6.36E-08	5.69E-08	-6.47E-09	6.84E-09
3	-4.94E-08	3.98E-07	-5.48E-09	5.78E-08
2	-2.97E-08	2.67E-08	-3.91E-09	4.13E-09
1	-1.93E-08	1.74E-08	-1.73E-09	1.83E-09

The composition profiles obtained are presented in Figures 2 and 3.

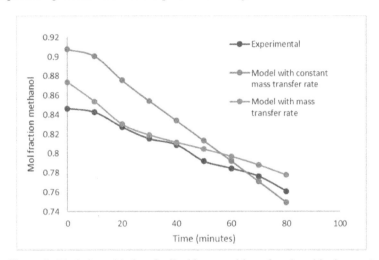

Figure 2.- Variation with time for liquid composition of methanol in the tray 1

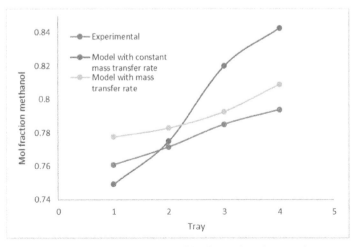

Figure 3.- Liquid composition profiles for methanol at 80 minutes.

Figure 2 shows the variation with time of the experimental and computed liquid composition of methanol in the tray 1. Methanol composition in tray 1 decreases as time progresses since it is the light component, thus, it is expected to concentrate in the distillate. Figure 2 shows a good agreement between the experimental data and the results predicted by Model 2. In the case of Model 1, the composition of methanol decreases more rapidly because the mass transfer rate is higher compared to that obtained with Model 2. The deviations between the experimental data Model 2 were ±1.41%.

Figure 3 shows a comparison between the experimental and simulation results for methanol in the final time. For Model 2, the average error is 1.64%. Figure 3 shows a good agreement between the experimental results and Model 2. The composition of methanol in the liquid phase increases in each tray since it is the lightest component.

4. Conclusions

The mass transfer rate is an important variable in the rate-based model. The most important variables in the mass transfer model are the diameter of the bubble and the bubble rising velocities. The lower the bubble rising velocity, the smaller the mass transfer rate is, and less variation in the compositions of methanol is obtained.

The proposed mass transfer rate model, which originates Model 2, allows a best fit with experimental data than Model 1. The mass transfer model predicts higher mass transfer rates than Aspen Plus, making use of the experimental information to compute the mass transfer rates.

Acknowledgements

The authors acknowledge the financial support provided by Universidad de Guanajuato and CONACYT, through the scholarship granted to M.M. May-Vázquez.

References

A. G. Gorak, G. Wozny, L. Jeromin, 1991, Industrial application of the rate-based approach for multicomponent distillation simulation. Proceedings of the 4th World Congress in Chemical Engineering.

H. A. Kooijman, R. A. Taylor, 1995, A nonequilibrium model for dynamic simulation of tray distillation columns, AIChE Journal, 41, 8, 1852-1863.

R. Krishnamurthy, R. Taylor, 1985, A nonequilibrium stage model of multicomponent separation processes. Part II: comparison with experiment, AIChE Journal, 31, 3, 456-465.

M. Lucet, A. Charamel, G. Guido, A. Chapuis, J. Loreau, 1992, Role of batch processing in the chemical process industry, Batch Processing Systems Engineering: Fundamentals and Applications for Chemical Engineering, 143, 43-48.

M.M. May-Vázquez, F.I. Gómez-Castro, M.A. Rodríguez-Ángeles, 2019, Rate-based modelling and simulation of pilot scale distillation column, Computer Aided Chemical Engineering, 46, 625-630.

B. Nada, K. Neran, S. Ibrahim, 2009, Rate-based model in bubble-cup batch distillation column, Engineering and Technology Journal, 27, 14, 2566-2583.

R. Tarikh, T. Fadilatul, N. Siti, A. Ali, 2019, Study of packed sieve tray column in ethanol purification using distillation process, Malaysian Journal of Fundamental and Applied Sciences, 15, 1, 69-74.

R. Taylor, R. Krishna, 1993, Multicomponent mass transfer, Wiley-Interscience.

Sauro Pierucci, Flavio Manenti, Giulia Bozzano, Davide Manca (Eds.)
Proceedings of the 30th European Symposium on Computer Aided Process Engineering
(ESCAPE30), May 24-27, 2020, Milano, Italy. © 2020 Elsevier B.V. All rights reserved.
http://dx.doi.org/10.1016/B978-0-12-823377-1.50004-5

Development of a Virtual Environment for the Rigorous Design and Optimization of Shell-and-tube heat Exchangers

Oscar Daniel Lara-Montaño [a], Fernando Israel Gómez-Castro [a,*], Claudia Gutiérrez-Antonio [b]

[a] *Departamento de Ingeniería Química, División de Ciencias Naturales y Exactas, Campus Guanajuato, Universidad de Guanajuato, Noria Alta S/N, Col. Noria Alta, Guanajuato, Guanajuato, 36050, México, fgomez@ugto.mx*
[b] *Facultad de Química, Universidad Autónoma de Querétaro, Av. Cerro de las Campanas s/n, Col. Las Campanas, Querétaro, Querétaro, 76010, México*

Abstract

Heat exchangers are one of the auxiliary equipment in industry, being the shell-and-tube heat exchangers (STHE) the most used. The design procedure of a heat exchanger is an iterative process, which is greatly affected by the designer experience; in spite of this, the designer can't know if the optimum design has been selected. Existing design methods involve solving a non-linear model with multiple decision variables. Therefore, it is convenient to use an optimization algorithm to select the best design. In order to solve this kind of optimization problems, meta-heuristic algorithms are the most promissory approach, which have exploration and exploitation capabilities. In this work, a virtual environment is created for the design and optimization of STHE, using the Kern and the Bell-Delaware methods, which are easily integrated with meta-heuristic algorithms. The STHE models and the optimization algorithms were coded in Python, supporting the particle swarm optimization and gray wolf optimization algorithms. Three constrains are always active, but the user can establish new ones easily if necessary. The default objective function is the total annual cost, but this can be also modified by the user.

Keywords: heat exchangers, meta-heuristic optimization, virtual environment.

1. Introduction

Shell-and-tube heat exchangers (STHE) are the most widely thermal equipment used in industry, and they provide a large heat exchange area in a small volume. Furthermore, they can be constructed using a wide range of materials to resist various kinds of fluids. Kern as well as Bell-Delaware methods are the most common strategies to design STHE. Kern method considers a single stream that advances in a zigzag flow pattern through the shell of the heat exchanger. On the other hand, Bell-Delaware method uses five factors to correct the shell-side heat transfer coefficient, and provide more accurate predictions of the actual thermal and hydraulic performance in shell-side as well as pressure drop calculations, since it takes into account leakage and bypass effects. Regard the optimization of STHE, there are plenty of works in which the main objective is to optimize thermal equipment using deterministic technics (Ponce-Ortega et al., 2006; Ravagnani and Caballero, 2007) or metaheuristic algorithms (Ponce ortega et al., 2009; Patel and Rao, 2010). The optimization of STHE represents a challenge due to the nonlinearity, nonconvexity and the presence of continuous and discrete variables in the mathematical model. Usually, a single tool is employed to perform the optimization of STHE; however, the availability of several optimization strategies in a toolbox could be useful to analyze the pros and cons of each one of them. Therefore, in this work, a computational tool to optimize STHE using metaheuristic algorithms is developed. The virtual environment uses Kern method and the Bell-Delaware method, while Particle Swarm Optimization (PSO) and Gray Wolf Optimization (GWO) methods are implemented in this first version.

2. Shell-and-tube heat exchanger models

The common equations of STHE models are the energy balances, the design equation, the mean logarithmic temperature differences. Each methodology are described next.

2.1. Shell-side calculations

2.1.1. Kern's method

The shell-side convective heat transfer coefficient, $h_{s,id}$, is computed with Equation (1). Re_s is the shell-side Reynolds number, Pr_s is the Prandtl number, k_f is the thermal conductivity of the shell-side fluid, j_h is the heat transfer factor, obtained from Sinnott (2005). μ_s is the fluid viscosity at mean temperature and μ_w is the fluid viscosity at wall temperature, this variable is calculated iteratively.

$$h_{s,id} = \frac{k_f}{d_e} j_h Re_s Pr_s^{\frac{1}{3}} \left(\frac{\mu_s}{\mu_w}\right)^{0.14} \tag{1}$$

For the equivalent diameter, d_e, either equations (2) or (3) are used, depending on the tube layout. Equation (2) is used for square layout, while equation (3) is for triangular layout. d_o is the outer tube diameter and p_t is the tube pitch.

$$d_e = \frac{1.27}{d_o}(p_t^2 - 0.785d_o^2) \tag{2}$$

$$d_e = \frac{1.1}{d_o}(p_t^2 - 0.917d_o^2) \tag{3}$$

Shell-side pressure drop, ΔP_s, is calculated using equation (4). ρ_s is the shell-side fluid density at mean temperature, v_s is the fluid velocity, L is the tube length, D_s is the shell diameter, B is the baffles spacing, D_e is the equivalent shell diameter, and f_s is the shell-side friction factor, which is calculated according to $f_s = 1.44Re_s^{-0.15}$, for $Re_s \leq 40,000$ (Peters and Timmerhaus, 1994). Full Kern model can be obtained from Sinnott (2005).

$$\Delta P_s = \frac{\rho_s v_s^2}{2} \frac{L}{B} \frac{D_s}{D_e} f_s \tag{4}$$

2.1.2. Bell-Delaware's method

Equation (1) is used to calculate an ideal shell-side convective heat transfer coefficient. In Bell-Delaware method, this value is modified using five correction factors (equation (5)), where J_c is the correction factor for baffle configuration, J_l is the correction factor due to the baffle leakage effect, J_b is the correction factor for bundle and pass partition bypass streams, J_s is the correction factor for larger baffle spacing at the inlet and outlet sections, and J_r is a correction factor for adverse temperature gradient in laminar flow (Shah & Sekulić, 2003).

$$h_s = h_{s,id} J_c J_l J_b J_s J_r \tag{5}$$

Shell-side pressure drop has three components, (i) pressure drop in the central section, (ii) pressure drop in the window area, and (iii) pressure drop at the inlet and outlet sections. Further details for thermal and hydraulic calculations for shell side using the Bell-Delaware method can be obtained from Shah and Sekulić (2003).

2.2. Tube-side calculations

For Kern's and Bell Delaware methodologies, thermal and hydraulic calculations are made using the following correlations. Where h_t is the tube-side convective heat transfer coefficient, k_t is the thermal conductivity of the tube-side fluid, f_t is the friction factor in tube side, d_i is the inner diameter of tubes, Re_t and Pr_s are the Reynolds and Prandtl number in tube-side, respectively. To calculate the tube-side convective heat transfer coefficient, equation (6) is used if $Re_t < 2300$, (7) if $2300 \le Re_t \le 10,000$, and (8) if $Re_t > 10,000$.

$$h_t = \frac{k_t}{d_i} 1.86 \left(\frac{Re_t Pr_t d_i}{L} \right)^{1/3} \tag{6}$$

$$h_t = \frac{k_t}{d_i} \left(\frac{\frac{f_t}{2} Re_t Pr_t}{1.07 + 12.7 \left(\frac{f_t}{2} \right)^{0.5} \left(Pr_t^{\frac{2}{3}} - 1 \right)} \right) \tag{7}$$

$$h_t = \frac{k_t}{d_i} 1.86 \left(\frac{Re_t Pr_t d_i}{L} \right)^{1/3} \tag{8}$$

3. Optimization algorithms

3.1. Particle Swarm Optimization

Particle Swarm Optimization (PSO), developed by Kennedy and Eberhart (1995), is inspired in the movement of a school of fishes or a flock of birds. It only uses two main equations:

$$v_i^{t+1} = v_i^t + \alpha r_1 (g^* - x_i^t) + \beta r_2 (x_i^* - x_i^t) \tag{9}$$

$$x_i^{t+1} = x_i^t + v_i^{t+1} \tag{10}$$

where x_i^t and v_i^t indicate position and velocity of particle i at iteration t, respectively. g^* is the best solution found so far by all particles, x_i^* is the best individual position and parameter α and β are set equal to 2.0. Equation (9) is used to calculate velocity for each particle and equation (10) is used to update the particle position. Finally, r_1 and r_2 are random parameters which are computed on each iteration.

3.2. Gray Wolf Optimization

Gray Wolf Optimization (GWO) algorithm, proposed by Mirjalili et al. (2014), emulates the hunting behavior and hierarchy of a wolf pack. The highest level in hierarchy is the alpha wolf, is the one who takes important decisions. The second level in hierarchy are beta grey wolves, which are subordinates that help the alpha one in decision making. Lowest level in hierarchy correspond to omega wolves; they must submit to all other levels. Other wolves who are not alpha, beta or omega, are delta. Delta wolves can be scouts, hunters, elders and caretakers, and they submit to alpha and beta wolves. This metaheuristic algorithm has three main phases (i) tracking, chasing and approaching to the prey (objective), (ii) pursuing, encircling and harassing the prey until stops moving, (iii) attack the prey.

4. Heat exchanger optimization system

The computational tool to optimize STHE, using metaheuristic algorithms, employs Python as codification environment. In the current version the user can choose between Kern's and Bell-Delaware methodologies, and also the optimization method, either PSO or GWO algorithms; the total annual cost is the objective function.

If Kern method is selected, the decision variables are shell diameter (D_s); outer tube diameter (d_o); tube layout (TL), square or triangular; number of tube passes (N_p), 1, 2 and 4; baffle spacing (B_s); diameter of tube bundle (D_{otl}); and diametrical clearance of shell to baffle (d_{sb}). For the Bell-Delaware method, the design variables are D_s; d_o; tube pitch (P_t, which can be either $1.25d_o$ or $1.5d_o$); TL (30°, 45° or 90°); number of passes (N_p, 1, 2 or 4); percentage baffle cut (B_c, 25%, 30%, 40% or 45%); baffle spacing at center (L_{bc}), defined from $0.2D_s$ to $0.55D_s$; baffle spacing at the inlet and outlet ($L_{bi} = L_{bo}$), defined from L_{bc} to $1.6L_{bc}$; d_{tb}, in the range $0.01D_s$ to $0.1D_s$; and diametrical clearance of tube to baffle (d_{tb}), in the range $0.01d_o$ to $0.1d_o$.

Figure 1 shows how this tool is designed. MainProgram is the run file, which allows the user to select the STHE model, metaheuristic algorithm and some parameters of the algorithm, such as population size, number of iterations, number of runs and design variable boundaries. MainProgram calls an optimization algorithm that links to the STHE design model. Both, Kern and Bell-Delaware methods are interconnected with a code that calculates the thermal convection coefficient in tube side (ThermalCoefConvTub). If Bell-Delaware model is selected the Geometry package is used to calculate geometrical parameters. Then, important variables for cost estimation are exported to CostCalculation to get the objective function value, this is the sum of operation and fixed cost. When the stop criterium is satisfied the STHE optimum design is showed.

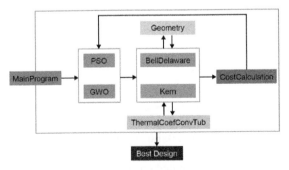

Figure 1. Design of STHE optimization tool.

Four constrains are applied: pressure drop in tube-side and shell side must be less or equal to a maximum pressure drop, fluid velocity in tubes must be between 1 m/s and 3 m/s, and the ratio between STHE length and shell diameter must be less or equal to 15. If one or more constrains are not satisfied a penalty value is applied to the objective function value.

5. Case studies

Case studies are taken from Taborek (1983); physical properties and process information is given in Table 1. For cost calculations interest rate of 5% per year is assumed; expected lifetime for STHE is 20 years; electricity cost is 0.1$/kWh; 5000 operational hours per year are used; and pump efficiency is 0.85. All codification was implemented in Python. 30 experiments were made to have enough information for a statistical analysis with 50 individuals and 50 iterations.

Table 1. Physical properties and process information for case studies.

	Case study 1		Case study 2	
	Tube side	Shell side	Tube side	Shell side
Fluid	Cooling water	Naphtha	Heavy gas oil	Crude oil
Flow rate (kg/m^3)	30	2.7	29.36	102.12
Inlet fluid temperature (°C)	33	114	319	209
Outlet fluid temperature (°C)	37.2	40	269	226
Density of fluid (kg/m^3)	1000	656	678	723
Heat capacity (kJ/kg-k)	4.187	2.646	3.161	2.679
Viscosity (Pa-s)	0.00071	0.00037	0.00032	0.00049
Thermal conductivity (W/m-K)	0.63	0.11	0.089	0.1
Fouling resistance ($m^2 K/W$)	0.0004	0.0002	0.0006	0.0006
Allowed pressure drop (Pa)	70,000	70,000	10,000	10,000
Material	Stainless steel	Carbon steel	Carbon steel	Carbon steel

6. Results

Table 2 summarizes the optimal design variables found for both case studies. It is important to notice that Table 2 only shows the results for the best (optimal) heat exchanger designs using the different combinations of design and optimization methods.

Table 2. Optimized STHE for using both design methods and optimization algorithms.

Parameter	Case study 1				Case study 2			
	Bell-Delaware		Kern		Bell-Delaware		Kern	
	PSO	GWO	PSO	GWO	PSO	GWO	PSO	GWO
Shell diameter (m)	0.3024	0.3024	0.3141	0.3148	0.5816	0.5806	1.0	1.0
Outer tube diameter (m)	0.01587	0.01587	0.015	0.015	0.01587	0.01587	0.015	0.015
Number of tubes	144	144	216	217	319	320	2762	2762
Area (m^2)	32.56	32.56	25.96	26.029	138.75	138.81	150.92	150.92
Length (m)	4.53	4.53	2.55	2.54	8.72	8.70	1.159	1.59
Operation cost (USD/year)	160.51	160.51	263.34	257.76	589.67	590.51	3430.25	3430.25
Fixed cost (USD/year)	3865.99	3806.01	3262.45	3275.97	9597.72	9600.51	10162.02	10162.02
Total annual cost (USD/year)	3966.50	3966.53	3525.80	3525.73	10187.40	10191.03	13592.27	13592.27

In a more detailed analysis, for case study 1 both optimization algorithms reach the same optimal solution. However, after 30 experiments the average total annual cost and standard deviation are 4,234.35 USD/year and 431.09 USD/year for PSO, and 4,074.93 USD/year and 52.15 USD/year for GWO, respectively. Therefore, GWO has a better performance for this problem and it is more likely to avoid local optima. When Kern's method is used, both optimization method has very similar statistical results. Average value for standard deviation are 3,535.72 USD/year and 16.64 USD/year for PSO, and 3,536.14 USD/year and 18.72 USD/year for GWO. It can be inferred that it is easier to have reproducibility between simulations when Kern method is used; this is because the model is simpler, contains less design variables, and less non-linear equations. Optimal designs calculated with Kern method have a lower cost than with Bell-Delaware. Nevertheless, results obtained with the Bell-Delaware method are expected to be more approximate to the actual performance of the exchanger.

The optimal STHE for case study 2 is larger than the first case. Considering Bell Delaware model, a better optimal design is calculated when PSO is used. The average total annual cost and standard deviation for PSO is 10,590.14 USD/year and 481.11 USD/year, while for GWO these values are 10,274.19 USD/year and 248.05 USD/year. In this case, the design calculates using Kern model is more expensive. For both PSO and GWO the minimum total annual cost is 13,592.07 USD/year. Nevertheless, an important difference occurs with standard deviation, having a value of 224.09 USD/year for PSO and 0.05 USD/year for GWO. This demonstrates that for all of 30 experiments GWO reached practically the same minimum value.

7. Conclusions

A tool for the optimization of STHE considering two models and two meta-heuristic approaches has been proposed. The design tool successfully optimizes STHE with no phase transition. Considering 30 experiments, both optimization methods calculates at least one design with the same minimum total annual cost value. GWO algorithm has a better ability to avoid local minima, this can be inferred by looking at the lower standard deviation compared to PSO algorithm. Although the user can choose between PSO and GWO, it is recommended to use GWO because of its better overall performance.

References

A.C. Caputo, P.M. Pelagagge, P. Salini, P, 2008, Heat exchanger design based on economic optimisation, Applied Thermal Engineering, 28, 10, 1151-1159.

J. Kennedy, R. Eberhart, 1995, Particle swarm optimization, Proceedings of ICNN'95 - International Conference on Neural Networks, 4, 1942-1948.

S. Mirjalili, S.M. Mirjalili, A. Lewis, 1995, Grey wolf optimizer, Advances in Engineering Software, 69, 46-61.

V.K. Patel, R.V. Rao, 2010, Design optimization of shell-and-tube heat exchanger using particle swarm optimization technique, Applied Thermal Engineering, 30, 11, 1417-1425.

M. Peters, K. Timmerhaus, 1994, Plant design and economic for chemical engineers. Mc Graw Hill.

J.M. Ponce-Ortega, M. Serna-González, L.I. Salcedo-Estrada, A. Jiménez-Gutiérrez, 2006, Minimum-investment design of multiple shell and tube heat exchangers using a MINLP formulation. Chemical Engineering Research and Design, 84, 10, 905-910.

J.M. Ponce-Ortega, M. Serna-González, A. Jiménez-Gutiérrez, 2009, Use of genetic algorithms for the optimal design of shell-and-tube heat exchangers. Applied Thermal Engineering, 29, 2, 203-209.

M.A.S.S. Ravagnani, J.A. Caballero, 2007, A MINLP model for the rigorous design of shell and tube heat exchangers using the TEMA standards. Chemical Engineering Research and Design, 85, 10, 1423-1435.

R.K. Shah, D.P. Sekulić, 2003, Fundamentals of heat exchanger design, Wiley.

R.K. Sinnott, 2005, Chemical Engineering Design, volume 6, 4th edition, Coulson & Richardson's Chemical Engineering Series, Elsevier.

J. Taborek, 1983, Shell-and-tube heat exchangers: single-phase flow, in "Heat exchanger design handbook" (Ed. G.F. Hewitt), Belleg House, 3.3.3.1-3.3.11.5.

Sauro Pierucci, Flavio Manenti, Giulia Bozzano, Davide Manca (Eds.)
Proceedings of the 30th European Symposium on Computer Aided Process Engineering
(ESCAPE30), May 24-27, 2020, Milano, Italy. © 2020 Elsevier B.V. All rights reserved.
http://dx.doi.org/10.1016/B978-0-12-823377-1.50005-7

A Multiscale Modelling Approach for the Design of new Polymer Materials

Alain Dequidt,[a] Sébastien Garruchet,[b] Benoit Latour,[b] Nicolas Martzel,[b] Ronald Blaak,[a] Etienne Munch,[b] Nicolas Seeboth,[b] Patrice Malfreyt[a]

[a]*Université Clermont Auvergne, CNRS, SIGMA Clermont, Institut de Chimie de Clermont-Ferrand, 63000 Clermont-Ferrand, France*
[b]*Manufacture Française des Pneumatiques Michelin, 23, place des Carmes, 63040 Clermont-Ferrand, France*
Patrice.Malfreyt@uca.fr

Abstract

We report examples of industrial interests for which only multi-scale simulations are able to provide bridges between consecutive scales. We focus here on the transfer of information between the atomic and mesoscopic scales. We treat the impact of the architecture of the polymer chains and the nature of the surface. We also investigate the phenomena of crystallization under shear and complete by a study of the deformation of an elastomer network.

Keywords: multiscale modelling, mesoscopic simulation, coarse-grain models, mechanical properties, polymer materials.

1. Introduction

Simulations have become an essential tool for analyzing, interpreting experimental data and generating new experiments. We can even imagine that in the near future (less than ten years) no experiment will be carried out without having launched before a simulation. It is now established that the improvement of the desired properties and of the performance of a material requires investigating the relationship between its structure at the atomic or molecular length and their macroscopic properties. However, the ability to perform molecular simulations of polymer materials over length scales that are relevant to experiments represents a grand challenge. Indeed, when studying polymer composite materials, polymers at the surface, we need to consider structures from the length scale of a single chemical bond (≈ 1 Å) to the persistence length (≈ 10 Å) to the coil radius (≈ 100 Å). The second factor that may control the practicality of the simulation is the time scales involved in the polymeric materials that can reach times of microsecond and beyond (full relaxation of the polymer chains, crystallisation).

One solution to simulate these time and length scales consists of reducing the degrees of freedom by coarsening the model. Each interaction center (called bead) may represent then few atoms or several monomers (see Figure 1). Numerous coarse-graining approaches have been developed in the past to conserve chemical information at the mesoscopic length scales. The idea behind our coarse-grained (CG) approach is to map atomistic configurations onto a coarser (Maurel et al., 2012; Maurel et al., 2015a, Maurel et al. 2015b; Kempfer et al., 2019a, Kempfer et al., 2019b, Kempfer et al., 2019c) configuration. We propose here to show the performance of the multi-scale approach for a quantitative prediction of thermodynamic and mechanical properties of different polymer materials.

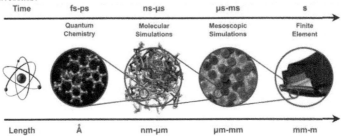

Figure 1: Different types of length and time scales associated with the methods of simulations from the quantum to macroscopic scales.

2. Coarse-grain simulations of polymer materials

2.1. Development of coarse grain (CG) models

We use the Statistical Trajectory Matching (STM) to develop the CG models. The reference trajectories are obtained from atomistic simulations from which the positions of the coarse-grains are determined. With the STM method, we use a degree of coarse-graining of 1 indicating that a grain corresponds to 1 monomer. This size of grain allows to reproduce both the structural properties of chains in the melt and the melt density. We are currently working for increasing the degree of coarse-graining to simulate larger systems on millisecond scales. The reader is redirected to the following papers [1-6] to have a comprehensive description of the STM method.

2.2. Effects of molecular structure on mechanical properties

Molecular structure of polymer materials is tightly correlated to their rheology and mechanical properties. Yet, molecular time-scales are very different from observable mechanical phenomena making it hard to link one with the other. Several models attempt to do so, and it is still a challenge for molecular modeling to develop tools to predict mechanical of polymer materials up to macroscopic timescales. This is partly due to the explicit simulation of molecular motions and partly to time limits from computational power.   The recent development of coarse-grain models allowed to overcome such limits. By reducing the complexity of the system while keeping a correct representation of polymer molecules, they gave access to time-scale up to the microseconds for polymeric systems. It is likely that fine tuned molecular model will be able to give quantitative prediction of material properties. For example, recent models of CG *cis*-1,4-polybutadiene (cPB) are able to reproduce molecular structure in agreement with experimental results (for example for cis-polybutadiene $\rho^{exp} = 0.90 \ g/cm^3$; $\rho^{sim} = 0.90 \ g/cm^3$, $\frac{R_{ee}^{exp}}{M} = 0.76 \ A^2 \frac{mol}{g}$, $\frac{R_{ee}^{sim}}{M} = 0.7 \ A^2 \frac{mol}{g}$) (Pearson et al., 2014). From stress auto-correlation up to the micro-second, plateau modulus is still overestimated with high coarse-graining $(G^{exp} = 0.76 \ MPa, \ G^{sim} = 1.12 \ MPa)$ (Maurel et al., 2012) as dynamics is difficult to reproduce and entanglements are lost. Nevertheless, it is already possible to see effects of molecular structure on rheological properties [8]. While it is not possible to simulate true polymeric structures with long enough molecules, we now try to see molecular effects of branching on mechanical properties and compare it with analytical models in order to validate our explicit simulation models. Our recent results show that G(t) decays slower for the star than for the linear polymer in line with recent experiments and simulations (Liu et al., 2018).

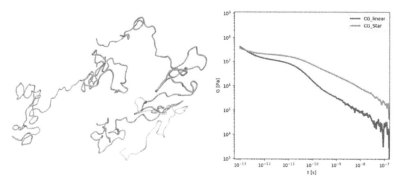

Figure 2 : Shear-modulus for linear (blue) and star polymers (orange) cis-1,4- polybutadiene polymer melts obtained from CG simulations.

2.3. Effects of free and grafted chains under shear

We show results of this methodology applied to polymers between confining surfaces that are grafted. We employ the model for cPB in contact with a cuprous oxide layer that was recently derived. The confining surfaces are represented by four layers of coarse-grained beads. For simplicity, we have assumed that each bead in the top layers of either surface can act as a grafting site for exactly one polymer. The grafting locations are selected randomly for a given grafting density. The grafted polymers themselves are short spacers of 5 beads and are attached at the other end to the middle of a normal polymer to create a ``Y"-like structure. In the current formulation the beads and bonds in grafted, attached, and free polymers are all identical to the *cis*-1,4-polybutadiene model. The separation between the two surfaces is chosen such that the density and pressure in the middle of the system, where there are just free polymers, are corresponding to the bulk value.

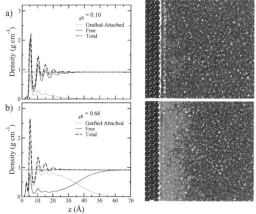

Figure 3 : Monomer density profiles for free and grafted polymers at (a) low ($\phi = 0.1$ nm^{-2}) and (b) ($\phi=0.66$ nm^{-2}) high grafting densities and corresponding representative snapshots. The blue

dashed line corresponds to the bulk density ρ =0.92 g/cm^3. The average position of the top layer of surface beads is found at z=0. The red, yellow, and green spheres correspond to surface, grafted, and free polymers.

Figure 3 shows two snapshots at low and high grafting densities for relative short polymers consisting of 41 beads (one bead corresponds to four united atoms). The grafting densities ϕ = 0.1 and 0.66 molecules/nm^2 correspond to the polymer chains to be grafted respectively at 7% and 45% of the available sites. The monomer density profiles show the characteristic oscillations of surface induced ordering. The slight sub-peak close to the surface is due to the short bond length between the grafted and the surface beads. The larger grafting density causes an effective thicker brush and expels the free polymers from the surface and ultimately from the brush. In future work, we will explore the behavior of this and similar systems when exposed to shear.

2.4. Strain-induced of polymers

A commonly used model to simulate the crystallization process of polymers as well as their properties, is the coarse-grained model for poly(vinyl alcohol) (PVA) that was introduced by Meyer and Müller-Plathe (2001). It takes the form of a simple bead-spring model, where individual grains represent single PVA-monomers rather than united atoms. The connectivity within polymers is modeled by means of a harmonic potential and the steric interaction is represented by a Lennard-Jones 9-6 potential. The angle and torsion potentials found in a united atom representation of this system, have been replaced by a single tabulated angle potential. In order to study the effects of strain on polymer systems, we have simulated a system of 2700 polymer chains with a length of 100 beads of this type at a pressure P*=8 in reduced units. An equilibrated melt configuration at T*=1 (reduced units) is quenched to T*=0.2 at the constant cooling rate $10^{-6}/\tau$, which is slow enough to avoid the glass and results in semi-crystalline order. Configurations from different temperatures during this process are subjected to a constant true strain-rate $10^{-5}/\tau$, under constant lateral pressure. Figure 4 shows two snapshots for the lowest temperature, one before and one after the maximum strain ε=1.59. Bonds in the polymers are color coded according to the local nematic order parameter N, which is the largest eigenvalue of the tensor $Q_{\alpha\beta} = \Sigma \, 3/2 \, b_{\alpha\beta} - 1/2 \delta_{\alpha\beta}$ in terms of the unit-vectors **b** associated to them. The average is taken over all bonds in proximity, i.e., within a distance 1.1σ The probability distribution functions P(N) of the local nematic order for different strains ε are shown in Figure 5 and indicate that the strain enhances the alignment in weakly ordered regions. Counterintuitively in some of the strongly ordered regions (N > 0.98) it will be somewhat lowered in favour of the range 0.6 <N <0.98, an effect that appears to be associated with those regions whose alignment direction differs significantly from the strain direction. Finally, the cooling to extremely low temperature not only results in alignment of the polymers, but also in some short range positional order as can be observed in the sub-structure in the PDF at zero-strain.

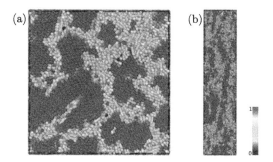

Figure 4: Snapshots representing the local nematic order parameter (a) before (ε=0) and (b) after ((ε=1.59) applying strain. Each sphere represents a bond in the polymer and the color coding corresponds to its local nematic order parameter N.

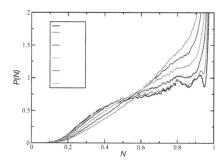

Figure 5: Probability distributions of the local nematic order parameter N at various strains ε

2.5. Molecular elastomer networks under high deformation

Resistance to fracture is a key property of materials in many practical applications. The optimization of the breaking strain and energy is thus a concern for the industry, in particular in elastomers (cross-linked polymers). In a cross-linked polymer under high deformation, the force felt by each chain depends on the local configuration of the network (chain length, entanglements, orientation of the neighboring chains...). The rupture of a chain is all the more likely that it is submitted to a great tension. During a rupture, the stress supported by the broken chain is distributed to its neighbors, whose stress increases and which may break in turn. In the end, this avalanche of ruptures leads to the rupture of the sample. To study the behavior of elastomer networks, we chose to develop a numerical model to simulate polymers at the scale of the cross-linked network. Our approach differs from previous analytical models (Wu, 1993) concerning network rupture by using a coarse grained model and method (based on Elastic Network Models (Rubinstein, 2002) with parameters estimated from quantum mechanics, dissipative particle dynamics and experimental data). In practice, in our simulations, the topological constraints (cross-links, entanglements...) are represented by a network of beads connected together by polymer chains with distributed lengths. To produce these systems, we adopt a specific network generation approach (Hansen, 2015) which takes into account polymer properties (Kuhn length, density) and network characteristics (cross-link density). We are able to measure the local stress distribution during the simulation. We show that stress is indeed distributed. Under strain, the stress distribution is not only shifted, but also broadened. The most remarkable element is that, under stretch, localized parts of the sample are under pressure, with a positive stress value along the stretch axis, while the average negative stress is of course negative. Rupture behavior will be obviously affected by this heterogeneity. Regions with high or low absolute stress value should correspond respectively to breaking zones and zones helping to relax constraint.

3. Conclusion

A multi-scale stratgey approach was used to link the atomistic and mesoscopic scales. The aim is to maintain a realistic chemical representation of the microstructure and to simulate the polymer materials at longer time scales. We have discussed the effects of the molecular structure on the mechanical properties, the impact of the grafting on the resulting rheological properties on the brush and of the shear on the crystallization process. We complete this paper by the simulation of molecular elastomer networks und high deformation.

Acknowledgments

This work was performed in SimatLab, a joint public-private laboratory dedicated to the modeling of polymer materials. This laboratory is supported by Michelin, Clermont Auvergne University (UCA), SIGMA Clermont and CNRS. It is a pleasure to thank F. Goujon, G. Clavier, J. S. Canchaya, J. Devémy, G. Munoz, H. Nagaraj.

References

D. E. Hanson, 2015, A new paradigm for the molecular basis of rubber elasticity, Contemp. Phys., 56, 319-337.

K. Kempfer, J. Devemy, A. Dequidt, M. Couty, P. Malfreyt, 2019a, Atomistic descriptions of the cis-1,4-polybutadiene/silica Interfaces, ACS Appl. Polym. Mater., 1, 969-981.

K. Kempfer, J. Devemy, A. Dequidt, M. Couty, P. Malfreyt, 2019b, Development of coarse-grained models for polymers by trajectory matching, ACS Omega, 4, 5955-5967.

K. Kempfer, J. Devemy, A. Dequidt, M. Couty, P. Malfreyt, 2019c, Realistic coarse-grain model of cis-1,4-polybutadiene: from chemistry to rheology, Macromolecules, 52, 2736-2747.

L. Liu, W. K den Otter, W. J. Briels, 2018, Coarse-grained Simulations of three-armed star polymer melts and comparison with linear chains, J. Phys. Chem. B, 122, 10210-10218.

G. Maurel; B. Schnell; F. Goujon; M. Couty; P. Malfreyt, 2012, Multiscale modeling approach toward the prediction of viscoelastic properties of polymers, J. Chem. Theory Comput., 8, 4570-4579.

G. Maurel; F. Goujon; B. Schnell, P. Malfreyt, 2015a, Prediction of structural and thermomechanical properties of polymers from multiscale simulations, RSC Adv., 5, 14065-14073.

G. Maurel; F. Goujon; B. Schnell, P. Malfreyt, 2015b, Multiscale modeling of the polymer−silica surface interaction: from atomistic to mesoscopic simulations, J. Phys. Chem. C., 119, 4817-4826.

H. Meyer and F. Müller-Plathe, 2001 Formation of chain-folded structures in supercooled polymer melts, J. Chem. Phys., 115, 7807.

D. S. Pearson, L. J. Fetters, W. Graessley, G. Ver Strate, E. von Meerwall, 2014, Viscosity and self-diffusion coefficient of hydrogenated polybutadiene, Macromolecules, 27, 711-719.

M. Rubinstein, 2002, Elasticity of polymer networks, Macromolecules, 35, 6670-6686.

P. D. Wu, 1993, On improved network models for rubber elasticity and their applications to orientation hardening in glassy polymers, J. Mech. Phys. Solids, 427-456.

Sauro Pierucci, Flavio Manenti, Giulia Bozzano, Davide Manca (Eds.)
Proceedings of the 30th European Symposium on Computer Aided Process Engineering
(ESCAPE30), May 24-27, 2020, Milano, Italy. © 2020 Elsevier B.V. All rights reserved.
http://dx.doi.org/10.1016/B978-0-12-823377-1.50006-9

Structured and Unstructured (Hybrid) Modeling in Precision Medicine

Linas Mockus, Gintaras V. Reklaitis, Yuehwern Yih

Purdue University, 610 Purdue Mall, West Lafayette, IN, 47907, USA
lmockus@purdue.edu

Abstract

One of the key objectives in precision medicine is to determine the right dose for the individual patient at the right time so that the desired therapeutic effect is achieved. The focus of this work is on modeling of pharmacokinetic/ pharmacodynamic data to facilitate the achievement of this goal. One novelty of our approach is to use structured models, such as physiologically-based compartment models and un-structured models, such as artificial neural networks or Gaussian Processes in a hierarchical fashion. The reason for using a hierarchical structure is that there are available well-established empirical compartmental and mechanistic physiologically based models, which do not explicitly account for various predictive covariates such as co-administered drugs or different laboratory measurements such as total protein, blood urea nitrogen, or urine output. Thus, we extend the structured models with the second hierarchical layer of an un-structured model and utilize the unstructured model to capture the effects of those covariates. Secondly, we employ Bayesian inference which allows direct quantification of uncertainty in the model predictions. Thirdly, utilization of Bayesian inference for the un-structured models (specifically Bayesian neural networks) allows the determination of important predictive covariates such as serum creatinine, blood urea nitrogen, or urine output.

Keywords: Pharmacokinetics, pharmacodynamics, Bayesian statistics, Artificial Intelligence.

1. Introduction

There is a plethora of literature on modeling of the drug kinetics in the human body, but the published models are typically structured (Colin, et al., 2019) with predictive covariates such as postmenstrual age, weight and serum creatinine. The literature on purely unstructured models is sparse (Roy, Dabbagh, Nguyen, & Hildgen, 2006), while the use of hierarchical approaches has not been reported. In this work we demonstrate the effectiveness of the hierarchical approach using the data from 2000 patients from Children's Hospital of Wisconsin. The data is imperfect – it has a large volume of missing vancomycin intermittent IVs. Moreover, for most patients there was a single concentration measurement at the trough per administration. The Bayesian framework allowed us to train the one-compartmental model combined with Bayesian neural networks models and Gaussian Process models for clearance and volume of distribution on data from patients for whom we have several concentration measurements. The predictive covariates were age, weight, height, gender, and serum creatinine. The results are encouraging – model predictions and actual measurements agree quite well. While these results must be viewed as only a proof of concept, they do suggest that such models can indeed help physicians to establish the right dose in a systematic way, accounting for different lab measurements, replacing the traditional approach in which the dosage is determined only based on weight and vancomycin half-life (the predominant practice). We expect that the proposed hybrid model may aid physician in prescribing the right dose at the right time as well as in facilitating Bayesian adaptive phase I/II trials. The problem with current trials is that the "applied dose" is controlled, rather than the achieved "exposure". One can imagine that with a "day one pharmacokinetic (PK) Profile" of a "low" dose, we could train a reasonable model to select a dose that would deliver the desired area under the curve for that specific patient. The achieved exposure would then be confirmed, and further dosing continued. The process is safe for the patient and further supports testing clinical hypotheses around how the actual exposure relates to pharmacodynamics (PD). In addition, our hypothesis is that establishing importance of various lab measurements will help to focus on those that are indicative for that particular disease.

2. Materials and Methods

In this work we use the data from 2000 vancomycin patients from Children's Hospital of Wisconsin. However, the data has a large volume of missing vancomycin intermittent IVs. Moreover, for most patients there was a single concentration measurement at the trough point per administration. In addition, age, height, weight were not recorded consistently nor were serum creatinine levels. There were approximately 100 patients that had several concentration measurements at the trough for the same administration as well as that had consistent records for age, weight, height, gender, and serum creatinine. We selected 20 patients at random to demonstrate the proposed approach. The predictive covariates were age, weight, height, gender, and serum creatinine.

The statistical analysis was performed using R (R: A Language and Environment for Statistical Computing, 2009) and Markov Chain Monte Carlo software Stan (StanDevelopmentTeam, 2019) by employing Extreme Science and Engineering Discovery Environment (XSEDE) (Towns, et al., 2014) environment. It was assumed that pharmacokinetics is defined by a one compartmental model (Buelga, del Mar Fernandez de Gatta, Herrera, Dominguez-Gil, & García, 2005).

3. Hierarchical modeling of structured and un-structured models

We assume that the structured pharmacokinetics/pharmacodynamics model is defined by a system of differential algebraic equations (DAE):

$$\tilde{y} = f\left(x(t), \theta\right)$$

$$\frac{dx}{dt} = g\left(x(t), \theta\right)$$

$$h\left(x(t), \theta\right) = 0$$

$$x(0) = x_0$$

In this model, $\tilde{y}$ is the predicted value for an experimental observation, while f is a function relating the state variables $x(t)$ to the predicted value. θ represents the vector of unknown parameters. The vectors of DAEs that define the predictive model are g and h, respectively. The vector of initial conditions is given by x_0. Assuming an exponential error, the relationship between the experimental observation (y) and its associated predictive value is established by $\ln(y) = \ln(\tilde{y}) + \varepsilon$ where ε is observation error. The exponential error model is more appropriate for PK data since it is always positive. For one compartmental PK models, for example, $\boldsymbol{\theta}$ consists of the clearance (CL) and the volume distribution (V_d).

In purely structured models V_d is often assumed to be a simple function of weight and CL as a simple function of creatinine clearance, using the Cockcroft and Gault equation which itself is a function of sex, age, weight, and serum creatinine (Buelga, del Mar Fernandez de Gatta, Herrera, Dominguez-Gil, & García, 2005; Cockroft & Gault, 1976). However, in practice there is a plethora of additional lab measurements collected, such as total protein, albumin, blood urea nitrogen (BUN), and urine output. In general, not all these lab measurements are included in the PK model. We propose to consider relevant lab measurements by extending the purely structured PK model with unstructured machine learning (ML) models (neural network, Gaussian Process, random forest etc.) for each or for at least some of the PK/PD parameters.

3.1. Neural network model

The architecture of neural network used in this work is depicted in Figure 1. A network consists of a layer of input units (which correspond to each line), one or more hidden layers with tanh activation function, and output unit (which corresponds to some PK parameter). Each hidden layer is connected to the preceeding hidden layer. The output is connected to the last hidden layer. Each unit in the hidden layers and output have a bias added to its input. The key difference between Bayesian Neural Networks (BNN) and traditional neural networks is that a probability distribution is associated with each weight and bias as opposed to the single point value used in conventional NNs. This allows estimating the uncertainty in the value of the output.

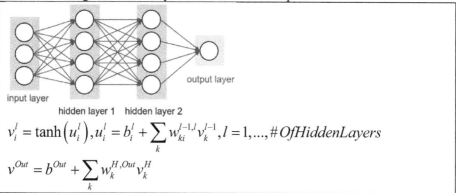

$$v_i^l = \tanh\left(u_i^l\right), u_i^l = b_i^l + \sum_k w_{ki}^{l-1,l} v_k^{l-1}, l = 1, \ldots, \#OfHiddenLayers$$

$$v^{Out} = b^{Out} + \sum_k w_k^{H,Out} v_k^H$$

Figure 1. The architecture of BNN

Here b_i^l is the bias for i^th unit in hidden layer l, b^{Out} is the bias for output unit, $w_{ki}^{l-1,l}$ is the weight from k^th unit in hidden layer l-1 to i^th unit in hidden layer l, $w_k^{H,Out}$ is the weight from k^th unit in the last hidden layer H to output unit, v_k^l is the value of the kth hidden unit, v_k^H is the value of the kth unit in the last hidden layer, v^{Out} is the value of the output unit (the value of PK parameter such as CL), and u_i^l is the value of the input to the ith hidden unit. The input layer may be interpreted as layer zero, i.c. v_k^0 is the value of the kth input (covariate). $w_{ki}^{0,1}$ corresponds to the weight from the kth unit in input layer to the ith unit in first hidden layer. The BNN model for the clearance parameter may be expressed as $CL \sim P\left(v^{Out}\right)$ where $P\left(v^{Out}\right)$ is a posterior of v^{Out}

In the case of Bayesian Neural Networks (BNN), the weights and biases have associated probability distributions (Neal, 1996). BNN model allows establishing the importance of critical covariates by using automatic relevance determination (ARD) (Husmeier, 1999) which is integral to BNN. The determination of important covariates allows the physician to concentrate on lab measurements relevant to specific disease.

3.2. Gaussian process model

The alternative to a neural network is the Gaussian Process (Rasmussen & Williams, 2006) which is another machine learning technique. The latent variable Gaussian Process model for the clearance parameter can be expressed as $CL = MVN\left(0, K\left(x \mid \theta\right)\right)$, where K is the kernel of the Gaussian Process, θ is the vector of parameters of kernel K, and MVN indicates a multivariate normal distribution. In this work we have used the squared exponential kernel with two parameters.

4. Results

We compared the predictions of these various models:

- **One compartmental PK model** with clearance and volume of distribution parameters specific to each patient. Such a model does not account for the change in clearance or volume of distribution that occur during treatment (i.e. renal function change or amount of liquid in the body)
- **Hybrid one compartmental PK model** with clearance represented as a BNN with one hidden layer and 10 nodes in the hidden layer with age, weight, height, gender, and serum creatinine as covariates.
- **Hybrid one compartmental PK model** with clearance represented as GP and the volume of distribution specific to each patient. This model does not account for change in weight and height in growing infants or the amount of liquid in the body.

The model predictions are summarized in Figure 2. It can be easily observed that the predictions enhanced with the Gaussian Process match the measured concentration more accurately since almost all blue lines cross the ideal line in red and uncertainty in estimates is lowest. The uncertainty (measured as a width of the 90% CR) is high because some patients have only few concentration observations at the trough. Uncertainty in the BNN estimates is similar to the predictions of the structural model.

The importance of covariates is summarized in Figure 2. If the weights of covariates are close to zero, then those covariates may be excluded from the model. In this case all covariates are important since 50% CR for all covariates are of comparable magnitude. The Bedside Schwartz equation confirms that height and serum creatinine are important for pediatric and adolescent patients (Schwartz & Work, 2009). The Cockcroft and Gault equation (Cockroft & Gault, 1976) confirms the importance of age, weight, and serum creatinine.

XSEDE environment allowed to parallelize training (or parameter estimation) of BNN and Gaussian Process (GP) models. For this dataset the training time was slightly less than 1 hour for the GP model and close to 15 minutes for the BNN model. Please note that it is possible to optimize parallelization to reduce training time significantly by exploring various approximations of Gaussian Process. Convergence was assessed visually as well as with R-hat statistics provided is stan (StanDevelopmentTeam, 2019).

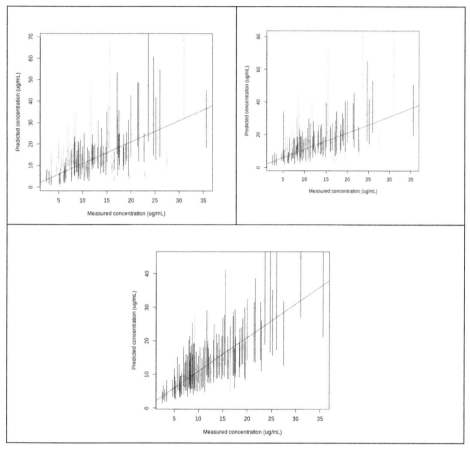

Figure 2. Predicted concentration for structured PK model (left panel), hybrid PK model where clearance parameter is represented as BNN (right panel), and the PK model where clearance parameter is represented as Gaussian Process (bottom panel). The green circles indicated the median of predicted concentration while the blue vertical lines indicate the 90% Credible Region (CR) of posterior distribution of predicted concentration. Vertical orange lines indicate where measured concentration is not within CR.

Table 1. Importance of covariates as determined by BNN

Covariate	50% CR of covariate for BNN
Weight	0.99
Serum creatinine	4.11
Age	2.76
Height	0.8
Sex	2.7

5. Conclusions

In this work we demonstrate the effectiveness of the hierarchical approach using the data from 2000 patients from Children's Hospital of Wisconsin. The data is not ideal – it has a large volume of missing vancomycin intermittent IVs. Moreover, for most patients there was single concentration measurement at the trough per administration. The Bayesian framework allowed us to train the one-compartmental model combined with Bayesian neural networks models and Gaussian Process models for clearance and volume of distribution on data from patients for which there were several concentration measurements available (20 patients). The predictive covariates were age, weight, height, gender, and serum creatinine. The results are encouraging – model predictions and actual measurements agree quite well. While these results must be viewed as only a proof of concept, they do suggest that such models can indeed help physicians to establish the right dose in a systematic way, accounting for different lab measurements, replacing the traditional approach in which the dosage is determined only based on weight and vancomycin half-life (the predominant practice). We also hypothesize that establishing the importance of various lab measurements will help to focus on those that are indicative for the disease.

We plan to validate those preliminary results on a large Cerner Heath Facts dataset (https://business.okstate.edu/chsi/cerner-health-facts.html). Instead of maintaining the volume of the distribution to be specific for each patient we are planning to have an non-structured model for volume of distribution to allow for changes in liquids content as well changes in weight and height for rapidly growing infants. Additional covariate to include would be urine output.

Acknowledgement

This work used the Extreme Science and Engineering Discovery Environment (XSEDE), which is supported by National Science Foundation grant number ACI-1548562, and is supported, in part, by the College of Engineering at Purdue University. We also would like to thank the Children's Hospital of Wisconsin for providing access to the dataset.

References

Buelga, D., del Mar Fernandez de Gatta, M., Herrera, E., Dominguez-Gil, A., & García, M. (2005). Population pharmacokinetic analysis of vancomycin in patients with hematological malignancies. *Antimicrob Agents Chemothe, 49*(12), 4934-41.

Cockroft, D., & Gault, M. (1976). Prediction of creatinine clearance from serum creatinine. *Nephron, 16*(1), 31-41.

Colin, P., Allegaert, K., Thomson, A., Touw, D., Dolton, M., Hoog, M., . . . Eleveld, D. (2019). Vancomycin Pharmacokinetics Throughout Life: Results from a Pooled Population Analysis and Evaluation of Current Dosing Recommendations. *Clinical Pharmacokinetics.*

Husmeier, D. (1999). Automatic Relevance Determination (ARD). In *Neural Networks for Conditional Probability Estimation.* London: Springer.

Neal, R. M. (1996). *Bayesian Learning for Neural Networks.* Springer.

(2009). *R: A Language and Environment for Statistical Computing.* Manual, R Foundation for Statistical Computing, Vienna, Austria.

Rasmussen, C., & Williams, C. (2006). *Gaussian Processes for Machine Learning.* Boston: MIT Press.

Roy, J., Dabbagh, N., Nguyen, A., & Hildgen, P. (2006). Application of an artificial neural network (ANN) for the monitoring of vancomycin IV in the intensive care unit. *Clinical Pharmacology & Therapeutics, 79*(2).

Schwartz, G., & Work, D. (2009). Measurement and estimation of GFR in children and adolescents. *Clin J Am Soc Nephrol, 4*(11), 1832-43.

StanDevelopmentTeam. (2019). CmdStan: the command-line interface to Stan. Retrieved from http://mc-stan.org/

Towns, J., Cockerill, T., Dahan, M., Foster, I., Gaither, K., Grimshaw, A., . . . Wilkins-Diehr, N. (2014). XSEDE: Accelerating Scientific Discovery. *Computing in Science & Engineering, 16*(5), 62-74.

Sauro Pierucci, Flavio Manenti, Giulia Bozzano, Davide Manca (Eds.)
Proceedings of the 30th European Symposium on Computer Aided Process Engineering
(ESCAPE30), May 24-27, 2020, Milano, Italy. © 2020 Elsevier B.V. All rights reserved.
http://dx.doi.org/10.1016/B978-0-12-823377-1.50007-0

A Two Carriers Reactor Configuration for Packed Bed Chemical-Looping for Power Generation

Erasmo Mancusi, Piero Bareschino, Annunziata Forgione, Francesco Pepe

Dipartimento d'Ingegneria, Università degli Studi del Sannio, Piazza Roma 21, Benevento, 82100, Italia

erasmo.mancusi@unisannio.it

Abstract

This work presents the model of a Chemical Looping Combustion fixed bed reactors network for CH_4 combustion. The network is made of couples of reactors arranged in series, the first one filled with a Cu-based oxygen carrier, already active at low temperature, while the second reactor exploits an Ni-based OC, which allows the achievement of high temperatures. The model developed will allow to evaluate the performances of the proposed reactor system in terms of both generated thermal power and flow and composition of gaseous current in output. The proposed two-stage CLC is shown to be able to reach same performances in terms of outlet gas temperature of a single carrier/single bed configuration while exposing each oxygen carrier to a narrower cyclic temperature increase.

Keywords: Chemical looping Combustion, CO_2 Capture, Two stages CLC, Packed Bed.

1. Introduction

The need for Carbon Capture (CC) from power plants has been thoroughly debated In the recent Paris Conference of the Parties (Rogelj *et al.* 2016). Within the framework of CC, several methods have been extensively studied. Although post-combustion capture seems to be well advanced in terms of maturity, pre-combustion capture using chemical looping processes retains an attractive thermodynamic potential for reducing energy penalty. Chemical Looping Combustion (CLC) is a two-step combustion technology for power generation that allows the inherent separation of CO_2, thus reducing the inherent penalties of the separation processes. In CLC, fuel and oxygen are not mixed but contacted via an intermediate, a metal oxide (oxygen carrier OC) able of being alternately oxidized and reduced. In this way, direct contact between fuel and combustion air is avoided and an N_2-free, CO_2 rich stream is produced (Adanez *et al.* 2012).

Generally, air is pressurized from ambient conditions up to 20-30 bar and a temperature of approximately 450-500°C is reached for the fed gas. To achieve a high electricity efficiency the flue gas for turbine system need to be produced at 1200°C (Hammers *et al.* 2015), so that the OC must withstand cyclic temperature jumps in order of ~700 °C, which puts its chemical and mechanical stability at great risk (Adanez *et al.* 2012). A strategy to reduce such danger could be to carry out the process in Two Stages-CLC (TS-CLC), so to avoid cyclical large thermal variations in a single stage. This goal can be pursued by pairing reactors in series (Hamers *et al*, 2015). The first reactor is responsible for first temperature rise, demanding that the oxygen carrier should be reactive at low temperature (e.g. copper-based materials), while the second bed is responsible for the remaining temperature rise, and thus the OC should be able to withstand higher temperatures. To circumvent the problem of maximum temperature achievable Hammers *et al.* (2015) and Kooiman *et al.* (2015) have proposed a TS-CLC using the pair Cu/Mn in the first case and Cu/Ni in the second one. In both cases the syngas is used as fuel. Differently from syngas methane is a reliable and an abundantly available energy source occurring in nature but the methane reduction is endothermic and therefore an accurate heat management strategy occurs (Diglio *et al* 2017a).

In this work the model of a CLC fixed bed reactor network for CH_4 combustion with a TS-CLC is numerically investigated. The network consists of two reactors arranged in series. The first reactor is filled with a Cu-based carrier, this metal has shown high reaction rates even at low temperature and, in addition, is cheaper than other carriers. The second reactor exploits an Ni-based OC, which allows the achievement of high temperatures even if used in low percentages (Adanez *et al.* 2012). The proposed model will allow to optimize and evaluate the performances of suggested reactor system in terms of developed thermal power and of the flow and composition of the gaseous current in output. It will be shown that this TS-CLC is a good alternative to the single bed configuration.

2. Kinetic scheme and mathematical model

The reaction kinetic model for Cu/CuO (Abad *et al.* 2007) and Ni/NiO (Iliuta *et al.* 2010) carriers on γ-Al_2O_3 is summarized in Table 1.

Table 1 – Kinetic scheme adopted.

Reaction	ΔH^0, kJ·mol^{-1}	
Oxidation Stage		
$2Cu\ O_2 \rightarrow 2CuO$	-296	R1
$2Ni\ O_2 \rightarrow 2NiO$	-479	R2
Reduction Stage		
$4CuO\ CH_4 \rightarrow 4Cu\ O_2\ H_2O$	-209	R3
$CH_4\ 2NiO \leftrightarrow 2Ni\ CO_2\ 2H_2$	161	R4
$H_2\ NiO \leftrightarrow Ni\ H_2O$	-2	R5
$CO\ NiO \leftrightarrow Ni\ CO_2$	-43	R6
$CH_4\ NiO \leftrightarrow Ni\ CO\ 2H_2$	203	R7
$CH_4\ H_2O \overset{Ni}{\leftrightarrow} CO\ 3H_2$	206	R8
$CH_4\ CO_2 \overset{Ni}{\leftrightarrow} 2CO\ 2H_2$	247	R9
$CO\ H_2O \overset{Ni}{\leftrightarrow} CO_2\ H_2$	-41	R10

Two main stages can be individuated during the CLC, namely Oxidation (OS), and Reduction (RS) stage. Over the OS air is fed to the TS-reactors and Cu (R1) and Ni (R2) oxidation in the first and second reactor occurs. When the second reactor is fully oxidized fed is switched to CH_4 and RS stage occurs. During RS the CuO is reduced to Cu (R3) in the first reactor while in the second reactor NiO reduction (R4-R7) occurs simultaneously to CH_4 reforming reactions. The kinetic expressions of reaction rate R1 and R3 are reported in Diglio *et al.* (2018a), while for R2 and R4-R10 see Diglio *et al.* (2017b, c).

To describe axial concentration and temperature profiles in TS-CLC reactors, a 1D pseudo-homogenous packed-bed model was used. The absence of radial concentration and temperature gradients, as well as the lack of both interphase and intra-particle concentration and temperature gradient has been validated and more details can be found for Cu OC in Diglio *et al* (2018a) and Ni OC in Diglio *et al.* (2017b). The model equations for both carriers are reported in Eqs. (1)-(4). TS-CLC is a periodically forced reactor (Altimari *et al.*, 2012) and when it is simulated the exit temperature and concentrations from the first reactor coincide with the inlet valued of the second reactor.

$$\varepsilon_g \frac{\partial c_i}{\partial t} + u_{sg} \frac{\partial c_i}{\partial z} = \varepsilon_g \frac{\partial}{\partial z}\left(D_{ax} \frac{\partial c_i}{\partial z} \right) - r_i \rho_{OC} \tag{1}$$

$$\frac{dX_k}{dt} = \sigma \frac{r_k}{C_{0k}} \tag{2}$$

$$\left[\varepsilon_g cp_g \rho_g + \left(1 - \varepsilon_g\right) cp_s \rho_{oc} \right]\frac{\partial T}{\partial t} + u_{sg} cp_g \rho_g \frac{\partial T}{\partial z} = \varepsilon_g \frac{\partial}{\partial z}\left(\lambda_{eff} \frac{\partial T}{\partial z} \right) + \rho_{OC} \sum_j \left(r_{Rj} \Delta H_{Rj} \right) \tag{3}$$

$$\frac{dP}{dz} = \frac{150 \mu_g \left(1 - \varepsilon_g\right)^2}{d_p^2 \varepsilon_g^3} u_{sg} + \frac{1.75\left(1 - \varepsilon_g\right)\rho_g}{d_p \varepsilon_g^3} u_{sg}^2 \tag{4}$$

Mass balance Eq. (1) has to be defined for each species, then i is the gas species (CH_4, H_2, CO_2, H_2O, CO, O_2, N_2), k is the solid species (Ni, Cu). C is the gas concentration in $mol \cdot m^{-3}$, C_{0k} is the initial concentration of solid species in the carrier, T is the temperature in K, X is the solid conversion, P is the pressure in Pa, z is the axial variable in m, t is the time in s, ε_g is the bed void fraction, u_{sg} is the gas superficial velocity in $m \cdot s^{-1}$, D_{ax} is the axial dispersion, ρ_{oc} and ρ_g are the density of oxygen carrier and gas, respectively, in $kg \cdot m^{-3}$, c_{pg} is the gas heat capacity in $J \cdot kg^{-1} \cdot K^{-1}$, λ_{eff} is the effective thermal conductivity in $W \cdot m^{-1} \cdot K^{-1}$, d_p is the particle diameter in m, ΔH is the reaction enthalpy in $kJ \cdot mol^{-1}$. The mathematical model Eqs. (1)-(4) is completed by the following set of boundary condition:

$$\frac{\partial c_i(0,t)}{\partial t} = \frac{u_{sg}}{\varepsilon_g D_{ax}}\left(c_i(0,t) - c_{i,in} \right), \frac{\partial c_i(L,t)}{\partial t} = 0 \tag{5}$$

$$\frac{\partial T(0,t)}{\partial t} = \frac{u_{sg} c_{pg} \rho_g}{\varepsilon_g \lambda_{eff}}\left(T(0,t) - T_{in} \right), \frac{\partial T(L,t)}{\partial t} = 0 \tag{6}$$

$$P(0,t) = P_{in} \tag{7}$$

The rates of consumption or formation of gas r_i solid, r_k species in $mol \cdot kg_{oc}^{-1} \cdot s^{-1}$ are determined according to the reaction scheme reported in Tab.1 by summing up the reaction rates of that species in all the reactions Rj (j=1,…,10). The numerical model was solved using the commercial software package Comsol Multiphysics®. Reactor length, L, for each reactor of the series was discretized with 500 nodes and it was carefully checked that further refinements of the spatial discretization did not produce any appreciable changes in the computed concentration and temperature profiles (Diglio *et al.*, 2018b).

3. Results and discussion Measurement units, numbers

In the proposed system the air is pressurized from ambient conditions up to 30 bar, a temperature of 500°C is obtained. The main idea behind the TS-CLC process is essentially that the heat developed during each stage in the first of the reactors should be transferred to the second so that from this it is possible, with fewer carriers than in the single stage, to achieve the desired temperature increase. In this way the burden of temperature variation is split between the two reactors instead of just one.

Two packed bed of same length are operated in series and the operating conditions, reactor and catalyst data used in the simulations are reported in Table 2.

Table 2 – Parameters used in the simulations

Parameter	Value
P_{in}, MPa	3.0
T_{in}, °C	520
$L_{Cu}=L_{Ni}$, m	1.0
d_r, m	0.65
$w_{act,Cu}$	0.12
$w_{act,Ni}$	0.1
$\rho_g V_{g,os}$, kg·m^{-2}·s^{-1}	2
$\rho_g V_{g,hr}$, kg·m^{-2}·s^{-1}	2
$\rho_g V_{g,ps}$, kg·m^{-2}·s^{-1}	4
$\rho_g V_{g,rs}$, kg·m^{-2}·s^{-1}	2/15

The TS-CLC process can be seen as a five stages sequence, namely: (I) reduction of carriers (RS): during this stage CH_4 is fed; (II) purge (PS): to avoid the formation of a potentially explosive mixture a purge stage is mandatory in industrial operation; (III) oxidation of carrier (OS): during this stage air if fed to the reactor and the oxidation of the carrier occurs generating heat at high temperature; (IV) heat removal (HR): at the end of OS the most of the heat produced is trapped inside the reactor and all the OC is in the oxidize form thus air is fed to the reactor in order to obtain a high temperature gas stream for subsequent power generation; (V) purge (PS): before to switch again the feed to CH_4 and restart the cycle. Then, the TS-CLC includes RS-PS-OS-HR-PS that cyclically follows each other in a fixed bed reactor. The length of each stage was not fixed a priori, but a controller automatically sets it. To clearly explain the adopted switching strategy, Figure 1 reports monitored outlet temperature (a) and gas concentrations (b) during a CLC cycle starting from RS. It can be inferred from Figure 1: i) the controller dictates the switch between RS and PS when CH_4 concentration at the second reactor outlet reaches about 90% its inlet value in order to fully reduce the OC in the reactor, ii) the subsequent PS length has been chosen equal to 15% of previous RS. iii) the switch between OS and HR is dictated when O_2 concentration at the reactor outlet reached 95% of its inlet value in order to fully oxidize the carrier in the reactor, iv) the subsequent HR is continued until outlet gas temperature drops below 1150°C in order to feed a gas stream at approximately constant temperature to a downstream unit, v) a quick purge is provided before switching to RS. The overall period of a CLC cycle is of 940 s and for the adopted gas flow rates and the percentage of the active phase the time length of OS is very similar to those of RS (~210 s), the HR stage has a time length of 460 s and both PS stages have a time length of 25 s. Moreover, as it is possible to observe in Fig.1, the time required to oxidize and/or reduce the first of the two reactors is the same as that required to complete the oxidation and/or reduction in the second reactor.

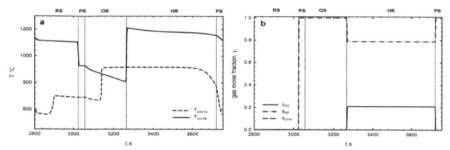

Figure 1 – Outlet temperature (a) and gas molar fractions during a CLC cycle

To gain insight about the TS-CLC process the spatial temperature profiles are depicted in Figure-2. During the RS (Fig.2a) in the first reactor the exothermic Cu reduction occurs (R3) while in the second the process of Ni reduction is strongly endothermic (R4-R10), therefore the temperature at the end of the RS is higher than the initial one in the first reactor while it decreases in the second. When both the carriers are oxidized (Fig.2b) two distinct temperature plateaus are observed, i.e. 970 °C and 1200°C for first and second reactor respectively. HR is extended until outlet gas temperature drops below 1150 °C.

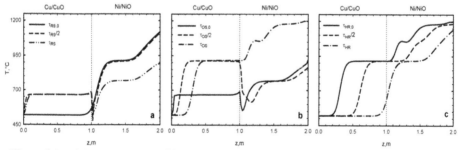

Figure-2 Spatial temperature profiles at several time instants during RS (a), OS (b) and HR (c)

Finally, the outlet gas temperatures at the outlet of first and second reactor are reported for several CLC cycles in Figure 3. It is possible to see that the temperature increase of 700°C between inlet and outlet, is equally split between the two oxygen carrier.

4. Conclusions

In this work, it has been demonstrated that a TS-CLC system based on Cu and Ni OC can guarantee a cyclical temperature variation of ~700 °C by evenly dividing it between two oxygen carriers. The TS-CLC system has two concurrent advantages: it is possible to reach higher outlet gas temperature than those achievable using only copper or to reduce the amount of carrier needed when only Ni is used. These results encourage a future detailed analysis of the costs of this process and a comparison with the most common CLCs.

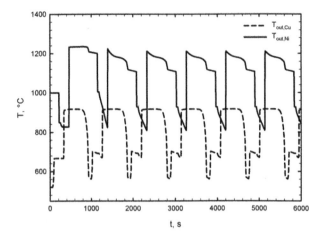

Figure 3 – Outlet gas temperature during multiple CLC cycles.

References

A. Abad, J. Adànez, F. Garcìa-Labiano, L.F. de Diego, P. Gayàn , J. Celaya , 2007,Mapping the range of operational conditions for Cu-, Fe-, and Ni-based oxygen carriers in chemical-looping combustion, Chem. Eng. Sci. 62, 533-54.

A. Adànez, F. Abad, P. Garcia-Labiano, L. Gayan, L. De Diego, 2012, Progress in chemical looping combustion and reforming technologies, Progress in Energy and Combustion Science 38, 2, 215–282.

P. Altimari, E. Mancusi, L. Russo, S. Crescitelli, 2012, Temperature wave-trains of periodically forced networks of catalytic reactors, AIChE J. 58 (3), 899-913.

G. Diglio, P. Bareschino, E. Mancusi, F. Pepe, 2017a, Numerical Assessment of the Effects of Carbon Deposition and Oxidation on Chemical Looping Combustion in a Packed-bed Reactor, Chem. Eng. Sci. 160, 86-96.

G. Diglio, P. Bareschino, E. Mancusi, F. Pepe, 2017b, Novel quasi-autothermal hydrogen production process in a fixed-bed using a chemical looping approach: A numerical study, International Journal of Hydrogen Energy, 42, 22, 15010-15023.

G. Diglio, P. Bareschino, R. Solimene, E. Mancusi, F. Pepe, P. Salatino, 2017c, Numerical simulation of hydrogen production by chemical looping reforming in a dual fluidized bed reactor, Powder Technol., 316, 614–627

G. Diglio, P. Bareschino, E. Mancusi, F. Pepe, 2018a, Techno-Economic Evaluation of a Small-Scale Power Generation Unit Based on a Chemical Looping Combustion Process in Fixed Bed Reactor Network, Industrial and Engineering Chemistry Research, 57, 33, 11299-11311.

G. Diglio, P. Bareschino, E. Mancusi, F. Pepe, F. Montagnaro, D.P. Hanak, V. Manovic, 2018b, Feasibility of CaO/CuO/NiO sorption-enhanced steam methane reforming integrated with solid-oxide fuel cell for near-zero-CO₂ emissions cogeneration system, Appl. Energy, 13, 241.

H.P. Hamers, M.C. Romano, V. Spallina, P. Chiesa, F. Gallucci, M. van Sint Annaland, 2015,Energy Analysis of Two Stage Packed-Bed Chemical Looping Combustion Configurations for Integrated Gasification Combined Cycles, Energy, 85, 489.

I. Iliuta, R. Tahoces, G. Patience, 2010, Chemical-looping combustion process: Kinetics and mathematical modeling, AIChE J., 56, 1063–1079.

R. F. Kooiman, H.P. Hamers, F. Gallucci, M. Van Sint Annaland, 2015, Experimental Demonstration of Two-Stage Packed Bed Chemical-Looping Combustion Using Syngas with CuO/Al₂O₃ and NiO/CaAl₂O₄ as Oxygen Carriers, Ind. Eng. Chem. Res, 54, 7, 2001-2011.

J. Rogelj, M. Den Elzen, N., Hohne, T. Fransen, H. Fekete, H. Winkler, R. Schaeffler, F. Shar, K. Riahi, M. Meinshausen, 2016, Paris Agreement Climate Proposal Need a Boost to Keep Warming Weel below 2 C. Nature , 534(7609), 631.

Sauro Pierucci, Flavio Manenti, Giulia Bozzano, Davide Manca (Eds.)
Proceedings of the 30th European Symposium on Computer Aided Process Engineering
(ESCAPE30), May 24-27, 2020, Milano, Italy. © 2020 Elsevier B.V. All rights reserved.
http://dx.doi.org/10.1016/B978-0-12-823377-1.50008-2

Modeling of Liquid-Liquid Phase Transfer Catalysis: Process Intensification via Integration of Process Systems Engineering and Computational Chemistry

Abhimanyu Pudi, Adam P. Karcz, Vahid Shadravan, Martin P. Andersson,
Seyed Soheil Mansouri*

*Department of Chemical and Biochemical Engineering, Technical University of
Denmark, Søltofts Plads 229, Kgs. Lyngby, DK-2800, Denmark*
seso@kt.dtu.dk

Abstract

Phase transfer catalysis is an important intensified extraction-reaction process and a powerful tool applied in a vast array of chemical synthesis applications. This technique allows for reactions that are generally not feasible through conventional synthesis routes via the introduction of a heterogeneous transfer catalyst that can carry a reactant species across two immiscible phases. These biphasic conditions enable novel synthesis routes, higher yields, and faster reactions, while also facilitating the separation of certain species. The economic viability and successful large-scale implementation of such processes are heavily contingent on the design and modelling of the systems under consideration. Although a few attempts have been made to create case-specific and generic models for phase transfer catalysis, they suffer from the lack of modelling considerations or thermodynamic model parameters. These limitations restrict the solution space to design new phase transfer catalysis-based processes. In the present work, an integrated and multiscale modelling framework is presented to overcome such limitations for liquid-liquid phase transfer catalysis. The proposed framework requires little to no experimental data and employs different tools at different scales of time and space to model nearly any liquid-liquid phase transfer catalytic system. The objective of this work is to apply this framework towards the process of H_2S recovery and conversion from an aqueous alkanolamine solution to value-added products as a means to improve process economics and sustainability, particularly in offshore oil and gas platforms. The framework is validated by comparing the preliminary results with known experimental behaviour. The final results are expected to contribute towards further developing a generic, systematic framework for biphasic reaction-separation processes.

Keywords: Phase transfer catalysis, multiscale modelling, resource recovery.

1. Introduction

Advances in computing have greatly revolutionized science and engineering. Coupled with massive progress in fundamental chemical physics theory, mathematics, and computer science, they have contributed to the constant evolution in the fields of chemistry and chemical engineering, essentially giving rise to the disciplines of computational chemistry and process systems engineering (PSE), respectively. These two disciplines play a major role in providing new understanding and development of computational procedures for the simulation, design, and operation of systems ranging from atoms and molecules to industrial-scale and enterprise-wide processes—an enormous span of scales of space and time that form the chemical supply chain. Despite being part of the same overarching field, chemistry and chemical engineering have generally remained two distinct areas working at different scales with partial overlap; while computational chemistry focuses on the small scale, PSE focuses on the intermediate and large scales. However, over the past two decades, it has become increasingly clear that the modelling, design and development of new and innovative reaction and separation processes requires going below the scale of unit operations—the holy ground of traditional process engineering—towards the underlying molecules, clusters and their behavior that make up the functions/tasks carried out by the unit operations (Babi et al., 2016). This trend of moving beyond traditional chemical engineering has emerged because the concept of unit operations, although useful and easy to understand, inherently restricts the solution space to a limited number of well-known and ready-made solutions (Freund and Sundmacher, 2008).

To overcome these limitations, engineers and industrial researchers have been working on novel equipment and techniques that could potentially transform our concept of chemical plants and lead to compact, safe, energy-efficient, and environment-friendly sustainable processes (Stankiewicz and Moulijn, 2000). These developments share a common theme: process intensification. In this regard, bridging computational chemistry and PSE to achieve process intensification could qualitatively change the way chemical products and processes are designed.

Phase transfer catalysis (PTC) is one such case of process intensification that could hugely benefit from a multiscale outlook. In liquid-liquid (L-L) PTC, the reactions take place in heterogeneous two-phase systems (organic-aqueous) with negligible mutual solubility of the phases. The catalyst, located in the aqueous phase, acts as a source of lipophilic cations and continuously introduces the reacting anionic species in the form of lipophilic ion pairs into the organic phase. However, the downside of PTC is the need to quantify exacting reaction conditions and parameters that are difficult to uncover and, in some cases, are counterintuitive. Although there has been some progress in terms of mathematical modeling of PTC systems (Anantpinijwatna et al., 2016), availability of accurate thermodynamic parameters still proves a major limitation as the chemical domain in the group contribution methods is inherently limited to the portion of the chemical design space for which every binary interaction parameter is available.

2. Modelling Framework

Anantpinijwatna et al. (2016) presented a systematic procedure for modelling biphasic systems that is based on the model generation method of Cameron and Gani (2011). The procedure serves to reduce the complexity of the modelling problem by breaking it into a series of sub-problems. A schematic of the various steps in the procedure can be seen in Figure 1.

The heart of a successful PTC modelling framework lies in the methods and/or tools used to describe the system in the three modules shown in Figure 1 since the methods used to calculate the molecular and mixture properties largely determine the breadth, accuracy and performance of the framework. The present work employs sequential multiscale modelling by using different tools for different scales of time and space to model and predict the behaviour of the PTC system. Although modules 2 and 3 remain largely the same as defined in Anantpinijwatna et al. (2016), the methods used in module 1 make the framework much more generic in terms of its application. The integration of quantum chemical calculations into a process modelling framework greatly expands the envelope of chemical species that can be modelled at a high level of accuracy. A more thorough description of the framework can be found in Pudi (2019).

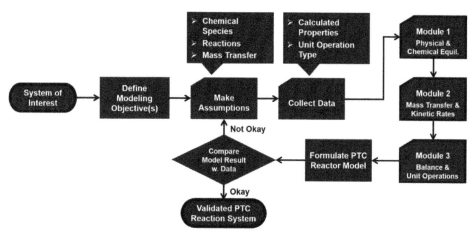

Figure 1 Generic Modelling Procedure for Biphasic Reaction Systems. Adapted from Anantpinijwatna et al. (2016)

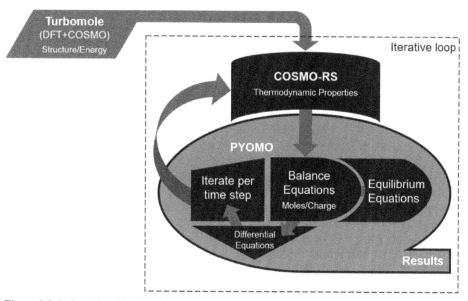

Figure 2 Solution Algorithm for the Proposed Framework

The algorithm is illustrated in Figure 2. With Python as the high-level interface, three different tools are employed at three different levels of space and time as follows:
- Molecular/electronic level: Turbomole
- Transport and reaction thermodynamics level: COSMOtherm

- Reactor level: Pyomo.

For each species in the system, geometric optimization calculations are performed in Turbomole to obtain their ground-state and gas-phase energies and screening charge density profiles. These are then transferred to COSMOtherm to obtain partition coefficients, activity coefficients, and chemical equilibrium constants, which are all parameters for the PTC model. These parameters are then input in Pyomo where the equations for equilibria, kinetics, and balances are solved to model the system behaviour.

3. Application and Validation

Hydrogen sulfide is a highly toxic chemical that is found as an impurity or an inhibitor in many petrochemical, chemical and biochemical processes. In fact, it is classified as a hazardous industrial waste. Environmental and/or process constraints often require the removal of this compound to trace amounts. This is usually accomplished by capturing H_2S and later oxidizing it to elemental sulfur, a process generally referred to as sulfur recovery. Recovered elemental sulfur is produced primarily during the processing of natural gas and crude petroleum. Due to the depletion of sweet oil and gas reserves around the world, players in the O&G industry are increasingly looking toward sour fields to meet our energy needs. In the past 2-3 decades, sulfur production has consistently outpaced the demand leading to the large stockpiles of block sulfur *waste* in several countries around the world. At a time when the world is striving to achieve a zero-waste and circular economy, sulfur disposal poses a serious barrier to such a transition. Therefore, it is vital to develop a viable alternative to the practice of converting H_2S to elemental sulfur.

L-L PTC offers one such alternative by converting H_2S to value-added products. Since alkanolamine-based processes are widely used for the removal of acid gases from gaseous streams, it is assumed that the capture of H_2S from a gas phase to a liquid phase uses a 30 % solution of methyldiethanolamine (MDEA). Traditional approach for the next step is the use of a stripping column to separate H_2S and regenerate MDEA; MDEA is then sent back to the absorber while H_2S is directed towards further process steps to convert it to elemental sulfur. However, the regeneration step requires high operational costs. In order to overcome the drawbacks of this process, PTC is explored as the cornerstone for the capture and utilization of H_2S. One major advantage of this route is the ability to target a wide variety of products, instead of only elemental sulfur or inorganic sulfates. Using L-L PTC in a continuous stirred tank reactor, the H_2S-rich aqueous phase is put in contact with an organic phase (here toluene) containing benzyl chloride (BC) to produce benzyl mercaptan (BM) in the presence of a PT catalyst such as tetrabutylammonium bromide (QBr). The objective is to model the complex interlinked phenomena—multiple reactions in each phase and partitioning of various species between the phases—occurring in such a system. The reactions presumed to occur in this biphasic system are given below.

Organic Phase:

$$QSH + BC \rightleftharpoons QCl + BM \tag{1}$$

Aqueous Phase:

$$2H_2O \rightleftharpoons H_3O^+ + OH^- \tag{2}$$

$$MDEAH^+ + H_2O \rightleftharpoons MDEA + H_3O^+ \tag{3}$$

$$H_2S + H_2O \rightleftharpoons HS^- + H_3O^+ \tag{4}$$

$$HS^- + H_2O \rightleftharpoons S^{2-} + H_3O^+ \tag{5}$$

$$QBr + HS^- \rightleftharpoons QSH + Br^- \tag{6}$$

$$QCl + HS^- \rightleftharpoons QSH + Cl^- \tag{7}$$

$$HBr + H_2O \rightleftharpoons Br^- + H_3O^+ \tag{8}$$

$$HCl + H_2O \rightleftharpoons Cl^- + H_3O^+ \tag{9}$$

$$QBr \rightleftharpoons Q^+ + Br^- \tag{10}$$

$$QCl \rightleftharpoons Q^+ + Cl^- \tag{11}$$

The PT catalysts, QBr & QCl, react with the inorganic sulfide anion in the aqueous phase to produce the active catalyst species, QSH. These active catalysts species partition into the organic phase transporting the hydrosulfide ion to participate in the nucleophilic substitution reactions with BC. A few of the reactor specifications are taken from the experimental data reported by Singh et al. (2016). Preliminary findings from the application of the modelling framework to this case are presented below.

3.1. Phase Partitioning

From the phase equilibrium calculations in COSMOtherm, affinities of each species in the system to each of the two phases can be understood. To this end, the partition coefficient values of a few important components calculated in the first iteration of the implicit solution method are listed in Table 1.

Table 1 Partition Behaviour Characteristics

Chemical Species	Partition Coefficient	Preferential Phase
H_2O	0.06	Aqueous
Toluene	1104.57	Organic
BM	1040.48	Organic
BC	912.15	Organic
QSH	100.86	Organic
QBr	26.82	Organic
QCl	24.31	Organic
MDEA	0.44	Aqueous
HS^-	0	Aqueous

A partition coefficient greater than 1 implies a relatively higher affinity towards the organic phase, while a value less than 1 implies a relatively higher affinity towards the aqueous phase. In this context, the reported values are consistent with and explain the experimental behaviour observed by Singh et al. (2016). The main reactant and product in the organic phase reaction, benzyl chloride and benzyl mercaptan, are heavily partitioned into the organic phase. This provides for a cleaner product separation in the downstream purification processes. The three catalyst species (QSH, QBr, and QCl) mildly prefer the organic phase. Among the three, the active catalyst form of QSH exhibits about four times higher affinity to the organic phase than the two inactive catalyst species. This enables the preferential partition of the necessary active form into the organic phase to undergo the reaction to form the required product BM.

3.2. General Performance

The first iteration found a 23 % conversion of benzyl chloride to benzyl mercaptan. Although the final rate of conversion is expected to be high, it is worth noting that the value from the first iteration matches the first data point obtained by Singh et al. (2016) in the first 5-10 minutes of the experiment. This shows that the current version of the modelling framework does indeed work and is headed in the right direction.

4. Conclusions

A rigorous multiscale modelling framework to describe the behaviour of a phase transfer catalysis system is presented. The framework incorporates a series of computational tools covering different scales of time and space in a sequential/dynamic modelling approach. The current implementation offers great advantages over the previously developed modelling framework reported in Anantpinijwatna et al. (2016). Due to the incorporation of quantum chemical and continuum solvation methods, the limitation due to the unavailability of accurate thermodynamic model parameters has been overcome in the present work. Further work is expected to fully develop the tool integration in the framework.

References

A. Anantpinijwatna, M. Sales-Cruz, S. H. Kim, J. P. O'Connell, and R. Gani, 2016, A systematic modelling framework for phase transfer catalyst systems, Chem. Eng. Res. Des., 116, 407-422

D. K. Babi, M. Sales-Cruz, and R. Gani, 2016, Fundamentals of Process Intensification: A Process Systems Engineering View, In: Segovia-Hernández J., Bonilla-Petriciolet A. (eds) Process Intensification in Chemical Engineering, Springer, Cham, Switzerland, 7-33

I. T. Cameron and R. Gani, 2011, Product and Process Modelling: A Case Study Approach, Elsevier, Amsterdam, Netherlands

H. Freund and K. Sundmacher, 2008, Towards a methodology for the systematic analysis and design of efficient chemical processes. Part 1. From unit operations to elementary process functions, Chem. Eng. Process., 47, 12, 2051-2060

A. Pudi, 2019, From Molecule to Process: Multiscale Modeling of Liquid-Liquid Phase Transfer Catalysis, M.Sc. Thesis, Technical University of Denmark, retrieved from https://findit.dtu.dk/en/catalog/2452812532

G. Singh, P. G. Nakade, D. Chetia, P. Jha, U. Mondal, S. Kumari, and S. Sen, 2016, Kinetics and mechanism of phase transfer catalyzed synthesis of aromatic thioethers by H2S-rich methyldiethanolamine, J. Ind. Eng. Chem., 37, 190-197

A. I. Stankiewicz and J. A. Moulijn, 2000, Process Intensification: Transforming chemical engineering, Chem. Eng. Prog., 96, 22-23

Sauro Pierucci, Flavio Manenti, Giulia Bozzano, Davide Manca (Eds.)
Proceedings of the 30th European Symposium on Computer Aided Process Engineering
(ESCAPE30), May 24-27, 2020, Milano, Italy. © 2020 Elsevier B.V. All rights reserved.
http://dx.doi.org/10.1016/B978-0-12-823377-1.50009-4

Investment Planning in Personalised Medicine

Despoina Moschou[a], Maria M. Papathanasiou[a], Matthew Lakelin[b], Nilay Shah[a]

[a]*Dept. of Chemical Engineering, Centre for Process Systems Engineering (CPSE), Imperial College London SW7 2AZ, London, U.K*

[b]*TrakCel Limited, 10/11 Raleigh Walk, Cardiff, CF10 4LN UK*

maria.papathanasiou11@imperial.ac.uk

Abstract

Personalised cancer therapies are gaining increasing attention due to their demonstrated clinical potential. Nonetheless, such patient-centric, 1:1 business models encompass significant manufacturing and distribution challenges that are directly associated with the patient schedule. In this work we focus on the development and solution of a mixed-integer optimisation problem to suggest cost-efficient candidate networks that guarantee responsiveness and successful delivery of the therapy. The developed model is tested under two demand scenarios, incorporating economies of scale elements.

Keywords: mixed integer programming, personalised medicine, optimisation, supply chain

1. Introduction

Personalised medicine is dedicated to the discovery, manufacturing and delivery of patient-specific therapy protocols that can more effectively target autoimmune diseases and malignancies related to patient-specific mutations, such as cancer. Chimeric Antigen Receptor (CAR) T cell therapy is one of the latest personalised therapies developed and approved in in the United States (Novartis, 2018), Europe (European Medicines Agency, 2018), Australia (Lymphoma Australia, 2018) and Japan (Biomedica, 2019). These use recombinant receptors for antigens that can make T lymphocytes tumour-specific. Through genetic modification, T cells are engineered to express the CAR receptor that redirects their specificity and function, enabling them to recognize and destroy cancer cells (Sadelain, Brentjens, Rivière, & Park, 2015). This individualized, emerging immunotherapy has shown promising results particularly in the treatment of B-cell lymphoma (Jackson, Rafiq, & Brentjens, 2016; Maude et al., 2018; Neelapu et al., 2017) and has encouraged further clinical research.

The delivery of gene-modified T cells is different from that of the traditional off-the-shelf medicines. CAR-T cell therapy is a dynamic treatment process that requires collaboration and effective communication between several parties (healthcare providers, cancer treatment centres, manufacturing facilities) (Novartis, 2017). Currently, this innovative therapy is provided through a service model, developed based on the requirements for allogeneic Blood and Marrow Transplantation (BMT)(NHS, 2018). The analogy between these two treatments lies in the pairing of one cell donor with one patient (Foley & Whitaker, 2012). The different stages of the treatment's delivery are illustrated in Figure 1. Currently, the end-to-end process comprises 7 steps, namely: leukapheresis (extraction of T cells from patient's blood stream), cryopreservation, manufacturing, quality control and cryopreservation, thawing and administration. It should be underlined that cryopreservation is a step highly dependent on the individual manufacturer models. Therefore, there may be processes where the patient T cell sample is transferred fresh (at -80°C). Following administration, patients are monitored short-term for side effects and long term for possible disease relapse.

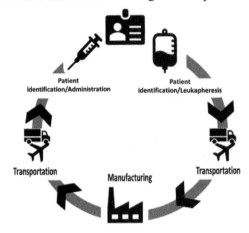

Figure 1 Different stages of CAR-T cell therapy delivery

The successful operation of such a supply chain model requires the orchestration of multiple components (Shah, 2004). In a typical supply chain model in the pharmaceutical industry there are usually established warehouses/distribution centres in place, responsible for the storage and distribution of the manufactured drug to the retailers. By contrast, in the case of CAR T cells, cells are transported directly from the clinical site to the manufacturing locations and back to the hospital, thus imposing additional constraints with respect to storage, activity coordination and sample tracking. Considering the uniqueness of the therapy's delivery, the supply chain of gene modified T-cells can be identified as a service starting and finishing with a specific patient (Wei Teng, Foley, O'Neill, & Hicks, 2014). CAR T cell therapy can be characterised as one-on-one autologous treatment (1:1 model) as cells are harvested form a single patient, manipulated and then returned to the same patient. Similar to classical pharmaceuticals, even more so in the case of CAR T cells, systematic decision making in the design and planning of supply chain networks can significantly reduce risk of failure and increase efficiency. In this framework, here we present for the first time the design of a comprehensive Mixed Integer Linear (MILP) model to allow decision-making in CAR T cell supply chain.

2. The model

2.1. Case under study

In this work we consider today's CAR T cell supply chain network (Figure 2), comprising 3 main nodes: (a) leukapheresis site, (b) manufacturing facility and (c) hospital. Often, the leukapheresis site and the hospital are either co-located or close to one another in the same city. Here, we consider the United Kingdom (UK) as the geographical area of interest and we develop two cases for 200 and 500 patients annually. The patient population is distributed in time based on a separate algorithm, considering the daily capacity of the leukapheresis centers.

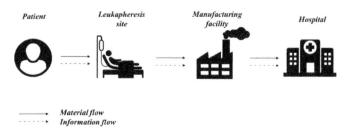

Figure 2 Classical CAR T cell supply chain network

2.2. Mathematical formulation

The optimisation problem described in the previous section is formulated as a mixed-integer linear programming (MILP) model, and the general formulation is presented in Table 1.

Table 1 Mixed Integer Linear Problem (MILP) formulation developed to solve the supply chain optimisation scenarios generated for the network as shown in Figure 2.

Index	Mathematical Formulation	Description
Objective function		
(1)	$TCO = C_{manufacturing} + C_{quality} + C_{apheresis} + C_{transportation} + C_{capital}$	Total Network Cost
OR (2)	$ART = \left. \sum_p T_{transport} + T_{manufacturing} + T_{leukap\,heresis} \right) / NP$	Average Return Time of Therapy
Constraints		
(3)	$Y1_{l,m} \leq E1_m \ \forall m,l, Y4_{m,h} \leq E1_m \ \forall m,h, \sum_m E1_m \leq 2,$ $Y2_{p,l,m,k,t} \leq Y1_{l,m} \ \forall p,l,m,k,t, Y3_{p,m,h,k,t} \leq Y4_{m,h} \ \forall p,m,h,k,t$	Network/Transportation
(4)	$XTA_{p,l,t} = \sum_m \sum_k XTAM_{p,l,m,k,t+TL} \ \forall p,l,m,k,t, XTAM_{p,l,m,k,t} = XTM_{p,l,m,k,t+TDEL_k},$ $\sum_l \sum_k XTM_{p,l,m,k,t} = \sum_h \sum_k XTMH_{p,m,h,k,t+TM+TQC} \ \forall p,m,t,$ $XTMH_{p,m,h,k,t} = XTHI_{p,m,h,k,t+TDEL_k}, \sum_m \sum_k XTHI_{p,m,h,k,t} = XTHO_{p,h,t+TH}$	Sequencing/ Scheduling
(5)	$\sum_p XTA_{p,l,t} = \sum_p \sum_m \sum_k XTAM_{p,l,m,k,t+TL} \ \forall l,t,$ $\sum_p \sum_l \sum_k XTM_{p,l,m,k,t} = \sum_p \sum_h \sum_k XTMH_{p,m,h,k,t+TM+TQC} \ \forall m,t, \sum_m \sum_k XTHI_{p,m,h,k,t} = XTHO_{p,h,t+TH}$	Sample Balances
(6)	$\sum_p \sum_l \sum_k XTM_{p,l,m,k,t} \leq MMCAP_m - \sum_p \sum_l \sum_k \sum_t^{t-TM} XTM_{p,l,m,k,t} \ \forall m,t,$ $\sum_p \sum_m \sum_k XTHI_{p,m,h,k,t} \leq MHCAP_h - \sum_p \sum_m \sum_k \sum_t^{t-TH} XTHI_{p,m,h,k,t} \ \forall h,t$	Capacity Constraints

Two functions are selected as candidate minimisation objectives; namely the total cost (Eq. (1)) and the average network response time, reflecting the urgency of the treatment (Eq. (2)). The total network cost is associated with the capital, fixed operational (leukapheresis and in-house quality control expenses), manufacturing and transportation cost (Eq. (1)). The responsiveness of the network is measured through the average lead time for the production and delivery of a therapy, which is the sum of the time a treatment spends at every stage of the supply chain. For the cost minimisation scenarios, an upper bound on the response time is introduced ($ART \leq U$, where U corresponds to the maximum time allowed before the therapy is be administered to the patient). A set of network and transportation constraints (Eq. (3)), ensures that only feasible connections are established inside the supply chain network. As regulatory authorities require manufacturers of biological medicinal products to conduct costly cooperabilities studies for the introduction of new manufacturing facilities, an upper bound constraint is introduced to prevent the establishment of more than two production sites. Sequencing constraints and material balances (Eq. (4)-(5)) at each supply chain node impose the correct sequence of events inside the supply chain for every treatment. Finally, capacity constraints on the treatment centres and the manufacturing sites (Eq. (6)) enforce upper bound limitations on the scheduling of therapies.

2.3. Model input

Here we consider 6 candidate locations for the manufacturing facilities with different annual capacities. Based on current standard practice, the choice of leukapheresis sites and hospitals is not entirely under the manufacturers' control and is tightly associated to regulations and reimbursement procedures. Therefore, in this case the latter are treated as inputs for the model formulation and the locations are depicted in Table 2. For the transportation of the therapies between the supply chain nodes two shipment options are considered (1-day and 2-day delivery). In addition, given the complex nature of the leukapheresis and administration procedures, we impose a daily demand equal to 10 patients for the leukapheresis sites and 5 patients for the hospitals.

Table 2 Model fixed and candidate location inputs for leukapheresis sites, manufacturing facilities and administration sites.

Leukapheresis site (fixed input)		Manufacturing facility (candidate locations)		Administration site (hospital) (fixed input)	
Geographical Location	Capacity (patients/day)	Geographical Location	Capacity (patients/year)	Geographical Location	Capacity (patients/day)
London	10	Stevenage	200	London	5
Glasgow	10	Glasgow	1500	Glasgow	5
Manchester	10	Berlin	500	Manchester	5
Birmingham	10	Belgium	200	Birmingham	5
		Pennsylvania	1500		
		Virginia	500		

3. Results and discussion

The optimisation algorithm presented above was modelled using the GAMS modelling system coupled with the CPLEX 12.9 solver. The optimal manufacturing facilities for each scenario and demand pattern are presented in Table 3. In general, the optimiser selected the establishment of manufacturing sites with annual production capacity higher than the demand of the scenario under investigation. This is attributed to the randomness of the demand distribution, a common characteristic of CAR T cell therapies. Higher production capacities ensure that enough production lines are available to serve patients in periods with high demand density. In addition, the proximity to the market influenced the solutions of the cost minimisation scenarios, as production sites located closer to the United Kingdom where selected, contributing to lower transportation costs.

Table 3 Model fixed and candidate location inputs for leukapheresis sites, manufacturing facilities and administration sites.

	Minimisation of ART	Minimisation of Total Cost with no time constraints	Minimisation of Total Cost with time constraints (ART<20)	Minimisation of Total Cost with time constraints (ART<21)	Annual patient population
Optima Manufacturing facilities	Stevenage, Virginia	Berlin	Berlin	Berlin	200
	Glasgow, Berlin	Glasgow	Glasgow	Glasgow	500

The economic performance of each network can be evaluated through the achievable average cost per therapy. Figure 2, shows that the cost significantly decreased with an increase in patient demand. The high demand scenarios presented reduced operational costs, due to higher manufacturing capacity utilisation. In addition, there is a clear cost trade-off between the supply chain responsiveness and economies of scale. Strict time constraints resulted in higher infrastructure and transportation costs, decreasing the profit gap per therapy. Finally, the capital costs are identified as the major cost contributor in the production of CAR-T cell therapies, while transportation costs only correspond to ~ 2% of the total therapy cost (Table 4).

Figure 2 Average cost per therapy for 200 and 500 patients annual demand for 4 different scenarios.

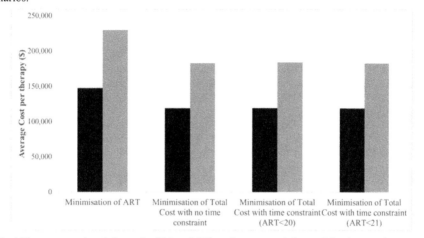

Table 4 Therapy cost breakdown for 200 and 500 patients annual demand for 4 scenarios.

	Minimisation of ART	Minimisation of Total Cost with no time constraints	Minimisation of Total Cost with time constraints (ART<20)	Minimisation of Total Cost with time constraints (ART<21)	Annual patient population
% Transport	2.07%	1.37%	1.99%	1.37%	200
% CAPEX/OPEX manufacturing	97.93%	98.63%	98.01%	98.63%	
% Transport	3.20%	0.97%	1.40%	0.97%	500
% CAPEX/OPEX manufacturing	96.80%	99.03%	98.60%	99.03%	

4. Conclusions

A complete optimisation algorithm able to design agile and cost-effective CAR T cell supply chain networks was developed. The case study on cost-time trade off at different demand patterns, revealed that the supply chain becomes more profitable as the number of patients receiving the treatment increases. The demand distribution uncertainty and the limiting production capacity were identified as the major supply chain bottlenecks, that lead to increased network costs. The current work considered the traditional supply chain model for delivering personalised cancer treatments. Future work will focus on novel network structures that introduce intermediate storage points and could possible increase the flexibility and efficiency of the current network.

Acknowledgements

Funding from the UK Engineering & Physical Sciences Research Council (EPSRC) for the Future Targeted Healthcare Manufacturing Hub hosted at University College London with UK university partners is gratefully acknowledged (Grant Reference: EP/P006485/1). Financial and in-kind support from the consortium of industrial users and sector organisations is also acknowledged.

References

Biomedica, O. (2019). Oxford Biomedica notes the Japanese approval of Kymriah® (tisagenlecleucel), the first CAR-T cell therapy authorised in Asia | OxfordBiomedica.

European Medicines Agency. (2018). First two CAR-T cell medicines recommended for approval in the European Union | European Medicines Agency.

Foley, L., & Whitaker, M. (2012). Concise Review: Cell Therapies: The Route to Widespread Adoption. *STEM CELLS Translational Medicine*. https://doi.org/10.5966/sctm.2011-0009

Jackson, H. J., Rafiq, S., & Brentjens, R. J. (2016). Driving CAR T-cells forward. *Nature Reviews Clinical Oncology*, *13*(6), 370–383. https://doi.org/10.1038/nrclinonc.2016.36

Lymphoma Australia. (2018). CAR-T cell therapy.

Maude, S. L., Laetsch, T. W., Buechner, J., Rives, S., Boyer, M., Bittencourt, H., … Grupp, S. A. (2018). Tisagenlecleucel in Children and Young Adults with B-Cell Lymphoblastic Leukemia. *New England Journal of Medicine*, *378*(5), 439–448. https://doi.org/10.1056/NEJMoa1709866

Neelapu, S. S., Locke, F. L., Bartlett, N. L., Lekakis, L. J., Miklos, D. B., Jacobson, C. A., … Go, W. Y. (2017). Axicabtagene Ciloleucel CAR T-Cell Therapy in Refractory Large B-Cell Lymphoma. *New England Journal of Medicine*, *377*(26), NEJMoa1707447. https://doi.org/10.1056/NEJMoa1707447

NHS. (2018). Axicabtagene Ciloleucel Chimeric Antigen Receptor T Cell (CAR T) Therapy for the treatment of adult patients with relapsed or refractory large B-cell lymphoma. *Nature Reviews Clinical Oncology*. https://doi.org/10.1038/nrclinonc.2017.148

Novartis. (2017). Starting Your Patients on Kymriah. *Novartis*.

Novartis. (2018). Kymriah® (tisagenlecleucel), first-in-class CAR-T therapy from Novartis, receives second FDA approval to treat appropriate r/r patients with large B-cell lymphoma. Retrieved July 24, 2018, from https://www.novartis.com/news/media-releases/kymriahr-tisagenlecleucel-first-class-car-t-therapy-from-novartis-receives-second-fda-approval-treat-appropriate-rr-patients-large-b-cell-lymphoma

Sadelain, M., Brentjens, R., Rivière, I., & Park, J. (2015). CD19 CAR Therapy for Acute Lymphoblastic Leukemia. *American Society of Clinical Oncology Educational Book*, *35*, e360–e363. https://doi.org/10.14694/EdBook_AM.2015.35.e360

Shah, N. (2004). Pharmaceutical supply chains: Key issues and strategies for optimisation. In *Computers and Chemical Engineering* (Vol. 28, pp. 929–941). Pergamon. https://doi.org/10.1016/j.compchemeng.2003.09.022

Wei Teng, C., Foley, L., O'Neill, P., & Hicks, C. (2014). An analysis of supply chain strategies in the regenerative medicine industry - Implications for future development. In *International Journal of Production Economics*. https://doi.org/10.1016/j.ijpe.2013.06.006

Sauro Pierucci, Flavio Manenti, Giulia Bozzano, Davide Manca (Eds.)
Proceedings of the 30th European Symposium on Computer Aided Process Engineering
(ESCAPE30), May 24-27, 2020, Milano, Italy. © 2020 Elsevier B.V. All rights reserved.
http://dx.doi.org/10.1016/B978-0-12-823377-1.50010-0

A Stochastic Modelling Approach to Describe the Effect of Drying Heterogeneity in the Lyophilisation of Pharmaceutical Vaccines

Gabriele Bano,[a,b] Riccardo De-Luca,[b] Emanuele Tomba,[c] Fabrizio Bezzo,[b] Massimiliano Barolo[b*]

[a] *GSK, Ware, United Kingdom*
[b] *CAPE-Lab, Department of Industrial Engineering, University of Padova, Italy*
[c] *GSK, Siena, Italy*
max.barolo@unipd.it

Abstract

In sterile drug product and vaccine manufacturing, reducing the duration of the primary drying stage of a lyophilisation cycle is pivotal to streamline process development and optimise commercial plant operation. Mathematical models can be used to assist this optimisation exercise. However, the models currently available in the literature usually neglect the effect of intra-lot drying heterogeneity in the optimization framework. In this study, we provide a description of drying heterogeneity using a deterministic model that mimics the behavior of a single vial, while treating the most impacting model parameter as a stochastic quantity. The novelty of the proposed approach lies in the description of drying heterogeneity using a single additional parameter, without further complicating the single-vial model structure. The prediction fidelity of the proposed model is assessed with experimental data obtained in an industrial equipment. Results show a robust prediction fidelity of the model in describing the effect of intra-lot drying heterogeneity on the process key performance indicators (KPIs).
Keywords: freeze-drying, lyophilisation, vaccines, quality by design.

1. Introduction

Freeze-drying is widely used in the biopharmaceutical industry to increase the shelf life of temperature-sensitive products (e.g., vaccines) that are processed in aqueous solution. The process first involves freezing the initial product, typically placed inside vials, then water removal by direct sublimation at low temperature and low pressure (*primary drying*). The residual water bounded to the product matrix is desorbed at higher temperature (*secondary drying*). Primary drying is the most energy-intensive and time-consuming process step (Liu *et al.*, 2008), and minimising its duration is crucial to reduce the overall process duration and energy requirement. However, primary drying protocols must respect hard constraints on both product temperature, which cannot exceed the collapse temperature of the product, and total sublimation rate, which cannot exceed the maximum capacity of the duct connecting the drying chamber with the condenser (to avoid choked flow). Different mathematical models have been proposed in the literature over the years, which could be used for primary drying optimisation (Pikal, 1985; Velardi and Barresi, 2008). These models describe the relevant heat and mass transfer mechanisms involved in ice sublimation and can be exploited to determine the optimal profiles of the manipulated variables (chamber pressure and shelf temperature) that minimise the drying time. Different attempts have also been made to embed in these models the intra-lot drying heterogeneity by describing the differences in heat and mass transfer mechanisms between vials placed at different locations inside the drying chamber, or accounting for parameter uncertainty (Barresi *et al.*, 2010; Scutellà *et al.*, 2018). These approaches typically result in a higher number of parameters to be estimated from experimental data, or in an amplification of the uncertainty in the model predictions due to parameter correlation. In this study, we propose a modelling framework that describes drying heterogeneity as stochastic uncertainty on the model parameter with the highest influence on the process KPIs. The proposed model is identified and its predictions verified through experiments conducted in an industrial lab-scale equipment.

2. Materials and methods

The experiments presented in this study were performed with a 5% w/w sucrose solution, processed in a VirTis Genesis 25EL freeze-dryer (SP Scientific, Stone Ridge, NY, USA); one full shelf out of a total of five was loaded for a total of 476 non-siliconized 3 mL vials filled with 0.6 mL of solution; the freezing step before primary drying was carried out at a freezing rate of –1 °C/min down to –50 °C. The condenser temperature was kept at –85 °C during the entire freeze-drying cycle. Product temperature measurements were obtained by placing thermocouple probes (T type, copper constantan wire, AWG 24) inside 12 different vials placed in different zones of the chamber. The software used for process simulation is gPROMS Model Builder v. 5.1 (Process Systems Enterprise, 2019).

3. Single-vial model

The proposed model has been derived from the model by Velardi and Barresi (2008) by introducing a dynamic energy balance to describe the time-varying system heat capacity.

3.1. Mass transfer

Since no radial gradients of temperature and ice composition during sublimation are assumed, the length of the frozen layer decreases along the axial direction, until the end of sublimation, according to Eq. (1):

$$\frac{dL_f}{dt} = -\frac{1}{\rho_f - \rho_d} J_w \tag{1}$$

where L_f [m] is the length of the frozen layer, ρ_f [kg m^{-3}] is the density of the frozen layer, ρ_d [kg m^{-3}] is the density of the dried layer and J_w [kg m^{-2} s^{-1}] is the sublimation flux. The sublimation flux is proportional to a driving force given by the difference between the water partial pressure at the sublimation interface $p_{w,in}$ [Pa] and the water partial pressure in the chamber $p_{w,c}$ [Pa] according to Eq. (2):

$$J_w = \frac{1}{R_p} \left(p_{w,in} - p_{w,c} \right) \tag{2}$$

where R_p [m s^{-1}] is the mass transfer resistance for the water flow. R_p depends on the length of the dried layer L_d [m] according to the experimentally verified empirical expression (Pikal, 1985):

$$R_p = R_0 + \frac{R_1 L_d}{1 + R_2 L_d} \tag{3}$$

with R_0 [m s^{-1}], R_1 [s^{-1}] and R_2 [m^{-1}] model parameters to be estimated from experimental data.

3.2. Heat transfer

The mechanisms through which heat is supplied to each vial inside the drying chamber are conduction and radiation. The dynamic energy balance for a single vial is given by:

$$\rho_f c_{p,f} A_v \frac{d(L_f T_p)}{dt} = Q_w + Q_r + Q_s - \Delta H_{sub} J_w A_v \tag{4}$$

where $c_{p,f}$ [J kg^{-1} K^{-1}] is the specific heat capacity of the frozen product, A_v [m^2] is the cross sectional area of the vial (assumed constant), T_p [K] is the temperature of the product (assumed constant along the axial direction) and ΔH_{sub} [J kg^{-1}] is the heat of sublimation. $\dot{Q}_w$ [J s^{-1}] is the heat rate supplied by the chamber walls through radiation; $\dot{Q}_r$ [W] is the radiant heat rate supplied by the rails along which vials are placed on the shelves; $\dot{Q}_s$ [J s^{-1}] is the heat rate supplied by the shelf upon which the vial is placed (lower shelf) and by the shelf placed on top of the vial (upper shelf) and involves both radiation and conduction mechanisms. The radiation from chamber walls is modelled according to a simplified expression of the Stefan-Boltzmann equation:

$$\dot{Q}_w = a_1 \sigma_{SB} \left(\bar{T}_w^4 - T_p^4 \right) \tag{5}$$

where σ_{SB} [W m^{-2} K^{-4}] is the Stefan-Boltzmann constant, $\bar{T}_w$ [K] is the mean temperature of the chamber walls and a_1 [m^2] is an equipment-dependent parameter to be estimated from experimental data. Similarly, the radiant heat rate from the rails is modelled as:

$$Q_r = a_2 \sigma_{SB} \left(\bar{T}_r^4 - T_p^4 \right) \tag{6}$$

where $\bar{T}_r$ is the mean temperature of the rails and a_2 [m^2] is an equipment-dependent parameter that needs to estimated from experimental data.

The heat rate supplied by the lower and upper shelves involves both conduction and radiation mechanisms. Mathematically, $\dot{Q}_s$ can be described as:

$$Q_s = Q_{sv} + Q_{sr} = (K_v + K_r) A_v (T_{shelf} - T_p) \tag{7}$$

with $\dot{Q}_{sv}$ [J s^{-1}] = heat rate supplied by conduction; $\dot{Q}_{sr}$ [J s^{-1}] = heat rate supplied by radiation and T_{shelf} [K] = shelf temperature. The conductive heat transfer coefficient K_v [W m^{-2} K^{-1}] depends on the total chamber pressure P_c [Pa] according to the experimentally verified empirical expression (Pikal, 1985):

$$K_v = C_1 + \frac{C_2 P_c}{1 + C_3 P_c} \tag{8}$$

where C_1 [W m^{-2} K^{-1}], C_2 [W m^{-2} K^{-1} Pa^{-1}] and C_3 [Pa^{-1}] are parameters to be estimated from experimental data. The effective radiation heat transfer coefficient K_r [W m^{-2} K^{-1}] can be derived according to a simplified Stefan-Boltzmann expression:

$$K_r = a_3 \sigma_{SB}(T_{shelf} + T_p)(T_{shelf}^2 + T_p^2) \tag{9}$$

with a_3 [-] an equipment-dependent parameter to be estimated from experimental data.

4. Effect of drying heterogeneity: multi-vial stochastic model

Describing the evolution of the partial pressure dynamics $p_{w,c}(t)$ is key to obtain an accurate description of the sublimation driving force, according to Eq. (2). A simple expression that can be used to this purpose is the one proposed by Scutellà *et al.* (2018):

$$\frac{dp_{w,c}}{dt} = \frac{R_g \bar{T}_w}{V_c M_w} (\dot{m}_s^{tot} - \dot{m}_{cd})$$ (10)

where R_g [J mol^{-1} K^{-1}] is the gas law constant, V_c [m^3] is the chamber volume, M_w [kg kmol^{-1}] is the molecular weight of water, $\dot{m}_s^{tot}$ [kg s^{-1}] is the total sublimation flow and $\dot{m}_{cd}$[kg s^{-1}] is the water vapor rate removed by the condenser. $\dot{m}_{cd}$ can be modelled as (Trelea *et al.*, 2015):

$$\dot{m}_{cd} = \frac{1}{\alpha \bar{T}_{cd}} \log \frac{(P_c - p_{w,cd})}{(P_c - p_{w,c})}$$ (11)

with $\bar{T}_{cd}$ = mean temperature of the condenser; $p_{w,cd}$ = water vapor partial pressure at the condenser interface and α [s kg^{-1} K^{-1}] = equipment-dependent parameter to be estimated from experimental data. The total sublimation flow can be derived as the sum of all the contributions from the different vials placed inside the drying chamber:

$$\dot{m}_s^{tot} = \sum_{n=1}^{N_v} \dot{m}_s^{(n)} = \frac{\pi d_v^2}{4} \sum_{n=1}^{N_v} J_w^{(n)}$$ (12)

with d_v [m] = vial diameter and N_v [-] = number of vials inside the drying chamber.

Vials placed at different positions on the shelf are exposed to different levels of radiation, meaning that the single sublimation rates $\dot{m}_s^{(n)}$ differ between vials of the same batch. In order to describe this intra-lot drying heterogeneity, we carried out the following sequential modelling activities:

1) global sensitivity analysis (GSA) to understand the effect of model parameters on the two process KPIs (product temperature and sublimation flow);
2) stochastic description of the parameter with the highest influence towards the process KPIs (with a given probabilistic distribution);
3) description of the total mass flow $\dot{m}_s^{tot}$ in Eq. (4) by sampling N_v samples from the distribution of the stochastic parameter using Monte-Carlo techniques;
4) model calibration using historical experimental data of product temperature and water vapor partial pressure.

We used Sobol's GSA (Saltelli *et al.*, 2008) to carry out the first step. The analysis was carried out by implementing 1100 scenarios that span the entire parameter domain to consider batch heterogeneity. The lower and upper bounds for the model parameters considered in the GSA are reported in Table 1. The analysis was performed at fixed values of shelf temperature (250.15 K) and chamber pressure (10 Pa). Dynamic sensitivities were collected every 10 min over a time horizon of 500 min. The dynamic profiles of the total sensitivity indices for all the model parameters with respect to product temperature (KPI) are shown in Fig. 1. Similar profiles were obtained for the other KPI (sublimation flow) and are not reported here for brevity.

Table 1. Model parameters and their lower and upper bounds used for global sensitivity analysis (uniform distributions).

Parameter	Bounds	Units
R_1	$[1 \times 10^8, 9 \times 10^8]$	$[s^{-1}]$
R_2	$[1 \times 10^2, 1 \times 10^4]$	$[m^{-1}]$
A	$[1000, 3000]$	$[s\ kg^{-1}\ K^{-1}]$
C_1	$[0, 10]$	$[W\ m^{-2}\ K^{-1}]$
C_2	$[0, 2]$	$[W\ m^{-2}\ K^{-1}\ Pa^{-1}]$
C_3	$[0, 2]$	$[Pa^{-1}]$
a_1	$[1 \times 10^{-5}, 9 \times 10^{-5}]$	$[m^2]$

Figure 1. Dynamic profiles of the global sensitivity indices for all model parameters.

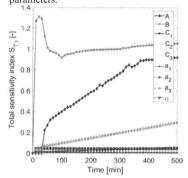

The results of GSA suggested three key considerations: (*i*) the parameter with the highest sensitivity towards the process KPIs is a_1, i.e. the parameter describing the effect of thermal radiation from the chamber walls; (*ii*) three parameters (a_2, R_2, C_3) have negligible impact on the process KPIs, and therefore can be set to their nominal values and do not need to be included in the model calibration activity; (*iii*) all the remaining parameters $(C_2, a_3, \sigma_{a_1}, \alpha)$ significantly affect at least one KPI; therefore, their values must be accurately estimated to guarantee a good model prediction fidelity.

Table 2. Estimated values for the model parameters together with their confidence intervals and *t*-values.

Parameter	Units	Value	95% CI	t-value
C_1	$[W\ m^{-2}\ K^{-1}]$	2.825	± 0.112	39.70
C_2	$[W\ m^{-2}\ K^{-1}\ Pa^{-1}]$	0.215	± 0.09	31.20
$\bar{a}_1$	$[m^2]$	7.625×10^{-5}	$\pm 8.213 \times 10^{-7}$	25.12
σ_{a_1}	$[m^2]$	1.545×10^{-5}	$\pm 9.416 \times 10^{-7}$	12.36
a_3	$[-]$	2.723×10^{-6}	$\pm 1.014 \times 10^{-7}$	4.12
R_1	$[s^{-1}]$	3.288×10^8	$\pm 8.935 \times 10^6$	68.12
α	$[Pa\ s\ kg^{-1}\ K^{-1}]$	2580	± 15	11.30
			Reference t-value (95%)	**1.645**

Based on these results, step #2 was carried out on the parameter a_1. We used a normal distribution for a_1 with mean $\bar{a}_1$ and standard deviation σ_{a_1}, i.e. $a_1 \sim N(\bar{a}_1, \sigma_{a_1})$. Both $\bar{a}_1$ and σ_{a_1} were treated as parameters to be estimated from experimental data.
Model calibration (step #4) was carried out using a maximum likelihood estimator and experimental data of product temperature and water vapor partial pressure from historical runs performed in the same equipment with the same formulation. The resulting optimal parameter estimates, together with their uncertainty statistics, are reported in Table 2. Model validation (step #4) was obtained by carrying out a new experiment and by comparing model predictions with the experimental observations. Fig.2a shows the dynamic profiles of the control variables (shelf temperature and chamber pressure) used in this experiment. The good agreement between the model predictions and the experimental data (see Fig.2b, c) confirms the ability of the proposed approach in describing both the contributions of the single vials to the total sublimation flow (Eq.11) and the maximum product temperature within the batch.

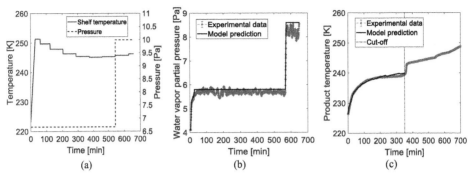

Figure 2. (a) Dynamic profiles of the control variables used during the validation experimental run. (b) Predicted trajectory for the water vapor partial pressure (black line) Vs experimental data (red dots). (c) Predicted trajectory for the maximum product temperature (black line) Vs experimental data (red dots).

5. Conclusions

In this study, we developed a stochastic modelling framework to describe the primary drying stage of a lyophilisation cycle by considering intra-lot heterogeneity. We showed that the proposed model formulation allows obtaining an accurate description of those KPIs (maximum product temperature and sublimation flow) for which hard constraints must be satisfied. Further work will focus on applying the proposed modelling framework to different pieces of equipment/formulated products.

Acknowledgments

This study was conducted under a cooperative research and development agreement between University of Padova and GlaxoSmithKline Biologicals SA. GSK co-funded this study in the framework of the University of Padova project "Uni-Impresa 2017 – DIGI-LIO – Towards digitalization of the pharmaceutical industry: generation of data with high information content for industrial freeze-drying process optimization". Gabriele Bano and Emanuele Tomba are employees of the GSK group of companies. Riccardo De-Luca, Fabrizio Bezzo and Massimiliano Barolo report no financial conflict of interest.

References

Barresi, A. A.; Pisano, R.; Rasetto, V.; Fissore, D. (2010) Model-based monitoring and control of industrial freeze-drying processes: effect of batch nonuniformity. *Drying Technol.*, **28**, 577-590.

Liu, Y.; Zhao, Y.; Feng, X. (2008) Exergy analysis for a freeze-drying process. *Appl. Therm. Eng.* **28**, 675 – 690.

Pikal, M. J. (1985). Use of laboratory data in freeze drying process design: heat and mass transfer coefficients and the computer simulation of freeze drying. *PDA J. Pharm. Sci. Technol.*, **39**, 115-139.

Process Systems Enterprise Ltd. (2019) gPROMS Model Builder v 5.1; Process Systems Enterprise Ltd: London, UK

Saltelli, A.; Ratto, M.; Andres, T.; Campolongo, F.; Cariboni, J.; Gatelli, D.; Saisana, M.; Tarantola, S. (2008) Global Sensitivity Analysis: The Primer; Wiley: Hoboken, NJ, USA.

Scutellà, B., Trelea, I. C., Bourlés, E., Fonseca, F., Passot, S. (2018). Use of a multi-vial mathematical model to design freeze-drying cycles for pharmaceuticals at known risk of failure. In *IDS 2018. 21st International Drying Symposium Proceedings* (pp. 315-322). Editorial Universitat Politècnica de València.

Trelea, I.-C.; Fonseca, F.; Passot, S.; Flick, D. (2015). A binary gas transport model improves the prediction of mass transfer in freeze drying. *Drying Technol.*, **33**, 1849-1858.

Velardi, S. A.; Barresi, A. A. (2008). Development of simplified models for the freeze-drying process and investigation of the optimal operating conditions. *Chem. Eng. Res. Des.*, **86**, 9-22.

Sauro Pierucci, Flavio Manenti, Giulia Bozzano, Davide Manca (Eds.)
Proceedings of the 30th European Symposium on Computer Aided Process Engineering
(ESCAPE30), May 24-27, 2020, Milano, Italy. © 2020 Elsevier B.V. All rights reserved.
http://dx.doi.org/10.1016/B978-0-12-823377-1.50011-2

CFD Simulation of Film and Rivulet Flows on Microstructured Surfaces

R. Bertling[a] , M. Hack[b], I. Ausner[b], M. Wehrli[b], E.Y. Kenig[a*]

[a] Paderborn University, Chair of Fluid Process Engineering, Pohlweg 55, 33098
Paderborn, Germany
[b] Sulzer Chemtech AG, Neuwiesenstrasse 15, 8401 Winterthur, Switzerland
eugeny.kenig@upb.de

Abstract

The flow of liquid-gas systems on surfaces of corrugated sheet packings was studied numerically and experimentally. In simulations the concept of "effective contact angles" was used to take surface microstructures into account. With this approach, resolving the microstructure geometries by the numerical grid can be avoided, which significantly reduces the numerical effort. Several combinations of liquid systems and surface structures were investigated under various liquid flow rates. Generally, the approach showed good capability to reproduce the different flow morphologies found in the experiments and to predict the flow behavior for different flow rates.

Keywords: CFD, Microstructure, Contact angle, Structured packings

1. Introduction

Corrugated sheet packings are the most common type of structured packings widely used in separation columns. Since the interfacial area is a key parameter affecting the column efficiency, the surface of corrugated sheet packings is usually microstructured to enhance liquid spreading. For most commercial packings, different types of microstructure are available.

In this work, a pyramidal structure used by Sulzer Chemtech AG was investigated. Since the size of microstructures is typically smaller than the size of packing channels by factors of up to 20, it is hardly possible to numerically resolve the microstructure of the packing surface simultaneously with the packing geometry in CFD simulations. Therefore, the concept of the so-called "effective contact angle", which is applied as a boundary condition on a smooth packing wall, has become established in the modeling of the surface wetting behavior and several studies reported significant influence of the effective contact angle on the liquid flow behavior in structured packings (e.g., Sebastia-Saez et al., 2015, Singh et al., 2018). However, to find the "correct" effective contact angle that would represent the effects of a given microstructure on a certain liquid flow is not at all easy and a consistent database or a methodology for reasonable selection of an effective contact angle for each microstructure–fluid combination is not yet available. Therefore, the aim of this study is to provide a method to find proper effective contact angles for realistic consideration of the microstructure within the modeling of structured packings. The commercial software ANSYS Fluent was applied, with the volume-of-fluid method used for the capturing of the free phase interface. Validation experiments for the investigation of the wetting behavior of microstructured plates were carried out at Sulzer Chemtech AG.

The value of the effective contact angle in the simulations was selected from the best fit of experimental results obtained for one fixed flow rate and one plate inclination angle of 30° to the vertical. Both flow rate and plate inclination angle were then varied to examine the predictivity of this approach. The most relevant physical liquid properties influencing the liquid flow are surface tension, viscosity and density. Furthermore, process parameters, especially the specific liquid flow rate, affect the liquid flow topology. The studied systems were water, ethanol and a mixture of water and triethyleneglycol (TEG). They were investigated under varied flow rates. These systems cover a broad range with respect to both surface tension and viscosity. The following cases were investigated experimentally and numerically:

- Surface structure: pyramidal grooving, smooth
- Liquid system: water, water/TEG mixture, ethanol
- Liquid loads:
  - water: $4.5 \text{ m}^3/\text{m}^2\text{h}$, $15\text{m}^3/\text{m}^2\text{h}$, $45\text{m}^3/\text{m}^2\text{h}$
  - water & TEG: $4.5 \text{ m}^3/\text{m}^2$, $15\text{m}^3/\text{m}^2\text{h}$, $45\text{m}^3/\text{m}^2\text{h}$
  - ethanol: $4.5\text{m}^3/\text{m}^2\text{h}$, $7.5\text{m}^3/\text{m}^2\text{h}$, $15\text{m}^3/\text{m}^2\text{h}$
- Plate inclination: 0° and 30° inclination to vertical

2. Experiments on inclined plates

A method which had already been successfully used by Sulzer Chemtech to evaluate the wetting performance of structured surfaces in lab-scale investigations served as a basis to characterize the liquid flow behavior. The test setup shown in Fig. 1 is applied to investigate microstructured packing sheets, while mesoscale packing features, such as sheet corrugations or contact points, are not included. In this setup, a free liquid jet leaves the vertically oriented pipe and hits the plate covered by a microstructured sheet. Originally, the plate had an inclination of 30° to the vertical. For the investigations on the vertically oriented plate, the relative orientation of the pipe remained the same, e.g. a pipe inclination of 30° to the vertical. The flow morphology and the wetted area on the sheet were evaluated optically using the open source software ImageJ.

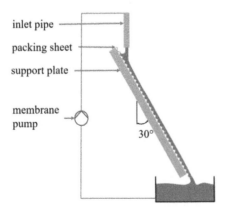

Figure 1: Experimental setup

The measured properties of the liquids are summarized in Table 1:

Table 1: Measured fluid properties at 20°C (literature values are marked with an asterics)

system	surface tension/ mN/m	density/ kg/m³	viscosity / mPas	contact angle with smooth steel
water	50.4	993	1.0	42° - 62°
ethanol	23.4	824.2	0.27	not measurable
water & TEG	38.7	1021.2	8.6	26°- 48°
air*	-	1.2	0.0179	-

Since a dye is used for increasing the contrast between liquid and background, this had an influence on the liquid properties, especially on the surface tension; hence the values somewhat differ from literature values. The surface tension was measured using a bubble tensiometer with a bubble formation time of five seconds. The contact angle on a smooth steel surface was measured optically on static droplets. This method bears some uncertainties; hence, a certain range is given for the contact angles. For the CFD simulations, the material data were set in accordance with Table 1.

3. CFD-Modeling

3.1. Governing equations

CFD simulations were performed with the software ANSYS Fluent (version 19.1). Both phases were assumed as incompressible and isothermal. The equations for continuity and momentum applied for both phases are as follows:

$$\nabla \cdot \boldsymbol{u} = 0 \tag{1}$$

$$\frac{\partial}{\partial t}(\rho \boldsymbol{u}) + \nabla \cdot (\rho \boldsymbol{u}\boldsymbol{u}) = -\nabla p + \rho \boldsymbol{g} + \eta \Delta \boldsymbol{u} + \boldsymbol{f}_\sigma \tag{2}$$

where $\boldsymbol{u}$ is velocity vector, t is time, ρ is density, η is dynamic viscosity, p is pressure; $\boldsymbol{g}$ is gravity and $\boldsymbol{f}_\sigma$ is a source term governing surface tension. The interface movement was captured by the volume of fluid (VOF) method (Hirt and Nichols, 1981), with the following transport equation for the liquid-phase volume fraction α:

$$\frac{\partial \alpha}{\partial t} + \boldsymbol{u} \cdot \nabla \alpha = 0 \tag{3}$$

The liquid-phase properties were calculated by

$$\Phi = \alpha \Phi_L + (1-\alpha)\Phi_G \text{ with } \Phi = \rho, \eta \tag{4}$$

For the consideration of the surface tension σ, the continuum surface force (CSF) model (Brackbill et al., 1992) was applied to determine $\boldsymbol{f}_\sigma$:

$$\boldsymbol{f}_\sigma = \sigma \kappa \boldsymbol{n} \text{ with } \boldsymbol{n} = \nabla \alpha \text{ and } \kappa = -\nabla \cdot \frac{\boldsymbol{n}}{|\boldsymbol{n}|} \tag{5}$$

The contact angle γ is considered in the calculation of the surface force term via the surface normal vector in the cells adjacent to the walls:

$$n = n_{wall} \cos \gamma + t_{wall} \sin \gamma \tag{6}$$

Where n_{wall} is the unit normal vector of the wall and t_{wall} is the corresponding unit tangential vector.

3.2 Boundary conditions and implementation

The discretization scheme used for Eq. 3 was the "Geo-Reconstruct" scheme available in ANSYS Fluent, which is based on the PLIC (piece wise linear interface construction) algorithm. The computational domain with the specified boundary conditions is displayed in Fig. 2. The initial conditions were zero values of liquid volume fraction (no liquid inside the domain) and velocity magnitude as well as ambient pressure.

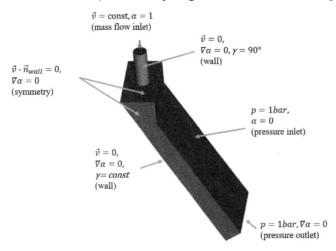

Figure 2: Computational domain and boundary conditions

3.3. Meshing

The meshes used in this work were generated using the "bloc structured" meshing function in ANSYS ICEM 19.1. As recommended for the VOF framework by ANSYS Fluent, exclusively hexahedral cells were used. The resolution was increased towards the bottom wall, in order to accurately resolve the phase interface near the triple line and velocity gradients normal to the wall. The cell growth rate in this direction was 1.1 (geometrical stretching), starting with a cell height of 20µm for water and the water-TEG mixture. This was equivalent to approximately 30 cells over the film thickness, depending on the liquid system and the simulated flow rate. For the simulation of ethanol, the cell size near the wall had to be decreased in order to resolve the film near the triple line where the solid, liquid, and gas phase are in contact properly. The first cell height was set to 10μm for this case.

4. Results

The introduced method showed good capability in predicting the flow behavior both qualitatively (see Fig. 3 and 4) and quantitatively (see Table 2).

Table 2: overview results

System	γ	u_L / m³/m²h	A_{sim} /A_{exp}
Water	32°	15	+19%
		45	-17%
Water & TEG	35°	15	+10%
		45	+3%
Ethanol	20°	4.5	-24%
		7.5	+3%
		15	+3%

For the lowest flow rate of 4.5m³/m²h droplet formation was observed in the experiments directly at the end of the pipe. This could not be reproduced by the simulations which, contrary to the experiments, showed a stable jet flow leaving the pipe. The problem also appeared for water as a working fluid with the same flow rate. The ethanol flow on grooved plates could be captured well (Fig. 3). Generally, the model had a slight tendency to overestimate the effect of the liquid flow rate on the wetted surface area, e.g. the wetted area in the simulations grew more significantly than in the experiments when a higher flow rate was applied. The contact angles that are specified in Table 2 were derived in a series of simulations, in which the contact angle was varied to find the best fit between simulations and experiments at a liquid flow rate u_L of 15m³/m²h. The ratio of the simulated wetted area A_{sim} and the wetted area measured in the experiments A_{exp} served to evaluate the agreement, while A_{exp} was calculated from processing photographs using the open source software ImageJ. In the process of searching for the contact angle that reproduces the flow morphology the best, it became clear that the flow morphology was strongly sensitive to the changes in the effective contact angle, especially for the water-TEG-mixture.

Figure 3: Simulated results (left) and experimental results (right) for ethanol flow on grooved plate with u_L=7.5m³/m²h and γ=20°

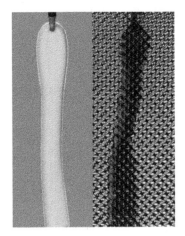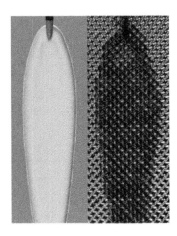

Figure 4: Water-TEG mixture on a grooved plate: $u_L = 15m^3/m^2h$ (left), $u_L = 45m^3/m^2h$ (right) with $\gamma=35°$

5. Conclusions

A new method to find effective contact angles that realistically reproduce the effects of common microstructures on rivulet and film flow was proposed. The methods novelty lies in the combination of experiments on non-corrugated, microstructured plates with CFD methods, which removes disturbing factors in evaluating how well a certain contact angle reproduces the effect of the investigated microstructures. The studies showed that the solutions are very sensitive to the effective contact angle variation, which underlines the importance of a proper choice of this parameter. Generally, the proposed method is capable of reasonably reproducing and predicting the flow morphology. Future work will focus on the application of the newly derived contact angles to packing structures.

References

J.U. Brackbill, D.B. Khote, C. Zemach, 1992, A continuum method for modelling surface tension, J. Comput. Phys. 100, 335–354.

C.W. Hirt, B.D. Nichols, 1981, Volume of fluid method for the dynamics of free boundaries, J. Comput. Phys. 39, 201–225.

D. Sebastia-Saez, S. Gu, P. Ranganathan, K. Papadikis, 2015, Meso-scale CFD study of the pressure drop, liquid hold-up, interfacial area and mass transfer in structured packing materials, Int. J. Greenh. Gas Control 42, 388–399.

R.K. Singh, J.E. Galvin, X. Sun, 2018, Multiphase flow studies for microscale hydrodynamics in the structured packed column, Chem. Eng. J. 353, 949–963.

Sauro Pierucci, Flavio Manenti, Giulia Bozzano, Davide Manca (Eds.)
Proceedings of the 30th European Symposium on Computer Aided Process Engineering
(ESCAPE30), May 24-27, 2020, Milano, Italy. © 2020 Elsevier B.V. All rights reserved.
http://dx.doi.org/10.1016/B978-0-12-823377-1.50012-4

Energy Reduction Potential in Natural Gas Processing through Heat and Process Integration

Mohamed Berchiche [a,b], Salah Belaadi [a], Grégoire Leonard [b]

[a] *Université des Sciences et de la Technologie Houari Boumediene, Laboratory of Reaction Engineering, FGMGP, BP32 El-Alia 16000, Algeria,*
[b] *Université de Liège, Department of Chemical Engineering, B6a Sart-Tilman, 4000 Liège, Belgium,*
mea.berchiche@doct.uliege.be

Abstract

Despite the advantages of Natural Gas (NG) over other fossil fuels, natural gas supply chain is still impacted by a high energy demand and a negative impact on the environment as a result. This work investigates the potential of reducing energy penalty of natural gas sweetening processes through energy integration with upstream compression units and the use of Organic Rankine Cycle as a bottoming technology.

The integration was studied over a range of inlet CO_2 content and admission pressure varying between 4 to 10% and 30 to 50 bar respectively. Results of heat integration showed an ample reduction in heating requirements ranging from 40 to 100%. Furthermore, the integration of an optimized ORC as a second recovery tool yielded in a net power output equivalent to 30% to 190% of the required pumping power and a reduction of cooling load ranging from and 4 to 16% respectively.

Keywords: Natural gas sweetening, Heat and process integration, ORC.

1. Introduction

Natural gas has the lowest CO_2 emissions rate per energy unit among fossil fuels; it is expected to play a significant role as a bridge fuel toward complete decarbonization of the global energy supply (BP Energy Outlook, 2016). Consequently, its demand is forecasted to witness a total increase of 60% by 2035 (Costello, 2017). Natural gas supply chain, however, is an energy intensive sector characterized by an important amount of waste heat which not only weights on the efficiency of the process and its profitability margin but also contributes to greenhouse gas emissions. Moreover, 50% of the remaining NG reserves are sour (i.e. containing more than 2% mole CO_2 or 4 ppmv of H_2S) implying the inevitable implementation of an additional sweetening step and further increasing the energy penalty (Brugers et al., 2011).

Several technologies were developed for NG sweetening purposes among which amine based absorption remains the most used. Despite its maturity and wide deployment, this technology is impacted by its high energy demand. Several improvement routes have been proposed in the literature, such as the development of new solvents with reduced regeneration requirement and the optimization of plant operating parameters using process simulation tools (Leonard et al., 2011 and Nuchitprasittichai et al. 2013).

In this regard, energy integration along with the use of low temperature waste heat recovery technologies, such as Organic Rankine Cycle (ORC), Heat pumps (HP) or

Absorption Chillers (AbC) can play a significant role in cutting emissions and alleviating the impact of this energy intensive process.

Because of the multiple advantages it presents, such as efficiency, simple layout and moderate operating conditions, the use of ORC as a waste heat recovery tool from energy intensive processes is receiving increasing interest. For instance, Yu et al. (2016) developed a systematic approach using waste heat composite curve for the optimization of the design of ORC as a tool of multiple-source waste heat recovery from refineries. In the context of CO_2 capture from natural gas supply chain, several studies focused on the energy integration of CO_2 capture with natural gas liquefaction and regasification processes. Abdulkareem et al. (2012) investigated the integration of several waste heat sources from the NG liquefaction process into a CO_2 capture and sequestration unit. They found that a 23% reduction in cooling loads could be achieved as a result of an improved heat integration and waste heat utilization. Zhao et al. (2016) integrated a two-stage ORC to recover cold energy from a regasification unit coupled with a CO_2 capture process.

In this paper, we have developed a two-steps approach to investigate the potential of energy integration in the context of upstream natural gas processing, first through the integration of waste heat and second, with the use of ORC as a bottoming technology.

Upstream natural gas compression is a crucial step to insure a constant pressure at the inlet of the processing unit. The exhaust of the compression process is therefore a non-intermittent source of waste heat that can potentially be integrated in the processing unit. In this work, we have assessed the direct use of high-temperature compression waste heat to satisfy the demand of the sweetening process and the integration of ORC as a secondary recovery tool to harness the low temperature waste heat.

2. Methodology

Process simulation tool Aspen Hysys V9 was used to simulate both processes, i.e. the amine based CO_2 capture and the natural gas driven turbo-compression. A feed of 5 MMSCM/Day of raw NG at different reservoir pressures (30, 40 and 50 bar) was considered in this study. CO_2 molar content in the feed was ranged between 3 to 10% whereas CO_2 content of the sweet gas outlet was set at the limit requested by pipeline transport constraint, i.e. 2%. The captured CO_2 is then compressed up to 200 bar.

The MDEA/DEA based acid gas sweetening unit was simulated using an equilibrium approach and Li-Mather thermodynamic model whereas the compression and turbine systems where simulated using Peng-Robinson equation of state. Sweetening and turbo-compression models were validated against plant and manufacturer data respectively.

For the NG sweetening unit, the predicted CO_2 content and temperature profiles in absorber and regeneration columns showed a deviation of less than 4% from plant data whereas, for the turbo-compression unit, the model presented a deviation of less than 2% from the overall efficiency and exhaust flow specified by the manufacturer.

The available exhaust waste energy depends on the pressure ratio of the compression unit. Consequently, three scenarios were investigated, P30, P50 and P60, referring respectively to inlet pressures of 30, 40 and 50 bar upstream the compression unit. The adequate turbine type was used for each scenario and a waste heat recovery unit (WHRU) was used to recover energy from the exhaust gas to the heating oil loop. A cold temperature limit of 140 °C was set as a technical constraint on the heating oil side to prevent Sulphur condensation in the exhaust gas. The remaining energy required to satisfy the solvent regeneration was provided by an external source.

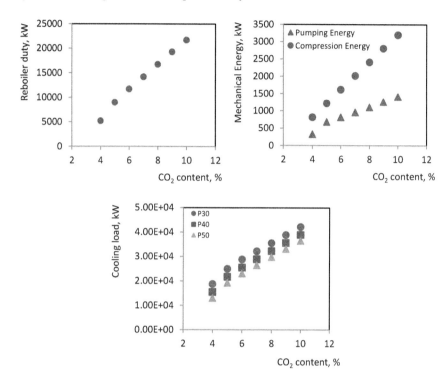

Figure 1 Energy demand of the process for different CO_2 molar fraction in the feed NG, a) Reboiler thermal energy, b) Mechanical energy, c) Cooling load

Low temperature waste heat from both processes (NG compression and CO_2 capture) was recovered by a set of heat exchangers and was used to power the ORC. The minimum temperature approach was fixed at 5 °C except for the WHRU where due to the restriction on pressure drop a minimum approach of 10 °C was chosen.

An ORC with a simple layout and R600 as a working fluid was used for recovering low grade waste heat. The optimal working conditions of the ORC, i.e. temperature, pressure and heating oil flow rate, corresponding to a maximal net power generation, were identified for each scenario by linking Aspen Hysys to Matlab and using Matlab's prebuilt optimization abilities.

In order to reduce computing time, the heat recovery network was solved separately for maximum outlet temperature versus heating oil flow rate. The resulting relationship was used as a constraint to the ORC optimization problem reducing thereby the number of variables and eliminating the necessity of solving both processes (heat recovery network and ORC) simultaneously.

3. Heat integration

Reboiler energy, pumping energy and cooling loads of the process were calculated for an inlet CO_2 molar content ranging from 4 to 10%. Figures 1a and 1b depict the regeneration energy and the mechanical shaft power demand of the sweetening process for the indicated range of CO_2 content in raw NG. With increasing CO_2 content, the amine flow rate required to achieve CO_2 specification increases which results in a subsequent increase in reboiler and pumping energy and cooling loads.

Also, the increase in CO_2 content in the raw NG will increase the amount of captured CO_2 and result in an increase of compression energy. Figure 1c shows the total cooling loads of both compression and sweetening processes for different inlet pressures 30, 40 and 50 bar and a CO_2 content ranging from 4 to 10%. The lower the reservoir pressure, the higher the compression duty and thus the higher the cooling loads. On the other side, with less CO_2 in the raw natural gas, the cooling duty decreases due to a lower release of absorption heat in the amine loop.

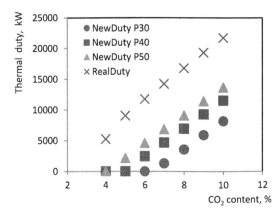

Figure 2 Reboiler thermal energy before and after integration for three inlet pressures 30, 40 and 50 bar

As explained in the previous section, waste heat from the compression units was used to supply the solvent regeneration reboiler. Figure 2 shows the reboiler duty before integration and the new reboiler duty after integration. For natural gas feed at low CO_2 content and at low inlet pressure the available waste energy is as high as the reboiler duty. We have found that it is therefore possible to cover all the regeneration energy from the waste heat sources.

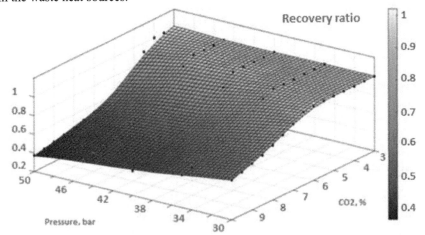

Figure 3 Ratio of recovered energy to the initial reboiler energy for different CO_2 contents and inlet pressures

As shown in figure 3, the potential of heat integration depends on both inlet pressure and CO_2 content and varies from 40 to 100%. Higher integration potential is met at lower CO_2 contents (less heat is required by the sweetening process) and lower inlet pressures (more heat is available from the NG compression step).

4. Secondary heat recovery

The use of Organic Rankine Cycle as a second recovery technology was investigated at the different scenarios of inlet pressure and CO_2 content discussed earlier. For each scenario, the optimal recovery temperature and working pressure yielding the highest energy output were identified. R600 was used as working fluid in this study as it was reported to demonstrate low global warming potential and high energy efficiency (Darvish et al. 2015).

The use of Organic Rankine Cycle presented a double advantage by harnessing a fraction of the waste heat into useful electricity and reducing the overall cooling load of the background process. Figures 4a and 4b show respectively the reduction in cooling load and the amount of maximal electricity output for three inlet pressures 30, 40 and 50 bar and for a CO_2 content ranging from 4 to 10%. The average efficiency of the Organic Rankine Cycle applied for the three inlet pressure scenarios P30, P40, and P50 was found to be 14%, 10%, and 9% respectively.

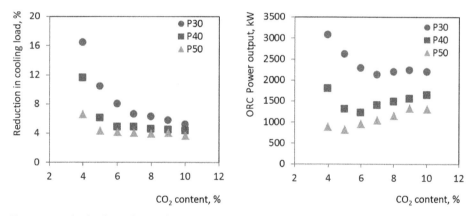

Figure 4 a) Reduction in cooling requirements for different CO_2 molar contents and inlet pressures, b) Energy optimal ORC energy output for different CO_2 contents and inlet pressures

The electricity output of the ORC is the contribution of the quantity of the available waste heat as well as its quality. Consequently, high energy output at low CO_2 contents is explained by the low energy demand of the capture process allowing more high-temperature waste heat to be recovered by the ORC whereas the slight increase of energy output at high CO_2 contents is due to the quantity of low-temperature waste heat available from the capture process.

5. Conclusion

Energy and process integration of amine based natural gas sweetening unit with upstream compression with ORC as a bottoming technology was investigated in this study. The potential of the integration was estimated for different compression ratios and CO_2 content scenarios.

The available waste heat from the compression units is a reliable source that showed an important potential for alleviating the energy demand of the natural gas sweetening process. The recovered waste heat varied from 40 up to 100% of the energy required for solvent regeneration. Maximal integration potential was found at low CO_2 content and high compression requirements where the available waste heat is high and the regeneration energy is low.

On another hand, the use of ORC as a second recovery technology allowed to further increase the energy efficiency of the process by using low temperature and fatal waste heat for power production. The energy output was found to vary from 30 to 190% of the required pumping power with a reduction in cooling loads of the process ranging from 4 to 16%.

References

Alabdulkarem A., Hwang H., Radermacher R., 2012, Energy consumption reduction in CO_2 capturing and sequestration of an LNG plant through process integration and waste heat utilization, International Journal of Greenhouse Gas Control, 10:215–228

BP Energy Outlook, 2016, BP p.l.c, London, United Kingdom,

Burgers1W., Northropb P., Kheshgic H., Valenciad J., 2011, Worldwide development potential for sour gas, Energy Procedia , 4:2178–2184

Costello K., 2017, Why natural gas has an uncertain future, The Electricity Journal, 30:18-22

Darvish K., Ehyaei A., Atabi F., Rosen M., 2015, Selection of optimum working fluid for organic rankine cycles by exergy and exergy-economic analyses, sustainability, 7:15362-15383

Leonard G., Heyen G., 2011, Modeling post-combustion CO_2 capture with amine solvents, Computer Aided Chemical Engineering, 29: 1768-1772

Nuchitprasittichai A., Cremaschi S., 2013, Optimization of CO_2 capture process with aqueous amines, a comparison of two SO approaches, Industrial and Engineering chemistry research, 52, 10236−10243

Yu H., Feng X., Wang Y., Biegler L., Eason J., 2016, A systematic method to customize an efficient organic Rankine cycle to recover waste heat in refineries, Applied Energy, 179:302–315

Zhao H., Dong H., Tang J., Cai. J., 2016, Cold energy utilization of liquefied NG for capturing carbon dioxide in the flue gas from the magnesite processing industry, Energy, 105:45-56

Sauro Pierucci, Flavio Manenti, Giulia Bozzano, Davide Manca (Eds.)
Proceedings of the 30th European Symposium on Computer Aided Process Engineering
(ESCAPE30), May 24-27, 2020, Milano, Italy. © 2020 Elsevier B.V. All rights reserved.
http://dx.doi.org/10.1016/B978-0-12-823377-1.50013-6

An adaptive data-driven modelling and optimization framework for complex chemical process design

Thomas Savage,[a] Hector Fernando Almeida-Trasvina,[a] Ehecatl Antonio del Río-Chanona,[b] Robin Smith,[a] Dongda Zhang[a,b]

[a]*Centre for Process Integration, University of Manchester, The Mill, Sackville Street, Manchester, M1 3AL, UK.*

[b]*Centre for Process Systems Engineering, Imperial College London, South Kensington Campus, London SW7 2AZ, UK.*

dongda.zhang@manchester.ac.uk

Abstract

Current advances in computer-aided chemical process design and synthesis take advantage of surrogate modelling and superstructure optimization techniques. Conventionally, this is completed by using first-principle physical models or data-driven models to replace the original rigorous models for optimization and selection of a specific unit operation. Despite its achievements, this strategy is inefficient when dealing with complex process flowsheets such as utility and refrigeration systems where a large number of unit operations are heavily connected by recycling streams. To address this problem, an integrated data-driven modelling and optimization framework is proposed in this work. The framework first constructs a hybrid machine learning based surrogate model to automatically reduce the system dimensionality and capture the nonlinearity of the underlying chemical process. Then, an efficient optimization algorithm, in specific, evolutionary algorithm, is embedded to identify the optimal solution of this surrogate model. Quality and accuracy of the estimated optimal solution is finally validated against the rigorous process model. Through an iterative approach, optimal operating conditions for the entire process flowsheet are efficiently identified. Furthermore, the novel CryoMan Cascade cycle system for large scale liquefied natural gas manufacturing is used as the case study. This framework is demonstrated to be superior regarding time-efficiency, solution quality, and flexibility over the rigorous model based optimization approach.

Keywords: large-scale chemical process, surrogate modelling, dimensionality reduction, Gaussian processes, artificial neural network.

1. Introduction

Developing disruptive digital technology to enable the design and operation of cost-effective and energy-efficient manufacturing systems is one of the grand research themes under the context of the 4th Industrial Revolution. Given the large amount of data accumulated from process industries, building data-driven models to enable rapid decision-making is of critical importance in order to guarantee the process performance and safety (Bhosekar and Ierapetritou, 2018). This directly triggers the development and application of surrogate modelling technology in the current industry and research community (McBride and Sundmacher, 2019).

Specific to the chemical industry, rigorous process models derived from mass and energy balances allow for accurate determination of states of a system, and can be directly constructed using multiple computer-aided software packages such as Aspen (Bhosekar and Ierapetritou, 2018; Zhang *et al.*, 2018) However, due to their complexity, the computational time to evaluate a rigorous model can be relatively large (e.g. potentially weeks to months), hence limiting their applications for process control and optimization (del Rio-Chanona *et al.*, 2018; McBride and Sundmacher, 2019). As a result, surrogate models have been adopted to replace rigorous models and help with identifying optimal operating conditions.

However, at present, surrogate models are predominantly used to replace single unit operations (Henao and Maravelias, 2011; Quirante, Javaloyes and Caballero, 2015), whilst their applicability in terms of substituting more complex systems such as entire process flowsheets has not been well explored. Therefore, in this study, different cutting-edge surrogate models are tested to simulate and optimize a novel liquefied natural gas (LNG) refrigeration cycle, with their performance thoroughly compared against the optimal solution identified through the rigorous model. The structure of this paper is organized as follows. Section 2 introduces the LNG production process. The approach to optimize the rigorous model and the associated primary challenges are also explained. Section 3 details the construction and optimization of different surrogate models. Section 4 summarizes the results of these surrogate models and compares them with the rigorous model's verification. A thorough discussion regarding the advantages of combining Gaussian processes and partial least squares for large scale complex chemical process simulation and optimization is presented in the Results and Discussion section.

2. Introduction to the CryoMan Cycle

Commercial scale production of LNG involves the use of large, complex and energy-intensive refrigeration cycles. The costs associated with the energy for refrigerant compression (shaft work energy) dominate the overall operating costs of the LNG plant. The CryoMan Cascade cycle recently developed by (Almeida-Trasvina and Smith, 2018) (shown in Fig. 1(a)) is a novel refrigeration configuration that can save significant energy demand in shaft work compared to current commercial processes. In this process, within the precooling cycle, a 'heavy' mixed refrigerant provides cooling in a series of two multi-stream heat exchangers (MSHEs); three stages are employed for refrigerant compression. In the liquefaction cycle, the 'light' mixed refrigerant is first fed into a liquid-vapour separator. The resulting outlet streams are partially mixed with each other to create the two refrigerant streams that provide cooling in a series of two MSHEs. Refrigerant compression is also carried out in three compression stages. In both precooling and liquefaction cycles, a pump after the second compression stage pumps any condensed refrigerant to the compressor discharge pressure.

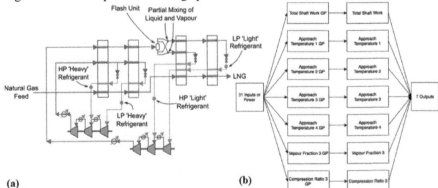

Figure 1: The CryoMan Cascade cycle (a), and its KPLS based surrogate model (b).

The rigorous model of the CryoMan Cascade cycle was implemented in Aspen HYSYS v8.2 and subsequently linked to MATLAB. This resulted in a callable function taking 31 inputs and producing 20 outputs. The inputs include the refrigerant mass flowrates, refrigerant compositions, discharge pressure, refrigerant evaporating pressures, MSHE outlet temperatures, compression ratios and refrigerant split fractions (where applicable) for both precooling and liquefaction cycles. The outputs from the process are eight values of shaft work demand, four MSHE approach temperatures, vapour fractions of four streams (to assess wetness at inlet of compressors), and four compression ratios.

The optimization problem for the rigorous model is defined as follows:

$$\min_{\varphi} \left(\sum_{i=1}^{N} W_1 \right) / m_{LNG}$$

s.t. $\Delta T_{min} \geq 2°C$; $P_{rat} \leq 3.5$; $\sum_{j=1}^{m} x_j = 1$, $x_j \in X^{MR}$; $VF^{ref} = 1$; $\varphi_{lb} \leq \varphi \leq \varphi_{ub}$

where the specific shaft work, defined as the sum of the individual shaft works W_i divided by the mass flow rate of LNG m_{LNG}, is the objective function to be minimized. The 31 inputs to the rigorous model are represented by φ with the set of inputs having corresponding upper and lower bounds φ_{ub} and φ_{lb}, respectively. Constraints include minimum approach temperatures for MSHEs ΔT_{min}, maximum compression ratios P_{rat} to discourage mechanical damage to compressors, valid molar compositions represented by x_j, and no wetness within compressors by constraining vapour fractions at the inlet of compressors VF^{ref} to zero. An evolutionary algorithm (EA) is first employed for the optimization of the rigorous model. The way on which constraints are dealt with in stochastic optimization is by applying penalties to invalid solutions. Successive Quadratic Programming (SQP) is next used to identify a local optimal solution around the best candidate resulting from the stochastic optimization.

3. Developing Surrogate Models

Directly optimizing the rigorous model is time consuming (over 17 hours per run), whilst the real-time decision-making of a commercial LNG plant is often around once per 4 hours. Therefore, surrogate models are used to resolve this challenge. Different from using surrogate models to substitute a unit operation, building a surrogate model to replace an entire process flowsheet is more challenging due to the high nonlinearity of the underlying process and high dimensionality of the involved design variables. To guarantee success, several surrogate model structures were proposed and their performance was thoroughly compared in this work. Furthermore, taking advantage of both supervised (dealing with nonlinearity) and unsupervised (dealing with dimensionality reduction) machine learning techniques is another strategy proposed in this work, as this may greatly simplify the process complexity for surrogate model construction and meanwhile obtain high quality optimal solutions.

3.1. Artificial Neural Network based surrogate models

To consider the nonlinearity of this highly interconnected process flowsheet, different structures of artificial neural networks (ANN) based surrogate models are constructed. These include: (1) a single ANN directly simulating the entire process (31 inputs and 20 outputs); (2) an ANN framework comprising 2 independent ANNs, one simulating the 8 shaft works, 4 compression ratios and 4 vapour fractions given the 31 inputs, and the other simulating the 4 temperature differences given the same inputs; (3) an ANN framework comprising 5 separate ANNs, one simulating the 8 shaft works, 4 compression ratios and 4 vapour fractions, and the other 4 each of which only simulating a specific temperature difference. The reasoning behind designing different ANN model structures is thoroughly discussed in the Results and Discussion section.

3.2. Kriging Partial Least Squares based surrogate model

In the method described by (Bouhlel *et al.*, 2016) to integrate partial least squares (PLS) into Gaussian Processes (GPs), PLS is performed in the data and the PLS weights (projected spaces of inputs and outputs) are used to construct a lower dimensional covariance matrix over which a GP model is constructed. By reducing the model dimensionality it allows for easier determination of the minimum log-likelihood resulting in a lower computational time cost, and more accurate mapping of between the input space and the output space. This integrated modelling strategy (embedding PLS into GP), namely KPLS, is adopted in this research to complete the construction of the GP based surrogate model superstructure. 7 GP models are constructed in this work to account for the 7 most important outputs. The structure of this model is shown in Fig. 1(b).

3.3. Data generation and selection

Three different datasets were generated with differing qualities and time costs in order to create the surrogate models: *Dataset 1:* 5000 random data points. Data points in this dataset were generated randomly within 10 minutes. Despite the negligible time cost, this dataset consists of mostly invalid solutions due to the nonlinearity and complexity of the LNG production process; *Dataset 2:* 500 refined data points. The input bounds were slightly more constricted to result in an increased proportion of valid solutions; *Dataset 3:* 350 high-quality data points. This dataset consists completely of valid solutions and was created by discarding invalid solutions. Despite the high accuracy, it takes 50 minutes to generate this dataset, thus the time cost is much higher than Dataset 1.

As the accuracy of a surrogate model heavily relies on the data quality, Dataset 1 was found incapable of constructing an accurate surrogate model. However, having a large size of data is also a prerequisite to build an accurate surrogate model, thus purely using Dataset 3 (*i.e.* only using feasible points) is not enough. Hence, Datasets 2 and 3 were combined (well mixed) to provide global representation of the rigorous model as well maintain a relatively large proportion of valid solutions. For a highly nonlinear system with 31 inputs and 20 outputs, 850 data points is not necessarily large. The ratio between feasible and infeasible data points in the combined dataset is approximate 3:1. Although extra high-quality data can be generated, the overall surrogate model construction time will be increased, diminishing its advantage over the rigorous model.

A specifically designed evolutionary algorithm was employed to optimize the surrogate models, taking advantage of tournament selection and single point crossover. A mutation rate of 3% and selection percentage of 98% were used over a population size of 100. The optimization scheme was chosen to run for 500 generations. Moreover, a linear penalty is implemented in order to guide the optimization initially towards a valid solution space. Finally, the ANN based surrogate models were implemented using PyTorch 1.2.0 and the KPLS based surrogate models were implemented using the SMT toolbox by (Bouhlel *et al.*, 2019), both within Python 3.7.3 on a Windows 10 operating system. Total construction of the KPLS models takes on average 2 minutes using 850 data points, and that for the ANN based surrogate models takes approximately 5 minutes.

4. Results, Discussion and Conclusions

4.1. Results of ANN based surrogate model frameworks

As shown in Fig. 2, after validation with the rigorous model, it is found that although the single ANN model can well predict total shaft work and vapour fractions, its predicted

MSHE approach temperatures (*i.e.* temperature constraints) are infeasible and greatly deviate from the rigorous model's verification result. The single large ANN is here unable to capture the nonlinearity of the process, and its accuracy is verified to be low. A straightforward improvement to the single ANN surrogate model is to split this large ANN into a two separate ANNs to deal with the nonlinear temperature constraints. In other words, a surrogate model framework can be built to include two independent ANNs, one only predicting the four highly nonlinear MSHE approach temperatures and the other estimating the remaining 16 outputs. Breaking a surrogate model up into a series of parallel sub-models may increase accuracy in capturing specific nonlinearities that are particularly prominent in a complex process flowsheet. Hence, a second surrogate model framework is constructed to further separate the MSHE approach temperature ANN into four separate ANNs, each predicting an individual approach temperature. This will allow the overall surrogate model to gain better accuracy still with regards to the individual approach temperatures, and ensure that a prediction made using the surrogate model remains feasible when validated with the rigorous model.

Indeed, through verification, the second framework (consisting of 5 ANNs) successfully meets all the constraints, hence resulting in feasible solutions (Fig. 2). Nonetheless, the optimal total shaft work identified in the third surrogate model is 160 MW, much higher than the optimal solution (144 MW) identified using the rigorous model. Hence, the surrogate model is still not efficient in terms of process optimization. Overall, the results from the three ANN based surrogate models suggest that due to the high nonlinearity and dimensionality of the underlying process and limited amount of data, it may not be ideal to use ANNs to construct surrogate models to simulate a whole process flowsheet.

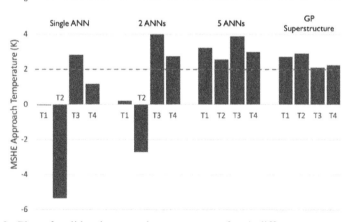

Figure 2: Plot of validated approach temperatures for 4 different surrogate model structures. Infeasible MSHE approach temperatures have values below the dotted red line.

4.2. Results of the KPLS superstructure model

Due to the system having a relatively large number of inputs and outputs, unsupervised learning techniques are adopted to reduce the dimension of the solution space (i.e. reducing the impact of the curse of dimensionality) for the construction and optimization of surrogate models. In addition, after assessing the rigorous optimization problem described in Section 2, it was observed that there exists no constraint on individual shaft works within the refrigeration cycle, thus using the summation of individual shaft works (*i.e.* total shaft work, one output) to substitute for the 8 individual shaft works (8 outputs) can potentially simplify the surrogate model construction. If the individual shaft works did need to be accessed after gaining a solution from the surrogate model with a reduced output such as this, the solution can be directly entered into the rigorous model to gain the relevant process information. Likewise, it was also observed from the ANN based surrogate models that the majority of data regarding 3 out of the 4 vapour fractions and 3 out of the 4 shaft works exist in feasible solution space all the time (*i.e.* redundant constraints). Due to this fact, it is decided to neglect to model these outputs in the first place to further reduce the dimension of the outputs. From Fig. 2, it is seen that the KPLS superstructure model (consisting of 7 GPs) satisfies all the practical constraints. Furthermore, its predicted total shaft work is verified to be accurate (147.4 MW verified by the Aspen model), and is comparable to the optimal result obtained using the rigorous optimization (144.4 MW). In addition, individual shaft works are found to be feasible after verification. Most importantly, the full time to train and optimize this surrogate model only takes around 10 minutes (*i.e.* 2 minutes for model construction and 8 minutes for stochastic optimization) as opposed to 17 hours spent when optimizing the rigorous model. This directly demonstrates the superiority and practical advantages of using the integrated KPLS modelling strategy for the optimization and real-time decision-making of high dimensional complex chemical systems (e.g. entire process flowsheet).

5. Conclusions

To conclude, Gaussian processes and artificial neural networks can be used as building blocks to construct efficient surrogate models to represent highly nonlinear systems such as an entire chemical process flowsheet. However, selection of surrogate model structure, fidelity of available data, and amount of data can greatly affect the accuracy and efficiency of surrogate models. Moreover, unsupervised learning techniques can also be taken advantage of to reduce the high dimensionality encountered in large scale processes simulation. Through the use of data-driven models and efficient stochastic optimization algorithms, it is possible to greatly reduce the computational time cost and meanwhile identify a high quality optimal solution for the operation of large scale systems.

References

Almeida-Trasvina, F. and Smith, R. (2018) 'Design and Optimisation of Novel Cascade Refrigeration Cycles for LNG Production', *Comput. Aided Chem. Eng.*, pp. 621–626.

Bhosekar, A. and Ierapetritou, M. (2018) 'Advances in surrogate based modeling, feasibility analysis, and optimization: A review', *Comput. Chem. Eng.*, 108, pp. 250–267.

Bouhlel, M. A. et al. (2016) 'Improving kriging surrogates of high-dimensional design models by Partial Least Squares dimension reduction', *Struct. Multidiscipl. Optim.*, 53(5), pp. 935–952.

Bouhlel, M. A. et al. (2019) 'A Python surrogate modeling framework with derivatives', *Advances in Engineering Software*, 135, p. 102662.

Henao, C. A. and Maravelias, C. T. (2011) 'Surrogate-based superstructure optimization framework', *AIChE J.*, 57(5), pp. 1216–1232.

McBride, K. and Sundmacher, K. (2019) 'Overview of Surrogate Modeling in Chemical Process Engineering', *Chemie Ingenieur Technik*, 91(3), pp. 228–239.

Quirante, N., Javaloyes, J. and Caballero, J. A. (2015) 'Rigorous design of distillation columns using surrogate models based on Kriging interpolation', *AIChE J.*, 61(7), pp. 2169–2187.

del Rio-Chanona, E. A. et al. (2018) 'Deep learning-Based surrogate modeling and optimization for microalgal biofuel production and photobioreactor design', *AIChE J.*, p. aic.16473.

Zhang, D. et al. (2018) 'Life cycle assessments of bio-based sustainable polylimonene carbonate production processes', *Sustain. Prod. Consum.*, 14, pp. 152–160.

Sauro Pierucci, Flavio Manenti, Giulia Bozzano, Davide Manca (Eds.)
Proceedings of the 30ᵗʰ European Symposium on Computer Aided Process Engineering
(ESCAPE30), May 24-27, 2020, Milano, Italy. © 2020 Elsevier B.V. All rights reserved.
http://dx.doi.org/10.1016/B978-0-12-823377-1.50014-8

Modelling and Optimisation of Middle Vessel Batch Distillation

Elena Cătălina Udrea, Romuald Győrgy, Costin Sorin Bîldea

University Politehnica of Bucharest, Department of Chemical and Biochemical

Engineering, Gh. Polizu street, no. 1-7, Bucharest, 011061, Romania

sorin.bildea@upb.ro

Abstract

This contribution demonstrates that middle vessel batch distillation can be conveniently studied using commercial process engineering software such as Aspen Plus and Aspen Dynamics. A steady-state model is initially developed in Aspen Plus, in order to obtain the starting point for the batch operation – total reflux operation. The model is exported to Aspen Dynamics as flow-driven or pressure-driven simulations. After the relevant controllers are added, the dynamic simulation model predicts the evolution of products composition. The optimal operation strategy can be easily found (for example, the setpoints of temperature and flow controllers which achieve the required product purities, while minimizing the energy requirements). This approach has significant advantages: rigorous distillation models including mass and energy balances; tray hydraulics calculations; temperature-dependent physical properties available from an extensive library; built-in models for other process units and control elements; robust numerical algorithms, including dynamic optimization.

Keywords: Middle vessel, batch distillation, control structure, dynamic optimisation.

1. Introduction

Batch distillation is extensively used in laboratory and chemical, pharmaceutical, biochemical and polymers industries. It is often preferred to continuous distillation because it provides a unitary solution and different separations can be performed in the same equipment by simply changing the operating conditions. Middle vessel batch distillation (MVBD) is a special configuration in which the mixture to be distilled is fed into a vessel placed between the rectifying section and the stripping section of a batch distillation column. During operation of a MVBD, the low- and high-boiling components are removed as distillate and bottoms products, respectively. At the end, the components with intermediate boiling points are found in the middle vessel. For ternary separations, this configuration is better compared with conventional batch distillation, having shorter operating time, lower energy requirements and higher product purities (Luyben, 2015, Li et al., 2018).

Various experimental and theoretical studies highlight the advantages of this configuration. Over time, MVBD processes have been developed for special scenarios, such as multi-component distillation (Wittgens et al., 1996), extractive distillation (Warter et al., 2000; Espinosa, 2002) and reactive distillation (Carmona et al., 2006; Arellano-Garcia et al., 2008). Many researchers have studied and contributed with improvements to the process by performing simulation and dynamic optimisation (Gruetzmann et al., 2008; Leipold et al., 2009; Rao et al., 2012; Luyben, 2015; Zhu et al., 2016).

2. Problem formulation

Mathematical models of middle vessel batch processes are useful for design and optimal operation studies. They include mass and energy balance equations, together with equilibrium relationships. This leads to a system of differential and algebraic equations which can be solved using general purpose software. However, reliable thermodynamic models for computation of physical properties (such as heat of vaporization, vapor pressure, density, viscosity, etc.) and access to a database with the parameters of the thermodynamic models are needed. Moreover, during the integration of the dynamic model the phase equilibria (vapor-liquid, liquid-liquid, or vapor-liquid-liquid) equations must be repeatedly solved by robust numerical methods. For all these reasons, the programming effort is significant, and the speed of execution is quite low.

The modelling approach suggested here makes use of available process simulation software such as Aspen Plus and Aspen Dynamics. In this way, new and efficient MVBD processes can be developed by process engineers faster, with reduced effort, and without requiring advanced modelling or programming skills. This approach has significant advantages: rigorous distillation models including mass and energy balances; tray hydraulics calculations; temperature-dependent physical properties readily available from an extensive library; built-in models for other process units and control elements; robust numerical algorithms, including dynamic optimization.

3. Development of the Aspen Dynamics model

This section considers the separation of an equimolar ethanol / 1-propanol / 1-butanol mixture in a laboratory-scale unit. The required purities are 0.95 (mole fractions). The upper (rectifying) and lower (stripping) sections house 20 and 10 theoretical stages, respectively. Including the condenser, middle vessel and reboiler, the total number of stages is 33. The column diameter is 5 cm. The reboiler duty is limited to 3 kW. The middle vessel, distillate and bottoms collector have 10 L each. The initial amount subjected to distillation is 134.5 moles (8.1 kg), which are fed into the middle vessel. Note that this is different from the approach taken by Luyben (2015), who considered that the mixture to be separated is initially at the bottom of the column. When operation begins, the liquid flows from the middle vessel towards the bottom of the column. Once enough liquid accumulates, the heating is started, vapour flows upwards, condenses, and returns as reflux. After a certain time, a stationary state is achieved – the total reflux operation. Our goal is to get a dynamic simulation model having the initial state as close to total reflux operation as possible. Thus, a steady state simulation is built in Aspen Plus (Figure 1, left). The feed flow rate is small (0.02 mol/min) and is distributed between the top (high purity ethanol), middle (ethanol / 1-propanol / 1-butanol, equimolar) and bottom (high purity 1-butanol) products. The reboiler duty is set to 1 kW, and the reflux ratio is very high (R = 375). This simulation is used to check that the hydrodynamic conditions are feasible, i.e. there is no flooding or weeping. Then, an Aspen Dynamics flowsheet is exported, including level controllers for the sumps of the upper and lower sections (not shown in Figure 1). After initialization of the dynamic simulation, the feed is cut off and no products are withdrawn. Finally, valves VE and VB are open, to empty the distillate and bottoms collectors, and the product streams (ETOH, PROH and BUOH) are simply deleted (Figure 1, right). The operation starts by increasing the lower reflux (L_i). The liquid level at the bottom of the lower section increases, and the bottoms product W is withdrawn. Fixing the operating variables to Q_{reb} = 1.2 kW, L_b = 1.5 mol/min, L_i = 2.5 mol/min (0.15 kmol/h), after 5 hours of operation the purities of the products are

$z_{EtOH,B2}=0.926$, $z_{PrOH,B1}=0.585$, $z_{BuOH,B3}=0.925$. Products of higher purity are obtained after adding temperature controllers for the upper and lower sections (Figure 1, left). Figure 2 presents the evolution of amounts of collected products and their purities, while a summary of the results for the initial operating conditions is shown in Table 1.

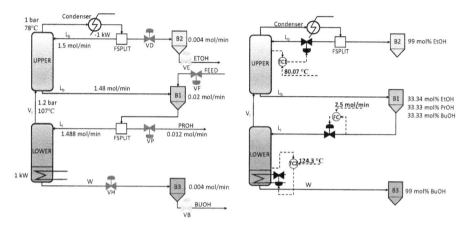

Figure 1. Steady state simulation (left); Dynamic simulation (right)

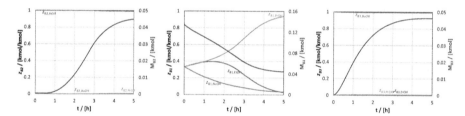

Figure 2. Simulation results (base case) showing the change of composition and holdup in the distillate vessel (left), middle vessel (center), and bottom vessel (right)

Table 1. Comparison between the values of the decision variables before and after the optimization

Variables	Base-case	Optimization	Dynamic optimization
TC1.Gain / [%/%]	1	0.1	4.63
TC1.Integral_time / [min]	20	16.46	19.88
TC1.SP / [°C]	80.07	82.5	81.79
TC2.Gain / [%/%]	1	5	2.81
TC2.Integral_time / [min]	20	40	19.97
TC2.SP / [°C]	124.3	124.5	115.15
Purities (top / middle / bottom)	0.99 / 0.94 / 0.99	0.95 / 0.95 / 0.95	0.95 / 0.95 / 0.95
Reflux (lower) / [mol/min]	2.5	2.6	Varying
Energy requirement / [kWh]	7.58	4.26	4.07

4. Process optimization

The base-case operating conditions lead to distillate and bottoms product with purities exceeding the specifications. To bring the unnecessarily high energy requirements down, a minimisation problem is formulated, with the cumulative reboiler duty as the objective function. The decision variables are the settings of the temperature controllers (setpoint, gain, integral time) and lower section reflux. The problem is completed by the constraints specifying that, at the end of distillation, the purities should exceed 0.95. The optimisation problem is solved using the facilities offered by Aspen Dynamics. As expected, the purity constraints are active and, compared with the initial case, the energy requirement is significantly reduced from 7.58 kWh to 4.26 kWh (Table 1).

Then, a dynamic optimisation is performed, with the lower reflux as the control variable, which is discretized into a 16-intervals piecewise constant function. The solution shows further decrease of the energy requirements (4.07 kWh) and of the batch time (4 h). Figure 3 presents the collected products and their purities, while the cumulative reboiler duty and the change of the control variable are shown in Figure 4. It should be noted that, during the entire process, the maximum heating duty does not exceed 2.5 kW.

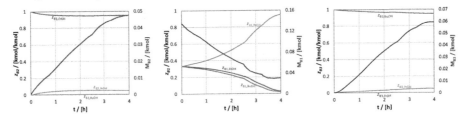

Figure 3. Simulation results (dynamic optimization) showing the change of composition and holdup in the distillate vessel (left), middle vessel (center), and bottom vessel (right)

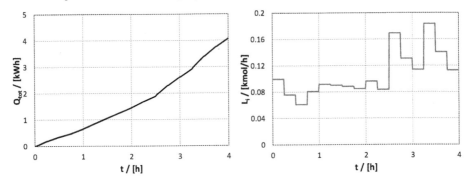

Figure 4. Results of the optimization study: total amount of heat (Q_{tot}, left side) and optimal reflux rate policy for the lower column (L_i, right side)

5. Complex operating sequence – separation of a quaternary mixture

This section describes the development of a model for separating 100 kmol of an equimolar methanol / ethanol / 1-propanol / 1-butanol mixture by MVBD. The required product purity is 0.99. The upper and lower sections have 20 and 30 theoretical trays, respectively. Methanol and ethanol are obtained as distillates, 1-butanol as bottoms. At the end of distillation, 1-propanol will be found in the middle vessel.

Figure 5 shows the process setup. The dynamic simulation is constructed as explained previously. However, the control structure is more complex, the products purities being controlled by concentration–temperature cascade loops.

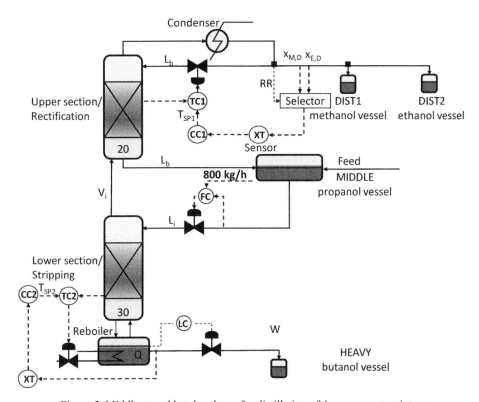

Figure 5. Middle vessel batch column for distillation of 4-components mixture

After the dynamic simulation reaches total reflux operating conditions, the lower section reflux rate is increased. At the bottom, high purity n-butanol is obtained. In the beginning, the methanol-rich distillate is collected in DIST1 vessel. As distillation proceeds, the lightest component (methanol) is depleted from the middle vessel. Consequently, it becomes increasingly difficult to achieve high-purity methanol product, and the required reflux ratio increases. When the reflux ratio becomes excessively high (200), the concentration sensor XT switches from measuring the ethanol concentration (the impurity in the methanol product) to measuring the n-propanol concentration (the impurity in the ethanol product), and the distillate is collected in the DIST2 vessel. The process stops when the n-propanol mole fraction in the middle vessel reaches the specification. It should be noted that this rather complex operating procedure can be reliably implemented by means of Aspen Dynamics "tasks":

```
Task etanol
    Runs Once When BLOCKS("B1").sf("LB") > 0.995 AND time >= 1
    Ramp (BLOCKS("B2").sf("ETOH"), 1, 0.1);
    BLOCKS("B11").SelSig : 2;
End
```

The amount of product collected in each vessel and their purities are shown in Figure 6. Throughout the process, methanol and n-butanol are obtained with the required purity (0.99 mole). At the end of the process, the n-propanol product also satisfies the specifications. However, the ethanol purity is only 0.95, due to impurification with methanol during the product switching. In order to improve the purity of the ethanol product, an off-cut vessel can be introduced.

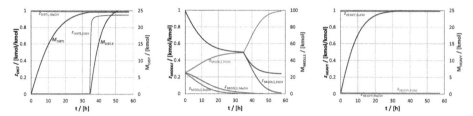

Figure 6. Simulation results (four-component mixture) showing the change of composition and holdup in the distillate vessel (left), middle vessel (centre), and bottom vessel (right)

6. Conclusions

Middle vessel batch distillation can be conveniently studied using commercial process engineering software such as Aspen Plus and Aspen Dynamics. In this way, models including rigorous physical properties, tray hydraulics, process control can be easily developed and solved using robust numerical algorithms. Such models are useful for simulating the behaviour of existing columns, designing new columns, or optimizing complex operating policies.

Acknowledgement

The financial support of the European Commission through the European Regional Development Fund and of the Romanian state budget, under the grant agreement 155/25.11.2016 (Project POC P-37-449, acronym ASPiRE) is gratefully acknowledged.

References

H. Arellano-Garcia, I. Carmona, G. Wozny, 2008, A new operation mode for reactive batch distillation in middle-vessel columns: Start-up and operation, Computers and Chemical Engineering, 32, 161-169.

J. Espinosa, 2002, On the Integration of Reaction and Separation in a Batch Extractive Distillation Column with a Middle Vessel, Industrial and Engineering Chemistry Research, 41, 3657-3668.

S. Gruetzmann, G. Fieg, 2008, Startup Operation of Middle-Vessel Batch Distillation Column: Modelling and Simulation, Industrial and Engineering Chemistry Research, 47, 813-824.

M. Leipold, S. Gruetzmann, G. Fieg, 2009, An evolutionary approach or multi-objective dynamic opimization applied to middle vessel batch distillation, Computers and Chemical Engineering, 33, 857-870.

X. Li, T. Zhao, Y. Wang, Y. Wang, Z. Zhu, 2018, Operational design and improvement of conventional batch distillation and middle-vessel batch distillation, Brazilian Journal of Chemical Engineering, 35, 2, 769-784.

W. L. Luyben, 2015, Aspen Dynamics simulation of a middle-vessel batch distillation process, Journal of Process Control, 33, 49-59.

C. S. Rao, K. Barik, 2012, Modeling, Simulation and Control of Middle Vessel Batch Distillation Column, Procedia Engineering, 38, 2383-2397.

M. Warter, J. Stichlmair, 2000, Batch Distillation of Azeotropic Mixtures in a Column with a Middle Vessel, European Symposium on Computer Aided Process Engineering, 10, 691-696.

B. Wittgens, B. Litto, E. Sørensen, S. Skogestad, 1996, Total reflux operation of multivessel batch distillation, Computers and Chemical Engineering, 20, 1041-1046

Z. Zhu, X. Li, Y. Cao, X. Liu, Y. Wang, 2016, Design and Control of a Middle Vessel Batch Distillation Process for Separating the Methyl Formate/Methanol/Water Ternary System, Industrial and Engineering Chemistry Research, 55, 10, 2760-2768.

Sauro Pierucci, Flavio Manenti, Giulia Bozzano, Davide Manca (Eds.)
Proceedings of the 30th European Symposium on Computer Aided Process Engineering
(ESCAPE30), May 24-27, 2020, Milano, Italy. © 2020 Elsevier B.V. All rights reserved.
http://dx.doi.org/10.1016/B978-0-12-823377-1.50015-X

Investigation of Heat Transfer Enhancement in a Microchannel Heat Sink with the Aid of Internal Fins: A Metamodel Approach

Vahid Hosseinpour, Mohammed Kazemeini *

Department of Chemical and Petroluem Engineering, Sharif University of Technology, Tehran, Iran

kazemini@sharif.edu

Abstract

Heat transfer enhancement with microchannel tools has been increased in recent year. In this study effect of geometric parameters as well as Reynolds number have been studied with experimental design approach. A metamodel was generated in this study for pressure drop and average Nusselt number passed all statistical tests. Order of an individual effect upon a response has been evaluated and interaction effects have been determined. Numerical results indicated that heat transfer increased significantly with inserting pyramidal micro fins.

Keywords: Metamodeling, Finned Microchannel Heat Sink (FMCHS), Experimental Design, Heat Transfer Enhancement Introduction

Heat transfer handling has a crucial role in the performance of engineering devices. Recently, miniaturized engineering devices such as micropumps (Liu et.al, 2018), microvalves(Huang et. Al, 2016), microsensors (Maegaard et. al, 2018) and high-performance electronic devices with a small size containing additional integrated circuits have been increasingly developed (Leela et. al, 2015). Accordingly, micro-size heat transfer devices have been favoured which opened new avenues for engineers to working on design and development of new micro heat sink systems (Kandlikar et.al, 2005, Naphon, et.al 2018). A higher heat transfer coefficient, a small inventory of coolant fluid and a large surface to volume ratio, are the most common excellence of Microchannel Heat Sink (MCHS) devices over conventional version of heat sink systems (Whitesides, 2006). However, several parameters affected the performance of these micro-scale devices including; the specific rate of heat dissipation, flow rate, pressure drop of coolant, fluid temperature rise, and the fluid inlet to surface temperature ought to be considered in microchannel designs.

Concerning the high capability of MCHS in heat transfer, various researches have been done for finding the proper design of microchannel and investigation of flow characteristics in these devices. Design, optimization and improvement for double layer microchannel heat sink performed by Wang et.al., (2015). In these studies, several parameters simultaneously optimized while minimization of thermal resistance chosen as an objective function. Lee et al. (2006) predicted the thermal behaviour of single-phase flow in a rectangular microchannel while correlating results with those of conventional sized channel. These results were validated through experimental data obtained in a microchannel with width ranging from 194 to 534 μm and depth range of five times of width in each case. Through investigation of heat transfer and fluid flow characteristics in MCHS, Philips (1987) developed a formulation for designing microchannel geometry. In this study microchannel with pyramid micro fins thoroughly investigated with statistical concepts. To verify effects of geometric parameters of pyramid fin on thermal performance of microchannel heat sink experimental design approach was used. Finally, a metamodel was developed for Nusselt number and pressure drop prediction as geometric parameter and Reynolds number.

1. Numerical Model

To save computation time only on channel of heat sink was modeled and simulated with the CFD technique. Dimension of single microchannel and computation domain presented in the figure 1 and Table 1. Geometrical parameters of micro-fins survived in this study was described as follows; ratio of cross-section of fins to microchannel width,

$\left(\alpha = \dfrac{d_f}{W_c}\right)$, the ratio of fin height to the height of the microchannel $\left(\beta = \dfrac{h_f}{H_c}\right)$, and

fins spacing (Sf) indicating the center to center distance of two adjacent fins.

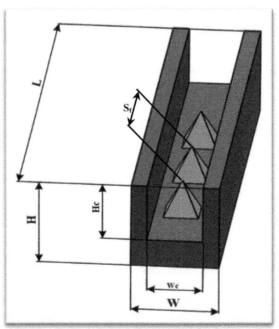

Figure 1) Schematic diagram of Computational domain

To solve governing equations some assumptions were accounted for. These included; steady state, laminar and no slipping flow, incompressible Newtonian fluid, uniform heat flux at the bottom wall, insignificant radiation, hydraulic and thermally fully developed flow; constant and varied thermos-physical properties for solid and fluid section;

respectively, and no gravity. Governing equation (continuity, momentum and energy balance) solved with the Finite Element Method with the tools of the in-house coding.

Table 1. Geometric parameters of computational domain and microchannel utilized in this study

Parameter	value
W	0.800 (mm)
H	0.800 (mm)
L	30 (mm)
W_c	0.325 (mm)
H_c	0.650 (mm)
α	0.3-0.9
β	0.0.3-0.9
S_f	0.5-2 (mm)
L_{int}	$3W_c$

2. Experimental Design

To evaluate fined microchannel heat sink performance, an experimental design approach was used. Central composite design at 5 levels was utilized to generate design points. Range of parameters displayed in table 2.

Table 2. Levels for input parameters used in the simulation of experiment in actual and coded values used in this research

Parameter	Description	Unit	Level				
			$-\alpha(-2)$	-1	0	+1	$+\alpha(+2)$
$A: \alpha$	$\dfrac{d_f}{W_c}$		0.3	0.45	0.6	0.75	0.9
$B: \beta$	$\dfrac{h_f}{H_c}$		0.3	0.45	0.6	0.75	0.9
$C: S_f$	adjacent fin's distance	(μm)	500	875	1250	1625	2000
$D: Re$	Reynold number		180	345	510	675	840

3. Developing a metamodel

Generated quadratic equations for prediction of Nusselt number and pressure drop for pyramidal FMCHS were presented in Eqs. (1) and (2). Power Box-Cox transformation with 0.32 for the pressure response and natural logarithm transforms for the average Nusselt number was performed.

$$(\Delta p)^{0.32} = 23.36 + 1.08A + 2.07B - 0.69C + 3.89D + 0.51AB + 0.22AD - 0.29BC \qquad (1)$$
$$+ 0.45BD - 0.12CD + 0.2B^2 + 0.11C^2 - 0.36D^2$$

$$\ln\left(Nu\right) = 3.13 + 0.054A + 0.070B - 0.058C + 0.12D + 0.025AB$$
$$-0.013AC - 0.021BC + 0.015C^2 - 0.024D^2$$

(2)

ANOVA table for the two responses presented in the table 3. Parameter in this table revealed that developed models passed statistical tests and these models. P-valuer less than 0.05 indicated models fits data properly. Adjusted R^2 and predicted R^2 were in less than 0.2 differential. This fact also confirmed that, the statistical tests passed properly.

Table 3. The ANOVA results for responses for pyramidal-FMCHS

Source	Sum of Square	DF	Mean Square	F-Value	p − value probability > F
ΔP					
Model	520.53	12	43.38	913.35	<0.00001
Residual	0.81	17	0.047		
R^2=0.9985, Adj- R^2=0.9974, Pred- R^2=0.9930, Adequate Precision= 128.82					
$\overline{Nu}$					
Model	0.64	9	0.071	168.41	<0.00001
Residual	0.008403	20	0.0004202		
R^2=0.9870, Adj- R^2=0.9811, Pred- R^2=0.9580, Adequate Precision= 57.098					

Equation (1) demonstrated that the Reynold number had the most significant effect on the pressure drop. Fin height ranked second in terms of importance and fin base diameter came third. Fin spacing had the least (and adverse) effect upon the pressure drop across the microchannel with pyramid micro-fins. The insignificant AC and A2 terms were removed from the quadratic equation.

According to equation (2), AD, BD, CD, A2, and B2 terms were determined to be trivial in the model regarding the design space and they were removed from the model. Water velocity had the greatest effect upon the average Nusselt number.

4. Overall Performance

The relationship between the thermal resistance and the Reynolds number is depicted in figure 2. In general, thermal resistances dropped with the enhancement of the Reynolds number due to improvement in the heat transfer coefficient. This Figure indicated that pyramid fins geometries enhanced the thermal performance of the considered microchannel. For a Reynolds number of 840, the thermal resistance of the plain microchannel was about 65% higher than that of the microchannel with pyramid micro-fins.

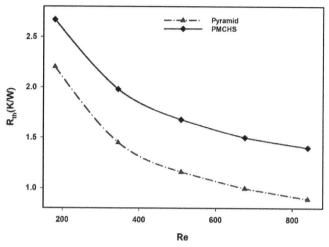

Figure 2. Comparison of pyramid fins microchannel with plain microchannel

Effect of micro-fins on convection heat transfer in microchannel heat sinks was examined by relative Nusselt number illustrated in figure 3. As shown, Nu0 stands for the average Nusselt number of PMCHS selected as the base case, for microchannel with pyramid fins, the relative average Nusselt number was greater than 1 implying that inserting micro-fins enhanced convection heat transfer due to increased heat transfer area as well as interruption in flow field. This behavior was considered as a typical characteristic of a microchannel. Moreover, this Figure emphasized that, the relative Nusselt number (Nu/Nu_0) increased through enhancement of the Re_{in} due to the fluid disturbance as a consequence of rising in flow velocity.

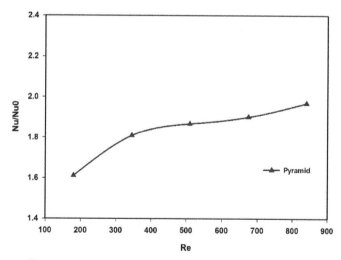

Figure 3. average Nusselt number for pyramid micro fins

5. Conclusion

In this research, inserting pyramid micro-fins onto microchannel were thoroughly investigated. To evaluate effects of geometric parameters as well as Reynolds number upon the performance of Finned Microchannel Heat Sinks, experimental approach was utilized. With the aid of the DOE software, a metamodel was generated for the pressure drop and average Nusselt number predictions. This metamodel passed all statistical tests that confirmed such model fitted data properly. These types of models might be used in the optimization of such microchannel greatly saving in computation time. Another benefit of the developed model is to determine the affect of parameters upon a selected response. Moreover, synergism of interaction of parameters for a particular response may also be determined.

References

B. Liu, Z. Zhang, J. Yang, J. Yang, D. Li, A rotary ferrofluidic vane micropump with C shape baffle, Sensors Actuators, B Chem. 263 (2018) 452–458.

B. bo Huang, M. jie Yin, A.P. Zhang, X. song Ye, On-chip microfabrication of thermally controllable PNIPAAm microvalves by using optical maskless stereolithography, Sensors Actuators, A Phys. 247 (2016) 397–402.

K. Maegaard, E. Garcia-Robledo, N.P. Revsbech, Microsensor for simultaneous measurement of H_2 and H_2S, Sensors Actuators, B Chem. 259 (2018) 560–564.

V. Leela Vinodhan, K.S. Rajan, Fine-tuning width and aspect ratio of an improved microchannel heat sink for energy-efficient thermal management, Energy Convers. Manag. 105 (2015) 986–994.

S. Kandlikar, S. Garimella, D. Li, S. Colin, M. King, Heat transfer and fluid flow in minichannels and microchannels, Elsevier, 2005.

P. Naphon, L. Nakharintr, S. Wiriyasart, Continuous nanofluids jet impingement heat transfer and flow in a micro-channel heat sink, Int. J. Heat Mass Transf. 126 (2018) 924–932.

G.M. Whitesides, The origins and the future of microfluidics, Nature. 442 (2006) 368–373.

C. Leng, X.D. Wang, T.H. Wang, An improved design of double-layered microchannel heat sink with truncated top channels, Appl. Therm. Eng. 79 (2015) 54–62.

P.S. Lee, S. V. Garimella, Thermally developing flow and heat transfer in rectangular microchannels of different aspect ratios, Int. J. Heat Mass Transf. 49 (2006) 3060–3067.

R.J. Phillips, Forced-convection, liquid-cooled, microchannel heat sinks, Massachusetts Institute of Technology, 1987.

Sauro Pierucci, Flavio Manenti, Giulia Bozzano, Davide Manca (Eds.)
Proceedings of the 30th European Symposium on Computer Aided Process Engineering
(ESCAPE30), May 24-27, 2020, Milano, Italy. © 2020 Elsevier B.V. All rights reserved.
http://dx.doi.org/10.1016/B978-0-12-823377-1.50016-1

Optimization of RFCC Process Considering Particle Deposition Model

Hyungtae Cho[a], Kwang Cheol Oh[a], Jiheon Lee[b], Seokyoung Hong[b], Junghwan Kim[a,*]

[a]*Green Materials & Processes Group, Korea Institute of Industrial Technology, 55 Jongga-ro, Jung-gu, Ulsan 44413, Republic of Korea*
[b]*Department of Chemical and Biomolecular Engineering, Yonsei University, 50 Yonsei-ro, Seodaemun-gu, Seoul, 03722, Republic of Korea*
kjh31@kitech.re.kr

Abstract

Formation of particle deposit in the reactor cyclone of the commercial residue fluidized catalytic cracking (RFCC) process is one of the major problems causing serious catalyst carryover into the fractionators and process shutdown. This problem has been considered as an unavoidable issue in sustainable operations and required an accurate forecasting model. The particle deposition model in the cyclone dipleg of RFCC process is developed considering both of mathematical particle deposit factors and actual operating data. The model for particle deposition was researched in the viewpoint of transport phenomenon of particle. Verification of the model is conducted with actual plant data using parameter estimation method. Optimization model of RFCC process is developed by combining particle deposition model and cracking reaction model to find optimal operating conditions. The optimal operating conditions are found by selection of reaction temperature, catalyst/oil ratio and feed rate, to minimize particle deposit thickness. As a result, the operating cycle time is increased from 31 to 47 months (52%) by the decreasing particle deposition rate and the productivity of gasoline is increased at about 46% by increasing RFCC operation period.

Keywords: Residue Fluidized Catalytic Cracking (RFCC), particle deposit, modeling and optimization

1. Introduction

A residue fluid catalytic cracking (RFCC), typical heavy oil upgrading (HOU) process, is a key process in refinery industry (Pinheiro, 2011). In this process, the residue from atmospheric distillation towers are converted into highly valuable light hydrocarbons such as gasoline and naphtha (Song, 2010). The RFCC unit is in the Ulsan Complex of SK energy, Korea. The unit has operated with atmospheric residue feed rates at ca. 58,000 BPSD (Kim, 2012). An RFCC process is composed of a reactor, and a regenerator. The cracking reaction occurs in the riser, and the product gas and catalysts are separated in a reactor cyclone. The riser is 60 m long; the upper section is 35 m long with a diameter of 1.6 m ID, and the lower section is 25 m long with a diameter of 1.0 m ID. The particle deposit, i.e. coking, has been commonly observed in the RFCC reactor as a black deposit on the surface of the cyclone barrels, reactor dome, and walls. It is also quite common for the deposit to form stalactites from the plenum chamber or dome steam rings. The deposit is often deposited on the cyclone barrels. Coking within the cyclones can be potentially very troublesome since any coke spalls going down into the dipleg could restrict catalyst flow or jam the flapper valve. Either situation reduces cyclone efficiency and can increase catalyst losses from the reactor. Also, the formation of deposit in the reactor cyclone dipleg incurs serious catalyst carryover in the fractionators and process shutdown (Kim, 2012).

In this study, Particle deposition on the wall of cyclone dipleg in a RFCC reactor is modeled. The different mechanisms of particle transport to the wall are considered, i.e., Brownian motion and turbulent diffusion. A boundary condition that accounts for the probability of particle sticking to the wall is suggested. An analytical solution for deposition of small Brownian particles is obtained. The model parameters are estimated: (1) the particle–wall sticking probability, (2) the shear removal constant parameter, (3) the shear removal exponent parameter. Also, developed particle deposit forecasting model and tuned cracking reaction model are combined in this optimization model. And its results of optimization are compared and discussed

2. Particle deposition model in the dipleg

The particle deposit forecasting model is considered the deposition from a turbulent steady-state flow of a particulate suspension on the wall of a cyclone dipleg in RFCC reactor. And the model is developed considering a dilute flow where particle–particle collisions and a particle effect on a fluid flow can be neglected over the entire computational domain. For accuracy, this model is adopted a poly-dispersed particulate system.

The deposition velocity of the dipleg, calculated as the fluxes caused by particle diffusion and advection, is

$$V_{deposit} = -(D_{Br} + D_{PT})\frac{dc}{dy} + cV_p^y \tag{1}$$

where D_{Br} is the Brownian particle diffusivity and D_{PT} is the particle turbulent diffusivity, c is the particle concentration by volume, y is the coordinate determining particle distance from the wall and V_p^y is the particle drift velocity caused by turbophoresis and the other forces affecting particle motion in the direction, normal to the wall (Brennen,2005).

2.1. Determination of critical particle diameter

The forces that act on a particle attached to the wall of dipleg are considered for determining a critical particle size. Figure 1 shows a diagram illustrating forces acting on a particle attached to the wall surface. The force balance of the maximum static liquid bridge force, F_{Liquid}, and the sum of the drag force, F_{Drag}, and gravity force, F_g is calculated for estimating of the order of magnitude of the critical particle diameter.

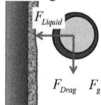

Figure 1. Diagram illustrating forces acting on a particle

2.2. The particle deposition model

The particle deposition flux, i.e. the deposition velocity, can be calculated by the product of the particle transport to the wall and the sticking probability. Though the concentration gradient in the wall vicinity is zero the chaotically moving particles reach the wall being transported by different mechanisms such as Brownian and turbulence.

First, the particles are involved into Brownian motion; that is, particles chaotically move due to multiple collisions with fluid molecules. The particle deposition flux caused by the Brownian motion is:

$$q_{Bi} = p_i \, m(d_i) \, N_i \, v_{dBi} \tag{2}$$

where p_i is the particle–wall sticking probability of the ith size fraction particle with the wall $m(d_i)$ is mass of ith size fraction, N_i is concentration of ith size fraction, v_{dBi} the most probable velocity directed to the wall.

As we already mentioned, small particles follow the fluid in fluctuation motion caused by turbulence. The deposition rate due to turbulence fluctuations is calculated based on the particle velocity at the time it touches the wall:

$$q_{Ti} = p_i \, m(d_i) \, N_i \, v_{dTi} \tag{3}$$

The total mass deposition flux of the ith size fraction particles is:

$$q_i = q_{Bi} + q_{Ti} = p_i \, m(d_i) \, N_i \, [v_{dBi} + v_{dTi}] \tag{4}$$

As a reasonable approximation for modelling such a complex system we assume that the particle–wall sticking probability is constant: that is, $p_i = p$.

The total deposition mass flux is:

$$q_\Sigma = \sum_{i=1}^{i_{cr}} q_i = p \sum_{i=1}^{i_{cr}} m_i \, N_i \, [v_{dBi} + v_{dTi}] \tag{5}$$

where i_{cr} is the size fraction number corresponding to the critical particle size d_{cr} that is a tuning parameter of our model.

According to Eskin et. Al. (2011) their experiments showed that increasing the Couette device rotation speed (i.e., the shear rate at the wall) leads to a reduction of the deposit mass. To account for the shear removal effect, the total depositing particle flux should be reduced as follows:

$$q_a = q_\Sigma - q_{SR} \tag{6}$$

The deposit thickness data of the commercial RFCC process is needed to identify the model parameters. The model parameters, included those for the shear removal model, are: (1) the particle–wall sticking probability, p; (2) the shear removal constant parameter, α_r; (3) the shear removal exponent parameter, n. For conducting calculation, every variable is collected from commercial RFCC process data. The particle size distribution (PSD) is adopted for robust simulation of the particle deposition. Also, fluid velocity and particle concentration are obtained from CPFD simulation result.

In Figure 6 a system boundary is presented. For accuracy of simulation, the system boundary is divided 4 zones and 6 blocks as height.

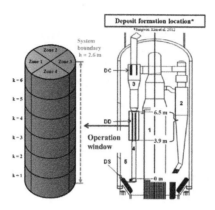

Figure 2. System boundary of particle deposit model

3. Results and discussion

3.1. Parameter estimation results

The deposit thickness data (thickness of the particle deposit at the different process operation times) were fitted to the simulation results upon identification of the following model parameters: (1) the particle–wall sticking probability, p= 0.023; (2) the shear removal constant parameter, α_r= 0.009; (3) the shear removal exponent parameter, n= 0.557.

Figure 3 shows the parameter estimation results and presents deposit thickness versus time at each zone of cyclone dipleg. As shown in Figure 3 (b), the two deposit thickness data (Plant data) points are also presented. One can see that agreement between the calculated and the plant data is good in this case

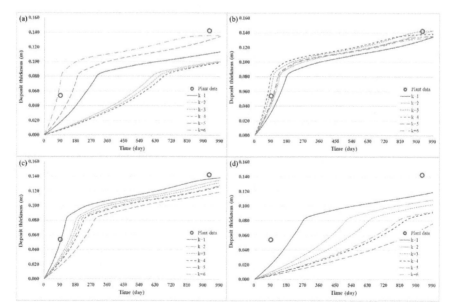

Figure 3. Parameter estimation results for deposit thickness versus time: (a) zone 1, (b) zone 2, (c) zone 3, (d) zone 4.

3.2. Optimization Results

The reaction model is assumed that the Residue is cracked into the most desired gasoline, and Cl-C4 gas and coke. One objective function is selected for the study. It is to minimize the deposit thickness at the certain operation day by using three decision variables: 1) the reaction temperature, 2) the catalyst oil ratio, 3) the feed flow rate, i.e. capacity of residue.

Optimization model is solved with constraints to search the optimum values of reaction parameters. In doing this, the reaction model and the particle deposit thickness is calculated again by using optimum values predicted by GA as shown in Table 1.

Table 1. Optimization results

Optimum operation conditions		
Temperature, T_f (°C)	Catalyst oil ratio, C/O	Feed rate, M_{feed} (BPSD)
505.429	8.981	72851.121

Reaction model result		
	Original operation conditions	Optimized operation conditions
Conversion	0.891	0.936

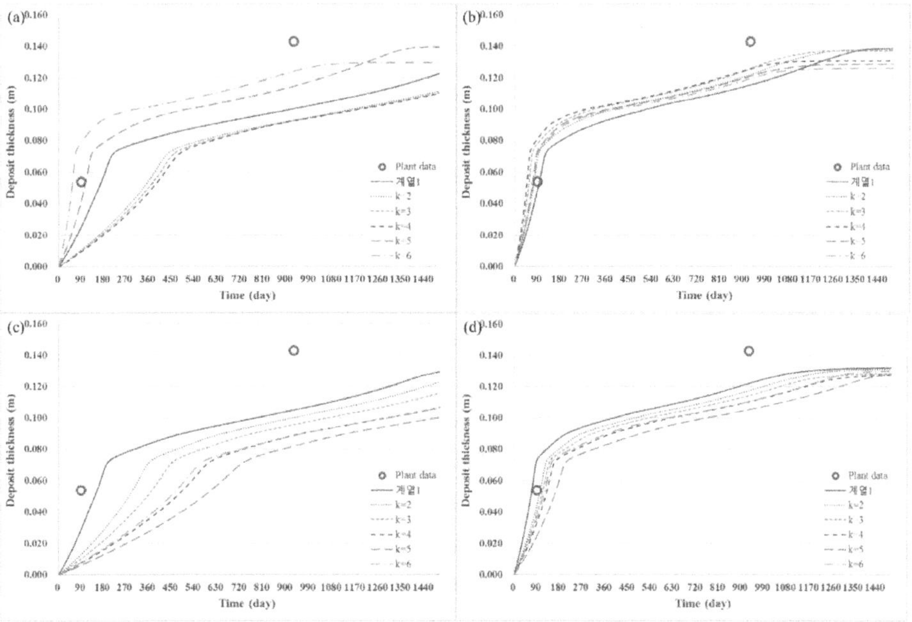

Figure 4. Minimized deposit thickness versus time: (a) zone 1, (b) zone 2, (c) zone 3, (d) zone 4.

Figure 4 shows the deposit thickness versus time at each zone of cyclone dipleg. And the maximum deposit thickness data (plant data) points is also presented. As shown in Figure 4 (b), the deposit thickness of optimized data is clearly lower than the plant data. The deposit thickness value of 0.126 cm that is lower than the values of experimental measurements, 0.146 cm in commercial RFCC process. Also, the operation period of optimized RFCC process is increased from 990 to more than 1400 days.

4. Conclusion

This study is developed the particle deposition model validated with real plant data and the optimization model including particle deposit effect. As a result, we found the optimal operating conditions, selection of reaction temperature, catalyst oil ratio and feed rate, to minimize particle deposit thickness. It has also demonstrated that feed conversion rate, amount of gasoline production and amount of C1-C4 production is increased about 4.5%, 3.5% and 79.2%, respectively. The operating cycle time expanded from 990 to 1400 years by the decreasing particle deposit rate. The proposed model is expected to benefit refinery industries by enabling them to determine optimal decision variables related to particle deposit formation.

References

Pinheiro, C. I., Fernandes, J. L., Domingues, L., Chambel, A. J., Graça, I., Oliveira, N. M., Cerqueira, H. S. & Ribeiro, F. R. (2011) Fluid Catalytic Cracking (FCC) Process Modeling, Simulation, and Control, Industrial & Engineering Chemistry Research, 51(1), 1–29.

Song, J., Sun, G., Chao, Z., Wei, Y. & Shi, M. (2010) Gas flow behavior and residence time distribution in a FCC disengager vessel with different coupling configurations between two-stage separators. Powder Technology, 201(3), 258-265.

Kim, S. W., Lee, J. W., Kim, C. J., Koh, J. S., Kim, G. R., & Choi, S. (2012). Characteristics of deposits formed in cyclones in commercial RFCC reactor. Industrial & Engineering Chemistry Research, 51(30), 10238-10246.

Kim, S. W., Lee, J. W., Koh, J. S., Kim, G. R., Choi, S., & Yoo, I. S. (2012). Formation and characterization of deposits in cyclone dipleg of a commercial residue fluid catalytic cracking reactor. Industrial & Engineering Chemistry Research, 51(43), 14279-14288.

Brennen, C. E. (2005) Fundamentals of multiphase flow. Cambridge university press

Guha, A. (2008). Transport and deposition of particles in turbulent and laminar flow. Annu. Rev. Fluid Mech., 40, 311-341.

Eskin, D., Ratulowski, J., Akbarzadeh, K., & Pan, S. (2011). Modelling asphaltene deposition in turbulent pipeline flows. The Canadian Journal of Chemical Engineering, 89(3), 421-441.

Eskin, D., Ratulowski, J., & Akbarzadeh, K. (2011). Modeling of particle deposition in a vertical turbulent pipe flow at a reduced probability of particle sticking to the wall. Chemical engineering science, 66(20), 4561-4572.

Cho, H., Kim, J., Park, C., Lee, K., Kim, M., & Moon, I. (2017). Uneven distribution of particle flow in RFCC reactor riser. Powder technology, 312, 113-123.

Cho, H., Cha, B., Kim, S., Ryu, J., Kim, J., & Moon, I. (2013). Numerical analysis for particle deposit formation in reactor cyclone of residue fluidized catalytic cracking. Industrial & Engineering Chemistry Research, 52(22), 7252-7258.

Sauro Pierucci, Flavio Manenti, Giulia Bozzano, Davide Manca (Eds.)
Proceedings of the 30th European Symposium on Computer Aided Process Engineering
(ESCAPE30), May 24-27, 2020, Milano, Italy. © 2020 Elsevier B.V. All rights reserved.
http://dx.doi.org/10.1016/B978-0-12-823377-1.50017-3

Dimethyl Carbonate Production by Urea Transesterification, Process Simulation and Environmental Assessment

Proceedings of the 30th European Symposium

Laurent Astruc, José Miranda, Ivonne Rodriguez Donis, Claire Vialle, Caroline Sablayrolles

Laboratoire de Chimie Agro-industrielle, Université de Toulouse, INRA, INPT, Toulouse, France

laurent.astruc@toulouse-inp.fr

Abstract

Evaluation of the environmental sustainability to synthesize dimethyl carbonate (DMC) from the urea transesterification with methanol is carried out by using Life Cycle Assessment (LCA) methodology for the first time. Foreground data for LCA analysis are supplied by simulation results using ProSimPlus®. The LCA is modelled with SimaPro, and Ecoinvent database provides background data. LCA results show that the urea production has the main impact in 10/11 impact categories whereas the ionizing radiation is mainly influenced by downstream separation. Finally, the urea route shows better results than the oxidative carbonylation of methanol.

Keywords: Life Cycle Assessment (LCA), urea route, DMC, ProSimPlus, Process design

1. Introduction

DMC is a highly attractive chemical that is considered as a green chemical with applications in pharmaceutics, coatings or battery electrolytes. DMC biodegrades readily in the atmosphere, and is non-toxic and noncorrosive to metal. Several studies have demonstrated that the synthesis of DMC via the methanolysis reaction with urea involves two-step reaction including methyl carbamate (MC) as the first intermediate product according to the following mechanism (Huang et al., 2015):

(R1) $NH_2CONH_2(Urea) + CH_3OH \overset{K_1}{\leftrightarrow} NH_2COOCH_3(MC) + NH_3$

(R2) $NH_2COOCH_3 + CH_3OH \overset{K_2}{\leftrightarrow} CH_3OCOOCH_3(DMC) + NH_3$

(R3) $CH_3NHCOOCH_3 + CH_3OCOOCH_3 \overset{K_3}{\leftrightarrow} NH_2COOCH_3(NMMC) + CH_3OH + CO_2$

MC is produced by reaction R1 with high yield even in the absence of catalyst. However, the conversion of MC into DMC by adding methanol requires the use of a solid catalyst at high temperature and pressure achieving a DMC yield up to 54% (Huang et al., 2015). Besides, the DMC yield is affected by a third side reaction with MC to form N-methyl,methyl-carbonate (NMMC). Kongpanna et al. (2015) carried out the simulation of the urea route process with ASPEN PLUS software including reactions R1 and R2 from CO_2 and ammonia as chemical feedstock. The commercial oxidative carbonylation of methanol (ENI Process) was selected as the base case design producing about $4x10^3$ kg/h of DMC with 0.998 of purity. They concluded that ethylene carbonate route is the most promising alternative. Nevertheless, they also highlighted that the energy consumption of the urea route process could be drastically reduced through process intensification and change of the operating conditions. Monteiro et al. (2009) compared the ethylene carbonate transesterification with the urea route including a reactive distillation (RD) column to produce DMC and using sustainability metrics in two domains gate to gate and cradle to gate. Simulation of the urea route process was carried out with HYSYS to produce about 13.5×10^3 kg/h of DMC in a RD column but omitting reaction R3. The ethylene carbonate transesterification showed better material and energy index as well as ecoefficiency. Later, Wang et al. (2010) developed a non-equilibrium model to simulate the RD column to synthetize DMC but also neglecting reaction R3. Experiments were carried out in a bench scale RD column and they were in good agreement with simulation results. Vazquez et al. (2018) run simulations with ASPEN Plus software including a RD column for synthetizing DMC considering the whole three reactions. Urea and methanol were the initial raw materials for a manufacturing production capacity of 74×10^3 t/y of DMC. The authors concluded that urea route process is an environmental friendly alternative without any environmental assessment. According to our knowledge, not much rigorous multicriteria methods as life cycle assessment (LCA) have been used for the sustainability evaluations of the urea route. This work focuses on the assessment of the environmental performance of the urea transesterification pathway in the light of LCA. The entire process with RD column is simulated using ProSimPlus® and the results from the mass and energy balance are used as foreground data for LCA. The main goal is to investigate this promising pathway from an environmental point of view and to highlight hotspots. To our knowledge, this work is the first to assess environmental performance of this DMC production alternative using LCA from cradle to gate.

2. Process simulation

2.1. Physicochemical properties and thermodynamic analysis

Simulation of the entire flowsheet requires the knowledge of the properties of the involved pure compounds as well as the thermodynamic information about the phase's equilibrium and the equilibrium constant or kinetic of the reactions. Group contribution methods is a suitable solution when experimental values are missing even for the computation of the variation of the Gibbs energy of the reactions ($\Delta_r G$) from the standard formation enthalpy and the standard absolute entropy of pure compounds.

2.1.1. Physicochemical properties database

Required physicochemical properties for the process simulation including CO_2, ammonia, urea, methanol and DMC are available in DIPPR database. MC and NMMC are missing. Many experimental data are available in NIST webBook for MC. However, NMMC has been scarcely studied and even the boiling point was hard to find. Hence, all required properties were computed from group contribution methods available in ProSimPlus®.

2.1.2. Equilibrium reactions

Since urea decomposes easily to MC and ammonia at temperature higher than 400K (Huang et al., 2015), in this work we use the kinetic model proposed by Zhao et al. (2012), where the Arrhenius parameters were computed from batch experiments without catalyst in the temperature range 403 – 433K. The Arrhenius frequency factor ($L.mol^{-1}.s^{-1}$) and the activation energy (kJ/mol) is 1.20×10^6 and 84.7, respectively. Kongpanna et al. (2015) and Vazquez et al. (2018) obtained a model for K_1 and K_2 vs temperature by fitting predicted values of the ($\Delta_r G$) at different temperatures using the Benson method in gas state (Poiling et al. 2001). This strategy seems not to be suitable because the reactions take place into the liquid phase. Similar to Monteiro et al. (2009), we use the kinetic model proposed by Wang et al. (2007) for reaction R2 based on experimental kinetic data with the solid ZnO catalyst at temperatures between 423 – 473K. For the forward R2, the Arrhenius frequency factor (g^{-1}.L.mol^{-1}.s^{-1}) and the activation energy (kJ/mol) are 1.10x10^3 and 101, respectively, while for the reverse reaction, the respective values are 1.464x10^{-3} and 49. Most of kinetic studies of the reaction R2 (Huang et al., 2015) have shown that there is an optimal residence time between 5 - 10 hours at temperature of 443 – 453K. The average yield of DMC is between 35-55% whereas NMMC yield varies from 2 to 12% depending on the catalyst. Vázquez et al. (2018) underlined that this residence time is unreachable in a real RD column. Hence, we also keep the assumption that the equilibrium is reached in the every reactive plate. An equilibrium constant K$_2$ model was fitted from the kinetic model proposed by Zhao et al. (2012):

$$K = 158.5 - 1.7027 * T + 0.0068 * T^2 - 1.10^{-5} * T^3 + 8.10^{-9} * T^4 \qquad (1)$$

Similar to Vázquez et al. (2018), the extension of reaction R3 was set at 4% of MC yield.

2.1.3. Vapor – liquid equilibrium

The DMC synthesis process involves seven compounds: ammonia, CO$_2$, urea, methanol, MC, DMC and NMMC. The maximum reaction temperature at normal pressure is limited by the boiling point of methanol (337.66K) and DMC (363.45K). The plug reactor for carrying out R1 and the RD column works at high pressure because the optimal reaction temperature exceeds 363.45K. Similar to previous works, the non-ideality in the liquid phase was only considered in the simulation study. There is a minimum boiling azeotrope methanol – DMC that boils at 337.35K with a methanol molar fraction of 0.85. The increasing of the pressure up to 16 atm allows increasing of the methanol purity up to 0.9625. Wilson thermodynamic model was chosen using the binary interaction parameters available in Wang et al. (2007). Binary ideal mixtures were set when missing binary parameters because the boiling temperature difference is higher than 30°C.

2.2. Process simulation results

Gate to gate domain process is simulated using ProSimPlus®. Figures 1.(a) and (b) display the final optimal flowsheet for the MC production in a plug reactor, the RD column to synthetize the DMC and the NMMC and the subsequent downstream process to produce DMC at 0.998 of mass fraction. The optimal conditions to reach 100% of conversion in the plug reactor are set. A sensitivity analysis was carried out to determine the optimal pressure for the RD column and the distillation columns of the downstream section (see Figure 1. (b)) where the heat duty, the total number of trays and the position of the feeds were set as key operating variables. The SPEC facility in ProSimPlus® software was used to optimize the reflux ratio satisfying the required purity constraints of each distillation column. The simulated process is similar to those proposed by Vázquez et al. (2018) but making some significant modifications. In the first section, the ammonia is separated with a distillation column instead of a flash separation. In the second section, the bottom product of RD column is recycled to the RD column. The DMC is separated from the methanol with only one distillation column at P =16 atm with a recovery yield of 99.88%. The conversion from MC to DMC in the RD column reached 94.7%.

(a)

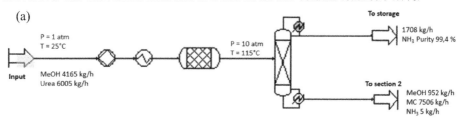

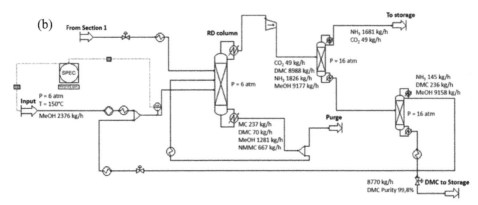

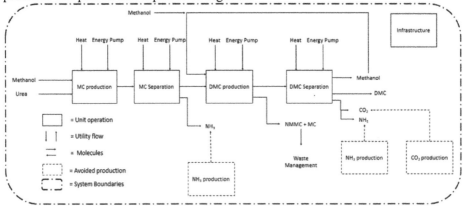

Figure 1. (a) Section 1: MC production and separation from the urea methanolysis (b) Section 2: DMC synthesis in the RD column and two distillation columns for DMC purification.

3. Environmental Assessment

The life cycle assessment (LCA) study is carried out in accordance with the ISO 14040/44 methodology (ISO, 2006a/b). SimaPro v8.5.0.0 Developer is used for the LCA modeling.

3.1. Goal and scope of the study

The system studied is described in the previous part about the process. The main goal of the study is to assess environmental performance of an emerging process of DMC production. The functional unit is the production of 1kg of DMC with a purity > 99% (molar). Hotspot analysis is performed to understand which part of the process has the higher impact and to identify opportunities of improvement. This study is conducted from cradle (raw material) to gate (DMC production). The geographical scope considers that the DMC production stems from a company located in France. The temporal scope considers the short-term horizon. The system boundaries comprise infrastructure and functioning: raw materials (extraction and production), utilities (production and use), process unit operations, transport, wastes end of life and avoided impacts link to co-products. The process tree is presented Figure 2.

Figure 2. Process tree of DMC production

3.2. Life cycle inventory

Foreground inventory data come from process simulation. Infrastructures are taken into account according to Althaus et al. (2007) recommendations. Direct emissions are calculated according to Hischier et al. (2005) recommendations. Background data are provided by Ecoinvent v3.4, Cut-Off database.

3.3. Life cycle impact assessment (LCIA)

ReCiPe Midpoint (H) 2016 v1.13 impact assessment method is chosen to calculate the following environmental impacts: Climate change, Ozone depletion, Particulate matter formation, Photochemical oxidant formation, Terrestrial acidification, Marine eutrophication, Freshwater eutrophication, Fossil depletion, Metal depletion, Water depletion (EC, 2013). The impact category Ionizing radiation is added because of the use of nuclear energy in the French electricity mix.

3.4. Results and interpretation

Over the entire life cycle, "MC production" is the mayor contributor to 10 categories out of 11 (Figure 3a), mostly due to the production and supplying of Urea (Figure 3b). The second hotspot is linked to "DMC separation" accounting for 50% of the category Ionizing radiation, due to electricity consumption. Infrastructure contributes to "Freshwater eutrophication" and "Metal depletion" because of the water, steel and copper consumption. Ammonia recovered permits to avoid from 12% to 46% depending on the category considered. It underlines the importance of recovering this gas during the process. The first clear improvement opportunity raised by this hotspot analysis is the urea production, which is mainly due to required ammonia. Ammonia is produced by a reaction of nitrogen from the atmosphere with hydrogen. This hydrogen currently produced from fossil fuel could be replaced by bio-based hydrogen or hydrogen produced from water electrolysis (Ni et al., 2006). Process simulation permits to face two LCA challenges: life cycle inventory collection and scaling up of an emerging process. The comparison of our emerging process with Eni process was performed. Eni process life cycle inventory is based on Garcia-Herrero et al. (2016). The results show that our emerging urea process has lower impact for 9 categories out of 11. Two co-products, carbon dioxide and ammonia, are considered as avoided production (avoided production of liquid under pressure). NMMC and MC contained in the purge are considered as wastes (incineration).

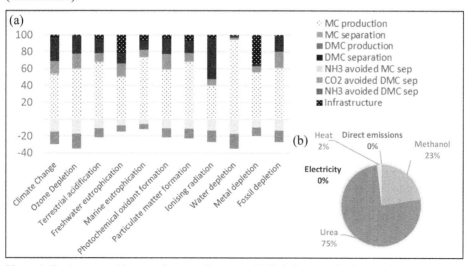

Figure 3. Environmental impacts from cradle to gate (a) Relative contributions to the corresponding impact categories of the different stages of the life cycle (b) Contribution of each foreground data to the climate change of "MC Production"

4. Conclusion

The environmental sustainability of the urea route for producing DMC has been evaluated and compared with the oxidative carbonylation of methanol (Eni process). Mass and energy balances of process are calculated by ProSimPlus simulations by considering the urea and methanol as chemical feedstock. A good conversion of 94.7% of MC is reached in the RD column. However, more experimental work have to be done for the NMMC side reaction to obtain a more realistic effect over the MC selectivity. The distillation columns are optimized to produce DMC at 0.998 of mass purity. The urea route to produce DMC appears as a promising alternative with improvement opportunities. The environmental assessment show better results than currently most used processes in Europe. The main issue in this synthesis pathway is the urea production and supply. Solutions can be proposed and further work can study these opportunities to show their environmental assets. Coupling process simulation with life cycle assessment has allowed us to face two LCA challenges, the scale up in LCA and the life cycle inventory collection.

Acknowledgments

The financial support allocated to this project by the French Ministry of Higher Education and Research (MESR) is gratefully acknowledged.

References

H.-J. Alhtaus, R. Hischier, M. Osses, A. Primas, S. Hellwag, N. Jungbluth, M. Chudacoff, 2007, Life Cycle Inventories of Chemicals, EcoInvent report No. 8

EC 2013, "Commission Recommendation of 9 April 2013 on the Use of Common Methods to Measure and Communicate the Life Cycle Environmental Performance of Products and Organisation"

I. Garcia-Herrero, R.M. Cuéllar-Franca, V.M. Enríquez-Gutiérrez, M. Alvare-Guerra, A. Irabien, A. Azapagic, Environmental Assessment of Dimethyl Carbonate Production: Comparison of a Novel Electrosynthesis Route Utilizing CO$_2$ with a Commercial Oxidative Carbonylation Process, ACS Sustainable Chemistry & Engineering, 4, 4, 2088-2097

R. Hischier, S. Hellweg, C. Capello, A. Primas, Establishing Life Cycle Inventories of Chemicals Based on Differing Data Availability, The Int Journal of Life Cycle Assessment, 10, 1, 59,67

S. Huang, B. Yan, S. Wang, X. Ma, Recent advances in dialkyl carbonates synthesis and applications, Chem. Soc. Rev., 2015, 44, 3079-3116

ISO, 2006a/b, ISO 14040/14044: Environmental Management – Life Cycle Assessment – Principles and framework / Requirements and Guidelines.

P. Kongpanna, V. Pavarajan, R. Gani, S. Assabumrungrat, 2015, Techno-economic evaluation of different CO2-based processes for dimethyl carbonate production, Chem. Engineering Research and Design, 93, 496-510

J.G.M-S. Monteiro, O. De Querioz Fernandes Araújo, J.L. De Medeiros, 2009, Sustainability metrics for eco-technologies assessment, Part II. Life cycle analysis, Clean Technologies and Environmental Policy, 11, 4, 459-472

M. Ni, D.Y.C Leung, M.K.H Leung, K. Sumathy, 2006, An overview of hydrogen production from biomass, Fuel Processing Technology, 87, 5, 461-472

B.E Poiling, J.M. Prausnitz, J.P O'Connel, 2001, The properties of liquid gases and liquids. Fifth edition. McGraw_Hill. Chapter 3, pages 3.14 - 3.50.

D. Vázquez, J. Javaloyes-Antón, J.D. Medrano-García, R. Ruiz-Femenia, J.A Cabellero, 2018, Dimethyl Carbonate Production Process from Urea and Methanol, Computer Aided Chemical Engineering, 43

F. Wang, J. Li, W. Zhao, F. Xiao, W. Wei, Y. Sun, 2007, Modeling of the Catalytic Distillation Process for the Synthesis of Dimethyl Carbonate by Urea Methanolysis Method, Industrial & Engineering Chemistry Research, 46, 26, 8972 -8979

W. Zhao, B. Han, N. Zhao, F. Xiao, W. Wei, 2012, Macro kinetics for synthesis of dimethyl carbonate from urea and methanol on Zn-containing catalyst, J Cent South Univ, 19, 1, 85-92

Sauro Pierucci, Flavio Manenti, Giulia Bozzano, Davide Manca (Eds.)
Proceedings of the 30th European Symposium on Computer Aided Process Engineering
(ESCAPE30), May 24-27, 2020, Milano, Italy. © 2020 Elsevier B.V. All rights reserved.
http://dx.doi.org/10.1016/B978-0-12-823377-1.50018-5

Modeling and Study of Hydrodynamic flow within the Preneutralizer Reactor using CFD Approach

S. Elmisaoui[a,b], L. Khamar[a,c], S. Benjelloun[a], M. Khamar[b], J.M. Ghidaglia[a,d]

[a] MSDA Modeling, simulation, and Data Analysis, Mohammed VI Polytechnic University Benguerir, Morocco

[b] LGCE, Laboratoire du génie civil et environnement, Mohamed V University, Rabat, Morocco

[c] LIPIM, Laboratoire d'ingénerie des procédés, informatique et mathématiques, ENSA-Khouribga, Sultan Moulay Slimane University, Khouribga, Morocco

[d] CMLA Centre des mathématiques et leurs applications, ENS Cachan, Paris Saclay University, Paris, France

Safae.elmisaoui@um6p.ma

Abstract

Mathematical modelling and numerical simulations are widely used in the petrochemical industries for operator training, design, and process optimization. However, there is a lack of rigorous numerical modelling and simulations in the phosphate fertilizer industry. There exist many challenges in the production systems of phosphate fertilizers including (i) multiphase flows in the system involving liquids, solids or gases, (ii) particles with different size distributions, and (iii) dynamic variations in the physical properties including rheology and thermodynamic behavior.

In the current study, using well-established techniques from computational fluid dynamics, we develop a model for the numerical simulation of multiphase flows in a conditioner operation unit used in the phosphate fertilizers facilities. The proposed model deals with the first step in the process, consisting on the preneutralizer, and it uses the Reynolds-averaged Navier-Stokes equations for modeling turbulent flow in the system. The preneutralization consist on a partial reaction between ammonia and phosphoric acid. Numerical results are presented for several scenarios and we particularly show the importance of the baffles on eliminating vortices, and also their effect on the different hydrodynamic performance criteria. This approach can be used to describe the behavior of reaction systems within this type of industrial plants and the analysis of the other sub-process of the fertilizer plant is an ongoing work.

Keywords: CFD; numerical simulation; multiphase flow; turbulence; vortex.

1. Introduction

Industrial manufacturing has relied on batch operation units mainly due to regulatory requirements (Driss Z. et al., 2012). However, the use of continuous processes and unit operations would provide a high flexibility in production capacity. Stirred tank reactors are encountered operation units in matter processing as in food, pharmaceutical, and chemical industries. Various research works (Khamar L et al., 2016) have been conducted in order to provide interesting information allowing to understand the complexity of the flow behavior in stirred tank reactors. This work uses CFD simulations of a chemical reactor characterized by a non- standard design in terms of the different characteristic dimension ratios of the vessel, and the shape. The stirred reactor is used in fertilizers manufacturing process as a preneutralization operation unit allowing to produce a chemical slurry with specific physicochemical characteristics and under special operating conditions. The main goal of this paper is to study the multiphase flow and mixing within the preneutralizer; and evaluate the effect of baffling on its hydrodynamic which should improve agitation performance and chemical species mixing.

2. Conceptual model of the preneutralizer reactor

2.1. CAD model and computational approach

Using a computational fluid dynamics (CFD) software package, we had defined the computational domain equipped with four baffles spaced uniformly around the preneutralizer periphery as shown in Figure 1. The mixing system is a pitched blade turbine (Figure 1.B) with inclined blade impellers. The CAD file is developed for the total reactor (Figure 1.A), and in order to study the hydrodynamic flow behavior, we had activated only the part that will be full of the mixture (Figure 1.C). On the other hand, two CAD models are developed: baffled and unbaffled cases.

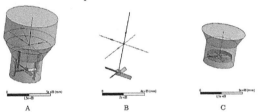

Figure 1: A: Preneutralizer geometry, B: Agitator Pitched blade turbine,
C: Simulated fluid using MRF

For the study and the simulation of the agitation mechanism within the targeted equipment using CFD, the preneutralization reactor was conceptually split by two separate and adjacent zones (Figure 1.C):

- A rotor defined by a rotating zone which surrounds the agitator;
- A stator as the stable and steady zone of the rest of the preneutralizer.

Hence, in this Multiple Referential Frame (MRF) approach, the flow domain is split in two parts. The first one is around the agitator that is simulated in a rotating frame with the stirrer and the equations are solved taking into consideration a Coriolis term. For the rest of the domain, the equations are solved in the fixed frame (T. Ian, et al.,2018 and Hadane A. et al., 2019). This approach is an approximate one but it has the advantage of involving stationary calculations (fixed mesh) and therefore faster simulation time.

2.2. Domain meshing

A mesh was generated to discretize the domain into small control volumes, where the governing equations (continuity and momentum) where be approximated by numerical schemes. Figure 2 represent the tetrahedral mesh grids for the unbaffled and baffled preneutralizers. It contains near to 287 843 cells for the first case and 389 772 cells for the second. As for the CFD model, grid dependence tests were carried out to choose the appropriate grid geometry for wich the grid density does not influence the simulation results.

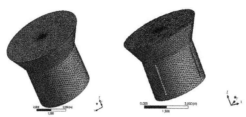

Figure 2: Meshing of the preneutralizer fluid domain (Mesh of the unbaffled preneutralizer (left), Mesh of the baffled preneutralizer (right))

3. Mathematical model and calculation setup

In the current study, we have considered that the multiphase flow behaves like an incompressible Newtonian viscous flow, and the system is isothermal.

3.1. Operational inputs of the preneutralizer

Some parameters are crucial for calculating and simulating mixing in the preneutralizer, which we summarize in the following table:

Table 1: Preneutraliser's operating parameters

Parameter	Value
Ammonia acid density (kg/m³)	0.6894
Phosphoric acid density (kg/m³)	1272.64
Ammonium acid viscosity (kg/m. s)	$1.015\ e^{-5}$
Phosphoric acid viscosity (kg/m. s)	0.0203
Rotational speed of the agitator (rpm)	68

3.2. Turbulence model

The aim of turbulence modelling is to predict the physical behavior of the turbulent flow generated in the system. A modelling method used should ensure accuracy, simplicity and computational efficiency (Dagadu C. P. K., 2015). In order to study the flow behaviour and the mixing quality in the preneutralizer, the chosen model is based on Reynolds Averaged Navier Stokes Equations (RANS). This model is indeed adapted for the majority of industrial problems. For turbulence modelling, the K-ε RNG model is used. It is a model where the smallest eddies are first resolved in the inertial range and then represented in terms of the next smallest eddies (Ansys. Inc., Canonsburg, 2011). More details on setting the solver for simulating the preneutralizer are given in the following table 2:

Table 2: Solver setup for the hydrodynamic flow in the preneutralizer

Turbulence model	K-Epsilon
Fluids in the stirred vessel (Preneutralizer)	Phosphoric Acid & Ammonia
Boundary conditions	Rotation MRF (68 rpm) Liquid level
Discretization - pressure	PRESTO!
Discretization - momentum	Second order upwind
Discretization	Species transport approach
Discretization-turbulent kinetic energy	Second order upwind
Discretization-turbulent dissipation rate	Second order upwind

3.3. Governing equations

The CFD software allow us to model the mixing and transport of chemical species by solving conservation equations describing convection, diffusion, and reaction sources for each component species. Multiple simultaneous chemical reactions can be modelled, with reactions occurring in the bulk phase (volumetric reactions) and/or on wall or particle surfaces. For this study we will use the transport species equation coupled to Navier Stokes equations and Turbulence equations:

(1) Mass conservation equation

$$\frac{\partial \rho}{\partial t} + \nabla.(\rho.\vec{v}) = S_m \tag{1}$$

The equation (1) is the general form of the mass conservation one and is valid for incompressible as well as compressible flows. The source S_m is the mass added to the continuous phase.

(2) Momentum conservation equation (Three-dimensional system)

$$\frac{\partial \rho.\vec{v}}{\partial t} + \nabla.(\rho.\vec{v}.\vec{v}) = -\nabla p + \nabla(\overline{\overline{\tau}}) + \rho\vec{g} + \vec{F} \tag{2}$$

With p is the static pressure, $\overline{\overline{\tau}}$ is the stress tensor, $\rho\vec{g}$ and $\vec{F}$ are respectively the gravitational body force and external body forces. For the turbulence model, as we had mentioned in section 3.2, the useful one is RNG K-ε, we have two equations to solve:

(3) Turbulent kinetic energy equation

$$\frac{\partial(\rho k)}{\partial t} + \frac{\partial(\rho.k.u_j)}{\partial x_i} = \frac{\partial}{x_j}[(\mu + \frac{\mu_t}{\sigma_k})\frac{\partial k}{\partial x_j}] + P_k - \rho.\varepsilon \tag{2}$$

(4) Turbulent dissipation equation

$$\frac{\partial(\rho\varepsilon)}{\partial t} + \frac{\partial(\rho.\varepsilon.u_i)}{\partial x_i} = \frac{\partial}{x_j}[(\mu + \frac{\mu_t}{\sigma_\varepsilon})\frac{\partial\varepsilon}{\partial x_j}] + C_{1\varepsilon}\frac{\varepsilon}{k}P_k - C_{2\varepsilon}^*\rho\frac{\varepsilon^2}{k} \tag{3}$$

Where $C_{e\varepsilon}^* = C_{2\varepsilon} + C_v\frac{\eta^3(1-\frac{\eta}{\eta_0})}{1+\beta\eta^3}$ and $\eta = \frac{Sk}{\varepsilon}$, with S is the modulus of the mean rate of strain tensor.

(5) Transport equations:

A prediction of the local mass fraction of each species (H_3PO_4 or H_2SO_4), through the solution of a convection-diffusion equation for the i_{th} species. This conservation equation takes the following general form:

$$\frac{\partial(\rho Y_i)}{\partial t} + \nabla.(\rho\vec{v}Y_i) = -\nabla.\vec{J}_i + R_i + S_i \tag{4}$$

Where R_i is the net rate of production by chemical reaction and S_i is the rate of creation by addition from the dispersed phase if it exists. For this stage of the study we don't take into account the reaction between the defined species. So, we have:

$$\frac{\partial(\rho Y_{H_3PO_4})}{\partial t} + \nabla.(\rho\vec{v}Y_{H_3PO_4}) = -\nabla.\overline{J_{H_3PO_4}} \tag{5}$$

$$\frac{\partial(\rho Y_{H_2SO_4})}{\partial t} + \nabla.(\rho\vec{v}Y_{H_2SO_4}) = -\nabla.\overline{J_{H_2SO_4}} \tag{6}$$

$$\vec{J}_i = -(\rho.D_{i,m} + \frac{\mu_t}{Sc_t})\nabla Y_i$$

With $D_{i,m}$ is the diffusion coefficient for species i in the mixture, μ_t the turbulent viscosity, and Sc_t is the turbulent Schmidt number.

(6) **The seventh equation is the Energy equation, for this study we suppose that we have an isothermal system, so this one doesn't make part of the system to solve.**

3.4. Boundary conditions

It is imperative to provide information on the flow at different boundaries of the flow domain. In this study, we have considered that the liquid level surface (The top of the geometry) is a symmetry surface, which mean that the free surface is assumed to be flat. This is generally the good assumption for stirred vessels with at least three baffles (Khamar et al. 2016). The agitator is divided in two parts, the first one is in the fixed reference frame and the second part is in the rotating reference frame.

4. CFD calculations and Simulation results

The CFD calculations and simulation are carried out for two cases. The first one is for the baffled preneutralizer with the characteristics mentioned before. The second case is for an unbaffled one, in order to evaluate the effect of baffles on the vortex formation.

4.1 Flow regime

Turbulence represents an important phenomenon that characterize the flow according to the value of Reynolds number (Ansys. Inc., Canonsburg, 2011). For this study Re = 3.8 10^7 which implies that the flow regime induced by the stirred is turbulent.

4.2 Type of flow induced by mechanical agitator

The analysis of the shape of the current's lines developed within the preneutralizer fluid sheath in the two studied cases (Figure 3) shows that the fluid is ejected from the blades of the agitator turbine towards the walls of the vessel and is divided into two parts. Thus, giving two loops of recirculation which develop, one below.

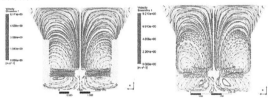

Figure 3: Streamlines inside the unbaffled (left) and baffled (right) preneutralizer

Consequently, it can be directly concluded that this stirrer ensures a radial flow of the mixture within the preneutralizer (Roustan M. 1997). Through a projection of the three-dimensional current lines on the longitudinal plane, we note the existence of two loops (Figure 3). A smaller one underneath the agitator turbine and relatively larger one that develops above the blades.

4.3 Balance of the torques exerted on the agitator

For a speed of rotation of 68 rpm, the main results from the CFD simulation are given in the following tables:

Table 3: Details of consumed power for unbaffled and baffled preneutralizer

Designation	Unbaffled (N.m)	Baffled (N.m)
Agitator	14501	27342.1102
Shaft in the static zone	0.0119	0.0186
Shaft in the MRF zone	0.0002	0.0159
Total	14501.0121	27342.1202

4.4 Power calculated using CFD

The general formula for the power is given by (Mununga L.,2003):

$$P = 2\pi NC \qquad (8)$$

With N: number of rotations per minute (Hz), and C: the torque (N.m). For a speed of 68 rpm, the power calculated using the CFD are given in table 4:

Table 4: Details of consumed power for unbaffled and baffled preneutralizer

Designation	Unbaffled (N.m)	Baffled (N.m)
Agitator	103.2084	194.1232
Shaft in the static zone	8.5230e^{-5}	1e^{-4}
Shaft in the MRF zone	1.0889e^{-6}	0.0113
Total	103.2084	194.4661

4.5 Number of power N_p

This parameter is dimensionless, and it's based on the hydraulic power calculated before Eq. (8), using the following formula (Mununga L.,2003):

$$N_P = \frac{P}{\rho N^3 D^5} \qquad (9)$$

The results of obtained using the CFD post processing tools gives a value of $N_{p\_unbf} = 0.2948$ for the unbaffled preneutralizer and $N_{p\_bf} = 0.5559$ for the baffled one. This values are similar with what is existing in the literature (Mununga L.,2003).

4.6 Pumping rate Q_p

The pumping rate is the volume flow rate of fluid that passes through the agitator turbine. Indeed, the stirrer rotating in the tank can be considered as a pump. This flow is also called the agitator pumping capacity noted Q_p From the results of the simulation $Q_{p\_unbf} = 79.72$ m³/s, and for the baffled preneutralizer the flow is $Q_{p\_bf} = 85.97$ m³/s.

4.7 Number of pumping N_q

It is the dimensionless formula of the pumping rate of an agitator. It depends essentially on the type of impellers and the hydrodynamic flow regime and it is given by the following expression:

$$N_q = \frac{Q_p}{ND^3} \tag{10}$$

With Q_p is the pumping flow (m³/s) and N is the rotation speed of the stirrer (rad/s), D is the turbine diameter. The results are $N_{q\_unbf} = 0.51$ and for the baffled one $N_{q\_bf} = 0.54$.

4.8 Vortex detection

The results presented in Figure 4 shows the vortex form in the preneutralizer using the Q-criterion parameter (G. Guyot, 2014), that define the vortex as a connected fluid region with a positive second invariant. This criterion also adds a secondary condition on the pressure, requiring it to be lower than ambient pressure in the vortex.

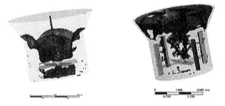

Figure 1 : Vortex inside the baffled and unbaffled preneutralizer

The Q represents the local balance between shear strain rate and vorticity magnitude, defining vortices as areas where the vorticity magnitude is greater than the magnitude of rate-of-strain. So, these results validate the baffles effect on the vortex appearance inside stirred vessels. For the baffled case baffles inhibit the vortex formation, which increase the mixing performance. On the other hand, the deformation of the free surface in the unbaffled preneutralizer make mixing operation more difficult and less efficient.

Conclusion

In this work, a modelling study and CFD calculations of a turbulent multiphase flow carried out for a mechanically agitated industrial reactor. It is a preneutralizer, with a specific geometry, used in the phosphate fertilizer industries. The effect of baffle's presence on the hydrodynamic performances and the vortex appearance inside the preneutralizer was studied. We have found that the baffles have a significant effect on the power consumption, they represent barriers to the flow which required the double of the normally consumed power. The high Reynolds number resulted from the simulation proves the right choice of RANS (k-ϵ) turbulence regime to model the system. Two recirculation loops are formed for the studied cases that confirm the radial flow generated by Pitched Blade turbine as known in the literature (Roustan M. 1997). Also, our calculation results affirm that baffles effectively break up the vortex generally observed in unbaffled preneutralizer. The developed CFD model is useful to understand the flow behavior, and in identifying the key parameters that affect directly the process effectiveness.

References

Driss Z., Karray S., Chtourou W., et al. 2012, a study of mixing structure in stirred tanks equipped with multiple four-blade Rushton impellers. Archive of Mechanical Engineering, vol. 59, no 1, p. 53-72.
Khamar L. et Samrane K. 2016, the use of the CFD for the hydrodynamic flow diagnostic and study in a Phosphoric Acid Reactor. Proceedia Engineering, vol. 138, p. 369-377.
T. Ian et J. Changying. 2018, a Study of the Mixing Performance of Different Impeller Designs in Stirred Vessels Using Computational Fluid Dynamics. Designs, vol. 2, no 1, p. 10.
Roustan Michel. 1997, agitation et mélange : caractéristiques des mobiles d'agitation. Techniques de l'ingénieur. Génie des procédés, vol. 4, no J3802, p. J3802. 1-J3802. 10.

Sauro Pierucci, Flavio Manenti, Giulia Bozzano, Davide Manca (Eds.)
Proceedings of the 30th European Symposium on Computer Aided Process Engineering
(ESCAPE30), May 24-27, 2020, Milano, Italy. © 2020 Elsevier B.V. All rights reserved.
http://dx.doi.org/10.1016/B978-0-12-823377-1.50019-7

Modelling and Optimization of a Multi-regional Hydrogen Supply System: a Case Study of China

Tianxiao Li,[a]Pei Liu,[*] Zheng Li

Department of Energy and Power Engineering, Tsinghua University, Beijing, 100084, China

liu_pei@tsinghua.edu.cn

Abstract

Hydrogen is likely to be widely used in the future due to its great potential to reduce carbon emissions. Planning and operation of a hydrogen supply system with multiple generation and transmission technologies, multiple consumers, and large infrastructure among regions are challenging tasks. Seasonal fluctuation of generation and demand would further make the problem more complex. In this paper, a long-period, multi-region and monthly-scale optimization model is developed, and China is taken as a case study. The optimal planning and operation strategy of China's hydrogen supply system before 2050 could be obtained by minimizing the overall system cost. Two scenarios are provided describing coal-based and power-based generation pathways. The overall costs in the power-based pathway is 2.4 times than the coal-based pathway due to higher cost of power. If zero carbon emissions are required, the economic balance point of two pathways would be when CCS cost is 525 yuan/tCO2. Furthermore, system planning is quite different in two pathways. Generation capacity would concentrate more in North China in the coal-based pathway, and nationwide pipeline networks are required in the power-based pathway.

Keywords: Hydrogen, Modelling, Optimization, Planning, China.

1. Introduction

Hydrogen is considered as a sustainable, clean and low-carbon energy carrier, and would have an important role in global low-carbon development. If hydrogen is widely used, a hydrogen energy supply system will be required in the future.

Planning and operation of a hydrogen supply system would be challenging. Firstly, multiple generation resources, transmission technologies, infrastructure and end-consumer in multi-regions are integrated in the supply system. Secondly, hydrogen generation and demand would fluctuate hourly and monthly, when hydrogen is generated from renewable resources. Thirdly, energy infrastructure requires large quantity of investment and a long construction period, which makes it difficult to maintain a high usage rate and secure economic return.

The planning of a hydrogen system in a long period has been studies in many studies, considering multi-regions and multiple resources. A linear programming model was developed to design the hydrogen delivery system for transportation demand towards 2040 in South Korea (2012). Almansoori, A. and A. Betancourt-Torcat (2016) developed a 16-region Mixed Integer Linear Programming (MILP) model and obtained the optimal layout of the generation capacity, storage facility and pipelines of hydrogen in Germany. Geographical Information System (GIS) method was also applied to develop planning models solving spatial issues (Baufume et al., 2013).

The planning of hydrogen supply systems could be further improved in two aspects. Firstly, intertemporal factors are not considered in most planning models, where monthly fluctuation of hydrogen demand and generation from renewable resources have great impacts on system layout. Li et al. (2019a) reviewed planning models for hydrogen systems and pointed out that integrating intertemporal factors into long-period planning would improve the planning outcome. Secondly, fossil-based hydrogen generation is neglected in most studies, which could be low-carbon when integrating carbon capture and storage technology. The difference between power-based and fossil-based pathway has not been pointed out.

In this paper, a long-period, multi-regional and monthly mathematical model of a hydrogen supply system is developed, and China is taken as a case study. China is facing duel challenges of more energy and low carbon. On the one hand, it is estimated that China's total energy demand would keep increase at an average rate of 1.5 % towards 2040 (BP, 2019). On the other hand, policy targets are set that non-fossil energy consumption would account for 50 % in 2050 (Commission, 2016). Hydrogen Industrial Technology Innovation Alliance of China (2019) made a positive estimation that hydrogen would account 10 % in final use in 2050 in China. The location of energy resources varies huge across the country, and renewable resources varies greatly within a year, which make planning and operation of China's hydrogen supply system more complicated. Therefore, in this model, monthly fluctuation of demand and power-based generation are described regionally. Two scenarios are set up to analyze the difference between power-based and coal-based generation pathway, assuming that hydrogen will account for 10 % in final consumption in 2050. This paper is organized as follows. In Section two, the methodology and scenario set are illustrated. In Section three, results are presented and discussed. In Section four, main conclusions are summarized.

2. Methodology and scenarios

2.1. Modelling framework

China Regional Hydrogen Supply System Optimization Model (CRHSSOM) includes 30 regions in China, and the planning period covers from 2019 to 2050. The input of CRHSSOM includes geographical data, cost data, technology choice as well as assumptions of economic growth, intensity decrease and hydrogen shares. The output includes monthly and regional hydrogen demand, and the optimal layout of the hydrogen supply system.

Hydrogen can be generated from eight resources in CRHSSOM, namely coal, natural gas, hydropower, nuclear power, onshore wind power, offshore wind power, solar power, and grid power, which describes generation without self-owned power plants. Hydrogen can be transmitted by pipeline and road, or stored in storage facility, to meet hydrogen demand.

CRHSSOM comprises of two parts, namely demand forecast and system planning. The demand forecast part generates monthly hydrogen demand, based on assumptions of economic growth, intensity decrease and hydrogen shares. The system planning part obtains the optimal layout of the hydrogen supply system applying the superstructure modelling method.

2.2. Mathematical model

The Mixed Integer Liner Programming (MILP) is applied to describe the hydrogen supply system. The input parameters are hydrogen demand, which is generated first, resources, transportation distance, geographical location and the cost in the supply chain. Yearly hydrogen generation capacity, pipeline transmission capacity and storage capacity are design variables. Monthly hydrogen generation, transmission and storage are operational variables. Equality constraints describe the monthly supply-demand balance in each region. Inequality constraints comprise of resources limitation, geographical limitation and infrastructure limitation. Objective function indicates the overall supply cost in a long period. The notation is listed below, and subscripts *e, r(rr), t, m* represent generation technologies, regions, year and month, respectively.

2.2.1. Demand forecast and equality constraints

Hydrogen demand is forecast in each region and each month, as shown in Eq.(1). Monthly fluctuation of demand in each region refers to fluctuations of natural gas (Li et al., 2019b). Total hydrogen supply comprises of domestic production, net import from other regions, and net reduction of storage, as shown in Eq.(2).

$$D_{r,t,m} = GDP_{r,t} \times ID_{r,t} \times HS_{r,t} \times MF_{r,m} \tag{1}$$

$$D_{r,t,m} = \sum_{e}{}^{'} ge_{e,r,t,m} + \sum_{rr}{}^{'}(tp_{rr,r,t,m} - tp_{r,rr,t,m} + tr_{rr,r,t,m} - tr_{r,rr,t,m}) + (bs_{r,t,m} - es_{r,t,m}) \tag{2}$$

2.2.2. Inequality constraints

Resources limitation indicates that hydrogen generation could not exceed its resources, as shown in Eq.(3). Yearly renewable resources come from a power system planning model of China, considering the expansion capability of power plants (Chen et al., 2019). Monthly renewable resources are generated from historical data in 2018, describing seasonal power generation fluctuation of hydropower, wind power and solar power (Statistic, 2019). Hydrogen generation capacity, pipeline capacity and storage capacity would limit hydrogen generation, transmission and storage, as shown in Eq.(4) – Eq.(6). Geographical limitation indicates that hydrogen could be transmitted only between adjacent regions, as shown in Eq.(7) – Eq.(8). Binary variables $b_{r,rr}$ are applied to describe the location of two regions. It would equal to 1, if two regions are adjacent, otherwise it would be 0.

$$R_{e,r,t,m} \geq ge_{e,r,t,m} \tag{3}$$

$$ge_{e,r,t,m} \leq \sum_{t \leq t0}{}^{'} ing_{e,r,t} / 12 \tag{4}$$

$$tp_{r,rr,t0,m} \leq \sum_{t \leq t0}{}^{'} inp_{r,rr,t} / 12 \tag{5}$$

$$es_{r,t,m} \leq \sum_{t \leq t0}{}^{'} ins_{r,t} \tag{6}$$

$$-L \times b_{r,rr} \leq tp_{r,rr,t,m} \leq L \times b_{r,rr} \tag{7}$$

$$(b_{r,rr} - 1) \times L \leq trt_{r,rr,t,m} \tag{8}$$

Table 1 Parameters

Symbol	Meaning and unit	Symbol	Meaning and unit
$DP_{r,rr}$	Distance by pipeline *km*	FC_e	Carbon factor *tCO2/t or bcm*
$DR_{r,rr}$	Distance by road *km*	$GF_{e,t}$	Fuel use *bcm/t or bcm or kwh*
$D_{r,t,m}$	Demand *bcm*	CTX	Transmission cost *yuan/(bcm*km)*
$GDP_{r,t}$	GDP *yuan*	$CG_{e,t}$	Generation capacity cost *yuan/(bcm/y)*
$ID_{r,t}$	Intensity *bce/yuan*	CP_t	Pipeline investment cost *yuan/km*
$HS_{r,t}$	Hydrogen share *%*	CS_t	Storage facility cost *yuan/bcm*
$MF_{r,m}$	Monthly factor	$CF_{e,r,t}$	Fuel cost *yuan/ton or bcm or kwh*
$R_{e,r,t,m}$	Resources limitation	DIS	Discount rate
CC_t	Carbon cost *yuan/t*		

Table 2 Variables

Symbol	Meaning and unit	Symbol	Meaning and unit
$ge_{e,r,t,m}$	Generation *bcm*	$ins_{r,t}$	Storage investment *bcm*
$tp_{r,rr,t,m}$	Pipeline transmission *bcm*	tct_t	Total transmission cost *yuan*
$tr_{r,rr,t,m}$	Road transmission *bcm*	tci_t	Total investment cost *yuan*
$bs_{r,t,m}$	Store at 1st *bcm*	tcf_t	Total fuel cost *yuan*
$es_{r,t,m}$	Store at 30th *bcm*	tcc_t	Total carbon cost *yuan*
$ing_{e,r,t}$	Generation investment *bcm/y*	c	Overall cost *yuan*
$inp_{r,rr,t}$	Pipe investment *bcm/y*		

2.2.3. Objective function

The objective function describes the overall costs during a long period, including transmission cost, infrastructure investment cost, fuel cost and carbon cost, and the overall costs could be calculated using a discount rate, as shown in Eq.(9) – Eq.(13).

$$c = \sum_t \left((tct_t + tci_t + tcf_t + tcc_t) / (1 + DIS)^{t-2019} \right) \tag{9}$$

$$tct_t = \sum_{r,rr,m} (tp_{r,rr,t,m} \times DR_{r,rr} \times CTP + tr_{r,rr,t,m} \times DR_{r,rr} \times CTR) \tag{10}$$

$$tcf_t = \sum_{e,r,m} ge_{e,r,t,m} \times GF_{e,t} \times CF_{e,r,t} \tag{11}$$

$$tci_t = \sum_{e,r} ing_{e,r,t} \times CG_{e,t} + \sum_{r,rr} inp_{r,rr,t} \times DR_{r,rr} \times CP_t + \sum_r ins_{r,t} \times CS_t \tag{12}$$

$$tcc_t = \sum_{e,r,m} ge_{e,r,t,m} \times GF_{e,t} \times FC_e \times CC_t \tag{13}$$

2.3. Scenarios

Basic assumptions are set in Table 3, and hydrogen would account for 10 % in total energy demand in 2050. Two scenarios are set, which are coal-based scenario and power-based scenario, by setting zero carbon price and high carbon price respectively.

3. Results and discussion

3.1. Costs

The overall costs and composition are shown in Figure 1. Over costs in the power-based scenario would be 2.4 times that of the coal-based scenario, and the fuel cost is the main reason. In the coal-based scenario, accumulated carbon emissions would be 28.88 bt, which indicates that the coal-based pathway would be more economic, if average cost of carbon capture and storage is less than 525 yuan/tCO_2.

3.2. Generation capacity

Generation technology would have great impacts on generation capacity distribution. Results show that generation capacity would concentrate more in North China, where coal resources are abundant, and coal is cheaper, whist it would concentrate more in Southwest and Northwest China, where renewable resources are abundant in the power-based scenario, as shown in Figure 2.

3.3. Pipelines and storage facility

National pipeline networks are required in the power-based scenario as shown in Fig.3, and would be helpful to manage monthly fluctuation. Therefore, total storage capacity would be required less, which is 26.6 bcm in 2050. On the country, pipelines networks are required mainly in North China, as shown in Fig.4, whilst other regions manage monthly fluctuation using their own storage facilities. In view of that, more storage capacity would be required in the coal-based scenario, which is 35.0 bcm in 2050.

Table 3 Basic assumptions

Year	2020	2030	2040	2050
GDP growth rate %	6.54	4.56	2.67	1.03
Energy intensity *tec/10⁴ yuan*	0.493	0.350	0.253	0.188
Total energy demand *btce*	4.99	6.05	6.16	5.45
Hydrogen share %	0.3	3.3	6.3	10.0
Hydrogen demand *Mtce*	14.96	199.54	387.95	544.60

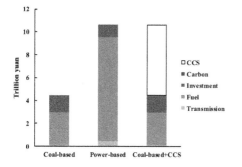

Figure 1 Overall costs and composition   Figure 2 Generation capacity distribution

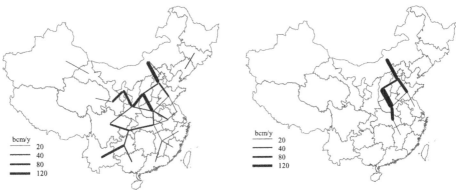

Figure 3 Pipelines in the power-based   Figure 4 Pipelines in the coal-based
                  scenario   scenario

4. Conclusions

In this study, China Regional Hydrogen Supply System Optimization Model is developed, and two scenarios are designed describing coal-based and power-based pathways. The overall costs in the power-based pathway are 2.4 times that of coal-based mainly due to fuel cost. The economic balance point of two pathways is when CCS cost is 525 yuan/tCO2. In the coal-based pathway, generation capacity concentrates more in North China, and pipelines are required mainly in North China. More storage capacity is required because of self-sufficiency in most regions. In the power-based pathway, nationwide pipelines are required, and less storage capacity is required.

Acknowledgement

The authors gratefully acknowledge the support by The National Key Research and Development of China (2018YFB0604301), National Natural Science Foundation of China (71690245) and the Phase III Collaboration between BP and Tsinghua University.

References

Almansoori, A., Betancourt-Torcat, A., 2016. Design of optimization model for a hydrogen supply chain under emission constraints - A case study of Germany. Energy 111, 414-429.
Baufume, S., Grueger, F., Grube, T., Krieg, D., Linssen, J., Weber, M., Hake, J.-F., Stolten, D., 2013. GIS-based scenario calculations for a nationwide German hydrogen pipeline infrastructure. International Journal of Hydrogen Energy 38, 3813-3829.
BP, 2019. BP Energy Outlook 2019 edition.
Chen, S.Y., Liu, P., Li, Z., 2019. Multi-regional power generation expansion planning with air pollutants emission constraints. Renewable & Sustainable Energy Reviews 112, 382-394.
Hydrogen Industrial Technology Innovation Alliance of China, 2019. China's hydrogen energy and fuel cell industry.
National Development and Reform Commission, 2016. Strategies on energy production and consumption (2016-2030).
Gim, B., Boo, K.J., Cho, S.M., 2012. A transportation model approach for constructing the cost effective central hydrogen supply system in Korea. International Journal of Hydrogen Energy 37, 1162-1172.
Li, L., Manier, H., Manier, M.-A., 2019a. Hydrogen supply chain network design: An optimization-oriented review. Renewable & Sustainable Energy Reviews 103, 342-360.
Li, T., Liu, P., Li, Z., 2019b. Modelling and optimization of a natural gas supply system at a transient stage: a case study of China. BMC Energy 1, 5.
National Bureau of Statistic, 2019. Monthly power generation in 2018.

Sauro Pierucci, Flavio Manenti, Giulia Bozzano, Davide Manca (Eds.)
Proceedings of the 30th European Symposium on Computer Aided Process Engineering
(ESCAPE30), May 24-27, 2020, Milano, Italy. © 2020 Elsevier B.V. All rights reserved.
http://dx.doi.org/10.1016/B978-0-12-823377-1.50020-3

A Hybrid Modelling Approach to Developing Digital Twins of an Ultra-supercritical Steam Turbine Control Stage

Jianxi Yu, Pei Liu,* Zheng Li

Department of Energy and Power Engineering, Tsinghua University, Beijing, 100084, China

liu_pei@tsinghua.edu.cn

Abstract

Modelling for digital twins is a key technology in smart power plants. A control stage is a key component for pressure and flow control in steam turbines of power plants. Its modelling and simulation for digital twins are important measures for steam turbine operation diagnosis and optimization. However, sequential operation modes of valves in a control stage result in dramatic changes in thermal and mechanical behaviours of the control stage, and modelling the change in behaviours still remains a challenge due to lack of measurements. In this paper, a hybrid modelling method based on the first-principle mechanism and actual operation data is proposed. Inlet flow of a control stage are obtained by calculating flow coefficient at the full range of sequential operation of valves. Then, characteristic functions of a control stage are obtained using the first-principle mechanism. In order to verify the reliability of the proposed method, a control stage of an ultra-supercritical steam turbine with typical sequential valves operation mode is modelled and simulated. Results show that the average value of the simulation relative error is less than 1%, which proves that the method has high simulation accuracy and reliability and lays a foundation for application of digital twins in smart power plants.

Keywords: Control stage; Sequential valve; First-principle mechanism; Digital twins

1. Introduction

Digital twins based on industrial big data plays an increasingly important role in industries with the advancement of information technology. It is a combination of physical principle and data science, which provides us precise and comprehensive guidance in design, operation and maintenance of manufactures (Tao et al., 2019). In power generation domain, digital twins are a key technology of smart power plant with operation diagnosis, optimization and smart control (Hua et al., 2019). Therefore, the development of power plant modelling and simulation for digital twins is very significant for promotion of smart power plants.

A control stage is one of the key components of a steam turbine worth further studying in a higher integration target of renewable power. A steam turbine is one of the main units of thermal power plant, the main components of which comprise valves, stages, pipes, heat exchangers and condensers. Its thermal characteristics have a critical impact on the overall cycle of power generation. Besides, the power output of a steam turbine need to be adjusted quickly due to continuous integration of renewable energy (Li and Wang J., 2018). A control stage is a key component which determines the power output of steam turbine. Therefore, quantitative study of its actual operating characteristics is significant for the performance monitoring and optimization of power plant. However, it still remains a challenge to establish the model of control stage based on digital twins due to sequential operation modes of valves and lack of measurement data. The sequential operation modes result in dramatic changes in thermal and mechanical behaviours of the control stage, which is difficult to quantity the changes with insufficient measurement data.

There are many studies which focus on steam turbine models for digital twins, however, lacking models of control stages of ultra-supercritical steam turbines which conform to physical mechanisms. Yu et al. (2019) developed a control stage model of a subcritical steam turbine rely on operation data, and simulation of digital twins was obtained through this model. Zhong (2014) established models of main components of a supercritical steam turbine using operation data, then obtaining simulation results of digital twins for online monitoring. The internal physical process of control stage was neglected and summarized into a quadratic function in this study, which cannot reflect the physical mechanisms of the control stage. Zhu (2015) established a modified model of the control stage of a supercritical steam turbine in Ebsilon software, which derived a linear function for simulation of digital twins. But the influence of valve opening degree on power output was neglected, which overshadowed the utility of the model. Zheng Y. (2018) established a big data model of thermal power plants for operation optimization based on pure data method, which lacked component models and cannot reflect actual operating characteristics. Despite these studies, a model of the control stage of ultra-supercritical steam turbines which can quantify its actual operating characteristics is rather lacking.

In this paper，a hybrid modelling method based on first-principle mechanism and actual operation data for digital twins is proposed. The paper is organized as follows. Modelling methodology is illustrated in Section 2. A case study and results are presented in Section 3. Some conclusions are summarized in Section 4.

2. Methodology

2.1. Flow calculation of sequential valves

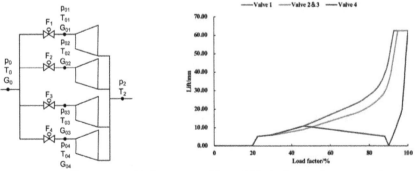

Figure 1 Overall structure with data illustration of a control stage system

Figure 2 Typical operation curves of sequential valves of ultra-supercritical steam turbines

Four high-pressure control valves are in front of a control stage which operate at certain modes. Figure 1 illustrates the control stage system consisting of four valves, four groups of nozzles and moving blades. Figure 2 shows typical operation curves of the four valves at sequential valve mode. The sequential valves are opened and closed in a certain order, regulating the flow and pressure in front of a control stage.

It's difficult to obtain the flow of sequential valves due to lack of measurement data. The main steam is separated through the four valves and then enter into corresponding group of nozzles. The only flow data we can get from measurement is the main steam. Although there are various formulas to calculate the theoretical flow of valves, flow characteristics of valves are required to obtain the actual flow. However, the flow characteristics of sequential valves are not available through experiment. So a calculation method rely on operation data is necessary.

We calculate the theoretical flow of the sequential valve on the analogy of nozzles, as shown in Eq.(1)- Eq.(3) (Xiao et al., 2008), where p_0 and p_{0i} is the inlet and outlet pressure of valve i, respectively. v_0 is the inlet specific volume. A_{Vi} is the opening area of valve i. ε_{cr} is the critical pressure ratio of steam flow.

$$G_{0i,t} = 0.648 \beta_i A_{Vi} \sqrt{\frac{p_0}{v_0}} \tag{1}$$

$$\beta_i = \sqrt{1 - \left(\frac{\varepsilon_{Vi} - \varepsilon_{cr}}{1 - \varepsilon_{cr}}\right)^2} \tag{2}$$

$$\varepsilon_{Vi} = \frac{p_{0i}}{p_0} \tag{3}$$

After calculating the theoretical flow of each valve, it is also necessary to obtain flow coefficient to match the actual flow. Flow coefficient of valves are determined by lift of valve core and fluid state (Wang Y. and Zheng Z., 2018). Since the structure of sequential valves are identical, and the influence of lift of valve core on flow is already contained in the opening area A_{Vi} in Eq.(1). Besides, the valves have the same inlet steam state under the same working condition. Therefore, we regard flow coefficient of each valve under the same conditions as equal. Then we can calculate the actual flow of each valve using Eq.(4)-Eq.(5), where G_0 is the measurement flow of main steam.

$$\mu = \frac{G_0}{\sum_i G_{0i,t}} \tag{4}$$

$$G_{0i} = \mu G_{0i,t} \tag{5}$$

2.2. First principles models of mechanisms

2.2.1. Flow characteristics model

For common stages, Flugel formula can be used to quantify the mathematical relationship between pressure and flow (Cao., 1991). Zhong (2014) derived flow capacity coefficient φ and reduced flow G' from flugel formula, which are used in the model of common stages. As for control stages, the definitions of φ and G' for each group of nozzles are shown in Eq.(6)-Eq.(7), where T_{0i} is the outlet temperature of valve i, p_2 is the outlet pressure of control stage.

$$\varphi_i = \frac{G_{0i} \sqrt{T_{0i}}}{\sqrt{p_{0i}^2 - p_2^2}} \tag{6}$$

$$G_i' = \frac{G_{0i}\sqrt{T_{0i}}}{p_{0i}} \tag{7}$$

Flow characteristics of control stages change as the opening degree of sequential valves change. We can obtain the change of characteristics through quantifying the relationship between flow capacity coefficient and reduced flow. Further more, the characteristics of each group of nozzles interact with each other due to the shared moving blades of control stages. Therefore, the first-principle mechanisms of flow model of control stages are reduced flow of all nozzles.

2.2.2. Efficiency characteristics model

The main loss of control stages occurred in the moving blades, which is the characteristics of efficiency model. Moving blades reduced enthalpy rise can reflect the efficiency characteristics of control stages, and the definitions are shown in Eq(8) -Eq.(10) (Yu et al., 2019), where h_2 is outlet enthalpy of control stages, h_{1i} is inlet enthalpy of moving blades.

$$\Delta h_b' = \frac{\Delta h_b}{\varepsilon} \tag{8}$$

$$\Delta h_b = \sum_i \frac{G_{0i}}{G_0}\left(h_2 - h_{1i}\right) \tag{9}$$

$$\varepsilon = \frac{p_2}{p_0} \tag{10}$$

Reduced flow is one of the dominant factor which determines efficiency of common stages (Zhu., 2015). For control stages, the efficiency is determined by all groups of nozzles and moving blades. So the first-principle mechanisms of efficiency model of control stages are reduced flow of all nozzles.

2.3. Characteristic functions of first principles models

We figure out characteristic functions which are the quantitative relationship between characteristics and the first-principle mechanisms using actual operation data. The form of characteristic functions of flow and efficiency model are shown in Eq.(11) - Eq.(12) according to the analysis in section 2.2. Then the parameters of the characteristic functions are calibrated from the actual operation data.

$$\varphi_i = a_{i0} + a_{i1}G_1' + a_{i2}G_2' + a_{i3}G_3' + a_{i4}G_4' \tag{11}$$

$$\Delta h_b' = b_0 + b_1G_1' + b_2G_2' + b_3G_3' + b_4G_4' \tag{12}$$

3. Case study

A control stage of an ultra-supercritical steam turbine is chosen to establish the model using the method proposed in this paper. One week of operation data are used for modelling and another week for simulation.

3.1. Modelling results

3.1.1. Flow model

A group of nozzles and moving blades are considered as one stage. The flow characteristics are obtained through Eq(11) and operation data, which are listed in Table 1. The R-Square of all functions exceeds 0.9, which proves high correlation of characteristics and the first-principle mechanisms. It also demonstrates the rationality of the method to some extent.

Table 1 Characteristic functions of flow model

Function	R^2
$\varphi_1 = -251.72 + 1.2556G_1' + 1.1219G_2' - 0.6833G_3' + 0.4394G_4'$	0.9236
$\varphi_2 = -255.13 - 0.0625G_1' + 2.5242G_2' - 0.7823G_3' + 0.3940G_4'$	0.9908
$\varphi_3 = -265.97 - 0.0723G_1' + 1.1711G_2' + 0.5995G_3' + 0.4041G_4'$	0.9904
$\varphi_4 = -97.718 + 0.0151G_1' + 0.5541G_2' - 0.4710G_3' + 1.5938G_4'$	0.9970

3.1.2. Efficiency model

We have to treat all the nozzles and moving blades as a whole when it comes to efficiency characteristic since the outlet temperature of corresponding moving blades of each group of nozzles is different. The four steam streams are blended after the control stage and reach the same post-stage temperature. However, we cannot calculate the individual outlet temperatures by the post-stage temperature. Besides, what we need to focus on is not the efficiency of each group of nozzles and moving blades, but the whole.

Table 2 Characteristic functions of efficiency model

Function	R^2
$\Delta h_b' = -78.96 + 0.2035G_1' - 0.0902G_2' + 0.0520G_3' - 0.0471G_4'$	0.6707

Therefore, the efficiency characteristic of the control stage is summarized as a function obtained through Eq(12) and operation data, which is shown in Table 2. The R-Square has a certain decline compared with flow characteristic functions. Since the loss in control stages is hard to quantify precisely. It decreases the correlation of efficiency characteristic and the first-principle mechanisms. But we can see that its correlation can still be acceptable for simulation in Section 3.2.

3.2. Simulation results

The data of another week are used for simulation in order to verify the models. The post-stage pressure p_2 and temperature T_2 are calculated through the two models and then compared with the actual measurement data.

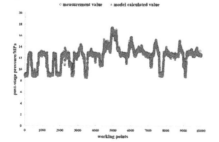
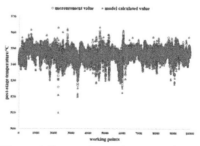

Figure 3 Comparison of measured values and simulated values of p_2

Figure 4 Comparison of measured values and simulated values of T_2

Results shown in Figure 3 and Figure 4 demonstrate that the simulated values match the actual measurement values under 10000 working points which cover full working range of the steam turbine. So digital twins models reflecting actual operating characteristics of the control stage are developed. The average value of relative error of post-stage pressure and temperature simulation is 0.53% and 0.20% respectively. It proves accuracy of the models and validity of the method, which lays a foundation for applications in smart power plants.

4. Conclusions

A hybrid modelling approach based on first-principle mechanism and operation data to the ultra-supercritical steam turbine control stage is developed in this paper. The flow characteristic of control stage is flow capacity coefficient and the efficient characteristic is moving blades reduced enthalpy rise. And the first-principle mechanisms of both characteristics are reduced flow of all nozzles. Results show that the hybrid approach can establish the models of control stage for digital twins effectively, and represent the change of operating characteristics. The average relative error of simulation is less than 1%, which proves accuracy and validity of the approach.

Acknowledgement

The authors gratefully acknowledge the support by The National Key Research and Development of China (2018YFB0604301) and the Phase III Collaboration between BP and Tsinghua University.

References

Tao F., Qi Q.L., Wang L.H., Nee A.Y.C., 2019, Digital Twins and Cyber–Physical Systems toward Smart Manufacturing and Industry 4.0: Correlation and Comparison, Engineering, 5, 4, 653-661

Hua Z.G., Guo R., Cui X., Wang Y., 2019, Discussion and Study on Technical Route of Smart Thermal Power Plant, Thermal Power Generation, 10, 8-14

Li D.C., Wang J.H., 2018, Study of supercritical power plant integration with high temperature thermal energy storage for flexible operation, Journal of Energy Storage, 20, 140-152.

Yu J.X., Liu P., Liu S.J., Li Z., 2019, Modeling of Variable Conditions of Steam Turbine Control Stage Based on Operation Data, Journal of Chinese Society of Power Engineering, 39, 7, 541-547

Zhong X.B., 2014, The Research of High Precision Model Used for On-line Monitoring of Thermal System of Thermal Power Units, Thesis, Tsinghua University, Beijing, China

Zhu H.L., 2015, The Research of Modeling, Monitoring and Optimizing for Thermal System of Thermal Power Plant Based on Ebsilon, Thesis, Tsinghua University, Beijing, China

Zheng Y., 2018, Operation Optimization of In-service Thermal Power Plants Based on Big Data Modeling, Thesis, Tsinghua University, Beijing, China

Xiao Z.H., Sheng W., Xia Y., 2008, Turbine Equipment and System, China Electric Power Press, 13-15 (in Chinese)

Wang Y.D., Zheng Z.J., 2018, Experimental and Numerical Research on Influence of Spool Stroke on Flow Characteristics of Angle Seat Valve, Chinese Hydraulics and Pneumatics, 327, 11, 46-51

Cao Z.Q., 1991, Turbine Variable Working Condition Characteristics, Water Power Press, 36-38 (in Chinese)

Sauro Pierucci, Flavio Manenti, Giulia Bozzano, Davide Manca (Eds.)
Proceedings of the 30th European Symposium on Computer Aided Process Engineering
(ESCAPE30), May 24-27, 2020, Milano, Italy. © 2020 Elsevier B.V. All rights reserved.
http://dx.doi.org/10.1016/B978-0-12-823377-1.50021-5

Stochastic Analyses on Relative Viscosity of Water-in-oil Emulsions

Ana M. Sousa,[*] Maria J. Pereira, Henrique A. Matos

[a]CERENA, Instituto Superior Técnico, Universidade de Lisboa, 1049-001 Lisboa, Portugal
ana.margarida.sousa@tecnico.ulisboa.pt

Abstract

Have not only water-in-oil emulsions been a ubiquitous flow assurance challenge in oilfield operations, but also future perspectives suggest its increasing importance. In fact, as oil reserves are becoming depleted, the crude oil is becoming heavier, and the quantity of produced water is increasing. Understanding water-in-oil emulsions behaviour is crucial to design or to optimize production, transportation and refining. This work provides a new approach to estimate water-in-oil emulsions viscosities given a certain crude oil viscosity value, since literature does not provide empirical correlations with excellent accuracy, especially for higher water fractions. Moreover, with this proposed methodology, the uncertainty metrics can be obtained by a statistical function, which best fits to the data histogram. This yields a valuable tool for matching of data to models. Stochastic analyses were developed using @RISK software and MATLAB programming. The proposed method suggests a solution for estimating the water-in-oil emulsion viscosity, which has been widely regarded as a major challenge.
Keywords: Water-in-oil emulsions (W/O), relative viscosity, waxy crude oils

1. Introduction

In a typical oil field, it is unusual to produce solely crude oil, since the presence of solids and water is frequent. This amount of water and solids, also named as Basic Sediment and Water (BSW), can cause several operational problems. Consequently, the measures to evaluate these problems need to be assessed.

The produced water can flow as 'free water' or as an 'emulsion'. At almost all the stages, emulsions can be encountered, namely in production, transportation, storage, and processing. This work will focus on the ability to describe emulsions rheological behaviour during the production phase. Through wellbores and pumps, crude oil and co-produced water are mixed, due to the high shear forces that occur. Knowing the amount of water in oil emulsions is essential to design the equipment, and to control and improve the operation.

Emulsions rheological properties and stability are dependent on the droplet size distribution, the volume fraction, the chemical composition which affects the continuous and dispersed viscosities, the shear rate, and the thermodynamic perturbations (Rønningsen 1995).

Depending on the crude oil properties and the range of operating conditions (Sousa et al. 2019b), different hydrodynamic behaviours can be found in an oil and water multiphase flow system. Although a considerable effort has been undertaken to generalize liquid-liquid models, there are not yet universal empirical correlations applicable for all types of crude oils. Fluid's global viscosity increases as emulsions are formed, attaining higher effective viscosities than the continuous oil phase. Due to the importance of knowing the fluid characteristics to design the production and process equipment, there are several methods to estimate the fluid relevant physical properties. Nevertheless, there is not an empirical correlation able to accurately predict the emulsion viscosity for each crude oil, still. It is important to highlight these methods for emulsion viscosity estimation not only face major challenges to provide vaguely accurate values, given emulsions' properties significantly sensitive nature, but also cannot offer insights about the uncertainty of such values.

This work provides a new approach to estimate water-in-oil emulsions viscosity, given a value for the crude oil viscosity. Moreover, the uncertainty metrics were also assessed, and it was obtained by the statistical function associated with the best fitting to the histogram data. The proposed method suggests a solution for such issue, which has been widely regarded as a significant hindrance from the industry point of view. One way to integrate a myriad of factors that influence the behaviour of emulsions into the computer-aided models is using a statistical approach. The research methodology to simulate emulsions viscosities encompassed the following steps:

i.   Performing experimental tests to measure the waxy crude oil viscosity, as a function of temperature;

ii.   Evaluating the accuracy of empirical correlations used to calculate the emulsions viscosities against the experimental data, gathered from literature;

iii. Developing a statistical approach to characterize the emulsions relative viscosities, in order to overcome the limitations found in the existent methods;

iv.   Performing stochastic analyses to evaluate the uncertainties.

2. Experimental methods

To determine the waxy crude oil viscosity, as a function of temperature, a set of experiments were performed using a Brookfield (DV-II+ Pro) viscometer, and a cryostat to guarantee the desired temperature. The experimental apparatus is presented in Figure 1. Viscosimetry tests were performed under ASTM D4402 guidelines.

Figure 1 – Cryostat and Viscometer (left), and waxy crude oil sample (right).

The viscosity rapidly decreases with the temperature, until it reaches the Wax Appearance Temperature (WAT), as presented in Figure 2. For higher temperatures, the viscosity will be less affected by the temperature, and the wax crystals will be dissolved in the fluid.

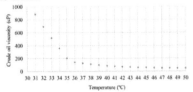 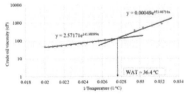

Figure 2 – Waxy crude oil viscosity as a function of temperature

The determination of the Wax Appearance Temperature resulted from intersecting two straight lines, adjusted to the attained test points, over a logarithmic scale. Eq. (1) enables to estimate the viscosity (cP) for this waxy crude oil, as a function of temperature (°C), for this specific crude oil:

$$\mu_{oil} = \begin{cases} 0.00049e^{453.46714\left(\frac{1}{T}\right)} & if \ T \leq WAT \\ 2.57171e^{141.98099\left(\frac{1}{T}\right)} & if \ T > WAT \end{cases} \tag{1}$$

3. Theoretical methods

Due to the importance of knowing the fluid characteristics to design the equipment, there are several methods to estimate the viscosity of the emulsion. Since 1906, the effective viscosity of a mixture of two immiscible liquid phases has been intensively discussed. This section will present the methods available in Aspen HYSYS, which is a software that enables modelling the upstream and downstream processes and has a worldwide crude oil database (Sousa et al. 2019a) which supports modelling the problem, even if the specific crude oil physical properties are unknown. The predefined method to estimate the emulsion viscosity is defined by Eq. (2):

$$\mu_{emulsion} = \begin{cases} \mu_{oil} \cdot e^{3.6(1-\phi_{oil})} & if \ \phi_{water} < 0.5 \\ \mu_{water} \cdot \left[1 + 2.5\phi_{oil}\left(\frac{\mu_{oil} + 0.4\mu_{water}}{\mu_{oil} + \mu_{water}}\right)\right] & if \ \phi_{water} > 0.7 \end{cases} \tag{2}$$

Where $\mu_{emulsion}$ is the emulsion viscosity, μ_{oil} and μ_{water} are the oil and water viscosity, respectively, ϕ_{oil} is the oil fraction (1-ϕ_{water}), and ϕ_{water} is the water fraction.

Brinkman method can be selected in the Aspen HYSYS pipe segment (Brinkman 1952), and it is defined by Eq. (3):

$$\mu_{emulsion} = \begin{cases} \mu_{oil} \cdot (1 - \phi_{water})^{-2.5} & if \ W/O \ emulsion \\ \mu_{water} \cdot \phi_{water}^{-2.5} & if \ O/W \ emulsion \end{cases} \tag{3}$$

Guth and Simha method (Guth and Simha 1936) can also be chosen in the Aspen HYSYS pipe segment, and it is described by Eq. (4):

$$\mu_{emulsion} = \begin{cases} \mu_{oil} \cdot (1 + 2.5\phi_{water} + 14.1\phi_{water}^2) & if \ W/O \ emulsion \\ \mu_{water} \cdot (1 + 2.5\phi_{oil} + 14.1\phi_{oil}^2) & if \ O/W \ emulsion \end{cases} \tag{4}$$

Levinton and Leighton method (Leviton and Leighton 1936) is another option, and it is expressed by Eq. (5):

$$\mu_{emulsion} = \begin{cases} \mu_{oil} \cdot e^{\left[2.5\left(\frac{0.4\mu_{oil} + \mu_{water}}{\mu_{oil} + \mu_{water}}\right)\left(\phi_{water} + \phi_{water}^{\frac{5}{3}} + \phi_{water}^{\frac{11}{3}}\right)\right]} & if \ W/O \ emulsion \\ \mu_{water} \cdot e^{\left[2.5\left(\frac{0.4\mu_{water} + \mu_{oil}}{\mu_{oil} + \mu_{water}}\right)\left(\phi_{oil} + \phi_{oil}^{\frac{5}{3}} + \phi_{oil}^{\frac{11}{3}}\right)\right]} & if \ O/W \ emulsion \end{cases} \tag{5}$$

For all these methods, Aspen HYSYS assumes that the inversion point occurs for a water fraction of 50 %. At that moment, when water-in-oil changes to oil-in-water, or vice-versa, the model will predict the highest viscosity.

These empirical correlations were analysed against experimental data gathered from the literature (Oliveira et al. 2018). The main conclusion was that in general, these equations could describe the rheological behaviour for lower water fractions (below 20 %). However, they show disagreements with the experimental data, especially when the water fraction increases, near the phase inversion.

The general polynomial method, expressed by Eq. (6), fulfils the need of specifying a correlation that fits the experimental data.

$$\mu_{emulsion} = \begin{cases} \mu_{oil} \cdot (1 + \beta_1 \phi_{water} + \beta_2 \phi_{water}^2 + \beta_3 \phi_{water}^3) \; if \; W/O \; emulsion \\ \mu_{water} \cdot (1 + \beta_1 \phi_{oil} + \beta_2 \phi_{oil}^2 + \beta_3 \phi_{oil}^3) \quad if \; O/W \; emulsion \end{cases} \quad (6)$$

This model enables to tune β_1, β_2, and β_3 parameters, as well as to define where the inversion phase occurs, for each emulsion. The parameters were obtained by fitting the function to the emulsion viscosities data. The main advantage of this method is the possibility of finding individual equations for each crude oil samples, which better resembles the emulsion rheological behaviour, rather than the other pre-settled methods. On the contrary, the main setback is that experimental tests are required to model the fluid dynamics.

All these methods describe the emulsion viscosity as a function of the continuous phase viscosity. For a water-in-oil emulsion, the relative viscosity is defined by Eq. (7):

$$\mu_{relative} = \frac{\mu_{emulsion}}{\mu_{oil}} \quad (7)$$

4. Results

4.1. Statistical analyses to characterize the emulsion relative viscosity

To overcome the limitation of fitting the parameters for each crude oil, a statistical analysis was performed upon available data for Brazilian crude oils. Experimental data was gathered from a set of 126 crude oil samples (Oliveira et al. 2018), and the relative viscosities of the water-in-oil emulsions are available for 10 %, 30 %, 50 % and 70 % water fractions, and for 4 °C, 30 °C and 50 °C, for a shear rate equals to $50 \; s^{-1}$. To perform this statistical approach, Newtonian behaviour was assumed.

Using the @RISK software a set of pre-defined statistical distributions were fitted to the relative viscosity experimentally determined, and the Akaike Information Criterion (AIC) estimator was used to compare the relative quality of the statistical models. The probability density function chosen (with the minimum global AIC value) was the Gumbel distribution, also known as Extreme Value distribution, which is defined by a location parameter (α), and a shape parameter (β). This probability density function is defined by the Eq. (8):

$$f(x) = \frac{1}{\beta} \left| \frac{1}{e^{\left[\frac{x-\alpha}{\beta} + \exp\left[-\frac{x-\alpha}{\beta} \right] \right]}} \right| \quad (8)$$

The cumulative distribution function is determined by the Eq. (9):

$$F(x) = \frac{1}{e^{\exp[-z]}} \quad (9)$$

To exemplify how the Gumbel distribution was fitted to relative viscosity for T = 50 °C and $\emptyset$ = 50 %, Figure 3 shows the probability density function and the cumulative distribution function.

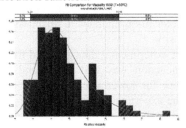 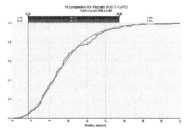

Figure 3 – Fitting Gumbel distribution to relative viscosity for T = 50 °C and $\emptyset$ = 50 %

Table 1 presents the location and shape parameters determined for the Gumbel probability density function.

Table 1 – Location and shape parameters for Gumbel probability density function

	Location parameters (a)			Shape parameters (b)		
	T = 4 °C	T = 30 °C	T = 50 °C	T = 4 °C	T = 30 °C	T = 50 °C
$\emptyset$=10 %	1.28235	1.24124	1.26947	0.18255	0.13486	0.13412
$\emptyset$=30 %	2.36553	2.46371	2.56775	0.62618	0.49967	0.4801
$\emptyset$=50 %	5.4988	7.8153	8.2369	2.3179	2.561	2.2401
$\emptyset$=70 %	12.6202	23.134	27.458	7.812	13.417	14.626

These parameters were plotted on two 3D graphs, and then two polynomial surfaces were fitted, applying the Eq. (10):

$$sf(T,\emptyset) = p_{00} + p_{10} \cdot \emptyset + p_{01} \cdot \emptyset + p_{20} \cdot T^2 + p_{11} \cdot T \cdot \emptyset + p_{02} \cdot \emptyset^2 + p_{21} \cdot T^2 \cdot \emptyset + p_{12} \cdot T \cdot \emptyset^2 + p_{03} \cdot \emptyset^3 \quad (10)$$

The fitted coefficients for the location and shape values, from Gumbel density function, are presented in Table 2.

Table 2 – Fitted coefficients for Gumbel distribution

Polynomial parameters	Location	Shape	Polynomial parameters	Location	Shape
p00	-1.244	-1.376	p02	-0.01077	-0.009001
p10	-0.005888	-0.04223	p21	-6.99E-05	-5.61E-05
p01	0.3509	0.2475	p12	0.0001631	5.88E-05
p20	0.001427	0.001333	p03	0.0001178	9.83E-05
p11	-0.004152	-0.0002101			

The fitted surfaces are presented in Figure 4.

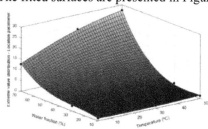 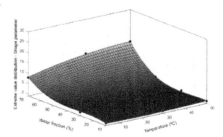

Figure 4 – Gumbel distribution. Location parameter (left) and shape parameter (right)

4.2. Monte Carlo Simulation applied to a case study

Monte Carlo simulation is a process that repeats an experiment many times and generates a large amount of randomized data in order to better describe the system. Such random data is gathered, organized and analysed to allow understanding the likelihood of an occurrence. Software @RISK was used to perform the Monte Carlo simulations. The results allow transforming analyses by considering probabilities, leaving the single point estimative to histograms.

A case study was simulated using the Monte Carlo approach to determine emulsions viscosities and their uncertainties for different well depths. Figure 5 represents the temperature density functions used as input, and the simulation results applied to the Eq. (3), after using the Gumbel distribution shown in Figure 4.

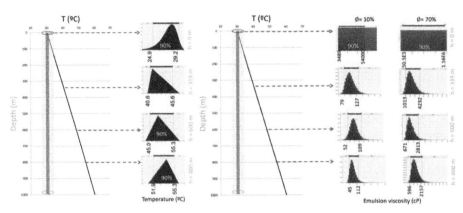

Figure 5 – Temperature distribution functions (left). Emulsion viscosities results for 10 000 Monte Carlo iterations (right), for different depths

5. Conclusions

It has been observed that W/O emulsions viscosity increases with the water fraction until reaching the inversion point. The herein proposed methodology allowed estimating emulsions viscosities, at temperatures ranging from 4 until 50 °C and water fractions between 10 and 70 %, for Brazilian crude oils. Using Monte Carlo simulations, it was possible to estimate the expected uncertainties on the emulsion viscosity, by incorporating the uncertainty on the temperature profile and the relative viscosity.

The major accomplishment of this work is the ability to predict the rheological behaviour of emulsions, not only for modelling processes but also for inside-wells equipment design. Matching the experimental data with computer-aided models is essential to accurately forecast the fluid properties. The employed statistical methodology can be applied in several other matters for assessing and validating models to data, making it a valuable tool for computer aided engineering.

Acknowledgements

The authors would like to acknowledge F.C.T., I.P. support through the PhD grant number SFRH/BD/131005/2017.

References

H. Brinkman, 1952, The viscosity of concentrated suspensions and solutions, The Journal of Chemical Physics, 20, 4, 571. DOI: 10.1063/1.1700493

V. Guth, R. Simha, 1936, Kolloid Zeitschrift, 74, 3, 266-275. DOI: 10.1007/BF01455734

A. Leviton, A. Leighton, 1936, Viscosity relationships in emulsions containing milk fat, Journal of Physical Chemistry, 40, 1, 71-80. DOI: 10.1021/j150370a010

M. Oliveira, L. Miranda, A. Carvalho, D. Miranda, 2018, Viscosity of Water-in-Oil Emulsions from Different API Gravity Brazilian Crude Oils, Energy & Fuels, 32, 3, 2749–2759. DOI: 10.1021/acs.energyfuels.7b02808

H. Rønningsen, 1995, Correlations for predicting Viscosity of W/O-Emulsions based on North Sea Crude Oils, SPE, SPE 28968, 1-7. DOI: 10.2118/28968-MS

A. Sousa, H. Matos, M. Pereira, 2019a, Modelling Paraffin Wax Deposition Using Aspen HYSYS and MATLAB, 29th European Symposium on Computer Aided Process Engineering, 46, 973-978. DOI: 10.1016/B978-0-12-818634-3.50163-6

A. Sousa, H. Matos, L. Guerreiro, 2019b, Wax deposition mechanisms and the effect of emulsions and carbon dioxide injection on wax deposition: Critical review, Petroleum. DOI: 10.1016/j.petlm.2019.09.004

Sauro Pierucci, Flavio Manenti, Giulia Bozzano, Davide Manca (Eds.)
Proceedings of the 30th European Symposium on Computer Aided Process Engineering
(ESCAPE30), May 24-27, 2020, Milano, Italy. © 2020 Elsevier B.V. All rights reserved.
http://dx.doi.org/10.1016/B978-0-12-823377-1.50022-7

Efficient Data-based Methodology for Model enhancement and Flowsheet analyses for Continuous Pharmaceutical Manufacturing

Pooja Bhalode[a], Nirupaplava Metta[a], Yingjie Chen[b], Marianthi Ierapetritou[b*]

[a]Department of Chemical and Biochemical Engineering, Rutgers University, 98 Brett Road, Piscataway, New Jersey, 08854, USA
[b]Department of Chemical and Biomolecular Engineering, University of Delaware, 150 Academy Street, Newark, Delaware, 19716, USA
mgi@udel.edu

Abstract

Accurate process predictability and efficient flowsheet analysis has been the focus of research in pharmaceutical manufacturing. Currently available mechanistic models, being unable to account for all complex powder variabilities, need to be improved for accurate digital twin framework of the manufacturing plant. In this work, we propose a novel methodology of integrated plant data for model enhancement. These enhanced models are applied for flowsheet analyses focusing on design space identification. Surrogate-based feasibility analysis is implemented using artificial neural network with adaptive sampling techniques. This strategy is demonstrated for a direct compaction line capturing realistic scenarios observed in the manufacturing plant.

Keywords: Pharmaceutical, Surrogate, Feasibility, Hybrid modeling, Industry 4.0

1. Introduction

Research efforts driven by FDA's Quality-by-design (QbD) initiative has led to development of detailed predictive models of continuous pharmaceutical manufacturing lines. These studies mainly focus on process flowsheet simulation using a combination of mechanistic and empirical models to demonstrate dynamic effects of process and material parameters on critical quality attributes, with tracking of powder material properties (Boukouvala et al. 2011; Wang et al. 2017). However, these models are not able to capture all observed process variabilities due to the inherent hard-to-predict nature of pharmaceutical powder materials. In this study, we aim to address these limitations by employing a data-based methodology for model enhancement focusing on inclusion of process data collected under Industry 4.0 framework. Developed process flowsheets models are applied for data-based system analyses. This study focuses on feasibility analysis to address the goal of identification of the design space of a process. In this analysis, a feasibility function which characterizes the maximum constraint violation, is evaluated. For a process with design variables d and uncertain parameters θ, the J constraints that represent feasible operation can be expressed as $g_j(d, \theta) \leq 0$. Following this, the feasibility function is defined as shown in Eq (1).

$$\psi(d,\theta) = \max_{j \in J} g_j(d,\theta) \qquad (1)$$

Since the constraints in the process models are not always available in closed form or are computationally expensive to evaluate, surrogate-based feasibility analysis methodology is implemented wherein a computationally efficient surrogate model is used to represent the feasibility function. The following sections focus on describing Industry 4.0 dataflow and methodology for model enhancement, followed by feasibility studies using the enhanced models. Concluding remarks are provided in Section 6.

2. Industry 4.0 Dataflow

Recent interest in application of Internet of Things (IoT) (Liao et al. 2017) aimed at developing an integrated data collection, storage, and knowledge extraction framework for efficient and effective manufacturing. This framework for pharmaceutical industry is illustrated in Figure 1, wherein the overall manufacturing plant data is stored to be used for predictive modelling. Data acquisition starts from the bottom up where all data are being generated. Data from Process Analytical Tools (PAT) and sensors are collected and sent to different prediction tools and OPC servers, whereas the raw data from the continuous pilot plant are sent to control software. To facilitate overall data storage and integration, data from these sources are sent to a local historian and then to a cloud storage infrastructure for ease of accessibility for predictive digital twin models. Material calibration and experimental data is stored using standardized data structures within cloud-based electronic laboratory notebooks (ELNs) for efficient data integration with the overall plant and extraction to modelling and simulation platforms.

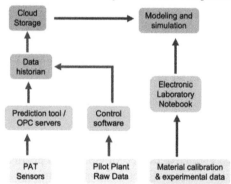

Figure 1: Data flow within Industry 4.0 framework for continuous pharmaceutical manufacturing

3. Methodology for Model Enhancement

In this section, the methodology for model enhancement based on the Industry 4.0 framework is presented. With this framework, process model outputs and actual plant data can be compared and analyzed to identify if a significant residual exists, indicating a potential departure between the model and the plant. The following sub-sections entail different methods for model enhancement with process data.

3.1. Identification and correction of process-model mismatch
A typical cause of departure can be attributed to the parameters used in the model (namely parametric mismatch). It is important to identify a suitable set of parameters that can appropriately describe the system. Using Industry 4.0 data framework, different parameter estimation methods including least squares fitting and Kalman filtering (Zhang 1997) can be applied to obtain a set of physically suitable parameters. Kravaris et al. (2013) identifies global optimization-based algorithms for parameter estimations under measurement uncertainty, and Wang et al. (2018) introduces a Bayesian approach for data from different scales. In certain situations, if the best set of parameters still does not yield

good model predictability, structural mismatches exist within the model, meaning that the functional forms within the model are not suitable to describe the actual system. For identification of structural mismatches, principal component analysis and correlation methods like partial correlation and mutual information are implemented (Badwe et al. 2009; Chen et al. 2013; Meneghetti et al. 2014). These methods can qualitatively determine the sources of structural mismatch. After identifying the source of mismatch, model selection and discriminations methods like posterior probability study and Akaike Information Criterion can be used to identify the most probable model (Wu et al. 2011; Wang et al. 2018).

3.2. Non-Parametric or Surrogate modeling

The non-parametric or surrogate model development method is implemented if the desired model predictability is not achieved after addressing process-model mismatch or when the cost of mismatch identification and correction is high. Non-parametric modeling includes developing an efficient surrogate based on input-output datasets. Kriging model, Artificial Neural Networks, and related methods are often used in developing the surrogate (Rogers et al. 2013). Datasets availed from the Industry 4.0 framework are applied to develop the computationally efficient surrogate models which captures the overall process without inclusion of mechanistic information.

3.3. Hybrid Modeling

Hybrid modeling approach focuses on capturing the mechanistic information along with data-driven surrogate models. The essence is to combine *a priori* knowledge like conservation and kinetic laws with nonparametric models built using process data (Stosch et al. 2014). Proposed hybrid structures can be broadly categorized as parallel and serial structure. For parallel structure, inputs are fed into both the mechanistic part and data-driven part of the model, and the model outputs are combined by superposition, multiplication, or weighting. This structure is often used to correct for errors of the original model. For serial structure, inputs are fed into the mechanistic and data-driven models in a sequential way, meaning that the output of the first part of the model serves as an input to the next, and the final outputs can be combined with appropriate weighting. The serial structure is prevalent when mechanism of the original model is not well-understood (Stosch et al. 2014). By integrating the mechanistic and data-driven models, the overall predictability of the model can be increased, and the enhanced model can then be integrated into flowsheet to conduct further flowsheet analyses.

4. Surrogate-based Feasibility Analysis

This section focuses on surrogate based feasibility analysis methodology where, an inexpensive feed-forward ANN model combined with Bayesian regularization (Burden and Winkler 2008) for network training is explained. The number of hidden neurons is determined in an initial model selection, minimizing the sum of squared errors between target and prediction data. In the model improvement stage, adaptive sampling is used to choose additional samples for improving the ANN model. In this work, a modified expected improvement function (EI_{feas}) proposed by Boukouvala and Ierapetritou (2012) as given in Eq. (2) is used to implement the adaptive sampling strategy.

$$EI_{feas}(x) = s\phi\left(\frac{-y}{s}\right) = s\frac{1}{\sqrt{2\pi}}e^{-0.5\frac{y^2}{s^2}} \tag{2}$$

where, y and s are the surrogate model predictor and standard error of the prediction at x respectively. Maximization of EI_{feas} identifies sample points close to the feasible region boundary or in the region of high prediction uncertainty. Thus, as samples are added, the surrogate model accuracy is improved focusing on identification of feasible region. In this work, the variance s^2 of ANN model predictor y at a sample point x is estimated using a statistical technique known as jack-knifing (Eason and Cremaschi 2014) wherein, sample set is divided into K disjoint sample sets. K neural networks are built for the sets and variance of prediction s^2 is estimated using Eq (3).

$$s^2(x) = \frac{1}{K}\sum_{k=1}^{K}\left(U_k(x) - \sum_{k=1}^{K}\frac{U_k(x)}{K}\right)^2 \tag{3}$$

Figure 2 illustrates the algorithm for implementation of the ANN based feasibility analysis methodology. This methodology is tested on Continuous Direct Compaction (CDC) process explained by (Wang et al. 2017), where the uncertain parameters used for the problem and their bounds are tabulated in Table 1. The constraints for the problem that define the feasible region is given in Table 2.

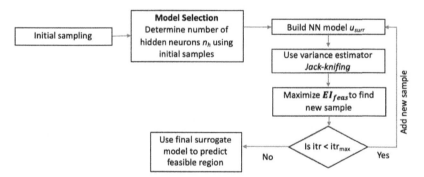

Figure 2: Algorithm for ANN based feasibility analysis methodology

Table 1: Variable bounds for CDC process feasibility case study

Factors	Units	Nominal	LB	UB
API flowrate	kg/h	3	2.85	3.15
Excipient flowrate	kg/h	26.7	25.36	28.03
Mill impeller speed	rpm	1120	1064	1176
Blender blade speed	rpm	250	237.5	262.5
Fill depth	m	0.01	0.0095	0.0105
Thickness	m	0.0025	0.002375	0.002625

Overall, the ANN based feasibility analysis is applied to the six-dimensional problem with 20 inequality constraints. 2^6 Latin Hypercube samples are used in the initial model selection phase. Using the initial samples, number of hidden neurons are varied. 8 hidden neurons yield the least sum of squared errors between predicted and target feasibility function values. 500 samples are iteratively added using the adaptive sampling strategy. Since this is a high dimensional problem, the feasible region is represented using a matrix of contour plots of feasibility function values as shown in Figure 3. For each contour plot, only two factors are varied, and the remaining two factors are set at nominal values. The feasible region boundary predicted by the final ANN model is represented using a red line. Feasible region boundary from the original process model is also plotted using red dashed line. Good agreement between the original and predicted feasible regions is observed.

Table 2: Constraints for the CDC process feasibility case study

Unit operation	Variable	Units	Limits based on % nominal value
Blender	Mean residence time	s	+/- 20%
	Delay time	s	
	Mass hold SS	kg	
	Mean bulk, true density	kg/m³	
	Mean d10, d50, d90	μm	
Comill	Mean d10, d50, d90	μm	+/-20%
	Mean bulk, true density	kg/m³	
	Mean residence time	s	
	Mass holdup SS	kg	
Tablet Press	Concentration	%	+/-5%
	Weight	kg	+/-10%
	Hardness	kp	
	Main compression pressure	MPa	
	Pre compression pressure	MPa	

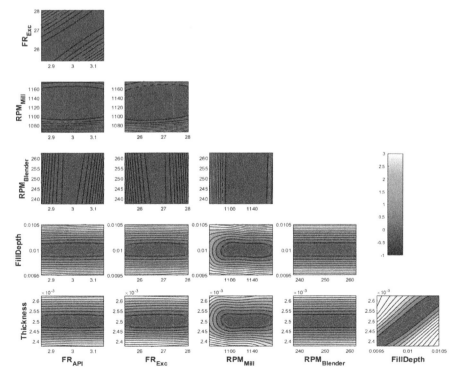

Figure 3: Matrix of feasibility function contour plots representing the feasible region of the continuous direct compaction process (Feasible region boundary from the original model and predicted by the ANN model are represented as red dashed lines and red solid lines respectively)

5. Conclusions

We propose an integrated methodology for data-based model enhancement using Industry 4.0 framework for surrogate-based feasibility analysis. Pilot plant and laboratory data collected from Industry 4.0 framework is applied for enhancement of mechanistic models. The enhanced flowsheets are proposed to be applied for feasibility analysis on a continuous direct compaction line. A good agreement between the actual and the predicted feasible regions is observed. For future work, we aim to extend the methodology to other continuous manufacturing lines with the inclusion of process dynamics.

Acknowledgement

The authors would like to acknowledge funding from U.S. Food and Drug Administration (FDA) through grant 1U01FD006487-01.

References

Badwe AS, Gudi RD, Patwardhan RS, Shah SL, Patwardhan SC. Detection of model-plant mismatch in MPC applications. Journal of Process Control. 2009;19:1305–13.

Boukouvala F, Ierapetritou MG. Feasibility analysis of black-box processes using an adaptive sampling Kriging-based method. Computers & Chemical Engineering. Pergamon; 2012 Jan 10;36:358–68.

Boukouvala F, Ramachandran R, Vanarase A, Muzzio FJ, Ierapetritou MG. Computer Aided Design and Analysis of Continuous Pharmaceutical Manufacturing Processes. Computer Aided Chemical Engineering. 2011;29:216–20.

Burden FR, Winkler D. Bayesian Regularization of Neural Networks. Methods in Molecular Biology. 2008;458:25–44.

Chen G, Xie L, Zeng J, Chu J, Gu Y. Detecting Model–Plant Mismatch of Nonlinear Multivariate Systems Using Mutual Information. Journal of Quality Technology. American Chemical Society; 2013 Jan 22.

Eason J, Cremaschi S. Adaptive sequential sampling for surrogate model generation with artificial neural networks. Computers & Chemical Engineering. Pergamon; 2014 Sep 4;68:220–32.

Kravaris C, Hahn J, Chu Y. Advances and selected recent developments in state and parameter estimation. Computers & Chemical Engineering. Pergamon; 2013 Apr 5;51:111–23.

Liao Y, Deschamps F, de Freitas Rocha Loures E, Ramos LFP. Past, present and future of Industry 4.0 - a systematic literature review and research agenda proposal. International Journal of Production Research. Taylor & Francis; 2017 Mar 28.

Meneghetti N, Facco P, Bezzo F, Barolo M. A Methodology to Diagnose Process/Model Mismatch in First-Principles Models. Ind Eng Chem Res. 2014;53(36):14002–13.

Rogers AJ, Hashemi A, Ierapetritou MG. Modeling of Particulate Processes for the Continuous Manufacture of Solid-Based Pharmaceutical Dosage Forms. Processes. 2013;1(2):67–127.

Stosch von M, Oliveria R, Peres J, de Azevedo SF. Hybrid semi-parametric modeling in process systems engineering: Past, present and future. Computers & Chemical Engineering. Pergamon; 2014 Jan 10;60:86–101.

Wang Y, Biegler LT, Patel M, Wassick J. Parameters estimation and model discrimination for solid-liquid reactions in batch processes. Chemical Engineering Science. Pergamon; 2018 Sep 21;187:455–69.

Wang Z, Escotet-espinoza MS, Ierapetritou MG. Process Analysis and optimization of continuous pharmaceutical manufacturing using flowsheet models. Computers and Chemical Engineering. Elsevier Ltd; 2017 Feb 21;107:77–91.

Wu S, McAuley KB, Harris TJ. Selection of simplified models: I. Analysis of model- selection criteria using mean- squared error. The Canadian Journal of Chemical Engineering. 2011 Feb;89:148–58.

Zhang Z. Parameter estimation techniques: a tutorial with application to conic fitting. Image and Vision Computing. Elsevier; 1997 Jan 1;15(1):59–76.

Sauro Pierucci, Flavio Manenti, Giulia Bozzano, Davide Manca (Eds.)
Proceedings of the 30th European Symposium on Computer Aided Process Engineering
(ESCAPE30), May 24-27, 2020, Milano, Italy. © 2020 Elsevier B.V. All rights reserved.
http://dx.doi.org/10.1016/B978-0-12-823377-1.50023-9

Artificial Neural Network to capture the Dynamics of a Dividing Wall Column

Eduardo Sánchez-Ramírez[a], Juan Gabriel Segovia-Hernández[a],

Esteban A. Hernández-Vargas[b,c]

[a] *Chemical Engineering Department, Universidad de Guanajuato, Noria Alta s/n, Guanajuato, Gto., 36050, México*

[b] *Instituto de Matematicas, UNAM, Unidad Juriquilla, Blvd. Juriquilla 3001, Juriquilla, Queretaro ,C.P. 76230, México*

[c] *Frankfurt Institute for Advanced Studies, Ruth-Moufang-Strae 1, 60438, Frankfurt am Main, Germany*
eduardo.sanchez@ugto.mx; esteban@im.unam.mx

Abstract

The forecasting ability of Artificial Neural Network (ANN) has made it received a widespread application in the field of engineering, biology, energy, and finance. One of the main advantages of ANN is its ability to capture complex dynamics, in fact, ANNs can approximate non-linear input-output relationships to any degree of accuracy in an iterative manner. Despite the forecasting ability of ANN, its application for the downstream process is still fragmented. This study applies an artificial neural network to model the dynamics of a dividing wall column that separates an effluent coming from fermentation producing acetone, butanol, and ethanol (ABE) for spark-ignition purposes. Considering the dynamic of the diving column simulated in Aspen Plus Dynamics, a 4-10-3 multi-layer perceptron with back-propagation algorithm was enough to reproduce the dynamics reported by the simulator. Two kind of dynamic studies were performed, an open-loop and closed-loop analysis. Four disturbances for six different percentages were applied in the open-loop policy; and three set point changes in the closed-loop policy. To ensure the reproducibility of the results, a dynamic simulation in Aspen Dynamics was performed. Results from the validated models show that the predicted versus actual values were bounded. Different input scenarios were evaluated promptly where the manipulated variables presented peaks in their values, and the result was relatively good. Between the two scenarios, the open-loop test, and closed-loop test, the closed-loop test showed a lower error percentage than the open-loop test. The largest error percentage values were close to 0.9%, however, the majority of errors were between 0.1 and 0.4%.

Keywords: Artificial Neural Network, Downstream process, ABE purification.

1. Introduction

The reproduction by simulation of chemical processes is associated with the reproduction of models; in such a way that the quality and reliability of said reproduction depends on the quality and certainty of the process model. Although the reproduction of these types of processes with variations in time can take a considerable period of. An interesting methodology to address complex models is that input and output data can be approximated as black boxes, with the main objective of obtaining reliable predictions. The problem then lies now in the quality of data with which the black box must be built. Artificial neural networks (ANN's) are a technique that can meet those requirements. The basic feedforward network is shown in Figure 1. The data enters the network at the input nodes, the data is propagated through the network through the hidden layers towards the output layer. Although ANNs have a relatively rudimentary structure, several studies conclude that any continuous and non-linear function can be successfully reproduced by an ANN (Cybenko 1989). One of the main advantages of using ANNs is the ability to initially use information to model complex systems, and predict results in a robust manner, since they can approximate non-linear input-output relationships of any degree of accuracy in an iterative manner (Safa and Samarasinghe 2011). Despite the great forecasting skills of the ANNs, their application to predict the behavior of separation processes is quite limited. One reason is the number of equations involved in the modeling of this kind of process, for example, considering that for each equilibrium stage and each component C, the total of MESH (mass and energy balance, thermodynamic equilibria, and purity constraint) equation solved are 2C +3. In addition, if the equations are modeling with variation in time the complexity increase. In the same way, the use of ANNs for more complex distillation systems has not been reported. That is, as far as the authors' knowledge is concerned, no work has been reported in which ANNs are used to model the dynamic behavior of intensified separation systems such as dividing wall columns (DWC). The interest of such intensified alternatives is the advantages that they represent over the conventional option regarding energy requirements and cost savings. In addition, due to the extra complexity it represents, no work has been reported that involves the handling of mixtures with high complexity relative to thermodynamic modeling. With this in mind, the aim of this work is to use an ANN to model and forecasting the dynamic behavior of a dividing wall column for the separation of a mixture composed of Acetone-Butanol-Ethanol and Water from a fermentation process. The modeling process was performed in two scenarios, *i)* modeling the dynamic behavior of the process under an open-loop analysis, *ii)* modeling the dynamic behavior of the process under a closed-loop analysis. The input data were obtained by means of Aspen Dynamics under both open-loop and closed-loop policy.

2. Case Study

Errico et al. (2017) presented a methodology to generate intensified alternatives to separate butanol from ABE fermentation. For the development of this methodology, they start from a hybrid design that considers a liquid-liquid extraction column and conventional distillation columns. Errico et al. (2017) apply a methodology to generate different intensified alternatives based on DWC. All the generated alternatives were evaluated and optimized by means of a robust optimization algorithm, differential evolution with tabu list (DETL), evaluating the total annual cost and the eco-indicator 99 as economic and environmental performance indices. As a result of their research, it was obtained several hybrid designs. Among those designs, the scheme in Figure 1 is considered as a case study. This scheme was initially simulated in Aspen Plus considering the NRTL-HOC as a thermodynamic model to describe phase equilibrium. The feedstream considered a mixture of Acetone, Butanol, Ethanol, and water in a proportion of 0.3018, 0.1695, 0.0073 and 0.5214 % wt respectively. Furthermore, the simulation was exported from Aspen Plus to Aspen Dynamics to obtain the dynamic behavior in both open-loop and closed-loop policy. The data from the dynamic simulation was used for being used as input data in the ANN.

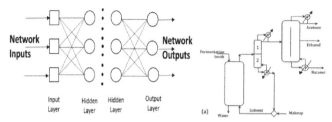

Figure 1. General topology of an ANN and DWC considered a case study

3. Methodology

3.1 Data Generation

The data to train the NNs were based on data using simulations for two cases, open-loop and close-loop policy in Aspen Dynamics. Regarding the open-loop, to generate the input data a step change of 5% every 5 hours in the manipulated variable was performed in a single manipulated variable until it reaches +20% of the nominal value. After that step change of -5% every 5 hours until reach again the nominal state, the other manipulated variables were kept as constant. The same procedure applied to the other variables in such a way that it was applied 3 different disturbances in 6 different percentages of the nominal point. Each manipulated variable was chosen according to each product stream, i.e., when a component was purified in the top of a distillation column, the manipulated variable was the reflux ratio; however, if the component purified remained in the distillation column as a bottom product, the manipulated variable was the reboiler heat duty, and so on. As output data, it was considered the composition profiles of all interest components obtained jointly the disturbances in Aspen Dynamics. Regarding the closed-loop test, the input data were obtained as follows. A setpoint change was implemented in the composition of each component of interest (Acetone-Butanol-Ethanol), in this way three changes of set points were performed and tuned at the same time. The analysis was based on the operation of a proportional-integral controller (PI). Because we considered PI controllers, the proportional gain (K_c) and the reset times (τ_i) were tuned up for each scheme studied here; in addition, we compared the dynamic performance by using the integral of the absolute error (IAE) criterion. To control the composition of distillate and funds, an LV structure was selected. As output data in this test, it was considered the composition profiles obtained. Once all input-output data was obtained, a 4-10-3 multi-layer perceptron with back-propagation algorithm was enough to reproduce the dynamics reported by the simulator.

3.2 Neural Network procedures

This subsection presents the procedures to establish the ANNs. The basic elements of the artificial neuron are: *i)* A set of synapses, or connecting links, each of which is characterized by weight or strength of its own. Specifically, a signal x_j at the input of synapse j connected to neuron k is multiplied by the synaptic weight w_{kj}. The first subscript in w_{kj} refers to the neuron in question, and the second subscript refers to the synapse's input end to which the weight refers. *ii)* An adder for summing the input signals, weighted by the respective synaptic strengths of the neuron; the operations described here constitute a linear combiner. *iii)* An activation function for limiting the amplitude of the neuron's output to the closed unit interval [0,1], or, alternatively, [-1,1]. However, there are exceptions like the linear activation function which covers the open range ($-\infty, \infty$). A neuron can be mathematically described by the following equations:

$$u_k = \sum_{j=1}^{m} w_{kj} x_j \quad \text{and } u_k = \sum_{j=1}^{m} w_{kj} x_j \tag{1}$$

where $x_1, x_2, ... , x_m$ are the input signals; $w_{k1}, w_{k2}, ... , w_{km}$ are the respective synaptic weights of the neuron k. u_k is the linear combiner's output due to the input signals. b_k is the bias. $\varphi()$ is the activation function. y_k is the neuron's output signal. The use of bias b_k has the effect of applying an affine transformation to the linear combiner's output u_k as shown by

$$v_k = u_k + b_k \tag{2}$$

where v_k is the induced local field or activation potential. The activation function considered in this work is the logistic function:

$$\varphi(v) = \frac{1}{1 + e^{-av}} \tag{3}$$

where a is the slope parameter of the logistic function. Note that the previous equation ranges from zero to one in a strictly increasing fashion and exhibits a graceful balance between linear and nonlinear behaviors. The Feedforward Network (FFN) used in this work is the Multilayer Perceptron (MLP) which consists of full connected consecutive layers of neurons that can be classified as input, hidden and output layers. The input layer contains independent variables that are connected to the hidden layer for processing. Each of the hidden layers contains neurons with logistic activation functions. These are responsible for the nonlinear mapping between the network's inputs and outputs. The output layer, which in this work is composed of neurons with linear activation functions, finishes the prediction or the classification process and presents the results with a small estimation error. The Matlab neural networks toolbox allows the use of multiple network architectures. Each one of the NARX networks was constructed by means of the feedforward neural network's command of the Matlab toolbox *Feedforwardnet Toolbox:feedforward net(hiddenSizes,trainFcn)*. This command creates a MLP with hidden layers. The hiddenSizes parameter is a row vector whose k_{th} element represents the number of neurons that compose the k_{th} hidden layer. Thus, the *hiddenSizes* vector length is the number of hidden layers composing the MLP. The parameter trainFcn defines the training algorithm for the new MLP. The algorithm backpropagation was considered in this work.

4. Results

4.1. Open-loop input data

Once the step changes in the manipulable variables were implemented, the variation of all of them in time was obtained. Despite all manipulated variables and all components were also monitored, Figure 2 A) shows only the variation of the reboiler duty over time, which together with the variation of the reflux ratio and the flow of the lateral current, were used as input data for the ANN. The composition profile of butanol in Figure 2 was used as output data together with the composition profiles of acetone and ethanol. With that input-output data, the neural network was trained. Both stages are shown in Figure 2. Regarding the closed-loop test, once the data for proportional gain (K_c) and the reset times (τ_i) were tuned with the minimum IAE. The values of the manipulated variables and the resulting composition profiles associated with those values of K_c and τ_i were considered as input-output data for training the ANN. Again, despite all variables were disturbed and the three components were studied, Figure 2 B) shows only the input and output data for Reboiler Heat duty and Butanol. According to Table 1, both AAN were able to reproduce the entire dynamic of the process with relatively good accuracy. Between both test, open-loop, and closed-loop, the ANN showed better accuracy to predict the complexity of the model under the presence of a PI controller. The K_c, τ_i and IAE values for all loops were 140/150/0.0677, 100/100/0.0183, 45/50/0.611 for acetone, butanol, and ethanol respectively.

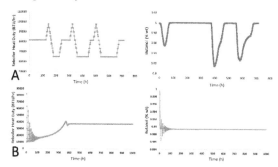

Figure 2. Input and output data Input and output data of the ANN in the open-loop test (A) and closed-loop policy (B).

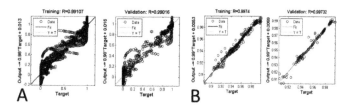

Figure 3. Training and validation data fit process for the open-loop test (A) and closed-loop policy (B).

Table 1. Data Validation for open-loop policy

INPUT			OUTPUT (%wt)		
			ANN	Aspen Dynamics	% Error
Time (h)	0.1	Acetona	0.9643	0.997	3.39106
Reb Duty (cal/s)	60413.5	Butanol	1.072	0.9992	6.79104
Reflux ratio (lb/lb)	24.3128	Etanol	0.9837	0.9864	0.27447
Side stream flow (lb/s)	0.724				
Time (h)	0.3	Acetona	0.8645	0.997	15.3268
Reb Duty (cal/s)	87014.5	Butanol	0.7313	0.9959	36.1821
Reflux ratio (lb/lb)	36.2144	Etanol	1.0488	0.9841	6.16895
Side stream flow (lb/s)	0.724				

Additionally, the computational time for reproducing in ANN was quite low (few seconds) in comparison with that in Aspen Dynamics (10-20 minutes). The values of the manipulated variables and the resulting composition profiles associated with those values of K_c and τ_i were considered as input-output data for training the ANN. Figure 2-3 shows the input and output data. According to Table 2, both AAN were able to reproduce the entire dynamic of the process with relatively good accuracy. Between both test, open-loop, and closed-loop, the ANN showed better accuracy to predict the complexity of the model under the presence of a PI controller. The K_c, τ_i and IAE values for all loops were 140/150/0.0677, 100/100/0.0183, 45/50/0.611 for acetone, butanol, and ethanol respectively. Additionally, the computational time for reproducing in ANN was quite low (few seconds) in comparison with that in Aspen Dynamics (10-20 minutes).

Table 2. Data Validation for closed-loop policy

INPUT		OUTPUT			
			Aspen Dynamics	ANN	% Error
Time (h)	3.6	ACETONE	0.995598	0.9889	0.672761496
Reflux ratio (lb/lb)	0	ETHANOL	0.959805	0.9686	0.916331963
Side stream flow (lb/s)	0	BUTANOL	0.992269	0.9902	0.208512006
Reb Duty (cal/s)	10555.8				
Time (h)	30	ACETONE	0.988805	0.9912	0.242211558
Reflux ratio (lb/lb)	0.617515	ETHANOL	0.970426	0.9724	0.203415819
Side stream flow (lb/s)	0.668623	BUTANOL	0.99086	0.9925	0.165512787
Reb Duty (cal/s)	11162				

5. Conclusions

Through de use of a 4-10-3 multi-layer perceptron with the back-propagation algorithm it was possible to reproduce the entire dynamic of a complex process to separate a highly nonideal mixture. The ANN showed the potential to reproduce the dynamic behavior of the process under two different test, an open-loop, and a closed-loop test. Between both tests, the ANN showed a minor error reproducing the closed-loop test in comparison with the open-loop test. Taking advantages of the capacities of ANN such as relative easy applications, computing time, and inferring on unseen data numerical convergence; it is possible to perform many studies considering the robustness, non-linearity, and complexity of the model involved in a divided wall column: controllability analysis, dynamic optimization, and model reduction for planning and scheduling works considering the application of the entire model of these complex schemes.

References

Cybenko, G., 1989, Approximation by Superpositions of a Sigmoidal Function. Mathematics of Control. Signals and Systems, 2, pp. 303-314.

Safa, M., & Samarasinghe, S.,2011,. Determination and modelling of energy consumption in wheat production using neural networks: "A case study in Canterbury province, New Zealand". Energy, 36(8), 5140-5147.

Errico, M., Sanchez-Ramirez, E., Quiroz-Ramìrez, J. J., Rong, B. G., & Segovia-Hernandez, J. G., 2017,. Multiobjective optimal acetone–butanol–ethanol separation systems using liquid–liquid extraction-assisted Divided Wall columns. Industrial & Engineering Chemistry Research, 56(40), 11575-11583.

Sauro Pierucci, Flavio Manenti, Giulia Bozzano, Davide Manca (Eds.)
Proceedings of the 30th European Symposium on Computer Aided Process Engineering
(ESCAPE30), May 24-27, 2020, Milano, Italy. © 2020 Elsevier B.V. All rights reserved.
http://dx.doi.org/10.1016/B978-0-12-823377-1.50024-0

An Optimal Design of Expansion-contraction Microchannel Based on Blockage Analysis

Lin Wang[*], De Yan, Shuzhi Song, Jiarui Liu

Department of Control Science and Engineering, Inner Mongolia University of Technology, Huhhot, 010080, China
lwang@imut.edu.cn

Abstract

Microchannel blockage is a common problem in microreactor applications. The principle of inertial aggregation in microchannel is used to analyze the formation of secondary flow and the wall effect of blockage. A heterogeneous microchannel structure combined with expansion and contraction is designed to achieve separation of blockage and solution. Finally, the designed microchannel is compared with the straight tube microchannel which has the same volume by CFD simulations, and the blockage distribution in the microchannel of the expansion-contraction structure is 340% larger than that of the straight tube structure, and the blockages are effectively collected in a predetermined separation position.

Keywords: Expansion and contraction structure, Blockage, Inertial Aggregation, Secondary Flow, Microchannel

1. Introduction

The microchannel reactor has the advantage of large surface volume ratio, fast mass and heat transfer and high safety (Luo et al., 2014). The size of the microreactor is between 10~1000 microns, and the microfluidics in the microchannel are more sensitive to the increasing intermolecular forces (Zhao et al., 2015). Moreover, microchannel is difficult to transport solid materials due to its structural characteristics. If there are solid impurities or solid particles formed by the reaction in the microchannel, the microchannels are prone to be blocked since the intermolecular forces cause the microparticle molecules to aggregate and adhere to the wall of the microchannel, thus, which interrupts production. At the same time, the manufacturing process of microchannels needs to be carried out in a clean room due to the rigorous production conditions of microreactors, which satisfies high requirements for solutions and reactants. Therefore, once a blockage occurs in the microchannel, the entire microreactor is scrapped, and the replacement cost is increased. Hence, it's necessary to study a method that can eliminate the solid-state blocking particles in microchannels.

Bayer et al. (2000) proposed a continuous radiation polymerization method using a micro premixer, which mentions that poor mixing conditions resulted in reactor clogging. Blockage could also be observed in the microfluidic-based systems of solid aggregation and precipitation, which ultimately leads to the blockage of the microchannels (Dressaire and Sauret, 2016). The accumulation of fouling of the microchannel surface is also led to the blockage formation and the progressively reduction of the flow rate until the entire microchannel cross-section is blocked in one or more areas. The deposition and aggregation growth are dominated by the interaction between particle-particle as well as particle-surface attraction/rejection forces and hydrodynamic forces, which depends on the flow state (Sicignano et al. 2018). Jespers et al. (2018) studied the fluid contact area of a microchannel disperser in the presence of a blockage. In order to prevent large blockage from appearing in the microchannels, the structure of the microchannel is optimized from the initial stage of the formation of blocking particles, i.e. the particles are still in the micro-nano stage. In the study, the stresses of the particles are analyzed, then the principle of inertial aggregation is used in the new designed structure to separate the blocking particles from the liquid phase flow for the purpose of filtering and separating the blocking body. Finally, the separation efficiency is compared by using CFD simulations.

2. Inertial aggregation and separation of particles in microchannels

2.1. Inertial aggregation

When a fluid with uniformly dispersed fine particles flows into a straight pipe at a low Re number of laminar flows, the particles are stably aggregated and move at a concentric annular position from the center of the pipe after a sufficiently long flow distance. This is inertial aggregation. In the experiments study of Segre and Silberberg (1961), the particles move at a concentric circular ring position, which is 0.6 times the distance from the center of the microchannel. The particle aggregation position is shown in Figure 1.

2.2. Dean secondary flow

When the fluid flows at a laminar flow in the straight channel, the fluid close to the channel wall is subjected to the frictional force of the channel wall, then hindering its movements and the fluid velocity near the channel wall is the lowest. Eventually, the velocity of the fluid is presented in a parabolic distribution, as shown in Figure 2 (Huang et al., 2011). The shear force gradient is generated along with this parabolic flow velocity distribution, which produces shear-induced lift force that pushes the particles suspended in the fluid toward the channel wall.

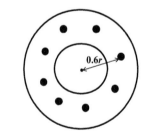

Figure 1 Particle aggregation location

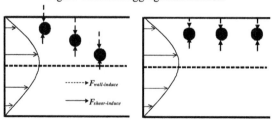

Figure 2 Schematic diagram of particle inertial focusing flow in linear micro-channel

However, when the particles move closer enough to the channel wall, the wall-induced lift force pushes the particles away from the channel wall i.e. wall effect (Zhang et al. 2018).

Furthermore, according to the fluid mass conservation equation, a pair of counter-rotating and symmetrical vortices is formed in a direction perpendicular to the flow of the fluid, respectively located at the upper and lower portions of the channel cross-section, i.e. Dean vortices. Therefore, the flowing particles are simultaneously subjected to the inertia lift and the Dean drag force in the curved channel, the relative magnitude of these two forces determines the flow situation of particles in the curved channel.

The expression of inertial lift is as follows:

$$F_L = \frac{\mu^2}{\rho} \mathrm{Re}_p^2 f_c(\mathrm{Re}_c, x_c) = \frac{\rho U_m^2 a^4}{D_h^2} f_c(\mathrm{Re}_c, x_c) \tag{1}$$

Where, Re_c and Re_p are the channel Reynold number and the blocking body Reynolds number, respectively. ρ is the fluid density, μ is the fluid viscosity, Um is the maximum flow velocity in microchannel, a is the diameter of the blocking body, D_h is the channel hydraulic diameter, f_c is the lift coefficient. When the blocking body is in the equilibrium position, f_c=0, and $f_c \approx 0.5$ at the center of the fluid flow line (Zhang et al. 2018). In this paper, it is assumed that the blocking body is generated from the center of the microchannel, that is f_c is taken as 0.5.

The Dean drag force satisfies the Eq. (2):

$$F_D \sim \rho U_m^2 a D_h^2 / r \tag{2}$$

Where, r is the radius of curvature of the curved channel. The scale of R_f is defined as the ratio of inertial lift to Dean drag force:

$$R_f = \frac{F_L}{F_D} \sim \frac{1}{\delta}(\frac{a}{D_h})^3 f_c(\mathrm{Re}_c, x_c) \tag{3}$$

Where, δ is the curvature ratio ($\delta=D_h/2r$). The radius of curvature is calculated by taking the arc of the midpoint of the opposite side for a square microchannel. If $R_f \geq 1$, the particles is pushed to the equilibrium position, and the flow of the fluid is dominated by the inertial lift. If $R_f < 1$, the particles is pushed toward the center of the streamline and the fluid is dominated by the Dean drag force, which leads to disorder of the particles. The microchannel where the blocking body is easy to be precipitated is designed to move the sedimentation position away from the center of the microchannel, instead of causing it to exit the microchannel with the fluid by using the secondary flow and the structure characteristic. When the diameter of the blocking body a is a constant, D_h is dominated by the characteristics of the channel. According to the Eq. (3), $R_f \geq 1$ is hoped.

3. Structure optimization of the microchannel

3.1. Structure of the microchannel

Based on above analysis, A microchannel with an expanding and contracting alternating structure is designed for the separation and elimination of the blocking body. In this configuration, the fluid flows from the contraction part to the expanded channel with a wide cross-section. The two structural microchannels are then alternately linked. When the fluid flows to the interface between the expansion unit and the contraction part, the secondary eddy current is formed at the top corner of the expanded structure due to the sudden enlargement of the cross-section of the microchannel. The vortex diagram in the structure is shown in Figure 3.

3.2. Parameters of the microchannel

The blocking body is subjected to the upward combined force, which will cause the body to deviate from the original motion trajectory and aggregate toward the walls of the microchannel. Meanwhile, the parameters of an expansion-contraction structure are calculated by combining with the inertial lift and Dean drag force. Its structure parameters are shown in Figure 3.

The optimized microchannel structure can be calculated based on the block size (4 μm) and the inlet channel size. The optimization problem is:

$$\max_{W_e, L_e} \quad R_f$$

$$\text{s.t.} \quad \Delta P < \Delta P^{\max} \tag{4}$$

$$W_c = W_1; L_c = L_1$$

$$0.6W_e > W_c$$

In the study, $\Delta P^{\max}=0.25\times10^4$ Pa, $W_1 = 40$ μm and $L_1 = 100$ μm are assumed, and the expansion structures adopt the cube structure, that is $W_e = L_e$. Therefore, there is only one optimal variable (W_e) in Eq. (4), the steepest gradient descent method is used to solve the optimization problem. The results are: $W_e = 187$ μm, $R_f^{\max} =3.1$, the flow rate is 1.39 m/s. Simulations are performed by using CFD with $W_e = 200$ μm for the convenience of computation.

4. Results and Discussions

The simulation is solved by Fluent, in which the expansion-contraction structure is composed of 3 expansion units and 4 contraction units. The results are compared with straight microchannel which has the equal volume and length. The design parameters are shown in Table 1. The simulation parameters are shown in Table 2. The model is shown in Figure 4(a) and the straight microchannel is shown in Figure 4(b).

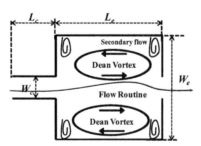

Figure.3 Vortex in the expansion structure

Table 1 Micro-channel model parameters

	Type	Inner diameter (mm)	Volume (mm³)	Length (mm)	Cross section (mm²)
	Straight channel	0.157	0.025	1	2.4649×10^{-2}
	expansion-contraction channel	0.04/0.2	0.025	1	1.6×10^{-3}

Table 2 Simulation parameters in CFD

Model	Inlet velocity	Turbulent energy	Turbulent ratio	Wall
DPM	1.39m/s	0.1	0.1	escape

(a)   (b)

Figure 4 Expansion-contraction microchannel and straight tube microchannel

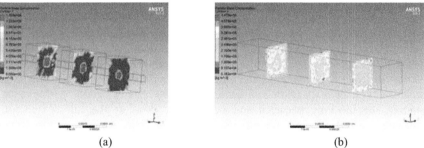

(a)   (b)

Figure.5 Location of YZ plane particle aggregation in (a) the expansion-contraction microchannel, (b) the straight microchannel

Figure 5(a) and Figgure 5(b) are the distribution of the concentration of the blocking body in the axial and longitudinal sections of the microchannel with two structures, respectively. From Figure 5(a), it can be seen that the effect of Dean secondary flow is apparent from the concentration profile of the blocking body in the microchannel with the expansion -contraction structure. The blocking body particles at the inlet are uniformly dispersed in the solution, but the focusing of the blocking body is clearly achieved when it reaches the extended structure. Meanwhile, the effect of two symmetrical Dean secondary vortex flow is shown clearly in the corner. From Figure 5(b), the concentration of the blocking body in the microchannel is represented as a green area, and the aggregation effect on the blocking body is not obvious. The simulation results verify the previous analysis that the use of straight microchannels requires a longer axial length to achieve the inertial aggregation of the blocking body.

Figure 6 is the histograms of the concentration distribution of the blocking body in the microchannel with the expansion-contraction structure and the straight microchannel respectively. It is shown that there are more low-density regions of the concentration distribution of the blocking body in the expansion-contraction microchannel. Compared with 25% ratio of the low-blocking density area of the straight microchannel, the proportion of the new designed microchannel with 85% ratio is increased by 340% in the low density area. That is to say, the larger the low-density area of the blocking body, the better the separation effect of the blocking body, which shows the optimal design of microchannel can effectively realize the separation of the blocking bodies.

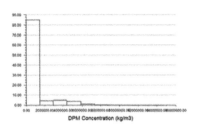
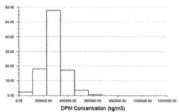

Figure 6 Histogram of blockage concentration distribution of the expansion-contraction
microchannel (left) and straight microchannel (right)

5. Conclusions

A new method concerning the exclusion of blocking particles is introduced based on
inertial aggregation principle and Dean secondary flow. By using the superposition of
the inertial lift and Dean drag force, a microchannel with expansion-contraction
structure is designed to achieve the aggregation separation and elimination of the
blocking particles. By conducting the CFD simulation experiments, the new designed
microchannel with expansion-contraction structure has a good performance of
separating the blocking particles and can collect them at the top corners of the
microchannel which are favourable for separation compared with the ordinary straight
microchannel under the same conditions including particles and inlet velocity. The
separation performance of the new designed microchannel is increased by about 340%
compared to the ordinary straight one since the particles are concentrated at the four
apex angles of the microchannel. The next work is to further optimize the expansion-
contraction structure to achieve the shortest axial length for the particles separation.

References

T. Bayer, D. Pysall, O. Wachsen. 2000, Micro mixing effects in continuous radical
    polymerization. IMRET 3: Proceedings of the Third International Conference on
    Microreaction Technology, 165-170.
E. Dressaire, A. Sauret, 2016, Clogging of microfluidic systems, Soft Matter, 13(1): 37-48.
W. Huang, H. Zhang, T. Xu, 2011, Separation of blood plasma by inertial focusing using
    microfluidic chips (in Chinese). Chinese Sci Bull (Chinese Ver), 56: 1711–1719.
S. Jespers, S. Deridder, G. Desmet, 2018, A microfluidic distributor combining minimal volume,
    minimal dispersion and minimal sensitivity to clogging, J Chromatography A, 1537, 75-82.
G. Luo, K. Wang, J. Xu, Y. Wang, Y. Lv, 2014, Advances in research of microstructured chemical
    process (in Chinese), Scientia Sinica Chimica (Chinese Ver), 44(9), 1404-1412.
G. Segre, A. Sillberberg. Radial particle displacements in Poiseuille flow of suspensions[J].
    Nature, 1961, 189 (4760): 209-210.
L. Sicignano, G. Tomaiuolo, A. Perazzo, 2018, The effect of shear flow on microreactor clogging,
    Chemical Engineering Journal, 341, 639-647.
B. Zhang, B. Yang, S. Yang, M. Su, G. He, X. Guo, H. Jin, 2018, Deposition behavior of barium
    sulfate in microchannel reactors (in Chinese), CIESC Journal (Chinese Ver), 69(4): 1461-
    1468.
S. Zhao, L. Bai, Y. Fu, Y. Jin, Y. Cheng, 2015, Fundamental research and applications of droplet-
    based microreactor (in Chinese), Chemical Industry and Engineering Progress (Chinese Ver),
    34(3), 593-616.

Sauro Pierucci, Flavio Manenti, Giulia Bozzano, Davide Manca (Eds.)
Proceedings of the 30th European Symposium on Computer Aided Process Engineering
(ESCAPE30), May 24-27, 2020, Milano, Italy. © 2020 Elsevier B.V. All rights reserved.
http://dx.doi.org/10.1016/B978-0-12-823377-1.50025-2

Comparative Study of Surrogate Modelling Techniques Applied to Three Different Chemical Processes

Ramón Mur, Ismael Díaz, Manuel Rodríguez

Departamento de Ingeniería Industrial y del Medio Ambiente, ETSI Industriales, Universidad Politécnica de Madrid, Calle de José Gutiérrez Abascal, 2, 28006 Madrid

r.mur@alumnos.upm.es

Abstract

In this paper, a comparative study of surrogate modelling techniques applied to chemical processes of different complexity is presented. The surrogate modelling techniques considered in this work are support vector regressions (SVR), Kriging and artificial neural networks (ANN). The surrogates were obtained by fitting to process data obtained from rigorous flowsheeting simulations previously developed in Aspen Plus v10. The processing schemes to be surrogated were (in order of decreasing complexity):1) the separation of aromatics-aliphatics mixtures by liquid-liquid extraction using ionic liquids as novel and more sustainable solvents, 2) the toluene hydrodealkylation process and 3) a simple distillation of organic solvents. Besides, in the first process (aromatics-aliphatics separation), advanced predictive thermodynamic models based on quantum chemical calculations (COSMO-SAC) were considered, allowing for the prediction of fluid phase equilibria properties of mixtures containing ionic liquids. In addition, the robustness of the surrogate techniques was assessed by adding a random noise contribution to the variables sampled. Thus, the paper is organized as follows: in section 1 an introduction to the surrogate modelling techniques is presented along with a short description of the chemical processes modelled in Aspen Plus. Afterwards, section 2 includes the methodology detailing the computational approach presented. The main results obtained in the study are presented in section 3 and the final the conclusions summarized in section 4.

Keywords: Surrogate Modelling, Process Modelling

1. Introduction

1.1. Surrogate modeling techniques

There are many advanced surrogate modelling libraries available for the scientific/engineering community, ready to be used in the fields of engineering for optimization, parametric analysis, etc. Three of the most widely employed are support vector regression (SVR), Kriging interpolation and artificial neural networks (ANN); which have been considered in this work to test their performance for the modelling of chemical processes.

1.1.1. Support vector regression

SVR surrogates are represented as the weighted sum of basis functions added to a constant term. A general form of SVR surrogate is given in Eq. (1).

$$\hat{f}(X) = \mu + \sum_{i=1}^{n} w^i \psi(X, X^i) \tag{1}$$

Assuming a simple basis function $\psi = X$, the surrogate can be written as per Eq. (2).

$$\hat{f}(X) = \mu + w^T X \tag{2}$$

The unknown parameters μ and w in the model are obtained by solving an optimization problem (Cortes et al (1995)).

1.1.2. Kriging

Kriging is based on the idea that a surrogate can be represented as a realization of a stochastic process. Kriging is a two-step process. First, the regression function f(x) is constructed on the basis of Generalized Least Squares (GLS) regression. Then, a stochastic Gaussian process that represents the uncertainty about the mean of Y (x) with expected value zero is constructed based on the residuals (Z(x)).

$$Y(x) = f(x) + Z(x) \tag{3}$$

Where f(x) is a regression function and Z(x) is a Gaussian process with mean 0, variance θ^2 and a correlation matrix Ψ. Depending on the form of the regression function f(x), Kriging has different prefixes. Simple Kriging assumes the regression function to be a known constant. On the other hand, Ordinary Kriging assumes an unknown constant regression function (f(x) = a). In general, Universal Kriging assumes amultivariate polynomial regression function:

$$f(x) = \sum_{i=1}^{p} \alpha_i b_i(x) \tag{4}$$

Given p the number of candidate functions, $b_i(x)$ the base functions and α_i the coefficients determined by regression. Further details can be found at (Krige et al (1960)).

1.2. Artificial Neural Networks (ANN)

The structure of ANN typically consists of three distinct layers: the input layer, the hidden layer(s), and the output layer. The connections of neurons across layers represent the transmission of information between neurons. A typical ANN with three layers and one single output neuron has the following form:

$$\hat{y} = \hat{f}(X) = \sum_{j=1}^{J} w_j f\left(\sum_{i=1}^{k} v_{ij} f(x_i) + \alpha_j\right) + \beta \tag{5}$$

Where X is an k-dimensional vector with $\{x_1, x_2,...,x_k\}$ as its elements, f is the transfer function, v_{ij} is the weight on the connection between the ith input neuron and j^{th} hidden neuron, α_j is the bias in j^{th} hidden neuron, w_j is the weight on connection between j^{th} hidden neuron and the output neuron, J is the total number of hidden neurons, and β is the bias of the output neuron. The weights and biases can be determined by the training procedure minimizing the training error (McCulloch et al (1943)).

1.3. Benchmark chemical processes

1.3.1. Aromatic-Aliphatic separation from low aromatic content naphta using ionic liquids

The liquid-liquid extraction process to separate aromatic components from a naphta stream using ionic liquids as solvents is studied in the present work as shown in Figure 1. For this purpose, an Aspen Plus flowsheet was developed based on the work of (de Riva et al (2016)). In this process, the naphtha entering the process (S-NAP-IN) contacts the extraction solvent stream (S7-IL) in a liquid-liquid extraction column (EXT). The raffinate (S-AL+N2) of this operation is the aliphatic product while the extract (S-AR+IL, rich in aromatic components) enters the intermediate stripper (STRIP) where the remaining aliphatic components are separated by an inert gas (N2) (S2) and exit the process in stream S-AL. After this gas stripping, the gas and the aliphatic hydrocarbons are separated in column SEP. The aromatic-rich stream (S1-IL) and the ionic liquid are separated in a vacuum distillation vessel (FLASH) after being conditioned (HEAT1). The aromatic components obtained in this vessel (S1-AR) are conditioned (HEAT2, PUMP1) before leaving the process as product (S3-AR). The regenerated ionic liquid (S3-IL) is recirculated as extraction solvent (S4-IL) to the extraction column (EXT-DIST), after being conditioned (HEAT1, HEAT3, PUMP2).

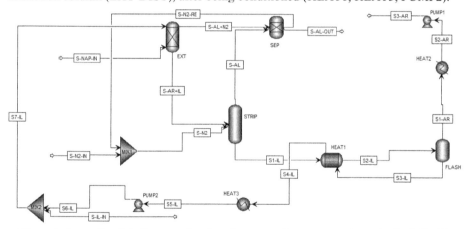

Figure 1: Aromatic-aliphatic separation from low aromatic content naphta using ionic liquids

The following process variables have been sampled (input of the model):
- Theoretical number of stages of the liquid-liquid extraction column (EXT): 2-30.
- Molar solvent to feed ratio of the liquid-liquid extraction column (EXT): 1-4.
- Recovery temperature of the ionic liquid (FLASH): 130-230°C.
- Nitrogen mass flow input into the stripper column (STRIP): 40-80 ton/h.

The final output variable to be regressed is the total mass fraction of aromatics (sum of all aromatics compound) in the product stream.

1.3.2. Toluene Hydrodealkylation

The purpose of this process is to produce benzene from toluene rich streams using H_2 as reagent, see Figure 2.The toluene entering the process (S1-TO-IN) contacts the recovery toluene (S3-TOL) as well as the hydrogen entering the process (S-H2-IN) contacts the recovery hydrogen (S3-H2). These streams after being conditioned (HEAT1) enter the reactor (REACT) where the hydrodealkylation reaction occurs. Afterwards, methane and hydrogen are separated from the S2-TO-BE stream by flash separators (FLASH1 and FLASH2) and then toluene and benzene are also separated using distillation columns (COL1 and COL2). Hydrogen and toluene are finally recycled to the process.

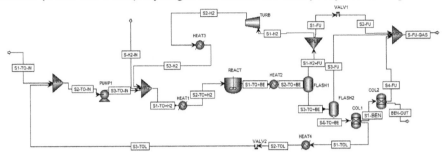

Figure 2: Toluene hydrodealkylation process

The following main chemical reaction has been assumed, and the kinetic equation and parameters adopted from (Dimian et al (2014)):

$$H_2 + C_6H_5CH_3 \rightarrow C_6H_6 + CH_4$$

The following process variables have been sampled (input of the model):

- Volume of the reactor (REACT): 0.8-200 m³.
- Temperature of the reactor (REACT): 550-850°C.
- Pressure of the reactor (REACT): 3-240 bar.
- Fraction of recovered toluene after the first distillation column (COL1): 0.2-0.95.

The final output variable to be regressed is the mass fraction of benzene in the product.

1.3.3. Distillation of organic solvents

A solvent mixture of acetone, methanol and water enters the first distillation column (COL1) along with a water stream and the acetone is separated as depicted in figure 3. Then, the bottom stream (S-WA-MET) enters the second distillation column (COL2) where methanol and water are separated; the process scheme is shown in Fig 3.

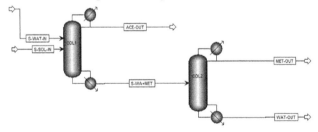

Figure 3: Distillation of organic solvents

The following process variables have been sampled (input of the model):

- Number of theoretical stages at the first column (COL1): 5-40.
- Number of theoretical stages at the second column (COL2): 5-40.
- Molar reflux ratio at the first column (COL1): 1-10.
- Molar reflux ratio at the second column (COL2): 1-10.

The final output variable to be regressed is the acetone mass fraction in the product.

2. Methodology

The methodology followed in this work can be split into three steps: the development of a communicating interface for sampling; the sampling and data preprocessing; and the fitting of the surrogate models. The first step is needed to call the variables values on the Aspen Plus models from MATLAB (COM interface), which is the main coding platform where the preprocessing and fitting steps are carried out. Both the input (before the execution of the process simulator) and the output variables (resulting from the Aspen Plus execution) were normalized to fit the [0,1] range. Data sampling was repeated 150 times using the LHS method adding a random noise value (low noise was considered to be $\eta \approx N(0,0.1)$ and large noise $\eta \approx N(0,0.2)$). The ranges of the input variables sampled are shortlisted for each process in sections 1.3.1 to 1.3.3. Then, data regression is carried out using different toolboxes available in MATLAB. Data fitting for Support Vector Regression and Artificial Neural Networks were performed using the built-in Statistics and Machine Learning and the Deep Learning toolboxes, whereas Kriging regressions were conducted using the ooDace toolbox developed by (Couckuyt et al (2014)) also available for MATLAB. The workstation used for the calculations was a computer with a 3.40GHz Intel Core i7-6700 CPU and 16 GB of RAM under Windows 10.

3. Results

In order to evaluate the performance of each surrogate modelling technique, the data sampling, noise addition (small or large) and regression process was repeated 25 times for each surrogate technique over each individual process in order to compute the average mean squared error (MSE) and the std deviation (the average and std deviation of the 25 surrogate models developed). Figures 4 to 6 show the average values and standard deviation for the three different processes studied in this work. The average and std deviation of the MSE values obtained have been normalized by dividing by the values obtained for SVR with large noise (deemed as the reference value).

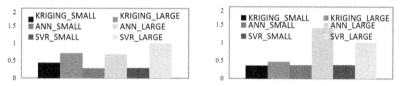

Figure 4: Average (a) and std deviation (b) of the MSE (aromatics-aliphatics separation).

Figure 5: Average (a) and std deviation (b) of the MSE (toluene hydrodealkylation)

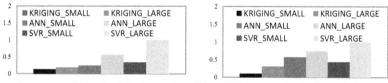

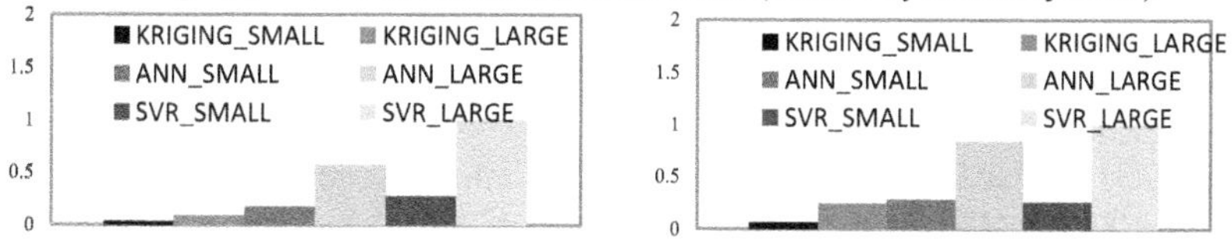

Figure 6: Average (a) and standard deviation (b) of the MSE (distillation of organic solvents).

Figure 4 shows that for the more complex process involving liquid-liquid extraction of aromatics-aliphatics mixtures with ionic liquids, the smaller MSE average value are obtained by ANN (SVR show similar performance), whereas the largest MSE standard deviation is also obtained by ANN (SVR show also similar values). In the other two processes (Figures 5 and 6, toluene hydrodealkylation and distillation of organic solvents), Kriging regression have shown to be the more accurate technique (lowest average deviations obtained) and the less sensitive to data changes (lowest standard deviation in the set of 25 regressions carried out). As it can be also seen in the previous figures, the imposed noise applied to the variables during the sampling step clearly influences the final deviation of the fitted models. It agrees with the fact that the more dispersed the sampled data to fit, more deviations are expected between the final surrogates fitted. However, the discussion presented herein is quite limited and is only valid in the restricted scope of this work. A broader study considering a larger pool of chemical processes, different variable nature (temperature, pressure, compositions, flows...) and different surrogate modelling parametrizations is under development at this moment which is expected to shed more light on the discussion presented herein.

4. Conclusions

In this work, a systematic study of surrogate modelling techniques (SVR, Kriging and ANN) applied to different chemical processes has been carried out. The performance of these techniques has been evaluated in the presence of imposed noise during variable sampling. Results show that for the more complex process model (aromatics-aliphatics separation), ANN and SVR have achieved the lowest MSE value. On the contrary, for the less complex processes (solvent distillation and toluene hydrodealkylation), Kriging regression was the most promising technique. However, a wider study is needed to obtain less case dependent results and deeper insights about the suitability of the different surrogate modelling techniques currently available.

Acknowledgements

The authors are grateful to the Com. de Madrid (project P2018/EMT-4348 SUSTEC) for financial support.

References

Cortes, C., & Vapnik, V. (1995). Support-vector networks. Machine learning, 20(3), 273-297.
Couckuyt I, Dhaene T, Demeester P (2014). OoDACE toolbox: A flexible object-oriented kriging implementation. J Mach Learn Res,15,3183–3186.
De Riva, J., Ferro, V. R., Moreno, D., Diaz, I., & Palomar, J. (2016). Aspen Plus supported conceptual design of the aromatic–aliphatic separation from low aromatic content naphtha using 4-methyl-N-butylpyridinium tetrafluoroborate ionic liquid. Fuel processing technology, 146, 29-38.
Dimian, A. C., Bildea, C. S., & Kiss, A. A. (2014). Integrated design and simulation of chemical processes (Vol. 13). Elsevier.
Krige, D. G. (1960). On the departure of ore value distributions from the lognormal model in South African gold mines. Journal of the Southern African Institute of Mining and Metallurgy, 61(4), 231-244.
McCulloch, W. S., & Pitts, W. (1943). A logical calculus of the ideas immanent in nervous activity. The bulletin of mathematical biophysics, 5(4), 115-133.

Sauro Pierucci, Flavio Manenti, Giulia Bozzano, Davide Manca (Eds.)
Proceedings of the 30th European Symposium on Computer Aided Process Engineering
(ESCAPE30), May 24-27, 2020, Milano, Italy. © 2020 Elsevier B.V. All rights reserved.
http://dx.doi.org/10.1016/B978-0-12-823377-1.50026-4

A Non-Autonomous Relativistic Frame of Reference for Unit Operation Design

Andres Carranza-Abaid,[*] Jana P. Jakobsen

Norwegian University of Science and Technology (NTNU), Department of Chemical Engineering, 7491, Trondheim, Norway

andres.c.abaid@ntnu.no

Abstract

This contribution presents an efficient systematic algorithm for unit operation design that uses a newly developed non–autonomous relativistic frame of reference (NARF). The NARF is aimed towards the conceptual design of unit operations that require solving systems of ordinary differential equations (ODE) where the system volume is unknown. The improved NARF algorithm was tested and compared against the classical modelling method that utilizes the Eulerian reference frame (ERF). To assess and validate the qualities of the NARF, a gas-liquid contactor was modelled using both frames of reference. The results show that the NARF significantly outperforms the computational speed of the ERF up to 1 order of magnitude, all of this, without compromising the accuracy of the results of the unit operation. The NARF can become invaluable in the conceptual design and optimization in computational chemical engineering.

Keywords: Modelling, Process Design, Multiphase Reactors, Absorption, CO_2

1. Introduction

The conceptual design and optimization of chemical processes has become a must in the later decades because of the ever-increasing economic competitive standards. Therefore, the optimization of chemical plants design has become common task in chemical engineering. Nevertheless, the optimization of a chemical process is a complex and computationally intensive problem that may require long periods of time to complete if the calculations are too extensive. This problem arises because unit operations are commonly designed using the ERF, that although useful, it jeopardizes the computational speed due to its iterative algorithm. The improved algorithm using NARF was conceived by making an analogy with the Galilean relativity principle: "if the laws of nature are valid in one frame of reference, they must be valid on a different frame of reference".

2. Modelling

2.1. Eulerian Reference Frame

In order to model a unit operation, the Lagrangian and Eulerian frames of reference are usually utilized. The last one being the most used because it is computationally more efficient (Jakobsen, 2008). In most 1-D problems, unit operations can be described in the ERF as an autonomous system of c ODEs. When using this reference frame, the modelled system is considered as a physical entity and the obtained solution describes how the dependent variables change within it. The ODE system has the following general form:

$$\frac{d}{d\theta}\left(\underline{\beta}(\theta)\right) = \underline{f}\left(\underline{\beta}(\theta), \underline{\mu}\right) \tag{1}$$

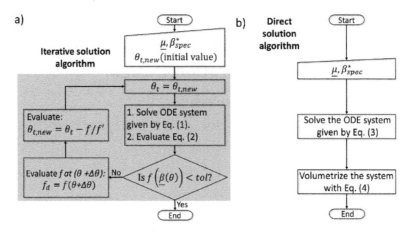

Figure 1: Algorithm to design a unit operation using a) Eulerian frame of reference and b) Non- Autonomous Relativistic Frame of Reference.

Where θ is the control volume (we refer to this variable as volume throughout the paper, but it can be time as well), $\underline{\beta}$ is the vector of state variables (mass or energy flow velocities), $\underline{\mu}$ is the vector of parameters. If a variable has a line _ underneath, it indicates that the variable is a vector, otherwise it is a scalar. Eq. (1) is said to be autonomous because it is not an explicit function of the independent variable (θ). A unit operation design problem fixes a design specification at a specific position (i.e. the outlet). Thus, a discrepancy function between the actual calculated value of the design variable Eq. (1) and the design specification must be set. This discrepancy function has the form:

$$f\left(\underline{\beta}(\theta)\right) = \beta^{*}(\theta) - \beta_{spec}^{*} \tag{2}$$

Where the superscript * indicates that it is the specified state variable and the subscript *spec* means that it is the fixed or specified variable in the problem. To solve a problem with the abovementioned characteristics, the procedure depicted in Figure 1a must be executed. Although this modelling approach has been used extensively, the procedure is computationally expensive because the ODE given by Eq. (1) must be solved as many times as necessary until Eq. (2) is satisfied (Figure 1a). Furthermore, a unit operation can be designed if and only if the solution of the state variables satisfies $\underline{\beta} \in \mathbb{R}$; hence, unit operation design implicitly assumes that the solution is within physical boundaries.

2.2. Non-Autonomous Relativistic Frame of Reference
Considering the main assumption of unit operation design: that the solution is within the real numbers ($\underline{\beta} \in \mathbb{R}$), it is possible to transform the ODE system from being autonomous to non-autonomous by deriving the conservation equations in terms of the design specification variable. This is done by performing a differentiation on the design specification conservation equation and substituting the result into all the remaining conservation equations of the ERF. The final non-autonomous ODE system has the form:

$$\frac{d}{d\beta^{*}}\left(\underline{\beta}^{r}\left(\beta^{*}\right)\right) = \underline{f}\left(\underline{\beta}^{r}\left(\beta^{*}\right), \underline{\mu}\right) \tag{3}$$

$$\frac{d\theta}{d\beta^{*}} = f\left(\underline{\beta}^{r}\left(\beta^{*}\right), \underline{\mu}\right) \tag{4}$$

Where the superscript *r* indicates a reduced vector that includes all the state variables except the design specification variable. Eq. (3) demonstrates that it is possible to determine the values of the state variables in an "spaceless" form before knowing the spatial dimensions of the system. Therefore, the solution given by Eq. (3) is a geometrical reduction of the solution given by the ERF. Even though Eq. (3) solves all the conservation equations, the unit operation volume has yet to be calculated. In order to transform the solution from the "spaceless" form to a solution with actual spatial dimensions, Eq. (4) must be used as a volumetrizing function to determine the required volume of the unit operation. A summary of the algorithm to design a unit operation in the NARF is illustrated in Figure 1b. It must be noted that a model based on the NARF describes how the non-design specification state variables behave with respect to the design specification variable (Eq. (3)) and how much volume is needed (Eq. (4)) to go from an initial state to a final state of the design specification variable.

2.3. Example Model

As an example, a design calculation of an amine-based CO_2 gas-liquid contactor has been performed in order to illustrate the equivalence between both frames of reference and to quantify the computational advantages that the NARF possess. The model of the CO_2 absorber is a boundary value problem (BVP) and was solved in Matlab 2018b with the bvp4 in-built function. The following assumptions were done:

- steady state and plug flow hydrodynamic regime
- four components are considered (CO_2, MEA, H_2O and N_2) and only CO_2 and H_2O go through a phase change. The mass transfer is assumed to go from the vapor to the liquid phase
- the two-film theory describes the mass and energy transfer
- the gas-phase mass transfer resistance is negligible
- the absorber is considered adiabatic and isobaric
- the kinetics are described by a second order irreversible enhancement factor model

2.3.1. Eulerian Conservation Equations

The conservation equations in the ERF are discretized in terms of the system volume. This method of developing the equations has been extensively discussed in the literature (Gabrielsen et al., 2007). The resulting equations that raise from this approach have the general form of Eq. (1), and for the current example the ODE system is described by:

$$\frac{d\underline{\beta}}{d\theta} = -\underline{r} \tag{5}$$

Where $\underline{r}$ is the rate of property transfer that can be either a mass or energy flow transfer rate. An absorber is usually a countercurrent unit operation, hence, there are two groups of boundary conditions. The first group describes the material and energy flows of the inlet vapor phase at the bottom of the absorber while the second group accounts for the material and energy flows of the liquid phase at the top of the absorber. The B.C. are:

$$\underline{\beta_v} = \underline{\beta_{v,0}} \quad at \quad \theta = 0 \; (Top) \qquad\qquad \underline{\beta_l} = \underline{\beta_{l,1}} \quad at \quad \theta = \theta_t \, (Bottom) \tag{6}$$

The subscripts indicate: *v* applies for the property flows in the vapor phase, *l* for the property flows in the liquid phase, *t* is the total volume of the system, *0* stipulates that the B.C. is at the bottom of the absorber while *1* shows that it is at the top of the absorber. It is clear from Eq. (6) that the B.C. of the system are the spatial boundaries of the absorber. In order to obtain the total volume of the unit operation, Eqs. (5) and (6) are to be solved along with a discrepancy function with the form of Eq. (2) where the value of the CO_2 molar flow at the top β_{v,CO_2} must be equal to the design specification β^*_{spec}.

2.3.2. Non-Autonomous Relativistic Conservation Equations

The conservation equations in the NARF are derived using the CO_2 molar flow as the independent variable. It is possible to do so because the boundaries are specified in the design problem, therefore the CO_2 molar flow will change from the CO_2 molar flow in the inlet stream to the specified CO_2 molar flow in the outlet stream. The following equations are obtained by following the procedure described in section 2.2:

$$\frac{d\beta^r}{d\beta^*} = \frac{r^r}{r^*} \tag{7}$$

$$\frac{d\theta}{d\beta^*} = -r^* \tag{8}$$

The B.C. of the ODE system given by Eq. (7) is numerically the same as the ones used in the ERF. Except for the fact that the B.C. for the CO_2 molar flow cannot be used because they are being utilized as the boundaries of the independent variable. Therefore, there is one less B.C. in the vapor phase in the NARF. The B.C. are:

$$\underline{\beta_v} = \underline{\beta_{v,0}} \;\; at \;\; \beta^* = \beta^*_0 \,(Initial\; state) \qquad \underline{\beta_l} = \underline{\beta_{l,1}} \;\; at \;\; \beta^* = \beta^*_{spec} \,(Final\; state) \tag{9}$$

Following the algorithm in Figure 1b, Eqs. (7) and (9) must be evaluated first, and after the solution is obtained, Eq. (8) can be evaluated. The B.C. for Eq. (8) are:

$$\theta = 0 \;\; at \;\; \beta^* = \beta^*_0 \,(Initial\; state) \qquad \theta = \theta_t \;\; at \;\; \beta^* = \beta^*_{spec} \,(Final\; state) \tag{10}$$

The volumetrizing function Eq. (8) along with the B.C. (Eq. (10)) must be solved to calculate the volume of the absorber. Eq. 8) is analogous to the performance equation for reactors developed by Levenspiel (2003); but Eq. (8) is not limited mass balances as the original equation.

2.3.3. Complementary Equations

The equations presented in this section apply for both frames of reference. The material balances source term is:

$$r_i^m = \frac{x_i \rho_l E k_{i,l} a}{\bar{M}_l H_i} \left(y_i - y_i^{eq} \right) \tag{11}$$

Where r^m is the mass transfer rate of component i, ρ_l is the liquid density, E is the enhancement factor, k_l is the mass transfer coefficient of the component i in the liquid phase, a is the ratio between the effective interfacial area and the gas-liquid contactor volume, $\bar{M}_l$ is the average molar fraction, H is the thermodynamic factor that relates the distribution of the component i between the vapor and the liquid phase, y_i is the molar fraction of component i in the vapor phase and the superscript ^{eq} indicates the equilibrium vapor composition of the liquid phase. The mass transfer coefficients and the effective interfacial area are calculated with Onda's correlation for random packings. For H_2O, the value of the enhancement factor is equal to 1, the equilibrium composition is given by

Raoult's law and the H_2O thermodynamic factor was estimated in Aspen Plus to be 0.117. The physical properties, the equilibrium composition of CO_2 and the enhancement factor are calculated using the SOFT model proposed by (Luo et al., 2014). The source term in the energy balance equations is calculated by:

$$\underline{r}^E = h_h \left(T_v - T_l \right) \tag{12}$$

Where $\underline{r}^E$ is energy transfer rate for both phases, h_h is the overall heat transfer coefficient, T_v is the bulk temperature of the vapor phase and T_l is the bulk temperature of the liquid phase. The heat capacities of the vapor and the liquid phase are estimated to be 30.1 and 85.1 kJ/kmol K respectively. The heat of phase change for CO_2 is 88,000 kJ/kmol (Gabrielsen et al., 2005) and 44,000 kJ/kmol for H_2O. The overall heat transfer coefficient was estimated using the Chilton-Colburn analogy and is considered constant and equal to 25.3 kJ/s m^2 K.

3. Results and Discussion

The problem statement of the study case is: Design an absorber that removes 90% of CO_2 from a flue gas (1 kmol/s) containing a 10/90% mol CO_2/N_2 mixture at 40 °C and 105 kPa with a solvent containing 30% wt. MEA, 70% wt. H_2O at 40 °C. The absorber packing is Mellapak 250Y and the superficial vapor velocity is set to be 1.5 m/s at the bottom. The design variables are the loading α (mol CO_2/mol MEA) at the solvent input and the molar liquid to gas ratio (LG) between the solvent and the flue gas. Note that the design specification is the outlet CO_2 mole flow given by the 90% reduction requirement and the volume is the unknown variable.

A set of 10,000 simulations were performed to show the equivalence between both frames of reference. The design variables values used were among the following ranges $\alpha = (0.05\text{-}0.24)$ and $LG = (4.0\text{-}8.0)$. The tolerance for the discrepancy function in the ERF was set to 10^{-5}. The profiles of the state variables with respect to the volume were compared in each one of the simulations by calculating the relative deviation between both frames of reference. The maximum, minimum and average deviations of the profiles of the CO_2 molar flow in the vapor phase, H_2O molar flow in the liquid phase, the energy flow in the liquid phase are presented in Table 1. In the last column of Table 1, the relative deviation the total volume of the absorber is also shown. As seen in Table 1 the NARF modelling scheme always gives the same results as the ERF; where the negligible differences are of numerical nature. This agrees with the principle of the Galilean invariance: all frames of reference are related to one another by a mathematical transformation.

Table 1. Relative deviation of the results of representative state variables between both frames of reference

Relative Deviation / 10^6	β_{v, CO_2}	β_{l, H_2O}	$\beta_{l, E}$	θ_t
Min	-1.5	-7.1	-0.5	-2.7
Max	0.7	7.4	4.2	1.2
Average	-0.1	-0.6	0.5	-0.2

The algorithmic and computational advantages of the NARF are shown in Figure 2. It compares the relative computational speed between both reference frameworks at different tolerances for convergence for the iteration loop described in Figure 1a. A total of 1,000 simulations were performed in each one of the runs. Figure 2 shows that as the ERF becomes more exact, the computational advantage of NARF increases. It is seen that this behavior is proportional to the amount of iterations that the ERF must perform in order to reach the desired design specification. Consequently, the NARF is more accurate than the ERF for unit operation design and, additionally, takes less time to solve.

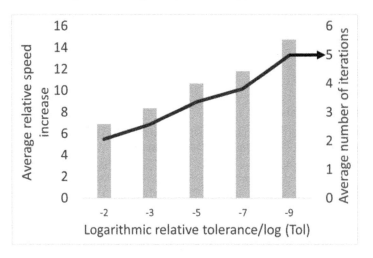

Figure 2: Computational comparison between both frames of reference. Left axis: how many times is the NARF compared to the ERF. Right axis: Average number of iterations.

4. Conclusions

An efficient algorithm for unit operation design calculations based on new non-autonomous relativistic reference frame was developed, numerically validated and tested on an example case of CO_2 absorption. The NARF unit operation design algorithm is faster and is even more accurate than using an algorithm developed in the ERF. This shows that this frame of reference can substitute the classical Eulerian frame of reference in the conceptual design of unit operation equipment. This frame of reference will be especially advantageous in the development of computationally demanding optimization and mapping frameworks for chemical engineering processes.

References

Gabrielsen, J, Svendsen H.F., Michelsen, M.L., Stenby E.H., Kontogeorgis, G.M., 2007, Experimental Validation of a Rate-Based Model for CO_2 capture using AMP solution, Chemical Engineering Science, 62, 2397-2413.

Jakobsen, H., 2008, Chemical Reactor Modeling Multiphase Reactive Flows, 2nd ed., McGraw-Hill, England, Chapters 1-2.

Levenspiel, O., Chemical Reaction Engineering, 3rd ed., John Wiley & Sons, Chapters 23-24.

Luo X., Hartono A., Hussain, S., Svendsen H., 2015, Mass transfer and kinetics of carbon dioxide absorption into loaded aqueous Monoethanolamine solutions, Chemical Engineering Science, 123, 57-59.

Tobiesen, F.A., Svendsen H.F., 2007, Experimental Validation of a Rigorous Absorber Model for CO_2 Postcombustion Capture, AIChE Journal, 53, 4, 846-865.

Sauro Pierucci, Flavio Manenti, Giulia Bozzano, Davide Manca (Eds.)
Proceedings of the 30th European Symposium on Computer Aided Process Engineering
(ESCAPE30), May 24-27, 2020, Milano, Italy. © 2020 Elsevier B.V. All rights reserved.
http://dx.doi.org/10.1016/B978-0-12-823377-1.50027-6

Evaluating the Transient Operation of PCC for fast Response gas Turbines in a Future Low-carbon Energy System

Mathew Dennis Wilkes, Solomon Brown[*]

Department of Chemical and Biological Engineering, University of Sheffield, Sheffield, S1 3JD, United Kingdom
s.f.brown@sheffield.ac.uk

Abstract

Dispatchable power generators with fast ramping capabilities are essential to combat the intermittency issues of renewable energy, and to ensure system security and flexibility. Quick starting gas turbines accompanied with post-combustion carbon capture utilisation and storage (CCUS), can play a vital role in decarbonising the energy sector.

To analyse the transient behaviour of post-combustion capture (PCC), a dynamic rate-based model is developed in gPROMS® gCCS 1.1.0. The aim of this paper is to simulate the flexible operation of a PCC plant attached to a small-scale (<50MW) open-cycle gas turbine (OCGT) power station. Model validation is carried out against a dynamic pilot-scale study, then scaled up to match the typical flue gas output from a modern gas turbine. Data from the Balancing Mechanism Reporting Service (BMRS) and industrial suppliers is used to assess transient nature of OCGT power generation. It is found that keeping utility streams constant causes a decrease in capture plant efficiency during the constant flowrate phases; however, the rapid transitioning between loads is beneficial as the time averaged capture rate remains above 90% capture.

Keywords: CO_2 capture, Dynamic Modelling, Post-Combustion Capture, Chemical Absorption, Flexible Operation

1. Introduction

It is internationally understood that the targets set to combat climate change cannot be achieved without Carbon Capture, Utilisation and Storage (CCUS). It is vital in developing a low-carbon electricity system, as well as decarbonising heavy polluting industries such as cement and steel production (Global CCS Institute, 2018). Energy systems with near-100% renewable power are feasible; however, a high penetration of intermittent renewables leads to realistic constraints on electricity grids with significant operational challenges (Heuberger & Mac Dowell, 2018).

For system security and flexibility, gas turbines are desirable due to their low greenhouse gas emissions (compared to other fossil sources), operational flexibility, reliability, fast ramping rates and short lead times (Parsons Brinckerhoff, 2014). With the role small-scale decentralised energy could play in decarbonising the electricity sector, the number of quick-response gas turbines is expected to increase (Heuberger & Mac Dowell, 2018). To have a low-carbon electricity system these generators will require CO_2 capture, and this paper focuses on post-combustion capture (PCC). The most commonly used and researched PCC technology is amine-based chemical absorption, with 30 wt. % monoethanolamine (MEA) the benchmark solvent (Oko, et al., 2017).

To ensure security of electricity supply, understanding the operational flexibility of fossil power generation coupled with PCC is essential. Several studies have tackled this issue experimentally and using dynamic models (Bui, et al., 2014). However, the focus in the literature has been on large scale system (>300MWe). To the author's knowledge, there are no examples in the literature for the flexible operation of PCC for small scale power generators (<50MWe), which has been highlighted as a key challenge by Bui et al. (2018a) due to economies of scale. The aim of this paper is to develop, validate and analyse a dynamic model of CO_2 absorption using the benchmark MEA solvent, for a small-scale quick response open-cycle gas turbine (OCGT) plant. The capture model is built in the equation-oriented systems modelling tool - gPROMS® gCCS 1.1.0 by Process Systems Enterprise Limited. Data from the Balancing Mechanism Reporting Service (BMRS) is used to assess the transient nature of OCGT power plants.

2. Model Development

2.1. Capture Plant

The complex reaction kinetics and the interaction between integrated system parts is difficult to accurately assess through steady-state modelling. Bui et al. (2014) reviewed dynamic modelling and optimisation of PCC CO_2 absorption using amine solvents, and rate-based models are more capable of handling transient operating scenarios. Figure 1 shows the model topology of a conventional amine-absorption process. The cooled exhaust gases enter the absorption column, with the 'lean' solvent flowing in a counter current direction. After absorbing the CO_2 the 'rich' solvent passes through a cross heat-exchanger before entering a stripping column. A reboiler maintains the elevated stripper temperature required for solvent regeneration and the condenser ensures a pure CO_2 stream (Bui, et al., 2014).

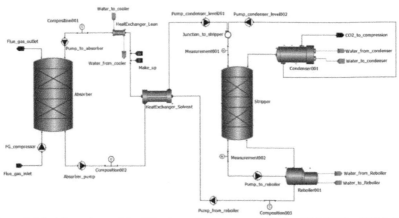

Figure 1: Model topology of the CO_2 absorption process, built in gPROMS® gCCS 1.1.0.

For absorption/desorption units, gCCS uses a rate-based approach where the multi-component mass and heat transfer is described through two-film theory. Each column is represented by a cascade of non-equilibrium stages, with the following assumptions:

- one-dimensional (axially distributed)
- reactions are treated implicitly and only occur in the bulk-liquid phase
- chemical equilibrium in the entire liquid phase
- phase equilibrium is assumed at the vapour-liquid interface
- negligible solvent degradation

Each column uses the Billet & Schultes pressure drop correlation and the Onda mass transfer correlation. The thermophysical properties are described through the Statistical Associating Fluid Theory (SAFT) properties package called gSAFT-VR (PSE, 2016).

2.1.1. Capture Plant Model Validation

Although a large number of pilot plant data is openly available, the number of dynamic operating data sets is limited. Currently only a small number of studies have validated dynamic models against dynamic pilot plant data (Bui, et al., 2018b). Tait et al. (2016) performed five different dynamic capture plant scenarios: startup, shutdown, capture plant decoupling, reboiler decoupling, and frequency reponse. A summary of the baseload operating conditions are shown in Table 1. The capture plant uses 30.16 wt.% MEA, and the flue gas is represessentative of a gas turbine (GT) with 4.27 vol.% CO_2.

Table 1: Baseload operating conditions from Tait et al. (2016)

Process Parameter		Value
Absorber	Packing material	Sulzer Mellapak 250.X
	Packing height (m)	6.92
	Packing diamater (mm)	158.00
Stripper	Packing material	Sulzer Mellapak 500.X
	Packing height (m)	5.00
	Packing diameter (mm)	350.00
Flue gas flowrate (Nm³/h)		120.50
Flue gas temperature (°C)		46.14
Flue gas CO_2 concentration (vol.%)		4.27
Solvent flowrate (L/h)		344.40
Solvent temperature into absorber (°C)		40.05
Solvent temperature into stripper (°C)		104.07
L/G ratio (L/m³)		2.86
Steam flowrate to reboiler (kg/h)		19.50
Steam pressure (bar)		4.00
Desorber pressure (bar)		1.80

For this study the shutdown procedure is used for dynamic validation. The flue gas and solvent flowrates are simultaneously decreased over 16 minutes to 40% baseload, then

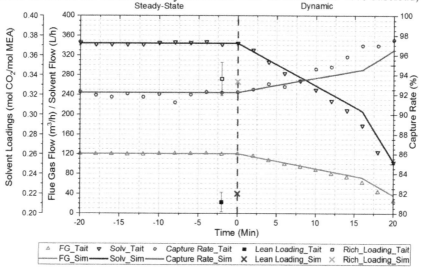

Figure 2: Model validation against steady-state and dynamic plant data from Tait et al. (2016)

further decreased to 30% baseload over the next 4 minutes. Figure 2 shows a comparison of the first 40 minutes of the shutdown procedure.

During steady-state operation the rich- and lean-loadings are 0.22 and 0.33 mol CO_2/mol MEA respectively, which are within the errors indicated by Tait et al. (2016). The average experiemental capture rate in the steady-state section is 92.28%, the predicted capture rate is 92.21%. Therefore, the model accurately simulates steady-state operation. In the capture plant shutdown experiment the steam flowrate to the reboiler is decreased to 0 kg/h between 0-10 minutes, however, due to model constraints this could not be included. This accounts for the small deviation in the capture rate during the dynamic operation, which has an increased gradient between 10-16 minutes, and showed a maximum deviation of 3.3% at 16 minutes.

2.2. Flexible Gas Turbine Operation

Data from the Balancing Mechanism Reporting Service (BMRS) and industrial suppliers is used to simulate the transient operation of an open-cycle gas turbine (OCGT) plant. BMRS is an open access electricity market databank providing data on the demand, generation and transmission of electricity in Great Britain (GB). The typical operating times and load changes follow a 30 minute time interval, based off the balancing and settlement period in GB (ELEXON, 2019). OCGT generation typically only comes on the system during periods of high strain, during the colder winter months in December, January and February. Figure 3 shows the time and load of OCGT's in January over the last 3 years in GB. The key points from the data set:

- over a 240 hour period an OCGT plant will start-up and shutdown on average five times
- typically coming on between 15:00-20:00
- used to deliver peak daily demand, which also have the highest peaks in the evening.
- the sporadic and inconsistent behaviour makes planning PCC operation difficult.

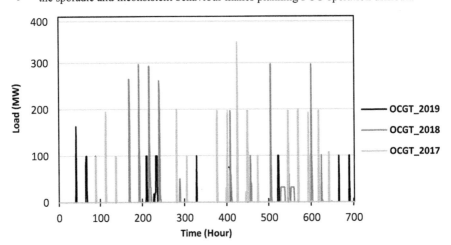

Figure 3: OCGT operation for 700 hours, data sourced from BMRS

This study uses the Siemens SGT-400 as an example modern gas turbine, the 11 MW version produces 33.80 kg/s of exhaust mass flow with low NO_X (≤25 ppm). The rated power output in open-cycle power generation is 10.40 MWe, and can be used for range of onshore and offshore applications (Siemens, 2019). For a typical OCGT power station, the average ramp rate is between 8-12% maximum load per minute, and the hot and cold start-up times are 5-11 minutes (Agora Energiewende, 2017).

Assuming the exhaust temperature can be reduced to a suitable inlet absorber temperature through a pinch analysis, the model is then scaled up to handle 33.80 kg/s of flue gas, and equipment sizes are scaled to maintain key process parameters highlighted in Table 1. The capture plant initially starts when the GT is at full load, the start-up procedure is not investigated in this study, and the shutdown time is 8 minutes. Initially, the capture plant is operated at full load (GT output = 10.40 MWe) for 1 hour, before progressing through two ramping cycle at 70% and 50% load. This study assumes a ramp rate of 10% full load per minute, therefore, the SGT-400 can increase or decrease power at 1.04 MWe/Minute. Flowrate changes follow the 30-minute balancing and settlement period in GB. The flue gas flowrate is assumed to be directly affected by load, i.e. 70% load correlates to 70% flowrate. The concentration of each emission is assumed to be constant, in reality power ramping effects the level of incomplete combustion, and thus the formation of CO and unburnt hydrocarbons, which will affect the capture plant. However, this is beyond the scope of this study.

3. Results

The flue gas flowrate entering the absorber column at maximum gas turbine load is 33.80 kg/s and the solvent flowrate is 83.04 L/s, consistent with the L/G ratio in Tait et al. (2016). Figure 4 shows the calculated capture rate is initially 92.48%, comparable to the 92.28% in Tait et al. (2016). The capture rate decreases to 90.37% over the initial hour due to the constant steam/water supply to the reboiler, condenser and lean solvent heat exchanger. This decrease during full load operation is also exhibited in the validation simulation, however, due to the smaller flowrates and column geometries it is not as substantial. Keeping the utility streams constant causes an increase in lean-loading, therefore, as more CO_2 is entrained in the solvent, less CO_2 can be removed from the flue gas. The increase in loadings was a result of the fraction of CO_2 released during the stripping process decreasing by 25%. The gas inlet and liquid outlet stripper temperatures decreased by 9°C and 2°C respectively, over the simulation prior to shut down; therefore, further work is required to analyse this decrease in recovery rate.

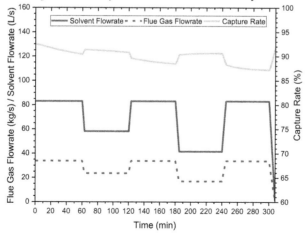

Figure 4: Flexible commercial scale post-combustion capture plant operation

Ramping to 70% load, the inlet absorber gas flowrate decreases to 23.66 kg/s in 3 minutes,during which the capture rate increases to 91.30%. Interestingly, once the flowrate is returned to full load the capture rate continues the original trajectory, going from 90.75 to 89.58%.

This pattern is also shown in the second ramping cycle at 50% load. Over both the cycles the capture plant efficiency drops 5.30%. If the plant was to have continuous operation this loss of efficiency would be alarming. However, when operating in the more dynamic future energy system, it is likely that gas-PCC systems will only be operating for short periods of time and the efficiency drop is less severe. The time-averaged capture rate including the shutdown procedure is 90.02%.

4. Conclusion

The fast ramping capabilities of modern gas turbines can be used as dispatchable generation, and accompanied with CCUS they can play a vital role in decarbonising the energy sector. This paper presents the steady-state and dynamic validation of a rate-based CO_2 absorption model, using the benchmark 30 wt.% MEA process. The process is scaled to capture CO_2 from the flue gas of a 10.40 MWe gas turbine in open cycle configuration. Capture plant operation during two ramping cycles, at 70% and 50% full load, shows the rapid load transitioning assists in maintaining a time-averaged capture rate above 90%. Therefore, while employing the right operating strategy for gas-PCC the time-averaged capture rate can be maintained without being a barrier to flexible operation. Future work should focus on optimising process parameters to minimise the energy penalty related to the desorption step, during various dynamic operating scenarios.

Acknowledgements

This work is funded by the Engineering and Physical Sciences Research Council (EPSRC) Centre for Doctoral Training in Carbon Capture and Storage and Cleaner Fossil Energy (EP/L016362/1), and Drax Group Plc.

References

Agora Energiewende, 2017. *Flexibility in thermal power plants* , Berlin: Agora Energiewende.
Bui, M. et al., 2018a. Carbon capture and storage (CCS): the way forward. *Energy & Environmental Science,* 11(5), pp. 1062-1176.
Bui, M. et al., 2014. Dynamic modelling and optimisation of flexible operation in post-combustion CO2 capture plants—A review. *Computers & Chemical Engineering,* Volume 61, pp. 245-265.
Bui, M., Tait, P., Lucquiaud, M. & Mac Dowell, N., 2018b. Dynamic operation and modelling of amine-based CO2 capture at pilot scale. *International Journal of Greenhouse Gas Control,* Volume 79, pp. 134-153.
ELEXON, 2019. *Balancing Mechanism Reporting Service (BMRS).* [Online]
Available at: https://www.bmreports.com
[Accessed 1 November 2019].
Global CCS Institute, 2018. *The Global Status of CCS - 2018,* Melbourne: Global CCS Institute.
Heuberger, C. F. & Mac Dowell, N., 2018. Real-World Challenges with a Rapid Transition to 100% Renewable Power System. *Joule,* 2(3), pp. 367-370.
Oko, E., Wang, M. & Joel, A. S., 2017. Current status and future development of solvent-based carbon capture. *International Journal of Coal Science & Technology,* Volume 4, pp. 5-14.
Parsons Brinckerhoff, 2014. *Technical Assessment of the Operation of Coal & Gas Fired Plants,* London: Department of Energy and Climate Change.
PSE, 2016. *gCCS Documentation,* London: Process Systems Enterprise Limited.
Siemens, 2019. *Gas Turbine Portfolio Brochure,* Munich: Siemens.
Tait, P. et al., 2016. A pilot-scale study of dynamic response scenarios for the flexible operation of post-combustion CO2 capture. *International Journal of Greenhouse Gas Control,* 48(2), pp. 216-233.

Sauro Pierucci, Flavio Manenti, Giulia Bozzano, Davide Manca (Eds.)
Proceedings of the 30th European Symposium on Computer Aided Process Engineering
(ESCAPE30), May 24-27, 2020, Milano, Italy. © 2020 Elsevier B.V. All rights reserved.
http://dx.doi.org/10.1016/B978-0-12-823377-1.50028-8

Increasing Power System Flexibility to Integrate High Share of Renewable Energy

Siyuan Chen, Pei Liu*, Zheng Li

State Key Lab of Power Systems, Department of Energy and Power Engineering, Tsinghua-BP Clean Energy Center, Tsinghua University, 100084 Beijing, China
liu_pei@tsinghua.edu.cn

Abstract

The variability and intermittency of renewable energy brings about technical challenges for its integration. In order to integrate high share of renewable energy, more flexibility is needed in the power system. Among all the flexibility options, taking customer-sited energy storage systems as demand response could be a promising measure addressing both grid needs and customer needs. In order to analyse the effect of customer-sited energy storage systems on renewable energy integration, an integrated power generation and customer-sited energy storage systems expansion planning model is proposed in this paper. The expansion and operation of energy storage systems are based on the objective of reducing total power generation costs. Sichuan province in China is taken as a case study due to its abundant renewable energy resources and increasing renewable energy share in the power system. The results indicate that: 1) demand response provided by customer-sited energy storage could partially replace coal power plants to provide flexibility for integrating high share of renewable energy into power system; 2) The utilization scale of renewable energy could be increased and CO_2 emissions could be reduced significantly. In order to encourage the deployment of customer-sited energy storage systems, more policy support for energy storage technology and electricity market mechanism improvement are needed to enhance the development of customer-sited energy storage systems.

Keywords: Renewable energy integration, Customer-sited energy storage, Modelling and optimization, Power generation expansion planning

1. Introduction

Renewable energy is expected to be the fastest growing source of energy, contributing half of the growth in global energy supplies and becoming the largest source of power by 2040 (BP, 2019). However, renewable energy output is highly dependent on weather conditions, which means it is variable and non-dispatchable. More flexibility is needed in the power system to balance the fluctuation of renewable energy in parallel with higher share of renewable energy. There are a range of measures to increase the power system flexibility including flexible power generation, demand side management, grid ancillary services, energy storage, power-to-gas and vehicle-to-grid (Lund et al., 2015). Among these measures, energy storage technologies have recently drawn much attention as a promising flexibility provider due to the technical maturity and decreasing costs (Hadjipaschalis et al., 2009). Existing researches mainly focus on using energy storage to provide flexibility on the supply side. However, if an energy storage system is located along the point of generation, its operation is tied to this individual facility and the potential utility is severely limited. Moreover, energy storage on the supply side will not change the power load profile. High capacity of power distribution networks and facilities are still needed in order to balance the peak load of consumers, while they remain idle in the rest of time. One way to manage power load profile is by demand response, which means customers shift their power demand among time periods in one day. However, the change of electricity usage pattern may cause discomfort for customers (Parrish et al., 2019). Using customer-sited energy storage systems as demand response could be a promising measure addressing both grid needs and customer needs. Peak load could be reduced without changing customers' usage pattern. Furthermore, the flexibility level that customer-sited energy storage can provide is higher than conventional demand response.

Wang et al. (2018) designed a user-side energy storage system and analyzed the effect on the grid side and user side. The simulation results demonstrate that power quality of the users is improved whilst reactive compensation is realized on the grid side in the presence of user-side energy storage. Hu et al. (2016) developed a scheduling model for customer-sited energy storage system, capturing the dynamics and operational constraints. A rolling-horizon approach is applied to optimize the schedule and assess the economics of energy storage system. They found that using customer-sited energy storage system to support only one or two of the services may not yield a positive profit based on current costs. Telaretti et al. (2015) proposed a charging strategy for customer-sited energy storage in presence of hourly electricity prices, aiming to maximize the profit for storage owners. A heuristic approach is applied to determine the optimal schedule of energy storage system regardless of the customer load profile.

Major concerns of existing literatures are to determine the optimal charging and discharging behavior of customer-sited energy storage system to maximize the profit. However, the resulting schedule of energy storage system may not be totally consistent with the grid needs. This inconsistency limits the potential effects of customer-sited energy storage on renewable energy integration and total social cost reduction. It is essential to consider the expansion and operation strategy of customer-sited energy storage systems from the perspective of whole society so that appropriate market mechanisms could be designed for customer-sited energy storage systems. In order to address this issue, we extended our previous power generation expansion planning model (Chen et al., 2019) to an integrated power generation and customer-sited energy storage systems expansion planning model. The expansion and operation of energy storage systems are based on the objective of reducing total power generation costs. The model is applied to the case study of Sichuan province in China, which has abundant renewable energy resources and increasing renewable energy share in the power system, to evaluate the effect of installing customer-sited energy storage facilities as demand response on the integration of renewable energy into power system.

2. Methodology

2.1. Model description

The integrated power generation and customer-sited energy storage systems expansion planning model proposed in this paper aims to optimize both long-term planning and short-term scheduling of power system. The optimal type, size, construction time and scheduling of both power generation units and customer-sited energy storage systems are obtained with this model. Five types of power generation technologies are included in this model: Pulverized Coal (PC) power plants, Natural Gas Combined Cycle (NGCC) power plants, Hydro (HD) power plants, Wind (WD) power plants and Solar Photovoltaic (PV) power plants. All power generation technologies are set a lifetime and assumed to be decommissioned at the end of their lifetime. The optimal development path is then calculated based on the objective function, which is to minimize the total system cost of power sector in the planning horizon. In order to reflect the fluctuation of variable renewable energy, the model takes hourly power balance into account to determine operational variables such as hourly power output of different power generation technologies. In this model, demand response is assumed to be implemented by installing customer-sited energy storage facilities without changing customers' usage patterns.

2.2. Mathematical formulation

Four sets, t, g, f and s stand for time, power generation technology type, fuel type, and time slice respectively. Parameters are expressed by upper-case characters and Greek alphabet whilst variables are expressed by lower-case characters.

2.2.1. Objective function

The objective function of this model is to minimize the total system cost of the power sector from 2018 to 2050. The total system cost comprises capital expenditure, operation and maintenance cost, fuel cost, start-up and shut-down cost. Eq. (1) shows the objective functions whilst all five parts of costs are listed in Eq. (2) - Eq. (5). Capital expenditure for power generation units are amortized equally to each year during the entire lifetime. Operation and maintenance costs equal the installed capacity multiplied by annual unit O&M cost. Fuel costs are the product of fuel prices and fuel consumption. Start-up costs equal unit start-up cost multiplying start-up capacity.

$$atc = \sum_{t=2018}^{2050} \frac{tinv_t + tom_t + tfc_t + tssc_t}{(1+I)^{t-2018}} \tag{1}$$

$$tinv_t = \sum_g inv_{t,g} = \sum_{t'=t-TLT_g+1}^{t} \left(CAP_{t',g} \cdot nb_{t',g} \cdot \frac{I \cdot (1+I)^{-1}}{1-(1+I)^{-TLT_g}} \right) \tag{2}$$

$$tom_t = \sum_g om_{t,g} = \sum_g OM_{t,g} \cdot ic_{t,g} \tag{3}$$

$$tfc_t = \sum_f FP_{f,t} \cdot \sum_{g,s} fd_{f,t,g,s} \tag{4}$$

$$tssc_t = \sum_{g,s} SSC_{t,g} \cdot (su_{t,g,s} + st_{t,g,s}) \tag{5}$$

2.2.2. Operational constraints

The power balance constraints ensure that power load in each time slice is satisfied by the sum of power generation from all types of generation units as shown in Eq. (6).

$$load_{t,s} = \sum_g pgs_{t,g,s} \tag{6}$$

In terms of renewable energy, power output is limited by capacity factor constraints which relate to the climate and weather. Renewable energy power generation in each time slice should not exceed the upper limit of capacity factor, as presented in Eq. (7).

$$pgs_{t,g,s} \le CF_{g,s} \cdot ic_{t,g} \quad g \in \{HD, WD, PV\} \tag{7}$$

For thermal power plants, unit commitment constraints are included to represent the status of operation, start-up, shut-down and reserve in Eq. (8) - (10).

$$ic_{t,g} = or_{t,g,s} + rs_{t,g,s} \quad g \in \{PC, NGCC\} \tag{8}$$

$$or_{t,g,s+1} = or_{t,g,s} + su_{t,g,s+1} - sd_{t,g,s+1} \quad g \in \{PC, NGCC\} \tag{9}$$

$$rs_{t,g,s+1} = rs_{t,g,s} + sd_{t,g,s+1} - su_{t,g,s+1} \quad g \in \{PC, NGCC\} \tag{10}$$

Thermal power plants can only operate in a specific load factor range, limited by the load factor constraints. Besides, the fuel consumption rate of thermal power plants is strongly influenced by the load factor. More fuel would be needed to generate electricity in off-design working conditions. Piecewise linearization method is used to reflect this relationship as shown in Eq. (11) - (12).

$$LFMIN_{g,s}^i \cdot or_{t,g,s} - M(1-x_i) \le pgs_{t,g,s} \le LFMAX_{g,s}^i \cdot or_{t,g,s} + M(1-x_i) \quad g \in \{PC, NGCC\} \tag{11}$$

$$pgs_{t,g,s} \cdot FCR_{f,t,g}^i - M(1-x_i) \le fd_{f,t,g,s} \le pgs_{t,g,s} \cdot FCR_{f,t,g}^i + M(1-x_i) \quad g \in \{PC, NGCC\} \tag{12}$$

Electricity consumption behavior is assumed to remain unchanged. Then, power load of the power grid is equal to the fixed power demand plus the power charged to customers' storage facilities minus the power discharged from customers' storage facilities as presented in Eq. (13). The storage balance constraints in Eq. (14) show that electricity storage level in each time slice equals the storage level in the previous time slice plus power charged minus power discharged in the current time slice.

$$load_{t,s} = PD_{t,s} + charge_{t,s} - discharge_{t,s} \tag{13}$$

$$storage_{t,s+1} = storage_{t,s} + charge_{t,s+1} \cdot \eta_{charge} - discharge_{t,s+1} / \eta_{discharge} \tag{14}$$

2.2.3. Investment constraints

Eq. (15) expresses the installed capacity of power generation units. The capacity of energy storage facilities is presented in Eq. (16).

$$ic_{t,g} = \sum_{t'=t-TLT_g+1}^{t} nb_{t',g} \tag{15}$$

$$ices_t = \sum_{t'=t-TLT_{es}+1}^{t} nbes_{t'} \tag{16}$$

Due to the limited renewable energy resources, an upper bound for the installed capacity of renewable energy is set in Eq. (17). Eq. (18) shows the policy targets for the development of renewable energy.

$$ic_{t,g} \le RL_g \quad g \in \{HD, WD, PV\} \tag{17}$$

$$ic_{t,g} \ge PT_{t,g} \quad g \in \{HD, WD, PV\} \tag{18}$$

3. Case study

The proposed model is implemented in General Algebraic Modelling System (GAMS) and solved using the CPLEX solver. It is applied in a case study for power generation expansion planning in Sichuan Province of China. Input parameters, including existing installed capacity, future power demand, techno-economic parameters of technologies, renewable energy resources endowment and capacity factor, power transmission limits, losses and costs are imported from previous work (Chen et al., 2019).

3.1. Scenario setting

Two scenarios are set in this case study. The first scenario is named as "Baseline Scenario". Power load curve is input as a fixed parameter to be satisfied in this scenario. The second scenario is named as "Demand Response Scenario". In this scenario, power load curve is relaxed to a variable and can be adjusted by demand response with customer-sited energy storage facilities.

3.2. Results and discussion

In "Baseline Scenario", the flexibility in the power system is provided by coal power plants with more frequent ramping processes as well as start-up and shut-down actions. More ramping processes mean that coal power plants are running at off-design conditions more often, which has lower efficiency and more emissions. In "Demand Response Scenario", demand response can provide flexibility for the power system from the demand side and reduce the need for flexible operation of coal power plants. Figure 1 shows the load dispatch profile of a winter day in 2050 in the two scenarios. It can be noticed that coal power plants are running flexibly in "Baseline Scenario". At noon time when the sunlight is strong, coal power plants have to run at low load to absorb PV power output. At about 19:00 – 20:00 when the power load is high whilst the PV power output is nearly zero, coal power plants have to ramp up to high load for peak regulation. In "Demand Response Scenario", peak load at 19:00 – 20:00 is shifted to low load time period (0:00 – 8:00) and noon time by demand response. After that, coal power plants can run at stable load at all times.

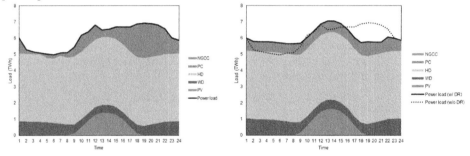

(a) Baseline Scenario   (b) Demand Response Scenario

Figure 1. Load dispatch profile of a winter day in 2050

As the power load is adjusted in consistent with the renewable energy power output, more variable renewable energy could be integrated into the power system whilst fewer coal power plants are needed for peak regulation. The comparison of installed capacity between the two scenarios is presented in Figure 2. In "Demand Response Scenario", wind and PV power plants increase by 5 GW and 4 GW respectively whilst coal power plants decrease by 15 GW by the year 2050 compared with "Baseline Scenario". Overall, demand response increases the utilization of renewable energy and reduces coal power generation simultaneously. The effect of these benefits is the significant CO_2 emission reduction. In "Demand Response Scenario", total CO_2 emissions in the planning horizon are reduced by 422 Mt compared with "Baseline Scenario".

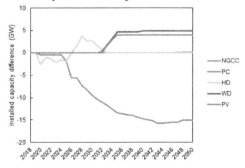

Figure 2. Installed capacity difference between the two scenarios

Despite the benefits that demand response brings about, it will also incur additional costs. In "Demand Response Scenario", 47.4 GW of energy storage capacity is needed by 2050 for demand response. It is noteworthy that power generation cost is reduced by 45 billion RMB whilst the additional storage cost is 117 billion RMB. Therefore, the benefits of demand response mentioned above are at the expense of the increased total cost (72 billion RMB). In order to encourage the installation of customer-sited energy storage facilities, policy-makers should enhance policy support for energy storage technology to promote technological innovation and cost reduction. Electricity market mechanism should also be improved to make it profitable for customers.

4. Conclusions

This paper analyses the effect of using customer-sited energy storage as demand response on integrating high share of renewable energy into power system. The results show that demand response provided by customer-sited energy storage increases the utilization of renewable energy, reduces the flexibility need for coal power generation and realizes significant CO_2 emissions reduction. In order to enhance the development of customer-sited energy storage systems, storage costs need further reduction with technology improvement and policy support. Electricity market mechanism needs to be improved to add more incentives for customer-sited energy storage systems, such as real-time pricing and two-part electricity tariff.

Acknowledgement

The authors gratefully acknowledge the support by The National Key Research and Development of China (2018YFB0604301) and the Phase III Collaboration between BP and Tsinghua University.

References

B. Parrish, R. Gross, P. Heptonstall, 2019. On demand: Can demand response live up to expectations in managing electricity systems?. Energy Research & Social Science, 51: 107-118.

BP Group, 2019. BP Energy Outlook 2019, BP p.l.c., London, United Kondom.

E. Telaretti, E.R. Sanseverino, M. Ippolito, S. Favuzza, G. Zizzo, 2015. A novel operating strategy for customer-side energy storages in presence of dynamic electricity prices. Intelligent Industrial Systems, 1(3): 233-244.

I. Hadjipaschalis, A. Poullikkas, V. Efthimiou, 2009. Overview of current and future energy storage technologies for electric power applications. Renewable and Sustainable Energy Reviews, 13(6-7):1513-1522.

P.D. Lund, J. Lindgren, J. Mikkola, J. Salpakari, 2015. Review of energy system flexibility measures to enable high levels of variable renewable electricity. Renewable and Sustainable Energy Reviews, 45:785-807.

Q. Wang, Y. Zhang, Z. Yun, X. Wang, D. Zhang, D. Bian, 2018. Research on Battery Energy Storage System Based on User Side. IOP Conference Series: Earth and Environmental Science. IOP Publishing, 108(5): 052122.

S. Chen, P. Liu, Z. Li, 2019. Multi-regional power generation expansion planning with air pollutants emission constraints. Renewable and Sustainable Energy Reviews, 112: 382-394.

W. Hu, P. Wang, H. B. Gooi, 2016. Assessing the economics of customer-sited multi-use energy storage. 2016 IEEE Region 10 Conference (TENCON). IEEE, 651-654.

Sauro Pierucci, Flavio Manenti, Giulia Bozzano, Davide Manca (Eds.)
Proceedings of the 30th European Symposium on Computer Aided Process Engineering
(ESCAPE30), May 24-27, 2020, Milano, Italy. © 2020 Elsevier B.V. All rights reserved.
http://dx.doi.org/10.1016/B978-0-12-823377-1.50029-X

A Discrete Modeling Approach for Excess Gibbs-energy Models Combined with Molecular Sampling

Christoph Mayer,* Thomas Wallek

Institute of Chemical Engineering and Environmental Technology, Graz University of Technology, Inffeldgasse 25C, 8010 Graz, Austria

cmayer@tugraz.at

Abstract

In this work, a modeling approach using the discrete states of molecules in an equilibrium lattice is introduced. The discrete states are considered in terms of probabilities to describe condensed phase mixtures. The molecules themselves are modeled with a dice-like geometry, providing the opportunity for up to six different energetic interaction sites per molecule. A link to real molecules is created by combining the model with a molecular sampling algorithm which determines the energetic interaction parameters for molecule clusters through a force field model. The comparison of model results with experimental data for the systems acetone – methanol and acetone – n-heptane shows that the deviations are comparable in magnitude to those of the UNIFAC model.

Keywords: chemical thermodynamics, lattice system, discrete modeling, UNIFAC

1. Introduction

Thermodynamic models for fluid phase equilibria calculations, such as equations of state and activity coefficients, are being challenged by the need to describe complex molecules. Especially systems with strong interactions which show large deviations from ideal mixture behavior are increasingly difficult to describe using conventional modeling approaches.

In this context, previous papers proposed 'discrete modeling' as a novel approach to incorporate a more detailed molecular picture into thermodynamics from scratch. The approach is characterized by the rigorous use of Shannon information equivalently to thermodynamic entropy (Pfleger et al., 2015; Wallek et al., 2016) and can be categorized among classical local-composition models and the more complex cluster variation method.

A previous application of discrete Markov-chains to thermodynamic modeling of two-dimensional lattices describing solid solutions, as developed by Vinograd and Perchuk (1996), was modified and extended from a flat lattice towards a three-dimensional, Ising-type model. The initial step of this model was the description of spherical molecules which are characterized by a uniform energetic interaction across the surface (Wallek et al., 2018).

In this paper, the molecules are modeled with a dice-like geometry, allowing there to be up to six different interaction sites per molecule, aiming at describing isomers and more complex molecules. This approach is combined with a molecular sampling algorithm to establish a link to real molecules. This link enables the possibility to compare the model based on this abstract molecule representation to both established models such as

UNIFAC and experimental data. This was impossible for prior stages of the model development where comparisons were limited to Monte-Carlo simulations of lattice systems and thus marks an important milestone for the approach.

Figure 1: Sequential lattice construction: neighborhood into which a new molecule is inserted.

2. Discrete modeling of dice-like molecules

In this work, molecules are modeled as dice in a simple cubic lattice. This means that at the current stage of model development all molecules are assumed to be of similar size and have up to six different energetic interaction sites positioned in a dice-like structure. Every molecule thus has 24 different orientations.

Each molecule interacts only with its nearest neighbors in the lattice. Further, each site interacts only with the closest site of the nearest neighbor. For a binary mixture, this results in 12 different interaction sites which can form 78 distinct pairwise interactions. The parameters which are the model input are the global composition of the mixture and a temperature-dependent interaction energy for each of the possible pairs of sites.

2.1. Sequential lattice construction

The basis of this work is an approach for two-dimensional solid solutions developed by Vinograd and Perchuk (1996). It was developed to create phase diagrams for crystals and works with uniform molecules, which have only one interaction property along the entire surface. The fundamental feature of this approach is a sequential construction of the lattice in equilibrium. Each molecule is placed into a partial neighborhood of previously inserted molecules. An example of one of these neighborhoods is given in Figure 1. Such an insertion process is only dependent on its particular neighborhood. This insertion of a molecule with a specific orientation into a neighborhood is described using conditional probabilities. The entropy and internal energy of a system are expressed using these conditional probabilities.

A previous work (Wallek et al., 2018) extended this approach to three-dimensional systems. This work focusses on dice-like binary mixtures and the combination of this approach with molecular sampling. The novelty of describing binary mixtures with dice-like components unlocks the desired determination of excess properties. This means that significant progress compared to previous works on this modeling methodology has been achieved.

2.2. Constrained optimization

The goal of the approach is to calculate the thermodynamic equilibrium state of the system of abstract, dice-like, molecule representations. This is achieved via a constrained minimization of the Helmholtz free energy, a.

$$a = u - T s \tag{1}$$

The free energy can be expressed using the internal energy, u, and the entropy, s, which is demonstrated in Eq. (1).

2.2.1. Constraints

The optimization is subject to constraints. These are based on the law of total probabilities or can be viewed as marginal probabilities. The constraints are formed by the sum of cluster probabilities over every possible state for all but one molecule. This sum must be equal to the global composition of the remaining molecule species divided by the number of possible orientations. The interpretation of a cluster probability is the probability of occurrence in the equilibrium lattice of a cluster of molecules each being in specific states concerning component and orientation. After consideration of symmetries, the number of constraints is reduced to 12.

2.2.2. Correlations between cluster of different sizes

The variables for the minimization are the probabilities of molecule pairs. Other equations are formulated with the neighborhood and insertion probabilities of the sequential construction step. These probabilities combined represent a larger cluster. A correlation between the larger cluster and the pairs of molecules is thus necessary. The used approach is chosen for its simplicity and equation size and connects the neighboring molecules to the newly inserted molecule via one-dimensional chains.

2.2.3. Internal energy

The internal energy of the system is expressed using the conditional probabilities of the insertion process. It is defined as the sum over all possible neighborhoods, n, of the probability of each neighborhood times the sum over all possible insertions, m, of the conditional insertion probability times the respective interaction energy, ε.

$$u = \sum_{j=1}^{n} p_j \cdot \sum_{i=1}^{m} p_{i|j} \cdot \varepsilon_{ij} \tag{2}$$

Eq. (2) expresses the internal energy as a function of the neighborhood probabilities and the insertion probabilities. Three new contact pairs are created per insertion step. By applying the constraints as well as the correlations between the different cluster sizes, the equation for the internal energy can be reduced to three times the sum of all pair probabilities multiplied by their respective interaction energy.

2.2.4. Entropy

The entropy is expressed using the neighborhood and insertion probabilities.

$$s = -R \left[\ln(24) + \sum_{j=1}^{n} p_j \cdot \sum_{i=1}^{m} p_{i|j} \cdot \ln\left(p_{i|j}\right) \right] \tag{3}$$

The particular way in which the entropy is formulated in Eq. (3) can also be interpreted as treating each orientation of the dice-like molecules as individual components. The constraints of the system then link every set of 24 components back to each respective molecule. In terms of entropy, this method for looking at the system contains too much information. Therefore it has to be corrected with ln(24) to account for the fact that there is in fact only one molecule behind these 24 pseudo-components.

3. Molecular sampling

The model based on dice-like molecules needs the interaction energy of every possible configuration as one of the inputs. These are specific to each pairing of components and provide the interface for linking the abstract model to real molecules. One possible strategy for this is a molecular sampling algorithm. Small molecular clusters, i.e., pairs of molecules, are formed and their potential interaction energy is subsequently evaluated.

The OPLS-AA force field, developed by Jorgensen et al. (1996), is chosen for the interaction energy calculations. It is well known and broadly accepted for potential energy calculations in the liquid phase. Since the focus of the model is to calculate the excess Gibbs-energy, only the intermolecular energy of the OPLS-AA force field is important. The intramolecular part is omitted.

The sampling procedure places each pair of molecules in specific rotations next to each other and reduces the distance until the smallest distance between the closest surfaces reaches a specific value. This procedure is similar to the sampling algorithm used by Sweere and Fraaije (2015). In their work, they have used different distances between molecules to better represent some mixture properties like a coordination number of ten. For the example systems presented in this work the distance between the molecules is reduced until the van der Waals surfaces are touching.

To establish a link between dice and molecules, the molecules are rotated in 90° steps until all 24 members of the cube symmetry group are sampled for each molecule in the cluster. From the point of view of contacting surfaces in a pair cluster of dice-like molecules, the sampling of all cube rotations leads to more than the 78 needed pairwise interactions for the current model formulation. Therefore, the mean of all combinations which lead to the same contact site pairing is calculated and used as resulting interaction energy.

The starting orientation of the molecules inside the dice-like model framework has an effect on how well components are represented by their dice counterpart. For the systems discussed in the results section, the orientation of acetone is such that the oxygen atom is pointing towards a corner of the dice. Heptane is placed on one of the room diagonals of the dice. The methanol molecule is oriented such that the hydroxy group is pointing at a face of the dice.

4. Results

Two systems are discussed to show the results of this modeling approach. The model is compared to experimental data, the (original) UNIFAC model (Fredenslund et al., 1975) as a representative state-of-the-art approach, and Monte-Carlo simulations. The Monte-Carlo simulations are performed using dice-like molecules in a regular lattice with the same interaction parameters as the model. They converge towards the real solution of these model assumptions and can be used to show the deviation of other model assumptions, for instance the sequential construction and the constraints which are part of the system of equations.

Figure 2 shows the excess Gibbs-energy of a mixture of acetone and methanol at a constant temperature of 323.15 K. The graph is plotted over the composition of acetone. The experimental data, as the base for comparison, are taken from Gmehling and Onken (2005) in the form of a Redlich-Kister polynomial.

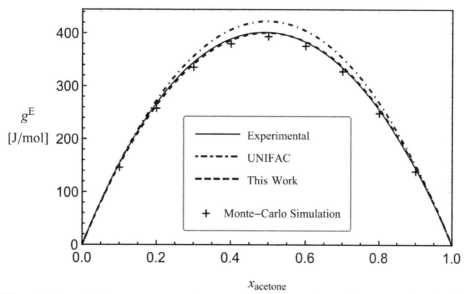

Figure 2: Excess Gibbs-energy over acetone composition for a mixture of acetone and methanol. Comparison between experimental data (Gmehling and Onken, 2005), UNIFAC (Fredenslund et al., 1975), Monte-Carlo simulations and this work.

The model presented in this work is slightly below the experimental data up to an acetone composition of 0.5 and slightly above for larger acetone amounts. The model shows in general a good agreement with the experimental data. Compared to the Monte-Carlo simulation of the dice-like molecules, the model displays a small positive deviation. The UNIFAC model, however, demonstrates a noticeably larger deviation from the experimental data for this case.

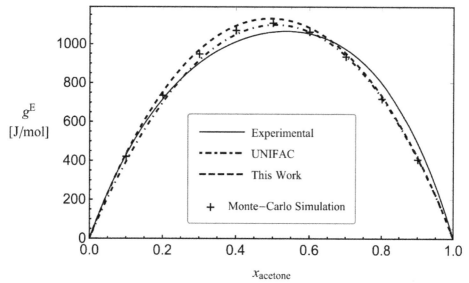

Figure 3: Excess Gibbs-energy over acetone composition for a mixture of acetone and n-heptane. Comparison between experimental data (Krenzer, 1985), UNIFAC (Fredenslund et al., 1975), Monte-Carlo simulations and this work.

The system acetone and n-heptane, given in Figure 3 at a temperature of 298.15 K, experiences slightly larger deviations compared to the previous one. This can be explained by the fact that n-heptane is, because of its elongated form, not as well described by a dice-like shape as methanol. Nevertheless, the magnitude of the deviation to the experimental data gathered from Krenzer (1985) is still comparable to the UNIFAC model. Again the model slightly overestimates the Monte-Carlo simulation data.

5. Conclusions

First results of the combination of the discrete modeling approach and molecular sampling show that small molecules, especially acetone and methanol, can be well described using dice-like molecules in a regular simple cubic lattice. For the example systems acetone – methanol and acetone – n-heptane it is shown that the deviations from experimental data are similar in magnitude to the UNIFAC model. In contrast to the simple cubic lattice with a coordination number of six, the UNIFAC model uses a coordination number of ten and the molecules are not restricted by a lattice.

The effect of the molecule orientation inside the dice and the link to the sampling algorithm are subject to further investigation. The results of this work show that discrete modeling approach is a promising basis for further investigation and development towards an activity coefficient model.

References

A. Fredenslund, R. L. Jones, J. M. Prausnitz, (1975), Group- contribution estimation of activity coefficients in nonideal liquid mixtures, AIChE J., vol. 21, no. 6, 1086–1099

J. Gmehling, U. Onken, (2005), Vapor-Liquid Equilibrium Data Collection, Dechema Chemistry Data Series, Vol. I, Part 2g

W.L. Jorgensen, D.S. Maxwell, J. Tirado-Rives, (1996), Development and testing of the OPLS all-atom force field on conformational energetics and properties of organic liquids, J. Am. Chem. Soc. 118, 11225–11236

G.M. Kontogeorgis, G.K. Folas, (2010), Thermodynamic models for industrial applications, From Classical and Advanced Mixing Rules to Association Theories

L. Krenzer, (1985), [in German] Untersuchungen zur Beeinflussung der Exzessenthalpie, der freien Exzessenthalpie und der Exzessentropie von binären Mischungen mit polaren Komponenten durch die Moleküleigenschaften, PhD thesis, Technische Hochschule Darmstadt

M. Pfleger, T. Wallek, A. Pfennig, (2015), Discrete modeling: Thermodynamics based on Shannon entropy and discrete states of molecules, Ind. Eng. Chem. Res. 54, 4643–4654

A.J.M. Sweere, J.G.E.M. Fraaije, (2015), Force-Field Based Quasi-Chemical Method for Rapid Evaluation of Binary Phase Diagrams, J. Phys. Chem. B. 119, 14200–14209

V.L. Vinograd, L.L. Perchuk, (1996), Informational models for the configurational entropy of regular solid solutions: flat lattices, J. Phys. Chem. 100, 15972–15985

T. Wallek, M. Pfleger, A. Pfennig, (2016), Discrete Modeling of Lattice Systems: The Concept of Shannon Entropy Applied to Strongly Interacting Systems, Ind. Eng. Chem. Res. 55, 2483–2492

T. Wallek, C. Mayer, A. Pfennig, (2018) , Discrete Modeling Approach as a Basis of Excess Gibbs-Energy Models for Chemical Engineering Applications, Ind. Eng. Chem. Res. 57, 1294–1306

Sauro Pierucci, Flavio Manenti, Giulia Bozzano, Davide Manca (Eds.)
Proceedings of the 30th European Symposium on Computer Aided Process Engineering
(ESCAPE30), May 24-27, 2020, Milano, Italy. © 2020 Elsevier B.V. All rights reserved.
http://dx.doi.org/10.1016/B978-0-12-823377-1.50030-6

Reliable Modelling of Twin-screw Extruders by Integrating the Backflow Cell Methodology into a Mechanistic Model

Maximilian Cegla, Sebastian Engell

TU Dortmund University, Biochemical and Chemical Engineering,
Process Dynamics and Operations Group, Emil-Figge-Straße 70,
44227, Dortmund ,Germany
maximilian.cegla@tu-dortmund.de

Abstract

Process modelling for twin-screw extruders is important for the optimal design, control and understanding of these machines. Existing models are often describing the residence time distribution (RTD) of the melt based on experimental data without the usage of further process knowledge. These completely data driven methods are unreliable for more advanced extrusion processes as a strong coupling between many internal states exists, which may not be reflected in the measurements. Therefore the use of a mechanistic model is beneficial to be able to address all important effects simultaneously. The standard mechanistic model describes the RTD as a series of continuous stirred tank reactors. However, this approximation is not capable of describing tailing effects that can occur when elements that promote distributive mixing are present. These effects can be described by the backflow cell model (BCM). Within the BCM the unidirectional flow is divided into an upstream flow and downstream flow with a fixed flow ratio for a series of tanks. This model can be in cooperated into the CSTR model, exploiting the similarities of the structure of the two models. In this work, the combination of the two methods is presented and applied to different screw geometries.

Keywords: Extrusion, Reactive Extrusion, Twin-Screw Extrusion, Backflow cell model, Residence Time Distribution

1. Introduction

Twin-screw extruders provide high mixing efficiency, high specific energy inputs and the ability to process solids and highly viscous material. Consequently, they are interesting for various industries such as the pharmaceutical and the chemical industry for blending, reacting and compounding purposes. The agile operation of these extruders creates a need for dynamic models that are capable of describing start-up, shut down, and product changeovers. Furthermore these models can be used for the optimization of screw setup and operating conditions. Pioneering work for the modeling of twin-screw extruders has been performed by Todd 1975. Todd approximated the residence time distribution with the help of an axial dispersion model. Based on the works of Todd, Vergnes 1998 presented a first twin-screw extruder model that describes the flow within the extruder and approximates the geometry as two C-shaped chambers. Further development led to a successful application of this model to the reactive extrusion of caprolactone by Poulesquen in 2001. A drawback of this method is the missing flexibility that results from the fact that the model relies on two nested iterative loops to converge the melt temperature and the conversion, and it is only usable at steady state. Choulak 2004 suggested a first dynamic model for the reactive extrusion of caprolactone that is based upon the approximation by a cascade of continuous stirred tank reactors (CSTR). The number of CSTRs as well as the internal flows were determined by parameter estimation on experimental data and therefore are not suitable for predictions. Eitzlmayr 2014 suggested a mechanistic twin-screw extruder model that describes the extruder as series of finite ideally mixed volumes that captures the dynamics of the extrusion process while maintain predictive capabilities. In this work, the model of Eitzlmayr is extended to account for the tailing effects in the RTD that were already reported by Todd in 1975. In the following sections the general modeling of twin-screw extruders is described, the investigated mixing elements and the BCM are presented, and a model extension is proposed and demonstrated for several typical screw geometries.

2. General

2.1. Twin-Screw Extrusion modeling

The mass-transport effects within a co-rotating twin screw extruder can be condensed to two simultaneously occurring effects. First, a flow that is being generated by conveying elements in the direction of the die or of the feed, depending on the screw geometry. The second effect is a pressure driven flow that transports the material into the direction of the die due to pressure differences. The pressure buildup within the extruder is realized by so called left handed or restrictive screw elements that convey material in the direction of the feeding port.

To describe the dynamics over the extruder length, the extruder can be discretized in finite volume elements as presented by Eitzlmayr 2016. These elements are connected by internal conveying and pressure driven flows as shown in Figure 1.

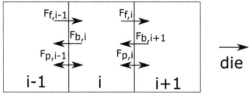

Figure 1: Schematic representation of the finite volumes and the internal flows.

The mass balance of each finite volume can be formulated in terms of the conveying flows F_f, F_b and the pressure flow F_p as:

$$\frac{df_i}{dt} V_i = F_{f,i-1} + F_{b,i+1} + F_{p,i} - F_{f,i} - F_{b,i} - F_{p,i} \tag{1}$$

With the screw volume V_i and the filling ratio f_i. Pressure can only build up in completely filled volumes. The flow contributions can be calculated as follows:

$$F_{f,i} = K_f \cdot n \cdot D^3 \qquad F_{b,i} = K_{fb} \cdot n \cdot D^3 \qquad F_{p,i} = K_p \cdot \frac{D^4}{\eta} \cdot \frac{\Delta p}{\Delta x} \tag{2),(3),(4}$$

With the speed of rotation of the screw n, the screw diameter D, the viscosity η and the pressure p. K_f and K_b describe the overall conveying capacity of a screw element in opposite directions, therefore classically only one of the values is nonzero depending on the geometry of the given element. K_p is factor that describes the pressure drop over an element. These factors are determined either experimentally as suggested by Kohlgrüber

2008 or mathematically by a rigorous modelling based on a two plate model in cylindrical coordinates as suggested by Vergnes 1996. Similar to Equation 4 the balances for heat, mass of species, pressure can be set up to take into account effects of temperature, dissipation, reaction as well as changing physical properties of the melt. By the nature of this model the RTD is described by a series of CSTRs with a small contribution of pressure induced backflow. This is reported to be a good accordance to literature for the classical conveying elements which can be described well by a cascade of 5 CSTRs (Poulesquen 2002b). However the model is not suitable for the description of distributive mixing. To describe this effect, the assumption of a uniform conveying capacity is relaxed in the following sections to take into account contributions in forward and backward direction in analogy to the BCM. This model describes a CSTR cascade with an additional countercurrent backflow.

2.2. Backflow cell model

Classically RTDs are described by a combination of ideal reactors, plug flow reactors and CSTRs. The BCM describes a series of CSTRs with a backflow countercurrent to the main flow direction. Mathematically the BCM was first described by Roemer in 1967. Figure 2 shows the graphical representation of the BCM and the comparison with figure 1 shows the obvious analogies. The BCM is defined by the number of cells N and the backflow ratio σ_B that is defined as: $\sigma_B = Q_B / Q$ (5)
Paux 2000 investigated different RTD models for extrusion applications and reports that the model describes processes accurately where the mixing is caused primarily by splashing and large eddies. Compared to other models such as the axial dispersion model, the double BCM, or an arithmetic progression the prediction error is comparable.

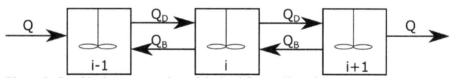

Figure 2: Graphical representation of the backflow cell model.

2.3. Investigated Screw Elements

Screw setups of twin-screw extruders consist of forward conveying elements, backward conveying elements and mixing elements. Forward conveying elements are used for material transport towards the die whereas backward conveying elements are used to generate a pressurized zone with completely filled elements. Mixing elements are used to achieve a maximum of distributive mixing with the minimal energy input. This distributive mixing has a significant impact on the RTD. Tooth mixing blocks (ZME), screw mixing elements (SME), turbine mixing elements (TME) and kneading blocks (KB) are shown in figure 2 and are investigated in the following section.

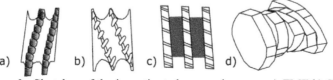

Figure 3: Sketches of the investigated screw elements. a) ZME b) SME c) TME d) KB

Tooth mixing elements are left handed elements with slots through the flight that provide a frequent flow division. Screw mixing elements are standard forward conveying elements with reverse conveying gaps milled into the profile. These gaps ensure a constant flow against the main conveying direction. Turbine mixing elements consists of rings with turbine blades which can have different orientations. Those elements have no pitch and are followed by empty sleeves and that have no conveying capacity. In this work only left handed TMEs are considered. Kneading blocks are typically multiple double flighted discs without pitch with a certain length of each disc staggered by a certain angle. Depending on the staggering angle they act as forward conveying elements with positive staggering angles or vice versa. Todd 1998 gives a broad overview of the advantages and application areas of the investigated screw types.

3. Method and Results

The goal of the presented method is the description of the effects of mixing elements on the RTD. The RTDs are characterized by a tailing of the distribution which the BCM can describe well. As the BCM and the existing extruder models show structural similarities, the results of the RTD model can be added to the existing extruder model. This is performed by the relaxation of the uniform conveying capacity to consider flows in both directions in the conveying parameters.

To validate this method, it was tested on experimental RTD data taken from Brouwer 2002 and Poulesquen 2003. These authors captured the contribution to the RTD of the special screw elements using a tracer method. This data was being normalized, nondimensionalized, and transformed into 100 equidistant data points. The theoretical RTD is calculated with the BCM as presented by Roemer 1967. The numbers of cells is calculated as the ratio of the measured length to the fixed discretization length of 1cm. The summed quadratic deviation of the calculated and experimental data is being minimized by optimizing the backflow ratio for the objective function

$$\min_{\sigma_B} \sum (E_{M,\exp}(\tau) - E_{M,theo}(\tau))^2 \tag{6}$$

The solution for the optimization problem is obtained with the MATLAB solver fmincon. The results are presented in table 1. For all screw elements but TMEs and kneading blocks with 30° staggering angle this method shows improvements compared to the classical CSTR cascade model. The results for the screw mixing elements show a perfect description with the backflow cell model at a backflow ratio of 0.684. The physical explanations for this result are the gaps within the elements that provide a frequent backflow and favor distributive mixing. In contrast, applying the method to the TME is not beneficial as the calculated optimum is a zero backflow ratio. The overall error is higher than for any other screw element. Potentially the influence of the empty sleeves after each TME element is not negligible and causes a very narrow RTD. In order to compensate this effect, one would have to increase the number of cells. This shows a significant reduction in the overall error but is not applicable in practice due to a uniform discretization length in the existing extruder model . The application of the BCM to the ZME shows a minor improvement with a small backflow. This is caused by the teeth that are not perfectly sealing. The optimum for kneading blocks with negative staggering angle is found at a backflow of about 0.456 and 0.497, respectively. It is possible to reduce the overall error compared to the representation as CSTR cascade to 1/4. It is not possible to generalize the results for positive and negative staggering angles as he kneading block with +60° staggering angle benefits from the backflow whereas the +30° block does not. For kneading blocks in general, the error decreases similar to the TME with an increasing number of cells because of a narrower RTD. A drawback of increasing the number of cells is the insufficient description of the tailing after 1.5 mean residence times as shown in figure 4. Moreover the presented method shows advantages over other methods for the description of RTDs for kneading blocks. Poulesquen 2003 reported the RTD of kneading blocks as a single CSTR with an unspecified delay time. The determination of this delay time is very inconvenient as experimental RTD measurements have to be carried out for different processing conditions. Consequently the proposed method is beneficial as it provides predictive capabilities such as the description of the mean residence time.

Table 1: Results of the optimization for the different screw elements for N=10. The experimental data was taken from Brouwer 2002[a] and Poulesquen 2003[b]. The total error is the summation for all 100 equidistant data points.

Screw Element	σ_B [-]	Error BCM [-]	Error CSTR Cascade [-]
SME[a]	0.684	0.074	4.521
TME[a]	0	3.848	3.848
ZME[a]	0.040	0.364	0.391
+60°KB[b]	0.247	2.856	4.837
+30°KB[b]	0	2.521	2.521
-30°KB[b]	0.497	1.580	6.263
-60°KB[b]	0.456	1.475	6.078

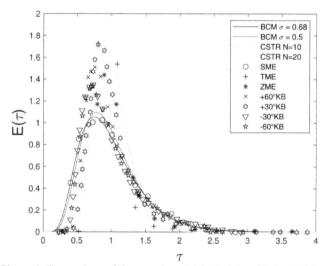

Figure 4: Comparison of the experimental RTD data with the BCM with 10 cells and with the series of CSTRs with 10 and 20 cells.

To apply the results to the existing extruder model, adapted conveying capacities $K_f{'}$ and $K_b{'}$ have to be calculated. No further structural changes within the model are necessary. The adapted screw parameters can be calculated as follows:

$$\sigma_B = \frac{K_b{'}}{K_f} \qquad\qquad K_f{'} = K_f - K_b{'} \qquad\qquad (7),(8)$$

4. Conclusion

In this work we presented incorporate the backflow cell model into a mechanistic extruder model to describe the effects of distributive mixing. By the application of the BCM, it is possible to improve the representation of the RTD and especially to reproduce the occurring tailing effects. Various types of mixing elements were investigated. Hereby it is possible to combine the information on the shape of the screw elements with the calculated backflow ratio to draw conclusions on the mixing efficiency. The results of the optimization of the backflow ratio show a sufficiently accurate description of the RTD especially considering the very limited number of fitted parameters. The obtained results can be directly used in an existing extruder model by simply modifying the forward and backward conveying capacities. With the help of the more complex mechanistic model it is possible to address the influence of changing processing parameters such as local filling ratios and melt temperatures within the extruder sections on the resulting residence time. This improves the prediction quality for RTDs over a broad range of operating conditions and can reduce or completely replace experimental investigations on the RTD during process development. In the future, the results of this work will be applied to the simulation and optimization of reactive extrusion processes. This makes the optimization of entire screw configuration with various screw geometries for complex processes possible, thus transforming the decision making process from being based upon expert knowledge to model-based science.

Acknowledgements

This was performed with funding from the European Union's Horizon 2020 research and innovation programme under grant agreement No 820716 (SPIRE project SIMPLIFY).

References

T.Brouwer et al., 2002, Flow Characteristics of Screws and Special Mixing Enhancers in a Co-rotating Twin Screw Extruder, Intern. Polymer Processing, Volume 17, Issue 1, pp. 26-32

S.Choulak et al., 2004, Generic Dynamic Model for Simulation Control Reactive Extrusion, Industrial Engineering Chemical Research, Volume 43, Issue 23, pp. 7373-7382

A. Eitzlmayr et al., 2014, Mechanistic modeling of modular co-rotating twin-screw extruders, International Journal of Pharmaceutics, Volume 474, Issues 1-2, pp. 157-176

Kohlgrüber et al., 2008, Co-Rotating Twin-Screw Extruders – Fundamentals,Technology and Applications, Carl Hanser Verlag, Munich

A.Poulesquen, 2003, A Study of Residence Time Distribution in Co-Rotatintg Twin-Screw Extruders. Part II: Experimental Validation, Polymer Engineering and Science, Volume 43, Issue 12, pp. 1849-1862

A.Poulesquen et al., 2001, Polymerization of Caprolatone in a Twin Screw Extruder, International Polymer Processing, Volume 16, Issue 1, pp. 31-38

J.P. Puaux et al., 2000, Residence time distribution in a corotating twin-screw extruder, Chemical Engineering Science, Volume 55, Issue 9, pp. 1641-1651

M. Roemer et al., 1967, Transient response and moments analysis of backflow cell model for flow systems with longitudinal mixing, Industrial and Engineering Chemistry Fundamentals, Volume 6, Issue 1, pp. 120-129

D.B. Todd, 1975, Residence time distribution in twin- screw extruders, Polymer Engineering Science,Volume 15 , Issue 6, pp. 437-443

D.B. Todd, 1998, Plastics Compounding, Carl Hanser Verlag, Munich

B.Vergnes et al., 1998, A Global Computer Software for Polymer Flows in Corotating Twin Screw Extruders, Polymer. Engineering Science, Volume 38, Issue 11, pp. 1781-1792

Sauro Pierucci, Flavio Manenti, Giulia Bozzano, Davide Manca (Eds.)
Proceedings of the 30th European Symposium on Computer Aided Process Engineering
(ESCAPE30), May 24-27, 2020, Milano, Italy. © 2020 Elsevier B.V. All rights reserved.
http://dx.doi.org/10.1016/B978-0-12-823377-1.50031-8

Comparison of two Meta-Heuristics for the Bi-Objective Flexible Job Shop Scheduling Problem with Sequence Dependent Setup Times

João Sacramento[a] , João Pedrosa[a], Nelson Chibeles-Martins[b] *, Tânia Pinto-Varela[a]

[a]Centro Estudos Gestão, Instituto Superior Tecnico, Universidade Lisboa, Lisboa, Portugal

[b]Centro de Matemática e Aplicações and Departamento de Matemática, Faculdade de Ciências e Tecnologia, UNL, 2829-516 Caparica, Portugal

npm@fct.unl.pt

Abstract

The increasingly competitivity in the plastic container market is driving companies toward a greater focus on efficiency, and mass production customisation, which triggers the increase of productivity by implementing more efficient and faster IT solutions. This work is based on a Portuguese case study, to develop a scheduling model considering the specific characteristics of this type of facilities and increase its competitiveness. To this end, two different approaches, the Tabu Search and Genetic Algorithm, were developed to solve a flexible job shop scheduling problem under a make-to-order production strategy. Each approach was validated using the case study, and the model's applicability were testes trough five instances. The results have shown that Tabu Search has a better efficacy and the Genetic Algorithm shows better efficiency.

Keywords: Flexible Job Shop Problem, Tabu Search, Genetic Algorithm, Metaheuristics, Multi-objective

1. Introduction

Nowadays, the industrial sector faces a new challenge. The traditional tactics used to increase productivity are outdated and companies are looking for new factors that may lead to improvement. Considering the fourth industrial revolution, Industry 4.0, more detailed and deep problem characterization is necessary. The speed of sharing information to and from the facility is crucial. The real-time information availability is required to support the decision making. To satisfy this challenge an agile and fast solution approach, with the aim of increasing flexibility and get competitive leverage is necessary. Therefore companies are becoming highly invested in developing customized information systems to manage, plan and schedule its manufacturing processes.

Despite some research has already been made using exact approaches, the FJSP's complexity and intractability usually lead to high computational times when these kind of algorithms are applied. On the other hand, meta-heuristics go towards the fourth revolution concepts, with lower computational burdens, being the Tabu Search (TS) and Generic Algorithm (GA), two of the most promising alternatives. Therefore the authors opted for focusing their efforts on the proposed Metaheuristics approaches.

Some of the work developed using a mono-objective TS were developed by Dell'Amico and Trubian (1993) with an algorithm that solve the classical Job-Shop Scheduling Problem (JSSP) makespan minimization. However, several authors, like Brandimarte (1993), Dauzère-pérès and Paulli (1997), Mastrolilli and Gambardella (2000), C. Scrich, V. Armentano (2004), and Abdelmaguid (2015) developed TS to solve the Flexible Job-Shop Scheduling Problem (FJSSP) in regards to makespan minimization, except C. Scrich, V. Armentano (2004) whom proposed to minimize tardiness. More recently the authors Saidi-Mehrabad and Fattahi (2007) and Shen et al. (2018) considered the sequence dependent setup times case of the FJSSP. GA approaches have also been applied to Scheduling problems. Pezzella et al. (2008) proposed several improvements to the generic GA in order to make them more efficient solving SP.

However, some research has been done concerning multi-objective approaches. Jia and Hu (2014) developed a TS procedure based on path relinking to solve a multi-objective FJSSP considering the minimization of the makespan, total workload and maximum workload, using the Pareto approach. Li et al. (2010) proposed a hybrid TS based algorithm to solve the multi-objective FJSSP with the three criteria chosen being makespan, total workload and maximum workload. Murata and Ishibuchi (1995) proposed a framework for GA with a weighted sum using randomly specified weights for each selection. It was already applied to several multi-objective optimization problems but never to a FJSSP. Morinaga et al. (2014) solved a FJSSP with MTO policy using a GA to minimize tardiness and setup-worker load. It was used a classic weighted sum approach to deal with the bi-objective problem.

The proposed work explores two multi-objective approach, a Genetic and a Tabu Search algorithm to define the production scheduling considering the tardiness and makespan minimization, as objective functions. The facility follows a make-to-order strategy, with sequence dependent setup time. To illustrate the methodologies applicability and its performance, not only a real case study is explored, but also, five more instances. This work is based on the same case studied in Chibeles-Martins et al. (2017).

2. Modelling Characterization

Multi-objective Genetic Algorithm - BObGA
A new multi-objective genetic algorithm is developed based on the classical algorithm proposed by the authors Murata and Ishibuchi in (1995) extending it with the integration of randomly weights for each selection of the best chromosomes. To take into account the mitigation of customers' service level impact, the tardiness has a higher importance than the makespan. This is achieved by introducing a new parameter defining a lower bound that controls the minimum weight that is applied to the tardiness. Finally, the BObGA uses a hill climbing heuristic introduced by Greiner (1992) to perform a local search. The BObGA algorithm pseudocode is shown in Figure 1.

Multi-objective Tabu Search Algorithm - BObTS
The Tabu Search proposed algorithm is based on Shen et al. in (2018) extended to explore a Lexicographic Multi-objective approach, considering the tardiness minimization, with highest priority and the makespan minimization as a second priority objective. It uses the neighborhood structure developed on the aforementioned work but is adapted to be applicable in a multi-objective perspective by assigning different importance levels to objective functions according to the stage the algorithm is in. A diversification strategy is employed to avoid a premature stop at local minima. The BObTS algorithm pseudocode is presented in Figure 2.

Algorithm: Bi-Objective Genetic Algorithm
---
begin
    Initialize parameters;
    Evaluate population;
    while *Generations number not reached* **do**
        Select the best-fit individuals for reproduction;
        Apply crossover;
        Apply mutation;
        Apply local search;
        Evaluate population;

Figure 1–Bi-objective Genetic algorithm pseudocode – BobGA

Algorithm: Bi-Objective Tabu Search
---
begin
    Initialize parameters;
    Evaluate initial solution;
    while *Tardiness not null or maximum iterations not reached* **do**
        Generate neighborhood;
        Evaluate neighbors;
        Select neighbor;
        Update tabu list;
    while *Maximum iterations not null* **do**
        Generate neighborhood;
        Evaluate neighbors;
        Select neighbor;
        Update tabu list;

Figure 2 – Bi-objective Tabu Seach pseudocode – BObTS.

3. Instances Characterization

The case study (CS) is based on a mould industry production of plastics containers. The plastic containers are characterized by a bottom and a cover, produced using an injection moulding process. The process requires different changeovers, based on the product sequence production, each one with different setup time associated. The production process requires mainly three tasks. However, each product manufacture follows a different path, triggering different setup times. Nevertheless, all machines are able to produce all the products. For confidential reasons detailed production process information is omitted. Beyond the case study implementation, five instances with increase complexity were explored over the two approaches. In Table 1 is shown instances' characterization with the respective number of orders, the produced quantity, due date and number of machines.

Table 1 – Instances characterization.

Instances	#orders	Quantity (units)	Average due date (minutes)	# Machines
CS	40	8888	40	8
1	70	2162	1765	8
2	30	9797	853	8
3	40	5000	880	8
4	40	8888	1765	7
5	100	7189	2091	8

4. Results

BObGA and BObTS algorithms were executed for the six instances on a PC with an Intel Core i7-6700HQ, 2.60GHz, 8 GB RAM. A detailed characterization of the results obtained are shown in Table 2, and its graphic representation in Figure 3 and Figure 4.

Table 2 – BObGA and BObTS performance results.

	Instance	(Order x Machine)	Tardiness		Makespan	CPU Time
			% Optimal values	Average (min)	Average (min)	Average (seconds)
Genetic Algorithm	CS	40 x 8	84%	8.6	1,510.2	27.7
	1	70 x 8	98%	0.2	1,160.1	143.1
	2	30 x 8	86%	19,4	1,018.2	17.1
	3	40 x 8	48%	46	1,040.3	32.1
	4	40 x 7	48%	130.3	1,950	34.9
	5	100 x 8	0%	718.4	2,892.5	364.3
Tabu Search	CS	40 x 8	100%	0	1,349.5	267
	1	70 x 8	100%	0	994.4	300
	2	30 x 8	100%	0	887.3	301
	3	40 x 8	87%	4	931.3	304
	4	40 x 7	0%	395	1,833.3	303
	5	100 x 8	0%	425.5	2,910.4	663

The BObTS reaches the optimum value for the tardiness objective function (which is zero value) in all iteration, in the Instances: CS, 1 and 2. In third Instance 87% of iterations reached the optimal value, followed by instances 4 and 5, with a non-optimum, justified by the decreased number of machines or the increase number of orders. The BObGA shown a decrease number of optimal solutions for the tardiness, as the complexity increases, with Instance 5, reaching only non-optimum solution. However, considering the case study, BObTS showed a 100% of optimum solutions for the Tardiness vs the 84% for the BObGA (Table 2). As is shown in Figure 4, the BObGA is more efficient, being less time consuming than BObTS. However, BObTS denotes a higher efficacy (Figure 3).

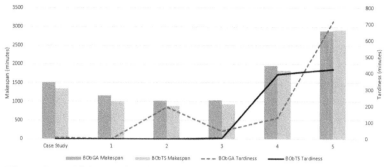

Figure 3 – BObGA and BObTS non dominated solution characterization

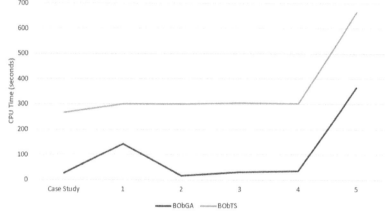

Figure 4 – BObGA and BObTS computational performance.

5. Conclusion

Nowadays, industry is triggered to increase its efficiency and productivity by developing tools to support decision making processes in real time. To overcome this challenge the authors propose two Meta-heuristic multi-objective algorithms (BObGA and BObTS) to explore the scheduling of a flexible job shop facility with product sequence setups. Both Meta-heuristics considered the tardiness and makespan minimization as objective functions. The MObGA explored the randomly weighted sum, while the MObTS a lexicographic approach. The Algorithm applicability and its performance comparison were made over a real case study, followed by five instances with increased complexity, to stress the algorithms. As the results showed, BObTS algorithm outperformed the BObGA in almost all cases, reaching better objective functions values denoting a higher efficacy. However, BObGA is less time consuming showing a higher efficiency. Nevertheless, further work should be done, exploring other production strategies and stressing the algorithm with tighter due dates.

Acknowledgements

The authors gratefully acknowledge the support of the Portuguese National Science Foundation through Portugal 2020 project POCI-01-0145-FEDER-016418 by UE/FEDER through the program COMPETE2020. This work was partially supported by the Fundação para a Ciência e a Tecnologia (Portuguese Foundation for Science and Technology) through the project UIDB/00297/2020 (Centro de Matemática e Aplicações).

References

T. F. Abdelmaguid, 2015, A neighborhood search function for flexible job shop scheduling with separable sequence-dependent setup times. Applied Mathematics and Computation, 260, 188–203. https://doi.org/10.1016/J.AMC.2015.03.059

P. Brandimarte, 1993, Routing and scheduling in a flexible job shop by tabu search. Annals of Operations Research, 41(3), 157–183. http://doi.org/10.1007/BF02023073

N. Chibeles-Martins, A. Marques, and T. Pinto-Varela, 2017, A Bi-objective two step Simulated Annealing Algorithm for Production Scheduling. Computer Aided Chemical Engineering, 40, 1351–1356. https://doi.org/10.1016/B978-0-444-63965-3.50227-0

C. R. Scrich, V. A. Armentano and M. Laguna, 2004, Tardiness minimization in a Flexible job shop/: A tabu search approach, Journal of Intelligent Manufacturing, 15, pp. 103–115, http://dx.doi.org/10.1023/B:JIMS.0000010078.30713.e9

S. Dauzère-Pérès and J. Paulli, 1997, An integrated approach for modeling and solving the general multiprocessor job-shop scheduling problem using tabu search. Annals of Operations Research, 70(0), 281–306. https://doi.org/10.1023/A:1018930406487

M. Dell'Amico and M. Trubian, 1993, Applying tabu search to the job-shop scheduling problem. Annals of Operations Research, 41(3), 231-252.

R. Greiner, 1992, Probabilistic Hill-Climbing: Theory and Applications. Proceedings of the Ninth Canadian Conference on Artificial Intelligence.

S. Jia and Z. Hu, 2014, Path-relinking Tabu search for the multi-objective flexible job shop scheduling problem', Computers and Operation Research. Elsevier, 47, pp. 11–26. DOI: 10.1016/j.cor.2014.01.010

J.-Q. Li, Q.-K. Pan and Y.-C. Liang, 2010, An effective hybrid tabu search algorithm for multi-objective flexible job- shop scheduling problems, Computers & Industrial Engineering, 59(4), pp. 647–662. https://doi.org/10.1016/j.cie.2010.07.014

M. Mastrolilli and L. M. Gambardella, 2000, Effective neighbourhood functions for the flexible job shop problem. Journal of Scheduling, 3(1), 3–20.

Y. Morinaga, M. Nagao and M. Sano, 2014, Optimization of flexible job-shop scheduling with weighted tardiness and setup-worker load balance in make-to-order manufacturing. In Joint 7th International Conference on Soft Computing and Intelligent Systems (SCIS) and 15th International Symposium on Advanced Intelligent Systems (ISIS) (pp. 87–94). https://doi.org/10.1109/SCIS-ISIS.2014.7044681

T. Murata and H. Ishibuchi, 1995, MOGA: Multi-objective genetic algorithms. In Proceedings of 1995 IEEE International Conference on Evolutionary Computation (Vol. 1, pp. 289-). https://doi.org/10.1109/ICEC.1995.489161

F. Pezzella, G. Morganti and G. Ciaschetti, 2008, A genetic algorithm for the Flexible Job-shop Scheduling Problem. Computers and Operations Research, 35(10), 3202–3212. https://doi.org/10.1016/j.cor.2007.02.014.

M. Saidi-Mehrabad and P. Fattahi, 2007, Flexible job shop scheduling with tabu search algorithms. The International Journal of Advanced Manufacturing Technology, 32(5), 563–570. https://doi.org/10.1007/s00170-005-0375-4.

L. Shen, S. Dauzère-Pérès and J. S. Neufeld, 2018, Solving the flexible job shop scheduling problem with sequence-dependent setup times, European Journal of Operational Research, 265(2), 503-516. DOI: 10.1016/j.ejor.2017.08.021

Sauro Pierucci, Flavio Manenti, Giulia Bozzano, Davide Manca (Eds.)
Proceedings of the 30th European Symposium on Computer Aided Process Engineering
(ESCAPE30), May 24-27, 2020, Milano, Italy. © 2020 Elsevier B.V. All rights reserved.
http://dx.doi.org/10.1016/B978-0-12-823377-1.50032-X

Simulation of the Crystallization Process based on Cellular Automata --- Snowflake Formation from Pure Water System

Jianmin Liu,[a] Jindong Dai,[a] Chengyu Han,[a] Junkai Zhang,[a] Jiali Ai,[a] Chi Zhai,[b] Xiaolin Liu[a]*, Wei Sun[a]*

[a]College of Chemical Engineering, Beijing University of Chemical Technology, North Third Ring Road 15, Chaoyang District, Beijing, 100029, China
[b]Faculty of chemical engineering, Kunming University of Science and Technology, Kunming 650500, China
liuxl@mail.buct.edu.cn
sunwei@mail.buct.edu.cn

Abstract

Crystallization is an important unit operation process in chemical industry production. Generally, there are a variety of morphology in most crystals and different crystal morphology varies greatly in physicochemical properties. As different crystal morphology may be obtained by changing its ambient conditions surrounding the crystal. In previous studies, the research for crystallization are usually conducted by experiments, which could be very time-consuming and resource-intensive. A cellular automata, CA, is a method by simulating the interaction among subsystems to obtain the description of the patterned system behavior. CA not only provides a description of the physical properties of the material but can also predict changes on the micro-level. Using the cellular automaton to simulate the crystallization process will be more efficient in terms of both time and computation load. In this paper, the crystallization process is simulated by the method of cellular automata. By changing the model parameters, the effects of the parameters on the crystal morphology are studied.

Keywords: crystallization, cellular automaton, simulation, morphology

1. Introduction

The crystallization process includes nucleation and crystal growth (Jungblut and Dellago, 2016). As the growth center of crystal, nucleus is composed of a set of regularly arranged particles, and exists stably in liquid phase. In the process of crystal growth, different crystal morphology of a substance can be generated under different conditions, such as temperature, saturation, solvent, seed crystals added, and the pH of solution. Furthermore, different crystal morphology varies greatly in physicochemical properties, exhibiting different thermodynamic and mechanical properties, such as particle size distribution, melting point, stability and habit. Suitable crystal morphology can improve the quality of products. (Wang et al., 2002). Therefore, it is promising to research on controlling the conditions to get effective crystal morphology.

Generally, the crystallization process is studied by experiments (Thompson et al., 2004). However, experiment study requires significant input of time and resource. With the development of computer technology, this situation can be improved through computer simulation.

According to classical diffusion theory, crystallization is achieved by the diffusion of solute molecules from the bulk of solution to the crystalline surface, the surface reaction in which the solute molecules are embedded in the crystal lattice, and the heat transfer of crystallization from crystalline surface to the bulk of solution.

Partial differential equation (PDE), as a commonly used mathematical tool, can be applied to describe crystallization process, which is established based on the mechanism theories of transfers. However, solving process of PDE is very time consuming and requires certain proficiency in professional software or programing.

In simulation practice, PDE is usually solved by dividing the solution area into subsets through methods, such as finite element or finite difference. And the subsets are related to adjacent regions through the law of diffusion. If the crystalline region is divided into grids, the crystal growth process can be regarded as the mass and heat transfer among adjacent grids, resulting in changes in the state of grids. Thus, from the system point of view, crystallization process can be also considered as a self-assembled complex system.

Cellular automata (CA) is a method to obtain the pattern of system behavior by simulating the interaction among subsystems. Through research on CA, S. Wolfram (Wolfram, 2002) thought that CA is suitable for simulating the self-assembled complex system, such as crystallization process. Then, the simulation of crystallization process by CA has attracted great attention of researchers (Mourachov, 1997).

In 2015, K. Libbrecht used CA model to research the effect of surface diffusion parameters on the columnar crystalline morphology of water (Libbrecht, 2015). However, the influence of density distribution parameters and the increment in three-dimensional spatial on the crystal morphology was not discussed. In this work, CA method is applied to simulate the crystallization of water into snowflake of different shapes. At the same time, the influence of the parameters on the crystal morphology was discussed by changing the parameters of crystal.

2. CA simulation: snowflake formation as an example

2.1. Basic hypothesis and Parameter setting

It is assumed that the system is pure water system with constant temperature and no impurities. The ideal process of water crystallizing into snowflakes was simulated without considering stirring, the influence of the outside environment of the wall and the crystal dissolution. Since the water molecules are arranged according to the rules of the hexagonal system (Figure. 1), the cell space is set to a regular hexagonal grid. Snowflakes are made by copying and shifting this structure (Nakaya, 1954).

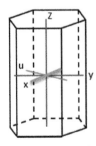
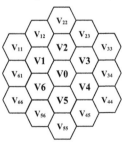

Figure. 1 The structure of hexagonal crystal system.   Figure. 2 The range of cellular neighbors.

The simulated region is R, that is, the distance from the most central cell to the outermost cell is R cells. There is a state value S for each cell. S is a number greater than

0, represented in grayscale. When the cell state $S \geq 1$, the cell is in the crystalline state and the color is white. When the cell state $S < 1$, the cell is in the uncrystallized state and is represented by different grey scales. In the initial state, $S = 1$ is set as the initial state of the cell at the most central point of the cell space. The growth and final shape of snowflakes are influenced by two parameters. One is the initial density distribution α, and the initial state of the cell is set to $S = \alpha$, except for the central cell. And the other one is the cellular capture of water at a three-dimensional level, called β. The neighborhood scope is shown in Figure. 2. The change of cellular state is influenced by its neighbors.

2.2. CA evolution rules

Based on the cellular automata method, all cells states are recognized simultaneously. When the state of cell is crystalline, that is, when its value is greater than or equal to 1, the state of cell remains unchanged at the next moment. The calculation of S at the next moment is shown in (1). And it can also be applied to the condition where the central cell is uncrystallized and there are no crystalline cells in either of the first and second circles.

$$S_{V0}^{t+1} = S_{V0}^{t} + \beta \tag{1}$$

When the cell state is not crystallized and the crystal cell exists in the two surrounding circles, this situation can be divided into three cases, in the first two cases, formula (2) is used to calculate the next value, and in the last case, formula (3) is used.

$$S_{V0}^{t+1} = S_{V0}^{t} + \beta + (V1 + V2 + V3 + V4 + V5 + V6)/12 \tag{2}$$

$$S_{V0}^{t+1} = 0.5 * S_{V0}^{t} + (V1 + V2 + V3 + V4 + V5 + V6)/12 \tag{3}$$

In the first case, crystallized cells only exist in the first cycle. It is worth noting that the values of cells in the crystalline state and the values of cells around the crystalline cell are represented by 0 when formula (2) is used.

In the second case, crystals both exist in the first and second cycles. Besides the rule in the previous paragraph, it is only necessary to add judgment on the cells in the second cycle and identify the crystalline cells in the second cycle. Then, the values of cells adjacent to the crystallized cells of second cycle are also regarded as 0 during calculation.

In the third case, if there is no crystalline cell in the first cycle but there are crystalline cells in the second cycle, formula (3) will be used to calculate the next value of central cell and the regulation is same as the second case.

It can be seen that the principle in the process of formulating rules is as follows. The crystallized cell is relatively stable, and its value is not affected by around cells in horizontal plane. Uncrystallized cells around crystalline cells tend to crystallize faster, and if there are no crystalline cells around the uncrystallized cell, its value will be contributed to cells closer to crystalline cells.

3. Results and discussion

The following image is set to $R = 200$ and the computer operation stops until the crystal grows to the boundary or iterates 10,000 times. The number of iterations for each crystal is below the figures.

3.1. The effect of changing the initial state value on snowflake

Under the condition of $\beta = 0$, the influence of α on crystal habit is studied by setting the value of α to 0.2, 0.4, 0.5 and 0.6.

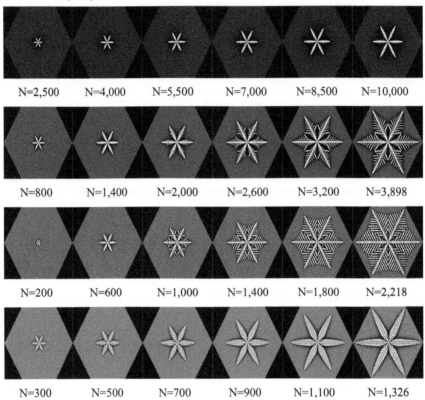

Figure. 3 Snowflake growth under different α conditions. Each row represents the process of snowflake growth under a set of parameters. *N* is the number of iterations. Different rows represent different α values. From top to next time, take 0.2/0.4/0.5/0.6.

These are a series of pictures of snowflake growth as shown in Figure. 3, and the last picture is the final state of the iteration. When α is 0.2, that is, the initial density distribution is 0.2, the calculation can still be iterated for 10,000 times before reaching the boundary, but when α is 0.4, the calculation is iterated for 3,898 times before reaching the boundary, and when α is 0.6, it is only iterated for 1,326 times before ending. With the increasing of α, the crystallization rate gets faster and faster and the branches appear earlier. Diffusion limits the growth as the crystal becomes larger, and eventually this causes branches to form. The two branches continued to grow outward after contacting and then stopped. When $\alpha = 0.4$, branches first meet at about 1/3 of the center of the dendrite. During the whole process of growing snowflakes, the growth rate of crystal branches is the fastest. When $\alpha = 0.5$, branches meet about 1/5 away from the center of the dendrite. When $\alpha = 0.6$, branches meet about 1/12 away from the center of the dendrites (Figure. 4). The voids in the central area are reduced and the structure is more compact. Six dendrites grow simultaneously and are identical in shape due to symmetry. The growth morphology of the branches on the dendrites became more regular and uniform gradually. In other words, the density distribution has an effect on the growth rate of the crystal and the location of the main branches. The greater the density distribution, the closer the branches meet to the center. The structure of the whole snowflake becomes tighter as the density distribution increases.

Figure. 4 From left to right α is 0.4/0.5/0.6, the growth state of the dendrites and branches.

Schematic diagram of crystal growth process of snowflake under set parameters β is an increment in three dimensions. The presence of β makes the snowflakes denser and the gaps between the branches smaller. Next, β is used to reflect the influence on crystallization habit.

3.2. The effect of changing the three-dimensional space increment on snowflake

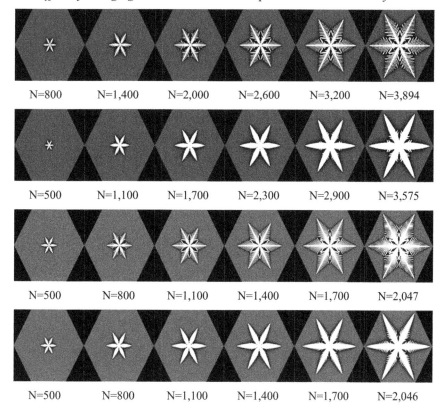

Figure. 5 Snowflakes grow under different conditions. Each row represents the snowflake's growth under a set of parameters. N is the number of iterations. The first two lines represent the case where α is 0.4 and β is 0.0005/0.002. The last two lines indicate the case where α is 0.5 and β is 0.001/0.002.

The effect of β on the rate of crystal growth is particularly significant because β is added directly to the cell value at each iteration. In order to study the influence of β on water crystal habit, the value of β was made smaller to observe the change of crystal morphology. When α is 0.4 and 0.5, two groups of pictures reflect the effect of β as shown in Figure. 5. When α is constant and the value of β is within consideration in this work, the change of β has less impact on the number of iterations, but the shape of the snowflakes is different significantly.

The presence of β makes the dendrite grow more robust, and the overall snowflake morphology tends to be more central, that is, the dendrite is closer to the length rather than the flake. The central area of a snowflake is less void and more compact. The branches have been reduced because the addition of β has increased the number of dendrites. Increased moisture content in the air has an effect on snowflake thickness. Its effect is on the upper and lower surfaces of the entire crystal. However, if the influence of the thickness of the crystal is not considered, it is equivalent to the growth only in the horizontal direction.

The overall complexity of the dendritic pattern increases with increasing supersaturation as well as with increasing crystal size. Libbrecht has reported that the growth is simple six-branch shape at the lower supersaturations, slenderer, often hollow columns at intermediate supersaturations, and firm crystals at higher supersaturations (Libbrecht, 2005). The shape of simulated crystal conforms to this situation.

4. Conclusion

In this work, CA method is used to simulate the process of snow crystal, and the effects of density distribution and three-dimensional spatial increment on snowflake are discussed. The effects on crystallization rate, dendrite and branch growth are studied. The model provides a basis for systematic studies with morphology substances. It can be concluded that it is a potential way to control the crystal growth process in order to obtain the effective crystal morphology and increase its yield. This method can also be applied to the systematic study of other substances with complex crystal morphology, which can be the starting point for controlling the growth process of crystals to increase the crystal yield with desired morphology in the future.

Acknowledgments

This work was supported by National Natural Science Foundation of China No. 21878012 and   No. 21576015.

References

S. Jungblut, C. Dellago, 2016, Pathways to self-organization: Crystallization via nucleation and growth. The European Physical Journal E, 39(8): 77.

K. Libbrecht, 2015, Incorporating Surface Diffusion into a Cellular Automata Model of Ice Growth from Water Vapor.

S. Wolfram, 2002, A New Kind of Science.

J. Wang, X. Huang, B. Liu, 2002, Research progress in predicting the habit of organic molecular crystals. Journal of Synthetic Crystals, 31(3): 218-223.

U. Nakaya, 1954, Snow crystals: Natural and Artificial.

C. Thompson, M. Davies, C. Roberts, 2004, The effects of additives on the growth and morphology of paracetamol (acetaminophen) crystals. International Journal of Pharmaceutics, 280(1-2): 137-150.

S. Mourachov, 1997, Cellular automata simulation of the phenomenon of multiple crystallization. Computational Materials Science, 7(4): 384-388.

K. Libbrecht, 2005, The physics of snow crystals. Reports on progress in physics, 68(4): 855-895.

Sauro Pierucci, Flavio Manenti, Giulia Bozzano, Davide Manca (Eds.)
Proceedings of the 30th European Symposium on Computer Aided Process Engineering
(ESCAPE30), May 24-27, 2020, Milano, Italy. © 2020 Elsevier B.V. All rights reserved.
http://dx.doi.org/10.1016/B978-0-12-823377-1.50033-1

A Thermo-Economic Analysis Method for Combined Cycle Power Plants under Flexible Operation Modes

Senjing Qin,[a] Pei Liu,[a,*] Zheng Li[a]

Department of Energy and Power Engineering, Tsinghua University, Beijing, 100084, China
liu_pei@tsinghua.edu.cn

Abstract

Gas steam combined cycle power plants have been playing an important role in peak shaving of a power grid. The increasingly complexity of power demand and power supply structure puts forward higher requirements for flexible operation, which is characterized by frequent load changes and start-stop operation. Under such circumstances, obtaining an optimal operation strategy becomes essential for profitability of combine cycle power plants. In this paper, a thermodynamic model comprising key functional modules of a combined cycle power plant and its overall cycle process are presented. An economic analysis method based on heat consumption rate is proposed. The proposed model is applied in a combined cycle power plant in China, and quantitative impacts of flexible operation on maintenance cost are discussed. Results show that the model can reflect the thermal economy of the power plant under variable environmental conditions. The economic analysis shows that there are significant economic differences between different flexible operation cases.

Keywords: Combined Cycle Power Plant, Thermo-Economic Analysis, Flexible Operation

1. Introduction

Gas steam combined cycle (GTCC) power plants perceives the advantages of high cycle efficiency and clean emissions. Also, due to its feature of very short-time start-up and load-change operations, GTCC have been playing an important role in peak shaving and demand respond of electricity grid. Recently, the availability of renewable energy and complex power demand have placed greater requirements on grid stability. Accordingly, GTCC faces a more arduous task of peak shaving and flexible operation. The economy of GTCC is highly sensitive to fuel cost, also frequent load changes will affect the service life of components, determining maintenance and replacement costs. It is essential to establish a thermo-economic analysis method applicable to GTCC under flexible operation modes.

Many studies have been done using different analysis methods to investigate the cost and economy of GTCC. Based on exergy analysis, the thermal economics model and cost equation of GTCC are established, and the exergy cost of each component of the system is calculated (Li et al., 2015). Considering the multiple benefits of the economy and environment, multi-objective optimization was carried out using three objective functions, concerned with exergy efficiency, total cost rate and CO_2 emission (Avval et al., 2011). Moreover, intelligent search techniques such as genetic algorithm was applied to find the

Pareto Frontier of exergy efficiency and total cost rate of GTCC, and best values of design parameters were presented (Ahmadi et al., 2011).

However, the existing research mainly focus on GTCC operating under design mode and aim at finding the best design values of cycle parameters. There are few studies focused on economy of an established GTCC under different flexible operation modes. Also the analysis of operation and maintenance cost related to drastic load changes is still lacking. In response to these research gaps, this paper proposes a thermal-economic analysis method, which is based on a thermal dynamic GTCC model. In terms of fuel cost, this paper calculates fuel consumptions under various operating conditions with different power output and environmental conditions. In terms of maintenance cost, this paper quantitatively describes the impact of start-stop and load-change operations by investigating equivalent operation hours. Moreover, a GTCC power plant in China is taken as a case study to verify the applicability of the method.

2. Methodology

2.1. Thermal dynamic model of GTCC

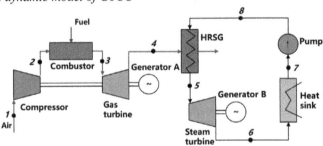

Figure 1 Schematic of GTCC

Figure 1 illustrates a gas steam combined cycle with a non-additionally heat recover steam generator (HRSG). In this study, thermo-dynamic models of gas turbine, steam turbine and HRSG are established, and parameters of gas and steam function as connections among each component model.

A typical gas turbine consists of a compressor, a combustor and a turbine. For compressor, parameters that characterizes its performance under off-mode operation are relative reduced pressure ratio π_C and relative reduced efficiency η_C, which are affected by relative reduced flow rate $\dot{M}_{red}$ and relative reduced speed $\dot{n}_C$. Empirical formula as Eq. (1) - Eq.(5). can be constructed based on compressor characteristic diagrams (Zhang et al., 2011). The two empirical parameters p and m can be obtained from Figure 2 and Figure 3.

$$\pi_C = c_1 \cdot \dot{M}_{red}^2 + c_2 \cdot \dot{M}_{red} + c_3 \tag{1}$$

$$\eta_C = [1 - c_4(1 - \pi_c)^2] \cdot \left(\frac{\dot{n}_{red}}{\dot{M}_{red}}\right) \cdot \left[2 - \left(\frac{\dot{n}_c}{\dot{M}_{red}}\right)\right] \tag{2}$$

$$c_1 = \frac{\dot{n}_c}{p\left(1 - \frac{m}{\dot{n}_c}\right) + \dot{n}_c(\dot{n}_c - m)^2} \tag{3}$$

$$c_2 = \frac{\left(p - 2mn_c^2\right)}{p\left(1 - \frac{m}{n_C}\right) + n_C(n_C - m)^2} \tag{4}$$

$$c_3 = \frac{-\left(pmn_c - m^2n_c^3\right)}{p\left(1 - \frac{m}{n_C}\right) + n_C(n_C - m)^2} \tag{5}$$

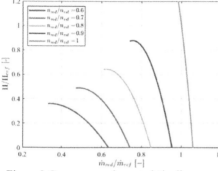

Figure 2 Compressor characteristic diagrams related to $\dot{\pi}_C$

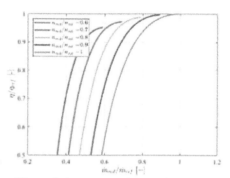

Figure 3 Compressor characteristic diagrams related to $\dot{\eta}_C$

The gas temperature at combustor outlet follows the energy balance equation Eq.(6). For turbine, the mathematical relationship between pressure and flow can be quantified by Flugel formula Eq.(7). Net power output of gas turbine is shown in Eq.(8).

$$m_{fuel} * \left[c_{p,fuel} * \left(T_{fuel} - T_{ref}\right) + LHV\right] + m_{air} * c_{p,air} * \left(T_2 - T_{ref}\right)$$
$$= m_t * c_t * \left(T_3 - T_{ref}\right) \tag{6}$$

$$\frac{M_t}{(M_t)_0} = \sqrt{\frac{p_3^2 - p_4^2}{(p_3^2 - p_4^2)_0}} * \sqrt{\frac{(T_3)_0}{T_3}} \tag{7}$$

$$P_{GT} = M_{air} \cdot c_{p,air} \cdot (T_2 - T_1) + M_t \cdot c_t \cdot (T_4 - T_3) \tag{8}$$

The steam turbine in GTCC usually operates under sliding pressure mode. The characteristics of it under off-mode operation also follow Flugel formula Eq.(7).Variables in the formula represent the state of superheated steam.

2.2. Operation and maintenance cost related to start-stop operation and load change
This study applied equivalent operating hours (EOH) to describe the life expenditure of gas turbine. And there exists a threshold of EOH for maintenance and replacement of parts. Start-stop operation and load change can be expressed quantitatively by adding additional EOH. Eq.(9) shows the calculation of EOH, where *AOH* represents actual stable operating hours. And *A* represents a correction coefficient, which shows the amount of actual stable operating hours equivalent to a normal Start-stop operation. The value of *A* is determined by the ratio of the thermal stress applied to the high-temperature components during start-stop operation to the thermal stress during stable operation.
The influence of load change is essentially similar to start-stop operation, so we can use Eq.(10) to describe the equivalent number of Start-stop during a period of time comprising *j* Start-stop operation and *n* load-change operation. *LC* is a correction

coefficient indicating the amount of equivalent number of start-stop operation of a single load-change operation. Fig 4 shows the value of LC as a function of percentage change in load and rate of load change, which is suggested by Mao (2010).

$$EOH = (AOH + A \times E) \times F \tag{9}$$

$$E = j + \sum_{i=1}^{n} (LC)_i \tag{10}$$

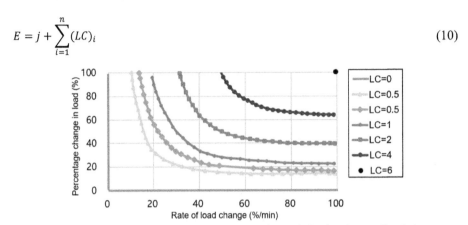

Figure 4 Value of LC as a function of percentage change in load and rate of load change

3. Case study

A GTCC power plant in China is chosen to carry out case study using the method proposed. The power plant consists of a 9E gas turbine, a non-additionally HRSG and a steam turbine. Values of operation parameters under design mode are listed in Table 1.

Table 1 Values of operation parameters under design mode of selected GTCC

Parameters of gas turbine	Value	Unit	Parameters of steam turbine	Value	Unit
power output	125.9	MW	power output	61.61	MW
speed	3000	rpm	HP steam pressure	62	bar
pressure ratio	12.3	-	HP steam temperature	519	°C
air/fuel inlet temperature	15	°C	HP steam flow rate	51.56	kg/s
air/fuel inlet pressure	1.013	bar	LP steam pressure	6.5	bar
mass flow of air	402.8	kg/s	LP steam temperature	259	°C
mass flow of fuel	8.3	kg/s	LP steam flow rate	8.72	kg/s
			back pressure	0.07	bar

3.1. Gas turbine simulation

This study takes power output, environment pressure and environment temperature as the input to figure out the fuel consumption. Then we select 1400 sets of measurement data for simulation, and the result is shown as Fig 5. Average relative error of simulation is 1.7%, and it demonstrate the accuracy of the model.

3.2. Steam turbine simulation

The HRSG produces high-pressure steam and low-pressure steam simultaneously. The high-pressure steam enters steam turbine at inlet directly, whilst the low-pressure steam enters at the middle of steam turbine and expands at remaining stages. Therefore, this study divides the steam turbine into high-pressure section and low-pressure section.

Simulation of the model is carried out with 2000 sets of operating data. Fig 6 shows the results and average relative error of simulation is 0.8%.

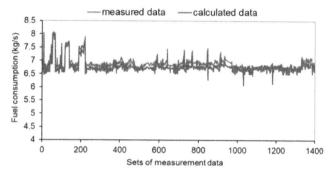

Figure 5 Comparison of measured values and calculated values of gas turbine fuel consumption

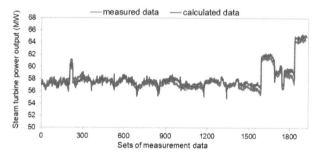

Figure 6 Comparison of measured values and calculated values of steam turbine power output

3.3. Operation and maintenance cost calculation

This study designs three scenarios with different load curve, as is shown in Fig 7. The most important factors that distinguish the three scenarios are the number and severity of start-stop operations and load changes. Scenario A reproduces the actual load curve of a given day of the GTCC power plant in China. The gas turbine starts and stops daily for the purpose of peak shaving. Scenario B shows that the gas turbine only starts and stops once a week, and the rest of the time it operates at continuous constant load. Scenario C indicates frequent start-stop operation and load change. The time range is one week and the output range of gas turbine under stable operation is between 80MW and 125.9MW. The *AOH* of the three scenarios are controlled as 95.08h, and the power generation is controlled as 11.1GW·h.

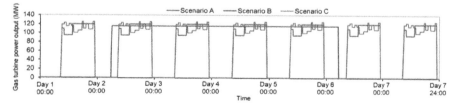

Figure 7 Different load curves of three scenarios

Table 2 displays the results of calculation. Compared to Scenario A, a constant-load operation strategy like scenario B will extend the service life of components to 2.06 times. However, frequent load change like scenario C will shorten the service life by 0.6%.

In general, the EOH threshold of components such as combustion chamber flame tube is 24,000h (Mao et al., 2010). This study supposes that a single maintenance and replacement cost is 26,000 EUR and the interest rate is 15%. Compared to scenario A, a constant-load operation strategy like scenario B can save 24.75% of the replacement and maintenance cost, whilst frequent load change like scenario C will increase 0.3% of the replacement and maintenance cost.

Table 2 Calculation results of three scenarios

	scenario A	scenario B	scenario C
EOH (h)	238.93	116	240.47
number of start-stop operations	7	1	7
number of load-change operations	14	0	70
service life (a)	1.93	3.97	1.91
discounted maintenance and replacement cost (EUR)	19,853	14,928	19,909

4. Conclusions

A thermo-economy analysis method based on thermo-dynamic GTCC model is proposed in this paper. Off-mode modeling is carried out for key components such as gas turbine and steam turbine. The simulation results indicate that average relative error of thermo-dynamic gas turbine model is 1.7%, and the average relative error of steam turbine model is 0.8%. This paper also applies equivalent running hours to quantify the cost of start-stop and load-change operations. Three scenarios with different load curves are studied. Results show that there are significant economic differences between different flexible operation scenarios. These differences are reflected in the huge difference in service life of equipment, which affects the maintenance and replacement costs.

Acknowledgement

The authors gratefully acknowledge the Phase III Collaboration between BP and Tsinghua University.

References

Li Y., Chen J.H.,2015, Thermoeconomic Analysis of Conbined Cycle Power Plants by Structure Theory, Thesis, Zhejiang University, Zhejiang, China.
https://kns.cnki.net/KCMS/detail/detail.aspx?dbcode=CMFD&dbname=CMFD201501&filename=1015539697.nh&v=MzEwNjJDVVI3cWZadWRuRmlublVyckxWRjI2RzdhN0Y5ZkZxSkViUElSOGVYMUx1eFlTN0RoMVQzcVRyV00xRnI= (in Chinese)
Zhang N., Cai R,.2002,Analytical solutions and typical characteristics of part-load performances of single shaft gas turbine and its cogeneration, Energy Conversion and Management, 43, 1323-1337
Avval H.B., Ahmadi P., Ghaffarizadeh A.R., et al., 2011,Thermo-economic-environmental Multiobjective Optimization of a Gas Turbine Power Plant with Preheater using Evolutionary Algorithm, International Journal of Energy Research, 35, 5, 389-403
Ahmadi P, Dincer I, Rosen M.A., 2011, Exergy, exergoeconomic and environmental analyses and evolutionary algorithm based multi-objective optimization of combined cycle power plants. Energy, 36, 10, 5886-5898
Mao D., Zhu Y.S., 2010, Maintenance Concept Analysis of Mitsubishi M701F Gas Turbine, Gas Turbine Technology, 3, 57-61 (in Chinese)

Sauro Pierucci, Flavio Manenti, Giulia Bozzano, Davide Manca (Eds.)
Proceedings of the 30th European Symposium on Computer Aided Process Engineering
(ESCAPE30), May 24-27, 2020, Milano, Italy. © 2020 Elsevier B.V. All rights reserved.
http://dx.doi.org/10.1016/B978-0-12-823377-1.50034-3

Two-phase Flow Modelling and Simulation of Gas Purification Column

Lívia Gyurik, Attila Egedy, Tamás Varga, Zsolt Ulbert

Department of process engineering, University of Pannonia, H-8200 Veszprém, Hungary

gyurikl@fmt.uni-pannon.hu

Abstract

In the technologies where harmful organic solvents are used it is necessary to purify the waste gases in order to ensure the protection of environment and the fulfillment of environment protecting laws. A wide-spread solution is to adsorb the undesired components on a porous fixed bed but it saturates during the operation and should be regularly regenerated resulting in an economic loss. One of the solutions to improve the process is the use of a moving bed equipment, where the regenerated particles are continuously fed to the adsorber and the saturated particles are transferred toward the regenerator providing this way a continuous operation. The objective of our research is to model and simulate the gas-solid two-phase flow using the immersed boundary method and calculate the particle movement and the adsorption process for the individual adsorber particles applying the principles of discrete element method. The surface of particles is discretized and the component transport to the surface element and the degree of saturation of surface element is calculated by a first-order adsorption kinetics. The calculation method is demonstrated on a single particle. The two-dimensional compressible Euler equations are discretized and solved by the second-order accurate TVD-MacCormack method to effectively handle the oscillations arising in the vicinity of steep spatial fronts. Furthermore, considering the physical bases of compressible gas flow, we used non-reflecting numerical boundary condition at the outflow boundary of calculation domain.

Keywords: adsorption, immersed boundary method, discrete element method, TVD-MacCormack, non-reflecting boundary condition

1. Introduction

Harmful organic solvents are used in many chemical technologies. For example, chlorinated hydrocarbons are applied during the swelling of ion-exchange resins (Kumagai et al., 2018) or gas emissions during the pyrolysis (Veksha et al., 2018). Waste gas purification is necessary for all related technologies since environment protection and sustainability are highly desired as well as decreasing the emission of greenhouse gases. A wide-spread solution of gas purification is to adsorb the undesired components on a porous fixed bed. The main operational characteristic of these units is that the fixed bed saturates during its operation and should be regularly regenerated. Improving the operational characteristic often two columns are used, while one of them operates in adsorption mode, the other one can be regenerated. Another approach is to use a moving bed equipment, where the regenerated particles are continuously fed into the adsorption column and the outgoing saturated particles are transferred into the regenerator equipment. This type of construction seems more effective, however it is challenging to control the two-phase flow inside both the adsorption and regenerator column, even more if temperature change plays an important role as in case of CO_2 capture technologies (Mondino et al., 2019). Both adsorber constructions can be investigated using models developed in the last decades in the research area of modeling gas-solid two-phase flows. However, they have to be completed with the model equations describing the component transport to the surface of adsorber particles and the diffusion toward the inside of particle.

One of the modeling approaches in modeling gas-solid two-phase flows is the direct numerical simulation (DNS) (Deen et al., 2014) which is basically coupled with the discrete particle treatment. In DNS models the Navier-Stokes equations are derived by the usual point variables and the fluid flow between the particles is fully resolved. Several DNS methods have been proposed by the authors. In the case of immersed boundary method the goal is to solve Navier-Stokes equations inside the complex calculation domain between the particles without using boundary-fitted or unstructured meshes. The flow equations are solved on a structured mesh over the entire calculation domain. The particles are virtually defined inside the flow by adding Lagrangian points on their surfaces. Then additional forcing terms are added to the Navier-Stokes equations to mimic the no slip boundary condition on these surface points. In this way a local force density is introduced to modify the flow field that realizes the particle boundaries. The motion of the particles calculated by the total surface force and torque evaluated on the surface of particles by one of the forcing approaches like direct forcing or feedback forcing (Fadlun et al., 2000). To describe the contacts between solid particles the discrete element method can be used.

The coupled application of immersed boundary method and discrete element method makes it possible to examine the gas purification process in detail. Modeling and simulation of gas-solid two-phase flow including the calculation of discrete particle motion and gas adsorption provides insight to the physical and chemical processes. By applying numerical investigation more information is available about the processes which take place in the equipment than measuring the properties of the waste gas only at the outlet. The aim of our research is to estimate the separation efficiency and the optimal operating parameters regarding both the adsorbent particles and the gas inflow. For this reason in our model the 2D Euler equation is completed with the mass balance equation of harmful organic gas component and the differential equation describing the adsorption process for the individual adsorbent particles. The applied model and simulation method can greatly help the process intensification and the tuning of operating parameters due to the better understanding of the detailed processes inside the gas purification column.

2. Model development and numerical solution

A two-dimensional flow model is set to model the compressible gas flow in the gas purification column shaped as a rectangular channel (Figure 1a). The inlet boundary is located at the bottom of left sidewall while the outflow boundary defined at the top of the column.

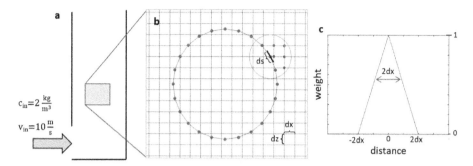

Figure 1. a) Geometry of the purification column. Inlet gas velocity is 10 m/s, concentration of the harmful gas component is 2 kg/m³. b) Immersed boundary, Eulerian and Lagrangian grid points with grid sizes dx, dz and ds respectively. c) Distance-based weight function for the extrapolation

The two-dimensional flow model consist of the continuity equation for the non-harmful gas components, the mass balance equation for the harmful gas component which is to be adsorbed, the two momentum and the energy balances:

$$\frac{\partial \rho_g}{\partial t} + \frac{\partial \left(\frac{m}{\rho}\rho_g\right)}{\partial x} + \frac{\partial \left(\frac{n}{\rho}\rho_g\right)}{\partial z} = 0 \tag{1}$$

$$\frac{\partial c}{\partial t} + \frac{\partial \left(\frac{m}{\rho}c\right)}{\partial x} + \frac{\partial \left(\frac{n}{\rho}c\right)}{\partial z} = R \tag{2}$$

$$\frac{\partial m}{\partial t} + \frac{\partial \left(\frac{m^2}{\rho}+p\right)}{\partial x} + \frac{\partial \left(\frac{n \cdot m}{\rho}\right)}{\partial z} = F_x \tag{3}$$

$$\frac{\partial n}{\partial t} + \frac{\partial \left(\frac{m \cdot n}{\rho}\right)}{\partial x} + \frac{\partial \left(\frac{n^2}{\rho}+p\right)}{\partial z} = F_z \tag{4}$$

$$\frac{\partial \rho E}{\partial t} + \frac{\partial \left(\frac{m}{\rho}(\rho E+p)\right)}{\partial x} + \frac{\partial \left(\frac{n}{\rho}(\rho E+p)\right)}{\partial z} = 0 \tag{5}$$

where ρ_g is the mass density of the mix of non-harmful gas components, c is the component mass density of the harmful gas component, ρ is the total mass density ($\rho=\rho_g+c$). m and n are the components of the mass velocity vector in x and z direction. R is the loss term describing the mass flow rate of harmful gas component to be adsorbed, p is the pressure (calculated according to the ideal gas law), F_x and F_z are the force densities introduced according to the immersed boundary method and ρE is the sum of the inner and kinetic energy.

The adsorption of harmful gas component is calculated for the individual adsorber particles. The surface of particles is discretized and the component transport to the surface element (c_S) and the degree of saturation of related particle volume element is calculated by the following first-order adsorption kinetics (Eq(6)).

$$\frac{\partial c_s}{\partial t} = k \cdot ds \cdot (c - c_0) \tag{6}$$

where c_s [kg/m³] is the harmful gas component concentration in the particle volume element, k [m⁻²·s⁻¹] is the mass transfer coefficient, ds [m²] is the area of surface element, c [kg/m³] is the mass density of the harmful gas component in the gas phase and c_0 [kg/m³] is the equilibrium mass density of harmful components on the solid surface, which is calculated as $c_0=bc_s$ (Bird et al., 2002), where b is a constant.

Eq(6) supposes the development of a homogeneous concentration profile in the individual particle volume element of the adsorber particle after the component transport to the surface element.

The source term R in Eq(2) is calculated by Eq(7). For a given grid point of gas phase it is the sum of component rates that absorbed through the surface elements (n) located in the vicinity of calculation cell i,j.

$$R_{i,j} = -\sum_{n=1}^{n=N} k \cdot ds \cdot \left(c_{i,j} - c_{0,n}\right) \qquad (7)$$

Eqs (1)-(5) are solved by the TVD-MacCormack second order accurate scheme (Yee, 1989) in order to get physically admissible solutions. In this scheme the two steps MacCormack's scheme is completed with a third step by introducing a dissipation term to avoid any unphysical oscillation in the vicinity of strong gradients in the numerical solution. At the outflow boundary, taking into account of the physical bases of compressible gas flow, non-reflecting numerical boundary condition is applied. The application of non-reflecting boundary condition at outflow boundary instead of constant physical boundaries prevents reflections of the unsteady compression and expansion waves back into the calculation domain. In our simulation study a generalized method of non-reflecting outflow boundary condition specification, developed by (Thompson, 1990) is applied. All the calculations are carried out in a self-developed program in MATLAB environment.

In order to calculate the flow field around the adsorber particle and the interaction between solid particle and gas-phase the immersed boundary method is used. The flow equations are solved on a structured and stationary mesh over the entire calculation domain and the solid adsorbent particles occur with a virtual boundary (Figure 1b). As the flow field around the particle is fully resolved, the size of the calculation grid should be approximately one order of magnitude smaller than the size of the particles, which is set in our simulation to 2 mm in diameter like a usual activated carbon adsorber particle. Lagrangian points (red dots in Figure 1b) are defined equidistantly around the particle. The distance (ds) is tuned to the Eulerian grid size and equal to 0.0002 m. Extrapolating between the two grid point locations are carried out by a distance-based weight function (Figure 1c), in our case a simple triangle function.

The calculation algorithm takes all the Lagrangian grid points of virtual particle and looks for the Eulerian grid points in a certain distance limit. In Figure 1b the orange colored circle shows the distance limit and the blue dots are the Eulerian grid points that influence the given Lagrangian grid point. The degree of influence of Eulerian grid points is a function of their distance to the Lagrangian grid point. The gas flow is forced to bypass the virtual solid body by the application of direct forcing method in which an extra force density terms are added to the momentum Eqs (3) and (4). The extra term balances the momentum equation such a way that the modified flow field realizes the particle boundary.

3. Results and discussion

The dynamic model given by Eqs (1)-(5) was solved by TVD-MacCormack scheme using non-reflecting outlet boundary condition. The inlet harmful gas component concentration was set to 2 kg/m^3. The non-harmful gas was considered as air. The inlet gas velocity was set to 10 m/s. The mass transfer coefficient k and constant b in the equations were equal to 1×10^8 m$^{-2} \cdot$ s^{-1} and 1.1. The time step of numerical solution was determined in each iteration step according to the Courant-Friedrich-Lewy criteria, and was changing around 2×10^{-7} s. At simulation time 5×10^{-3} s the velocity field of the gas phase around the particle is shown in Figure 2a and the concentration field of harmful gas component show in Figure 2b. The concentration of harmful gas component in the particle volume elements around the particle is shown in Figure 2c giving a picture of the saturation state of the particle surface. The saturation state around the particle shows a distribution due to the dynamically changing concentration values of those gas phase elements which interact the surface of adsorber particle. Figure 2d shows the dynamic change of saturation at six highlighted surface points. It can be seen that surface points located at the different points of the particle surface are saturated by different velocity depending on the concentration of interacting gas-phase elements.

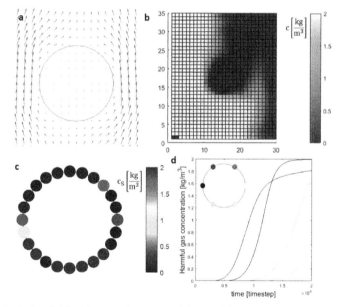

Figure 2. a) Velocity field of the gas phase around the particle. b) Concentration field of the gas phase around the particle. c) Degree of saturation around the adsorbent particle after 2×10^4 timesteps. d) Saturation curves at specific surface points of the adsorber particle.

As it is seen from the simulation results the model is able to calculate the saturation curves of particle surface points and can provide information about the necessary residence time of particles in the purification column at given operating parameters and this way it can help in the optimal design of column.

4. Conclusions

Adsorption process is modeled for a single particle by a first order adsorption kinetics with the fully resolved dynamic gas flow around the particle. The gas flow around the motionless adsorber particle is modeled by immersed boundary method, and the gas-solid interaction is calculated regarding the velocity field and the harmful component adsorption. The adsorber material is considered a layer on the carrier particle in our case, in which the diffusion is fast, therefore homogenous concentration field is assumed. However, the main achievement of this study is to calculate the saturation state of the adsorber layer resolved for the small segments of particle surface. This knowledge helps to define the overall saturation time of particle more accurately, and could also help in other process development issues.

Motion and collision of particles is not calculated in the current work, however the next step in improving our detailed model is to populate the gas purification column with more particles, which can interact with the gas flow and each other. Using our extended model it will be possible to simulate the whole purification column and the operating parameters can be designed more efficiently.

Acknowledgment

We would like to express our acknowledgement for the financial support of Széchenyi 2020 under the GINOP-2.2.1-15-2017-00059, MOL Group and Peregrinatio I. Foundation.

References

Bird, R.B., Stewart, W.E., Lightfoot, E.N., 2002. Transport phenomena, 2nd, Wiley international ed ed. J. Wiley, New York.

Deen, N.G., Peters, E.A.J.F., Padding, J.T., Kuipers, J.A.M., 2014. Review of direct numerical simulation of fluid–particle mass, momentum and heat transfer in dense gas–solid flows. Chem. Eng. Sci. 116, 710–724. https://doi.org/10.1016/j.ces.2014.05.039

Fadlun, E., Verzicco, R., Orlandi, P., Mohd-Yusof, J., 2000. Combined Immersed-Boundary Finite-Difference Methods for Three-Dimensional Complex Flow Simulations. J. Comput. Phys. 161, 35–60. https://doi.org/10.1006/jcph.2000.6484

Kumagai, S., Lu, J., Fukushima, Y., Ohno, H., Kameda, T., Yoshioka, T., 2018. Diagnosing chlorine industrial metabolism by evaluating the potential of chlorine recovery from polyvinyl chloride wastes—A case study in Japan. Resour. Conserv. Recycl. 133, 354–361. https://doi.org/10.1016/j.resconrec.2017.07.007

Mondino, G., Grande, C., Blom, R., Nord, L.O., 2019. Moving bed temperature swing adsorption for CO2 capture from a natural gas combined cycle power plant. Int. J. Greenh. Gas Control 85, 58–70. https://doi.org/10.1016/j.ijggc.2019.03.021

Thompson, K.W., 1990. Time-dependent boundary conditions for hyperbolic systems, II. J. Comput. Phys. 89, 439–461. https://doi.org/10.1016/0021-9991(90)90152-Q

Veksha, A., Giannis, A., Oh, W., Chang, V., Lisak, G., 2018. Upgrading of non-condensable pyrolysis gas from mixed plastics through catalytic decomposition and dechlorination.   Fuel   Process.   Technol.   170,   13–20. https://doi.org/10.1016/j.fuproc.2017.10.019

Yee, H.C., 1989. A class of high resolution explicit and implicit shock-capturing methods. NASA Technical Memorandum 101088

Sauro Pierucci, Flavio Manenti, Giulia Bozzano, Davide Manca (Eds.)
Proceedings of the 30th European Symposium on Computer Aided Process Engineering
(ESCAPE30), May 24-27, 2020, Milano, Italy. © 2020 Elsevier B.V. All rights reserved.
http://dx.doi.org/10.1016/B978-0-12-823377-1.50035-5

Parameters Influencing the Rate-based Simulation of CO_2 Removal units by Potassium Taurate Solvent

Stefania Moioli[a,*], Minh T. Ho[b], Laura A. Pellegrini[a], Dianne E. Wiley[b]

[a]GASP, Group of Advanced Separation Processes and GAS Processing, Dipartimento di Chimica, Materiali e Ingegneria Chimica "Giulio Natta", Politecnico di Milano, Piazza Leonardo da Vinci 32, I-20133 Milano, Italy
[b]The University of Sydney, School of Chemical and Biomolecular Engineering, 2006 Australia
stefania.moioli@polimi.it

Abstract

CCS (Carbon Capture & Storage) is being widely considered for reducing the emissions of greenhouse gases to the atmosphere and is already industrially applied by use of chemical absorption with aqueous amines, as MonoEthanolAmine (MEA). This solvent is well performing, though being characterized by several drawbacks as high regeneration energy requirements, corrosion and toxicity.

The excessive use of toxic solvents is environmentally detrimental and recognized as an unstable practice. In the efforts to address the issues of sustainability established in the 2030 Agenda for Sustainable Development, also the carbon dioxide absorption process is being studied and one key point is the employment of more environmentally friendly solutions.

Aqueous amino acid salt solutions have been considered in the last years a viable alternative to traditional solvents for carbon dioxide removal. Moreover, some of them, such as the potassium taurate solvent, are characterized by precipitation at specific conditions during absorption, thus providing further advantages in terms of potential reduction in energy requirement to the process and/or costs.

For any system, a validated process and thermodynamic model and simulation is one essential tool used by process engineers to assist with a thorough evaluation of different process options and designs. Choice of model parameters is fundamental to the accurate and reliable representation of the process. This work focuses on the analysis of the parameters influencing the rate-based simulation of the carbon dioxide removal section of a 500 MW coal-fired power plant. Results confirm that for the considered system the mass transfer coefficient is strongly influenced by the viscosity of the solvent and the diffusivity of CO_2 in the aqueous solution. The results also show that different values of the film discretization can lead to differences in the required solvent flowrate.

Keywords: CO_2 removal; rate-based simulation; potassium taurate solvent; physical properties, film discretization.

1. Introduction

The application of Carbon Capture & Storage (CCS) technology, that can significantly reduce the emissions of CO_2 produced in electricity generation and in industrial processes, is getting more and more attention.

The mostly employed method of removing CO_2 from industrial gaseous streams is chemical absorption (Kohl and Nielsen, 1997; Rochelle, 2009), with aqueous solutions of MonoEthanolAmine (MEA) being the benchmark solvent. Though being well performing, this solvent is corrosive and toxic and for its regeneration high energy consumption (Moioli and Pellegrini, 2019) is needed.

For this reason different types of amine solvents started to be considered (Moioli and Pellegrini, 2015, 2016; Rochelle et al., 2011) and, recently, with the aim of achieving the goals of the 2030 Agenda for Sustainable Development, innovative solvents, with environmentally friendly characteristics, are being studied (Lerche, 2012; Majchrowicz, 2014; Sanchez-Fernandez, 2013).

Among these, some amino acids (as taurine (Lerche, 2012)) in aqueous solution favor CO_2 absorption by forming a precipitate at high CO_2 loadings (Kumar et al., 2003a; Kumar et al., 2003b; Sanchez Fernandez et al., 2013) and may favor a reduction of the steam to be employed for the reboiler of the regeneration section (the most energy demanding section of the plant) by variations of pH of the solution (Moioli et al., 2019c). Compared to the MEA solvent, in addition, they are much less corrosive (Ahn et al., 2010) and with lower enthalpy of reaction (Brouwer et al., 2009).

1.1. The considered process

The process taken into account in this work employs an aqueous solution of potassium taurate (4M KOH, 4M taurine) for removing 90% of CO_2 from a flue gas stream of a 500 MW coal-fired power plant, before emitting it to the atmosphere (Moioli et al., 2019a).

The flue gas has a flowrate of 19.60 kmol/s and a molar fraction (y) of CO_2 equal to 0.13, in the range of the ones typical of flue gas from coal generation. Water (y = 0.07), N_2 (y = 0.75) and O_2 (y = 0.05) are the other main components. The stream is available at atmospheric pressure and 40°C.

The process scheme, with also some possible alternative configurations for energy saving, is described in (Ho et al., 2019).

1.2. Rate-based simulation

For the rate-based simulation of the process, the commercial software ASPEN Plus® V9 has been employed. Because some species are not present by default in the database, the tool has been customized by adding these species and by developing a thermodynamic model with good agreement with the experimental vapor-liquid-solid equilibrium data (Moioli et al., 2018).

The physical properties such as density and viscosity of the solvent and the diffusivity of carbon dioxide in the liquid phase are variables used for the estimation of the mass transfer coefficient, which in rate-based calculations is employed for the evaluation of mass transfer on each stage of the column.

In order to understand the impact that the values used for these variables have on the estimation of the amount of carbon dioxide absorbed, a sensitivity analysis has been carried out, by estimating the mass transfer coefficient and the terms composing it.

The mass transfer resistance is taken into account through a film, which is present both for the vapor phase and for the liquid phase. In the liquid film, reactions occur, therefore a further influence on mass transfer is obtained. In ASPEN Plus® the reacting film can be modeled by choosing "filmrxn" or "discrxn" as options: according to the first one, the film is divided into two segments, while according to the second one, the number of segments for discretization of the film can be chosen by the user.

The number of segments in which subdividing the film is important for the description of the mass transfer in that region. A high number of segments can guarantee a more rigorous analysis, though requiring high computational times, while a low number of segments may lead to differences in results.

2. Methodology

This work focuses on both the study of the influence of the physical properties on the mass transfer coefficient and on the choice of the film discretization in simulation.

As for the former, the analysis has been focused on the variation of density and viscosity and of diffusivity of carbon dioxide in a range of possible values occurring for the potassium taurate process. The expression of mass transfer coefficient from the correlation by Onda (AspenTech, 2016) has been considered for the calculation.

The number of segments in which the film must be subdivided has been determined by performing several simulations with different number of discretization points of the absorption column. The column is characterized by the same height and the same diameter and is fed with a sour gas stream and a solvent with lean loading equal to 0.27, as considered in previous works on this topic (Moioli et al., 2019b). No liquid-solid separator is considered. The obtained outputs have been considered for the analysis.

3. Results and discussion

3.1. Influence of the physical properties on the mass transfer coefficient

The results are reported in terms of relative sensitivity, defined as the ratio of the difference of the considered output variable, for instance the mass transfer coefficient, and the difference of the input variable (*i.e.* the density, the viscosity or the diffusivity of CO_2). A low value of this ratio indicates that the output variable is not significantly influenced by variations in the input variable, while high values of the relative sensitivity mean that the value of the input variable should be chosen carefully, since it strongly influences the value of the output variable.

Figure 1a) shows that the value of density of the liquid phase has not a significant influence on the mass transfer coefficient. On the right axis of the same figure also the Schmidt number is reported, being the variable that shows the highest difference between the value of density at 1000 kg/m^3 and 2000 kg/m^3. However, the variation is low, in the range of order of magnitude of 10^{-5}.

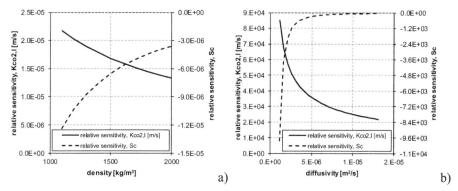

Figure 1. Relative sensitivity of mass transfer coefficient (left axis) and of Schmidt number (right axis) for different values of a) density of the solvent and b) diffusivity of carbon dioxide in the solvent.

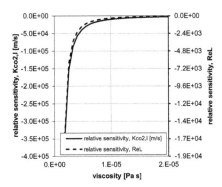

Figure 2. Relative sensitivity of mass transfer coefficient (left axis) and of Reynolds number (right axis) for different values of viscosity of the solvent.

The viscosity of the aqueous solution and the diffusivity of carbon dioxide in the solvent, on the contrary, exerts a high influence on the estimation of the mass transfer coefficient. In particular, a relative sensitivity of the viscosity of the liquid phase on the Reynolds number of order of magnitude of 10^4 is obtained, which contributes in the evaluation of a relative sensitivity for the mass transfer coefficient resulting in the order of magnitude of 10^5 (Figure 2).

As for the diffusivity of carbon dioxide in the solvent, the Schmidt number is reported in Figure 1b) because one of the parameter most influenced by the variation of the input variable considered. The relative sensitivity results in the order of magnitude of 10^4 both for the Schmidt number and for the overall mass transfer coefficient.

The proper description of these properties is therefore fundamental for obtaining a good representation of the process. For the considered system, the values of density and viscosity of the potassium taurate solution estimated in ASPEN Plus® have been compared with the available experimental data (Kumar et al., 2001; Wei et al., 2014). The density of the lean solvent is within 10 % of the experimental data. As resulting from the analysis carried out in this work, this variation in density does not exert a significant influence on the description of mass transfer. As for viscosity, the values calculated by ASPEN Plus® have been considered as representing with good approximation the experimental data.

Data of loaded solutions are not available for the potassium taurate solvent, so the description of these two properties may be further improved if additional experimental data becomes available.

The diffusion coefficient of carbon dioxide is calculated by means of the Wilke-Chang correlation, in ASPEN Plus® considering water as solvent. The results have been compared with the values estimated by Wei et al. (Wei et al., 2014) using a correlation of diffusivity of N_2O as a function of viscosity of the potassium taurate solvent, resulting within the range of those obtained by Wei et al. (Wei et al., 2014).

3.2. Choice of the film discretization

As can be seen from Figure 3a), the addition of two discretization points to the default values results in an increase in the amount of carbon dioxide present in the purified gas of 5%. The amount of carbon dioxide reacted also influences the temperature along the column, in particular at the top, where variations up to about 1.5 K have been obtained, though not shown here for reasons of limiting space.

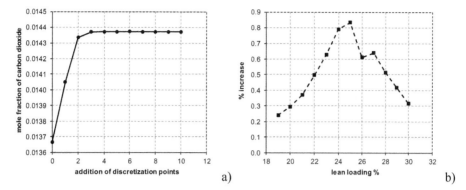

Figure 3. a) Mole fraction of carbon dioxide in the purified flue gas for simulation of the absorption column with different numbers of discretization points for the film; b) % variation in the amount of solvent flowrate calculated with "filmrxn" and with "discrxn" with addition of 3 discretization points for removing 90% of carbon dioxide for different lean loadings.

When the number of added segments is higher than 8, no changes in the results are obtained. However, no significant changes are also obtained when adding three points for discretization, with the result that the time for the calculation is significantly reduced. Since the variation between adding three points and adding eight points can be considered not remarkable and about half computational time is required, the "discrxn" option with the addition of three points has been considered for the simulations.

The discretization ratio, *i.e.* the ratio of the extension of each segments of the film to the following one, has been found not affecting significantly the results of the simulation, therefore the default values have been maintained.

The choice of the film discretization has an influence on the results obtained from the simulation of the process, with all the other parameters and variables set equal for the two simulations. In detail, Figure 3b) shows results obtained in estimating the solvent flowrate needed for removing 90% of carbon dioxide for different lean loadings when the option "filmrxn" is considered or when simulations are performed with the option "discrxn" with addition of 3 segments. Depending on the considered lean loading, a maximum percentage increase in the solvent flowrate of 0.83 % is obtained. This difference in the circulating flowrate has an influence also on the required reboiler duty, to which it is strongly related.

4. Conclusions

This paper has analyzed the influence that different values of density and viscosity of the solvent and diffusivity of CO_2 in the solvent can have on the estimation of the mass transfer coefficient. It has also taken into account the variation of results related to the choice of how to discretize the film.

Results confirm the need of an accurate representation of properties, in particular the viscosity of the solvent and the diffusivity of CO_2 in the liquid phase. Experimental data of CO_2 loaded solutions would help in achieving higher accuracy in their description and thus in the estimation of mass transfer. Moreover, the option "discrxn" with addition of three segments results the best choice for film discretization.

References

S. Ahn, H.-J. Song, J.-W. Park, J.H. Lee, I.Y. Lee, K.-R. Jang, 2010, Characterization of metal corrosion by aqueous amino acid salts for the capture of CO_2, Korean Journal of Chemical Engineering 27, 1576-1580.

AspenTech, 2016, ASPEN Plus® Guidelines. AspenTech, Burlington, MA.

J.P. Brouwer, P.H.M. Feron, N.A.M. ten Asbroek, 2009, Amino-acid salts for CO_2 capture from flue gases.

M.H. Ho, E.G.C. Conde, S. Moioli, D.E. Wiley, 2019, The effect of different process configurations on the performance and cost of potassium taurate solvent absorption, International Journal of Greenhouse Gas Control 81, 1-10.

A.L. Kohl, R. Nielsen, 1997, Gas Purification, 5th ed. Gulf Publishing Company, Book Division, Houston, Texas, USA.

P.S. Kumar, J.A. Hogendoorn, P.H.M. Feron, G.F. Versteeg, 2001, Density, viscosity, solubility, and diffusivity of N_2O in aqueous amino acid salt solutions, Journal of Chemical and Engineering Data 46, 1357-1361.

P.S. Kumar, J.A. Hogendoorn, P.H.M. Feron, G.F. Versteeg, 2003a, Equilibrium solubility of CO_2 in aqueous potassium taurate solutions: Part 1. Crystallization in carbon dioxide loaded aqueous salt solutions of amino acids, Industrial & Engineering Chemistry Research 42, 2832-2840.

P.S. Kumar, J.A. Hogendoorn, S.J. Timmer, P.H.M. Feron, G.F. Versteeg, 2003b, Equilibrium solubility of CO_2 in aqueous potassium taurate solutions: Part 2. Experimental VLE data and model, Industrial & Engineering Chemistry Research 42, 2841-2852.

B.M. Lerche, 2012, CO_2 Capture from Flue gas using Amino acid salt solutions. Technical University of Denmark, Lyngby, Denmark.

M.E. Majchrowicz, 2014, Amino Acid Salt Solutions for Carbon Dioxide Capture. University of Twente, Twente, The Netherlands.

S. Moioli, M.H. Ho, L.A. Pellegrini, D.E. Wiley, 2019a, Application of Absorption by Potassium Taurate Solutions to Post-Combustion CO_2 Removal from Flue Gases with Different Compositions and Flowrates, Chemical Engineering Transactions 74, 823-828.

S. Moioli, M.H. Ho, D.E. Wiley, L.A. Pellegrini, 2018, Thermodynamic Modeling of the System of CO_2 and Potassium Taurate Solution for Simulation of the Process of Carbon Dioxide Removal, Chemical Engineering Research and Design 136, 834-845.

S. Moioli, M.H. Ho, D.E. Wiley, L.A. Pellegrini, 2019b, Assessment of carbon dioxide capture by precipitating potassium taurate solvent, International Journal of Greenhouse Gas Control 87, 159-169.

S. Moioli, L.A. Pellegrini, 2015, Physical properties of PZ solution used as a solvent for CO_2 removal, Chemical Engineering Research and Design 93, 720-726.

S. Moioli, L.A. Pellegrini, 2016, Modeling the methyldiethanolamine-piperazine scrubbing system for CO_2 removal: Thermodynamic analysis, Frontiers of Chemical Science and Engineering 10, 162-175.

S. Moioli, L.A. Pellegrini, 2019, Operating the CO_2 absorption plant in a post-combustion unit in flexible mode for cost reduction, Chemical Engineering Research and Design 147, 604-614.

S. Moioli, L.A. Pellegrini, M.T. Ho, D.E. Wiley, 2019c, A comparison between amino acid based solvent and traditional amine solvent processes for CO_2 removal, Chemical Engineering Research and Design 146, 509-517.

G. Rochelle, E. Chen, S. Freeman, D. Van Wagener, Q. Xu, A. Voice, 2011, Aqueous piperazine as the new standard for CO_2 capture technology, Chemical Engineering Journal 171, 725-733.

G.T. Rochelle, 2009, Amine Scrubbing for CO_2 Capture, Science 325, 1652-1654.

E. Sanchez-Fernandez, 2013, Novel Process Designs to Improve the Efficiency of Postombustion Carbon Dioxide Capture. Technische Universiteit Delft, Delft, The Netherlands.

E. Sanchez Fernandez, K. Heffernan, L.V. van der Ham, M.J.G. Linders, E. Eggink, F.N.H. Schrama, D.W.F. Brilman, E.L.V. Goetheer, T.J.H. Vlugt, 2013, Conceptual Design of a Novel CO_2 Capture Process Based on Precipitating Amino Acid Solvents, Industrial & Engineering Chemistry Research 52, 12223-12235.

C.C. Wei, G. Puxty, P. Feron, 2014, Amino acid salts for CO_2 capture at flue gas temperatures, Chemical Engineering Science 107, 218-226.

Sauro Pierucci, Flavio Manenti, Giulia Bozzano, Davide Manca (Eds.)
Proceedings of the 30th European Symposium on Computer Aided Process Engineering
(ESCAPE30), May 24-27, 2020, Milano, Italy. © 2020 Elsevier B.V. All rights reserved.
http://dx.doi.org/10.1016/B978-0-12-823377-1.50036-7

Innovative Hybrid Energy System for stable Power and Heat Supply in offshore oil & gas Installation (HES-OFF): System Design and Grid Stability

Luca Riboldi[a*], Erick F. Alves[b], Marcin Pilarczyk[a], Elisabetta Tedeschi[b], Lars O. Nord[a]

[a]*Department of Energy and Process Engineering, Norwegian University of Science and Technology-NTNU, Trondheim 7491, Norway*
[b]*Department of Electric Power Engineering, Norwegian University of Science and Technology-NTNU, Trondheim 7034, Norway*
luca.riboldi@ntnu.no

Abstract

This paper presents an innovative hybrid energy system for stable power and heat supply in offshore oil & gas installations (HES-OFF). The hybrid concept integrates offshore wind power with gas turbines and a H_2 energy storage solution based on proton exchange membrane fuel cells and electrolysers. The objectives are: 1) improve the environmental performance of offshore installations by maximizing the exploitation of offshore wind and partially decarbonizing the gas turbines by co-feeding H_2; 2) minimize the negative effects that wind power variability has on the electrical grid frequency stability. This study presents a first assessment of the HES-OFF concept performance using an offshore platform in the North Sea as case study. The results show that the HES-OFF concept: 1) cuts CO_2 emissions up to 40 % when compared to the reference case but requires large H_2 storage capacity to fully exploit wind power throughout the year; 2) allows higher wind power penetration without infringing on the grid frequency requirements.

Keywords: offshore energy, hybrid system, energy storage, system design, grid stability.

1. Introduction

Due to the long-term character of the energy transition and the many technical limitations to replace fossil fuels with renewable energy sources (RESs), hybrid energy systems (HESs) with energy storage (ES) can be affordable alternatives. The choice of the HES configuration and its specification depends on the availability of RESs and the general purpose of the system. Optimum design can be achieved through comprehensive analyses and optimisation of layouts and the size of system components. Offshore oil and gas (O&G) production is likely to increase in the near future and thus its related CO_2 emissions. In Norway, the petroleum sector is the main contributor to greenhouse gas emissions, making up 27 % of the total emissions in 2018 (Statistics Norway, 2018). Several options to reduce the carbon footprint of the O&G sector have been investigated (Riboldi and Nord, 2017), including the electrification of offshore facilities (Riboldi et al., 2019). The utilization of RESs is a very promising opportunity, though there are challenges for their efficient exploitation offshore. This article presents the concept of an innovative hybrid energy system for stable power and heat supply in offshore oil & gas installation (HES-OFF), which considers wind energy along with H_2 ES using a proton exchange membrane (PEM) fuel cell (FC) and electrolyser (EL) system.

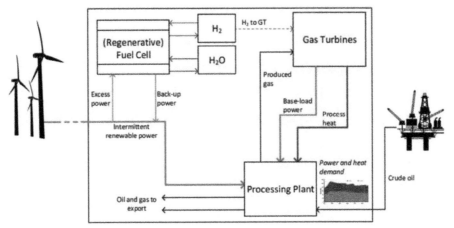

Figure 1. Schematic of the HES-OFF system proposed.

2. The HES-OFF hybrid concept

The HES-OFF concept consists of a HES integrating an offshore wind farm, stacks of PEM FC and EL for ES and back-up power supply, and a gas turbine (GT). The ES is further integrated with the GT, where the possibility to co-feed H_2 is envisioned. Fig. 1 depicts the HES-OFF system layout.

Within this energy system, the GT operation meets the process heat demand and supplies base-load power to a processing plant. Wind turbines (WTs) provide the remaining load. The FC and EL stacks smooth out the intermittent wind power output by: 1) storing excess power in the form of gaseous H_2 when production is larger than demand; 2) providing back-up power on the contrary. This HES is expected to reduce CO_2 emissions from an offshore facility due to: 1) enhanced exploitation of RESs; 2) clean fuel to GTs; 3) improved operational strategy of the GTs.

3. Modelling framework

Two main areas of the modelling activity are distinguished, namely (1) process components and (2) offshore grid modelling. The general intention is to pre-screen the feasibility of the HES-OFF concept and to assess the potential reduction of CO_2 emissions.

3.1. Process components

The HES-OFF process components are modelled in MATLAB and are presented below.

GTs: Two types of gas turbines are considered for the study, namely a GE LM2500+G4 (rated power 32.2 MW) and a GE LM6000 PF (rated power 41.9 MW). To simulate the GTs, two data-defined models are used. Those are based on performance curves retrieved from tabulated data and assess the effect of changing working conditions as well as off-design operation. The models were validated against the Thermoflow library (Thermoflow Inc, 2016). The performance of the LM2500+G4 model was further checked against real operational data by Riboldi and Nord (2018), showing good agreement, and used in previous publications (e.g., Riboldi and Nord, 2017).

FCs&ELs stacks: The models used in this study are based on zero-dimensional, static models of PEM FC and EL stacks, which describe the electrical domain of cells. The FC stack model is based on Spiegel (2008), improved and tuned according to Dicks et al.

(2018). The EL stack model is based on Zhang et al. (2012) with further improvements based on Millet (2015). The output of the model is the overall performance of the FC and EL stacks as a function of load expressed in MJ/kgH_2 and kgH_2/MJ, respectively. The obtained results reflect the state-of-the-art for high capacity PEM systems on the market. **WT:** The conversion of wind speed into power was simulated through the power curve of the Hywind Scotland WT (Nielsen, 2018). The wind speed distribution throughout a year was based on the measurements from a platform in the North Sea made available by the Norwegian Meteorological Institute (reported in Korpås et al., 2012).

3.2. Offshore grid
A surrogate model of the electrical grid (Alves et al., 2019) was developed in Simulink. It evaluates frequency dynamics using Eq. (1):

$$\dot{\omega} = \frac{P_a - k_d \omega^2}{2H_{GT}\omega} \tag{1}$$

$$P_a = P_{GT} + P_{FC} + P_{WT} - P_{EL} - P_{LD} \tag{2}$$

where ω is the frequency in per unit[1] (pu), the model state and output; P_a is the net accelerating power in pu and the model input; H_{GT} and k_d are model parameters, defined as the equivalent inertia constant in s and the equivalent damping constant of the plant in pu/pu. Base values are: $\omega_b = 2.\pi.60$ rad/s; $P_b = 44.7$ MW.

P_a is defined by Eq. (2) where P_{GT}, P_{FC}, P_{WT}, P_{EL}, P_{LD} are respectively the power in pu of GT, FC, WT, EL and loads. The model from Eq. (1) is extended to include PID controllers for the GT, FC and EL (Alves et al., 2019 and Sanchez et al., 2017). Those keep the grid frequency at its rated value. The choice of controller parameters follows the magnitude optimum criteria as outlined by Papadopoulos (2015).

4. Results

The developed methodology was tested on a case study: an offshore facility in the North Sea, for which an estimation of the energy requirements throughout its lifetime was made available by the operator (18 years). To ease the analysis, the power and heat supply demand was discretized: 1) Peak (2 years): 43.6 MW electrical power, 14.0 MW heat power; 2) Mid-life (4 years): 35.2 MW electrical, 11.0 MW heat; 3) Tail (12 years): 32.9 MW electrical, 8.0 MW heat.

4.1. Long-term system design
The long-term analysis sizes the components of the HES by: 1) ensuring that power and heat demand is always met; 2) maximizing the reduction of CO_2 emissions; 3) removing one GT; 4) avoiding waste of wind power.

The discretized lifetime energy demand of the offshore installation is considered, where each year is simulated with an hourly resolution. Table 1 reports the input parameters varied to define a design.

The storage strategy adopted ensures a net-zero balance of H_2 at the end of the year and the storage size is determined by the largest variation in the storage level. At first the design is tested over one year without ES.

---

[1] per unit (ou) is a system for expressing values in terms of a reference or base quantity.

Table 1. Input parameters for the long-term system design

INPUT PARAMETERS	
GT type	GE LM2500 or LM6000
Max. GT load	95 %
Min. GT load	40 %
Max. H_2 in GT	20 % vol.
Wind turbine	Hywind Scotland
Wind farm size (MW)	12-18-24

Table 2. Input parameters for the short-term grid stability analysis

INPUT PARAMETERS	
H_{GT}	1.85s for LM2500 1.8s for LM6000
k_d	7 pu/pu
GT PID controller	Kp = 3.8, Ki=1.6, Kd=0, Td=100
EL / FC PID controllers	Kp = 0, Ki=0, Kd=6, Td=50

In case of a net deficit of power (typical of peak years), the strategy: 1) evaluates total H_2 needed; 2) when possible, increases GT load and uses extra power to produce H_2; 3) stops when reaching a maximum storage level; 4) stops when reaching overall H_2 needed. In case of a net surplus of power (typical of tail years), the strategy: 1) evaluates total H_2 produced due to surplus power; 2) when possible, decreases GT load and use fuel cells to produce power; 3) when the level of H_2 storage reaches a maximum, uses H_2 in the GT; 4) if some H_2 is still unused, sends H_2 to GT. Table 3 and
Table 4 shows results obtained for the small and large GTs, respectively.

The designs of the HES-OFF concept reduce CO_2 emissions both compared to the reference case (only GT) and to the basic integration of wind power (GT+WIND). The lowest cumulative CO_2 emissions are obtained by the HES-OFF designs based on the small GT (LM2500). However, those are also characterized by extremely large (possibly unfeasible) sizes of the H_2 storage and fail to remove one GT. Conversely, the HES-OFF design based on the large GT obtain a more limited CO_2 emission reduction but with more acceptable sizes of the H_2 storage and with a single GT.

The size of the H_2 storage is given in kg of H_2 as the storage technology is not specified. Cryogenic option has been ruled out because of the significant energy requirements. H_2 storage in gaseous form has been considered as more appropriate for this application. The very large volumes connected with this option would require a storage on the seabed. Some technologies have been qualitatively investigated such as the utilization of gas balloons (Pimm et al., 2014), gas pipes and underground formations (Kruck et al., 2013). Additional analyses are planned to identify the most promising option.

Table 3. Output results of the HES-OFF concept based on the LM2500 GT

INPUTS		Only GT	GT + WIND			HES-OFF		
GT type		LM2500	LM2500	LM2500	LM2500	LM2500	LM2500	LM2500
No. GT		2	2	2	2	2	2	2
Max. GT load	%	90 %	90 %	90 %	90 %	95 %	95 %	95 %
Min. GT load	%	40 %	40 %	40 %	40 %	40 %	40 %	40 %
Wind farm size	MW	-	12	18	24	12	18	24
OUTPUTS								
Size H_2 storage	kg	-	-	-	-	175334	81605	71062
Size EL stacks	MW	-	-	-	-	6	6	6
Size FC stacks	MW	-	-	-	-	4	4	4
CO_2 emissions	Mt	3.51	2.71	2.42	2.25	2.50	2.27	2.09
Max. frequency	Hz	60.00	60.15	60.23	60.31	60.12	60.19	60.25
Min. frequency	Hz	59.22	59.02	58.91	58.79	59.13	59.04	58.95
Max. dP/dt GT	%/s	1.52	1.88	2.11	2.33	1.68	1.86	2.03

Table 4. Output results of the HES-OFF concept based on the LM6000 GT

INPUTS		Only GT	GT + WIND			HES-OFF		
GT type		LM6000	LM6000	LM6000	LM6000	LM6000	LM6000	LM6000
No. GT		2	2	2	2	1	1	1
Max. GT load	%	90 %	90 %	90 %	90 %	95 %	95 %	95 %
Min. GT load	%	40 %	40 %	40 %	40 %	40 %	40 %	40 %
Wind farm size	MW	-	12	18	24	12	18	24
OUTPUTS								
Size H$_2$ storage	kg	-	-	-	-	10010	8014	11824
Size EL stacks	MW	-	-	-	-	4.0	4.0	6.6
Size FC stacks	MW	-	-	-	-	1.1	1.1	1.1
CO$_2$ emissions	Mt	2.92						
Max. frequency	Hz	60.00	60.15	60.23	60.31	60.14	60.22	60.30
Min. frequency	Hz	59.21	59.02	58.90	58.78	59.06	58.92	58.75
Max. dP/dt GT	%/s	1.05	1.30	1.46	1.61	2.49	2.88	3.32

4.2. Short-term grid stability analysis

This step verifies if each proposed design of the long-term analysis: 1) is stable from the frequency stability perspective (Kundur et al., 2004); 2) complies with industry requirements (IEC, 2015) for frequency deviations (± 2%) during normal operation conditions; 3) complies with technical specifications of GT ramp rates.

For that, it simulates the offshore grid model presented in section 3.2. Inputs are obtained as following: 1) P_{GT}, P_{FC}, and P_{EL} are results from the long-term analysis of the process model and are assumed as constants; 2) P_{WT} and P_{LD} are results from analyses of 1-year long datasets of wind speeds and loads sampled every minute and are assumed as variables. These datasets are stored in an NTNU repository and are not publicly available. To reduce total simulation time, two synthetic time series reflect the worst-case scenarios of operation during the offshore platform lifetime. Those are 3-minutes long and contain the most sharp and common positive and negative variations of P_{WT} and P_{LD}. Parameters for the short-term grid stability analysis are reported in Table 2.

The bottom part of Table 3 and

Table 4 presents the obtained results. Note that as the wind farm size increases: 1) the frequency deviations increase and, in the extreme cases (24 MW wind farm), the minimum frequency limit (58.8 Hz) is always violated, except for the LM2500 HES-OFF concept; 2) the rate of change of power (*dP/dt*) of the GT increases, which translates into increased actuation of the governor and consequently additional wear and tear. The HES-OFF concept contributes to decrease frequency deviations and GT ramp rates. Note that, in the LM6000 HES-OFF concept with 24 MW wind farm, the minimum frequency limit can be respected if the FC increases to 1.6 MW. This shows the importance of considering grid requirements in the design phase of a HES.

5. Conclusions

The HES-OFF concept was presented and tested on a case study. Six configurations were assessed using two GTs of different rated power. Long- and short-term analyses verified the HES potential to reduce CO$_2$ emissions and to provide a stable offshore grid. The HES-OFF concept demonstrated the ability to reduce the cumulative CO$_2$ emissions of an O&G platform not only compared to a reference case using only GTs but also compared to a concept integrating GTs and WTs without ES. The designs based on the small GT return the highest CO_2 emission reductions (between 29 % and 40 % depending on the wind farm size) but are unable to remove one of the GTs and involve very large H_2 storage capacity. Conversely, the designs based on the large GT return lower CO_2 emission reductions (between 16 % and 24 % depending on the wind farm size) but use a single GT and more limited H_2 storage capacity. It is also shown that the addition of ES helps reducing the frequency variations in the offshore grid. The minimum frequency specification is generally met by the HES-OFF solutions but at 24 MW wind capacity for the large GT. However, an increase in the FC stack size would allow the frequency to be within the required limits. Not least, GTs ramp rates are reduced as well, with potential advantages in terms of decreased wear, tear and maintenance requirements. Further work in this ongoing research project envisions the development of more complex models, optimization of the HES and validation by means of hardware-in-the-loop simulation.

References

E. Alves, S. Sanchez, D. Brandao, E. Tedeschi, 2019, Smart load management with energy storage for power quality enhancement in wind-powered oil and gas applications, Energies, 12, 1-15.

A.L. Dicks, D.A.J. Rand, 2018, Fuel Cell Systems Explained, Wiley&Sons

IEC 61892, 2015, Mobile and fixed offshore units - Electrical installations, 3.0. ed, IEC, Geneva, Switzerland.

M. Korpås, L. Warland, W. He, J. O. G. Tande, 2012, A case-study on offshore wind power supply to oil and gas rigs, Energy Procedia, 24, 18–26.

O. Kruck, F. Crotogino, R. Prelicz, T. Rudolph, 2013, Overview on all known underground storage technologies for hydrogen, HyUnder, Deliverable 3.1.

P. Kundur, J. Paserba, V. Ajjarapu, G. Andersson, A. Bose, C. Canizares, N. Hatziargyriou, D. Hill, A. Stankovic, C. Taylor, T. Van Cutsen, V. Vittal, 2004 Definition and classification of power system stability, IEEE Transactions on Power Systems 19, 1387–1401.

P. Millet, 2015, PEM Water Electrolysis, in book: Hydrogen Production by Electrolysis, ed. Agata Dodula-Jopek, Wiley-WCH Verlag, Weinheim.

F. G. Nielsen, 2018, Hywind – From idea to world's first wind farm based upon floaters. Available at: https://bit.ly/2QYQIGM

K.G. Papadopoulos, 2015, PID controller tuning using the magnitude optimum criterion. Springer International Publishing, Cham.

A. J. Pimm, S. D. Garvey, M. de Jong, 2014, Design and testing of Energy Bags for underwater compressed air energy storage, Energy, 66:496–508.

L. Riboldi, L. O. Nord, 2017, Concepts for lifetime efficient supply of power and heat to offshore installations in the North Sea, Energy Convers Manag, 148:860–75.

L. Riboldi, L. O. Nord, 2017, Lifetime Assessment of Combined Cycles for Cogeneration of Power and Heat in Offshore Oil and Gas Installations. Energies, 10:744.

L. Riboldi, L. O. Nord, 2018, Offshore Power Plants Integrating a Wind Farm: Design Optimisation and Techno-Economic Assessment Based on Surrogate Modelling. Processes.

L. Riboldi, S. Völler, M. Korpås, L. O. Nord, 2019, An Integrated Assessment of the Environmental and Economic Impact of Offshore Oil Platform Electrification. Energies, 12.

S. Sanchez, E. Tedeschi, J. Silva, M. Jafar, A. Marichalar, 2017, Smart load management of water injection systems in offshore oil and gas platforms integrating wind power, IET Renewable Power Generation 11, 1153–1162.

C. Spiegel, 2008, PEM Fuel Cell Modeling and Simulation Using Matlab, Academic Press.

Statistics Norway, 2018, Table 1: Emissions to air of greenhouse gases, Available at: https://www.ssb.no/en/natur-og-miljo/statistikker/klimagassn

Thermoflow Inc., 2016, Thermoflex Version 26.0, Fayville, MA, USA.

H. Zhang, S. Su, G. Lin, J. Chen, 2012, Efficiency Calculation and Configuration Design of a PEM Electrolyzer System for Hydrogen Production, International Journal of Electrochemical Science, 7, 4143-4157.

Sauro Pierucci, Flavio Manenti, Giulia Bozzano, Davide Manca (Eds.)
Proceedings of the 30th European Symposium on Computer Aided Process Engineering
(ESCAPE30), May 24-27, 2020, Milano, Italy. © 2020 Elsevier B.V. All rights reserved.
http://dx.doi.org/10.1016/B978-0-12-823377-1.50037-9

Nonlinear Prediction Model of Blast Furnace Operation Status

Pourya Azadi[a,*], Saeid Ahangari Minaabad[a], Hauke Bartusch[b], Rainer Klock[c],
Sebastian Engell[a]

[a]*Process Dynamics and Operations Group, Department of Biochemical and Chemical Engineering, TU Dortmund, Emil Figge Straße 70, 44227 Dortmund, Germany*
[b]*Process Optimisation Iron and Steel Making Department, VDEh-Betriebsforschunginstitut GmbH, Sohnstraße 65, 40237 Düsseldorf, Germany*
[c]*thyssenkrupp Steel Europe AG, Kaiser-Wilhelm-Straße 100, 47166 Duisburg, Germany*
pourya.azadi@tu-dortmund.de

Abstract

The operation status of a process in the steel industry is mainly defined by three aspects, efficiency, productivity and safety. It provides guidance for the operators to make decisions on their future actions. The abrasive process environment inside a blast furnace (BF) makes it demanding to analyse the operation status by direct internal measurements. The blast furnace gas utilization factor (ETACO) is an essential indicator of the process efficiency. Besides efficiency, productivity and safety can, to some extent, be derived from the pressure drop (DP) and the top gas temperature (TG). This paper presents a nonlinear autoregressive network with exogenous inputs (NARX) model for the simultaneous multistep ahead prediction of ETACO, DP and TG, based upon a new set of fast and slow dynamic input attributes. Validation results using real industrial plant measurements show that this approach not only enables monitoring of the current operation status but also provides prediction capability by including the slow dynamics of the blast furnace into the model.

Keywords: Blast furnace operation status, NARX model, Multistep ahead prediction

1. Introduction

The ironmaking blast furnace (BF) is a very energy-intensive metallurgical process and the prime route for steel production, from which about 70% of the world's steel consumption is produced (Geerdes et al., 2015). The BF system receives coke and ore solid raw material along with hot blast air and continuously produces hot metal as the main product, as well as top gas and slag as the by-products. The performance of a BF is commonly characterized by its efficiency, productivity and safety. Currently, the BF industry is very focused on energy-saving and environmental-friendly operation. Productivity is a function of fuel efficiency and the amount of available gas in the process (Seetharaman, 2013). The complex physical and chemical phenomena inside the BF, with nonlinearly interconnected process variables in three dimensions, make the application of dynamic first-principle models demanding. Alternatively, in recent years, data-based modelling and prediction algorithms have shown great potential and been used more often for representing the BF process with less effort than the first-principle models. High temperatures and the corrosive internal environment of the blast furnace make continuous direct internal measurements impossible and hence the operation status must be monitored via the conditions at the boundaries (Saxén et al., 2013). The gas utilization factor, defined as the ratio of the carbon dioxide and carbon monoxide concentration of the BF top gas, is an essential indicator of the process efficiency. In (Li et al., 2018) and (Zhang et al., 2018), the authors established a soft sensing scheme to predict the gas utilization ratio based on hot blast flowrate, temperature and pressure, as well as top gas pressure and permeability index input attributes. However, there are several shortcomings in these works. Firstly, the gas utilization ratio is additionally dependent on the physical, chemical and metallurgical properties of the solid feedstock (Geerdes et al., 2015). However, these attributes have not been considered in the development of the models. As explained below, in order to ensure the productivity and safety of the BF operation by control strategies, the model prediction should also incorporate pressure drop and top gas temperature (Geerdes et al., 2015). In (Zhang et al., 2016), a nonlinear autoregressive and moving average (NARMA) model was developed to predict the BF operation status. However, this model does not consider exogenous inputs and therefore cannot be used to determine future actions.

In this work, we propose a new set of exogenous input variables and develop a nonlinear autoregressive with exogenous input (NARX) model for the multistep prediction of the BF efficiency, productivity and safety. The paper is structured as follows. First, the process is described in more detail. Then, the selection of the input variables based on the process knowledge and the data pre-processing are explained. The structural parameters of the NARX model are discussed, followed by a discussion on the multistep prediction results of the outputs of interest. Finally, an outlook on future research is given.

2. Process description

The overview of a blast furnace with its basic terminology is related to Figure 1. The internal part of a blast furnace is divided into five major zones: the throat, the stack, the belly, the bosh and the hearth. A blast furnace is a counter-current gas-solid reactor where the ascending gas reacts with the descending solid bed, producing hot metal as the main product. The coke and iron-ore bearing burden (lump ore, sinter and pellets) along with flux materials are fed from the top until the BF is filled with alternating layers of coke and ore at the level of the stockline at the bottom of the throat. Compressed hot blast air (1000 – 1300 °C) containing oxygen, nitrogen and moisture, along with additional enriching pure oxygen and pulverized coal is blown into the furnace via the tuyeres. The hot blast oxidizes all carbon-based materials (coke and coal) in the raceways and produces the reducing agent, gaseous carbon monoxide (CO) and hydrogen (H_2) with a flame temperature of 1900 – 2300 °C. The gas ascends through the furnace while heating up the materials, melting the iron ore and conducting chemical reactions. This gas leaves the top of the BF at around 100 °C after 6 – 10 seconds. On the other hand, the iron-ore is first heated up to about 600 °C at the top of the furnace until the indirect reduction reactions, Eqs. (1) and (2), start in the stack.

$$FeO_x + CO \rightarrow FeO_{x-1} + CO_2 \tag{1}$$

$$FeO_x + H_2 \rightarrow FeO_{x-1} + H_2O \tag{2}$$

The reduced iron-ore materials descend further to the belly and bosh regions at the softening/melting temperature of 1000 – 1100 °C. At this stage, the molten wustite (FeO) undergoes the cyclic reactions, Eqs. (3) and (4), to produce the molten iron.

$$FeO + CO \rightarrow Fe + CO_2 \qquad \text{(Direct reduction reaction)} \tag{3}$$

$$CO_2 + C \rightarrow 2CO \qquad \text{(Boudouard reaction)} \tag{4}$$

Afterwards, the liquid iron and slag, which is mainly formed from the burden gangue materials (CaO, MgO, Al_2O_3 and SiO_2) and the coke ash, drip through the active coke and accumulate in the voids between the inactive coke particles (deadman) in the hearth. The hot metal is cast via the taphole at a temperature around 1500 °C. The residence time of the solid is around 6 – 10 hours. More detailed information can be found in (Geerdes et al., 2015).

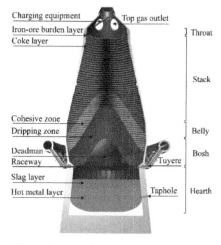

Figure 1: Overall sketch of a blast furnace

3. Analysis of the process variables

In this section, an overview of the input and output variables of the model is given.

3.1. Model outputs

The BF operation status can be monitored through the gas utilization factor (ETACO), the pressure drop (DP), and the top gas temperature (TG). Eq. (5) gives the definition of the gas utilization factor:

$$\eta_{CO} = \frac{CO_2}{CO + CO_2} \tag{5}$$

where CO_2 and CO stand for the concentration of carbon dioxide and carbon monoxide in the top gas. This factor reflects the amount of indirect and direct reduction reactions of the iron oxide and ranges between 0.45 – 0.52. The higher the value of ETACO is, the more efficient the BF operation is, which indicates that the oxygen is removed from the ore using less coke and coal (Geerdes et al., 2015). Another significant aspect of the operation status is productivity. The BF productivity can be assessed through the maximum pressure drop and the top gas temperature. Operating the BF above the maximum DP (1.4 – 1.7 bar) results in decayed burden descent and hence decreased productivity (Geerdes et al., 2015). Furthermore, since the BF is a gas-solid reactor, the productivity increases when more gas is produced at the tuyeres. The more oxygen is injected through the tuyeres, the more gasification takes place in the raceways, resulting in higher productivity. However, too much oxygen injection results in higher temperatures at the raceways. All reactions shift to the lower furnace regions and the wall, resulting in higher heat loss and delayed indirect reduction reaction. This leads to a lowered top temperature. If the top gas temperature becomes too low (less than 100 °C), the effective volume of the furnace, the bed permeability for the gas and liquid flows and thus the productivity decrease (Geerdes et al., 2015). In addition, the drying of the burden materials is prolonged and the BF process becomes more sensitive to wet and low-quality raw materials, rising the risk of process instabilities such as hanging and slipping of the burden (irregular burden descent) and channelling (a direct gas tunnel from the tuyeres to the BF top). In the worst case, the risk extends to a chilled hearth where the connection between tuyeres and hearth is lost and the outflows of the produced hot metal and slag are ceased (Schwalbe et al., 2015; Geerdes et al., 2015). This event can be identified in top gas temperatures falling below 80 °C (Seetharaman, 2013). Based on these insights, ETACO, DP and TG are considered as the model outputs for monitoring the BF operation status.

3.2. Model inputs

The proposed set of input variables are listed in Table 1. The hot blast is the origin of the produced gas at the tuyere level of the furnace. Its parameters affect the reaction conditions. Due to the very short residence time of the gas, changes in the hot blast variables can be directly detected in the top gas. More oxygen in the raceways results in more gasification. Then, not only a large amount of heat is released, but also more gaseous reducing agents are produced, promoting the reduction reactions, which can be identified through the gas utilization rate and the top gas temperature. The blast moisture reacts with the available carbon in front of the tuyeres and produces H_2. Part of the oxygen in the iron-ore is removed by H_2. Therefore, varying the hot blast moisture changes the portion of the reduction reactions between CO and H_2, which is reflected in the gas utilization factor. The gas flow distribution depends on the blast volume and the bed permeability. The bed permeability is an essential characteristic in the BF process. It is influenced by fine particles and the reduction disintegration (RDI) feature of the sinter. Generally, FeO, SiO_2 and MgO make the burden more resistant, and CaO

Table 1: Input variables

Variable name	Symbol	Unit
Blast volume	VB	m^3/h
Blast temperature	TB	°C
Top pressure	PG	bar
Oxygen enrichment	OE	m^3/h
Coal injection	PCI	m^3/h
Blast moisture	MB	g/m^3
Burden depth	BD	m
Coke reactivity index	CRI	-
Coke mass flow	Coke	t/min
Sinter mass flow	Sinter	t/min
Pellet mass flow	Pellet	t/min
CaO mass flow	CaO	t/min
MgO mass flow	MgO	t/min
Al_2O_3 mass flow	Al2O3	t/min
SiO_2 mass flow	SiO2	t/min
FeO mass flow	FeO	t/min
Permeability index	PI	-

and Al_2O_3 more prone to RDI. The changes in RDI also affect the pressure drop and the gas utilization factor. The top pressure is an independent control variable in the process that is regulated by the annular gap elements of the exhaust system. It influences the gas velocity and the pressure drop, the intensity of the chemical reactions and, thus, the gas utilization factor. The sinter materials contain less oxygen than pellets to be removed. Thus, the effect that the amounts of sinter and pellet have on ETACO should also be incorporated into the model. For further details see (Geerdes et al., 2015).

A principal component analysis (PCA) is used to support the choice of the input

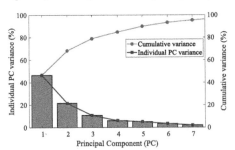

Figure 2: PCA scree plot

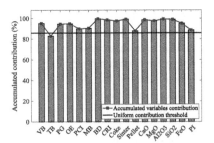

Figure 3: Variables contribution to all 7 PCs

variables. As Figure 2 reveals, 95% of the major variations in the input variables are incorporated by 7 principal components. The accumulated contribution of all input variables, except the blast temperature (TB), to all 7 principal components, as shown in Figure 3, is above the uniform contribution threshold, approving the importance of the variables influencing TG, DP and ETACO. As a result, the set of input attributes is finalized with 16 variables, excluding the blast temperature: VB, PG, OE, PCI, MB, BD, CRI, Coke, Sinter, Pellet, CaO, MgO, Al2O3, SiO2, FeO and PI. This is also motivated by the fact that, in practice, this variable is highly correlated (more than 0.8) with the pulverized coal injection which is an input variable.

4. Multistep ahead prediction of operation status

In this work, a nonlinear autoregressive model with exogenous inputs (NARX) is used to represent the nonlinear relation between the input and output variables. NARX is a feedforward neural network-based model with external memory. Such a model can mathematically be stated as follows:

$$y(t) = f(y(t-1), \ldots, y(t-d_y), u(t), u(t-1), \ldots, u(t-d_u)) \tag{6}$$

where y represents the output vector and u is the set of exogenous inputs. The blast variables, due to the gas residence time being shorter than the sampling time (1 minute), are considered to have no time delay with respect to the output variables. A time delay of 5 minutes is chosen for the slow dynamic (solid phase) variables based on the influence of burden loading on the output variables. The output autoregressive order and the number of hidden layers of the embedded network (p) are chosen based on the Bayes Information Criterion (BIC), defined in Eq. (7), with SSR and T as the sum of squared regression and number of data points:

$$BIC(p) = \ln\left(\frac{SSR(p)}{T}\right) + (p+1)\frac{\ln T}{T} \tag{7}$$

The first term penalizes the error of the model, while the second term penalizes the complexity of the network. The parameters with the minimum BIC value are chosen for the network. Table 2 summarizes the BIC analysis.

The dataset for the model with 400000 samples was obtained from plant measurements of the large-scale blast furnace 2 Schwelgern in thyssenkrupp Steel Europe with the working volume of about 4800 m³. In our study, 98% of the samples were used for training and cross-validation and the rest for testing. One-step ahead prediction based training was carried out. Figure 4 depicts the free-running forward simulation results of the multistep ahead prediction (MSAP) of the BF operation status, over a horizon of 3 hours, using the proposed input variables. The quality of the predictions over such a long horizon in comparison with the test

Table 2: Bayes information criterion analysis

Autoregressive order	Hidden layers	Hidden neuron per layer	BIC	R^2
1	3	30	6.6500	0.9509
15	**5**	**30**	**6.6355**	**0.9623**
30	6	30	6.6361	0.9689
60	6	30	6.6457	0.9696

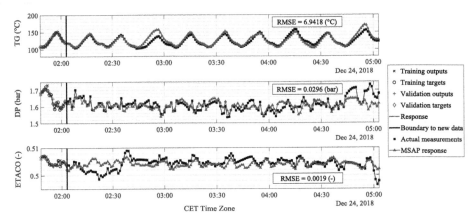

Figure 4: Multistep ahead prediction of BF operation status – validation results (TG: top gas temperature; DP: pressure drop; ETACO: gas utilization factor)

dataset demonstrates the reliable prediction of the operation status when using the proposed input attributes. Despite the influence of unknown disturbances, the root mean squared errors (RMSE) of the predictions are small (see **figure 4**) so the model can be used in a model-based control scheme.

5. Conclusions and outlook

A nonlinear data-based prediction model of blast furnace operation status with a set of carefully selected exogenous inputs has been developed and validated by real plant measurements. The validation results show that the model is able to predict the main trend of the BF operation status under the stable working condition over a long prediction horizon. In the future, we plan to apply the model to compute control strategies for optimal decision-making on the future input variables to the process.

Acknowledgement

The project leading to this publication has received funding from the Bundesministerium für Wirtschaft und Energie under the grant agreement number 03ET1524B. The responsibility for the content of this publication lies solely with the authors.

References

M. Geerdes, R. Chaigneau, I. Kurunov, O. Lingiardi, J. Ricketts. 2015. Modern blast furnace ironmaking: an introduction. Amsterdam, NL: IOS Press BV.

Y. Li, S. Zhang, Y. Yin, J. Zhang, W. Xiao. 2018. A soft sensing scheme of gas utilization ratio prediction for blast furnace via improved extreme learning machine. Neural Process. Lett 1-23.

H. Saxén, C. Gao, Z. Gao. 2013. Data-driven time-discrete models for dynamic prediction of the hot metal silicon content in the blast furnace - a review. IEEE Trans. Ind. Informat. 9 (4): 2213 - 2225.

R. Schwalbe, R. Klock, U. Janhsen, P. Schmöle, M. Peters. 2015. Influence of intentionally deteriorated coke properties on performance of blast furnace 2 schwelgern. METEC & 2nd ESTAD.

S. Seetharaman. 2013. Treatise on Process Metallurgy, Volume 3: Industrial Processes. Oxford, UK: Elsevier.

L. Zhang, C. Hua, J. Li, X. Guan. 2016. Operation Status Prediction Based on Top Gas System Analysis for Blast Furnace. IEEE Trans. Control Syst. Technol. 25 (1): 262-269.

S. Zhang, H. Jiang, Y. Yin, W. Xiao, B. Zhao. 2018. The prediction of the gas utilization ratio based on TS fuzzy neural network and particle swarm optimization. Sensors 18 (2): 625.

Sauro Pierucci, Flavio Manenti, Giulia Bozzano, Davide Manca (Eds.)
Proceedings of the 30th European Symposium on Computer Aided Process Engineering
(ESCAPE30), May 24-27, 2020, Milano, Italy. © 2020 Elsevier B.V. All rights reserved.
http://dx.doi.org/10.1016/B978-0-12-823377-1.50038-0

CFD Simulation of a Solid-Liquid Counter-Current Screw Extractor

Annemarie Lehr,[a*] Gábor Janiga,[a] Andreas Seidel-Morgenstern,[a,b] Dominique Thévenin[a]

[a]*Otto von Guericke University Magdeburg, Universitätsplatz 2, 39106 Magdeburg, Germany*
[b]*Max Planck Institute for Dynamics of Complex Technical Systems, Sandtorstraße 1, 39106 Magdeburg, Germany*
annemarie.lehr@ovgu.de

Abstract

More efficient processes to obtain artemisinin from *Artemisia annua* leaves via a solid-liquid extraction process are desirable, since artemisinin is increasingly needed as anti-malaria drug. As a substitute for conventional batch extraction technology, continuously operated counter-current processes are highly attractive for that purpose. To get first a better understanding of the hydrodynamics controlling the extraction, a multiphase 3D computational fluid dynamics (CFD) simulation model has been developed in the present project. It relies on the Volume of Fluid (VoF) model, leading to a purely Eulerian description of the flow. Using VoF, the distribution of the different phases within the screw extractor can be obtained. When varying the two inlet flow rates, different residence times for the liquid and the solid phases are obtained. This is particularly important, since the residence time is the most important process parameter to adjust. Currently, the predicted residence times for the liquid solvent amount to only one third of the experimentally determined values. However, accurate measurements are difficult, the assessment of residence times is different in the experiments and in the simulations, and the numerical model does not consider mass exchange processes between the phases yet. In spite of this discrepancy, a very good qualitative agreement is obtained, and these first results can be used to support the development of a compartment model, able to capture later both hydrodynamic and mass exchange processes with short computational times.

Keywords: CFD, fluid dynamics, mass exchange, screw extractor, VOF

1. Introduction

Counter-current extraction processes are widely used in the food industry, where they are applied, for example, in the solid-liquid extraction of beet sugar or rapeseed oil. With this method, higher final concentrations of the target substance in the solvent can be obtained compared to the direct current method. Additionally, the yield of the extraction process can be increased. This leads in the pharmaceutical industry to a growing interest in continuously operated counter-current processes. High yields are required for the extraction of plant substances from natural materials, used further for the preparation of drugs (Lack, 1985). Following this concept, the Max Planck Institute (MPI) Magdeburg has developed a continuous process based on a solid-liquid counter-current screw extraction to gain artemisinin from *Artemisia annua* leaves. Derivatives of artemisinin (e.g., artesunate) are increasingly used as efficient anti-malaria drugs (Gilmore et al., 2014). According to the World Malaria Report 2018, 219 million people worldwide were infected with malaria in 2017. About 435,000 people died as a result of malaria infection, of which 61 % were children under 5 years (World Health Organisation, 2018). These facts demonstrate the importance of efficient extraction of artemisinin, which would allow a higher treatment rate thanks to a decrease in production costs. For this aim an appropriate solvent is necessary. For this particular separation problem, toluene is a promising substance (Lapkin et al., 2010, Gilmore et al., 2014). However, this organic solvent is highly explosive and requires a lot of safety procedures. Experimental counter-current extraction studies have just started in our group. Here, the use of CFD in preliminary studies is an advantage and can contribute to a better understanding of the process. The implemented counter-current screw extractor at the MPI Magdeburg represents a combination of screw extractor and extruder. The complexity of the system is very high as it involves a multiphase (solid-liquid) flow with a free surface, and rotating components. A detailed overview of the state of the art regarding CFD for modelling positive displacement screw machines is provided by Kovacevic et al. (2016), who focus on the importance of capturing the leakage gaps on the grid. Bahadar et al. (2013) performed a CFD simulation of a screw expeller for performance analysis regarding massive Jatropha biomass in connection with oil extraction. Lübke and Wünsch (2012) dealt with free-surface flows of highly viscous liquids in single screw extruders, using a combination of an Euler-Euler approach with the Volume of Fluid method.

In this work, a 3D investigation relying on the industrial CFD software package StarCCM+ has been performed in order to represent the extraction process. Due to the high complexity of this configuration, mass exchange processes and reactions between the natural material and the solvent are first neglected. The results are compared with experimental data using water as a solvent. In addition, the results are currently used to derive and parameterize a compartment model. Ultimately, this model will be used to optimize solvent choice and extraction process.

2. Methods and Implementation

The geometry used for the preliminary simulations corresponds to the original pilot plant of the screw extruder. This has a length of 321 mm, smaller than the production extraction device now used for all experiments at MPI Magdeburg, with a length of 640 mm. As all other dimensions are identical, a first analysis of the flow behaviour can be obtained more rapidly with the smaller geometry, imported as a CAD file (Figure 1). Since only the screw shall rotate, the domain has been separated into a rotating and a stationary domain. The employed mesh was created with a polyhedral mesher, with a base size of $\Delta x = 8$ mm.

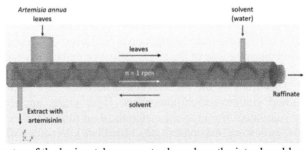

Figure 1: Geometry of the horizontal screw extruder, where the introduced leaves are transported in axial direction by the screw, while the solvent flows in counter-current direction due to a perforated disc at the outlet of the raffinate. This corresponds to the experimental procedure. The length of the geometry amounts to $l = 321$ mm and the diameter has a value of $d = 29.7$ mm.

Refinements at the interface between the domains were implemented to accurately capture the occurring leakage flows. A total number of roughly 1 million finite-volume cells were generated. For the considered flow, a Reynolds number of 26 can be computed, so that the flow is laminar. The flow simulation is based on a purely Eulerian approach. In addition, the VoF model has been activated to track the boundary of the two involved phases. As the complexity of the process is very high (three phases: gaseous, liquid, and solid), with additional rotation of the screw, separate CFD simulations have been performed. First simulations consider a free-surface flow between solvent and air, neglecting the solid phase; this simulation shall deliver information regarding the steady-state position of the liquid surface. A second simulation set was performed to investigate an extruder filled with liquid, neglecting the gas and the solid phase; this simulation is used to get first estimates concerning residence times and deliver information for fitting a compartment model.

2.1. Two-Phase Flow: Liquid – Gas

Since the gas phase is not significantly influenced by the low-speed liquid and screw, it can be regarded as incompressible. In order to capture the free surface between the liquid and the gaseous phase, the VoF model is suitable. For the simulation, the default material properties of water and air provided by the employed software (StarCCM+) at room temperature have been used. At the start of the simulation the screw extruder is filled with water by 60 % in volume. This corresponds to the initial filling degree with solid matter in the experiments. Starting screw rotation at a speed of $n = 1$ rpm, water is continuously injected into the system with a volumetric flow-rate of $\dot{V} = 1$ L/h, again mimicking the experimental procedure. The time step of this unsteady simulation was set constant to $\Delta t = 0.01$ s; this small value was necessary to get a stable free surface.

2.2. Two-Phase Flow: Liquid – Highly Viscous Phase

As the numerical simulation of a solid phase is very complex, the water-soaked *Artemisia annua* leaves have been represented in an approximate manner as a Newtonian fluid with a very high viscosity of $\eta = 1,000$ Pa·s, chosen after viscosity measurements of the raffinate using an available rotational rheometer (Kinexus pro+, Malvern). Since mass exchange processes between the phases are not considered yet, the effects of density and viscosity differences on the residence time of the liquid phase will be analysed instead by setting constant, linear profiles of these quantities in the device. In addition, the values of the injected liquid volumetric flow-rate and of the rotational speed of the screw have been varied in order to quantify the corresponding changes in residence time and compare these numerical predictions with experimental data. Finally, the residence time of the solvent toluene has been compared with that obtained for water, keeping all other conditions identical. This will help preparing corresponding modifications of the experimental studies.

3. Results and Discussion

3.1. Two-Phase Flow: Liquid – Gas

Figure 2 illustrates the distribution of the water and air phases along a vertical cross-section of the extractor (y-z plane). This result is obtained by VoF after a process time of 120 s, which corresponds to two complete revolutions of the screw and could be obtained with a computational time of four days using 6 cores. This state corresponds visually to near steady state.

Figure 3 shows the evolution with time of the air/water interface. It corresponds to a volume fraction of $0 \leq \alpha_{water} \leq 1$, which extends over one to three control volumes in the present simulations. Due to the slow rotation of the screw, the interface is found to remain stable even when the screw crosses it. With time, a movement of the interface starting from a horizontal state, is observed as expected (Figure 3), due to the conveying of the screw in axial direction. At steady-state, the height of the interface increases continuously over the length of the reactor from left to right in axial direction x (with $x = 0$ at the left side, where the outlet of the extract is located). Its position can be approximated by $z = -0.044x^2 + 0.036x + 0.001$.

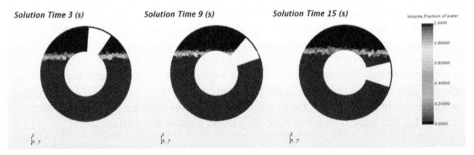

Figure 2: Distribution of the phases water (bottom) and air (upper) along a vertical cross-section (y-z plane) during the passage of the screw (white) through the interface (from air into water).

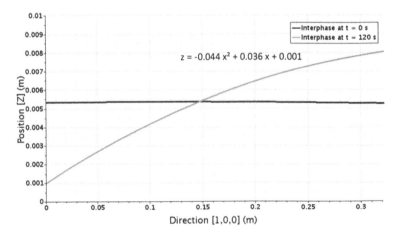

Figure 3: Height curve of the interface between water and air caused by the conveying of the screw in axial direction at the solution times $t = 0$ s (initial) and $t = 120$ s (steady-state). The value $z = 0$ corresponds to the axis of the extractor.

3.2. Two-Phase Flow: Liquid – Highly Viscous Phase

Implementing a fixed linear density difference between the left and right end of the plant for the highly viscous phase varying from $\Delta\rho$ = 140 to 420 kg/m³ leads with increasing values to a decrease of the residence time of water from τ = 3.78 min to τ = 3.05 min (Figure 4). For comparison, the residence time of water in the extractor without any density difference using the value corresponding to the dry leaves, leads to a higher value of τ = 4.5 min. This must be compared to the experimental residence time, estimated as 10.7 min. In addition, the implemented viscosity difference for the highly viscous phase, which leads to a linear decrease of the viscosity value from η = 1,000 Pa·s at the left end of the screw to a value of η = 100 Pa·s at its right end, results in an increase of the residence time from 3.15 min to 3.42 min. To analyse the most relevant quantities for the process, a constant viscosity of η = 1,000 Pa·s and a density difference of $\Delta\rho$ = 340 kg/m³ were set. Keeping these conditions but doubling the volumetric flow-rate of water injected into the extractor, a halving of the residence time from 3.15 min to 1.53 min is observed in the CFD (Figure 5), as expected, since water is then the dominant phase. Hence, it is shown that the residence time can be tuned to a desired value by setting in an appropriate manner the water flow-rate entering the extractor. Comparing the numerical residence times for changing volumetric flow-rates with experimental values determined at the MPI Magdeburg (Figure 5), a good qualitative agreement can be observed despite quantitative differences by a factor 3.5. The residence times increase exponentially for smaller volumetric flow-rates. In contrast, changing the rotational speed from n = 1 to 1.5 rpm (increase by 50 %) has only a minor influence on the numerical residence times. This also corroborates experimental observations. Switching now the liquid phase from water to toluene as solvent by changing the corresponding density and viscosity values while keeping all other parameters identical, the residence time increases slightly from 3.15 min to 3.31 min. This must be kept in mind when planning the modifications of the experimental set-up.

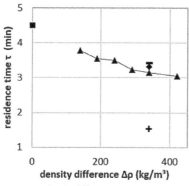

— density difference
■ constant density leaves
— viscosity difference
+ double volumetric flow-rate
♦ toluene

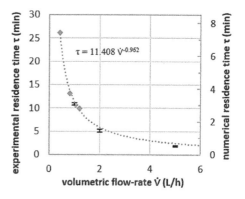

I numerical - rotational speed n = 1 - 1.5 rpm
♦ experimental (MPI) - rotational speed n = 1 rpm
······ interpolation of experimental data

Figure 4: Change in residence time of the solvent predicted by numerical simulation when varying different flow quantities with density differences for the highly viscous phase ranging from $\Delta\rho$ = 140 to 420 kg/m³.

Figure 5: Comparison between numerical and experimental (MPI Magdeburg) residence times of water (in min) as a function of the volumetric flow-rate injected into the extractor and of the rotational speed of the screw.

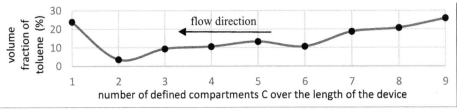

Figure 6: Volume fraction of toluene in defined compartments (C), C1-outlet, C9-inlet

The obtained numerical results show lower residence times compared to the experimental observations of 10 min. The predicted residence times are shorter by a factor 3.5. Apart from the smaller length of the used geometry compared to the experiments (factor 2), at least three reasons can be proposed to explain this discrepancy: 1) Currently, all mass exchange processes between the phases are neglected; 2) The numerical model contains simplifications, e.g. concerning material properties; 3) The residence time is measured in the simulations by tracking the first appearance of solvent at the outlet, while a different protocol based on a pulse injection is used in the experiments.

4. Conclusions and Outlook

A 3D multiphase CFD model for a counter-current extraction process has been developed. This model has been used to investigate the effect of different quantities. For instance, the rotational speed of the screw is not significant for small values, while the injected volumetric flow-rate of the solvent can be modified to set a desired value of the residence time. Both findings corroborate well with experimental observations, even if quantitative differences by a factor 3.5 are still found, due to the different lengths of the reactors but also to limited model and measurement accuracy. This will be further refined in on-going studies. The developed CFD approach is currently used to parametrize a compartment model for toluene with a view toward process optimization. As a first step, the volume fractions of toluene in manually-defined compartments have been obtained on the basis of pressure (Figure 6) where a decrease from inlet to outlet can be observed, which is in qualitative agreement with the expectations for this system. Additionally, mass exchange processes between the different phases will be implemented in the solver in the future.

References

A. Bahadar, M.B. Khan, T. Mehran, 2013, Design and development of an efficient screw press expeller for oil expression from Jatropha Curcas seeds, 2013, Industrial & Engineering Chemistry Research, 52, 5, 2123-2129

K. Gilmore, D. Kopetzki, J. W. Lee, Z. Horvath, D. T. McQuade, A. Seidel-Morgenstern, P. H. Seeberger, 2014, Continuous synthesis of artemisinin-derived medicines, Chemical Communications, 50, 12652-12655

A. Kovacevic, S. Rane, N. Stosic, 2016, Computational fluid dynamics in rotary positive displacement screw machines, 16th International Symposium in Transport Phenomena and Dynamics of Rotating Machinery, Honolulu, United States, hal-01879361

E. A. Lack, 1985, Kriterien zur Auslegung von Anlagen für die Hochdruckextraktion von Naturstoffen, PhD Thesis, Graz, Austria

A. A. Lapkin, M. Peters, L. Greiner, S. Chemat, K. Leonhard, M. A. Liauw, W. Leitner, 2010, Screening of new solvents for artemisinin extraction process using *ab initio* methodology, Green Chemistry, 12, 2, 241-251

M. Lübke, O. Wünsch, 2012, Two-Phase Flow in Single Screw Extruders, Proceedings in Applied Mathematics and Mechanics, 12, 1, 509-510

World Health Organisation, 2018, World Malaria Report (accessed on: November 08, 2019)

Sauro Pierucci, Flavio Manenti, Giulia Bozzano, Davide Manca (Eds.)
Proceedings of the 30th European Symposium on Computer Aided Process Engineering
(ESCAPE30), May 24-27, 2020, Milano, Italy. © 2020 Elsevier B.V. All rights reserved.
http://dx.doi.org/10.1016/B978-0-12-823377-1.50039-2

Optimum Utilization of *Jatropha* Seedcake Considering the Energy, Water and Food Nexus

Mohammad Alherbawi,[a] Ahmed AlNouss,[a] Gordon Mckay,[a] Tareq Al-Ansari [a,b*]

a Division of Sustainable Development, College of Science and Engineering, Hamad Bin Khalifa University, Qatar Foundation, Doha, Qatar.

b Division of Engineering Management of Decision Sciences, College of Science and Engineering, Hamad Bin Khalifa University, Qatar Foundation, Doha, Qatar.

talansari@hbku.edu.qa

Abstract

Biofuel production has attracted significant attention from researchers and policymakers as a carbon-neutral source of energy. However, corresponding intensive land and water requirements have hindered the advancement of the biofuel industry. Consequently, second-generation biofuels from non-edible biomass have been promoted as suitable alternatives. In this context, the *Jatropha curcas* has proved to be a promising feedstock for various types of biofuels due to its competences over other oil-bearing crops, and its suitability to grow in non-arable lands with minimal water and energy requirements. In addition to utilising *Jatropha* oil as a source of energy, *Jatropha* seedcake has been used to produce energy and food-related products. Although, there are several processing pathways of seedcake which have been investigated, there are no conclusions on the optimum overall pathway. Meanwhile, the Energy-Water-Food (EWF) Nexus approach has recently become an important tool to ensure efficient and optimum management of the three vital resources by considering the inter-dependencies amongst them. It can also guide decision making in terms of identifying optimal processing and utilisation pathways. Therefore, this study presents an analysis of different production routes, and defines the optimum utilisation of *Jatropha* seedcake, by ensuring that the highest possible net energy, water and food are achieved. Required data are obtained via Aspen Plus' simulation of potential processes, while MATLAB is used to develop the mathematical optimisation model. The model produced 77 different solutions, with gasification being the dominant pathway in most of the given solutions, followed by livestock feed and fertilizers production.

Keywords: *Jatropha*, Biofuels, Seedcake, EWF Nexus, Optimisation.

1. Introduction

Biofuel production has been widely investigated throughout the past two decades to mitigate the carbon emissions and to combat global warming. Various energy crops have been tested for biofuel production worldwide. However, the widely used feedstock such as sunflower and corn oils have been criticized for being used as a source of energy at the expense of food, land and water resources. Since then, vast efforts have been directed towards a second generation of feedstock represented in non-edible biomass, where *Jatropha curcas* has been selected because of its properties compared to various other energy crops. *Jatropha*, a non-food competing crop can tolerate difficult soil conditions and is able grow in non-arable and arid lands (Tomar et al., 2014). In addition, *Jatropha* is well known for its minimal demand of water and energy. Not only its oil can be converted to biofuel, but also the fruit residues of *Jatropha* such as the seedcake can be transformed into multiple energy and food-related products as presented in Figure 1. Furthermore, *Jatropha* seedcake can be processed into livestock feed as it contains approximately 60 % of crude protein (Islam et al., 2011). However, it must be detoxified first to decompose its toxic phorbol esters content (Makkar, 2016). *Jatropha* seedcake contains up to 4.44 % nitrogen, 2.09 % phosphorus and 1.68 % potassium which makes it a good candidate to be used as a fertilizer (Islam et al., 2011). Several studies have highlighted the attractive multiple uses of *Jatropha* fruit residues in energy and food production. Yet, no conclusions are drawn on the optimum utilization of these residues. In terms of managing resources, the energy, water and food (EWF) Nexus concept has been used to promote efficient management of the three vital resources considering the inter-dependencies amongst them (AlNouss et al., 2019). It can also serve as a decision-making methodology to identify the synergies and trade-offs amongst different process pathways and product utilization options. Using an EWF Nexus approach, this article investigates the optimum processing routes of *Jatropha* seedcake to produce energy and food-related products.

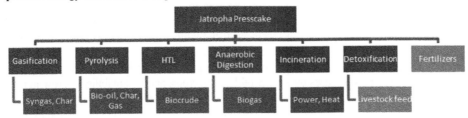

Figure 1: *Jatropha* seedcake processing routes into energy and food-related products.

2. Methodology

The net energy, water and food$_{(eq)}$ outputs of different processing pathways of seedcake is assessed from cradle to gate. For the cultivation and pre-processing stages, the required data are dependent on literature reports. Whereas, at processing level, Aspen Plus (V.9) is used to simulate all processes, except for the production of fertilisers, as it is assumed that the seedcake can be utilised directly as a fertiliser without further processing. The data obtained is then used to run an optimisation mathematical model using MATLAB (R2016b) to determine the optimum processing routes. All models are developed based on the assumptions of steady state and isothermal processes. In this study, 10,000 hectares of *Jatropha* plantations considered at a (3x3m) spacing, which is assumed to yield 100,000 tonnes of *Jatropha* fruits per year. The seedcake accounts for 40 wt.% of the whole-fruit (Singh et al., 2008) and 32 % of its net heating value (Jourabchi et al., 2014). Seedcake is defined based on its proximate and elemental analyses reported earlier (Ramírez et al., 2019).

2.1. Flowsheets Development

Gasification: The *Jatropha* seedcake is initially converted into conventional components using an "Ryield" reactor associated with a calculator block (AlNouss et al., 2018). The ash is then separated using solid separator before introducing the stream into the gasifier. The Cl_2, S and N_2 compounds are first converted completely to HCl, H_2S and NH_3 in a stoichiometric reactor and removed from the inlet stream to the gasifier. Steam is used as a gasifying agent at a steam to biomass ratio of 0.75. While the process is conducted in "RGibbs" reactor at 850 °C and 1 atm. The heat of the gasifier is provided by means of external combustion for a small portion of the carbon.

Pyrolysis: The seedcake is decomposed at 500 °C in "RGibbs" block into pre-defined conventional components. The stream is then introduced into a cyclone unit for solid removal, while the gas stream is cooled down to separate the low boiling-point components to yield bio-oil and syngas products. Besides, the solid stream is further processed into a solid separator, yielding an ash-free biochar (Elkhalifa et al., 2019).

Hydrothermal liquefaction (HTL): The seedcake is initially decomposed into conventional components using a calculator block. The stream is then fed into the main reactor following the removal of ash. A hot and pressurized water is pumped to create a slurry with the presence of sodium hydroxide catalyst. The reaction is conducted at 300 °C and 150 bars using "RGibbs" reactor. Besides, predicted product are defined with reference to earlier reports (Pedersen et al., 2017).

Anaerobic digestion (AD): The process is simulated with reference to literature published models (Salman et al., 2017). The seedcake is converted into conventional components in an "RYield" block based on specific defined yields. The stream is then introduced into a solid separator to remove the solid digestate, while the gaseous stream is further processed into "RStoic" reactor, in which all carbon content is converted into methane and carbon dioxide.

Incineration: The model is simulated as a combined cycle process. Whereby, the seedcake is initially converted into conventional components using a calculator block connected to an "RYield" reactor. In addition, the ash content is removed using a solid separator. The flow is then introduced along with air into an "RStoic" block representing a combustion chamber, in which the process stichometry is defined, yielding a mixture of gases at 8 bar that pass through a gas turbine to generate power. Furthermore, a turbine is used to generate power out of the high-pressure stream generated from the excess heat of the effluent gases.

Detoxification: The model is developed based on the experimental work of Diwani et al. (2011). The process aims at degrading the toxic content of phorbol ester in seedcake, which is assumed to account for 0.29 wt.% (Gogoi et al., 2014). Sodium bicarbonate solution is added to seedcake in an "RGibbs" reactor, then the seedcake is separated and sent to an "RYield" reactor for thermal treatment at a temperature level of 120 °C. The defined yield assumes that all phorbol ester content has been degraded.

2.2. EWF Quantification

The net energy, water and food of the different investigated systems are assessed throughout the process lifecycle including cultivation, transportation, extraction and processing. At pre-processing stages, the EWF inputs are allocated over the *Jatropha* fruit parts based on their calorific values. The energy requirements for cultivation, transportation and extraction are adapted from studies reported by Neto et al. (2018), Han et al. (2013) and Ju et al. (2010) respectively. While the processing energy requirement are estimated by the Aspen Plus simulations. For net water analysis, an average watering value of 1200 mm/year is considered to ensure an optimum seed production (Tomar et al., 2014). Whereas, Aspen Plus estimates the water requirement for processing and cooling, as well as the process' water generation.

Furthermore, the plantation and processing of *Jatropha* do not consume or generate food directly, as it is a non-edible fruit. However, the land used to grow *Jatropha* could have been used at the expense of growing food crops. The area of the land used is converted into a food equivalent (food-$_{eq}$) quantity. For conversion purpose, "cereals" were used as reference crops, as they account for nearly 80 % of global food supply (Markussen and Østergård, 2013). One hectare of land can yield up to 2.25 tonnes of cereals (Roser and Ritchie, 2018), therefore a hectare of land is converted intoa quantity of 2.25 tonnes of food$_{(eq)}$. Besides, the food-related products such as fertilizers and livestock feed are also converted into food$_{(eq)}$ quantity. For fertilizers, the conversion is conducted based on seedcake's nitrogen content (wt.%) versus N-fertilizer requirement to grow cereals (Ladha et al., 2016). While the livestock feed is converted into food$_{(eq)}$ quantity in the form of meat instead of crops. For this purpose, beef is selected as a reference meat, whereby the conversation is conducted based on the seedcake's protein content (wt.%) versus protein requirement to raise cows (kg/kg) (Mekonnen and Hoekstra, 2010).

2.3. Optimization

A mathematical model to define the optimum processing routes for *Jatropha* seedcake is developed as presented in Table 1. The model aims at maximizing the net energy, water and food outputs. All seedcake shall be processed; therefore, the sum of all technologies' share shall be equal to 100 %. The Genetic Algorithm process of MATLAB is used for the optimization. The constants of the objective functions are obtained from simulations, calculations and literature reports as explained in section 2.2.

Table 1: Mathematical formulation of the optimization problem.

Objective functions	Definitions
$Z_E = (\sum_{i=1}^{7} E_i\, X_i)$	Z_E: net energy outcome.
	E_i: Net energy generated from process (i).
$Z_W = (\sum_{i=1}^{7} W_i\, X_i)$	X_i: Share of process (i).
	Z_W: net water outcome.
$Z_F = (\sum_{i=1}^{7} F_i\, X_i)$	W_i: Net water generated from process (i).
	Z_F: net food$_{(eq)}$ outcome.
	F_i: Net food$_{(eq)}$ generated from process (i).
Constraints	
$\sum_{i=1}^{7} X_i = 1$	All seedcake must be utilized.
$X_i \geq 0$	Positivity condition.

3. Results and Discussion

3.1. Processes Outputs

The different investigated processing pathways have yielded significant quantities of energy and food-related products. The energy products are in the form of direct power generation, gaseous fuels such as syngas and biogas, liquid fuels like bio-oil/biocrude or solid fuels like biochar. The food-related products including fertilizers and livestock feed are produced in almost a similar quantity as the feed flow (seedcake). The different processes outputs are illustrated in Figure 2.

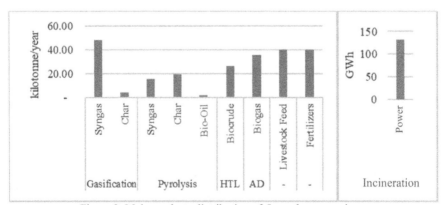

Figure 2: Main products distribution of *Jatropha* processing.

3.2. Net Energy, Water and Food Outputs

The net EWF evaluation of the *Jatropha* seedcake processing pathways is illustrated in Figure 3. The most energy-intensive stage throughout the lifecycle of all products is the cultivation, which is a common stage amongst them. All energy producing pathways are energy efficient with high energy return. Overall, the gasification process is the most energy efficient pathway. Besides, all the processing pathways are water-consuming, with insignificant water generation. Moreover, pyrolysis is the most water consuming pathway, while incineration is the most water generating process. Amongst all energy producing pathways, anaerobic digestion is the least water consuming as no system cooling is required. Obviously, the food$_{(eq)}$ consumption for all pathways is equal, since it accounts for the land use only. Whereas, livestock feed and fertilizers production are the only food$_{(eq)}$ producing pathways, with livestock being the highest food producing in terms of quantity.

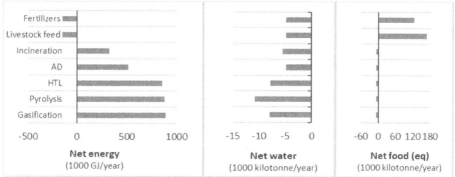

Figure 3: Net value of energy, water and food$_{(eq)}$ outputs for different pathways.

3.3. Optimum Technology

The MATLAB optimization model predicted 77 optimum solutions. The optimum technology share (%) with their corresponding outputs are presented in Figures 4 and 5 respectively. Since the variations in net water values are not great amongst all pathways, it is noticeable that the model conducted a trade-off mainly between both, the net energy and food$_{(eq)}$. The main suggested pathways are gasification followed by livestock feed and fertilizers production.

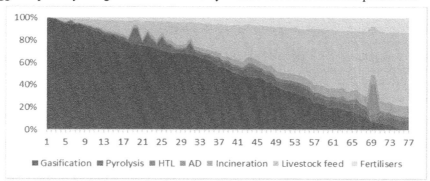

Figure 4: Optimum technology share (%) for *Jatropha* seedcake utilization.

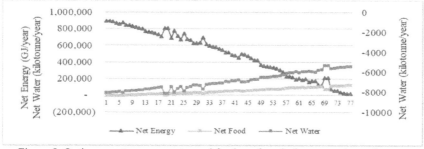

Figure 5: Optimum net energy, water and food$_{(eq)}$ of seedcake processing pathways.

4. Conclusions

Jatropha curcas proved to be a good source for both, energy and food-related production, though, it is still a water-consuming biomass as indicated throughout the various analyses in this study. Seven processing routes of *Jatropha* seedcake were investigated to identify the optimum amongst them in the light of the energy, water and food (EWF) Nexus. The optimisation model yielded 77 different solutions, with gasification being the dominant pathway in most of the given solutions, followed by livestock feed and fertilizers production.

References

A. K. M. A. Islam, Z. Yaakob & N. Anuar, 2011, Jatropha: A multipurpose plant with considerable potential for the tropics. *Scientific Research and Essays*, *6*(13), 2597–2605.

A. AlNouss, G. Mckay & T. Al-ansari, 2018, Optimum Utilization of Biomass for the Production of Power and Fuels using Gasification. In *28th European Symposium on Computer Aided Process Engineering* (Vol. 43, pp. 1481–1486). Elsevier Masson SAS.

A. AlNouss, S. Namany, G. McKay, and T. Al-Ansari, 2019, Applying a Sustainability Metric in Energy, Water and Food Nexus Applications; A Biomass Utilization Case Study to Improve Investment Decisions, Computer Aided Chemical Engineering, 46, 205-10.

C. A. Salman, S. Schwede, E. Thorin & J. Yan, 2017, Predictive Modelling and Simulation of Integrated Pyrolysis and Anaerobic Digestion Process. *Energy Procedia*, *105*, 850–857.

H. P. S. Makkar, 2016, State-of-the-art on detoxification of Jatropha curcas products aimed for use as animal and fish feed: A review. *Animal Feed Science and Technology*, *222*, 87–99.

J. Han, A. Elgowainy, H. Cai & M. Q. Wang, 2013, Life-cycle analysis of bio-based aviation fuels. *Bioresource Technology*, *150*, 447–456.

J. K. Ladha, A. Tirol-Padre, C. K. Reddy, K. G. Cassman, S. Verma, D. S. Powlson, H. Pathak, 2016, Global nitrogen budgets in cereals: A 50-year assessment for maize, rice, and wheat production systems. *Scientific Reports*, *6*, 19355.

L. P. Ju & B. Chen, 2010, Embodied energy and emergy evaluation of a typical biodiesel production chain in China. *Ecological Modelling*, *222*(2011), 2385–2392.

M. M. Mekonnen & A. Y. Hoekstra, 2010, *The green, blue and grey water footprint of farm animals and animal products*.

M. Roser & H. Ritchie, 2018, Yields and Land Use in Agriculture. *Our World In Data*.

M. V. Markussen & H. Østergård, 2013, Energy Analysis of the Danish Food Production System: Food-EROI and Fossil Fuel Dependency. *Energies*, *6*, 4170–4186.

N. S. Tomar, M. A. Ahanger & R. M. Agarwal, 2014, Jatropha curcas: An Overview. In P. Ahmad & M. R. Wani (Eds.), *Physiological Mechanisms and Adaptation Strategies in Plants Under Changing Environment: Volume 2* (pp. 361–383). New York, NY: Springer New York.

O. Neto, A. Santos, M. V. Folegatti, B. P. Lena, A. V. Diotto, J. P. Francisco & T. L. Romanelli, 2018, Energy analysis of Jatropha curcas under irrigation and rainfed at the Southeast Brazilian humid subtropical. *CIGR Journal*, *20*(3), 116–126.

R. Gogoi, U. K. Niyogi & A. K. Tyagi, 2014, Reduction of phorbol ester content in jatropha cake using high energy gamma radiation. *Journal of Radiation Research and Applied Sciences*, *7*(3), 305–309.

R. N. Singh, D. K. Vyas, N. S. L. Srivastava & M. Narra, 2008, SPRERI experience on holistic approach to utilize all parts of Jatropha curcas fruit for energy. *Renewable Energy*, *33*(8), 1868–1873.

S. A. Jourabchi, S. Gan & H. K. Ng, 2014, Pyrolysis of Jatropha curcas pressed cake for bio-oil production in a fixed-bed system. *Energy Conversion and Management*, *78*, 518–526.

S. Elkhalifa, A. AlNouss, T. Al-Ansari, H. R. Mackey, P. Parthasarathy & G. Mckay, 2019, Simulation of Food Waste Pyrolysis for the Production of Biochar: A Qatar Case Study. In *29th European Symposium on Computer Aided Process Engineering* (Vol. 46, pp. 901–906). Elsevier.

T. H. Pedersen, C. U. Jensen, L. Sandström & L. A. Rosendahl, 2017, Full characterization of compounds obtained from fractional distillation and upgrading of a HTL biocrude. *Applied Energy*, *202*, 408–419.

V. Ramírez, J. Martí-Herrero, M. Romero & D. Rivadeneira, 2019, Energy use of Jatropha oil extraction wastes: Pellets from biochar and Jatropha shell blends. *Journal of Cleaner Production*, *215*, 1095–1102.

Sauro Pierucci, Flavio Manenti, Giulia Bozzano, Davide Manca (Eds.)
Proceedings of the 30th European Symposium on Computer Aided Process Engineering
(ESCAPE30), May 24-27, 2020, Milano, Italy. © 2020 Elsevier B.V. All rights reserved.
http://dx.doi.org/10.1016/B978-0-12-823377-1.50040-9

Potential Integrated Pathways for Jet Biofuel Production from Whole Fruit of *Jatropha*

Mohammad Alherbawi,[a] Tareq Al-Ansari,[a,b] Gordon Mckay [a*]

[a] *Division of Sustainable Development, College of Science and Engineering, Hamad Bin Khalifa University, Qatar Foundation, Doha, Qatar.*

[b] *Division of Engineering Management of Decision Sciences, College of Science and Engineering, Hamad Bin Khalifa University, Qatar Foundation, Doha, Qatar.*

gmckay@hbku.edu.qa

Abstract

Civil Aviation is responsible for nearly 5 % of total radiative forcing of climate and 2.5 % of annual global CO_2 emissions, while the demand on Jet fuel is rising rapidly. As such, Jet Biofuel (JBF) has been recognised by the aviation industry as the best option to mitigate its carbon footprint. In this regard, *Jatropha curcas* has proved to be a promising biomass for JBF production due to its unique competences over other energy crops. Not only can its oil be converted into high performance fuels, but also its fruit residues are considered a valuable source for multiple energy carriers. However, *Jatropha* is not yet fully utilized in the Jet Biofuel industry. Therefore, this study presents three novel integrated systems that utilize all parts of the *Jatropha* fruit to produce JBF. These systems integrate the conventional hydroprocess along with one of three thermochemical processes including gasification, pyrolysis and hydrothermal liquefaction. Aspen Plus® is used to develop the systems and investigate the optimum amongst them based on Jet Biofuel yield. All the three systems resulted in significant increments in the JBF yield. While, the hydroprocess-gasification system demonstrated promising results; whereby, 65 wt.% of the *Jatropha* whole-fruit is converted into green liquid fuels with 57 % Jet Biofuel selectivity. The results indicate over a 90 % increment in JBF yield as compared to the utilization of *Jatropha* oil alone in the best reported scenarios.

Keywords: *Jatropha*, Jet Biofuel, Hydroprocess, Fischer-Tropsch, Gasification, Pyrolysis, Hydrothermal liquefaction.

1. Introduction

Civil aviation contributes to nearly 2.5 % of global carbon emissions, which is predicted to double in the coming three decades (ICAO, 2016). Meanwhile, Jet Biofuel (JBF) produced from renewable resources has been intensively investigated and proved to be a promising technology to mitigate the carbon footprint of aviation sector. As airplanes depend exclusively on liquid fuels as compared to road transportation, the shifting of the refining process towards maximizing JBF becomes a favorable practice (Anand et al., 2016).

Currently, four main JBF production pathways have been certified, including Oil to Jet (OTJ) by the conventional hydroprocess, Gas to Jet (GTJ) by gasification of biomass followed by Fischer-Tropsch technology, Alcohol to Jet (ATJ) by bio-alcohol upgrading and Sugar to Jet (STJ) by the catalytic upgrading of sugar (Gutiérrez-Antonio et al., 2017). Though, the hydroprocess is still identified as the most cost-effective pathway (de Jong et al., 2015).

Since the feedstock price accounts for up to 75 % of JBF net cost (de Jong et al., 2015), great efforts have been paid to identify the best feedstock in terms of cost and sustainability. In this context, *Jatropha curcas* is considered a promising feedstock due to its high competences as compared to other oil-bearing crops. Several demonstration and commercial flights have already been operated using different blending ratios of *Jatropha* JBF (Wang and Tao, 2016). The JBF industry has been greatly developed in a relatively short time, yet, it is still facing great challenges related to the availability of sufficient feedstock to fulfill future JBF demands, as well as offering biofuels with competitive prices as compared to conventional Jet-A fuels.

Amongst the various attempts to lower JBF production costs, Zech et al. (2018) reported that a 30 % cost reduction can be achieved by running the process in diesel-mode rather than jet-mode; as diesel has a higher market value. While, Gutiérrez-Antonio et al. (2016) integrated the heat among the process subsystems to reduce the energy consumption. In addition, Wang (2016) has utilized the *Jatropha* fruit's shells and seedcake for power generation and bio-oil production respectively to enhance the process' efficiency. Although previous attempts have managed to lower the production cost, but the yield of JBF is not enhanced or even dropped. Meanwhile, experimental studies reported a maximum JBF selectivity of around 70 % (YaJie et al., 2017), which corresponds to less than 20 wt.% of the *Jatropha* fruit.

Although the *Jatropha* fruit residues have been earlier converted into multiple energy carriers, no reports were found in literature on the utilization of these residues directly in JBF production, to the knowledge of the authors. As such, this study investigates three novel integrated systems to utilize all parts of the *Jatropha* fruit including its oil, shells and seedcake for JBF production. The proposed systems integrate the conventional hydroprocess technology along with one of three thermochemical processes including gasification, pyrolysis and hydrothermal liquefaction. The optimum utilization of *Jatropha* residues is believed to be a key factor to enhance the JBF yield, and therefore lower its production cost. The integrated systems are simulated in Aspen Plus to investigate the potential JBF yields and to identify the highest-yielding system amongst them.

2. Methodology

Aspen Plus (V.9) is used to develop the proposed integrated systems based on the assumptions of steady state and isothermal processes. A plant feed capacity of 100 tonne/hour is considered. Besides, *Jatropha* fruit feed is assumed to split into (30 wt.%) oil, (35 wt.%) shells and (35 wt.%) seedcake upon the deshelling and extraction processes (Singh et al., 2008). The *Jatropha* oil is defined based on its triglycerides' content (Chen et al., 2014), while the shells and seedcake are defined based on their proximate and elemental analysis (Ramírez et al., 2019). All nitrogen and sulphur contents are assumed to be converted into NH_3 and H_2S respectively, while char is assumed to be composed of carbon only. The *Jatropha* oil is processed by the conventional hydroprocess, while the residues are processed by three different thermochemical processes before introducing the resulting oils into the hydroprocessing reactors. All the three systems are optimized for the highest liquid fuels production and highest JBF selectivity. The simplified process flow diagrams are presented in Figure 1.

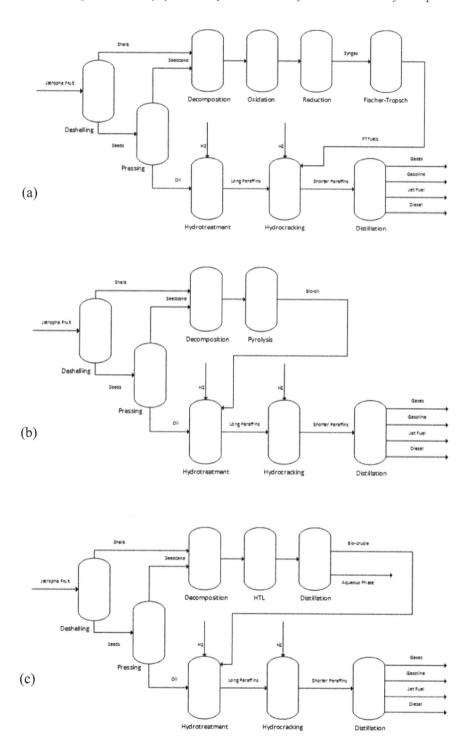

Figure 1: Process flow diagrams of integrated systems of (a) Gasification and hydroprocess, (b) Pyrolysis and hydroprocess and (c) HTL and hydroprocess.

2.1. Hydroprocess

In the hydroprocess model, the triglycerides of *Jatropha* oil are broken down into saturated fatty acids and propane in a hydrogenation reactor. The oxygen content of fatty acids is then removed in a deoxygenation reactor, yielding long-chain paraffins (C15-C18) along with H_2O, CO and CO_2. The former two steps are conducted in an "RGibbs" block at 300 °C and 45 bars. The long paraffins are transferred into a hydrocracking and isomerizing reactor to obtain paraffins with carbon chain lengths that correspond to kerosene (C8-C16). The cracking step is performed in an "RYield" block at 350 °C and 80 bars, whereby, all paraffins of chain lengths (C1-C20) are defined. The flow is then directed to a distillation column.

2.2. Gasification and Fischer-Tropsch

The *Jatropha* shells and seedcake are initially dried in "RYield" block at 120°C, in which the proximate analysis is modified by setting the moisture content to zero. A calculator block is used to convert the non-conventional components of *Jatropha* residues into their corresponding conventional compounds (Alnouss et al., 2018). Consecutively, the flow is introduced into oxidation and reduction reactors, while all related chemical equations are defined. Produced syngas is introduced into a Fischer-Tropsch (FT) reactor, where potential products are predicted based on the Anderson-Schulz-Flory (ASF) distribution (Al-Yaeeshi et al., 2019). The FT process is conducted at 250 °C and 25 bars. The produced FT fuels are finally introduced into the hydrocracking and isomerising reactor.

2.3. Pyrolysis

Similar to gasification model, the *Jatropha* residues are initially dried and decomposed into conventional compounds before being introduced into the pyrolysis reactor at 400 °C. The possible products are defined according to the study reported by Murata et al. (2012). Solids and gases are separated before introducing the bio-oil into the hydrotreatment reactor.

2.4. Hydrothermal Liquefaction

The *Jatropha* residues are initially converted into conventional compounds using a calculator block. The HTL process does not require a drying step, but rather pumping a hot and pressurized water to decompose the *Jatropha* residues with the presence of alkaline catalyst. The main reaction is conducted using an "RGibbs" reactor at 300 °C and 150 bars. Predicted products are adapted from earlier studies (Pedersen et al., 2017). Ash is removed using a solid separator, while the aqueous phase is separated from the bio-crude in a distillation column. The biocrude is then introduced into the hydrotreatment reactor.

3. Results and Discussions

The simulation results indicated a significant increment in liquid fuel yields for all the proposed integrated systems. The gasification-hydroprocess pathway has shown the best overall yield. Whereby, nearly 65 wt.% of the *Jatropha* whole-fruit is converted into liquid fuels, which represents double the initial oil content of the fruit. Nevertheless, 12 wt.% of the fruit is converted into useful gaseous fuel that can be directly used for power generation. The yields of the integrated systems as compared to the hydroprocess alone are illustrated in Figure 2. The increment in the fuel yield may contribute to enhancing the sustainability of *Jatropha* fruit and saving land, water and energy.

Besides, the selectivity of different liquid fuels is illustrated in Figure 3. A jet fuel selectivity of around 60% has been achieved for all processes. Whereas, the best JBF yield has also been achieved via the gasification-hydroprocess integrated system, where nearly 37 wt.% of the fruit has been converted into JBF, which represents over a 90% increment in JBF yield as compared to processing the oil alone in the conventional hydroprocess.

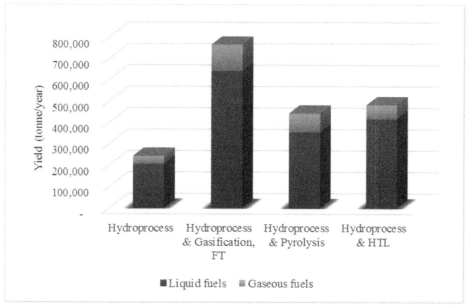

Figure 2: Yields of Integrated systems as compared to the hydroprocess alone.

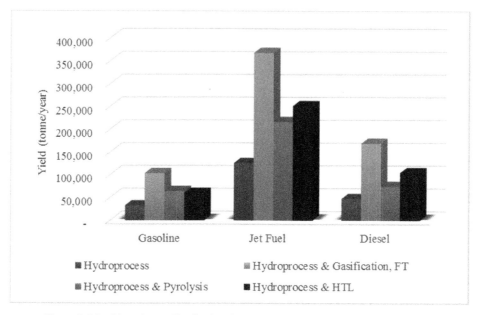

Figure 3: Liquid products 'distribution for the proposed integrated systems.

4. Conclusion

The optimum utilization of all parts of *Jatropha* fruit has been proved to be a key factor in enhancing the feedstock sustainability. In this study, three novel integrated systems have been investigated with the goal of boosting the JBF yield. The systems integrated the conventional hydroprocess with one of three thermochemical processes including gasification, pyrolysis and hydrothermal liquefaction. 65 wt.% of *Jatropha* whole-fruit is converted into green liquid fuels with 57 % Jet Biofuel selectivity. The results indicated over a 90 % increment in JBF yield as compared to the utilization of *Jatropha* oil alone.

References

A. Alnouss, G. Mckay & T. Al-ansari, 2018, Optimum Utilization of Biomass for the Production of Power and Fuels using Gasification. In *28th European Symposium on Computer Aided Process Engineering* (Vol. 43, pp. 1481–1486). Elsevier Masson SAS.

A. Al-Yaeeshi, A. AlNouss, G. McKay & T. Al-Ansari, 2019, A Model based analysis in applying Anderson–Schulz–Flory (ASF) equation with CO2 Utilisation on the Fischer Tropsch Gas-to-liquid Process. In A. A. Kiss, E. Zondervan, R. Lakerveld, & L. B. T.-C. A. C. E. Özkan (Eds.), *29 European Symposium on Computer Aided Process Engineering* (Vol. 46, pp. 397–402). Elsevier.

C. Gutiérrez-Antonio, F. I. Gómez-Castro, A. G. Romero-Izquierdo & S. Hernández, 2016, Energy integration of a hydrotreating process for the production of biojet fuel. In Z. Kravanja & M. B. T.-C. A. C. E. Bogataj (Eds.), *26 European Symposium on Computer Aided Process Engineering* (Vol. 38, pp. 127–132). Elsevier.

C. Gutiérrez-Antonio, F. I. Gómez-Castro, J. A. de Lira-Flores & S. Hernández, 2017, A review on the production processes of renewable jet fuel. *Renewable and Sustainable Energy Reviews, 79,* 709–729.

H. Chen, Q. Wang, X. Zhang & L. Wang, 2014, Hydroconversion of Jatropha oil to alternative fuel over hierarchical ZSM-5. *Industrial & Engineering Chemistry Research, 53*(51), 19916–19924.

H. YaJie, C. YuBao, L. Qiang, Z. ShaoPeng, H. BenYong & D. JunChen, 2017, Preparation of biological aviation kerosene from Jatropha curcas oil by one-step hydrogenation with Pt/SAPO-11 as catalyst. *China Oils and Fats, 42*(6), 110–114.

ICAO, 2016, *On Board a Sustainable Future: 2016 Environmental Report.*

K. Murata, Y. Liu, M. Inaba & I. Takahara, 2012, Catalytic fast pyrolysis of jatropha wastes. *Journal of Analytical and Applied Pyrolysis, 94,* 75–82.

K. M. Zech, S. Dietrich, M. Reichmuth, W. Weindorf & F. Müller-Langer, 2018, Techno-economic assessment of a renewable bio-jet-fuel production using power-to-gas. *Applied Energy, 231,* 997–1006.

M. Anand, S. A. Farooqui, R. Kumar, R. Joshi, R. Kumar, M.G. Sibi & A. K. Sinha, 2016, Optimizing renewable oil hydrocracking conditions for aviation bio-kerosene production. *Fuel Processing Technology, 151,* 50–58.

R. N. Singh, D. K. Vyas, N. S. L. Srivastava & M. Narra, 2008, SPRERI experience on holistic approach to utilize all parts of Jatropha curcas fruit for energy. *Renewable Energy, 33*(8), 1868–1873.

S. de Jong, R. Hoefnagels, A. Faaij, R. Slade, R. Mawhood & M. Junginger, 2015, The feasibility of short-term production strategies for renewable jet fuels - a comprehensive techno-economic comparison. *Biofuels, Bioproducts and Biorefining, 9*(6), 778–800.

T. H. Pedersen, C. U. Jensen, L. Sandström & L. A. Rosendahl, 2017, Full characterization of compounds obtained from fractional distillation and upgrading of a HTL biocrude. *Applied Energy, 202,* 408–419.

V. Ramírez, J. Martí-Herrero, M. Romero & D. Rivadeneira, 2019, Energy use of Jatropha oil extraction wastes: Pellets from biochar and Jatropha shell blends. *Journal of Cleaner Production, 215,* 1095–1102.

W. C. Wang, 2016, Techno-economic analysis of a bio-refinery process for producing Hydro-processed Renewable Jet fuel from Jatropha. *Renewable Energy, 95,* 63–73.

W. C. Wang & L. Tao, 2016, Bio-jet fuel conversion technologies. *Renewable and Sustainable Energy Reviews, 53,* 801–822.

Sauro Pierucci, Flavio Manenti, Giulia Bozzano, Davide Manca (Eds.)
Proceedings of the 30th European Symposium on Computer Aided Process Engineering
(ESCAPE30), May 24-27, 2020, Milano, Italy. © 2020 Elsevier B.V. All rights reserved.
http://dx.doi.org/10.1016/B978-0-12-823377-1.50041-0

Environmental Impacts of the Future German Energy System from Integrated Energy Systems Optimization and Life Cycle Assessment

C. Reinert[a], S. Deutz[a], H. Minten[a], L. Dörpinghaus[a], S. von Pfingsten[a], N. Baumgärtner[a], and A. Bardow[a,b,*]

[a] *Institute of Technical Thermodynamics, RWTH Aachen University, Aachen, Germany*
[b] *Institute of Energy and Climate Research IEK-10, Jülich Research Center, Jülich, Germany*
andre.bardow@ltt.rwth-aachen.de

Abstract

Climate change mitigation requires a fundamental transition of our energy systems to reduce greenhouse gas (GHG) emissions. At the same time, ambitions to reduce GHG emissions should not shift burdens to other environmental impacts. Environmental impacts of technologies can be evaluated holistically using Life Cycle Assessment (LCA). Classical LCA is static and relies on historic process data. In contrast, dynamic LCA incorporates future changes in production processes and therefore allows for a consistent assessment of future environmental impacts. In this work, we develop a dynamic LCA model for the German energy transition. For this purpose, we combine LCA with energy systems optimization. We model the German electricity, heat, and transport sectors. For a given GHG target, the model designs the cost-optimal transition of the energy system. Environmental impacts are evaluated using dynamic LCA based on global energy scenarios. Compared to static LCA, dynamic LCA shows a 75 % higher impact in agricultural land occupation and smaller impacts in 15 out of 18 impact categories, demonstrating the need for the consistent assessment by dynamic LCA.

Keywords: Dynamic LCA, Supply chain analysis, Synthesis optimization, Energy transition, Background changes

1. Introduction

The significant reductions in greenhouse gas (GHG) emissions needed to mitigate climate change require a fundamental transition of our energy systems. This energy transition is expected to increase sector coupling and fluctuating renewable electricity supply. We therefore need sector-coupled optimization models of energy systems that account for renewable electricity supply while achieving the GHG emission targets.

However, the ambition to reduce GHG emissions should not shift burdens to other environmental impacts. To achieve an environmentally sustainable design, the planning of energy systems should therefore consider environmental impacts beyond GHG emissions. Such a holistic assessment of environmental impacts is enabled by Life Cycle Assessment (LCA). LCA has therefore been combined with energy systems optimization for the electricity sector in Germany (Rauner and Budzinski 2017), the energy system in Switzerland (Volkart et al. 2017), and the US electricity sector (Algunaibet and Guillén-Gosálbez 2019).

The available methods for the design and environmental assessment of national energy systems currently face one major issue: the studies use static Life Cycle Inventories (LCI's) for the environmental assessment. As a result, improvements in energy systems are not reflected for newly installed infrastructure produced in other countries. Because such changes in the background affect environmental impacts of the energy transition (Mendoza Beltran et al. 2018), it is necessary to include global developments in national long-term assessments, leading to a dynamic LCA approach (García-Gusano et al. 2016). Global energy models already integrate dynamic LCA: future impacts of global, low-carbon electricity system scenarios are examined by Pehl et al. (2017) and Luderer et al. (2019). The global, multi-sectoral energy transition is optimized by updating LCI's model endogenously by Volkart et al. (2018); however, endogenous LCI updating is not applicable for national studies.

In this work, we present a national energy model that uses dynamic LCA to integrate global developments for the electricity sector. Using Germany as an example, we present a fully sector-coupled energy systems optimization for the years 2016-2050 based on dynamic LCA and global electricity transition scenarios. In section 2.1, we briefly describe the optimization model SecMOD. In section 2.2, we dynamize electricity processes in Life Cycle Inventories using a regionalized energy transition scenario. In section 3, the resulting dynamic LCA database is integrated in SecMOD. We then compare the economic and environmental results of the energy optimization to using the static database.

2. Dynamization of the optimization model SecMOD

First, we present our optimization model SecMOD, a national energy model combining optimization and LCA. In section 2.2, SecMOD is expanded by dynamic LCA (Figure 1).

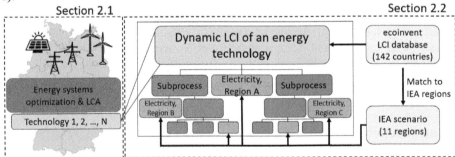

Figure 1: Optimization of an energy system using dynamic LCA using the SecMOD model (section 2.1). The electricity-related background processes of the Life Cycle Inventories (LCI's) are modified using a multiregional scenario (section 2.2).

2.1. SecMOD: Combined energy systems optimization and Life Cycle Assessment

SecMOD (Baumgärtner et al. 2020) is an optimization model of the sectors electricity, heat (household and industrial), and private transport in Germany. The linear model optimizes a least-cost transition pathway to a low-carbon economy for the years 2016 – 2050. The existing capacity of the starting year 2016 is modeled to represent the actual technology mix in Germany. The model consists of 18 geographic zones (as defined by the German Energy Agency) which are interconnected by a grid following the DC load-flow approach (Egerer 2016). For each zone, the mass and energy balances are solved for each time step.

We simultaneously optimize the design and the operation of the energy system, using an aggregated time series (Bahl et al. 2018) of 60 time steps. The GHG emissions resulting from the operation of the energy system are constrained to achieve a GHG emission reduction of 85% in year 2050. Existing infrastructure is extended by infrastructure investments to meet the electricity, heat and transport demands at each time step (Baumgärtner et al. 2020). Subsequent to the optimization, we perform a complete LCA study to evaluate the energy system in 18 environmental categories, as proposed in the ReCiPe 2008 method (Goedkoop et al. 2009). Environmental impacts for the energy system are based on the LCI database ecoinvent 3.5 APOS (Wernet et al. 2016).

2.2. Dynamization of LCA database

The ecoinvent database relies on static data and thus does not consider improvements in the background systems of the newly installed infrastructure. To improve the assessment of energy technologies in future energy systems, we present a method to incorporate long-term energy scenarios in national energy systems optimization. Since electricity processes contribute by up to 70 % to the global warming impact (GWI) of the considered technologies, we focus on the electricity sector. Based on a multiregional energy scenario, we modify the ecoinvent 3.5 database by updating the electricity processes in the background to generate dynamic Life Cycle Inventories for all investment periods. The dynamic LCI's are then included in the SecMOD optimization for transition pathways of the electricity, heat, and transportation sectors in Germany.

As scenario for regionalized technology mixes from year 2014 to 2050, we select the "2 °C sustainable development scenario" (IEA scenario) (International Energy Agency 2017). The scenario provides the annual electricity generation by technology for 11 world regions and is used here to modify the Life Cycle Inventories of all technologies in SecMOD.

Similarly to Mendoza Beltran et al. (2018), we use Brightway 2 (Mutel 2017) to identify the background processes of the LCI's and modify the electricity processes according to the IEA scenario. First, electricity processes are identified in all LCI's used in SecMOD and classified by region. Second, all ecoinvent regions (comprising 142 countries) are matched to the 11 regions of the IEA scenario. The region matching is a necessary step for dynamization; however, the matching also causes some loss of spatial detail. For each region, a new electricity market mix is defined for every considered future year, corresponding to the electricity mix of the IEA. The new regional market mixes generate electricity by various technologies. The Life Cycle Inventories of the electricity generation technologies depend on the region of electricity generation – if no matching region is found, we use a dataset from the nearest geographic region. Some LCI's do not exist in ecoinvent and were added based on literature data: carbon capture and storage (Volkart, 2013), wave power plants (Thomson et al. 2011), hydroelectric power stations (Douglas et al. 2008), and concentrated solar power plants (Mendoza Beltran et al. 2018). For each investment period, we generate a dynamic LCI, updating the electricity processes in the LCI with the regional market mix from the IEA scenario.

In summary, we modify the ecoinvent 3.5 database based on the IEA scenario, updating the electricity mix for all investment periods to generate dynamic LCI's. In section 3, the LCI's are employed in the SecMOD optimization.

3. Results: Optimal energy transition from SecMOD using static and dynamic LCA

In the following, we compare the SecMOD optimization using static and dynamic LCI's. The functional unit of our assessment is the total energy supply for Germany, comprising all technologies and their operation to satisfy the electricity, heat, and private transport demands in one year. We compare the total annualized costs and the environmental impact during the transition to a low-carbon economy.

Figure 2 shows the total annualized costs for the design and operation of the energy system during the transition pathway (left: static, right: dynamic). The cost difference between both transitions pathways does not exceed 1.2 % of the total annualized costs.

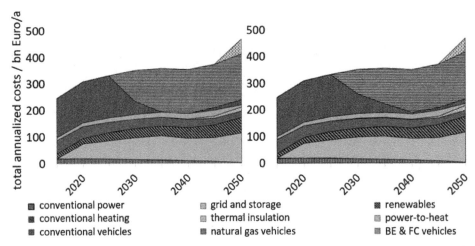

Figure 2: Comparison of total annualized costs: optimization using static LCA (left) and dynamic LCA (right). BE & FC vehicles: battery electric and fuel cell vehicles.

However, the choice of technology is affected by the dynamic LCA database most strongly for transportation: in year 2050 the optimization using dynamic LCA leads to higher shares of natural gas vehicles and lower shares of conventional and battery electric vehicles (Figure 3, left). The share of power-to-heat and thermal insulation is higher in the static case. These changes can be attributed to electricity background processes, which vary and thus change per technology; the change in GHG emission intensity leads to a shift in technology preference. As a result, the total annualized costs in year 2050 vary by up to 15 % for the different technologies.

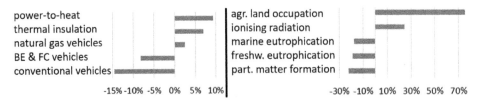

Figure 3: Largest changes in technology-specific cost (left) and environmental impacts (right) in the dynamic assessment of year 2050 compared to the static case. BE & FC vehicles: battery electric and fuel cell vehicles.

Additionally, dynamic LCA changes the results of the environmental evaluation of the energy system: in the dynamic case, we find higher impacts for ionizing radiation (24 %) and agricultural land occupation (75 %) compared to the static case in year 2050 (Figure 3, right). The higher impact in agricultural land occupation compared to the static assessment is caused by the globally increasing use of biomass. All other impacts (15 out of 18) are smaller in the dynamic assessment of year 2050.

4. Conclusions

In this work, we present a long-term energy systems optimization model. We assess the resulting energy system using dynamic LCA instead of the typically used static LCA. A comparison between integrating static and dynamic LCI data shows differences both in the optimal transition pathway and in the environmental assessment. The total cost of the static and the dynamic pathway are almost the same, however, the total annualized costs for specific technologies differ by up to 15 %. In the dynamic LCA for year 2050, 15 out of 18 impact categories are smaller compared to the static case. However, the impact of agricultural land occupation is higher in dynamic LCA, due to the globally increasing share of biomass in the electricity mix.

In conclusion, we show that fundamental trends and costs of the German energy system are predicted with sufficient accuracy even with static LCA. However, dynamic LCA is necessary to consider individual technology developments. Further, the dynamic assessment leads to fundamentally different results for some environmental impacts.

Acknowledgements

This study was funded by the Ministry of Economics, Innovation, Digitalization and Energy of North-Rhine Westphalia (Grant number: EFO 0001G). The support is gratefully acknowledged.

References

Algunaibet, I. M.; Guillén-Gosálbez, G. (2019): Life cycle burden-shifting in energy systems designed to minimize greenhouse gas emissions: novel analytical method and application to the United States. *Journal of Cleaner Production* (229), pp. 886–901.

Bahl, B.; Söhler, T.; Hennen, M.; Bardow, A. (2018): Typical periods for two-stage synthesis by time-series aggregation with bounded error in objective function. *Front. Energy Res.* (5), 35.

Baumgärtner, N.; Deutz, S.; Reinert, C.; Nolzen, N.; Küpper, E.; Hennen, M. et al. (2020): Life-cycle assessment of sector-coupled national energy systems: environmental impacts of future electricity, heat & transportation in Germany. In preparation.

Douglas, C. A.; Harrison, G. P.; Chick, J. P. (2008): Life cycle assessment of the seagen marine current turbine. *Proceedings of the IMechE* 222 (1), pp. 1–12.

Egerer, J. (2016): Open source electricity model for Germany (ELMOD-DE). Data Documentation. DIW Berlin, German Institute for Economic Research (83). Available online at https://www.diw.de, checked on 11/27/2019.

García-Gusano, D.; Martín-Gamboa, M.; Iribarren, D.; Dufour, J. (2016): Prospective Analysis of Life-Cycle Indicators through Endogenous Integration into a National Power Generation Model. *Resources* 5 (4), 39.

Goedkoop, M.; Heijungs, R.; Huijbregts, M.; Schryver, A.; Struijs, J.; Zelm, R. (2009): ReCiPE 2008. A life cycle impact assessment method which comprises harmonised category indicators at the midpoint and the endpoint level. Available online at http://www.lcia-recipe.net, checked on 11/27/2019.

International Energy Agency (2017): Energy technology perspectives 2017. Catalysing energy technology transformations. Edited by OECD/IEA.

Luderer, G.; Pehl, M.; Arvesen, A.; Gibon, T.; Bodirsky, B. L.; Boer, H. Sytze de et al. (2019): Environmental co-benefits and adverse side-effects of alternative power sector decarbonization strategies. *Nature communications* 10 (1), 5229.

Mendoza Beltran, A.; Cox, B.; Mutel, C.; Vuuren, D. P.; Font Vivanco, D.; Deetman, S. et al. (2018): When the background matters. Using scenarios from integrated assessment models in prospective life cycle assessment. *Journal of Industrial Ecology* 7 (6), pp. 1-16.

Mutel, C. (2017): Brightway: An open source framework for life cycle assessment. *The Journal of Open Source Software* 2 (12), 236.

Pehl, M.; Arvesen, A.; Humpenöder, F.; Popp, A.; Hertwich, E. G.; Luderer, G. (2017): Understanding future emissions from low-carbon power systems by integration of life-cycle assessment and integrated energy modelling. *Nat Energy* 2 (12), pp. 939–945.

Rauner, S.; Budzinski, M. (2017): Holistic energy system modeling combining multi-objective optimization and life cycle assessment. *Environ. Res. Lett.* 12 (12), 124005.

Thomson, R. C.; Harrison, G. P.; Chick, J. P. (2011): Full life cycle assessment of a wave energy converter. In : IET Conference on Renewable Power Generation. IET, pp. 63–68.

Volkart, K.; Mutel, C. L.; Panos, E. (2018): Integrating life cycle assessment and energy system modelling. Methodology and application to the world energy scenarios. *Sustainable Production and Consumption* 16, pp. 121–133.

Volkart, K.; Weidmann, N.; Bauer, C.; Hirschberg, S. (2017): Multi-criteria decision analysis of energy system transformation pathways. A case study for Switzerland. *Energy Policy* 106, pp. 155–168.

Wernet, G.; Bauer, C.; Steubing, B.; Reinhard, J.; Moreno-Ruiz, E.; and Weidema, B. (2016): The ecoinvent database version 3 (part I): overview and methodology. *The International Journal of Life Cycle Assessment* (21 (9)), pp. 1218-1230.

Sauro Pierucci, Flavio Manenti, Giulia Bozzano, Davide Manca (Eds.)
Proceedings of the 30th European Symposium on Computer Aided Process Engineering
(ESCAPE30), May 24-27, 2020, Milano, Italy. © 2020 Elsevier B.V. All rights reserved.
http://dx.doi.org/10.1016/B978-0-12-823377-1.50042-2

A General Dynamic Model of a Complete Milk Pasteuriser Unit Subject to Fouling

Mengjia Zhu, Federico Lozano Santamaria, Sandro Macchietto

Department of Chemical Engineering, Imperial College London South Kensington

Campus, London SW7 2AZ, UK

Abstract

Heat treatment of milk for hygiene and preservation is carried out in energy integrated pasteurisers units which include several plate heat exchangers (PHEs), a holding tube and ancillary piping. Fouling reduces energy efficiency and cleanings generate downtime and wastes. No detailed dynamic models are currently available of full heating-cleaning cycles for an overall unit. Using a first principle modelling approach, a 2D dynamic thermal model, coupled with semi-mechanistic fouling and cleaning in place (CIP) models, is developed for the whole pasteurisation process, and used to test various heating-cleaning cycles. The model generality and flexibility are demonstrated for high temperature short time (HTST) and ultra-high temperature (UHT) treatments. The whole unit thermal model is validated against experimental data for a HTST process, with excellent agreement. Fouling evolution, distribution and impact are assessed for both processes. A UHT heating-cleaning cycle simulation enables quantifying the amounts of cleaning agent and waste water produced. The new model is suitable for control, optimisation of heating and cleaning strategies, and waste reduction studies.

Keywords: food processing, pasteurisation, plate heat exchanger, milk fouling, dynamic modelling.

1. Introduction and background

Heat treatments eliminate pathogenic microorganisms in raw milk for safety and extended shelf life. A typical pasteuriser unit (Figure 1) includes a preheater (regenerator), a main heater, a cooler, using plate heat exchangers (PHEs), as well as a holding tube, and ancillary pipework (Wang, et al., 2007). Fouling leads to economic (e.g. energy use, downtime for cleaning) and environmental problems (e.g. cleaning water and chemicals use, waste treatment). Fouling mitigation treatments (Müller-Steinhagen, et al., 2011), mostly focus on a qualitative analysis. Experimentation is time-consuming and costly, and results are often difficult to extrapolate to other conditions. In spite of much modelling research over many years (e.g. Georgiadis et al. 1998a, 1998b), no current model can comprehensively and accurately (1) capture the main thermal and hydraulic behaviours of fluids within the PHEs; (2) reflect the interactions among different sections of the pasteuriser; (3) predict deposit severity, location and composition during heating and cleaning; (4) optimize the overall operation of a full pasteuriser. Here we present a general model for the whole pasteuriser with all these features, and demonstrate it for high temperature short time (HTST) and ultra-high temperature (UHT) milk treatments. The thermal model of the whole unit is validated vs. experimental data for a HTST process. The evolution and impact of fouling are then assessed for both HTST & UHT.

Finally, a UHT full heating-cleaning cycle simulation calculates the amount of cleaning agent and rinsing water required, as well as the cleaning time needed and cycle time.

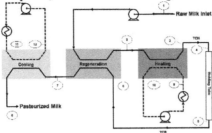

Figure 1. Schematic diagram of a pasteuriser unit (reproduced from Gutierrez et al *(2014)*).

2. Pasteurisation system modelling

The structure of the overall pasteuriser model and sub-models involved (Figure 2) includes heating, regeneration and cooling PHEs, a non-isothermal holding tube and two non-isothermal tubular connections (TCH & TCR). Initial conditions, equipment data and configurations are specified in the main unit model, and passed to the section models for PHEs and tubes, enabling continuity of fluid and temperature among sections. The thermal model in each section (PHE or tube) is coupled with fouling and CIP models.

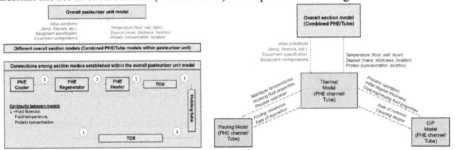

Figure 2. Overall model of the pasteuriser (left) and model components in each section (right).

The PHE dynamic model is modified from those proposed by (Guan & Macchietto, 2018) for single channel and (Sharma & Macchietto, 2019a). Here, each internal PHE channel is delimited by the two side half-plates, the end channels by a half (internal) plate and a full (end) plate. Any desired PHE arrangement is then assembled as a collection of individual channels (Figure 3), using a hierarchal model building design which sets the appropriate boundary conditions. For the two end plates, adiabatic condition is assumed. All models are implemented in gPROMS (PSE, 2018). The holding tube "holds" the heated milk at a desired temperature for a specified time. For skimmed milk, the requirement is to hold milk for at least 15 seconds at or above 72 °C in a HTST process, and for 2 to 5 seconds at 135-140°C in a UHT process (FDA, 2018). The thermo-hydraulic tube model used, adapted from (Diaz-Bejarano, et al., 2016) consists of working fluid, deposit layer, and tube wall domains connected via suitable boundary conditions. Previous holding tube models in milk pasteurisation either assumed isothermal condition or a constant temperature drop based on experimental data (Grijspeerdt, et al., 2004) (Aguiar & Gut, 2014) (Gutierrez, et al., 2014). Here, non-isothermal condition was used, with an average external heat flux determined from experimental data, assuming convective heat transfer to air around uninsulated holding tube and tubular connections. Reaction mechanisms in milk fouling were discussed in Sharma and Macchietto (2019b).

For HTST processes, protein fouling (type A) is the dominant fouling type; while for UHT process, both protein and mineral fouling (type B) are known to occur in different temperature ranges (Khaldi et al., 2015). Only type A fouling was used, so the calculated

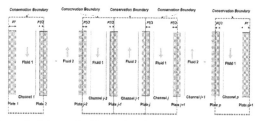

Figure 3. Schematic illustration for PHE channel modelling.

deposit mass is expected to be lower than the experimental one in UHT process. The fouling model of Georgiadis and Macchietto (2000), Sharma and Macchietto (2019a) was adopted with minor modifications. Two β-lg reaction schemes are considered: fouling due to (1) aggregated protein (Dep$_A$) and (2) unfolded protein (Dep$_U$) deposition (Figure 4). Here, N, U and A represent the native, unfolded and aggregated β-lg protein, respectively. Reactions of $N \rightarrow U$ and $U \rightarrow A$ occur in both bulk fluid as well as the thermal boundary layer. Fouling can occur anywhere in the pasteuriser unit and its severity is temperature dependent. The fouling model is coupled with the thermal model of both PHE channel and tube (Figure 2). In the combined models, all equations in the thermal and fouling models are solved simultaneously, using a standard DAE solver in gPROMS (PSE, 2018).

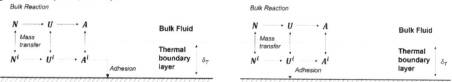

Figure 4. β-lg reaction schemes with fouling due to aggregated protein (Dep$_A$) and unfolded protein (Dep$_u$) (adapted from Georgiadis and Macchietto (2000)).

3. Validation of full pasteurisation unit model

A well-documented steady state experimental case for a HTST process was simulated (Gut and Pinto, 2004; Gutierrez, Diniz and Gut, 2014). The heating, regeneration and cooling PHEs consists of 12, 20 and 8 channels, respectively, each with a single-inlet-multiple-pass configuration. Details of experimental apparatus and experimental conditions, at steady-state, for a thermal test with water as both heating/cooling and process fluid are given in the references. The water physical properties, assumed constant within each section at average conditions, estimated from correlations based on the NIST database (Linstrom and Mallard, no date) are detailed in Zhu, 2019. The average external heat flux in the tubes was estimated to be 467 W/m^2 (Zhu, 2019). The key experimental and calculated temperatures in the entire pasteuriser (Figure 5 left.) show excellent agreement. The simulated temperature profiles of the working fluid in different PHE channels within the heating section (Figure 5 right) are very plausible, although no experimental data were available. This validation test confirms that the thermal model of the whole integrated pasteuriser unit matches well the experimental results.

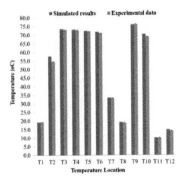
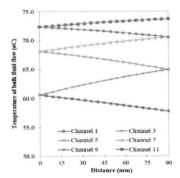

Figure 5. Thermal model validation: Key calculated and experimental temperatures - Exp. Data from Aguiar and Gut *(2014)* – left. Temperature profiles of the working fluid (water) within the heating section - right.

4. Operation and cleaning cycles - full pasteurisation unit

A fouling simulation for the HTST process, with the same experimental conditions used for thermal model validation, shows that fouling is not significant for the first 2.1 days. As a result, a heating-cleaning cycle of the complete pasteuriser unit was studied for the UHT process. As no experimental data on configuration or measured performance of a unit was available in literature, a realistic case was defined based on a typical UHT process (Tetra-Pak, 2015) (FDA, 2018). The PHE plate geometry is adopted from Georgiadis and Macchietto (2000). The heating, regeneration and cooling PHEs, all of single-inlet-multiple-pass configuration, have 12, 8 and 12 channels. The holding, TCH and TCR tubes have lengths of 1.0, 0.42, 1.06 m, internal diameter 40, 30, 30 mm and outer diameter 44, 33 and 33 mm, respectively. Milk, heating water and cooling water enter at 4, 140 and 4 °C. The milk physical properties (Fernández-Martín, 1972; Kessler, 2002; Minim et al., 2002) are detailed in Zhu, 2019. The Dep_U fouling mechanism was used, with $\beta = 15.1$, as estimated for the PHE heating section in previous studies (Zhu, 2019).

The two-stage CIP model of Bird and Fryer (1992), detailed in Sharma and Macchietto (2019b), is used for cleaning, however applied to the whole system, in a CIP procedure with Heating, cleaning and rinsing phases (Figure 6). Heating is terminated when the total deposit mass in any of the sections reaches a certain critical mass. A 3 minutes Rinsing phase follows, where it is assumed that no heat transfer and deposit removal occur. The Cleaning phase then starts, using the above cleaning model. Process-side fluid properties are switched from milk to cleaning solution in both the thermal and fouling models, the latter causing deposit removal. The Cleaning phase stops when the mass left on each plate in any PHE is less than 0.1 g., followed by a final Rinsing phase. Multiple fouling-cleaning cycles can be implemented back to back using this model.

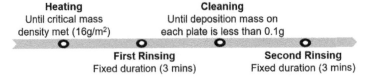

Figure 6. Heating-CIP operation cycle.

The predicted deposit mass over time in the heating PHE and the holding tube are shown in Figure 7. Relative to HTST, much more severe fouling is found in the main PHE heater for the UHT process. The switch from heating to first Rising is triggered by the deposit mass in the main heating PHE. No significant deposit is observed in most of the regeneration PHE channels, although there is deposit in some of them, and the cooling PHE. For numerical reasons, a small initial deposit thickness (1.0E-7 m) was applied to all tubes, while zero initial deposit thickness was set for PHEs. This explains the rapid initial jump of the deposition mass in the holding tube. Cleaning starts before significant drop in the exit milk temperature of the main PHE heater occurs. Considering the overall interactions between the sections of the pasteuriser unit, fouling effects in one section have limited impact on the overall processing temperature. This suggests that a less stringent global stopping criteria could be used for heating phase termination. With the cleaning lasting about 30 minutes, the total cycle time is rather short. The CIP requires 404 Kg of Cleaning fluid (caustic solution) and 85.3kg of wastewater (both circulated at a rate of 0.237 Kg/s).

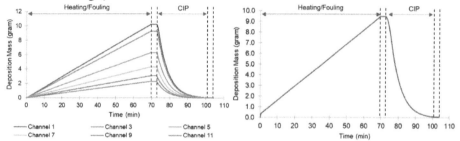

Figure 7. UHT Pasteuriser - Deposit mass during Heating-CIP cycle in the heating PHE (left) and holding tube (right).

5. Conclusions and perspectives

This work extended to a full pasteuriser the 2D distributed model developed by Guan & Macchietto (2018) and Sharma & Macchietto (2019) respectively for a single PHE channel and a PHE. This model is general, modular and versatile. Its predictions have been validated with good agreement against available experimental results. Fouling is considered in all the pasteurisers elements, reflecting configuration and operating conditions. Coupling fouling and cleaning models enables the simulation of heating-cleaning cycles for the whole unit, based on user-defined procedures and phase switching conditions. The model may be used to optimize of the overall operation, considering complex trade-offs between energy for heating, use of cleaning agents and rinsing water for CIP, downtime due to cleaning and cycle length (hence throughput and productivity). It could also be used to optimise continuous and sequential control strategies, and provide diagnostic information. There is scope for further validation of all models, in particular the prediction of local deposit growth/removal and its distribution over time. Only protein fouling was considered here. Further work and validation are also needed to improve the kinetic models, to better link process performance to the inlet milk properties.

References

Aguiar, H. F. & Gut, J. A. W., 2014. Continuous HTST pasteurization of liquid foods with plate heat exchangers: Mathematical modeling and experimental validation using a time-temperature integrator. *Journal of Food Engineering,* 123, 78-86.

Bird, M. R. & Fryer, P. J., 1992. An analytical model for cleaning of food process plant. *Food Engineering in a computer climate. ICHEME Symposium Series,* Issue 126, 325–330.

Diaz-Bejarano, E., Coletti, F. & Macchietto, S., 2016. A new dynamic model of crude oil fouling deposits and its application to the simulation of fouling-cleaning cycles. *AIChE Journal,* 62(1), 90-107.

FDA, 2018. *CFR - Code of Federal Regulations Title 21.* https://www.accessdata.fda.gov/scripts/cdrh/cfdocs/cfcfr/CFRSearch.cfm?fr=1240.61 [Accessed 9 9 2019].

Fernández-Martín, F., 1972. Influence of temperature and composition on some physical properties of milk and milk concentrates. II. Viscosity. *Journal of Dairy Research,* 39(1), 75–82.

Georgiadis, M. C. & Macchietto, S., 2000. Dynamic modelling and simulation of plate heat exchangers under milk fouling. *Chemical Engineering Science,* 55(9), 1605–1619.

Georgiadis, M.C. Rotstein, G.E. Macchietto, S., 1998a. Modelling and simulation of complex plate heat exchanger arrangements under milk fouling. *Computers and Chemical Engineering*, 22 (SUPPL.1), 331-338

Georgiadis, M.C. Rotstein, G.E. Macchietto, S., 1998b. Optimal design and operation of heat exchangers under milk fouling. *AIChE Journal*, 44(9), 2099-2111.

Grijspeerdt, K., Mortier, L., De Block, J. & Van Renterghem, R., 2004. Applications of modelling to optimise ultra high temperature milk heat exchangers with respect to fouling. *Food Control,* 15(2), 117–130.

Guan, S. & Macchietto, S., 2018. A novel dynamic model of Plate Heat Exchangers subject to fouling. Computer-Aided Chemical Engineering Vol. 43 Part B, 1679-1684, Elsevier, Amsterdam.

Gutierrez, C. G. C. C., Diniz, G. N. & Gut, J. A. W., 2014. Dynamic simulation of a plate pasteuriser unit: Mathematical modeling and experimental validation. *J. Food Eng.,* 131, 124-134.

Gut, J. A. W. & Pinto, J. M., 2004. Optimal configuration design for plate heat exchangers. *International Journal of Heat and Mass Transfer,* 47(22), 4833–4848.

Kessler, H. G., 2002. *Food and bio process engineering: dairy technology.* 5th ed. Munich, Germany: Verlag A. Kessler.

Khaldi, M., Blanpain-Avet, P., Guérin, R., Ronse, G., Bouvier, L., André, C., Bornaz, S., Croguennec, T., Jeantet, R., Delaplace, G., 2015. Effect of calcium content and flow regime on whey protein fouling and cleaning in a plate heat exchanger. *J. Food Eng.* 147, 68–78.

Linstrom, W. G. & Mallard, P. J. eds., (no date), *NIST Chemistry WebBook, NIST Standard Reference Database Number 69.* Gaithersburg MD, 20899: National Institute of Standards and Technology.

Minim, L. A., Coimbra, J. S. R., Minim, V. P. R. & Telis-Romero, J., 2002. Influence of Temperature and Water and Fat Contents on the Thermophysical Properties of Milk. *Journal of Chemical & Engineering Data,* 47(6), 1488–1491.

Müller-Steinhagen, H., Malayeri, M. R. & Watkinson, A. P., 2011. Heat exchanger fouling: Mitigation and cleaning strategies. *Heat Transfer Engineering,* 32(3-4), 189–196.

PSE, 2018. *gPROMS,* s.l.: Process System Enterprise Limited.

Sharma, A. & Macchietto, S., 2019a. Fouling and cleaning of Plate Heat Exchangers for Milk Pasteurisation: a moving boundary model. Computer Aided Chemical Engineering 46, Part B, 1483-1488, Elsevier, Amsterdam.

Sharma, A. & Macchietto, S., 2019b. Fouling and cleaning of Plate Heat Exchangers for Milk Pasteurisation: Dairy Application. Heat Exchangers Foulingand Cleaning – XIII, Warsaw, Poland, 2-7 June 2019.

Tetra-Pak, 2015. *Dairy Processing Handbook.* [Online].

Wang, L., Sundén, B. & Manglik, R., 2007. *Plate heat exchangers : design, applications and performance.* s.l.:WIT Press.

Zhu, M., 2019. *A general dynamic model of a complete milk pasteuriser unit subject to fouling,* Imperial College London.

Sauro Pierucci, Flavio Manenti, Giulia Bozzano, Davide Manca (Eds.)
Proceedings of the 30th European Symposium on Computer Aided Process Engineering
(ESCAPE30), May 24-27, 2020, Milano, Italy. © 2020 Elsevier B.V. All rights reserved.
http://dx.doi.org/10.1016/B978-0-12-823377-1.50043-4

A Nonsmooth Approach to Multicontaminant Mass and Water Integration

Caroline J. Nielsen[a,*], Paul I. Barton[a]

[a]*Massachusetts Institute of Technology, 77 Massachusetts Ave., Cambridge, MA, USA*
cjn1994@mit.edu

Abstract

This work presents a novel approach for process integration that accounts for the presence of multiple contaminants in fixed-load water integration problems and mass exchange networks with a single solvent source. Existing approaches to the multicontaminant problem are either unable to solve for contaminant concentrations or use superstructures that grow rapidly with problem size and require solving nonconvex mixed-integer programs. To address these limitations, we have extended previous work on solving single contaminant problems using the generalized nonsmooth integration operator. By assuming mass transfer relations and scaling the concentrations according to the limiting contaminant, we can directly apply a nonsmooth integration operator to solve the mass integration problem. The result is a simple nonsmooth system of two equations for each mass exchange system regardless of the system size that can be used to solve for any selection of unknowns including contaminant concentrations.

Keywords: Water Integration, Mass Integration, Multicontaminant, Nonsmooth

1. Introduction

There are significant incentives to reduce the use of water and other materials in chemical processes including resource scarcity and regulations on waste discharge. Process integration methods have been widely proposed and utilized to address this challenge by minimizing resource use through optimal reuse, beginning with heat recovery problems (Linnhoff and Flower, 1978) which were later extended to the recovery of materials in mass exchange networks (El-Halwagi and Manousiouthakis, 1989) and fixed-load water networks (Wang and Smith, 1994). However, the body of work on solving the heat integration problem cannot be directly generalized to mass and water integration in real systems where multiple components or contaminants are present. In these systems, contaminant transfer cannot occur independently, so considering each component independently will underestimate the required external utilities and provide infeasible results. Therefore, it is necessary to develop methods to consider multiple contaminants simultaneously to improve the usefulness and accuracy of process integration approaches.

As summarized in the review of Khor et al. (2014), the existing approaches to solving multicontaminant process integration problems primarily use complex heuristics or superstructures to solve the network design problem by including multicomponent mass transfer relations in each mass exchange unit. However, superstructure approaches typically scale exponentially with the number of mass or water streams in the problem and also require solving potentially nonconvex mixed-integer nonlinear programs. To reduce problem size and intractability, alternative approaches have been presented that use heuristics or solve the resource targeting problem, which determines the minimum external mass or water utilities without the network design step. These approaches scale the contaminant concentrations for each operation to account for simultaneous mass transfer and then use the scaled concentrations with classical pinch analysis methods such as graphical pinch analysis or the transshipment formulation (Wang and Smith, 1994; Alva-Argáez et al., 1999). Although these methods can significantly reduce the size of the problem, they also require the construction of concentration intervals through nonsmooth mappings that prevents them from solving for unknown concentrations in the system or being embedded in process optimization problems.

In this work, we present an alternative approach to solving the resource targeting problem for multiple contaminants and a single fresh solvent source. We extend our previous work on the nonsmooth integration operator, which is able to solve the general targeting problem using a system of two nonsmooth equations per integrated resource regardless of system size (Nielsen and Barton, 2019). We adapt the concentration-scaling approach for the nonsmooth integration operator whose unique structure makes it ideal for incorporating the nonsmooth mappings. Our new approach retains the compact scaling of the integration operator and is also able to solve for any unknown process variable, including contaminant concentrations, making it a good candidate for solving large-scale integration and process optimization problems.

2. Problem Statement

This work considers a specific instance of the general integration problem. For each resource n in a set T with a set of resource sources, SR_n, and a set of sinks, SK_n, the general integration problem seeks to determine the system specifications, either resource targets or process variables, at which minimal feasible resource use and waste production occur. Mathematically, this problem can be represented by a system of equations describing a process model, $\mathbf{h}$, and a set of embedded optimization problems that minimize the fresh loads of each resource and are parametric in the process variables, $\mathbf{x}$, as outlined below:

$$0 = \mathbf{h}(\mathbf{x}, \mathbf{y}_1, \ldots, \mathbf{y}_{|T|})$$

$$\left. \begin{array}{l} \{\mathbf{y}_n\} = \arg \min_{\mathbf{y}_n} R_{SR,n}(\mathbf{x}) \\ \text{s.t. Resource balance holds and transfer is feasible} \end{array} \right\} \forall n \in T, \qquad (1)$$

where, for each resource type, $\mathbf{y}_n = (R_{SR,n}; r_{SK,n})$, where $R_{SR,n}$ is the fresh resource supply and $r_{SK,n}$ is the waste resource flow. The feasibility of resource transfer between the sources and sinks for each resource is limited by their qualities $Q_i^{in,out}$ and $q_j^{in,out}$, respectively, which change with resource transfer at a rate determined by their constant states, $S_{i,n}$ or $s_{j,n}$. In the general integration problem, we assume that the qualities are linearly related to the resource transfer by the state and that the transfer of each resource is independently limited at a pinch point based on enforced or driving force limitations.

Here we consider an instance of the general integration problem in which we wish to determine the minimum solvent requirement to remove multiple contaminants from a set of rich streams. A commonly addressed problem of this type is the fixed-load water integration problem, which considers process units with constant water flow rates as rich streams for mass integration. The minimum feasible fresh water supply for removing the contaminant loads from the process units is then determined as a single lean stream in the mass integration problem. In this problem type, the resource quantities are contaminant mass load flow rates, the states are the solvent mass flow rates, and the qualities are the concentrations of contaminants scaled to a chosen reference stream using equilibrium relations. For this analysis, we assume that the external mass loads for each contaminant are zero and a single solvent stream is available for contaminant removal.

In this problem type, the feasibility of the contaminant transfers to the solvent cannot be independently considered using pinch analysis because contaminant transfer between streams occurs simultaneously. Considering each component independently will underestimate the required external utilities and provide infeasible results. Therefore, traditional approaches to solving the embedded optimization problems in Eq. (1) must be adapted to account for the dependent mass transfer of the contaminants. In the following section, we present one such adaptation for the nonsmooth integration operator.

3. Nonsmooth Approach

The nonsmooth integration operator is a system of two equations per resource to express the solutions to the minimization problems in Eq. (1). The first equation is an overall resource balance, and the second is a pinch point balance which enforces the resource balance to be nonnegative at each quality value for feasibility and zero at one pinch quality for optimality. Neglecting the index n for clarity, the nonsmooth integration operator for a given resource is:

$$0 = \sum_{i \in SR} S_i (Q_i^{in} - Q_i^{out}) - \sum_{j \in SK} s_j (q_j^{out} - q_j^{in}) + R_{SR} - r_{SK} \tag{2}$$

$$0 = \min_{p \in P} \{RBP_{SK}^p - RBP_{SR}^p\} + r_{SK} \tag{3}$$

Where P is the finite index set of pinch point candidates and

$$RBP_{SR}^p := \sum_{i \in SR} S_i [\max\{0, Q^p - Q_i^{out}\} - \max\{0, Q^p - Q_i^{in}\} - \max\{0, Q^{min} - Q^p\}$$

$$+ \max\{0, Q^p - Q^{max}\}], \quad \forall p \in P,$$

$$RBP_{SK}^p := \sum_{j \in SK} s_j [\max\{0, (Q^p - \Delta Q_{min}) - q_j^{in}\} - \max\{0, (Q^p - \Delta Q_{min}) - q_j^{out}\}$$

$$+ \max\{0, (Q^p - \Delta Q_{min}) - q^{max}\} - \max\{0, q^{min} - (Q^p - \Delta Q_{min})\}], \quad \forall p \in P,$$

where ΔQ_{min} is the minimum feasible quality difference at which resource transfer can occur and the source qualities at the potential pinch points are

$$Q^p = \begin{cases} Q_i^{in}, & \forall p = i \in SR, \\ q_j^{in} + \Delta Q_{min}, & \forall p = j \in SK, \ q_j^{in} \neq 0. \end{cases}$$

$Q^{min,max}$ and $q^{min,max}$ are the minimum and maximum qualities across the sources or sinks, respectively, and the max terms containing these variables create nonphysical extensions to the cumulative resource quantities, which ensure the difference between the source and sink resource balances is always defined.

To solve the general integration problem, one nonsmooth operator is constructed for each resource, and these are combined with a process model to form a system of nonsmooth equations. In addition to retaining the same size regardless of the number of sources and sinks in the system, one of the advantages of the generalized nonsmooth integration operator is that it can be directly applied to any pinch-constrained resource as long as the resource states and qualities are correctly defined, even if they are nonsmooth functions of other process variables. This property allows us to easily incorporate elements of previous scaling approaches to solve the multicontaminant problem presented above.

Wang and Smith (1994) first proposed the scaling approach for the fixed-load water integration problem which was later extended by Alva-Argáez et al. (1999). These approaches assume a mass transfer relation between contaminants in a given operation and use this relation to determine both the limiting contaminant for the operation and the transfer of the other contaminants in the limiting case. The adjusted concentrations for the limiting case describe a pinch-constrained integration problem that can be solved using pinch analysis methods. Note that for these scaled concentrations to fully describe the mass integration problem, the system must have a single, uncontaminated, lean solvent stream for mass removal. Otherwise, the lean stream concentrations must also be adjusted to the limiting case based on the rich streams present in the same concentration interval. While these scalings are a good candidate for nonsmooth approaches, they are beyond the scope of this paper and remain a subject of future work.

This paper considers the case of fixed mass load distribution in which the contaminant load transferred for any contaminant c in the set C in the rich stream i to the fresh solvent stream is proportional to its inlet concentration. However, in theory, this approach can be extended to any functional mass transfer relation and can even vary between operations. For the case of a fixed mass load distribution, Alva-Argáez et al. (1999) show that the concentration scaling in an outlet rich stream with relative use RU_i is

$$\overline{C}_{c,i}^{out} = RU_i C_{c,i}^{in}, \quad RU_i = \min_{c \in C} \left(\frac{C_{c,i}^{out}}{C_{c,i}^{in}} \right). \tag{4}$$

These equations assume that the unscaled concentrations $C_{c,i}$ have already been transformed to their equilibrium values in the lean solvent streams as required for the single contaminant problem. In this formulation, the inlet concentrations remain unscaled, so to maintain the overall contaminant mass load balances, the rich stream flow rates must also be scaled according to

$$\overline{G}_{c,i} = \frac{C_{c,i}^{in} - C_{c,i}^{out}}{C_{c,i}^{in} - \overline{C}_{c,i}^{out}} G_i. \tag{5}$$

To solve the multicontaminant integration problem, the scaled outlet concentrations and solvent flow rates are selected as the source outlet qualities and states, respectively, and the source inlet qualities and sink properties take their unscaled values. Using this scaling, any contaminant can be selected equivalently as the reference contaminant. Since the problem is now pinch constrained, the nonsmooth integration operator in Eqs. (2) and (3) can be applied directly to solve for a selection of unknowns. Because the equation system is already nonsmooth, the rich stream concentrations can be selected as unknowns even though they are the arguments of nonsmooth functions in Eqs. (4) and (5). To solve the nonsmooth system, we use a semismooth Newton method implemented in MATLAB. Generalized derivative elements are automatically calculated from LD-derivatives using a vector forward mode of automatic differentiation developed by Khan and Barton (2015).

4. Example

To demonstrate the ability of our method to solve for both water targets and concentration limits in multicontaminant systems, we consider a fixed-load water integration problem with three contaminants and three water-using operations. The data for this problem is adapted from Alva-Argáez et al. (1999). The concentration and flow rate values for the contaminant-rich operations are given in Table 1. We assume this data is already transformed to the equilibrium values in the water lean stream, that the single lean water stream is supplied free of any contaminants, and that there are no additional external mass sources or sinks. We also assume that contaminants are transferred to the water stream according to a fixed mass load distribution.

Table 1: Data for the example problem, adapted from Alva-Argáez et al. (1999).

Operation	Contaminant	$C_{c,i}^{in}$ (ppm)	$C_{c,i}^{out}$ (ppm)	$\bar{C}_{c,i}^{out}$ (ppm)	RU_i
Operation 1	HC	1	0	0	0
$G_1 = 45$ t/h	H₂S	400	0	0	0
	SALT	35	0	0	0
Operation 2	HC	90	30	30	0.33
$G_2 = 34$ t/h	H₂S	1200	600	400	0.5
	SALT	90	54	30	0.6
Operation 3	HC	220	120	4.6	0.55
$G_3 = 56$ t/h	H₂S	45	20	0.95	0.45
	SALT	9500	200	200	0.02

We applied the nonsmooth approach as described above for two selections of unknowns, using HC as the reference contaminant. For the first case, we solved the typical integration problem to find the water target for known rich stream data. Table 1 gives the reuse factors and scaled outlet concentrations for this case. Solving this problem gave a minimum fresh water flow rate of 47.8 t/h and an outlet HC concentration of 160.6 ppm. The outlet concentrations of the other contaminants can be determined from these results through mass balances. Figure 1 shows the resulting pinch plots for both the scaled and unscaled HC concentrations. These results demonstrate that in the multicontaminant case, limiting resource transfer may not result in a pinch point for any single contaminant. In the second case, we demonstrate the ability of our approach to solve for rich stream concentrations by determining the limiting inlet HC concentration in Operation 2 required to reduce the fresh water consumption to 45 t/h. We calculated the new concentration limit to be 73 ppm which gives an outlet HC concentration in the water stream of 158.9 ppm.

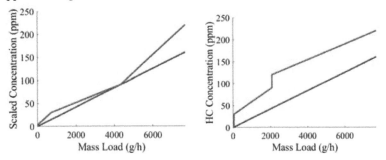

Figure 1: Pinch plots for the example problem with unknown water flow rate. The red curves shown the rich streams for each operation and the blue are the lean water streams. Left shows the scaled HC concentrations and right the unscaled.

5. Conclusions

This paper represents a new approach to solving the multicontaminant mass integration problem to determine the minimum feasible flow rate for a single pure solvent stream. This approach adapts known scaling methods based on the limiting contaminant to be used with the nonsmooth integration operator. The resulting formulation solves a system of two nonsmooth equations per independent set of contaminants regardless of system size. We present a fixed-load water-integration problem to demonstrate the success of this approach for solving for both unknown water flow rates and contaminant concentrations. In future work, we plan to extend our approach to include multiple lean streams with varying inlet contaminant concentrations and to adapt the results to the fixed-flow rate water integration problem. Compared to existing methods, our formulation both significantly reduces the problem complexity and retains the ability to solve for unknown concentrations in the system or be embedded in process optimization problems, making it an ideal candidate for solving large-scale multicontaminant problems.

Acknowledgements

We are grateful to the OCP Group financial support and to the Université Mohammed VI Polytechique - MIT Research Program for supporting and facilitating this collaboration.

References

A. Alva-Argáez, A. Vallaintos, A. Kokossis, 1999. A multi-contaminant transhipment model for mass exchange networks and wastewater minimisation problems. Computers and Chemical Engineering 23, 1439-1453.

M. M. El-Halwagi, V. Manousiouthakis, 1989. Synthesis of Mass Exchange Networks. AIChE Journal 35 (8), 1233–1244.

K. A. Khan, P. I. Barton, 2015. A vector forward mode of automatic differentiation for generalized derivative evaluation. Optimization Methods and Software 30 (6), 1185–1212.

C. S. Khor, B. Chachuat, N. Shah, 2014. Optimization of Water Network Synthesis for Single-Site and Continuous Processes: Milestones, Challenges, and Future Directions. Industrial & Engineering Chemistry Research 53. 10257-10275.

B. Linnhoff, J. R. Flower, 1978. Synthesis of heat exchanger networks: I. Systematic generation of energy optimal networks. AIChE Journal 24 (4), 633–642.

C. J. Nielsen, P. I. Barton, 2019. A Generalized, Nonsmooth Operator for Process Integration. Computer Aided Chemical Engineering 46, 385-390.

Y. P. Wang, R. Smith, 1994. Wastewater Minimisation. Chemical Engineering Science 49 (7), 981-1006.

Sauro Pierucci, Flavio Manenti, Giulia Bozzano, Davide Manca (Eds.)
Proceedings of the 30th European Symposium on Computer Aided Process Engineering
(ESCAPE30), May 24-27, 2020, Milano, Italy. © 2020 Elsevier B.V. All rights reserved.
http://dx.doi.org/10.1016/B978-0-12-823377-1.50044-6

Systematic Generation of a Robust Compartment Model for Counter-current Spray Dryers

Borja Hernández[ab], Mark A. Pinto[a], Mariano Martín[b].

[a]*Procter and Gamble R&D, Newcastle upon Tyne NE12 9TS, United Kingdom.*
[b]*Chemical Engineering Department, University of Salamanca, 37008 Salamanca, Spain.*
hernandezblazquez.bh@pg.com

Abstract

This work presents a novel methodology using machine learning techniques to generate a robust compartment model for unit operations that process particulate materials. The methodology is based on generating a multi-level model from multiple CFD simulations. The reduced-order model comprises flexible phenomenological compartments that modify their size, fluxes and momentum properties according to the different operating conditions of the unit. Each compartment is represented by a set of equivalent CSTR reactors that are used to reproduce the residence time distribution (RTD) for the entire compartment. In each of the CSTR reactor, mass and population balances for continuous and discrete phases are performed along with calculations addressing physical properties and phase momentum. The methodology has been developed for the complete operating space of a counter-current spray dryer. It is able to reproduce the mean residence time and average volume fraction of each compartment with an average error of 21% in the contact region and 11% at the bottom of the counter-current dryer.

Keywords: CFD based compartment model, Population balances, model reduction, robust modelling, multiphase flows.

1. Introduction

Multiphase particulate processes have been traditionally modelled using detailed methods such as CFD-DPM (Computational Fluid Dynamics coupled with Discrete Particle Dynamics) or DEM (Discrete Element Method). Besides helping to understand the mass and energy fluxes in the unit, they provide details of (1) the dispersion of momentum and (2) the spatial variation of phase properties for the continuous and discrete phases (Bezzo et al. 2003). However, CFD-DPM and DEM methods involve a high computational cost; they are not recommended for process optimization and design, or when a complex process phenomenon is considered (Tajsoleiman et al. 2019). In this context, the use of tools that combine CFD and process system engineering (PSE) approaches have shown to provide a significant benefit, without missing the spatial distribution of the phases within a unit. One of the most relevant approaches in this area was introduced by Bezzo et al. (2003). A hybrid CFD-compartment framework was developed, with both models connected by a 2-way coupling approach. This hybrid method was able to reproduce the fluxes with accuracy, with the properties of this flow highly dependent on the procedure used to construct the compartment model. If turbulent dispersion is to be reproduced, zoning is controlled by Damköler and Peclet numbers (Le Moullec et al. 2010); if kinetics is governing, the number of compartments needs to be high enough to capture the speed of the kinetics (Yang et al. 2019). The use of this method has been applied beyond single-phase fluid CFD simulations to multiphase and particulate processes. For example, a DEM-compartment method was developed for modelling particle dispersion and RTD in a particle mixer (Portillo et al. 2007). In this case the number of compartments was homogeneously distributed through the system. However, if more complex cases are to be studied, a phenomenological distribution of the compartments is critical in terms of computational cost and accuracy (Freireich et al. 2011). Freireich et al. (2011) presented a methodology based on (1) characterizing a region where there is a predominating phenomenon and (2) generating a compartment model within each region that is able to reproduce the RTD of the particles. The RTD of each bin of the population balance was introduced by generating two new variables for the 1st and 2nd moments of the RTD, with the 2nd moment of the RTD fitted to an exponential function. The method accurately reproduced the RTD for a mixer-coater under fixed operating conditions. Similarly, Tajsoleiman et al. (2019) recently proposed an automatic method for identifying such regions within CFD codes. However, in all the previous cases, the methods were always studied under a single fixed operating condition. Changes in the size and distributions of the zones, fluxes and momentum as a function of the operating conditions have not been considered. It is necessary to generate a new compartment model every time a change in the operation conditions modifies the distribution of the system's properties (Jourdan et al. 2019). Thus, the aim of this work is to propose a novel methodology for generating a robust compartment model that will be able to reproduce the change in the size of the zones, the particle fluxes and RTD under different operating conditions without the need of repeating CFD or DEM simulations every case. Furthermore, a physics-based approach based on the equivalent number of CSTRs is proposed for reproducing the 2nd moment of the RTD within each phenomenological region. For the demonstration of this methodology a counter-current spray dryer is used.

2. Methodology for robust compartment model generation based on CFD-DPM simulations.

Figure 1 shows the methodology for generating a robust compartment model based on CFD-DPM simulations. It consists of two parts. In the first part, mass balance models for continuous and discrete phases are generated based on monodisperse distributions. In the second part, the characteristic parameters of the discrete phase are determined. Some of the dimensionless groups used for computing the momentum balances and the fluxes are dependent on a single particle diameter, and it is necessary to identify the characteristic diameter (For example, Sauter or mean) of the PSD that is used in each group.

2.1. Description of the stages.

The generation of the models in the first stage is carried out following the procedure presented in Figure 1. In the following paragraphs, the systematic methodology is presented using the case of an industrial counter-current spray dryer:

- The first stage of the process is the generation of a design of experiments (DOX) for studying the mass fluxes with monodispersed particles. A fast-flexible filling method is selected since fouling in the walls is introduced as a discrete variable and the method ensures non duplicity for the remaining continuous variables studied. The DOX is built with a statistical software. In the current case, JMP ® was used to define 20 experiments.
- In the second stage, the experiments are run in a CFD software such as ANSYS® Fluent. The CFD-DPM model used for running the virtual experiments is based on the methodology previously presented by Hernández et al. (2018). This methodology has been extended by validating particle dispersion for different particle sizes, air fluxes and injection characteristics. For each experiment, the

spray dryer is divided into the following phenomenological zones based on differences in the momentum behavior of the particles: injection, elutriates, falling region with concentrated particles, center of the dryer and bottom cone, see left part of Figure 1. Since the RTD and fluxes of particles can also change within each of the zones, each phenomenological zone is also internally analyzed to obtain the fluxes and momentum of air and particles. After obtaining this information, the experiments are evaluated together against each zone. A minimum number is needed to generate the reduced order models. For example, only 2 of the initial experiments resulted in elutriated particles so more we needed to model the fluxes in this zone. It is assumed that the number of representative experiments must be at least one half of the original size.

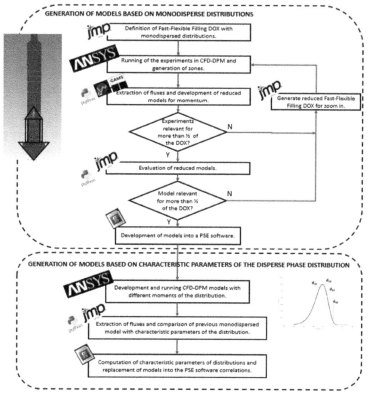

Figure 1. Methodology for the generation of a robust compartment model for multiphase flows based on CFD fluxes.

- In the third stage, reduced models are generated from the fluxes extracted from the CFD simulations. If the data needs post-processing, a data science software such as Python ®TM can be used. The models generated should preferably be based on dimensionless groups as this facilitates scale-up and application to units with similar geometry. For determining the dimensionless groups that are needed and the model to be applied for calculate the momentum in each compartment, machine learning techniques such as Bayesian Information Criteria (BIC) minimization are used. In simple cases BIC minimization can be performed with software such as Alamo (Cozad et al. 2014). In most complex cases where the correlation is included within other models, the terms and parameters are determined by developing the BIC minimization problem in an optimization software as GAMS ® and optimizing with a suitable solver as BARON.

- Once the reduced models are developed for the size of the zones, fluxes of air and particles, momentum and number of equivalent CSTR in each of the zones, the results are validated with the CFD model. If there are enough valid experiments for obtaining the reduced order models and if the models are representative enough of the complete space of operating conditions, the model can be applied to the zone. Otherwise, a new DOX is generated and the new experiments are added to the previous ones. In the current case we assumed that the new DOX needs to have at least half of the experiments of the original DOX.
- The last stage using the monodisperse experiments is the implementation of the reduced order models into a process modeling software. In this work gProms ® is used. The compartment model is structured using a multi-level approach as presented in Figure 2. The first layer contains the phenomenological zones and the core model for computing the size of such zones and the number of equivalent reactors within each of them. In the second layer, the equivalent number of CSTR tanks are modelled. They are modeled with an internal by-pass in case the CSTR equivalent is less than one. The maximum number of tanks is also limited by the accuracy of the model of the momentum in each region. Each tank contains the general mass and energy balances for the air and the population balances for the particles. In order to address the individual phenomena such as drying, lower levels are defined within each CSTR. In this study, the models in the third level are the continuous and discrete phase property models and the momentum model.

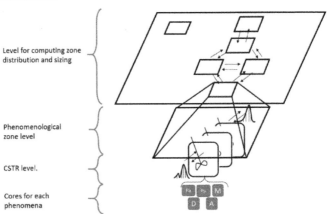

Level for computing zone distribution and sizing

Phenomenological zone level

CSTR level.

Cores for each phenomena

Figure 2. Structure of the compartment model.

Since different PSDs are processed within the unit, the second part of the work focuses on identifying the characteristic diameter of the PSD for properties that depend on particle size. For example, the airflow dynamics are affected by the Stokes number of the particle since it produces a drag on it. This Stokes number can be computed with a characteristic Sauter mean or mass mean diameter.

- The first stage of this part focuses on performing a comparative analysis where four PSDs with (1) different Sauter and similar mass mean and (2) with different mass mean a similar Sauter mean are run in Ansys ® Fluent.
- The second stage involves the extraction of the zone characteristics, fluxes, and momentum properties and performing a comparative analysis for each of them in order to identify the one that governs each property.

- The final stage is the modification of the models in the process modeling tool to make use of the characteristic numbers based on the simulated PSD. For example, to make the Stokes number as function of the characteristic diameter that govern the property for the one that this number is used.

3. Results

In this section the results obtained from the compartment model are presented. To validate the results, the mean residence times predicted, the volume fraction in the most relevant region (the region with falling particles near the wall), and the RTD curves are used. For computing the cumulative error in the RTD of the particles, the differences between the mass fraction predicted by the compartment model, w_{comp}, and the mass fraction predicted by the CFD-DPM model, $w_{CFD-DPM}$, are approximated as presented in Eq. (1) for intervals of 0.5 s.

$$\varepsilon = \sqrt{\sum (w_{comp} - w_{CFD-DPM})^2}$$ Eq. (1)

3.1. Results for monodispersed particles.

In the case of monodispersed particles, the average volume fraction in the falling region and one example of the RTD curves is provided in Figure 3. The average error in the prediction of the volume fraction and mean residence times is 26% and the case with highest error has an average volume fraction 48% lower than the one obtained from CFD. However, evaluating the error of the cumulative RTD, an average 21% of the mass fraction is missed before the cone (a maximum of 65% is missed) and an average of 11% (maximum of 17%) is missed when the recovered mass is evaluated at the bottom of the dryer. From these results, it is determined that the main source of error is due to the mean residence time. That error is especially significant at the beginning of the introduction of the particles as also observed by Portillo et al. (2007). Here, the dispersion of the flux is much smaller than in the cone, where the particles spent more time (up to 90% of the total residence time) and have much higher dispersion.

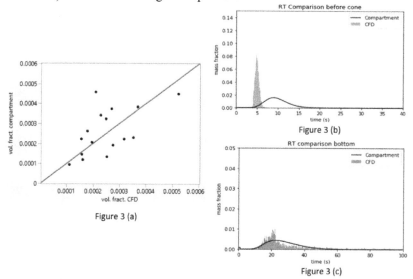

Figure 3. (a) Parity plot of the volume predicted for different monodispersed injection experiments, (b) RTD comparison before the cone and (c) at the bottom of the dryer.

3.2. Results for particles distribution.

In this second part, the results for the concentration of particles and the RTD curves have been studied. Since different sizes are considered, the cumulative error computed by Eq. (1) is averaged between them, with values up to 21% of mass lost and an average missed mass of 18.5% before the bottom cone. At the bottom of the dryer the maximum mass not captured is 9% and the average error is 8.4%. This lower error is obtained because the particle size bins are not captured individually, but as group. Thus, the use of monodisperse particles proves more reliable for validation.

4. Conclusions

In the current work a novel methodology for generating a robust compartment model for multiphase unit operations is developed. The methodology, using machine learning approaches, focused on generating different phenomenological zones that are flexible and that compute the fluxes and momentum for the entire range of operating conditions. This eliminates the need of generating a new CFD-type model for each new operating condition. The method has been applied to modelling an industrial counter current spray dryer. Particle concentration and momentum have been used to validate this methodology. The results show that errors of up to 48% are obtained for the prediction of the mean residence time. A large part of this error is generated due to lack of accuracy in determining the mean residence time. The substitution of the Navier-Stokes equations in the CFD-DPM model by correlations of dimensionless numbers does not allow the accurate reproduction of the mean residence time in the zones where such particles spend very low residence times. However, the methodology shows better results when the residence time and dispersions are higher, for example in the bottom cone of the spray dryer.

References

F. Bezzo, S. Macchietto, C. Pantelides, 2004, General hybrid multizonal/CFD approach for bioreactor modeling. AIChE Journal. 49,8, 2133-2148.

A. Cozad, N.V. Sahinidis, D.C. Miller, 2014, Learning surrogate models for simulation-based optimization. AIChE J. 60 (6), 2211-2227.

B. Freireich, J. Li, Lister, J. C. Wassgren, 2011, Incorporating particle flow information from discrete element simulations in population balance models of mixer-coaters. Chemical Engineering Science, 66, 3592-3604.

B. Hernández, B. Fraser, L. Martín de Juan, M. Martín, 2018 Computational Fluid Dynamics (CFD) Modeling of Swirling Flows in Industrial Counter-Current Spray-Drying Towers under Fouling Conditions. Ind. Eng. Chem. Res. 57, 35, 11988-12002.

N. Jourdan, T. Neveux, O. Potier, M. Kanniche, J. Wicks, I. Nopens, U. Rehman, Y. Le Moullec, 2019, Compartmental Modelling in chemical engineering: A critical review. Chemical Engineering Science 210, 115196.

Y. Le Moullec, C. Gentric, O. Potier, J.P. Leclec, 2010, Comparison of systemic, compartmental and CFD modelling approaches: Application to the simulation of a biological reactor of wastewater treatment. Chemical Engineering Science, 65, 1, 343-350.

Portillo, P.M. Muzzio, F.J. Ierapetritou, M.G, 2007, Hybrid DEM-Compartment Modeling Approach for Granular Mixing. AIChE Journal, 53, 1, 119-128.

Tajsoleiman, T. Spann, R. Bach, C. Gernaey, K.V. Huusom,J.K. Krühne, U, 2019, A CFD based automatic method for compartment model development. Computers and Chemical Engineering, 123, 236-245.

Yang, S. Kiang, S. Farzan, P. Ierapetritou, M.G., 2019, Optimization of Reaction Selectivity using CFD-Based Compartmental Modeling and Surrogate-Based Optimization. Processes, 7(1), 9.

Sauro Pierucci, Flavio Manenti, Giulia Bozzano, Davide Manca (Eds.)
Proceedings of the 30th European Symposium on Computer Aided Process Engineering
(ESCAPE30), May 24-27, 2020, Milano, Italy. © 2020 Elsevier B.V. All rights reserved.
http://dx.doi.org/10.1016/B978-0-12-823377-1.50045-8

Multiobjective Dynamic Optimization of Slow Freezing Processes for Human Induced Pluripotent Stem Cells by Modeling Intracontainer Condition

Yusuke Hayashi[a,*], Ikki Horiguchi[b], Masahiro Kino-oka[b], Hirokazu Sugiyama[a]

[a]*Department of Chemical System Engineering, The University of Tokyo, 7-3-1, Hongo, Bunkyo-ku, 113-8656, Tokyo, Japan*

[b]*Department of Biotechnology, Osaka University, 2-1, Yamadaoka, Suita, 565-0871, Osaka, Japan*

y-hayashi@pse.t.u-tokyo.ac.jp

Abstract

This work presents multiobjective and dynamic optimization of temperature profile for the slow freezing of human induced pluripotent stem (hiPS) cells. A single-cell model was developed that can quantify (i) temperature distribution in a container that causes intracontainer conditional variation, (ii) cell volume change through transmembrane water transport, (iii) intracellular ice formation during freezing, and (iv) cell survival rate after thawing. The phenomena (i) to (iii) were described by white-box (ODE/PDE) models. The phenomenon (iv) was statistically modeled, for which experiments using hiPS cells provided the necessary parameter values. The overall hybrid model can produce cell survival rate and required freezing time as the quality and the productivity objectives, respectively. Multiobjective dynamic optimization was performed on the freezer temperature profile. Among the Pareto optimal solutions, a specific profile was identified that maximized the joint objective of quality and productivity.

Keywords: Regenerative medicine, Cells, Cryopreservation, Hybrid modeling, Numerical simulation

1. Introduction

Human induced pluripotent stem (hiPS) cells are one of the most promising sources of regenerative medicine products. Along with the successful clinical studies, e.g., Parkinson's disease (Morizane, 2019) and spinal cord injuries (Goulão et al., 2016), the demand of hiPS cells is increasing. It is now an urgent task to establish cell freezing process that is necessary for the supply chain with storage and transportation.

As the technique of cell freezing, slow freezing is considered more appropriate for commercial production than vitrification because of scalability, simplicity in operation, and no direct contact with liquid nitrogen. On the other hand, attention needs to be paid to various process conditions that can have significant influence on process performance. Xu et al. (2014) investigated the choice of cryoprotective agent, and observed the consequential influence on cell survival rate. Li et al. (2018) measured the influence of temperature profile on intracellular ice crystals of hiPS cells after freezing. Most recently, we published a single-cell model that defined the estimated cell quality and productivity as a function of the process conditions, e.g., temperature profile of the freezer (Hayashi et al., 2020). However, rigorous temperature optimization was yet to be performed.

In this work, we present multiobjective and dynamic optimization of temperature profile in the slow freezing of hiPS cells. The basis here is the single-cell model that can account for intracontainer temperature distribution. On top of the mechanistic models on heat transfer, transmembrane water transfer, and crystallization of water inside the cell, we developed a statistical model to estimate cell survival rate after thawing. Freeze/thaw experiments using hiPS cells provided the required parameter values. The overall hybrid model was applied for dynamic optimization of temperature profile using quality and productivity objectives.

2. Experimental Methods

hiPS cells in a container, namely vial, with a cryoprotective agent were cooled in a direct-contact freezer at a determined cooling rate. The side of the vial contacted the duralumin freezer plate. The initial temperature of all elements was 277 K and the freezing process was completed when the center temperature of the vial was 193 K. The frozen cells were stored in liquid nitrogen. In order to investigate the cell survival rate, the frozen cells were thawed at 310 K in water. The living cells were counted by trypan blue extrusion test with an automated cell counter before/after freezing-thawing. The cell survival rate was derived by calculating the rate of the number of living cells before/after freezing-thawing.

3. Single-cell Model

Figure 1 shows the structure of the developed model. The mechanistic part consists of the models on heat transfer, mass transfer, and crystallization, which produces the cell volume change and the ice crystal volume. The statistical part, which was newly added in this work, relates these two parameters further with the cell survival rate. The overall model produces the quality and productivity indicators given the process conditions. The modeling concept was based on so-called two-factor hypothesis by Mazur et al. (1972). They investigated the slow freezing of animal cells, and determined the cell volume change by dehydration and the intracellular ice formation as the major cause of damage.

3.1. Heat Transfer Model

Considering conduction as the primary mode of heat transfer in a vial, we adopted the following equation to calculate the temperature profile inside a vial:

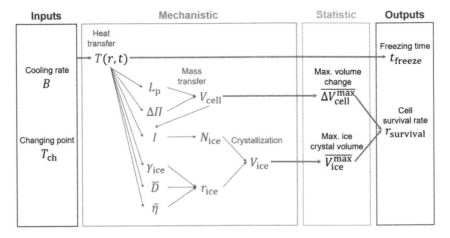

Figure 1. Overview of the developed model.

$$\frac{\partial T}{\partial t} = \alpha \left(\frac{\partial^2 T}{\partial r^2} + \frac{1}{r} \frac{\partial T}{\partial r} \right) \tag{1}$$

where T [K] is the temperature, t [s] is the time, α [m^2 s^{-1}] is the thermal diffusion coefficient, and r [m] is the radial distance from the center of a vial. The position of the solid–liquid interface from the vial center, δ [m], can be calculated as follows:

$$\frac{\rho_{ice} \Delta H_f}{M_{ice}} \frac{d\delta}{dt} = k_{ice} \left(\frac{\partial T}{\partial r} \right)_{r=\delta} - k_w \left(\frac{\partial T}{\partial r} \right)_{r=\delta+d\delta} \tag{2}$$

where ρ [kg m^{-3}] is the density, ΔH_f [J mol^{-1}] is the molar heat of fusion of ice, M [kg mol^{-1}] is the molar mass, k [J s^{-1} m^{-1} K^{-1}] is the thermal conductivity, and the subscripts of w and ice represent water and ice. The required time for completing the freezing, t_{freeze} [min], was defined as the productivity indicator:

$$t_{freeze} = t|_{T(0,t)=193\,K} \tag{3}$$

3.2. Mass Transfer Model

Transmembrane mass transport of water by the osmotic pressure difference was modeled using the following equations (Xu et al., 2014):

$$\frac{dV_{cell}}{dt} = \frac{L_p A_{cell} RT}{v_w} \left[\frac{\Delta H_f}{R} \left(\frac{1}{T_0} - \frac{1}{T} \right) - \ln \left\{ \frac{V_w}{V_w + v_w(\mu_s n_s + n_{cpa})} \right\} \right] \tag{4}$$

$$\frac{dn_{cpa}}{dt} = \frac{(C_{ex} + C_{in})(1 - \sigma)}{2} \frac{dV_{cell}}{dt} + A_{cell} P_{cpa} (C_{ex} - C_{in}) \tag{5}$$

where V [m^3] is the volume, L_p [m s^{-1} Pa^{-1}] is the water permeability, A [m^2] is the surface area, R [J mol^{-1} K^{-1}] is the gas constant, v [m^3 mol^{-1}] is the partial molar volume, μ [–] is the dissociation constant, n [mol] is the molar amount, C [mol m^{-3}] is the cryoprotective agent concentration, σ [–] is the reflection coefficient, and P_{cpa} [m s^{-1}] is the cryoprotective agent permeability. The subscripts of cell, 0, s, cpa, in, and ex represent cell, reference, salt, cryoprotective agent, intracellular, and extracellular, respectively. Normalized maximum cell volume change, $\overline{\Delta V_{cell}^{max}}$ [–], was defined as follows:

$$\overline{\Delta V_{cell}^{max}} = \max \left\{ \frac{|V_{cell}^{fin}(r) - V_{cell}^{init}|}{V_{cell}^{init}} \right\} \tag{6}$$

where the superscripts init and fin represent the initial and final state of freezing, respectively.

3.3. Crystallization Model

The radius of an intracellular ice crystal was defined using the following equation (Karlsson et al., 1994):

$$r_{ice,i} = \begin{cases} 0 & (0 \leq N_{ice} < 1) \\ \sqrt{\int_{\tau_i}^{t} \gamma_{ice}^2 \overline{D} \, dt} & (N_{ice} \geq 1) \end{cases} \tag{7}$$

where r_{ice} [m] is the radius of an ice crystal, N_{ice} [–] is the number of intracellular ice crystals, γ_{ice} [–] is the non-dimensional ice crystal growth parameter, τ [s] is the starting time of ice crystal formation, and $\bar{D}$ [m² s⁻¹] is the average water diffusion coefficient. The total volume of intracellular ice crystals $V_{\text{ice}}(r)$ [m³] can be calculated using the following equation:

$$V_{\text{ice}}(r) = \sum_{i=1}^{N_{\text{ice}}} \frac{4}{3}\pi r_{\text{ice},i}^3 \tag{8}$$

Normalized maximum ice crystal volume, $\overline{V_{\text{ice}}^{\max}}$ [–], was defined as follows:

$$\overline{V_{\text{ice}}^{\max}} = \max\left\{\frac{V_{\text{ice}}^{\text{fin}}(r)}{V_{\text{cell}}^{\text{fin}}(r)}\right\} \tag{9}$$

3.4. Cell Survival Rate Model

As the output of the model, the cell survival rate after thawing, r_{survival} [–], was defined as follows:

$$r_{\text{survival}} = \omega_1\left(\overline{\Delta V_{\text{cell}}^{\max}}\right)^2 + \omega_2\overline{\Delta V_{\text{cell}}^{\max}} + \omega_3\left(\overline{V_{\text{ice}}^{\max}}\right)^2 + \omega_4\overline{V_{\text{ice}}^{\max}} + \omega_5 \tag{10}$$

where ω_1 [–] to ω_5 [–], are the fitting coefficients to the experimental results. The experiments presented in Chapter 2 provided the necessary values.

4. Results and Discussion

4.1. Freeze/thaw Experiments Using Constant Cooling Rates

The circles in Figure 2 show the results of freeze/thaw experiments using constant cooling rates. The highest cell survival rate was observed at $B = 1.0$ K min⁻¹. This result can be explained by the two-factor hypothesis advocated by Mazur et al. (1972). In the range of $B \leq 0.50$ K min⁻¹, the survival rate decreased because the value of $\overline{\Delta V_{\text{cell}}^{\max}}$ increased along with the decrease of B. In contrast, in the range of $B \geq 3.0$ K min⁻¹, the value of $\overline{V_{\text{ice}}^{\max}}$ increased with the increase of B, which decreased the cell survival rate. The solid line in Figure 2 shows the fitted curve for the experimental results. The coefficient of determination was 0.83. The curve was used in the succeeding dynamic optimization.

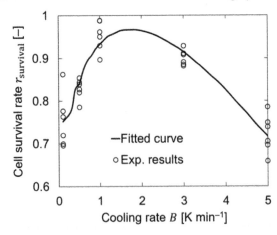

Figure 2. Experimental results of the cell survival rate after thawing and fitted curve for the experimental results.

4.2. Dynamic Optimization of Freezer Temperature Profile

With assuming two-stage temperature profile, multiobjective and dynamic optimization was performed on the first cooling rate, the changing point of the temperature, and the second cooling rate. The optimization problem was formulated as shown in Eq. (11):

$$\min S_{\text{total}}\{r_{\text{survival}}(B_1, T_1^{\text{ch}}, B_2), t_{\text{freeze}}(B_1, T_1^{\text{ch}}, B_2)\} \tag{11}$$

subject to

$$
\begin{aligned}
B_1 &\in \{0.50, 1.0, 1.5, 2.0, 2.5, 3.0, 3.5, 4.0, 4.5, 5.0\} \\
T_1^{\text{ch}} &\in \{-5.0, -10, -15, \ldots, -65, -70, -75\} \\
B_2 &\in \{0.50, 1.0, 1.5, 2.0, 2.5, 3.0, 3.5, 4.0, 4.5, 5.0\}
\end{aligned}
$$

where B_1 [K min^{-1}] is the first cooling rate, T_1^{ch} [°C] is the changing point of the freezer temperature, B_2 [K min^{-1}] is the second cooling rate. The joint objective function, S_{total}, [–] was defined as follows:

$$S_{\text{total}} = \left(\frac{1 - r_{\text{survival}}}{1 - r_{\text{survival}}^{\text{min}}}\right) + \left(\frac{t_{\text{freeze}}}{t_{\text{freeze}}^{\text{max}}}\right) \tag{12}$$

where $r_{\text{survival}}^{\text{min}}$ [–] is the minimum cell survival rate in the all considered temperature profiles, and $t_{\text{freeze}}^{\text{max}}$ [min] is the maximum required freezing time in the all considered temperature profiles.

Figure 3(a) shows the relationship between the calculated survival rate and the required freezing time for 1,360 different temperature profiles considered. Large difference is observed even at the same required time depending on the profile. A trade-off between the quality and the productivity can be seen from the increase of the survival rate along with the increase of the required time. The red dot in Figure 3(a) represents the optimal solution to the problem in Eq. (11). The solution is $(B_1, T_1^{\text{ch}}, B_2) = (2.0, -45, 5.0)$. Figure 3(b) shows the temperature profile of this optimal solution. This profile can reduce the damage due to both dehydration and intracellular ice formation, and at the same time, achieve short freezing time. The profile can be appropriate for practical use.

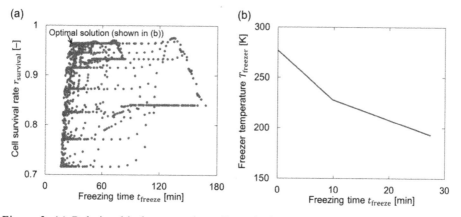

Figure 3. (a) Relationship between the cell survival rate and the required freezing time for each temperature profile, (b) Optimal temperature profile obtained by Figure 3(a) for both the cell quality and the productivity.

Runge-Kutta/Crank-Nicolson methods were used for solving the ODEs/PDEs, and the algorithm was implemented in Python 3.7. The total CPU time for the results in Figure 3 was ca.10 h using Intel® Xeon® Platinum 8160T CPU @ 2.1 GHz with 512 GB RAM.

5. Conclusions and Outlook

We presented multiobjective and dynamic optimization of slow freezing processes for hiPS cells considering an intracontainer condition. A single-cell model was developed by integrating models describing temperature profile, cell volume change, intracellular ice formation, and cell survival rate. The developed model can produce the survival rate and the required freezing time as the quality and the productivity objectives, respectively. We applied the model to evaluate 1,360 different temperature profiles. The optimal temperature profile for both the cell quality and the productivity was obtained, which is suitable for practical application. In an ongoing work, we are conducting freeze/thaw experiments to validate the obtained optimal profile, and also investigating the impact of the choice of cryoprotective agent on the results. In the field of computer aided process engineering, regenerative medicine related researches are becoming increasingly relevant, e.g., Győrgy et al. (2017) and Wang et al. (2018). More model- and simulation-based researches in this area are encouraged to move away from empirical approaches in product and process development.

Acknowledgements

This study was supported by the Japan Agency for Medical Research and Development (No. P14006) and the Japan Society for the Promotion of Science (No. 17H04964). We thank Mr. Yuki Uno in Osaka University for the support in experiment.

References

M. Goulão, A. C. Lepore, 2016. iPS cell transplantation for traumatic spinal cord injury. Curr. Stem Cell Res. Ther. 11, 321-328.

R. Győrgy, M. E. Klontzasb, M. Kostoglouc, N. Panoskaltsisd, A. Mantalarisb, M. C. Georgiadisa, 2017. A Population Balance Model for Stem Cell Differentiation Bioprocesses. Comput. Aided Chem. Eng. 40, 2761-2766.

Y. Hayashi, I. Horiguchi, M. Kino-oka, H. Sugiyama, 2020. Slow freezing process design for human induced pluripotent stem cells by modeling intracontainer variation. Comput. Chem. Eng. 132, 106597.

J. O. M. Karlsson, E. G. Cravalho, M. Toner, 1994. A model of diffusion-limited ice growth inside biological cells during freezing. J. Appl. Phys. 75, 4442-4455.

R. Li, G. Yu, S. Azarin, A. Hubel, 2018. Freezing Responses in DMSO-Based Cryopreservation of Human iPS Cells: Aggregates vs. Single Cells. Tissue Eng. Part C Methods 24, 289–299.

P. Mazur, S. P. Leibo, E. H. Y. Chu, 1972. A two-factor hypothesis of freezing injury: Evidence from Chinese hamster tissue-culture cells. Exp. Cell Res. 71, 345–355.

A. Morizane, 2019. Cell therapy for Parkinson's disease with induced pluripotent stem cells. Rinsho Shinkeigaku 59, 119–124.

X. Wang, Q. Kong, M. M. Papathanasiou, N. Shah, 2018. Precision healthcare supply chain design through multi-objective stochastic programming. Comput. Aided Chem. Eng. 44, 2137-2142.

Y. Xu, L. Zhang, J. Xu, Y. Wei, X. Xu, 2014. Membrane permeability of the human pluripotent stem cells to Me2SO, glycerol and 1,2-propanediol. Arch. Biochem. Biophys. 550–551, 67–76.

Sauro Pierucci, Flavio Manenti, Giulia Bozzano, Davide Manca (Eds.)
Proceedings of the 30th European Symposium on Computer Aided Process Engineering
(ESCAPE30), May 24-27, 2020, Milano, Italy. © 2020 Elsevier B.V. All rights reserved.
http://dx.doi.org/10.1016/B978-0-12-823377-1.50046-X

Optimal Design of a Non-isothermal Hybrid Catalyst Pellet based on POD-DEIM Reduced-order Methodology

Katarzyna Bizon[a*], Gaetano Continillo[b]

[a]*Faculty of Chemical Engineering and Technology, Cracow University of Technology, ul. Warszawska 24, 31-155 Kraków, Poland*
[b]*Dipartimento di Ingegneria, Università degli Studi del Sannio, Piazza Roma 21, 82100 Benevento, Italy*
katarzyna.bizon@pk.edu.pl

Abstract

The problem of the optimal design of a catalyst pellet occupied by different types of active sites was formalized and solved for a non-isothermal system of two consecutive chemical reactions. The maximization of the desired product yield was tackled with model-order reduction techniques. *Proper Orthogonal Decomposition* (POD) and *Discrete Empirical Interpolation Method* (DEIM) were employed to reduce the catalyst pellet balance equations that need to be resolved to evaluate the objective function. It was demonstrated that the pellet performance may be significantly improved by choosing proper fractions of two types of catalytic active centers. Moreover, application of the model-order reduction procedure permitted to solve the problem with a minimal numerical effort without affecting significantly the accuracy.

Keywords: hybrid catalyst pellet, process integration, model-order reduction, POD.

1. Introduction

Hybrid catalyst pellets, also referred as to multifunctional catalyst pellets, enable to integrate different functionalities, including different types of catalytic active centers or catalyst and adsorbent on a single particle level (Grünewald and Agar, 2004). In contrast to the chemical processes carried out in multifunctional reactors integrating different functionalities on an apparatus level, mass transport by diffusion in hybrid pellets takes place over much smaller distances, and this may improve the product yield.

While the optimization of the distribution of a single type of catalytic active centers was examined extensively in the past (Morbidelli et al., 2001), there are very little reports dealing with optimal distribution of two or more functionalities within the pellet. In a previous study (Bizon and Continillo, 2019a) concerning isothermal catalyst pellets integrating two types of active centers, it was demonstrated that optimal distribution of the catalysts within the pellet may lead to a substantial increase of the product yield.

In this study, the analysis of the yield maximization is extended to a non-isothermal catalyst pellet integrating two types of catalytic active sites. The case of two consecutive reversible chemical reactions is investigated. To keep the computational costs low, the optimization algorithm is coupled with *Proper Orthogonal Decomposition* (POD) and a Galerkin projection method (Holmes et al., 1996) employed for the order reduction of the model of a single catalyst pellet. Moreover, since when modelling a non-isothermal hybrid catalyst pellet, the computational efficiency of the standard POD method may fall down, due to the presence of a highly nonlinear Arrhenius term, to reduce the computational burden the POD approach was additionally combined with a *Discrete Empirical Interpolation Method* (DEIM) (Chaturantabut and Sorensen, 2010).

2. Mathematical model and computational methods

2.1. Mathematical model of a single non-isothermal catalyst pellet

Let us consider a system of two reversible first-order chemical reactions:

$$A \underset{k_{-1}}{\overset{k_1}{\rightleftharpoons}} B \underset{k_{-2}}{\overset{k_2}{\rightleftharpoons}} C \tag{1}$$

taking place in a non-isothermal spherical catalyst pellet of radius R_p including two types of active centers. Steady-state mass and energy balance in the pellet are written as:

$$\frac{d^2 \beta_A}{d\zeta^2} + \frac{2}{\zeta} \frac{d\beta_A}{d\zeta} - \Phi_1^2 f_1 \frac{\hat{r}_1}{\hat{r}_{1,ref}} = 0 \tag{2a}$$

$$\frac{d^2 \beta_B}{d\zeta^2} + \frac{2}{\zeta} \frac{d\beta_B}{d\zeta} + \Phi_1^2 f_1 \frac{\hat{r}_1}{\hat{r}_{1,ref}} - \Phi_2^2 f_2 \frac{\hat{r}_2}{\hat{r}_{2,ref}} = 0 \tag{2b}$$

$$\frac{d^2 \theta}{d\zeta^2} + \frac{2}{\zeta} \frac{d\theta}{d\zeta} + \Phi_1^2 \delta_1 f_1 \frac{\hat{r}_1}{\hat{r}_{1,ref}} + \Phi_2^2 \delta_2 f_2 \frac{\hat{r}_2}{\hat{r}_{2,ref}} = 0 \tag{2c}$$

where:

$$\beta_A = C_A / C_{ref}, \quad \beta_B = C_B / C_{ref}, \quad \theta = \frac{T}{T_{ref}}, \quad \zeta = r / R_p \in [0,1] \tag{3a}$$

$$\hat{r}_1 = k_{01} \exp\left(-\frac{\gamma_1}{\theta}\right)\left(\beta_A - \frac{1}{K_{p1}} \beta_B\right), \quad \hat{r}_2 = k_{02} \exp\left(-\frac{\gamma_2}{\theta}\right)\left(\beta_B - \frac{1}{K_{p2}} \beta_C\right), \quad \gamma_j = \frac{E_j}{R T_{ref}} \tag{3b}$$

$$\hat{r}_{j,ref} = k_{0j} \exp(-\gamma_j)\left(1 + \frac{1}{K_{pj}(T_{ref})}\right), \quad \Phi_j^2 = \frac{R_p^2 \hat{r}_{j,ref}}{D_{eff}}, \quad \delta_j = \frac{D_{eff}\left(-\Delta h_j\right) C_{ref}}{\lambda_{eff} T_{ref}}, \quad j = 1, 2 \tag{3c}$$

whereas f_1 and $f_2 = 1 - f_1$ are the volume fractions of the pellet occupied by active sites catalyzing, respectively, the first and the second step of the process given by Eq. (1). The boundary conditions associated with Eq. (2) are:

$$\left.\frac{d\beta_i}{d\zeta}\right|_{\zeta=0} = 0, \quad \left.\frac{d\beta_i}{d\zeta}\right|_{\zeta=1} = \text{Bi}_m\left(\beta_{i,bulk} - \beta_i(1)\right), \quad i = A, B \quad \text{where} \quad \text{Bi}_m = \frac{k_m R_p}{D_{eff}} \tag{4a}$$

$$\left.\frac{d\theta}{d\zeta}\right|_{\zeta=0} = 0, \quad \left.\frac{d\theta}{d\zeta}\right|_{\zeta=1} = \text{Bi}_q\left(\theta_{bulk} - \theta(1)\right) \quad \text{where} \quad \text{Bi}_q = \frac{\alpha_q R_p}{\lambda_{eff}} \tag{4b}$$

More detailed description of the model, including its formulation and definition of state variables and parameters, can be found in Bizon et al. (2019b), where the intensification of catalytic processes through pellet structuring is investigated by means of parameter continuation of steady-state properties of a bifunctional catalyst pellet.

2.2. Formulation of the optimization problem

Assuming for simplicity that each type of catalytic active centers is distributed uniformly along the pellet radius, and that C is the desired product, the optimization problem consists in finding the value of f_1 and $f_2 = 1 - f_1$ that maximizes the yield of C with respect to reactant A (Morbidelli et al., 2001; Bizon and Continillo, 2019a):

$$Y_{CA} = \frac{3\int_0^1 f_2 k_{02} \exp(-\gamma_2/\theta)(\beta_B - \beta_C/K_{p2})\zeta^2 d\zeta}{k_{01}\exp(-\gamma_1/\theta_{bulk})(\beta_{A,bulk} - \beta_{B,bulk}/K_{p1}(T_{bulk}))} \quad \text{where } 0 \le f_1, f_2 \le 1 \tag{5}$$

2.3. Model-order reduction techniques

Evaluation of the cost function (Eq. (5)) requires the numerical resolution of Eq. (2) at every iteration of the optimization algorithm. To keep the computational expenses at a reasonable level, the reduced-order modelling technique based on POD (Holmes et al., 1996) was employed to reduce the number of equations resulting from the discretization of the model equations. In the second step, the POD approach was additionally combined with DEIM (Chaturantabut and Sorensen, 2010), that permits to further increase the computational efficiency in case of occurrence of nonlinearities in the equations.

Let us consider the following system of N algebraic equations, referred to as *full-order model* (FOM), resulting from the discretization of spatial derivatives in Eq. (2) in N discrete nodes distributed uniformly along the particle radius:

$$\mathbf{Ay} + \mathbf{G}(\mathbf{y}) = 0 \tag{6}$$

Employing the method of POD that consists in the resolution of the eigenvalue problem:

$$\mathbf{C\Phi} = \mathbf{\Lambda\Phi} \quad \text{where} \quad \mathbf{C} = \frac{1}{M}\mathbf{YY}^T \tag{7}$$

the state variable vector, $\mathbf{y}$, can be represented in a truncated form as a linear combination of modal coefficients, $\mathbf{c}_K$, and K leading POD modes, that is $\mathbf{\Phi}_K = [\phi_1, \phi_2, ..., \phi_K] \in \square^{N \times K}$, $K \ll N$. Symbol $\mathbf{Y}$ in Eq. (7) denotes a matrix of the model solutions obtained for M values of a selected parameter. Introduction of the truncated state variable into Eq. (6) followed by the Galerkin projection onto the POD basis, $\mathbf{\Phi}_K$, yields the following *reduced-order model* (ROM) consisting of K algebraic equations:

$$\mathbf{\Phi}_K^T \mathbf{A}\mathbf{\Phi}_K \mathbf{c}_K + \mathbf{\Phi}_K^T \mathbf{G}(\mathbf{\Phi}_K \mathbf{c}_K) = 0 \quad \text{where} \quad \mathbf{y} \approx \mathbf{\Phi}_K \mathbf{c}_K \tag{8}$$

When dealing with strongly nonlinear algebraic equations the reduction of the number of equations from N to K usually does not result in computational savings since the value of the nonlinear term $\mathbf{G}$ in Eq. (8) still depends on the full set of variables of the FOM. Computational costs related to the evaluation of the nonlinear terms can be decreased by applying DEIM. DEIM permits to determine a relatively small number of grid nodes optimally distributed along the domain, in correspondence of which the model nonlinearities are evaluated. Following the procedure described in (Chaturantabut and Sorensen, 2010; Bizon, 2017), Eq. (8) can be recast as follows:

$$\mathbf{\Phi}_K^T \mathbf{A} \mathbf{\Phi}_K \mathbf{c}_K + \mathbf{\Phi}_K^T \mathbf{\Psi}_J (\mathbf{P}^T \mathbf{\Psi}_J)^{-1} \mathbf{G}(\mathbf{P}^T \mathbf{\Phi}_K \mathbf{c}_K) = 0 \qquad (9)$$

where $\mathbf{\Psi}_J = [\psi_1, \psi_2, \dots, \psi_J] \in \square^{N \times J}$ is the POD basis determined from Eq. (7) based on the snapshots of the nonlinear term, whereas $\mathbf{P} = [e_{p_1}, \dots, e_{p_J}] \in \square^{N \times J}$, $J \ll N$ is a matrix of interpolation indices, that is the grid nodes at which the nonlinear terms are evaluated, with $e_{p_i} = [0, \dots, 0, 1, 0, \dots, 0] \in \square^{N \times J}$ being the p_i^{th} column of the identity matrix $\mathbf{I} \in \square^{N \times N}$. The interpolation indices can be determined using the algorithm presented in (Chaturantabut and Sorensen, 2010; Bizon, 2017).

3. Results and discussion

Table 1 reports the main parameters of the model employed in the numerical simulations. The values of dimensionless concentrations and temperature of the bulk gas were set, respectively, to $\beta_{bulk,A} = 1$, $\beta_{bulk,B} = 0$ and $\theta = 1$. To construct the FOM, the derivatives in Eq. (2) were approximated by finite differences at $N = 51$ discrete nodes. Both the POD modes and DEIM indices were calculated from FOM solutions obtained for 25 random values of f_1.

Table 1. Main model parameters used in the numerical simulations.

Parameter	Value	Parameter	Value
D_{eff}	10^{-6} m²·s⁻¹	k_m	0.03 m·s⁻¹
$E_1 = E_2$	$6 \cdot 10^4$ kJ·kmol⁻¹	k_m	0.03 m·s⁻¹
Δh_1	$-7 \cdot 10^4$ kJ·kmol⁻¹	k_q	0.02 kW·m⁻²·K⁻¹
Δh_2	$-5 \cdot 10^4$ kJ·kmol⁻¹	R_p	$2.5 \cdot 10^{-3}$ m
$k_{01} = k_{02}$	10^7 s⁻¹	λ_{eff}	10^{-4} kW·m⁻¹·K⁻¹

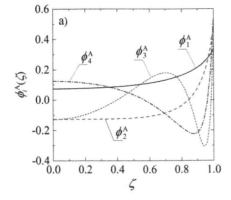 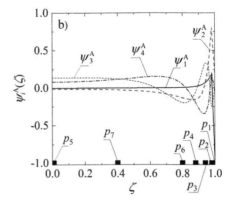

Figure 1. Leading POD modes of the concentration of A, β_A (a) and nonlinear term present in mass balance of component A together with first 7 interpolation indices (b).

Figure 1 shows leading POD modes of β_A (ϕ_i^A, Fig. 1a) and of the nonlinear term present in the component A mass balance (ψ_i^A, Fig. 1b), together with location of the first

$J = 7$ interpolation indices (marked with ■). The non-smooth character of ψ_i^A close to $\zeta = 1$ results from the incorporation of the boundary conditions in **G**. Higher density of DEIM indices is observed in the outer part of the pellet, characterized by larger variations of the state variables.

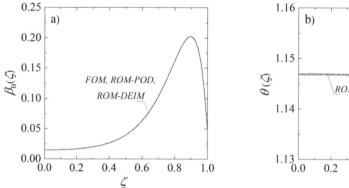

Figure 2. Intraparticle concentration of intermediate product B, β_B (a) and temperature, θ (b) obtained for $f_1 = f_2 = 0.5$ using FOM, ROM-POD ($K = 7$) and ROM-DEIM ($K = 7$ and $J = 7$).

Representative solutions obtained using full-order (FOM) and reduced-order models (ROM) are presented in Fig. 2. It can be observed that employing $K = 7$ POD modes gives a very accurate approximation, when compared with the FOM solution, both for concentration (Fig. 2a) and temperature (Fig. 2b). Actually, the three profiles are virtually indistinguishable. A slight discrepancy between FOM and ROM temperature profiles is encountered when coupling the POD approach with DEIM and the nonlinear term evaluated at only $J = 7$ points of the domain (curve denoted with ROM-DEIM in Fig. 2b). It must be emphasized here that the number of POD modes, K, does not have to be necessarily equal to the number of DEIM indices, J, however in this case such a combination resulted to perform best. The ROM-POD model constructed using 7 modes to approximate each state variable resulted to be about 6.2 faster than FOM, whereas ROM-DEIM with $K = 7$ and $J = 7$ was about 6.8 faster than FOM.

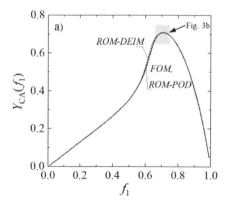
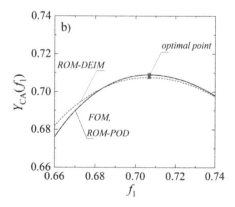

Figure 3. Values of the yield of C with respect to reactant A, Y_{CA}, obtained using FOM, ROM-POD ($K = 7$) and ROM-DEIM ($K = 7$ and $J = 7$) and positioning of the optimum.

Figure 3 shows the values of Y_{CA} determined for varying value of f_1 with the aid of FOM, ROM-POD and ROM-DEIM, together with the positioning of the optimum (Fig. 3b) determined using the interior-point algorithm coupled with FOM and ROM. Both ROMs approximate the objective function and the optimum very accurately. To better visualize the great accuracy of ROMs, representative results of the optimization are reported in Table 2, where FOM is to be regarded as the reference solution.

Table 2. Comparison of the optimal solutions obtained using FOM, ROM-POD and ROM-DEIM.

Model	FOM	ROM-POD $K = 7$	ROM-POD $K = 8$	ROM-DEIM $K = 7, J = 7$	ROM-DEIM $K = 8, J = 8$
f_1	0.70701	0.70696	0.70698	0.70679	0.70842
f_2	0.29299	0.29304	0.29302	0.29321	0.29158
Y_{CA}	0.70899	0.70897	0.70902	0.70762	0.70739

4. Conclusions

The resolution of the optimization problem consisting in the maximization of the product yield demonstrates that properly selected fractions of different types of catalytic active centers may significantly increase the catalyst pellet performance. The proposed computational methodology based on reduced-order modelling gives considerable computational savings without affecting significantly the solution accuracy. For demonstrative reasons it was assumed that both catalysts are uniformly distributed in the entire pellet volume, however, the methodology can be easily adapted for determination of the optimal non-uniform intraparticle distribution of the catalytic active sites.

Acknowledgements

The research was partly financed by the Polish National Science Centre, project number 2017/26/D/ST8/00509.

References

K. Bizon, 2017, Assessment of a POD Method for Dynamical Analysis of a Catalyst Pellet with Simultaneous Chemical Reaction, Adsorption and Diffusion: Uniform Temperature Case, Computers & Chemical Engineering, 97, 259-270.

K. Bizon, G. Continillo, 2019a, Determination of the Optimal Distribution of Active Centers in a Multifunctional Catalyst Pellet Using Global Searching Combined with Reduced-order Modeling Approach, Computer Aided Chemical Engineering, 46, 1015-1020.

K. Bizon, K. Skrzypek-Markiewicz, D. Pędzich, N. Reczek, 2019b, Intensification of catalytic processes through the pellet structuring: steady-state properties of a bifunctional catalyst pellet applied to generic chemical reactions and the direct synthesis of DME, Catalysts, 9 (12), 1020.

S. Chaturantabut, D.C. Sorensen, Nonlinear Model Reduction via Discrete Empirical Interpolation, SIAM Journal of Scentific Computing, 32, 5, 2737–2764.

M. Grünewald, D.V. Agar, 2004, Enhanced Catalyst Performance Using Integrated Structured Functionalites, Chemical Engineering Science, 59, 22-23, 5519-5526.

P. Holmes, J.L. Lumley, G. Berkooz, 1996. Turbulence, Coherent Structures, Dynamical Systems and Symmetry, Cambridge University Press, Cambridge, UK.

M. Morbidelli, A. Gavriilidis, A. Varma, 2001, Catalyst Design. Optimal Distribution of Catalyst, Pellets, Reactors, and Membranes, Cambridge University Press, UK.

Sauro Pierucci, Flavio Manenti, Giulia Bozzano, Davide Manca (Eds.)
Proceedings of the 30th European Symposium on Computer Aided Process Engineering
(ESCAPE30), May 24-27, 2020, Milano, Italy. © 2020 Elsevier B.V. All rights reserved.
http://dx.doi.org/10.1016/B978-0-12-823377-1.50047-1

Cyclopentane Purification from Multicomponent Azeotropic Mixtures

Nuchteera I.,[a] Thirasak P.,[b] Chavagorn M.,[c] Thanyalak C.,[a] Kitipat S.[a]

[a,]*Chulalongkorn University, The Petroleum and Petrochemical College, Bangkok 10330, Thailand*
[b]*Thaioil Public Company Limited, Chonburi 20230, Thailand*
[c]*Sak Chaisidhi Company Limited, Rayong 21150, Thailand*
Kitipat.S@chula.ac.th

Abstract

The distillation technique plays a key role in a separation and purification of multicomponent mixtures. Several alternative designs using conventional distillation for purifying cyclopentane with high purity have been done using Pro/II Process Engineering Software. Using conventional distillation process for purifying cyclopentane from close boiling point mixture is uneconomic and impractical. The distillation technique is also applied in the cyclopentane production. However feed mixture contains multicomponent of hydrocarbons including cyclopentane and 2, 2-dimethylbutane forming azeotrope. Only 80-85%wt cyclopentane purity can be achieved from the conventional distillation. Therefore, a widely used technology, extractive distillation is applied for purifying cyclopentane with 95%wt purity. High-purity cyclopentane gains higher benefit from a larger cyclopentane market.

Keywords: distillation, azeotropic and close boiling point mixture, extractive distillation

1. Introduction

Distillation is a purification technique based on a separation of different volatility or boiling point of the components. In practice we often deal with system of the nonideal mixtures and azeotropic behavior. One kind of azeotropic mixtures is a close boiling point mixture, having the same vapor and liquid composition at a specific temperature and pressure. Then the proper selection of a separation technology depends on the physical or chemical properties between components in the mixtures. Due to the azeotropic properties, a conventional distillation technology cannot be applied to achieve high purity because it requires a large number of trays, which is an economic inefficiency. Several techniques have been developed to eliminate the azeotrope to get higher product purity such as the pressure-swing distillation, azeotropic distillation and extractive distillation (Luyben and Chien, 2010).

The simplest technique for the cyclopentane production is fractionating a light naphtha fraction and natural gas liquid by using the conventional distillation. Due to a presence of an azeotrope within the mixtures or feeds like naphtha fraction, a cyclopentane purity could be achieved only 80-85%wt (Lavanya et al, 2007). Therefore, other feeds and technologies were invented. A high cyclopentane purity can be obtained by processing a feed of partially pyrolysis gasoline using conventional distillation and selective hydrogenation unit (Kanne et al, 1997). Dicyclopentadiene can be used as a feedstock processing through the distillation and hydrotreating unit to produce high cyclopentane purity (Halsey, 2003).

2. Separation and purification processes

This work focuses on distillation, which is a widely used techniques in the chemical and petroleum industries. Distillation principle is operated based on the differences in volatility between mixtures. The higher volatility substances or the lighter molecules are vaporized to the top of column. The vapor molecules are then condensed at the condenser. The condensed liquid is drawn from column as distillate called overhead product. While lower volatility substances or heavier molecules are drawn from the bottom of column as a bottom product (Wankat, 2013). Relative volatility plays a key parameter in the separation process. The relative volatility is a parameter to measure the volatility of components in a liquid mixture. The relative volatility (α_{AB}) can be expressed as shown in following equation (1):

$$\alpha_{AB} = \frac{y_A / x_A}{y_B / x_B} \tag{1}$$

Where x_A and y_A are the molar fractions of the most volatile, having high purity in the top product in the liquid and vapor phase, respectively. While x_B and y_B are the molar fractions of the least volatile substance, having high purity in the bottom product in the liquid and vapor phase, respectively. For their meaning, if the relative volatility (α) equals to one, the separation of the mixtures would be impossible. Conversely, the separation becomes possible for mixtures with relative volatility greater than one (Doherty and Malone, 2001).

In practice, we often deal with the nonideal, azeotropic or close boiling point mixtures. Azeotropic phenomenon or close boiling point mixtures occurs at the same vapor and liquid compositions (Gmehling and Kleiber, 2014). And their relative volatility equals to one. The formation of close boiling point mixtures of this work is the mixtures of cyclopentane and 2, 2-dimethylbutane. The difference in boiling point between cyclopentane and 2, 2-dimethylbutane is less than 1 degree Celsius. Then close boiling point mixtures limit purity of the products. Only 80-85%wt purity of cyclopentane and 15-20%wt purity of 2, 2-dimethylbutane obtained via conventional distillation.

The data used in this work are acquired from hydrocarbon feed (HC-FEED) stream from the solvent plant in Thailand. HC-FEED contains more than 10 components of hydrocarbon. HC-FEED is fed into the complex distillation column (T1) with total 80 trays and weight reflux ratio of 21. By product from the process is withdrawn as overhead product from the top of column T1. Cyclopentane rich stream is then sent to the second column (T2) for purifying with 80-85%wt along with 15-20%wt purity of 2, 2-dimethylbutane as bottom product from column T2. The top product stream of column T2 is recycled to column T1 to improve concentration of cyclopentane in the system. Process simulation by Pro/II Process Engineering Software has been applied for the cyclopentane purifying process as shown in Figure 1.

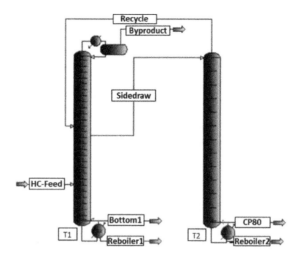

Figure 1: Base-case cyclopentane purifying process by Pro II simulation program

3. Sensitivity analysis

95%wt purity of cyclopentane can be obtained by retrofitting the base-case distillation columns giving 80-85%wt purity cyclopentane. The sensitivity analysis in ProII program was applied to increase cyclopentane purity by modifying base-case process as shown in the Figure 1 into many alternative designs with 95%wt cyclopentane purity. First alternative design was done by decreasing from 12 to 5% yield of cyclopentane from the bottom of column T2, to very low amount as shown in Figure 2. Side-draw tray position from column T1 was moved from trays number 40 to 24 as shown in Figure 3. This helps increase separation ability of cyclopentane at column T1. Then it helps decrease the loss of cyclopentane at column T1. Higher cyclopentane content in the side draw stream from column T1 is sent to further purify at column T2. Moreover weight reflux ratio of column T1 was increased from 21 up to 36.5 as shown in Figure 4. The increase of reflux ratio in column T1 helps reduce loss of cyclopentane to bottom of column T1 and increase by-product content in the overhead stream of column T1. From these conditions, only less than 10 trays was added to the column T1. However, only 35%wt recovery of cyclopentane at the bottom of column T2 was obtained.

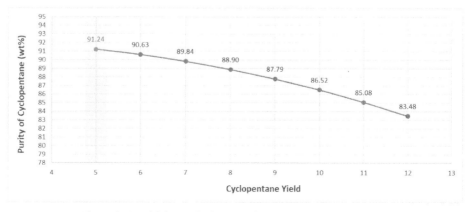

Figure 2: Sensitivity analysis on production yield of cyclopentane

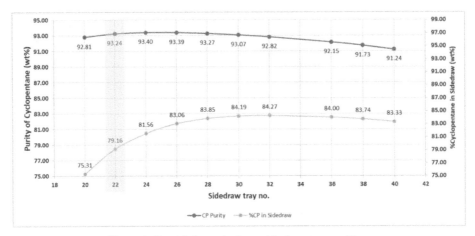

Figure 3: Sensitivity analysis on side draw tray position

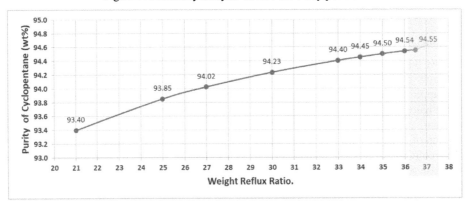

Figure 4: Sensitivity analysis on weight reflux ratio at column T1

For second alternative design, total trays at column T1 are increased about twice of base-case ones as shown in Figure 5. Side-draw tray position at column T1 was moved from trays number 40 to 24. Weight reflux ratio was changed from 21 to 29 to reduce loss of cyclopentane in both distillate and bottom streams at column T1. All of process modifications enhance separation ability of cyclopentane in column T1. Moreover, high purity of by product could be obtained at distillate stream. Higher cyclopentane content will be sent to purify in the column T2. Moreover, flow of cyclopentane was also reduced some amount to meet higher cyclopentane purity. Then 70%wt recovery of cyclopentane at the bottom of column T2 was obtained. Besides higher tray numbers and weight reflux ratio, more column modification of column was also required. From these two alternative designs using base-case distillation column is impractical and uneconomical. Therefore other alternative technology and design, like extractive distillation, becomes more concerns.

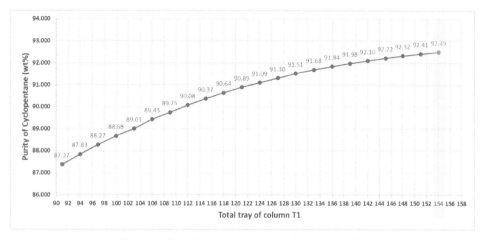

Figure 5: Sensitivity analysis on total tray required

4. Extractive distillation

Extractive distillation is an effective separation technique for azeotrope mixtures or close boiling point mixture. A polar solvent, entrainer or separating agent with high boiling point is added to interact with the components in the azeotropic or close-boiling mixtures. The solvent changes the relative volatility of the component to be separated. This work is focused on the simulation of extractive distillation for purifying cyclopentane with 95%wt purity, which based on the extractive distillation process from a publication (Lehuan Wu et al, 2018). In the publication, the extractive distillation simulation from Aspen 9.0 program was applied to simulate a cyclopentane and 2, 2-dimethylbutane separation process using solvent DMF. In this work, solvent NMP has been used as a solvent for purifying cyclopentane with 95%wt purity in column simulated by Pro/II Process Engineering Software as shown in Figure 6.

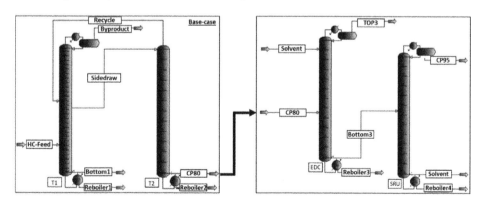

Figure 6: Extractive column (EDC) and recovery unit (SRU) added to base-case process

The bottom product stream containing 80-85%wt (CP80) along with 15-20%wt 2, 2-dimethylbutane from column T2 of the base-case distillation has been used as the close boiling point mixture feed stream in the extractive distillation simulation. The solvent NMP is used and fed to the top section to be the liquid phase in all stages of the extractive distillation column (EDC). While the close boiling point mixture is fed into the middle section of the EDC column. Once the mixture is distilled, solvent NMP will come out with high concentrated cyclopentane at the bottom of EDC column. Mixture of solvent NMP and cyclopentane is then separated apart from each other at a solvent recovery unit (SRU). 95%wt of cyclopentane and 100%wt of solvent NMP are withdrawn at column SRU as the distillate and bottom product, respectively. And 70%wt recovery of cyclopentane at the top of the solvent recovery unit (SRU) was obtained as shown in Figure 6.

5. Conclusions

Base-case distillation models for separating extremely nonideal azeotropic mixture have been generated via Pro/II Process Engineering Software. Simulation results show large numbers of trays and reflux required. It can be concluded that it is impractical and uneconomical for purifying the close boiling mixture by base-case distillation column. While extractive distillation technology can reduce 30% and 25% of total condenser and reboiler duty, respectively. Moreover, only two additional small columns are needed in the extractive distillation process. Therefore, extractive distillation is the most promising techniques for separating and purifying of the azeotropic and close boiling mixture.

Acknowledgments

This work was funding supported by the 30th Years PPC 30 Scholarships of The Petroleum and Petrochemical College (PPC) and Pro/II Process Engineering Software was supported by Thai Oil Public Company Limited. Authors also thank Damrong Taksanont from Thai Oil Public Company Limited and Supanan Suppawatin from Sak Chaisidhi Company Limited to promote the cooperation between academic and industry.

References

W. L. Luyben, I- Lung Chien, 2010, Design and Control of Distillation Systems for Separating Azeotropes, John Wiley & Sons, Ltd., ISBN:9780470448625

M. Lavanya, M. N. S., and B. Sairam, K. Balu, 2007, Petroleum Science and Technology. Effect of Solvents for the Production of Cyclopentane by Extractive Distillation Taylor & Francis: 12

U. Kanne, F. J. H., B. Dürkheim; T. Krug, Worms, all of Germany Production of cyclopentane and/or cyclopentene from partially hydrogenated pyrolysis gasoline, BASF Aktiengesellschaft, Ludwigshafen, Germany

Richard B. Halsey, H., TX (US) (1998). METHOD OF PRODUCING PURIFIED CYCLOPENTANE. US, Equitar Chemicals, LP, Houston, TX (US).

P. C. Wankat, 2013, Separation process engineering : includes mass transfer analysis, PEARSON Education, Inc., 3rd edition

M. F. Doherty and M. F. Malone, 2001, Conceptual Design of Distillation Systems, McGraw-Hill Science/Engineering/Math, Chemical Engineering Series

J. Gmehling, M. Kleiber, 2014, Chapter 2 - Vapor–Liquid Equilibrium and Physical Properties for Distillation, Distillation: Fundamentals and Principles, Pages 45-95

Z. Lei , C. Li and B. Chen, 2003, Extractive Distillation: A Review. Separation and Purification Reviews - SEP PURIF REV. 32. 121-213. 10.1081/SPM-120026627

K. Anton, 2013, Distillation | Extractive Distillation. 10.1016/B978-0-12-409547-2.05949-7

L. Wu, L. W., Y. Liu*, X. Guo, X. Hu, R. Cao,X. Pu, X. Wang, 2018, "Conceptual design for the extractive distillation of cyclopentane and neohexane using a mixture of N,N-dimethyl formamide and ionic liquid as the solvent." Elsevier-Chemical Engineering Research and Design: 197-208.

Sauro Pierucci, Flavio Manenti, Giulia Bozzano, Davide Manca (Eds.)
Proceedings of the 30th European Symposium on Computer Aided Process Engineering
(ESCAPE30), May 24-27, 2020, Milano, Italy. © 2020 Elsevier B.V. All rights reserved.
http://dx.doi.org/10.1016/B978-0-12-823377-1.50048-3

Rigorous Simulation and Optimization of a Plant-wide Glycerol Carbonate (GC) Production Process

Bor-Yih Yu[*] and Wei-Jen Chen

Department of Chemical and Materials Engineering, Chang Gung University No. 259, Wenhua 1st Road, Guishan District, Taoyuan City, 333, Taiwan
boryihyu@mail.cgu.edu.tw

Abstract

The spurring increase in bio-diesel production produces a large amount of glycerol as side product, which causes its over-supply. Hence, converting glycerol (GLY) into other value added chemicals would be a promising solution. In this work, the design and optimization of a plant-wide glycerol carbonate (GC) production processes of GLY and dimethyl carbonate (DMC) is firstly proposed, which is consisted of a reactive distillation section and an extractive distillation-based separation section. The research scope includes regressing the thermodynamic parameters suitable for representing both vapour-liquid and liquid-liquid equilibrium, correcting the kinetic parameters, developing process flowsheets, and optimization.

Keywords: glycerol, glycerol carbonate, process design, optimization, reactive distillation

1. Introduction

The production of bio-diesel has been spurred in the recent years, in order to fight against the oil depletion and global warming. Yet large amount of glycerol (GLY) is also generated as the side product in accompany with bio-diesel. Hence, how to convert glycerol into the other value-added chemicals has attracted wide attention. Among the various GLY utilization routes, a very promising one is to convert it into glycerol carbonate (GC). Holding favorable properties such as low volatility, low toxicity, high bio-degradability and good reactivity, GC finds its uses as solvents, adhesives, chemical intermediate, monomers of polymers and so on.

The process studied in this work is the transesterification reaction between GLY and DMC to produce GC. Considering the difficult handling of using homoogeneous catalyst such as the need of separation from the product, the possibility of equipment corrosion, catalyst deactivation and so on, heterogeneous catalyst is used in the process design. To this end, the kinetic parameters proposed from Singh et al. (2014), in which the performance of zinc/lanthanum mixed-oxide (Zn4La1) catalyst was evaluated for temperature from 120 to 140 °C and DMC excess ratio from 2 to 6. According to this contribution, there are two reactions included in this process. The main reaction is to react GLY with DMC to become GC and MeOH. This is a reversible reaction, indicated by the following eq. (1) and (2). The side reaction is that GC dissociates into glycidol (GLC) and CO_2 under higher temperature, as indicated by the following eq. (3).

$$GLY + DMC \xrightarrow{r_1} GC + 2MeOH \tag{1}$$

$$GC + 2MeOH \xrightarrow{r_2} GLY + DMC \tag{2}$$

$$GC \xrightarrow{r_3} GLC + CO_2 \tag{3}$$

The main contribution of this work is to develop the plant-wide process for GC production based on reactive distillation. The proposed process is then optimized, and the limitations for operation are summarized. This paper will provide another baseline for further studies, especially in scale-up, control, operation and economical evaluation.

2. Overview of this work

In this work, simulations were performed in Aspen Plus V10. NRTL is selected as the thermodynamic model in simulation. There are seven components included in this work, which are glycerol (GLY), dimethyl carbonate (DMC), methanol (MeOH), glycidol (GLC), glycerol carbonate (GC), carbon dioxide (CO2) and aniline (ANI). The Aspen built-in binary parameters are used if they exist. Otherwise, they are estimated by UNIFAC. Note that the binary pairs in between DMC, GLY, MeOH, and GC were regressed based on the liquid-liquid equilibrium data found in the paper by Esteban et al. (2014), and the vapour-liquid equilibrium data from NIST. The regressed parameters are listed in Table 1.

Table 1. Re-regressed binary interaction parameters in between the selected components

Comp i	Comp j	Temp. Unit	a_{ij}	a_{ji}	b_{ij}	b_{ji}	c_{ij}
GLY	MEOH	C	-0.89448	0.200844	162.205	259.384	0.3
GLY	DMC	C	-2.04183	-0.75795	1300.07	1063.04	0.2
GLY	GC	C	0	0	980.274	-402.219	0.3
DMC	MEOH	C	-1.22636	-1.19606	563.468	669.367	0.1
DMC	GC	C	0	0	143.475	-127.974	0.2
MEOH	GC	C	0	0	58.5085	1638.81	0.3

The reaction kinetic is referenced from Singh et al. (2014), which is a power-law model. The kinetic parameters are re-regressed to reach a better fit of reaction conversion and GC selectivity. The rate equations are listed in eq. (4) to (6).

$$r_1 = 2.29 \times 10^{15} \exp\left(\frac{-138719}{RT}\right) X_{DMC} X_{GLY} \tag{4}$$

$$r_2 = 1.04 \times 10^{7} \exp\left(\frac{-77500}{RT}\right) X_{GC} X_{MeOH}{}^2 \tag{5}$$

$$r_3 = 2.72 \times 10^{9} \exp\left(\frac{-115346}{RT}\right) X_{GC} \tag{6}$$

In the optimization part, the objective function was to minimize total annual cost (TAC), which was calculated as the following eq. (7). Correlation provided by Luyben was used to calculate the capital and operating cost (Luyben , 2011), with the assumption of 3-year payback period and 8000 hours of annually operation. In eq. (7) the correction term on the GC production rate (in kg/year) is included, in which GC$_{optim}$ represents the GC production rate in the final optimal case, GC$_i$ means the GC production rate in any other case. GC$_{cost}$ is the price of GC, which is assumed to be 2.4 USD/kg. With this expression, the difference of GC production rate comparing with the optimal case is quantified as a correction term in TAC.

$$TAC(kUSD/yr) = \frac{Capital\ Cost}{Payback\ Period} + Operating\ Cost + (GC_{optim} - GC_i) \times GC_{cost} \tag{7}$$

3. Process Design and Optimization

One intuition when mentioning reactive distillation technique is that, whether the stoichiometric ratio of DMC to GLY (ER=1) can be used to achieve the targeted (99% in this work) in a single reactive distillation column. However, it may not be feasible in this process, and the reason is two-fold. Firstly, if ER=1 is used for reactive distillation, the bottom stream will be high-purity GC. But GC holds a very high normal boiling point, which makes the bottom temperature unfavourably high. If this is the case, then electricity (or other higher grade heat sources) must be used at the column bottom. Secondly, a very high column temperature may lead to more GC decomposition, which is also undesired.

One solution to this condition is to operate the reactive distillation column under vacuumed condition in order to let HPS usable. However, this means that the reaction would be operated at a relatively lower temperature region. As Singh et al.'s kinetic data is used in this work, we would keep the reaction temperature in between 120 to 140 °C.at which the interested operating temperature is in between 120 to 140 Hence we consider this aspect outside the scope of this paper. The possibility of a vacuumed distillation column was not ruled out, but would be discussed if there is a more suitable kinetic data in the future.

In this work, we analysed the case which also uses excess of DMC in the reactive distillation process. The optimized flowsheet with ER=2 is illustrated in Figure 1, with the details of optimization addressed later.

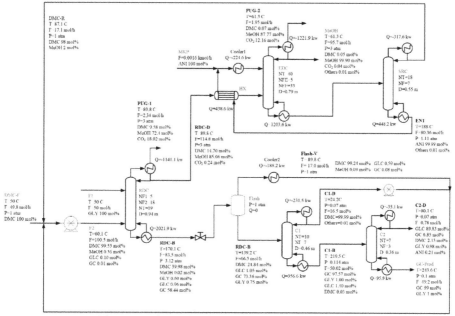

Figure 1. The optimal flowsheet of the RD process.

Firstly, the GLY feed enters at the upper section (5th tray), and the combined DMC stream enters at the lower section (18th tray) into a reactive distillation column (RDC). The reactive section is in between these two feed locations, in which each tray packed with 50% volume of the solid catalyst. The catalyst holdup is calculated by the following equation:

$$\text{holdup} = \frac{\pi D^2}{4} \times WH \times 0.9 \times 0.5 \times \rho_{cat} \tag{8}$$

Where D is the column diameter in meter; WH is the weir height which is set to be 0.1016 meter (4-inch), and ρ_{cat} is the catalyst density (1000 kg/m³). A downcomer area of 10% is also assumed. The calculated holdup is in unit of kg catalyst.

From RDC, a near-azeotropic DMC/MeOH mixture is obtained at the top, while the bottom stream contains the generated GC, the remaining DMC, the unreacted GLY and the slight amount of side product GLC. Besides, as slight amount of CO_2 is formed by GC dissociation, a partial vapour-liquid condenser is equipped in this column, setting 2% vapour purged from the column. The optimal column pressure is 3 atm, with 0.0068 atm pressure drop per tray. The bottom stream from RDC is then depressed to 1 atm, and is flashed. The flash liquid is sent to downstream columns, C1 and C2, for GC recovery. The flash vapour stream contains very high purity of DMC, so it is condensed to become saturated liquid, combined with the C1 distillate, and is then recycled to RDC. The purity for the final GC product is set at 99 mol%, and other specifications for the units in the processes can be found in Figure 1. In order to let the high pressure steam usable (254 °C) as the reboiler heat source, both C1 and C2 are operated under 0.07 atm. The pressure drop of these two vacuumed columns are set at 0.005 atm per stage.

On the other side, the distillate from the RDC is sent to the extractive distillation section to separate DMC and MeOH, which uses ANI as an entrainer. The design concept is similar to that in Yu et al's previous work (Yu et al., 2018). The entrainer to feed molar ratio is set to be 0.7 in this case. The DMC purity from the SRC top is set at 98 mol%, which is determined from optimization, and is going to be discussed in more detail in the following.

The proposed RD process is also optimized by sequential iterative method to minimize TAC. Due to the text size, only the most influential variables are discussed here. These variables are the pressure of the reactive distillation column (P_{RDC}), excess ratio (ER) and the DMC purity from the extractive distillation section. Figure 2(a) shows the TAC change of the optimal cases with varying ER under P=3 atm, while Figure 2(b) and 2(c) records the temperature profiles and the reaction profiles of these cases. It is found that the TAC continues to drop with decreasing ER, which means that the reduction in separation cost dominates. From the temperature profile, it is observed that the bottom temperature becomes higher with decreasing ER. The corresponding bottom temperature is 156.3 °C for ER=2.5, and 170.0 °C for ER=2. Under these cases, the MPS should be used as the heat sources in the RDC reboiler. On the opposite, the bottom temperature is 149.6 °C for ER=3, in which the low pressure steam (LPS, 6 bar, 160 °C) may still be used. Although it requires a lower grade of heating source, the cost saving do not make up for the higher cost resulted from the increased system loading in the ER=3 case comparing with those lower ER cases.

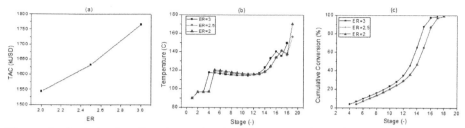

Figure 2. Optimization Results under P_{RDC}=3 atm and varying ER. (a) TAC; (b) Reaction temperature; (c) Reaction conversion profile in RDC.

Figure 3(a) shows the TAC variation of the optimal cases with different P_{RDC} under ER=2, while Figure 3(b) and 3(c) recorded the temperature profile and the reaction profile of these cases, respectively. From these figures, it is observed that TAC becomes lower as P_{RDC} decreases, although greater P_{RDC} leads to higher column temperature which benefits the reaction rate. This represents again the fact that the system loading plays a dominant role in this process. The large drop at P_{RDC}=3 atm in Figure 3(a) is because the cheaper MPS can be used in RDC reboiler. While in P_{RDC}=3.25 and 3.5 atm cases, HPS is needed. Also, it is clear that the number of reaction trays becomes larger as P_{RDC} decreases. From Figure 7(b) it is noted that under P_{RDC}=2.5 atm, the temperature in the reactive section mostly lies below 115 °C, with the lowest tray temperature at 111.7 °C. Hence, we do not consider this case as the optimal one, as the temperature is too far away from the lowest validated value (120 °C). For the case at P_{RDC}=3 atm and 3.25 atm, it is also observed that at some of the reactive trays have temperature lower than 120 °C. The lowest tray temperature at P_{RDC}=3 atm case is around 116 °C, and in P_{RDC}=3.25 atm case it is 117.6 °C. For the P_{RDC}=3.5 atm case, almost all the tray temperature lies in the range between 120 to 140 °C, with the lowest temperature at 119.7 °C. But when considering the highest temperature on the reactive section, they are 141.3 °C, 142.5 °C and 143.6 °C for P_{RDC}=3, 3.25 and 3.5 atm, respectively. In the 3 atm case, only one tray exceeds 140 °C, while two trays exceed this limit for the 3.25 and 3.5 atm cases. Because high reaction temperature leads to greater GC decomposition, here we consider exceeding the temperature upper limit to be more undesired. Hence, the P_{RDC}=3 atm case would be viewed as the optimal one, as it shows a reasonable length of reactive section in RDC as well as a low TAC.

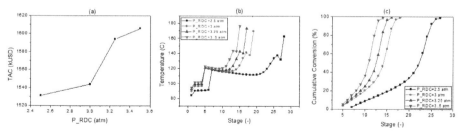

Figure 3. Optimization Results under ER=2 and varying P_{RDC}. (a) TAC; (b) Reaction temperature; (c) Reaction conversion profile in RDC.

The test results on how the DMC purity from SRC distillate affects the performance are illustrated in Figure 4. Previously, we found that the case operating at P=3 bar and

ER=2 is the best case. Here, the analysis starts from this case, varying the DMC purity from 0.995 down to 0.96. From Figure 4(a) it is observe that the DMC purity slightly affects the TAC for this case, and the optimal point is at 0.98. However, the difference is very small. The reason is due to the fact that the recycled DMC from the extractive distillation accounts only for less than 20% of the total flowrate in the combined feed. Even if the small variation, the trade-off caused by different DMC purity can be discovered. Based on this fact, the optimal cases under different P, ER, and DMC purity are compared, and the results are shown in Figure 9(b) and 9(c). From this figure, it is observed that in all cases, DMC purity at 98mol% has a slightly better economic performance comparing with the 99.5 mol% case.

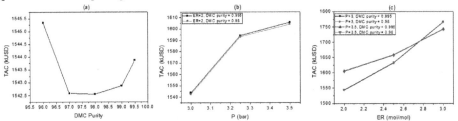

Figure 4. TAC comparison under DMC purity=99.5 and 98 mol%. (a) Optimized TAC comparison; (b) TAC comparison at ER=2 and different P_{RDC}; (c) TAC comparison at P_{RDC}=3 and 3.5 bar under varying ER.

4. Conclusions

In this work, two plant-wide processes to produce GC based on reactive distillation and extractive distillation were rigorously simulated and optimized. The investigation started from regressing the binary interaction parameter sets in the GLY/DMC/MeOH/GC quaternary system. The regressed parameters can be used to represent both the vapour-liquid equilibrium, and also the LLE equilibrium under different temperatures. Besides, the reaction kinetics parameters were also re-regressed to better fit the experimental data. Then, the process was rigorously simulated, and then optimized by sequential iterative method to minimize TAC. The variation of TAC caused by three important variables (P_{EDC}, ER and DMC purity) were clearly illustrated. Note that the process was designed at ER=2 in this work. From the viewpoint of adopting reactive distillation, we suggest that the future kinetic research focus more on the reaction performance at a lower temperature, and also for a larger temperature range. This would lead to another possible improvement in the operation of the RD process.

References

J. Esteban, M. Ladero, L. Molinero, F. Garcia-Ochoa, 2014, Liquid-liquid equilibria for the ternary systems DMC-methanol-glycerol, DMC-glycerol carbonate-glycerol and the quaternary system DMC-methanol-glycerol carbonate-glycerol at catalytic reacting temperatures, Chem Eng Res Des, 92 (12), 2797-2805.

W. L. Luyben, 2011, Principles and Case Studies of Simultaneous Design, Chap. 5. Wiley: New York.

D. Singh, B. Reddy, A. Ganesh, S. Mahajani, 2014, Zinc/Lanthanum Mixed-Oxide Catalyst for the Synthesis of Glycerol Carbonate by Transesterification of Glycerol, Ind Eng Chem Res, 53 (49), 18786-18795.

B. Y. Yu, M. K. Chen; I. L. Chien, 2018, Assessment on CO2 Utilization through Rigorous Simulation: Converting CO2 to Dimethyl Carbonate, Ind Eng Chem Res, 57 (2), 639-652.

Sauro Pierucci, Flavio Manenti, Giulia Bozzano, Davide Manca (Eds.)
Proceedings of the 30th European Symposium on Computer Aided Process Engineering
(ESCAPE30), May 24-27, 2020, Milano, Italy. © 2020 Elsevier B.V. All rights reserved.
http://dx.doi.org/10.1016/B978-0-12-823377-1.50049-5

CFD-based Design Optimization of Air Quenching Equipment to Enhance the Cooling Effect

Jiwon Roh,[a,b] Hyungtae Cho,[a] Yeongryeol Choi,[a] Hyundo Park,[a] Il Moon,[b]
Junghwan Kim[a,*]

[a]*Korea Institute of Industrial Technology, 55 Jongga-ro, Jung-gu, Ulsan 44413, Republic of Korea*
[b]*Yonsei University, 50 Yonsei-ro, Seodaemun-gu, Seoul 03722, Republic of Korea*
kjh31@kitech.re.kr

Abstract

To improve the productivity and quality of industrial products, it is necessary to improve the cooling effect of the air quenching equipment. To optimize the design of the air quenching device, case studies involving numerical analyses using the computational fluid dynamics (CFD) technique were performed. The reliability of the CFD model was validated by comparing the product temperature results obtained using the CFD model with the experimental results obtained using an actual commercial equipment to cool an aluminum alloy product weighing 36 kg. It was observed that the main variables influencing the cooling effect of the air quenching equipment included the distance between air inlet and the product, air velocity at the inlet, and inlet design. A smaller distance between the inlet and the product corresponded to a better cooling effect. The air velocity at the inlet was dependent on the inlet design and flow rate of the air, and the cooling effect varied with the inlet design. When the products at a temperature of 535 °C were cooled for 1200 s, the average temperatures of the cooled products were 190 °C and 117 °C in the cases involving air quenching equipment with a non-optimized and optimized inlet design, respectively. Thus, the optimization of the inlet design could lead to a higher cooling effect, with a temperature reduction of 73 °C. It is expected that the findings of this work can be used to design air quenching equipment with an excellent cooling effect.

Keywords: CFD, air quenching, air cooling, numerical analysis, design optimization, cooling effect.

1. Introduction

Quenching is a crucial part of the heat treatment process of hardening in metals. Alloys are subjected to the quenching process to convert the pearlite grain structure, which is soft and unsuitable for practical uses, into a considerably harder form known as martensite. Previous studies employed different types of simulation techniques to produce high-quality alloys via the quenching process. Xiao et al. (2010) studied the heat transfer during the water quenching process of aluminum alloys, and Yang et al. (2013) performed a finite element method (FEM)-based investigation of the residual stress distribution on the surface of a metal after quenching. Based on the cooling rate required for each alloy type, different types of heat media, such as air, water, and oil, can be used. However, when using a liquid heat medium such as water or oil, it is difficult to remove the generated by-products or liquid waste during the quenching process. Furthermore, it is difficult to ensure a uniform residual stress distribution on the alloy surface. Consequently, the use of air quenching, which is a relatively environmentally friendly technique, has recently become popular in the industry. Although the cooling rate of air quenching is lower than that of other quenching techniques, this technique allows the realization of an advanced heat treatment, and the products can be cooled uniformly without the generation of any additional by-products or waste.

Despite the usefulness of this technique, no existing study has reported on the improvement of the cooling efficiency of air quenching equipment by analyzing the cooling stream inside the device and changing the inlet design of the air flowing from the blower. To allow a wider implementation of air quenching in the industry, the objective of this study was to enhance the cooling effect of the air quenching equipment via design optimization using CFD techniques. The inlet design parameters influencing the cooling efficiency were identified by performing case studies, and the design optimization was carried out accordingly.

2. CFD Simulation

The model setup and simulation analysis were performed using the commercial software Star CCM+. Each case required approximately one hour of computation time.

2.1. Numerical analysis procedure

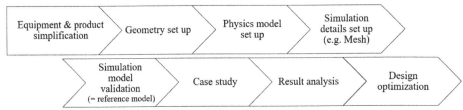

Figure 1. CFD simulation set up and numerical analysis procedure

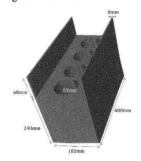

Table 1. Equipment properties

Set up region	Specific heat capacity	Density
Tray	25.10 J/mol·K (25°C)	7.324 g/cm^3
Conveyor	27.23 J/mol·K (25°C)	7.850 g/cm^3

Table 2. Product properties

Set up region	Specific heat capacity	Density
Product	24.14 J/mol·K (25°C)	2.701 g/cm^3

Figure 2. Product geometry

The model setup and numerical analysis procedure for the design optimization using a CFD simulation is shown in Figure 1. Similar to the actual device and product, a model simplification is required to design a shape suitable for the CFD analysis. However, the characteristic parts of the shape, such as the wings and corners, should be the same as those in the actual device to accurately reflect the flow distribution in the CFD analysis. In addition, the physical information and mass of the device and the product should be the same to ensure that the heat capacity is the same in both cases. In this study, a product model with a mass of 34 kg and composed of the same aluminum alloy as the actual product is simplified, as shown in Figure 2. The physics model is required to be established carefully, and the governing equations used in this work are described in detail in Section 2.2. Among the simulation details, the post-processing settings must be set appropriately for displaying the research results; in addition, it is important to suitably set the shape type and number of meshes to perform accurate calculations and obtain accurate results. The validation of the simulation model is shown in Figure 3. By analyzing the quenching results for each inlet design through a case study, the most optimum design was identified, and the design parameters for the optimized design were determined.

2.2. CFD modeling equations

The CFD simulations were performed based on the Navier–Stokes equation. The heat transfer method involved a thermal analysis of a high temperature model, with a temperature of more than 500 °C; however, only conduction and convection were considered and the radiation phenomenon was ignored to improve the convergence of the result data and reduce the calculation cost. The flow used in the simulation was evaluated using the k-epsilon turbulence model.

2.3. Equipment geometry

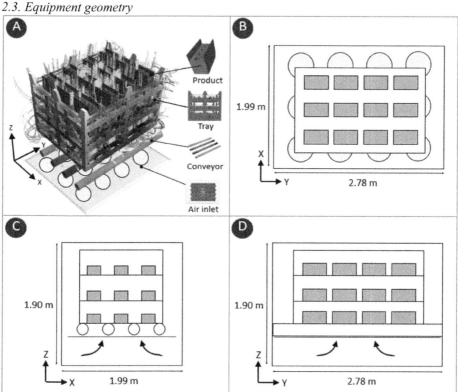

Figure 3. (A) Geometry model of the equipment in the CFD simulation. (B) Side view; (C) front view; and (D) top view of the equipment

The geometry of the simulation model used in this study is shown in Figure 3. Figure 3 (A) shows the overall geometry. Air is supplied from the lower air inlet, and the conveyor is located in the upper area adjacent to the air inlet. The total number of layers is 3. A total of 36 products are considered, and the tray of each layer above the conveyor has 12 products. The product placement and other internal geometry parameters of the equipment are shown in Figures (B), (C), and (D) using the orthogonal coordinate system represented in Figure (A).

2.4. Simulation conditions

The boundary conditions of the CFD simulation can be defined as follows. The external air enters through the air inlet located at the bottom of the device, cools 12 products per layer on the tray, and is later vented through the top air outlet. The product and tray are heated to 535 °C in the furnace and supplied to the equipment by the conveyor. In this study, the heat exchange in the equipment for only one cycle of cooling was considered.

Table 3. Summary of simulation conditions

Domain	Value
Air inlet speed [m/s]	9.037
Air inlet temperature [°C]	80
Gravity [m/s^2]	-9.81

2.5. Inlet design

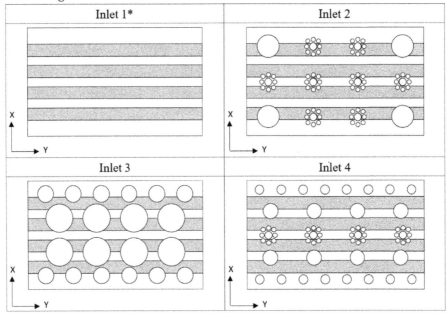

Figure 4. Inlet design

The inlet design used in the simulation is shown in Figure 4. The four long rectangles in Figure 4 represent the conveyor, and the circles represent the inlet. When air enters the equipment using the same number of blowers, a larger size of the inlet and more number of inlets correspond to a lower airspeed per unit through the inlet. Furthermore, the conveyor acts as a type of baffle that changes the flow distribution upon contact, and thus it is important to distribute the inlets to ensure that the flow does not change around the conveyor position. To investigate the effect of the inlet design on the cooling effect, the reference model (inlet 1) is compared with inlets 2, 3, and 4 without setting up a detailed inlet.

3. Model validation

The simulation results for the reference model, that is, inlet 1 indicated that the cooling rates of the product, as obtained using the model and the actual experimental equipment were nearly equivalent with a value of -4.9628 °C/ s

4. Results and discussion

The results of the CFD case studies corresponding to the inlet design are presented in Table 5. After 1200 s, inlets 1 and 2 exhibited a temperature difference of more than two times.

Figure 5. Average temperature of the products with different quenching times

Inlet	Average temperature for quenching time of 600 s	Average temperature for quenching time of 1200 s
1	329.91	215.47
2	182.13	99.30
3	221.23	130.90
4	202.86	130.96

Figure 6 shows the average temperature for different quenching times. The results indicated that an excellent cooling effect occurs when a separate inlet exists.

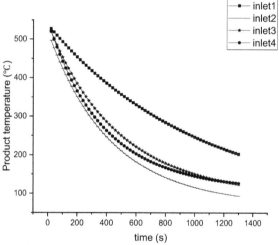

Figure 6. Comparison of average temperature of the products for different quenching times and inlet designs

The flows of inlets 1 and 2, which exhibited a notable difference in the cooling, were compared, as shown in Figure 7, to identify the cause of the difference. As shown in Figure 7 (A), the products located on the outside of the inlet 1 case experienced only a few cooling streams and a low flow rate, resulting in a relatively small cooling. However, the flow distribution of the inlet 2 case involved several cooling streams passing around the product and the flow rate was high, leading to a high cooling effect, as shown in Figure 7 (B). As shown in Figure 7 (C), the flow rate of the upper layer was approximately 30 m/s, which is relatively low compared to the flow rate of 40–60 m/s observed in Figure (D). Consequently, the cooling effect of the quenching equipment with inlet 1 was not satisfactory, since the cooling flow disappeared after impacting the wall and efficient cooling was not performed. As shown in Figure 7 (D), the upper part involved a flow faster than 40 m/s, which passed the product at a high speed, thereby generating an excellent cooling effect. In the case of inlet 2, the air passing through the inlet hit the conveyor and was evenly distributed, thereby effectively cooling the first-floor products. Rapid flows through the small-sized inlets often moved to the top without disappearing.

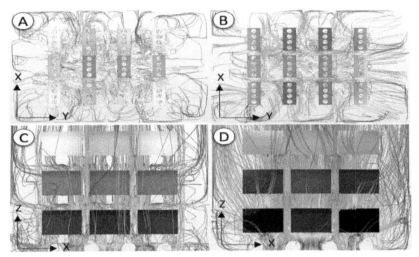

Figure 7. Flow distribution in the air quenching equipment. Top view for (A) inlet 1 and (B) inlet 2. Front view for (C) inlet 1 and (D) inlet 2

5. Conclusions

In this study, four case studies were investigated using CFD to increase the cooling effect of the air quenching equipment. The results indicated that the cooling effect of the different inlet designs was significantly different from that of the reference model. To enable the application of the findings in the actual industry, design optimization was performed in terms of the design optimization parameters. The flow of inlet 2, which led to the best cooling effect, was analyzed, and the following two factors were noted to increase the cooling effect.

(1) If the flow through the air inlet hits the conveyor and is evenly distributed, the cooling effect of the first-floor products is improved. Therefore, it is more desirable to place the inlet close to the conveyor to ensure that it can be directly cooled.

(2) The cooling rate is higher when the air inlet is smaller. Consequently, a smaller air inlet is more desirable, as it can improve the cooling of the products located in the upper layer of the third floor of the tray.

In future studies, the layout and size for the inlet can be numerically formulated for the optimization. The optimized inlet design will be applied directly to the equipment.

References

B. Xiao, Q. Wang, P. Jadhav, K. Li, 2010, An experimental study of heat transfer in aluminum castings during water quenching, Journal of Materials Processing Technology, Volume 210, Issue 14, Pages 2023-20281

X. Yang, J. Zhu, Z. Nong, Z. Lai, D. He, 2013, FEM simulation of quenching process in A357 aluminum alloy cylindrical bars and reduction of quench residual stress through cold stretching process, Computational Materials Science, Volume 69, Pages 396-413

L.Huiping, Z. Guoqun, N. Shanting, H. Chuanzhen, FEM simulation of quenching process and experimental verification of simulation results, Materials Science and Enginering: A, Volumes 452–453, Pages 705-714

Sauro Pierucci, Flavio Manenti, Giulia Bozzano, Davide Manca (Eds.)
Proceedings of the 30th European Symposium on Computer Aided Process Engineering
(ESCAPE30), May 24-27, 2020, Milano, Italy. © 2020 Elsevier B.V. All rights reserved.
http://dx.doi.org/10.1016/B978-0-12-823377-1.50050-1

Integration of Computational Chemistry and Artificial Intelligence for Multi-scale Modeling of Bioprocesses

Nima Nazemzadeh, Laura Wind Sillesen, Rasmus Fjordbak Nielsen, Mark Nicholas Jones, Krist V. Gernaey, Martin P. Andersson, Seyed Soheil Mansouri[*]

Process and Systems Engineering Centre, Department of Chemical and Biochemical Engineering, Technical University of Denmark, Building 229, 2800, Lyngby, Denmark

Seso@kt.dtu.dk

Abstract

Bio-based manufacturing is playing an increasingly important role. Flocculation is an important step in bio-manufacturing, and in water, wastewater treatment and the food industry. Flocculation is a multi-scale process with phenomena that span from the nano-scale all the way beyond the microscale. The control and monitoring of such a process is a difficult task due to the lack of knowledge towards modeling the process across the scales. The intention of this work is to develop a hybrid systematic model-based framework, which integrates the computational methods in chemistry and stochastic modeling approaches for monitoring and control of the flocculation process above microscale. The framework therefore utilizes a hybrid model structure. Since industry resorts to either manual control or no control at all for flocculation, it is aimed to reduce the time required for manual control and to avoid unnecessary product losses and unwanted process variations during the operation.

Keywords: Flocculation, Hybrid Modeling, Computational Chemistry, Artificial Intelligence

1. Introduction

Separation of particles from a suspension in a liquid can be studied in different research areas and applications. The removal of particles from suspensions can be facilitated by flocculation in a stirred reactor [1], since the velocity gradient in the system brings the particles close enough to each other to collide and make an aggregate [1].

Figure 1 represents a schematic figure of shear induced flocculation with polymers as surfactant. Flocculation is a process where two or more particles of the dispersed phase collide and cluster as an aggregate. This process consists of different phenomena including aggregation/agglomeration, fragmentation, breakage and erosion. The mathematical modeling of flocculation, leads to employing a population balance model (PBM) [2] similar to other applications of modeling particle processes. In this work, flocculation dynamics are simulated with a basic form of a PBM represented in Eq. (1). The first and third terms in Eq. 1 account for the generation of flocs of size class *i* due to the aggregation of smaller size aggregates and fragmentation of larger size aggregates respectively, while the second term represents the destruction of such aggregates due to the fragmentation, and the remaining terms stand for the destruction of flocs considering breakage and erosion [2].

$$\frac{dN_i}{dt} = \sum_{\substack{j,k \\ v_{i-1} \le (v_j + v_k) \le v_{i+1}}}^{j \ge k} (1 - \frac{1}{2}\delta_{j,k})\eta_i\alpha_{j,k}\beta_{j,k}N_jN_k - N_i\sum_k \alpha_{i,k}\beta_{i,k}N_k$$
$$+ \sum_k \gamma_{j,i}S_jN_j - S_iN_i \tag{1}$$

Where N_i is the number of flocs in size class i, v_i stands for the volume of a size class i. $\delta_{j,k}$ is the delta-dirac function in order to avoid considering the collisions twice, η is a proportional coefficient that shows how the generated floc size should be assigned to the size classes of the model, while α is the collision efficiency and β is the kernel corresponding to aggregation. S is the breakage kernel and γ is the breakage distribution function that determines the fraction of daughter particles in each size class. The subscripts j and k represent the size classes collide. This PBM is implemented with the python based package TensorFlow in a hybrid framework [3].

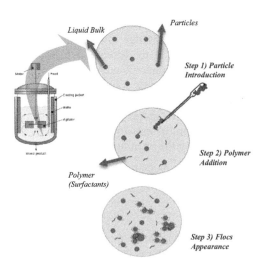

Figure 1: Schematic overview of a flocculation in three sequential steps

2. Hybrid Framework

The aim of this study is to develop a hybrid framework that uses computational methods in chemistry as the first-principles model and a data driven method as the black box element to train the model to find the best fitting flocculation kinetics for the PBM presented previously. Figure 2 represents the overview of this hybrid framework. The model of the process can be represented through the use of constitutive equations and balance equations. The variable u is a vector of input variables including the particle size distribution and process variables from the sensor measurements, while x is the vector of state variables retrieved from density functional theory (DFT) calculations, and together with the process variables the interfacial tension (IFT) between the particles is determined. The machine learning algorithm receives the constitutive variables and the input variables, in order to train the neural network and to predict the kinetic rates of the population balance model (y; vector of output variables). The output variables are used to update the constitutive equation. Then the particle size distribution during the operation is predicted by the model during the operation of the process and it is compared with the experimental results to validate the model.

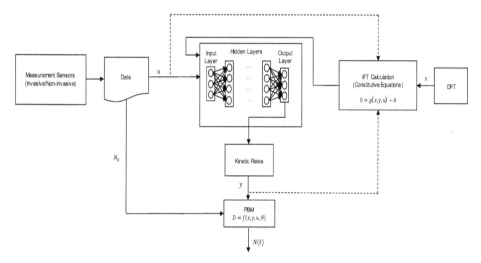

Figure 2: General overview of the hybrid framework

The framework uses computational quantum chemistry as the means to provide a more precise phenomenological understanding of the process. The first-principles model employs DFT calculations to carry out a geometry optimization on the molecules in the system by Turbomole®. Afterwards, possible conformers of these molecules are determined by using COSMOconfX® with BP-TZVPD-FINE basis set. Then, the conformers are introduced in COSMOthermX® to generate the σ surfaces profiles (COSMO surfaces). The σ surface shows the screening charge density, σ, on the molecule surface [4]. The σ surface is then used to calculate the interfacial tension between the particles in the system. The interfacial tension between particles has to be calculated for a solid-liquid interface, which is developed based on the liquid-liquid model of this property in Andersson et al. [4].

The data-driven model is composed of a neural network, which is utilized to find the best kinetics of agglomeration and breakage for the flocculation process. The framework is structured such that the data collected from the first-principles model is used to determine the parameters required for the kinetics of the process. In order to provide the machine learning algorithm with the process variables and floc properties, an experimental setup is prepared. The experimental setup consists of an optical scanning device (oCelloscope by ParticleTech ApS) and an in-line pH measurement for the suspension and an impeller with velocity data transmission. The deep learning algorithm uses the data from the first-principles model (at non-observable scale) and the measurements at microscale to find the best fitting expression governing the system. The proposed framework in this study includes an array of technologies at different technology readiness level (TRL) from fundamental research in nano-scale (low TRL) to using advanced optical measurements (high TRL). Thereby, this facilitates the industry to use a systematic design framework for such complex processes towards industrial implementation. An optimal or near optimal solution will be the outcome of the framework. For instance, by using such framework the polymer usage for flocculation can be optimized during the operation, which is one of the important variables that industry can hardly optimize it in lack of an efficient control and monitoring strategy.

3. Experimental Procedure

A thorough literature study has been carried out to determine the most important parameters for flocculation processes. Among different process variables, pH and velocity gradient induced by the impeller are studied in this work. A design of experiments (DoE) is carried out using the Sobol method [5]. The DoE analysis is carried out for the two variables pH and the shear induced in the range of 2-8 and 50-500 s^{-1}, respectively [6,7]. The Sobol method applies a quasi-random sequences over the parameter space. This will allow to re-use the measurements when conducting more physical experiments with additional process parameters and to use the same sample set for the computational model by applying Monte Carlo based statistical analysis. In this way a cyber-physical setup for the automation of experiments in future research work will be prepared.

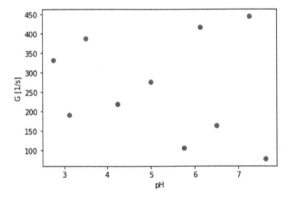

Figure 3: Sampling points for the Sobol method for pH and induced shear

Silica nanoparticles (7631-86-9, size range 0.5-10 μm, Sigma Aldrich) were used as received. 5 M hydrochloric acid and 5 M sodium hydroxide solutions were prepared and used for pH adjustment. The experimental procedure was carried out using the image analysis device (oCelloscope by ParticleTech ApS) and the reactor setup (by Applikon biotechnology) was used for pH measurement and an impeller velocity control system. The sample was agitated by ultrasonication (UP200S Ultrasonic Processor by Hielscher).

A silica suspension was prepared with demineralized water (0.02% wt/wt), 200 mL were ultrasonicated for 5 minutes at an amplitude of 60%, and then transferred to the reactor, which has an impeller to provide shear and a pH probe for measurement. The pH was adjusted and a sample taken (t=0). The samples were taken with a syringe and transferred to a well in a titer plate. Images were made from the silica solution every 5 min. over a 30 min. time span.

4. Case study and results

The application of the hybrid framework is highlighted with a simple binary suspension of silica particles in water. The experimental setup discussed in the previous section is applied to generate the data required for the flocculation of these particles. The particle size distribution of silica in water is plotted every $5\ min$ for $30\ min$ of process operation. Figure 4 illustrates the size distribution of the silica particles at $pH = 2.25$ and an impeller velocity of $N = 200\ rpm$. It can be seen that the mean value of the equivalent diameter is decreased within the first $10\ min$. Then the mean diameter of the particles starts to increase.

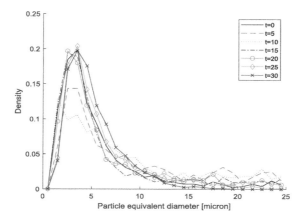

Figure 4: Silica size distribution for $pH = 2.25$, $N\ (impeller\ velocity) = 200\ rpm$,
$t = [0.30]\ min$

The optimized geometry of the components in the system shall be introduced to the IFT calculation routines in the framework. In order to determine the state variables, it is aimed in this study to use DFT calculation for geometry optimization of the molecules present in the system. Hence, a pentamer of polyacrylamide is built in Avogadro® and a geometry optimization is carried out in Turbomole® by using DFT calculations.

Table 1: Sigma surfaces of polyacrylamide conformers

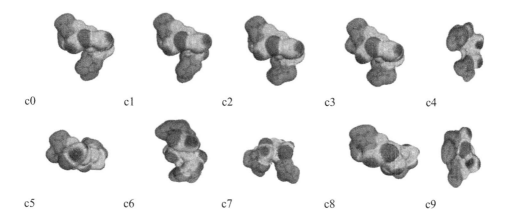

c0   c1   c2   c3   c4

c5   c6   c7   c8   c9

A conformer search is conducted for all possible conformers of this polymer in COSMOconfX® by using BP-TZVPD-FINE basis set. Subsequently, the conformers of the molecule are provided in COSMOthermX® in order to simulate the polymer and to generate the σ surfaces for each conformer. For all of the conformers, it is considered that the weight fraction of the two edges of the molecule is zero. It is an approximation of a larger polymer chain, where the edge effects will be minimal and the ends of of the model molecule will not be included. A pentamer has been chosen for the simulation of the polymer in order to avoid a too large effect of the edges in further calculations. All determined conformers are illustrated in Table 1.

5. Conclusions and future developments

In this work it is shown that a silica particles suspension in water can be observed with the oCelloscope and its image analysis algorithms. A fine segmentation is performed on this system. Hence, most of the silica particles in the sample can be identified by the segmentation algorithm and the process of silica flocculation can be monitored above microscale by the experimental setup. In order to have a phenomenological understanding of the process in nano-scale (i.e. non-observable state) a DFT calculation is carried out to determine all possible conformers of a polyacrylamide molecule. It can clearly be seen from the conformer presented in Table 1 that each conformer has different sigma surfaces. Therefore, the interaction of silica particles will be different with each possible conformer. In the next step of this study it is intended to determine the sigma surface for silica particles and calculate the solid-liquid interfacial tension between the silica and polyacrylamide molecules. Moreover, the population balance model of flocculation is under implementation as a hybrid model combining first-principles with process data driven neural networks.

Acknowledgement

We would like to thank Novozymes A/S, ParticleTech ApS and Greater Copenhagen Food Innovation (CPH_FOOD) for co-financing this research and also for their support during this project.

References

[1]   J.C. Flesch, P.T. Spicer, S.E. Pratsinis, Laminar and turbulent shear-induced flocculation of fractal aggregates, AIChE J. 45 (1999) 1114–1124.

[2]   Z. Li, P. Lu, D. Zhang, F. Song, Simulation of Floc Size Distribution in Flocculation of Activated Sludge Using Population Balance Model with Modified Expressions for the Aggregation and Breakage, Math. Probl. Eng. 2019 (2019) 1–10.

[3]   F. Nielsen, Rasmus, K. V. Gernaey, S.S. Mansouri, Hybrid machine learning assisted modeling framework forparticle processes, Comput. Chem. Eng. (2019) (Submitted).

[4]   M.P. Andersson, M. V. Bennetzen, A. Klamt, S.L.S. Stipp, First-principles prediction of liquid/liquid interfacial tension, J. Chem. Theory Comput. 10 (2014) 3401–3408.

[5]   M. Cavazzuti, Optimiization Methods: From Theory to Design Scientific and Technological Aspects in Mechanics, Springer, 2013.

[6]   J. Rubio, J.A. Kitchener, The mechanism of adsorption of poly(ethylene oxide) flocculant on silica, J. Colloid Interface Sci. 57 (1976) 132–142.

[7]   J. Gregory, S. Barany, Adsorption and flocculation by polymers and polymer mixtures, Adv. Colloid Interface Sci. 169 (2011) 1–12.

Sauro Pierucci, Flavio Manenti, Giulia Bozzano, Davide Manca (Eds.)
Proceedings of the 30th European Symposium on Computer Aided Process Engineering
(ESCAPE30), May 24-27, 2020, Milano, Italy. © 2020 Elsevier B.V. All rights reserved.
http://dx.doi.org/10.1016/B978-0-12-823377-1.50051-3

Performance Enhancement of Acid Gas Cleaning Units in the Natural Gas Processing via Design Modification

Umer Zahid[*], Amr Al-Amri

Department of Chemical Engineering, King Fahd University of Petroleum and Minerals, Dhahran, 34464, Saudi Arabia

uzahid@kfupm.edu.sa

Abstract

Acid gas cleaning is one of the natural gas processing steps where the acid gases are removed to satisfy the quality of the sweet gas. Conventionally, this is achieved by processing the sour gas through an acid gas removal (AGR) unit to produce the desired sweet gas, while concentrating the H_2S gas in the acid gas enrichment (AGE) unit. In this study, a novel acid gas cleaning design has been proposed that can significantly reduce the energy requirement while maintaining all the streams design specifications. The proposed design recommends to first produce acid gas with the required purity and then producing the sweet gas in another AGR unit. The results show that the proposed design requires 22 % lower operational energy compared to the base design.

Keywords: Acid gas removal, energy efficiency, economic analysis, amines.

1. Introduction

Natural gas goes through a series of processing units where various impurities are removed to meet the desired product specification. Removal of acid gases from the natural gas is known as gas sweetening which is a critical process. Acid gases if not removed may cause corrosion in the pipeline, formation of SOx after the fuel combustion and a decrease in the fuel heating value. In addition, H_2S is an extremely toxic gas, hence, the sales gas must not contain more than 16 ppmv of H_2S. There are several methods that can be used to clean the natural gas from acid content. The selection among various methods rely on factors such as concentrations of H_2S and CO_2 in the feed gas, the required product specifications, feed flowrate, and feed gas pressure and temperature (Kidnay et al., 2011). Chemical absorption using amines is the recommended process for the treatment of natural gas at high pressure containing high acid gas content with the requirement of sweet gas to contain very low acid gas concentration. Various efforts have been reported in the literature to improve the performance of AGR plants by different methodologies. Abotaleb et al., (Abotaleb et al., 2018) studied the impact of selective amine application with different additives concentrations on the energy consumption. They reported that based on the acid loading, an addition of piprazine (PZ) to MDEA can increase the absorption and reduce the circulation rate leading to an enhanced performance. Nejat et al., (Nejat et al., 2018) studied the impact of blending a chemical amine solvent with the physical solvent on the energy requirement. They reported an energy savings of 30 – 42 % when using MDEA with a physical solvent such as Sulfinol compared to the chemical amine system. The acid gases separated in the AGR unit are sent to the sulfur recovery unit (SRU). The most common sulfur recovery process in the oil and gas industry is Claus process which can achieve more than 95 % recovery of elemental sulfur. However, the quality of the acid gas feed stream to SRU is critical for its efficient operation. For a straight-through Claus process, the minimum H_2S amount in the acid gas stream should be at least 30 % for an effective operation (Weiland and Khanmamedov, 2010). This becomes an issue especially with high CO_2 content natural gas because a single absorber cannot meet the desired H_2S concentration in the acid gas stream. Hence, the use of acid gas enrichment (AGE) unit is typically employed for increasing the H_2S concentration to enhance the Claus plant performance. The purpose of the AGE unit is to maximize the CO_2 slip in the reject gas stream while minimizing the H_2S loss from the system. The novel contribution of this study is the design development of an integrated acid gas cleaning unit which considers the downstream quality requirements of both the sweet gas and acid gas streams with reduced energy requirements compared to the conventional design.

2. Process Details

2.1. Basis and Assumptions

The simulation models in this study have been developed using a commercial process simulator Aspen HYSYS V.9. Acid gas removal – Chemical solvent fluid package has been used in this study, which is suitable for the amine systems (Dyment and Watanasiri, 2015). The feed specifications used in this study with CO_2 to H_2S ratio of 3.95. The sweet gas HHV must be maintained above 930 BTU/SCF and the hydrogen sulfide content must be below 1 grain/100 SCF or 16 ppmv (Russell et al., 2004).

2.2. Existing Design

Acid gas cleaning for the sour gas with CO_2 to H_2S ratio of more than 2 takes place in two amine units arranged in series (Rufford et al., 2012) namely AGR and AGE, respectively. Since, the CO_2/H_2S ratio of sour feed gas is almost 4, the base case design consists of AGR and AGE units as shown in figure 1. The base case design employs MDEA solvent in both the AGR and AGE units. AGR unit has a lean amine (MDEA) circulation rate of 4,633 USGPM to sweeten the sour gas. Approximately 457.6 MMSCFD of sweet gas with a HHV of 950 BTU/SCF containing 6.8 ppmv of hydrogen sulfide content leaves at the top of the AGR absorber. The rich amine leaving at the bottom of the AGR absorber is flashed in a drum where the flash gas at a flow rate of 2 MMSCFD with HHV of 538 BTU/SCF and H_2S content of 68 ppmv is produced which is sent to the tail gas thermal oxidizer. The rich amine from the AGR absorber is sent to the AGR regenerator where 45 MMSCFD of acid gas containing 23 % of H_2S content is produced at the top. Since the H_2S in the acid gas stream is very dilute, it is sent to the AGE unit. The acid gas from AGR unit enters the bottom of AGE contactor where it contacts the lean MDEA with circulation rate of 3,810 USGPM. Since MDEA selectively removes the hydrogen sulfide, the overhead product of the AGE absorber is the waste gas which contain minimal amount of H_2S. Waste gas mainly containing CO_2 with a flowrate of 19.14 MMSCFD with 104 ppmv of H_2S leaves at the top of the AGE absorber and is fed to thermal oxidizer. Unlike the design of AGR unit, AGE unit is not equipped with flash drum after the absorber due to the low hydrocarbon content. The rich amine from the bottom of the absorber is sent to the AGE regenerator, where 24 MMSCFD of acid gas with 43 mol% H_2S content is produced at the top of the column. The key parameters of the base case model have been validated against the GPSA guidelines to ensure the accuracy of the model results as shown in Table 1. The key material balance results are shown in Table 2.

Table 1: Comparison of base case parameters with GPSA guidelines

Operating Parameters	Normal Range (MDEA)	AGR (MDEA)	AGE (MDEA)
Acid Gas Pickup Ratio (SCF/gal)	3 – 7.5	6.5	4.4
Lean Amine Residual Acid Gas (mol/mol amine)	0.005 – 0.01	0.006	0.005
Re-boiler Heat Duty Ratio (Btu/gal)	800 - 1200	935	916

2.3. Proposed Design

In this study, a novel design has been proposed that can potentially reduce the overall energy consumption of the AGR and AGE units. The idea of the proposed design is to first produce acid gas stream with a desired H_2S content instead of the sweet gas. The off-spec sweet gas is then treated in another AGR unit to produce the desired quality sweet gas. Therefore, this alternative design consists of two AGR units in series, the first unit will produce the acid gas stream while the second AGR unit will produce the sweet gas with the desired specifications. Similar to the base case design, MDEA has been used to analyze the process performance for the proposed design. Figure 2 shows the process flow diagram for the proposed design. The sour gas is counter contacted with the lean MDEA in the first AGR absorber, where the low HHV sweet gas leaves at the top of the column while the rich amine leaves at the bottom of the contactor and is flashed in a flash drum. The rich amine after exchanging heat with the lean amine is fed to the regenerator, where acid gas stream containing 34 mol % H_2S content is produced at the top of the column. The off-spec sweet gas produced at the top of the first AGR absorber has a CO_2 content of more than 5 mol% which reduces the HHV of the sweet gas compared to the desired value of 930 BTU/SCF. Therefore, this off-spec sweet gas is sent to the second AGR unit where more CO_2 is removed to meet the desired purity. MDEA is employed in the second AGR unit with the circulation rate of 2470 USGPM. The off-spec sweet gas and the lean MDEA contacts in the second AGR absorber, where sweet gas with HHV of 949 BTU/SCF containing 1 PPMV H_2S content is produced at the top of the column. The rich amine leaves at the bottom of the absorber and is flashed to release the hydrocarbons. The combined flashed stream with a HHV of 779 BTU/SCF and H_2S content of 42 ppmv is sent to the thermal oxidizer. The rich amine stream after flashing exchanges heat with the lean amine and is sent to the regenerator. The regenerator produces a waste gas stream at the top of the column while the lean amine leaves at the bottom.

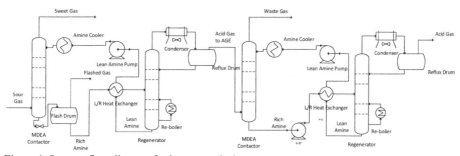

Figure 1. Process flow diagram for base case design

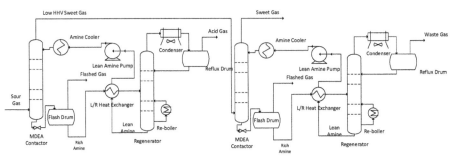

Figure 2. Process flow diagram for the proposed design

Table 2: Stream specifications for the conventional and proposed designs

	Feed	Conventional Design			Proposed Design		
		Sweet Gas	Acid Gas	Waste Gas	Sweet Gas	Acid Gas	Waste Gas
Temperature (°C)	37.8	47.4	47.6	41.2	48.9	60.7	62.9
Pressure (bar)	63.1	61	2	1.8	59.6	2.3	2.3
Composition (mol. fr.)							
H_2O	0.001	0.003	0.055	0.037	0.003	0.093	0.103
Nitrogen	0.060	0.065	0.000	0.000	0.065	0.000	0.000
CO_2	0.082	0.020	0.512	0.958	0.021	0.558	0.890
H_2S	0.021	0.000	0.431	0.000	0.000	0.345	0.001
Methane	0.802	0.874	0.000	0.002	0.873	0.001	0.003
Ethane	0.028	0.031	0.000	0.000	0.031	0.000	0.000
Others	0.007	0.007	0.003	0.002	0.007	0.003	0.003

3. Results

3.1 Energy Analysis

Energy analysis has been performed in order to identify the most energy consuming units in the gas cleaning plant. The main utilities of amine acid gas cleaning systems are power (electricity), cooling agent (cooling water) and heating agent (MP/LP stream). A high amount of steam is required in the reboiler for the regeneration of rich amine. The results show that the base case design requires a total of 274.7 MW energy in comparison to the proposed design which consumes 208.8 MW of the total energy. The proposed design requires 22 % less energy than the base case design mainly because of the reduction in the steam and cooling water usage. The base case design has a high steam consumption because the major amount of acid gas is first stripped in the AGR unit and then the same acid gas goes through the AGE unit. The cooling load in the proposed design could be reduced because of the decreased lean amine circulation rates in both the AGR units. Figure 3 shows the main utilities consumption for the base case and the proposed design. The results show that the proposed design requires 23.3 % less steam compared to the base case. Similarly, the cooling water consumption reduced by 25.5 % for the proposed design in comparison to the base case design. However, the electricity consumption increased slightly in the case of the proposed design. The consumption of utilities shown in figure 3 have been translated into the cost as shown in figure 4.

3.2 Economic Analysis

Economic analysis has been performed to study the impact of new design on the overall cost of the process. The computation of process economics follows the estimation of capital expenditures (CAPEX) and operating expenditures (OPEX) to calculate the total annual cost (TAC). The gas processing cost (GPC) is then calculated by dividing the TAC and the annual plant sweet gas production. The plant life and investment interest rate are assumed to be 30 years and 10 % respectively for the both cases. Annual plant availability also known as stream factor has been assumed as 95 %.

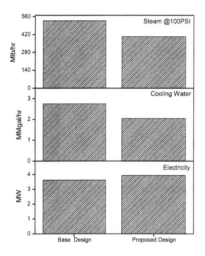

Figure 3. Utilities requirement for the base case and the proposed design

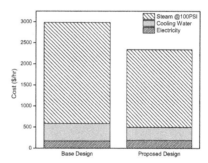

Figure 4. Utilities cost for the base case and the proposed design

The results show that the main contributor to the CAPEX is the cost of the towers. The total equipment cost for the base case and the proposed design is calculated as M$ 54.9 and M$ 47.4 respectively. The lower equipment cost for the proposed design is mainly because of the lower amine circulation rate and reboiler duties compared to the base case design. Figure 5 shows the annualized capital cost for the two designs. The results show that the proposed design requires 20 % less variable operating and maintenance cost (VOM) annually compared to the base case as shown in figure 6. The utilities for the proposed design cost around 21.4 % less compared to the base case design. The huge utility savings for the proposed design comes mainly from the reduced steam requirement. The results show that the amine makeup cost for the two designs is almost the same. The TAC for the base case and proposed design comes out to be M$ 39.2 and M$ 31.9 respectively. The results show that the gas processing cost for the proposed design is $ 201.8 per MMSCF which translates into the cost reduction of around 18.5 % compared to the base case.

4. Conclusion

A novel acid gas cleaning system for the natural gas with high CO_2 content has been proposed in this work that can potentially reduce the energy requirement and gas processing cost compared to the conventional design. The proposed design employs two AGR units for the acid gas cleaning instead of a typical AGR-AGE setup while maintaining the specifications for the sweet gas, acid gas, waste gas and amine unit flashed gas. The new design consumes 22 % less energy compared to the base case because of the reduced amine circulation flow leading to a decrease in reboiler duties. The study compared the two designs in terms of energy and economics to ascertain the process improvement. The results show that the proposed design requires 18.6 % lower total annual cost compared to the base case. In order to have a fair comparison, MDEA has been employed for both the designs in this study.

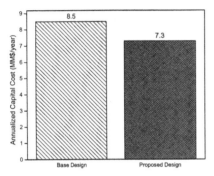

Figure 5. Annualized capital cost for the base case and the proposed design

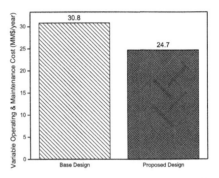

Figure 6. Variable operating and maintenance cost for the base case and the proposed design

Acknowledgment: The authors would like to acknowledge financial support from King Fahd University of Petroleum & Minerals (KFUPM).

References

Abotaleb, A., El-Naas, M.H., Amhamed, A., 2018. Enhancing gas loading and reducing energy consumption in acid gas removal systems: A simulation study based on real NGL plant data. J. Nat. Gas Sci. Eng. 55, 565–574.

Dyment, J., Watanasiri, S., 2015. Acid gas cleaning using DEPG physical solvents: validation with experimental and plant data. USA Aspen Technol. Inc.

Kidnay, A.J., Parrish, W.R., D.G.M, 2011. Fundamentals of natural gas processing 218.

Nejat, T., Movasati, A., Wood, D.A., Ghanbarabadi, H., 2018. Simulated exergy and energy performance comparison of physical–chemical and chemical solvents in a sour gas treatment plant. Chem. Eng. Res. Des. 133, 40–54.

Rufford, T.E., Smart, S., Watson, G.C.Y., Graham, B.F., Boxall, J., Da Costa, J.C.D., May, E.F., 2012. The removal of CO2 and N2 from natural gas: A review of conventional and emerging process technologies. J. Pet. Sci. Eng. 94, 123–154.

Russell, F.G., Adler, S., Albaugh, L.R., Aldana, G.J., 2004. GPSA Engineering Data Book. Gas Process. Suppliers Assoc. 821.

Weiland, R.H., Khanmamedov, T.K., 2010. Acid Gas Enrichment Flow Sheet Selection. Sulphur, Sept.

Sauro Pierucci, Flavio Manenti, Giulia Bozzano, Davide Manca (Eds.)
Proceedings of the 30th European Symposium on Computer Aided Process Engineering
(ESCAPE30), May 24-27, 2020, Milano, Italy. © 2020 Elsevier B.V. All rights reserved.
http://dx.doi.org/10.1016/B978-0-12-823377-1.50052-5

Profitability Increase of a Formaldehyde Plant

Catarina G. Braz[a], J. Rocha[b], R. Alvim[b], Henrique A. Matos[a*]

[a]*Centro de Recursos Naturais e Ambiente, Instituto Superior Técnico, Universidade de Lisboa, Av. Rovisco Pais 1, 1049-001 Lisboa, Portugal*
[b]*EuroResinas – Indútrias Químicas S.A., Plataforma Industrial de Sines – Lote Industrial I, 7520-064 Sines, Portugal*
henrimatos@tecnico.ulisboa.pt

Abstract

This work aimed at the development of a model of an industrial formaldehyde production plant, to identify the process variables that will have the most impact in the improvement of the process efficiency and the increase of its profitability. The model of the process was developed and implemented in *gPROMS® Modelbuilder 5.1.1,* and the system analysed. From the scenarios tested, it was possible to conclude that smaller production costs are obtained for lower operation regimes and when higher oxidation reactor inlet temperatures and methanol concentrations are used.

Keywords: Formaldehyde, Industrial data, Process Modelling, Dynamic Simulation

1. Introduction

The increase of energy costs and the stringent environmental regulations observed in the last years has proved to be a great challenge to chemical industries that try to maintain their product quality and secure their profit and market share. Process modelling and optimisation becomes a powerful tool, using mathematical models based on the chemical and physical phenomena that allow to have a better understanding of the systems and help to make better decisions. Optimal operating conditions and modifications in the plant design can be implemented to improve efficiency, reduce waste and increase the profitability.

The aim of this work was the development of a process model of the above described industrial formaldehyde production unit, and identify the process variables that will have the most impact in the enhancement of the process efficiency and the increase of its profitability. It is the first time that a study on a formaldehyde production unit includes the effects of the deactivation of the catalyst, which, as the results suggest, will have a major impact on the overall plant profitability throughout its lifetime.

Formaldehyde is produced in large amounts due to its broad application as a raw material in industrial and end-use products in more than 50 industrial segments. The *Formox* process is one of the main formaldehyde production processes, in which formaldehyde is obtained by partial oxidation of methanol on an iron-molybdenum catalyst, according to reaction (1).

$$CH_3OH + 1/2O_2 \rightarrow CH_2O + H_2O \tag{1}$$

In the industrial unit subjected to study and presented Figure 1, there are two independent lines producing formaldehyde, which join at the bottom of the absorption column T-1. System 1 is used as an example throughout the description of the process.

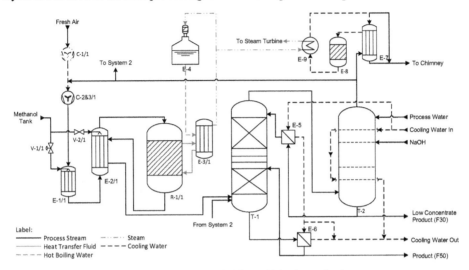

Figure 1 – Scheme of the industrial formaldehyde production process.

Methanol is fed to the formaldehyde plant and is divided into two lines, where the mainline goes into the pre-vaporiser E-1/1, while the second one goes into the vaporiser E-2/1. This division is controlled by the remote-controlled valve V-1/1 and the manual valve V-2/1.

Fresh air is introduced in the processing system, through the pressurisation fan C-1/1 and mixed with the recycled gas coming from the absorption column T-2. The recycling rate is determined by the oxygen content of the gas stream after the recirculation fans C-2&3/1, which must be close to 11 %. During normal operation, approximately one-third of the total gas flow is fresh air. The gas from the recirculation fans is heated by compression in C-2&3/1 and mixed with methanol at the top of the pre-vaporiser E-1/1. In the vaporiser E-2/1, the gas from E-1/1 is further heated by the hot outlet gas coming from reactor R-1/1.

The air-methanol mixture leaving the vaporiser E-2/1 enters at the top of the multitubular reactor with a fixed bed of iron-molybdenum oxide (R-1/1) with a methanol concentration between 8.4 and 8.6 %. . The shell side is filled with boiling heat transfer fluid (HTF) to remove the heat of reaction.

HTF vapours condensate later in the HTF condenser E-3/1 by evaporating bolling feed water (BFW), coming from the BFW tank E-4, into saturated steam at 21 barg, which is later superheated in E-9 to be used in a steam turbine and produce electricity.

In the oxidation reactor R-1/1, the gas mixture reacts into formaldehyde and water and cool down in the vaporiser E-2/1 before entering the absorption column T-1.

In the absorption system, columns T-1 and T-2 remove the formaldehyde from the gas stream to produce aqueous solutions with concentrations of about 55 (F50) and 35 wt % (F30), collected at the bottom of column T-1 and column T-2, respectively. Recirculation from the column T-2 is used to achieve the required flow of liquid. In column T-2, a caustic solution is added at the top to promote absorption, especially at this stage, where the concentration of formaldehyde in the gas is very low.

Finally, the tail gases from the absorption column T-2 are split up between the recirculation fans C-2&3/1, and the Emission Control System (ECS). In the ECS, the process gas is pre-heated in E-7 before reacting in the catalytic reactor E-8, where all organic compounds suffer total oxidation over a catalytic bed. The gases leave reactor E-8 and are cooled down in the steam superheater E-9 before heading to the pre-heater E-7 and afterwards to the plant chimney.

2. Model development and assumptions

The methanol oxidation reactor was described as a pseudo-homogeneous plug-flow reactor model and the kinetic and deactivation parameters estimated in Braz et al. (2017) and Braz et al. (2019). Afterwards, a rate-based model of the absorption columns was developed, that took into account the chemical reactions occurring in the liquid phase and the thermodynamic non-idealities, described in Braz et al. (2018). These models were later revised and validated in Braz (2019), and implemented together with the models of the remaining process units, to analyse the entire production system. Physical properties were obtained using *Aspen Plus V8.8* through the Thermo CAPE-OPEN Standard properties system with the Formaldehyde-Methanol-Water Data Package. In order to simulate the formaldehyde production process, some simplifications and assumptions had to be employed:

- **Operation regime**

The simulation of the different operation scenarios was accomplished, assuming that only one of the formaldehyde production lines is functioning and that the results are the same for the other production line. The formaldehyde production unit operates during the year in four main methanol inlet flowrates, defined here as operation regimes and presented in Table 1. Regime 1 is the maximum methanol capacity (MMC) of one production line, meaning that the maximum methanol capacity of the entire industrial unit is two times Regime 1.

Table 1 – Definition of the four main operation regimes implemented at the formaldehyde industrial unit and their terminology.

Name	% of MMC
Regime 1	100
Regime 2	92
Regime 3	85
Regime 4	66

- **Oxygen and methanol concentrations**

The control of the oxygen content in the methanol oxidation reactor R-1/1 is achieved by regulating the flow of recycle gas to the recirculation fans C-2&3/1, while the normal flow of methanol is calculated as the volumetric percentage of the total gas entering reactor R-1/1. During the process simulation, the operation regime was defined, the methanol concentration fixed to 8.9 and the flowrate of the mixture of fresh air and recycled gas calculated. The fraction of fresh air inserted into the system was then calculated by fixing the concentration of oxygen in the gas mixture at 11 %. At oxygen concentrations above 13 %, there is a risk of explosion due to pressure surge, and at too low concentrations (< 9.5 %), there is a risk of damaging the catalyst because of the reduction and volatilisation of the active centres, according to Andersson et al. (2016).

- **Cost of the production of 1 t of formaldehyde**

The cost of the production of one ton of formaldehyde (C_{CH_2O}) is calculated considering the cost of the catalyst purchase (C_{cat}). After each simulation, the total amount of methanol and electricity consumed (M_{CH_3OH} , C_{MWh}), and the formaldehyde and electricity produced (M_{CH_2O} , P_{MWh}) during the catalyst lifetime were calculated, and the cost of the production of one ton of formaldehyde was determined by equation (2).

$$C_{CH_2O}(\text{€}/t_{CH_2O}) = \frac{M_{CH_3OH} \times Price_{CH_3OH} + (C_{MWh} - P_{MWh}) \times Price_{MWh} + C_{cat}}{M_{CH_2O}} \tag{2}$$

3. Process analysis

A sensitivity analysis of several operating variables was carried out to the industrial formaldehyde production plant for three main operating variables: Process operation regime; Opening of valve V-1/1; Methanol concentration. The effect of these operating variables was observed in four process key performance indicators (KPIs): Lifetime of the catalyst; Formaldehyde production capacity; Superheated steam production; Cost of production of 1 ton of formaldehyde.

Each simulation was carried out throughout time until the catalyst had to be replaced. It was defined that the catalyst reached its end of life when the molar yield of the process was less than 80 %.

3.1. Process operation regime

The first operating variable studied was the operation regime. The four main regimes implemented at the industrial plant were tested, and the results presented in Table 2.

Table 2 – Analysis of the effect of the operation regime in the performance indicators.

	Catalyst lifetime (days)	CH₂O Prod. Variation (%)	Steam Prod. Variation (%)	CH₂O Cost Variation (%)
Regime 1	297	NA	NA	NA
Regime 2	331	3.5	3.9	-0.49
Regime 3	372	7.0	7.8	-0.94
Regime 4	525	18.2	20.9	-2.45

NA – Not applicable (base case)

Table 2 shows that the operation regime will have a significant influence on the catalyst lifetime. If operating on the lowest regime, the catalyst lifetime will increase by 77 %

compared with the highest regime. Moreover, although the operation in higher regimes will increase the methanol conversion and the production of steam in the HTF condenser, the selectivity of the reactions to formaldehyde will decrease, increasing the amount of methanol necessary to produce 1 t of formaldehyde. The result is that the cost of the production of formaldehyde is lower for the lowest operation regime. This is because, according to Andersson et al. (2016), about 94 % of the cost of the formaldehyde comes from the methanol consumed.

Assuming that with the two formaldehyde production lines operating at the same time, the unitary production costs will not increase, with both lines working at Regime 4, the same amount formaldehyde produced during the catalyst lifetime running in one line at Regime 1, would be achieved in 218 days with savings of about 329 k€.

3.2. Opening of valve V-1/1

Later, the effect of the opening of the valve V-1/1 to increase the ratio of fresh methanol flowing to the methanol pre-vaporiser E-1/1 was studied. Opening valve V-1/1 will raise the inlet temperature of reactor R-1/1 and increase the amount of HTF vaporising inside the oxidation reactor.

During the model simulations, it was considered that the opening of valve V-1/1 (%) is equal to the percentage of fresh methanol flowing to pre-vaporiser E-1/1. For the initial simulation, a valve opening of 60 % was implemented, followed by openings of 10 % until valve V-1/1 was completely open. The results presented in Table 3 show that the lifetime of the catalyst is not significantly affected, and an increase in the total formaldehyde and steam produced is observed, decreasing the final production cost of formaldehyde.

Table 3 – Analysis of the effect of valve V-1/1 opening (VO) for Operation Regime 1.

VO (%)	Catalyst lifetime (days)	CH_2O Prod. Variation (%)	Steam Prod. Variation (%)	CH_2O Cost Variation (%)
60	297	NA	NA	NA
70	297	0.17	4.1	-0.10
80	297	0.34	8.2	-0.20
90	298	0.51	12.3	-0.30
100	298	0.69	16.5	-0.40

NA – Not applicable (base case)

3.3. Methanol concentration

The effect of the methanol concentration on the process KPIs was studied by increasing the reactor R-1/1 inlet methanol volumetric concentration until the maximum limit was reached before it could damage the catalyst [112]. The increase of methanol concentration was achieved by decreasing the recycling fraction of the process gas coming from Column T-2, meaning that more gas was directed to the Emission Control System (ECS) for the combustion of the hydrocarbons, and the production of superheated steam.

Table 4 shows that, although the production of formaldehyde decreases with the increase of methanol concentration, the cost of production continually decreases. The main contributor to the fall of the production cost is the reduction of the expenses with electricity because less gas is being introduced into the reactor. Secondly, the catalyst is operating for fewer days, reducing the total consumption of methanol. And finally, the production of steam also increases, reaching a maximum value at a methanol concentration between 10.1 and 10.5 %.

Table 4 – Analysis of the effect of the reactor R-1/1 inlet methanol concentration at Operation Regime 1.

Met %	Catalyst lifetime (days)	CH$_2$O Prod. Variation (%)	Steam Prod. Variation (%)	CH$_2$O Cost Variation (%)
8.9	297	NA	NA	NA
9.3	297	0.01	1.37	-0.30
9.7	296	-0.15	2.49	-0.60
10.1	294	-0.84	3.02	-0.92
10.5	291	-2.07	2.97	-1.25

4. Conclusions

In this work, a dynamic model of an industrial formaldehyde production unit was developed, and the effect of several process variables analysed. From the analysis of the formaldehyde production process, some recommendations aroused. Methanol accounts for about 94 % of the formaldehyde production cost; therefore, all operating changes that reduce the consumption of fresh methanol will have the highest impact on the operation costs. In this work, it is showed that lower operation regimes would increase the lifetime of the catalyst and the total amount of formaldehyde produced compared with the highest one. Moreover, the inlet methanol concentration on the oxidation reactor R-1/x should be increased by reducing column T-2 exhaust gas recirculation fraction, and finally, the opening of valve V-1/x will increase the production of steam without compromising the production of formaldehyde, nor the lifetime of the catalyst.

Acknowledgements

The authors greatly acknowledge EuroResinas and FCT support through the project UID/ECI/04028/2013 and the PhD grant number PD/BDE/113539/2015.

References

A. Andersson, J. Holmberg, R. Häggblad, 2016, Process Improvements in Methanol Oxidation to Formaldehyde: Application and Catalyst Development. Topics in Catalysis, 59, 17–18, 1589–1599.

C.G. Braz et al., 2018, Model of a Formaldehyde Absorption System Based on Industrial Data. In *Computer Aided Chemical Engineering*. Elsevier, pp. 25–30.

C.G. Braz et al., 2019, Model of an Industrial Multitubular Reactor for Methanol to Formaldehyde Oxidation in the Presence of Catalyst Deactivation. Chemical Engineering Science, 195, 347–355.

C.G. Braz et al., 2017, Model of an Industrial Reactor for Formaldehyde Production with Catalyst Deactivation. In *Computer Aided Chemical Engineering*. pp. 121–126.

C.G. Braz, 2019, Profitability Increase of a Formaldehyde Production Plant, PhD Thesis.

Sauro Pierucci, Flavio Manenti, Giulia Bozzano, Davide Manca (Eds.)
Proceedings of the 30th European Symposium on Computer Aided Process Engineering
(ESCAPE30), May 24-27, 2020, Milano, Italy. © 2020 Elsevier B.V. All rights reserved.
http://dx.doi.org/10.1016/B978-0-12-823377-1.50053-7

Automatic Improved Hybrid Scheduling and Worker-task Allocation Method Applied to Multi-purpose Production Plants

Raul Calvo Serrano,[a*] Matteo Luigi Abaecherli,[b] Ruben Jungius,[c] Thomas Kreuzer,[b] Gonzalo Guillen Gosalbez,[a]

*a*ICB Institute of Chemical and Bioengineering, ETH Zürich, Vladimir-Prelog-Weg 1, 8093 Zürich, Switzerland
*b*Pharma Biotec & Nutrition, Lonza AG, Rottenstrasse 6, 3930 Visp, Switzerland
*c*Ecole polytechnique federale de Lausanne, Station 7, 1015 Lausanne, Switzerland

raulc@ethz.ch

Abstract

Contract Development and Manufacturing Organisations (CDMOs) are becoming a key element in the pharma and fine chemical industries during the development and production of precursor components. Most CDMOs provide their services to several companies, having to operate and organise several production lines simultaneously, complying with specific production and product requirements for each customer. Under this scenario, the operation of CDMOs depends on market changes as well as customer and product regulations, these conditioning the definition and optimization of operational plans, and in turn, hindering the definition clear routines for workers. Ultimately, the difficulties may cause planning inconsistencies, generating production delays or disruptions. For that purpose, here we present a novel methodology able to automate the scheduling and worker-task allocation for several simultaneous production lines. This is done through the sequential application of specifically designed scheduling and allocation optimization models, first identifying the optimal periodic production plan and then finding the optimal transition from current to optimal operation conditions. This approach has been applied to a real industrial process with several simultaneous production lines, successfully identifying periodic production strategies and optimal transition and worker-task allocation plans for the different lines. Overall, the proposed tool presents a first step towards the automatic integrated optimisation of production planning in fine chemical and pharmaceutical multi-purpose production plants.
Keywords: Scheduling, Allocation, Python, Optimisation, Multi-purpose process

1. Introduction

The Pharmaceutical and fine chemical industries have long relied on Contract Development and Manufacturing Organizations (CDMOs) to carry out the scale-up of synthesis processes as well as the production of some key products, ranging from early precursors to final products ready for encapsulation or tableting. This tendency has increased in both popularity and volume in the last years, with big companies exclusively relying on CDMOs for their bulk production (Miller, 2017). In turn, this model of production exerts substantial pressure on CDMOs, which have to supervise simultaneously several production lines for different products and customers. Furthermore, these CDMOs need to accommodate all the customers' requirements in their production processes, the tightness of which make disruptions in one or more production lines critical. In order to address these disruptions, CDMOs need to rely on agile strategies for adapting and planning their operational strategies. The common practice nowadays is to solve the planning problem manually by a panel of experts, a task that is highly time consuming and cannot guarantee the optimality of the solutions found. In this work we present a novel methodology to identify potentially optimal process and operating plans and apply it to a real industrial problem. Our approach is based on the sequential optimization of several scheduling and allocation optimization models, while accounting for technical and workers availability constraints. The core optimization models here considered are based on the work by (Castro et al., 2003), but have been modified to consider several simultaneous production lines and handle both the design of the full production schedule and the rescheduling of tasks to cope with disruptions.

2. Methodology

The presented methodology is divided in two stages: first, the calculation of the optimal operational plan, and second, the rescheduling of operations and the corresponding worker-task allocation. Figure 1 provides a graphical summary of the presented methodology, describing the information required and models solved in each of the two stages.

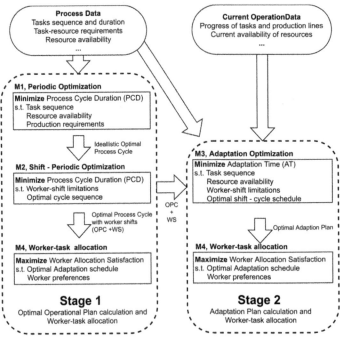

Figure 1, graphical representation of the proposed methodology, describing for the two considered calculation stages, the different data requirements and a general description of the models, broadly defining the respective objective functions and constraints considered in each model.

2.1. Stage 1: Optimal Operational Plan calculation and Worker-task allocation

The first stage of the proposed methodology aims to identify the optimal operational plan for the different production lines considered, providing the ideal plan to be followed assuming normal behaviour of the production process without disturbances or disruptions. The models we use here are based on the on the continuous-time resource-task network periodic scheduling approach presented by Castro et al., (2003), on which some significant modifications have been applied to better characterize the processes present in CDMO companies. In particular, the starting, progress and ending at a given time t of task i are characterized by three binary variables y_{it}^S, y_{it}^P and y_{it}^E, these taking a value of 1 if task i starts, is taking place or ends, respectively, at a time reference point t, and taking a value of 0 otherwise. These three new variables modify most of the formulation of the original problem, with Eqs. (1) to (8) below representing the most significant modifications.

$$\sum_t y_{it}^S \geq 1, \forall i \tag{1}$$

$$\sum_t y_{it}^E \geq 1, \forall i \tag{2}$$

$$\sum_t y_{it}^S - y_{it}^E = 0, \forall i \tag{3}$$

$$y_{it}^S \leq \sum_{t'=t+1}^{|t|} y_{it'}^E, \forall i \tag{4}$$

$$y_{it}^E \leq \sum_{t'=1}^{t-1} y_{it'}^S, \forall i \tag{5}$$

$$y_{it}^P = \sum_{t'=1}^{t} y_{it'}^S - \sum_{t'=1}^{t} y_{it'}^E, \forall i, t \tag{6}$$

$$\tau_{t'} - \tau_t \geq \delta_i - M\left(2 - y_{it}^S - y_{it'}^E + \sum_{t''=t}^{t'-1}(1 - y_{it''}^P)\right), \forall i, t, t' \| |t| \geq t' \geq t \tag{7}$$

$$R_{rt} - R_{r\,t-1} = \sum_i \mu_{ir}^S y_{it}^S + \mu_{ir}^E y_{it}^E, \forall r, t > 1 \tag{8}$$

Eqs. (1) to (6) characterise the starting, progress and ending binary variables. For example, Eq. (6) calculated the difference between the amount of times a task has started and ended prior to a particular reference time, obtaining as a result whether a task is taken place at that time. Eq. (7) characterises the reference time values τ_t from the continuous-time approach, to that end using the previously defined binary variables and the task durations δ_i. Eq. (8) represents the balance of resources between two consecutive time reference points, calculating the change of each resource r using the amounts generated or consumed either at the start (μ_{ir}^S) or end (μ_{ir}^E) of a particular task. Among other equations, the balance of resources is particularly critical for the correct definition of the models in the proposed methodology, with resource availability being a major limitation on the scheduling of tasks (e.g. workers are here modelled as a resource required to carry out manual tasks). Furthermore, the sequence of tasks (i.e. in which order or priority should tasks be carried out) is here enforced through the use of resources. This approach provides a direct and systematic approach to define complex task sequences (i.e. recipes), enhancing the automation of the presented models. The presented eight equations represent the core of the scheduling optimization models in the proposed methodology, with each of these models presenting a different variation on the general scheduling optimization model in order to achieve their individual objectives. Model M1 is used first to identify the "idealistic optimal process operation", disregarding restrictions on the scheduling of manual tasks derived from the worker-shifts. To this end, this model aims to identify the minimum possible Production Cycle Duration using a periodic scheduling optimization approach. In this approach, since the specific time values are calculated variables in the model (τ_t), it is fundamental to define the amount of time reference points t that ensures the feasibility of the problem and leads to a model of reasonable size. In this case, the amount of time reference points used has been defined as twice the minimum required to achieve a feasible solution. In order to include the effects of the worker-shifts into the general scheduling, model M2 aims to adapt the solution found from model M1, again minimising the Process Cycle Duration while enforcing manual tasks to be completed by the available amount of workers in no more than one shift. To this end, model M2 only considers constraints directly related with the timing of the manual tasks (e.g. Eq. (7)) and their interaction with the worker-shifts. In addition, model M2 fixes the starting, processing and ending task binary variables (i.e. y_{it}^S, y_{it}^P and y_{it}^E) from the solution of M1, only modifying the reference time values τ_t. The operational plan obtained in model M2 is then used in the worker-allocation model M4, which uses binary variables x_{iwt} that take a value of 1 if worker w is allocated to task i at reference time t. These variables are used to determine the allocation that minimises the maximum workload among the workers.

2.2. Stage 2: Adaptation Plan calculation and Worker-task allocation

The second stage of the proposed methodology aims to identify the task schedule that minimises the time required to transition from a set of initial operation conditions to an optimal production plan operation (i.e. adaptation time). This, in turn, is aimed to minimise the disruption caused by process irregularities, which are assumed to be more frequent than major changes in the process, thus making the application of this second stage more frequent than the first. Unlike the previous stage, this schedule optimisation is done in a single model M3, which aims to minimise the adaptation time again using Eqs. (1) to (8) as the core of the model, also considering the limitations imposed by the worker-shifts in the scheduling of manual tasks. Furthermore, this model uses the starting, processing and ending task binary variables values from the optimal schedule obtained in the first stage (i.e. $y_{it_2}^{CS}$, $y_{it_2}^{CP}$ and $y_{it_2}^{CE}$) and a binary variable (z_{t_2}) in order to identify the optimal operational time reference point (t_2) to which transition, as enforced by Eqs. (9) to (12).

$$y_{i|t|}^S = \sum_{t_2} z_{t_2} y_{it_2}^{CS}, \forall i \tag{9}$$
$$y_{i|t|}^E = \sum_{t_2} z_{t_2} y_{it_2}^{CE}, \forall i \tag{10}$$
$$y_{i|t|}^P = \sum_{t_2} z_{t_2} y_{it_2}^{CP}, \forall i \tag{11}$$
$$\sum_{t_2} z_{t_2} = 1 \tag{12}$$

The particular amount of time reference points $|t|$ used in model M3 is the same as in model M1 ($|t_2|$), as it has been considered sufficient to cover most potential current production scenarios regardless of the level of their similarity with any of the optimal production plan reference points. As in the previous stage, the worker-task allocation model M4 is then used on the adaptation schedule from model M3, obtaining particular schedules for each one of the individual workers. Altogether, all the models included in the proposed methodology present Mixed Integer Linear Programming (MILP) structures. Furthermore, the presented methodology can be easily automated, as the only information required is generally fundamental process information generally measured and recorded (e.g. task durations, resource consumption and availability, current progress of the production lines …).

3. Case Study

The methodology here presented was developed in collaboration with LONZA AG Pharma, Biotech & Nutrition. In particular, our approach was applied to two production lines (L1 and L2) consisting of 6 (E1 to E6) and 11 (E7 to E17) equipment units, respectively, in total considering 114 tasks, 29 of which are manual tasks require one or more workers to be completed.

4. Results

The models here presented (M1 to M4) were implemented in PYOMO (Hart et al., 2012) and solved interfacing with the solver GLPK 4.65 (Sottinen, 2009), using an Intel Core i5-4570 3.20 GHz computer. Model M1 contains 2400 continuous and 5600 binary variables, and 54000 equations. A computation time limit of 24 CPU-hours was set for the models in the first stage of the methodology (i.e. models M1, M2 and M4). This time was sufficient to identify a potentially optimal feasible solution (i.e. optimality gap of 20%), although longer calculation times or more effective commercial solvers may reach better solutions. On the other hand, only 2 CPU-hour was more than enough for the models in the second stage (i.e. models M3 and M4) to reach optimal solutions. Figure 2a presents the resulting Gantt chart, indicating the distribution of automatic and manual tasks and which of these are bottlenecks of the process. Figure 2b provides the corresponding worker-task allocation schedule of the considered production lines.

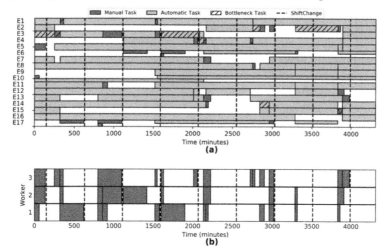

Figure 2, (a) Schedule structure of the operating cycle and (b) corresponding worker-task allocation schedule obtained in the first stage of the methodology.

The optimal production cycle schedule obtained presents manual tasks fairly distributed across the calculated 9 shifts, with all shifts having at least one manual task. This indicates that the schedule of the process is mostly determined by the limitations imposed by the worker-shifts and the availability of workers. At the same time, the obtained schedule hints that faster process cycles could be achieved, as most tasks are being carried out longer than their minimum required durations, with only a few automatic and manual tasks acting as bottlenecks. The obtained operation schedule was then used to determine the adaptation schedule using the second stage in the methodology. In this case, both models M3 and M4 reached global optimality, providing the adaptation and worker schedule presented in Figure 3.

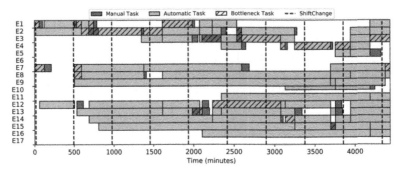

Figure 3, Schedule structure of the obtained adaptation in the second stage of the methodology.

The adaptation schedule obtained significantly contrast with the production cycle schedule, as the former presents significantly more tasks acting as bottlenecks, with one or more tasks being a bottleneck of their respective production line at almost all times. This, in turn, confirms the global optimality of the obtained adaptation schedule, as there are no clear windows for improvement in the schedule.

5. Conclusions

This work presents a methodology that aims to facilitate the planning and management of Contract Development and Manufacturing Organizations (CDMOs), enabling the automatic long and short term scheduling of specific tasks and workers. To that end, the methodology is divided into two stages, with the first stage sequentially solving three optimization models to identify the optimal production cycle and the corresponding worker-task allocation. The second stage encompasses two optimization models that aim to minimize the impact of production irregularities by identifying the schedule that minimizes the adaptation time to optimal process conditions, also identifying the corresponding worker-task allocation. This methodology has been applied to a real process involving two production lines and 114 different tasks. The methodology's first stage was only able to identify a feasible solution with potential for further optimization. In contrast, the second stage was able to identify the optimal adaptation schedule and corresponding worker-task allocation. Overall, the presented methodology has been able to automatically generate feasible and potentially optimal operational planning schedules and their corresponding worker schedules. These results highlight how scheduling approaches specifically designed for particular processes may significantly reduce the time and resources spent in the design of production and work organization, also supporting the transition to a more automated production industry.

References

Castro, P.M., Barbosa-Póvoa, A.P., Matos, H.A., 2003. Optimal periodic scheduling of batch plants using RTN-based discrete and continuous-time formulations: A case study approach. Ind. Eng. Chem. Res. 42, 3346–3360. https://doi.org/10.1021/ie0203781

Hart, W.E., Laird, C., Watson, J.-P., Woodruff, D.L., 2012. Pyomo – Optimization Modeling in Python. Springer Optim. Its Appl. 67, 13–28. https://doi.org/10.1007/978-1-4614-3226-5

Miller, J., 2017. Contract manufacturing through the years. BioPharm Int. 30, 12–13.

Sottinen, T., 2009. operatins research with GNU Linear Programming Kit.

Sauro Pierucci, Flavio Manenti, Giulia Bozzano, Davide Manca (Eds.)
Proceedings of the 30th European Symposium on Computer Aided Process Engineering
(ESCAPE30), May 24-27, 2020, Milano, Italy. © 2020 Elsevier B.V. All rights reserved.
http://dx.doi.org/10.1016/B978-0-12-823377-1.50054-9

Efficient Amine-based Carbon Capture in a Power-to-Jet process under varying Renewable Electricity supply

Mahmoud Mostafa,[a*] Christopher Varela,[a] Elvis Ahmetović,[b] Edwin Zondervan,[a]

[a]University of Bremen, Leobener Straße 6, 28359 Bremen, Germany
[b]University of Tuzla, Faculty of Technology, Univerzitetska 8, 75000 Tuzla, Bosnia and Herzegovina
mmostafa@uni-bremen.de

Abstract

To comply with the outcomes of the Climate Change Conference in Paris (COP 21), the ever-growing greenhouse gas (GHG) emissions has to be drastically reduced. With the soaring growth rates of GHG emissions in the aviation sector, the need for a near zero-net greenhouse emission alternative is essential. The novel concept of the Power-to-Jet pathway directly utilizes renewable electricity, carbon dioxide and water to synthesize a sustainable kerosene fuel that chemically resembles the one produced from fossil sources, having 'Drop-in' capability allowing the use and distribution within existing architectures. In the Power-to-Jet process, hydrogen is produced via water electrolysis. Captured CO_2 (from rich point sources) then reacts with hydrogen to produce the intermediate methanol, before being upgraded to the final synthetic jet fuel along with by-products (Schmidt et al., 2012). With fluctuating electricity inputs due to the variability in photovoltaic and wind power generation, the process units within the Power-to-Jet process have to be adjusted at each time-instant to satisfy the production constraints. To find the best operating strategy for these fluctuating conditions, dynamic models are needed. In this work, we will propose a model that describes the dynamic behaviour of the carbon capture section in the Power-to-Jet process. Several dynamic scenarios can be introduced for the carbon capture rate by altering the lean solvent concentration, flue gas flow rates and re-boiler duty. The dynamic information obtained from the simulations (such as: Open loop gain, time constants and dead time) can be used to device an appropriate control scheme under varying electricity inputs, while satisfying all operational constraints.

Keywords: Dynamic, Carbon Capture, Amine, Aspen, Renewables

1. Introduction

According to the International Air Transport Association (IATA), more than 3.8 billion passengers and 54.9 Mt of goods (worth around 5.5 trillion US dollars) were transported by air in 2016. By producing around 781 Mt of CO_2 in 2015, the aviation sector is responsible for 2 % of the world's total anthropogenic emissions of carbon dioxide. With new technologies emerging from electric vehicles to hydrogen-powered buses, airplane engines will still run on high quality paraffinic fuel for quite some time in the future increasing the total share of emissions. Synthetic kerosene is considered a promising answer to the every growing aviation demand, being carbon neutral is an essential aspect in complying with the strict environmental regulations.

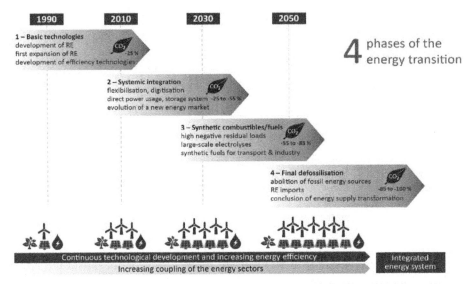

Figure 1 - Timeline of the four-energy transition phases (Acatech, 2018)

Photovoltaic, wind and biomass technologies have matured and built over the last 30 years, decreasing the costs strongly. As shown in Figure 1, we are currently ending the systemic integration phase and entering a phase of utilizing renewable electricity. A serious challenge we face currently is the volatile behavior of supply of renewable energy, where there are periods during which large amounts of electricity aren't utilized due to short-term storage and load management (Acatech, 2018). The Power-to-Jet pathway enables us to convert this unutilized intermittent production into valuable aviation kerosene.

The process is divided into 4 main stages namely: carbon capture (CC) and electrolysis stage that provide the raw materials. The raw materials then react to produce the intermediate product methanol. Methanol is subsequently converted into olefins (mixture of ethylene and propylene) by passing it over a zeolite catalyst, oligomerized/isomerized and finally hydro-treated to achieve the final synthetic fuel (Schmidt et al., 2018). This fuel has advantageous chemical and physical properties as compared to the fossil-based kerosene. It also complies with the ASTM-D7566 standard and offers a far superior environmental performance with overall GHG emissions of 1 g CO_2 per MJ of final fuel (German Environment Agency, 2016). This research will focus on the CC stage simulation using Aspen Plus for the steady-state model and Aspen Plus Dynamics for the dynamic analysis. The feedstock for the model is the flue gas of a refinery (Raffinerie Heide located north of Germany) with a concentration of 15.36 wt % CO_2. Post-combustion scrubbing using the base monoethanolamine (MEA) is the most suitable technology, with a technology readiness level of nine. This technology can be easily integrated into an existing infrastructure of a plant with minimal modifications. MEA high reactivity with CO_2 makes it the most studied solvent, but with this high reactivity, large amounts of steam are required in the desorber stage to regenerate the gas. Dynamic scenarios will be investigated with a specific control strategy ensuring a stable operation for the various units.

2. Model description

2.1. Steady-state rate-based model

The flow sheet of an amine based CO_2 capture process consists of a packed absorber unit where countercurrent contact of the incoming flue gas with an amine solution occurs. The structured packing 250Y FLEXIPAC are considered in this study with HETP of 315 mm. The flue gas rich in CO_2 enters the absorber at the bottom with a flow rate of 325,130 kg/hr while the lean amine solvent is introduced at the third equilibrium stage with a flow rate of 958,371 kg/hr (L/G 2.9). The treated flue gas is then washed in a water-wash section (accounting for two equilibrium stages) to remove any entrained valuable solvent droplets and to meet any environmental regulations concerning the solvent emission. MEA solution of 30 % by weight is chosen to reduce the energy requirement of the solvent regeneration. The rich solvent stream leaves at the bottom of the absorber and is sent to a stripper where the reverse of what happened in the absorber occurs. Before entering the stripper, the stream absorbs some of the heat in the lean solvent exiting the stripper and heading towards the absorber in the closed loop recycle. In the stripper, the rich amine is introduced at the top and the CO_2 is released by the upward flowing steam generated by the reboiler. The exiting stream passes through a condenser and all of the condensed liquid is returned to the top of the stripper as reflux stream. The uncondensed stream is mainly CO_2 with 98.95 % purity, which will be later on delivered to the methanol reactor. The absorber and stripper are both modeled using the Aspen RadFrac model unit, the Unsymmetric Electrolyte NRTL property method is adopted which uses the Redlich-Kwong equation of state for vapour phase properties. All reactions in the absorber and stripper units are assumed to be in equilibrium except those of CO_2 with OH^- and CO_2 with MEA. The chemistry of EQU consists of the following equilibrium reactions (Agbonghae et al., 2014):

$$MEAH^+ + H_2O \longleftrightarrow MEA + H_3O^+ \tag{1}$$

$$MEACOO^- + H_2O \longleftrightarrow MEA + HCO_3^- \tag{2}$$

$$2H_2O \longleftrightarrow H_3O^+ + OH^- \tag{3}$$

$$CO_2 + 2H_2O \longleftrightarrow HCO_3^- + H_3O^+ \tag{4}$$

$$HCO_3^- + H_2O \longleftrightarrow CO_3^{2-} + H_3O^+ \tag{5}$$

The reaction models of the Absorber/Stripper consist of the instantaneous reactions (1), (3), (5) and the following finite rate reactions governed by the power law:

$$CO_2 + OH^- \longrightarrow HCO_3^- \tag{6}$$

$$HCO_3^- \longrightarrow CO_2 + OH^- \tag{7}$$

$$MEA + CO_2 + H_2O \longrightarrow MEACOO^- + H_3O^+ \tag{8}$$

$$MEACOO^- + H_3O^+ \longrightarrow MEA + CO_2 + H_2O \tag{9}$$

The column diameters were designed based on 70 % of the flood point velocity and a capture rate of 90 % was adopted, as it's a commonly used basis for amine-based capture design in open literature. Reboiler duty was adjusted to achieve the desired CO_2 loading. The value of 0.19 was maintained for the lean loading stream while the rich

MEA stream had a loading ratio of 0.43. The specific reboiler duty achieved was 3.9 MJ/ton CO_2.

2.2. Dynamic equilibrium-based model

After converging the steady-state model in Aspen Plus, additional data (such as the vessel geometry e.g. sump volume and heat transfer data) is required to export the model into Aspen Plus Dynamics. The flow-driven dynamic mode was selected and the equilibrium equations had to be split into forward and backward reactions to export the model. Once the model is exported, controllers are added to the desired units. In our model, we focus on the behaviour of the absorber/stripper unit. The goal is to smoothly run the process by keeping the controlled variable within the specified limits. The controllers were assigned default tuning-parameters, which proved inefficient when tested.

2.3. Controller tuning

An open-loop dynamic run was implemented; first, the process was run for 2 hours before ramping down the flue gas flow rate by 50 %. The process then stabilizes before ramping up again 50 %. The controller has no feedback from the process, and the scenario caused a deviation in the parameters from the set point as shown in figure 2. The pressure and temperature both take one hour to stabilize to a new steady state condition.

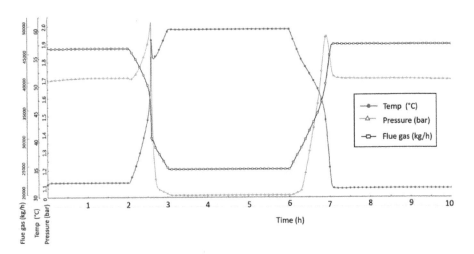

Figure 2 – open-loop simulation for a ramp down/up of the flue gas flow rate for 10 hours

Aspen Plus Dynamics tuning tool, was used to tune the controllers. The controller is tuned handling both set-point and load disturbances by causing 5 % step up on the process output range. The open loop steady-state gain, dead-time and time constant are estimated and the values are used to calculate the tuning parameters using Ziegler-Nichols method, giving approximate values of gain and integral time for each PI controller. Table 1 shows the tuning results from 2 different tests indicating the effect of the sump volume on the dead-time and time constant.

Table 1 - Tuning parameters for 2 different sump heights (P=Pressure controller, LC= Level controller, TC= Temperature controller, L= sump level height)

	Absorber				*Stripper*		
L = 1m	Gain	Dead time	Time constant		Gain	Dead time	Time constant
	%	min	min		%	min	min
P	-6.1	0.6	2.44	P	-0.6	0.058	0.599
LC	-9.15	23.16	13.86	LC	-9.22	5.86	5.95
				TC	0.33	0.60	0.5058
L = 2m							
P	-6.18	0.6	2.49				
LC	-9.24	30.05	18.36				

The height of the sump was increased by one meter to analyze the effect on the tuning parameters, the dead time increase by 6.89 minutes while the time constant increased by 4.5 minutes.

3. Results

A disturbance was introduced to the dynamic model representing the worst-case scenario to test the flexibility of the process. The model was allowed to run at initial conditions to ensure steady-state operation, and then a ramp up of 50 % was implemented to the flue gas flow rate for a duration of 1 hour. The temperature and pressure were stabilized in a matter of a few minutes. A more severe disturbance of ramp down 50 % in 5 minutes was introduced at the 7th hour and a small disturbance was caused that also lasted for a few minutes before stabilizing back to the set-point conditions. The capture rate was maintained at 90 %.

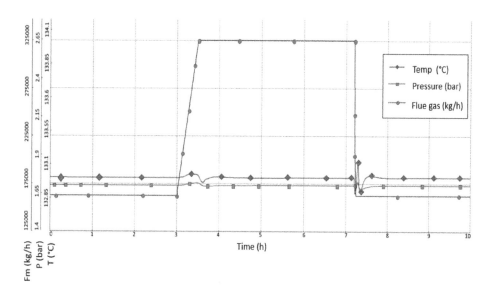

Figure 3 - Dynamic behaviour to disturbances in the flue gas flow-rate showing the stability in the temperature and pressure of the column

4. Conclusion

Utilising renewable energy to produce synthetic combustibles will be an important element in achieving the carbon reduction objectives. Dynamic models help us in studying the effect of various controlled and uncontrolled disturbances on the operation of the carbon capture plant, to be able to implement a control strategy and apply and necessary improvements to the design. It was noticed that the sump volume has an effect on the dead time, time constants and steady-state gain meaning that a reasonable sump volume has to be calculated for each plant. The controllers were tuned using an open loop test and a dead time of 23.16 minutes was noticed in the level controller for the absorber (sump height of 1 m). Sudden and abrupt disturbances are introduced in 1 hour and in 5 mins to study the effect on the pressure and temperature of the column and the results proved flexibility of the capture process. Further tuning tests are required in closed loop with alternative control strategies that covers the whole plant, to successfully maintain the process parameters at the desired set points while flexibility adjusting to the change in inputs such as flue gas flow rates.

Acknowledgements

The authors are grateful to the German Federal Ministry of Economic Affairs and Energy for funding the KEROSyN100 project (funding code 03EIV051A).

References

Chikukwa, A., Enaasen, N., Kvamsdal, H. M., & Hillestad, M. (2012). Dynamic Modeling of Post-combustion CO_2 Capture Using Amines - A Review. *6th Trondheim Conference on CO_2 Capture, Transport and Storage, 23*, 82-91. doi:10.1016/j.egypro.2012.06.063

Jung, H., Im, D., Kim, S. H., & Lee, J. H. (2018). Dynamic Modeling and Analysis of Amine-based Carbon Capture Systems. *Ifac Papersonline*, 51(18), 91-96. doi:10.1016/j.ifacol.2018.09.263

Schmidt, P., Batteiger, V., Roth, A., Weindorf, W., & Raksha, T. (2018). Power-to-Liquids as Renewable Fuel Option for Aviation: A Review. *Chemie Ingenieur Technik, 90*(1-2), 127-140. doi:10.1002/cite.201700129

Cames, M. (2019, February 12). The global decarbonization challenge and aviation within it: Where are we now, where are we going ? Lecture presented at Aviation Decarbonization Forum in Canada, Montréal.

Coupling the different energy sectors – options for the next phase of the energy transition. (2018, August). Retrieved from https://www.acatech.de/wp-content/uploads/2017/11/ESYS_Summary_Position_Paper_Coupling_the_energy_sectors-1.pdf.

Aspen Technology, Inc. Rate-based model of the CO_2 capture process by MEA using Aspen Plus. Burlington (USA);2012.

Zhang, Y.; Chen, C.-C. Modeling CO2 Absorption and Desorption by Aqueous Monoethanolamine Solution with Aspen Rate-Based Model. Energy Procedia 2013, 37, 1584–1596.

Agbonghae, E. O.; Hughes, K. J.; Ingham, D. B.; Ma, L.; Pourkashanian, M. Optimal Process Design of Commercial-Scale Amine-Based CO2 Capture Plants. Ind. Eng. Chem. Res. 2014, 53 (38), 14815−14829.

Sauro Pierucci, Flavio Manenti, Giulia Bozzano, Davide Manca (Eds.)
Proceedings of the 30th European Symposium on Computer Aided Process Engineering
(ESCAPE30), May 24-27, 2020, Milano, Italy. © 2020 Elsevier B.V. All rights reserved.
http://dx.doi.org/10.1016/B978-0-12-823377-1.50055-0

Analysis and Optimization of Carbon Supply Chains Integrated to a Power to Gas Plant in Italy

Grazia Leonzio,[a*] Edwin Zondervan[b]

aDepartment of Industrial and Information Engineering and Economics, University of L'Aquila, Via Giovanni Gronchi 18, 67100 L'Aquila, Italy
bLaboratory of Process Systems Engineering, Department of Production Engineering, Universität Bremen, Leobener Str. 6, 28359 Bremen, Germany

grazia.leonzio@graduate.univaq.it

Abstract

Italy should solve the problem related to carbon dioxide emissions for the next years and carbon supply chains can be a strategic solution. In this research work, mixed integer linear programming models are developed for carbon capture, utilization and storage supply chains in Italy with multiple storage sites (saline aquifers) while one main utilization section, producing methane via power to gas, is considered. Currently, there are no carbon supply chains integrated to a power to gas system. The systems under investigation are designed and optimized minimizing the total costs. A supply chain with the offshore Adriatic sea as storage site is the best solution: a lower value of methane production cost (19.1 €/MWh) and incomes (carbon tax of 80 €/t and economic incentives of 260 €/MWh) are required as compared to the other cases. The total costs of this supply chain are of 7.34·104 million €/y, while 16.1 Mt/y of methane are produced.

Keywords: carbon supply chain, mathematical model, optimization, reduction of carbon dioxide

1. Introduction

Globally, carbon dioxide emissions increased over the last years amounting to 33.1 Gt with a concentration of 395 ppm in 2018 (IEA, 2019; Goel et al., 2015). Emissions lead to a climate change and an increase of global average temperature. Different countries in the world agreed to reduce carbon dioxide emissions of 40% by 2030 and of 80% by 2050, compared to the level of 1990 (IPCC, 2013). Italy must decrease carbon dioxide emissions to a value of 275 Mt by 2030, considering that in the 2016 they were 352 Mt (Gracceva et al., 2017). To this aim, carbon supply chains, as carbon capture utilization and storage (CCUS), carbon capture and utilization (CCU) and carbon capture and storage (CCS) technologies have an important and strategic role. In these systems, carbon dioxide is captured at the source site, transported generally via pipeline, and then stored and/or utilized according to the specific case (Hasan et al., 2015). In addition to methanol, formic acid, dimethyl ether, methyl formate, ethylene glycol, acetic acid and other compounds, are considered. Also, carbon dioxide can be valorized and used in the utilization section to produce methane, through the Sabatier reaction (Vooradi et al., 2018; Schiebahn et al., 2015). In this case, hydrogen can be provided by water electrolysis, as in a common power to gas process, exploiting renewable energies (Leonzio, 2017). Studies where a power to gas system is used in the utilization section of a carbon supply chain are rarely considered: they are mainly focused on the production of other compounds (Leonzio et al., 2019a,b;

Hasan et al., 2015). On the other hand, the technical potential for wind and solar power generation, at the base of power to gas processes, as well as the potential application of power to gas systems in Italy are assessed in several studies (Hoefnagels, 2011; Guandalini et al., 2017). This encourages the study of a carbon supply chain integrated to a power to gas system as a possible solution to reduce carbon dioxide emissions in Italy, satisfying at the same time the national methane demand. This research work wants to overcome this gap. Mixed integer linear programming (MILP) models are developed for different CCUS supply chains with different storage sites (mainly saline aquifers), with the same utilization site, producing methane. These systems are compared in terms of topology, costs and required economic incentives to find the best scenario. A comparison with a CCU supply chain is also analyzed.

2. Mathematical model of carbon supply chains

2.1. Problem statement

For the formulation of the mathematical model, a number of realistic and simplified assumptions are made. Intrinsic assumptions are the following: i) capture plants and carbon dioxide sources are located at the same place; ii) one source node can be connected to only one capture node in the storage and utilization section; iii) carbon dioxide is transported via pipeline; iv) the hydrogen required for the Sabatier reaction is provided by a PEM electrolyzer using renewable energy power, but a portion of electricity from the network is any case present (Matzen and Demirel, 2016); v) the network structure is designed for steady state conditions over a period of 25 years; vi) methane production is constant over time, due to the stationary conditions and it is sent to the gas grid; vii) methane is sold a stable price set by the market. Moreover, some information (i.e. locations, costs, capture materials/technologies, carbon dioxide compositions, etc.) is provided about carbon dioxide sources, capture and compression technologies, carbon dioxide transportation, utilization and storage sites. The model can be used to find the best connection between each element inside the supply chain, the amount of considered carbon dioxide and produced methane through the minimization of the total costs, setting a target for emissions reduction: economic and environmental are both considered for the optimization.

2.2. CCUS supply chain model

The considered model, like others developed by us, is based on the work of Hasan et al. (2015). More details (the expressions of equations) of the CCUS supply chain model can be found in our recent work (Leonzio et al 2019a). In these sections, we shortly describe the main features of this model, that can be widely applied in other similar problems.

2.2.1. Sets

As in the most of carbon supply chains, each element inside the considered supply chains is defined by a set: carbon dioxide sources are defined by *"i"*, capture technologies are defined by *"j"*, geological storage and utilization site by *"k"*.

2.2.2. Parameters and variables

Some parameters are considered for the developed mathematical model and these are related to the minimum target of carbon dioxide reduction (Gracceva et al., 2017), to carbon dioxide emissions from each source i (Green, 2014), to flue gas flow rate from source i calculated by carbon dioxide composition (Zhang et al., 2018), to the lowest and highest carbon dioxide composition processed by the capture technology j (Zhang et al., 2018), to the maximum storage capacity (Moia et al., 2012). As in our previous work, binary and continuous variables are introduced to define the selected storage site ($X_{i,j,k}$), the selected capture technology ($Y_{i,j,k}$), the amount of carbon dioxide that is stored ($FR_{i,j,k}$) and sent to the utilization ($MR_{i,j,k}$) for methane production.

2.2.3. Constraints and equations

The same constraints set in the model presented in Leonzio et al. (2019a) are considered (regarding the selection of capture technologies and storage site based on one to one coupling, maximum storage capacity that can not be exceed, minimum target for emissions reduction that should be achieved, purity on carbon dioxide that should be ensured and glover linearization). However, the constraint for the national demand of methane, that should be satisfied, equal to 46.5 Mt/y (Alverà et al., 2017), is not considered because, the amount of captured carbon dioxide is not sufficient to produce methane at this rate. Equations are defined to express the capture and compression costs (Hasan et al., 2014), carbon dioxide transportation costs (Knoope et al., 2013), carbon dioxide storage costs (Hendriks, 1994). The methane production cost through a power to gas system including also the electrolysis process is of 300 €/MWh, due to the high cost of electricity (Ma et al., 2018; Reichert, 2012).

2.2.4. Objective function

As in our models, the objective function of the developed mathematical model contains the total costs of the supply chain that are the sum of carbon dioxide capture and compression costs, carbon dioxide transportation costs, carbon dioxide storage costs and methane production costs. The objective function is minimized to design an optimal system.

2.3. Case study

Italy must reduce carbon dioxide emissions to 275 MtCO$_2$ by 2030 (Gracceva et al., 2017). To suggest a solution for this objective, CO$_2$ source, utilization and storage sites are defined in the supply chain. Ten Italian regions, those with higher emissions, are selected as sources: Puglia (68.64 MtCO$_2$/y), Lombardy (46.8 MtCO$_2$/y), Sicily (41.53 MtCO$_2$/y), Lazio (28.16 MtCO$_2$/y), Sardinia (26.4 MtCO$_2$/y), Veneto (22.5 MtCO$_2$/y), Emilia Romagna (21.82 MtCO$_2$/y), Piedmont (19.71 MtCO$_2$/y), Liguria (17.6 MtCO$_2$/y), Tuscany (16.9 MtCO$_2$/y) (Green, 2014). The nodes for the system are located at the capital cities of each region. Seven carbon dioxide storage sites with a defined storage capacity, as saline aquifers, are selected: Malossa San Bartolomeo, Pesaro sea, offshore Adriatic sea, Cornelia, offshore Marche, offshore Calabria ionic sea, Sulcis area (Moia et al., 2012). Verbania is chosen as the utilization site, with an infinite capacity, replacing an existing biogas plant and supposing that in the next future solar energy will be available (Colbertaldo et al., 2018). Monoethanolamine (MEA) and ionic liquid absorption, membrane, pressure swing adsorption (PSA) and vacuum swing adsorption (VSA) are the capture technologies available inside the supply chain.

3. Results and discussion

The AIMMS software (Version 4.3) is used to solve MILP models with CPLEX 12.7.1 as selected solver. The computer processor is 2.5 GHz while the memory is 4 GB. For the different CCUS supply chains, MILP models are made of 711 variables (50 integer) and 684 constraints. The solutions are found in some seconds and with a maximum of 100 iterations. For the CCU supply chain, the MILP model is composed by 460 variables (50 integer) and 482 constraints. The problem is solved in 1.69 s with 142 iterations.

The topologies of different carbon supply chains, connecting sources and utilization sites, obtained by the optimization, are shown in figure 1. For each system, a specific capture technology is selected to achieve the minimum target of carbon dioxide reduction of 77

MtCO$_2$. Table 1 shows the economic analysis: total costs, methane yields, set carbon tax and economic incentives, net methane production costs are presented for each considered supply chain. Then, carbon tax and economic incentives are required to have a profitable system (Di Costanzo, 2017). By comparing the different case studies, it is evident that the CCUS supply chain with the offshore Adriatic sea as storage site has a lower value of economic incentives and production cost (lower than the selling price of 25 €/MWh (ec.europe.eu)), compared to other case studies. For this scenario, the methane production cost is 19.1 €/MWh while the economic incentives are 260 €/MWh. Considering economic incentives and carbon tax, the net total costs of supply chain is, instead, of 59.69 €/tCO$_2$ captured, comparable with other studies (Zhang et al., 2018). The CCU supply chain, producing only methane, is not a profitable solution because, with the highest economic incentives of 260 €/MWh, a high methane production cost is obtained.

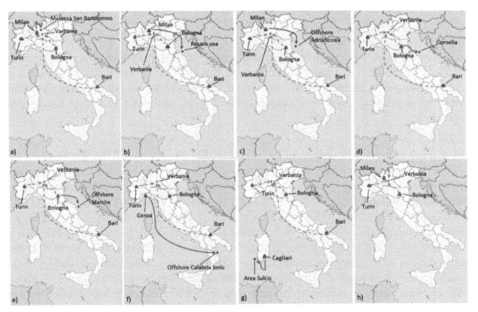

Figure 1 Results of carbon supply chains: a) CCUS supply chain with Malossa San Bartolomeo as storage site; b) CCUS supply chain with Pesaro sea as storage site; c) CCUS supply chain with Offshore Adriatic sea as storage site; d) CCUS supply chain with Cornelia as storage site; e) CCUS supply chain with offshore Marche as storage site; f) CCUS supply chain with offshore Calabria Ionic as storage site; g) CCUS with Area Sulcis as storage site; h) CCU supply chain. (Legend: ▲ CO$_2$ source; * CO$_2$ storage site; ° CO$_2$ utilization site, − − CO$_2$ transportation from a source to the utilization site, ▬ CO$_2$ transportation from a source to the storage site)

For all scenarios, the methane production cost including hydrogen production via electrolysis has the highest contribution to the total costs. The designed system allows to reduce methane importation. Currently the Italian methane production is 3.9 Mt/y (yearbook.enerdata.net), and to satisfy a methane demand of 46.5 Mt/y, 43 Mt/y of methane should be imported. With the proposed best system, producing 16.1 Mt/y of methane, it is possible to reduce the methane importation to 26.9 Mt/y.

Table 1 Economic results of the analyzed carbon supply chains

Storage site	Total costs (million€/year)	Methane yield (Mt/y)	Carbon tax (€/t)	Economic incentives (€/MWh)	net Methane production costs (€/MWh)
Malossa San Bartomeo	$10.17 \cdot 10^4$	22.5	80	260	23.4
Pesaro sea	$11.09 \cdot 10^4$	24.5	80	260	24.6
Offshore Adriatic sea	$7.34 \cdot 10^4$	16.1	80	260	19.1
Cornelia	$11.32 \cdot 10^4$	25.1	80	260	24.4
Offshore Marche	$10.07 \cdot 10^4$	22.2	80	260	24.1
Offshore Calabria Ionic	$12.15 \cdot 10^4$	26.5	80	270	19.4
Area sulcis	$12.51 \cdot 10^4$	27.8	80	270	15.2
-	$12.88 \cdot 10^4$	28	80	270	21.8

4. Conclusions

In this research, mathematical models for CCUS and CCU supply chains integrated to a power to gas system are compared and developed to solve CO_2 emission problem in Italy. Carbon dioxide is used to produce methane and in the literature no similar work have been considered before. Mainly, CCUS supply chains with different storage sites and a CCU supply chain are compared in terms of topology,costs and required economic incentives. The CCUS system with the offshore Adriatic sea as storage site provides the best case, due to a lower methane production cost and required incentives, that are needed to have a profitable process. Without considering economic incentives before, the total costs of the best framework is of $7.34 \cdot 10^4$ million €/y producing 16.1 Mt/y of methane, at a production cost of 19 €/MWh when a proper level of incomes are considered (carbon tax of 80 €/t and economic incentives of 260 €/MWh). The national import of methane is in this way reduced significantly. In addition, it result that the storage is important inside the carbon supply chain, to have the most economically profitable solution, with a fixed carbon dioxide reduction rate. Only utilization is not sufficient to achieve the target set by the environmental policies at an advantage cost and this motivats the support of carbon storage.

References

1. M. Alverà, 2017, Snam Rete Gas Ten-year network development plan of the natural gas transmission network 2017-2026, Document prepared by Snam Rete Gas S.p.A. In compliance with the D.L. 93 of 11 June 2011 and subsequent amendments and additions.
2. P. Colbertaldo, G. Guandalini, S. Campanari, S., 2018. Modelling the integrated power and transport energy system: The role of power-to-gas and hydrogen in long-term scenarios for Italy, Energy 154, 592-601.
3. F. Di Costanzo, 2017. Analisi energetica ed economica di un sistema "Power to gas" con produzione biologica di metano. [Laurea magistrale], Università di Bologna, Corso di Studio in Ingegneria energetica [LM-DM270], Documento full-text non disponibile.
4. F. Gracceva, E. De Luca, A. Fidanza, P. Del Nero, L.G. Giuffrida, B. Felici, C. Pona, A. Zini, 2017, Analisi trimestrale del sistema energetico italiano. Report 1/2017. ISSN 2531-4750.
5.Green, 2014, https://www.google.de/search?q=percentuale+emissioni+co2+regioni+italiane&source=lnms&tbm=isch&sa=X&ved=0ahUKEwi22_WKvtHeAhVJFywKHaQTACUQ_AUIDigB&biw=1366&bih=608#imgrc=_Q4uMiUoDub58M:

6. C. Goel, H. Bhunia, P.K. Bajpai, 2015. Development of nitrogen enriched nanostructured carbon adsorbents for CO2 capture. J. Environ. Manag. 162, 20-29.

7. G. Guandalini, M. Robinius, T. Grube, S. Campanari, D. Stolten, 2017. Long-term power-to-gas potential from wind and solar power: A country analysis for Italy, International Journal of Hydrogen Energy, 42, 13389-13406.

8. M.M.F. Hasan, L.E. First, F. Boukouvala, C.A. Floudas, 2015, A multi-scale framework for CO2 capture, utilization, and sequestration: CCUS and CCU, Computers and Chemical Engineering 81, 2–21.

9. M.M.F. Hasan, F. Boukouvala, E.L. First, C.A. Floudas, (2014). Nationwide. regional. and statewide CO2 capture. utilization. and sequestration supply chain network optimization. Ind Eng Chem Res 53. (18). 7489–7506.

10. C.A. Hendriks. Carbon Dioxide Removal from coal-Fired power plant. In department of science. technology. and society. Utrecht University. 1994: Utrecht. Netherlands.

12. R. Hoefnagels, M. Junginger, C. Panzer, G. Resch, A. Held, 2011, Reshaping project e long term potentials and costs of RES-Part I: potentials. diffusion and technological learning. [Online]. Available: www.reshaping-res-policy.eu [Accessed 09 March 2017].

12. https://ec.€europa.eu/€eurostat/statistics-explained/index.php?title=File:Gas_prices_for_non-household_consumers,_second_half_2017_(EUR_per_kWh).png#filehistory

13. https://yearbook.enerdata.net/natural-gas/world-natural-gas-production-statistics.html

14. IEA (International Energy Agency), 2019. Global energy & CO2 status report. https://www.iea.org/geco/emissions/.

15. IPCC, 2013. Climate Change 2013: the Physical Science Basis. Technical Report. Intergovernmental Panel on Climate Change.

16. M.M.J. Knoope, A. Ramirez, A.P.C. Faaij, 2013. A state of the art review of techno-economic model predicting the costs of CO2 pipeline transport. Int. J. Greenh. Gas Control 16. 241-270.

17. G. Leonzio, 2017, Design and feasibility analysis of a Power-to-Gas plant in Germany, Journal of Cleaner Production, 162, 609-623.

18. G. Leonzio, P.U. Foscolo, E. Zondervan, 2019a, Sustainable utilization and storage of carbon dioxide: Analysis and design of an innovative supply chain, Computer and Chemical Engineering, 131, 106569.

19. G. Leonzio, D. Bogle, P.U. Foscolo, E. Zondervan, 2019b, Optimization of CCUS supply chains in the UK: a strategic role for emissions reduction, Chemical Engineering Research and Desing, under review.

20. J. Ma, Q. Li, M. Kühn, N. Nakaten, 2018, Power-to-gas based subsurface energy storage: A review, Renewable and Sustainable Energy Reviews 97, 478–496.

21. M. Matzen, Y. Demirel, 2016, Methanol and dimethyl ether from renewable hydrogen and carbon dioxide: alternatve fuels production and life cycle assessment, Journal of Cleaner Production, 139, 1068-1077.

22. F. Moia, S. Fais, F. Pisanu, G. Sardu, P. Casero, R. Guandalini, G. Agate, S. Beretta, F. Cappelletti, F. Colucci, 2012. La fattibilità dello stoccaggio geologico della CO2 negli acquiferi salini profondi nell'onshore e offshore italiano, 1° Congresso dell'Ordine dei Geologi di Basilicata,"Ricerca, Sviluppo ed Utilizzo delle Fonti Fossili: Il Ruolo del Geologo", Potenza, 30 Novembre - 2 Dicembre 2012.

23. F. Reichert, 2012, Wind-to-Gas-to-Money? Economics and Perspectives of the Power-to-Gas Technology. Aalborg University Department of Development and Planning MSc (Eng) Sustainable Energy Planning and Management. master thesis.

24. R. Vooradi, M.O. Bertrana, R. Frauzema, S.B. Anne, R. Gani, 2018. Sustainable chemical processing and energy-carbon dioxide management: Review of challenges and opportunities, Chemical Engineering Research and Design, 131, 440-464.

25. S. Schiebahn, T. Grube, M. Robinius, V. Tietze, B. Kumar, D. Stolten, 2015. Power to gas: Technological overview, systems analysis and economic assessment for a case study in Germany, International Journal of Hydrogen Energy, 40, 4285-4294.

26. S. Zhang, L. Liua, L. Zhang, Y. Zhuang, J. Du, 2018. An optimization model for carbon capture utilization and storage supply chain: A case study in Northeastern China, Applied Energy 231, 194–206.

Sauro Pierucci, Flavio Manenti, Giulia Bozzano, Davide Manca (Eds.)
Proceedings of the 30th European Symposium on Computer Aided Process Engineering
(ESCAPE30), May 24-27, 2020, Milano, Italy. © 2020 Elsevier B.V. All rights reserved.
http://dx.doi.org/10.1016/B978-0-12-823377-1.50056-2

Effect of Selective Size Extraction of Microalgae from a Photobioreactor

Ergys Pahija[a], Chi-Wai Hui[b,*], John M. Woodley[a], Gürkan Sin[a]

[a]*Process and Systems Engineering Research Center (PROSYS), Department of Chemical and Biochemical Engineering, Technical University of Denmark, 2800 Kgs. Lyngby, Denmark*
[b]*Department of Chemical and Biological Engineering, The Hong Kong University of Science and Technology, Clear Water Bay, Hong Kong SAR*
kehui@ust.hk

Abstract

A good understanding of population dynamics can give relevant insights and process understanding to improve the production of microalgae. To this end, population balance modelling (PBM) can be used to study population dynamics that can provide information such as the size distribution of cells. This detail can then be used to comprehend whether and how certain process strategies are beneficial to the population growth. The objective of this work is to understand how different cell removal strategies can affect the production of microalgae, using a model-based approach.

Keywords: microalgae, harvesting, population dynamics, population balance.

1. Introduction

A good understanding of microalgae dynamics can be particularly beneficial to improve the efficiency of the production process. Several models of microalgae growth can be found in the literature (Lee et al., 2015). Likewise, models for harvesting cells have been considered to reduce the costs of the process (Salim et al., 2013; Lee et al., 2018). Among others, the PBM can give relevant information about biological systems, and unicellular organisms in particular (Pahija et al., 2019b). Looking at these two processes separately is relevant to develop an essential strategy in their design and select the best operating conditions.

A possible scenario for a microalgae production plant consists of a production or biomass growth unit, where microalgae grow in a photobioreactor (PBR), and a harvesting unit, where the microalgae are collected. Part of the solution flows from the PBR to a sedimentation tank, where cells tend to settle on the bottom as sludge and from there to a downstream process (e.g., extraction, recovery, and isolation of valuable products from inside the cells). Although this paper focuses on the growth unit, future works should consider the integration of all units operating in the process to maximise the production of microalgae.

Microalgae size and internal composition are affected by environmental conditions and are dependent upon which stage of the life cycle the cell is located (Morimura, 1959).

The aim of this work is to apply a population balance model (PBM) to simulate the growth and show the effect of extracting a specific size distribution of cells from the PBR. Several examples will be used to illustrate the impact and importance of the size distribution in this process. In particular, we will demonstrate how extracting a specific size of microalgae from the bioreactor will affect the overall performance and yield of cells. The effects on the harvesting unit will be taken into account in future studies.

2. Methodology

The PBM is used to simulate the population dynamics of microalgae inside the PBR. The population balance is solved using a discretization method and it appears as shown in Equation (1).

$$N_i^{j+1} = N_i^j + \Delta t \left[-\frac{G_i}{\Delta L_i} S_i N_i^j + \frac{G_{i-1}}{\Delta L_{i-1}} S_{i-1} N_{i-1}^j \right] - S_i N_i^j \Delta t + \sum_{k=L_{cr}}^{L_{max}} \left(XS_k b_{ki} N_k^j \Delta t \right) \tag{1}$$

Where N_i^j is the number of particles in the size interval i at time j, G_i is the growth rate of interval i, S_i is the size-specific division rate and X is the number of daughter cells. b_{ki} is the probability for particles of size k to divide into particles of size i. Finally, Δt and ΔL_i are the time and size interval i, respectively. In case the size discretization is uniform, then it can be assumed that $\Delta L = \Delta L_i$. In this first example, b_{ki} is taken as equal to 1 for the first size interval ($i=1$) and equal to 0 for all other size intervals ($i \neq 1$). It is assumed that the new-born cells are generated in the first interval and division starts only after the size of microalgae is larger than 5 μm. The equation was solved following the methodology proposed by Pahija et al. (2019b), and the growth and division rates are a function of temperature and light intensity. The PBM was implemented and solved in MATLAB and is used to evaluate different extraction strategies. Although this paper proposes only simulations, all initial conditions shown in the results below are taken from experimental data. The measurements of the number density of cells and their size distribution were conducted as explained by Pahija et al. (2019a).

Three strategies are considered in order to demonstrate the importance of size distribution in the production of microalgae:

- Removal from a perfectly mixed PBR
- Removal from a perfectly mixed PBR including the stationary phase
- Removal of a selected size of cells from the PBR

3. Results

3.1. Extraction from a perfectly mixed PBR
This first basic application consists of the continuous removal of microalgae cells from a perfectly mixed PBR. Figure 2 shows the change in cell population in case different flowrates are removed from the PBR. The size distribution of particles is not affected by the removal of microalgae. The volumetric removal rate can be addressed as a fraction of the total population collected. Let's assume a PBR containing 300,000 L of microalgae solution. A specific flowrate is then removed from the reactor and sent to the harvesting unit. The volume of the solution inside the PBR is assumed constant and we suppose that BG11 (NaNO$_3$, K$_2$HPO$_4$, MgSO$_4$·7H$_2$O, CaCl$_2$·2H$_2$O, Citric Acid·H$_2$O, Ferric Ammonium Citrate, Na$_2$EDTA·2H$_2$O, Na$_2$CO$_3$, Trace Metal Solution, Sodium

Thiosulfate Pentahydrate) is used as a medium, being the initial condition taken from experimental data.

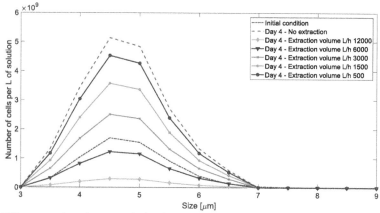

Figure 1 Effects on microalgae population by cell removal at different flowrates from the PBR.

Figure 1 and Figure 2 depict that there is a value of flowrate that allows the population to slightly increase, even when cells are removed. Intuitively, a decision should be taken according to the given process objectives. In this case, our goal is to maximise the production of microalgae. Removing 12,000 L/h of solution from the PBR can provide a good production rate for a small amount of time, while after two to three days, the production is reduced considerably. The reason is that the population growth of microalgae is not as fast as the removal rate, resulting in a reduction in the overall population inside the PBR. Reducing the flowrate to 500 L/h has a much lower impact on the population inside the reactor, but only a small mass of microalgae is collected. Figure 2 indicates that there is an optimal flowrate to guarantee the maximum production of microalgae in a certain period. From the proposed graph, in order to maximize the production, we need to make a trade-off between collected cells and population growth in the reactor.

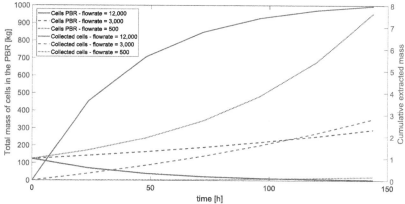

Figure 2 Effect of different flowrates on the total mass of microalgae collected and the total mass of cells inside the PBR.

Figure 2 shows the increase in the concentration of cells with time. In this case, the mass of cells in 144 hours is equal to almost 900 kg of cells; the value is not a dry weight, according to literature the water content depends on the cell species, composition, and may vary according to the conditions can be higher than 90 %, as described by Kanda and Li (2011).

3.2. Considerations on the stationary phase

However, it is common to work with a higher concentration of microalgae in order to collect more biomass. Therefore, a possible approach could consist of reaching the stationary phase to have a higher biomass concentration. Nevertheless, the composition of cells in the stationary phase must be in line with the production requirements; the environmental condition should allow the achievement of high microalgae concentration and the health condition of the population should be monitored. If all these requirements are met, maintaining the population in the stationary phase would be beneficial in terms of biomass production.

In the case of limited nutrients concentration (0.5 BG11) in continuous production of microalgae, if the removal rate of cells from a PBR of 300 m³ of solution is limited to 500 L/h, the stationary phase would be reached after several days.

Figure 3 represents an extension of Figure 2. Here more appropriate values of removal flowrates are selected, and the simulation is extended for a relevant period in order to see the effect of the cumulative biomass removed and how the population inside the PBR responds. The maximum number of cells in the reactor is related to the concentration of nutrients and, as shown below, the maximum biomass concentration inside the selected reactor, and the proposed conditions. It is now particularly evident that there is an optimal removal rate, and it would beat the value that causes the cumulative removal of biomass to increase fastest. The increase in cumulative biomass collected becomes linear after the stationary phase is reached.

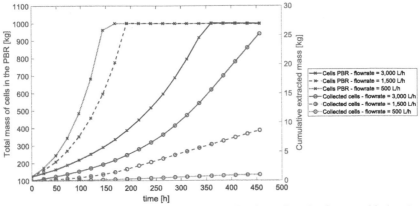

Figure 3 Effect of different flowrates for 20 consecutive days of production, considering the stationary phase.

The specific growth rates and division rates are considered equal to zero when the population becomes higher than the set limit (stationary phase). In case no cells are removed from the PBR, the number of cells remains constant. After reaching the removal, the population stops growing, while removal of the solution is in progress. As shown in Figure 4, the case with a higher extraction rate reaches the limit later than the other cases. The reason the maximum concentration remains constant is that the stationary phase is generally long, and we assume that all the medium removed from the reactor is instantly recirculated while eventual losses of the volume are reintroduced by using deionized water. If these assumptions are respected, the maximum population would approximately maintain the same value. Notice that Figure 4 the axes are adjusted to focus on the differences in the stationary phase.

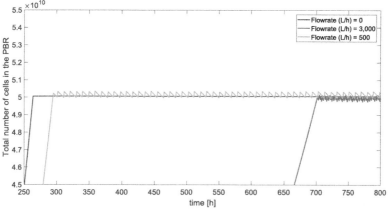

Figure 4 Stationary phase with a continuous collection of cells.

3.3. Extraction of a selected size of cells

Finally, the extraction of a specific size of microalgae is now proposed. Let us suppose that an ideal harvesting system is used to collect microalgae and that it is able to collect 100 % of a defined size range of cells. This test would allow to better visualize the population dynamics in case a specific size is continuously removed from the system.

As a case study, the growth of microalgae at 30°C and 600 lumens is considered. The medium is BG11. The time interval is equal to 0.5 h while the size interval is fixed to 0.5 μm.

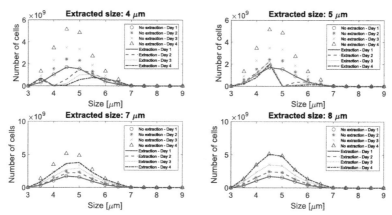

Figure 5 Growth of microalgae in case a specific size of microalgae is continuously extracted from the PBR.

Figure 5 shows the effect of extracting a different size of microalgae. The number of cells per litre of solution is affected by the size range of removed cells. Looking at the four graphs, it is clear that extracting small cells affects the population more than extracting larger sizes. This is because we assume new-born cells are generated in the first interval, and the division starts only after the size of microalgae is larger than 5 μm. Therefore, removing smaller cells would reduce the overall younger population, that can grow to the mature phase. Furthermore, this demonstrates the importance of cells in the range 5-8 μm, where the majority of divisions occur. Removal of cells larger than 7.5

µm can be considered as negligible for the simulation because of the low number of cells, and the resulting dynamics with be very similar to the one without any extraction. An additional consideration can also be made with respect to the model. Looking at the figure with size 4 µm removal, it is noticeable that the concentration of cells of size 4.5 µm in day 2 is not zero. This is due to the fact that in this case, we are not assuming the Courant–Friedrichs–Lewy condition to be equal to unity when trying to solve the population balance model. Consequently, we have a residual number of cells remaining in the interval but, because of microalgae growth, the number of cells in the interval is reduced at each time step.

4. Conclusions and future work

The results show the effect of microalgae size distribution in a photobioreactor. Several case studies have been simulated in this work. In particular, the first case has demonstrated how removing more cells than those obtained from the population growth, the concentration of cells drops. Similarly, a case study by including the stationary phase shows that an optimal extraction flowrate should be calculated. Following, the example of specific size removal of cells indicates it can strongly affect the dynamics, and it is a function of the size distribution. This work is a simulation-based work and although the results give some relevant information on the possibility of size-specific microalgae removal. The simulation results provided some relevant information on the population dynamics and process performance, which will be tested using experimental investigations for improving the microalgae production process.

The achieved results are relevant in the case a specific size of microalgae wants to be concentrated inside the photobioreactor. This allows a higher concentration of cells in a specific stage of the life-cycle, and it can be further correlated to the concentration of desired substances inside the cells. However, the proposed work could also be applied to other biological and non-biological reactors when a specific internal coordinate (size of cells or particles) wants to be achieved.

References

E. Lee, M. Jalalizadeh, and Q. Zhang, 2015, Growth kinetic models for microalgae cultivation: A review, Algal Research, 12, 497–512.

P. Y. Lee, E. Pahija, Y. Z. Liang, K. P. Yeoh, and C. W. Hui, 2018, Population Balance Equation Applied to Microalgae Harvesting, Computer Aided Chemical Engineering, 43, 1299–1304.

Y. Morimura, 1959, Synchronous Culture of Chlorella, Plant and Cell Physiology, 1, 49–62.

E. Pahija, and C.W. Hui, 2019a, A systematic study on the effects of dynamic environments on microalgae concentration, Algal Research, 42, 101599.

E. Pahija, P. Y. Lee, and C. W. Hui, 2019b, A Revision of Population Balance Equation Applied to Microalgae with Birth, Growth, and Death, Process Integr. Optim. Sustain., 3, 1, 125–141.

S. Salim, L. Gilissen, A. Rinzema, M. H. Vermuë, and R. H. Wijffels, 2013, Modeling microalgal flocculation and sedimentation, Bioresour. Technol., 144, 602–607.

H. Kanda, and P. Li, 2011, Simple extraction method of green crude from natural blue-green microalgae by dimethyl ether, Fuel, 90(3), 1264-1266.

Sauro Pierucci, Flavio Manenti, Giulia Bozzano, Davide Manca (Eds.)
Proceedings of the 30th European Symposium on Computer Aided Process Engineering
(ESCAPE30), May 24-27, 2020, Milano, Italy. © 2020 Elsevier B.V. All rights reserved.
http://dx.doi.org/10.1016/B978-0-12-823377-1.50057-4

Numerical Modelling for Environmental Impact Assessment of Sediment Dispersion in Port Areas

Stefania Magrì[a*], Patrizia De Gaetano[a], Alessandra Feola[b], Iolanda Lisi[b], Andrea Salmeri[b], Francesco Venti[b], Andrea Pedroncini[c]

[a]ARPAL - Agenzia Regionale per la Protezione Ambiente Liguria, Via Bombrini 8, 16149 Genova, Italy
[b]ISPRA - Istituto Superiore per la Protezione e la Ricerca Ambientale, Loc. Brondolo, 30015 Chioggia, Italy
[c]ISPRA - Istituto Superiore per la Protezione e la Ricerca Ambientale, Via Brancati 48, 00144 Roma, Italy
[d]DHI Italia, Via Bombrini 11, 16149 Genova, Italy

stefania.magri@arpal.gov.it

Abstract

In port areas, sediments resuspension can be critical for the presence of contaminants (such as metals from industrial effluents), which may be dispersed to unpolluted areas under different hydrodynamics forces. In the framework of the interregional project SE.D.RI.PORT (SEdimenti, Dragaggi e RIschi PORTuali) project, the Institute for Environmental Protection and Research (ISPRA) and Regional Agency for Environmental Protection–Liguria (ARPAL) have implemented a numerical model to simulate the sediment plume dynamics for bed levelling operation in the pilot area of La Spezia harbour (Italy). The area is characterized by a diffused pollution and subjected, since the 90s, to different dredging and reclamation activities, as well as monitoring and environmental characterization, providing data for the model. According to sectors references, different modelling tools has been applied to characterize the area interested by sediment plume dynamics, in term of significant variations of suspended sediment concentration (SSC) and sediment deposition rates (DEP). Model results are presented by means of synthetic maps showing the meaningful effects of operations at different water depths and at different key sites in order to support the dredging project and the environmental monitoring planning and optimization.

Keywords: Dredging and bed levelling, environmental assessment, mathematical modelling, port areas, sediment dispersion.

1. Introduction

The removal of sediments from the bottom of harbours is often necessary to maintain or increase the depth of navigation channels or berthing areas, thus ensuring the functionality of the port. The increase of suspended solid concentration due to resuspended bottom sediments can determine negative environmental effects both on the abiotic and biotic marine ecosystem, as reported by Wilber & Clark (2001), Erftemeijer et al. (2012). In coastal marine systems at high level of anthropization, like harbours, sediments represents a sink and a source for contaminants, and resuspension can contribute to propagate pollution even in clean areas (e.g. PIANC, 2006; Lisi et al., 2017 e 2019; CEDA/IADC, 2018). Most dredged material in ports are rich in fine sediments and often contain many anthropogenic substances, some of which have a toxic character: heavy metals, tributyltin (TBT), polycyclic aromatic hydrocarbons (PAHs), polychlorinated biphenyls (PCBs), pesticides and biocides whose effects on health are multiple (carcinogenic, mutagenic, toxic for reproduction) and attempts have been made to define protocols to determine the dangerousness of contaminated sediments (Garbolino et al., 2014). The problem of metal contamination in marine sediments have recently lead to proposed techniques for environmentally friendly strategies for removal, such as bioleaching (Fonti et al., 2013) or nano-based products site-remediation (De Gisi et al., 2017).

For projects that involve the handling of sediments, a detailed Environmental Impact Assessment (EIA, Directive 2014/52/UE) should be carried out to determine the potential environmental impacts, evaluate technical alternatives and design appropriate mitigation, management and monitoring measures. Recently, in absence of local legislation, guidelines for the use of numerical modelling to support environmental studies have been published (Lisi et al., 2017).

The present paper describes an application of the Integrated Modelling Approach for simulating Sediment Dispersion (IMAforSED) proposed by Lisi et al. (2017, 2019) and of the Dredging Environmental Assessment Module (Dr-EAM) proposed by Feola et al. (2015, 2016), specifically developed by ISPRA as supporting tools for dredging activities. The approach is applied to bed levelling operations with grab dredger planned for 2019 in the harbour basin in La Spezia, Italy. Bed levelling is a technique consisting in removal of sediments from an area and their consequential re-disposal in an adjacent area. The main objective of the work is to test the replicability of the methodology to a sea bed levelling activity and capture the spatial (vertical and horizontal) and temporal variability of the modelled SSC and DEP levels by means of maps showing statistical measures usable for decision support and environmental management.

2. Material and Methods

2.1. The study area

La Spezia harbour basin, located in Liguria region (Italy) covers an area of about 16 km², bounded to the south-east by a breakwater, of about 2.8 km. The basin is connected to the open sea by two entrances about 400 m and 200 m wide. The enclosed bay is influenced by the runoff of several small rivers, characterized by seasonal and discontinuous discharges, as well as civil and industrial discharges, in particular by the Enel thermoelectric power plant. The heavy industrial, military, commercial and anthropic activities have caused terrestrial as well as marine widespread contamination. Since 2006 many sectors of the harbour area have been dredged for environmental reclamation and depth maintenance.

2.2. Integrated Modelling Approach

An Integrated Modelling Approach for simulating Sediment Dispersion (IMAforSED), developed by ISPRA (Lisi et al., 2017; 2019) has been applied to provide a characterization of the area interested by sediment passive plume dynamics, in term of significant variations of suspended sediment concentration (SSC) and sediment deposition rates (DEP). Basically, the IMAforSED consists in the implementation in series of three numerical modules, hereinafter referred to as the hydrodynamic module, source term module and transport module. Finally an Environmental Assessment Module (Dr-EAM) is implemented, to synthesize numerical results and to make them usable for decision support. Available data (e.g. ARPAL and ISPRA seabed sediment characterization and environmental monitoring of dredging activities in the area) have been used to feed the numerical models implemented in the proposed methodology.

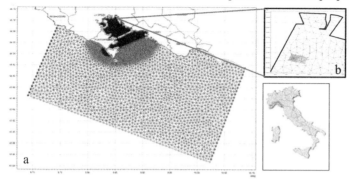

Figure 1. a) Model domain and b) location of the area object of the bed levelling activity (left area for removal and right area for deposition)

2.2.1. Hydrodynamic Module (HM)

The characteristics of La Spezia harbour have suggested the application of a three-dimensional hydrodynamic model. The three-dimensional finite volume MIKE 3 Flow Model FM (DHI, 2019) was used to model the stratified flow field and to obtain hydrodynamic parameters at a high-resolution scale for a full reference year. The model uses a three-dimensional, Reynolds averaged, Navier-Stokes equations for solving the full non-linear equations of continuity and conservation of momentum. On-field data from monitoring activities were used to calibrate the coefficient that parametrizes vertical dispersion. A flexible mesh with maximum horizontal resolution of 50 m was chosen to properly describe the complex geometry and dynamics of the site (Figure 1). An hybrid vertical discretization system (σ and z) was used to account for the stratification effects. An entire reference year of climatic conditions was used, and, in particular, 2015 was chosen. At the open boundaries, reanalysis from the 3D model of the Mediterranean sea, available through the Copernicus Service (Marine Environment Monitoring Service, marine.copernicus.eu), were applied. For the tidal component of water level and current, data from the OSU Tidal Prediction Software (OTPS) were used. Wind forcing from the meteorological model MOLOCH, developed and run at the Meteo Hydrological Functional Centre for Civil Protection (CFMI-PC) in ARPAL, was introduced. While runoff of the several small rivers, characterized by seasonal and discontinuous discharges, were not considered, the input from the thermoelectric power plant was introduced as input of warmer water, with a constant flow of 15 m³/s and an exceeding temperature of 5 °C. Also, Magra river freshwater input, obtained from the hydrological model DRiFt, also developed at the CFMI-PC in ARPAL, was considered in the domain.

2.2.2. Definition of the source for levelling operations

The simulation of the plume evolution requires the definition of the potential dredging source and the sediment loss rate in the "near-field" area, related to the equipment and operational techniques, as well as operational cycle of the specific case study.

The sediment source, as flux of fine sediment released during operations, is defined taking into account: dredged volume, percentage of sediments fine fraction ($d_{50} < 63$ μm) and sediment spill related to the used operational technique. Based on information provided by La Spezia Port Authority (AdSP MLO) and on the available sediment characterization data (ISPRA - ARPAL, 2016), a suspended sediments flux rate of 18 kg/s was estimated, for a source term representative of bed leveling operation with grab dredge, considering different spill coefficient for the removal (σ_{dr}=0.1) and the disposal (σ_{ds}=0.75) operational phases (Table 1). These spill coefficients were settled according to a specific sensitivity analysis.

Table 1. Detail of bed levelling activities

Total volume to be removed (m³)	4,000	Operational technique	grab dredge
Daily production (m³/d)	800	Spill coefficient for removal	σ_{dr}=0.1
Operations time (days)	5	Spill coefficient for disposal	σ_{ds}=0.75
Operations time (hs/d)	16	Release depth	Bottom layer

2.2.3. Transport Module (TM)

The application of the sediment transport and deposition model is applied to a series of 51 independent consecutive dredging scenarios, covering the entire reference year, and thus the action of different seasonal conditions. The Mud Transport module (MIKE 3 MT) was used, decoupled from the hydrodynamic module, to simulate transport and deposition of the fine sediments, as suggested in ISPRA Guidelines (Lisi et al., 2017), considering the two different sediment fractions d_{50}=32 μm, and d_{50}=16 μm. Each scenario represents the whole bed levelling activity, covering 5 days operations and 2 days to take into account the deposition of all the suspended sediment.

2.2.4. Dr-EAM Module

Dr-EAM tools, specifically developed by ISPRA to provide maps that synthesize the modeling results of sediment dispersion for long-term modeling scenarios (Feola et al., 2015; 2016), was applied. In order to compare numerical results, obtained within the local model domain (Figure 2A), a regular grid (step 160 m, Figure 2B) was used to synthetize results of both hydrodynamics and Mud Transport simulations. For each regular grid element (Figure 2E), time series of the current speed, SSC, and DEP output parameter were extracted from corresponding elements (Figure 2C) and statistically analyzed. In particular, statistics were calculated for specific layers: the bottom layer, the surface layer and two layers (sub and intermediate) in between. Maps of different statistical parameters (mean, max) were produced for specific periods (i.e. seasonal and annual mean).

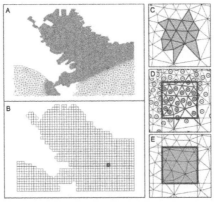

Figure 2. A) Mesh of the model domain; B) regular grid for result synthesis. Association between mesh elements and model results within (C) through centroids (D) to a specific regular grid element (E)

3. Results and Discussion

The output maps obtained from the model show that the considered activity show a limited influence area. In particular, as shown Figure 3, in the area within 500 metres of the dredging area, SSC shows mean values below 3 mg/L while maximum values do not exceed 11 mg/L. The maximum values of DEP, which near the dredging/levelling area have recorded mean values higher than 10,000 g/m², decrease rapidly in the first 500 meters (average values of about 3,500 g/m² and maximum values of about 5,600 g/m²). Within 1,000 m of the dredging area, the mean and maximum values are less than 6 and 10 g/m² respectively. Significant variations for SSC > 1 mg/L and DEP > 1 g/m² are confined within 500- 1,000 meters from the source.

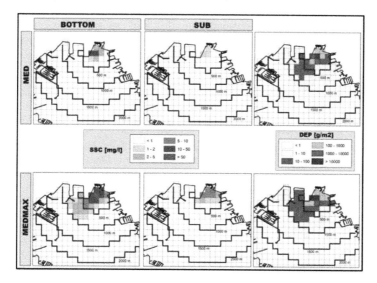

Figure 3. Distribution of the mean values, and mean of the maximum values of SSC in the deepest levels and DEP in reference to the distance from the dredging/levelling area (step 500 m)

Table 2. Mean and maximums annual values of SSC (modeled for bottom, sub and intermediate layers) and DEP calculated at regular distance from the intervention area

distance [m]	N	SSC [mg/L]						DEP [g/m2]	
		bottom		sub		intermediate		bottom	
		mean	max	mean	max	mean	max	mean	max
0-500	24	2.9	10.9	0.4	2.6	0.2	1.3	3544.6	5601.2
500-1000	48	0.1	0.8	0.0	0.2	0.0	0.2	5.5	9.8
1000-1500	69	0.0	0.1	0.0	0.1	0.0	0.0	0.4	0.9
1500-2000	83	0.0	0.0	0.0	0.0	0.0	0.0	0.1	0.2
2000-3000	207	0.0	0.0	0.0	0.0	0.0	0.0	0.0	0.1
>3000	666	0.0	0.0	0.0	0.0	0.0	0.0	0.0	0.0

4. Conclusions

This work proposes an application of the Integrated Modelling Approach for simulating Sediment Dispersion (IMAforSED) reported in Lisi et al. (2017, 2019) and of the Dredging Environmental Assessment Module (Dr-EAM) reported in Feola et al. (2015, 2016) and specifically developed by ISPRA as supporting tools to dredging activities. The approach was tested on bed levelling operations with grab dredger, to characterize the sediment plume dynamics and the areas interested by significant variations of suspended sediment concentration (SSC) and sediment deposition rates (DEP). Results of the present work has shown that the proposed methodology can be easily applied to any area and to different activities of sediment displacement, where information of the specific technology used is known. In addition, maps comparing results for different climatic conditions can show the ability of the applied methodological approach to support the management of dredging project (e.g. selection of the appropriate operating windows in relation to the presence of different sensitive receptors) and the environmental monitoring planning (e.g. sampling station location and frequency).

References

CEDA/IADC, 2018. Dredging for Sustainable Infrastructure. CEDA/IADC, The Hague, The Netherlands. Revision no. 1021 logged at 2017-10-05 13:35

DHI, 2019. MIKE 21 & MIKE 3 Flow Model FM, Hydrodynamic and Transport Module – Scientific documentation. Release 2019

Erftemeijer P.L.A., Riegl B., Hoeksema B.W., Todd P.A., 2012. Environmental impacts of dredging and other sediment disturbances on corals: a review. Mar.Pollut.Bull.64 (9),1737-65

Feola A., Lisi I., Venti F., Salmeri A., Pedroncini A., Romano E., 2015. A methodological modelling approach to assess the potential environmental impacts of dredging activities. In Proc. Of CEDA. Dredging Days, Innovative Dredging Solutions for Ports, Rotterdam

Feola A., Lisi I., Salmeri A., Venti F., Pedroncini A., Romano E., 2016. Platform of integrated tools to support environmental studies and management of dredging activities, J. Env. Manag. 166

Fonti V., Dell'Anno A., Beolchini F., 2013, Mutualistic interactions during bioleaching of marine contaminated sediment, Chemical Engineering Transactions, 32, 979-984 DOI:10.3303/CET1332164

Lisi I., Feola A., Bruschi A., Di Risio M., Pedroncini A., Pasquali D. & Romano E., 2017. La modellistica matematica nella valutazione degli aspetti fisici legati alla movimentazione dei sedimenti in aree marino-costiere. Manuali e Linee Guida ISPRA, 169/2017, pp.144

Garbolino E., Aqua J.L., Abriak N.E., 2014, Applicability of h14 protocol for sediments in order to consider their valorization: limits and benefits, Chemical Engineering Transactions, 36, 631-636 DOI: 10.3303/CET1436106

Lisi I., Feola A., Bruschi A., Pedroncini A., Pasquali D., Di Risio M., 2019(b). Mathematical modeling framework of physical effects induced by sediments handling operations in marine and coastal areas. J. Mar. Sci. Eng., 7, 149

PIANC, Permanent International Association of Navigation Congresses, 2006. Environmental risk assessment of dredging and disposal operations. Report of Working Group 10 of the Environmental Commission. pp.40

De Gisi S., Minetto D., Lofrano G., Libralato G., Conte B., Todaro F., Notarnicola M., 2017, Nano-scale Zero Valent Iron (nZVI) treatment of marine sediments slightly polluted by heavy metals, Chemical Engineering Transactions, 60, 139-144 DOI: 10.3303/CET1760024

Wilber DH., Clarke DG., 2001. Biological Effects of Suspended Sediments: A Review of Suspended Sediment Impacts on Fish and Shellfish with Relation to Dredging Activities in Estuaries. North American Journal of Fisheries Management 21(4). 855-875

Sauro Pierucci, Flavio Manenti, Giulia Bozzano, Davide Manca (Eds.)
Proceedings of the 30th European Symposium on Computer Aided Process Engineering
(ESCAPE30), May 24-27, 2020, Milano, Italy. © 2020 Elsevier B.V. All rights reserved.
http://dx.doi.org/10.1016/B978-0-12-823377-1.50058-6

An Efficient Hybridization of Gaussian Processes and Clustering for Electricity Price Forecasting

Aaron S. Yeardley, Diarmid Roberts, Robert Milton, Solomon F. Brown*

Department of Chemical and Biological Engineering, University of Sheffield, Sheffield, S1 3JD, United Kingdom
s.f.brown@sheffield.ac.uk

Abstract

Electricity retailers and power generators have an increasing potential to profit from selling and purchasing electricity as wholesale electricity prices are encouraged to be introduced to both industrial and domestic customers. Hence, this paper focuses on developing an efficient method to aid decision-makers in forecasting the hourly price of electricity 4 weeks ahead. The method developed in this paper uses an approach to hybridize Gaussian Process (GP) regression with clustering to improve the predictive capabilities in electricity price forecasting. By first clustering all the input data and introducing a cluster number as a new input variable, the GP is conditioned to aid predictive process through data similarity.

This proposed method has been successfully applied to real electricity price data from the United Kingdom, comparing the predictive quality of the novel method (GPc1) to that of an original GP and that of a method which pre-clusters and filters the data for numerous GPs (GPc2). By comparing the predictive price distributions to the observed prices in the month of December 2018, it was found that clustering improves the predicted mean values of a GP while the mean predictive quality of GPc1 and GPc2 are of equal standing. Therefore, the number of outliers at 2 STD's were compared, showing GPc1 to have a predicted distribution with uncertainty that covers more of the true electricity prices than that of GPc2. In conclusion, the novel method provides the decision-maker with greater reliability so that the true electricity prices will be within the confidence limits predicted.

Keywords: Gaussian Process, hierarchical clustering, hybridization, forecasting, electricity prices.

1. Introduction

Increasingly, the rollout of intermittent renewable power sources with zero marginal cost of generation is resulting in a more dynamic electricity supply price curve. Coupled with variation in demand, this has the potential to increase the volatility of wholesale electricity prices. Within the existing electricity market structures, all of the proposed approaches to dealing with intermittency – storage, demand-side response and spatial interconnection - may be encouraged by exposing all customers, from domestic to industrial, to these variations. Hence accurate price forecasting will be of the utmost importance in the coming years.

Attempts to construct bottom-up models for electricity price based on predictions of demand and supply price curve at a given time run into difficulties due to the non-transparency of constraints in the system (Staffell and Green, 2016) and high levels of residual variance are associated with this approach (Pape *et al.*, 2016). There is, therefore, a role for statistical models in improving predictions of the electricity price. A common choice of a statistical model is the Gaussian process (GP) (Milton *et al.*, 2019), which is computationally efficient and the use of it for regression (Zanella *et al.*, 2019) has been proven to be effective for electricity price forecasting (Kou *et al.*, 2015; Mori and Nakano, 2015). The flexibility of GPs allows the clustering of the inputs to be directly incorporated into the prediction of the output, so combining GPs with clustering techniques allows them to learn from data points of similar nature. In this work, we introduce a hybrid method which uses clustering to improve the predictive capabilities of a GP by first applying a hierarchical clustering technique and using this to condition a single GP. The cluster number becomes an additional input variable that aids the GP learning process through data similarity.

This new hybridization method is then compared to a GP without the hybridization with clustering and to a known method by Mori and Nakano (2015) which applies individual GPs to each cluster of inputs. The comparison is achieved through an analysis of electricity price forecasting using real data from the United Kingdom (NordPool) which is split at a specific date to give two datasets, a past and a future, providing results which show the forecasting capabilities of each GP method. The forecasted results of each GP are then compared to the true observed prices proving that the proposed method can be used by power generators and electricity retailers for electricity price forecasting while considering the uncertainties of the proposed predictions.

2. Method

2.1. Clustering

In clustering processes, a set of vectors is divided into subsets based on a proximity measure. In the present work, five potential predictors of electricity price at the UK national level are taken as input variables; electricity demand, CCGT generation, coal generation, wind generation and solar generation (BMReports).

For each day, the hourly profiles of each predictor were normalized to the maximum observed value, then concatenated. Hierarchical clustering was then performed on the 5×24 D vectors, as this approach makes no prior assumption regarding the number of clusters. The Ward algorithm was used to judge the intercluster distance (SciPy.org). The second derivative of the merge distance plot was used to judge the emergence of genuine clusters (Hees). By this measure, the data set was judged to contain 5 clusters (see). The centroids of the corresponding 5 clusters are shown in Fugure 1. It is worth noting that the price input vectors contain several outliers, which is why the normalized profile is highly   compressed (coordinates 1 to 24).

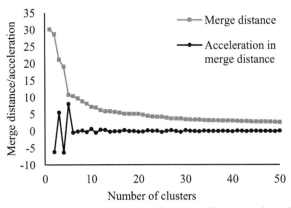

Figure 1: An elbow plot showing the merge distance and acceleration for the last 50 cluster merges.

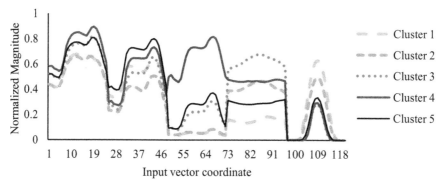

Figure 2: Centroids for the five clusters identified in the 5 x 24D predictor vector set.

2.2. Gaussian Process Regression

The use of GPs for regression begins with standard Bayesian conditioning of Gaussian priors to derive a predictive process. This creates a GP which takes a $(1 \times d)$ row vector of input variables $\mathbf{x}$ and returns a Gaussian random variable through calculations using the predictive equations

$$y(\mathbf{x}) \sim \mathcal{N}\left[\bar{f}(\mathbf{x}), \Sigma_y + \sigma_e{}^2\right] \tag{1}$$

where

$$\bar{f}(\mathbf{x}) := k(\mathbf{x}, \mathbf{X})(k(\mathbf{X}, \mathbf{X}) + \sigma_e{}^2 \mathbf{I})^{-1} \mathbf{y} \tag{2}$$

$$\Sigma_y = k(\mathbf{x}, \mathbf{x}) - k(\mathbf{x}, \mathbf{X})(k(\mathbf{X}, \mathbf{X}) + \sigma_e{}^2 \mathbf{I})^{-1} k(\mathbf{X}, \mathbf{x}) \tag{3}$$

The mean $\bar{f}(\mathbf{x})$ and variance Σ_y is learnt using n amounts of training data $\mathbf{y} = f(\mathbf{X}) + e$. Standard Bayesian inference has been used to express the mean prediction in terms of the $(n \times 1)$ observed responses $\mathbf{y}$ to $(n \times d)$ training inputs $\mathbf{X}$. In this work, the observed responses $\mathbf{y}$ are the electricity price at a given time from the 01/02/2017 to the 30/11/2018 corresponding to the training inputs $\mathbf{X}$. The predictions are then made using Eq. (1), the predictive equation, which takes test data from December 2018, allowing comparisons to the true electricity prices for that timeframe. At the heart of these equations lies the kernel function k which expresses the correlation between the responses to the input variables. Exclusively, this work uses the automatic relevance determination (ARD) kernel (Wipf and Nagarajan, 2009):

$$k(\mathbf{x}', \mathbf{x}) := \sigma_f{}^2 exp\left(-\frac{(\mathbf{x} - \mathbf{x}')\mathbf{\Lambda}^{-2}(\mathbf{x} - \mathbf{x}')^{\mathrm{T}}}{2}\right) \tag{4}$$

where $\mathbf{\Lambda}$ is a $(d \times d)$ diagonal positive definite lengthscale matrix. This choice can be entirely justified from the assumption that the similarity function $k(\mathbf{x}', \mathbf{x})$ is differentiable at $\mathbf{x}' = \mathbf{x}$, together with the assumption that the output is normal. The learning from the training data requires optimizing $d + 2$ hyperparameters, constituting of $\mathbf{\Lambda}$, σ_f, and σ_e, through the optimization of the marginal likelihood $p[\mathbf{y}|\mathbf{X}]$ using the ROMCOMMA software library (Milton and Brown, 2019).

2.3. Hybridization Method

On a given day, we wish to predict the hourly electricity price for 4 weeks ahead given the input variables. We apply a novel method, combining the clustering technique in Section 2.1 with the GP in Section 2.2 to create a hybridized method (GPcl).

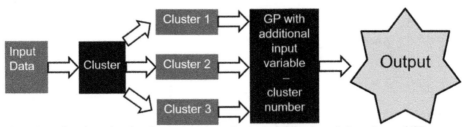

Figure 3: A flowchart showing the methodology for the hybridization of clustering and GPs.

Figure 3 describes the methodology for predicting the electricity profile as the input data for both training and testing are put through the clustering method creating clusters of data which are similar. The cluster number then becomes an additional input variable (along with the time, date, day of the week, price 4 weeks previously, electricity demand and electricity generation from various types) used in the GP for both the training data and the test data.

3. Results

In this section, the methodology developed above is applied to the December 2018 electricity price test data with direct comparison to a GP without hybridization and a method which uses clustering to create individual GPs as developed by Mori and Nakano (2015) (GPc2).

The forecasted results for three full weeks in December can be seen in Figure 4 for each method. In each sub-figure, the black dots show the true electricity price every hour from 00:00 on the 03rd of December to 23:00 on the 23rd of December. Within these time-dependent graphs, the Gaussian Process' predictive distributions can be seen by the mean centre grey line and the 95 % confidence intervals that bound the line. Throughout the three weeks, it can be seen that all three methods have difficulties predicting the extremely high and low electricity prices. The predictions using GPc2, shown in Figure 4 (c), has a distribution that varies closest to the true prices almost capturing the extremely high price on the 4th of December at 17:00. However, the predicted uncertainty in GPc2 tends to be smaller in comparison to the GPc1 and so more of the true prices are captured within the predicted distribution of the third novel method, shown in Figure 4 (b). Table 1 presents the correlation coefficient r^2, the root mean squared error (RMSE) and the outliers at 2 STD's for each of the methods for the December 2018 predictions. The introduction of clustering has improved the predictive quality of an original GP as shown by an increase in the r^2 and a decrease in the RMSE. Furthermore, the two values are very similar for GPc1 and GPc2 showing the mean predictions are equal in quality with respect to the nearness to the observed electricity price. Given that a major advantage of GPs is that they produce uncertainty in the predictions allowing the decision-maker to further understand the range of values that the electricity price could be instead of the singular mean predicted value. Therefore, the outliers at 2 STD's is a preferred diagnostic for this type of predictive model as it measures the number of true values outside of the predictive distribution. As can be seen, Table 1 shows the third method, GPc1, produces the lowest amount of outliers at just 2.55 %. Therefore, this method of forecasting allows the decision-maker to reliably estimate the degree of uncertainty in the electricity price efficiently, trusting that the true price is within the predicted distribution.

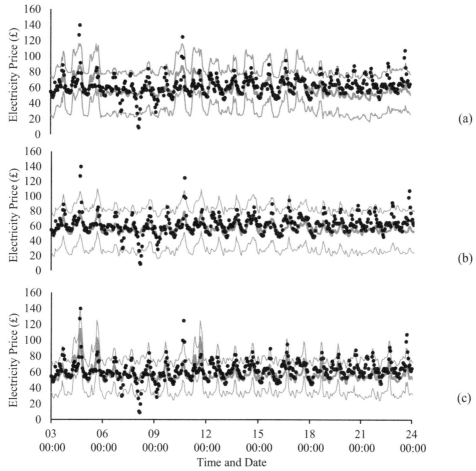

Figure 4: Forecasted electricity price distribution and true electricity price for 3 weeks in December from the 3rd to the 24th using (a) a GP without hybridization, (b) GPc1, and (c) GPc2.

Table 1: The diagnostic results for testing the three methods with electricity price data from December 2018.

Method	r^2	RMSE	Outliers at 2 STD's
GP without hybridization	0.216	0.904	3.90 %
GPc1	0.358	0.840	2.55 %
GPc2	0.405	0.833	3.90 %

4. Conclusion

In this work, a novel hybridization method was produced to effectively forecast the hourly price of electricity for 4 weeks ahead. The method used hierarchical clustering to create an extra input variable for a GP regression model. This extra input variable gives the GP additional information on the electricity data due to data similarity.

The method was applied to real wholesale electricity price data for the United Kingdom from 2017 to 2018 using the month of December 2018 as test data allowing a comparison to the capabilities of the novel forecasting method to an independent GP and to individual GPs produced for each cluster number. In conclusion, the results found that introducing clustering to a GP improves the mean predictive quality for electricity price forecasting, with both clustering methods being equal with respect to the nearness of the predicted price to the observed price. However, GPs have the advantage of producing a predicted distribution which includes the uncertainty in the predictions. Hence, this gives electricity retailers and power generators more insight into the forecasted price. Therefore, the outliers at 2 STD's were an important diagnostic which discovered the novel hybridization method produces a predicted distribution which covers the most observed values compared to the other two methods.

Overall, the method is proven to be reliable, giving the decision-maker greater confidence when compared to other prediction methods so that the true price will be within the 95 % confidence interval predicted by the GP. However, this work does have limitations as some of the input variables do need to be forecasted, such as the electricity demand and the electricity generated by various types. Although the national grid does provide forecasted demand profiles, further work will need to be dedicated to understanding the importance of each of the input variables and how errors in the forecasted input variables may affect the forecasted electricity price in this method. Additionally, comparing the relative computational efficiency of the two hybridization methods in an attempt to understand how the data size, dimensionality and number of clusters scale with the efficiency would further benefit the development of this technique.

References

BMReports (no date) *Balancing Mechanism Reporting Service (BMRS)*. Available at: https://www.bmreports.com/bmrs/?q=help/about-us.

Hees, J. (no date) *SciPy Hierarchical Clustering and Dendrogram Tutorial*. Available at: https://joernhees.de/blog/2015/08/26/scipy-hierarchical-clustering-and-dendrogram-tutorial/.

Kou, P. *et al.* (2015) 'Probabilistic electricity price forecasting with variational heteroscedastic Gaussian process and active learning', *Energy Conversion and Management*. Elsevier Ltd, 89, pp. 298–308. doi: 10.1016/j.enconman.2014.10.003.

Milton, R. A. and Brown, S. F. (2019) 'ROMCOMMA'. Available at: https://github.com/C-O-M-M-A/rom-comma.

Milton, R., Bugryniec, P. and Brown, S. (2019) 'Parameter Estimation for Thermal Runaway of Li-ion cells: a Gaussian Process approach', *Computer Aided Chemical Engineering*. Edited by A. A. Kiss et al. Elsevier (Computer Aided Chemical Engineering), 46, pp. 775–780. doi: https://doi.org/10.1016/B978-0-12-818634-3.50130-2.

Mori, H. and Nakano, K. (2015) 'Development of advanced Gaussian Process for LMP forecasting', *2015 18th International Conference on Intelligent System Application to Power Systems, ISAP 2015*. IEEE, pp. 1–6. doi: 10.1109/ISAP.2015.7325553.

NordPool (no date) *Historical Market Data*. Available at: https://www.nordpoolgroup.com/historical-market-data/.

Pape, C., Hagemann, S. and Weber, C. (2016) 'Are fundamentals enough? Explaining price variations in the German day-ahead and intraday power market', *Energy Economics*. Elsevier B.V., 54, pp. 376–387. doi: 10.1016/j.eneco.2015.12.013.

SciPy.org (no date) 'Clustering package (scipy.cluster)'. Available at: https://docs.scipy.org/doc/scipy/reference/cluster.html.

Staffell, I. and Green, R. (2016) 'Is There Still Merit in the Merit Order Stack? The Impact of Dynamic Constraints on Optimal Plant Mix', *IEEE Transactions on Power Systems*. IEEE, 31(1), pp. 43–53. doi: 10.1109/TPWRS.2015.2407613.

Wipf, D. and Nagarajan, S. (2009) 'A new view of automatic relevance determination', in *Advances in Neural Information Processing Systems 20 - Proceedings of the 2007 Conference*.

Zanella, L. *et al.* (2019) 'Real-time determination of optimal switching times for a H2 production process with CO2 capture using Gaussian Process Regression models', *Computer Aided Chemical Engineering*. Elsevier, 46, pp. 1219–1224. doi: 10.1016/B978-0-12-818634-3.50204-6.

Sauro Pierucci, Flavio Manenti, Giulia Bozzano, Davide Manca (Eds.)
Proceedings of the 30th European Symposium on Computer Aided Process Engineering
(ESCAPE30), May 24-27, 2020, Milano, Italy. © 2020 Elsevier B.V. All rights reserved.
http://dx.doi.org/10.1016/B978-0-12-823377-1.50059-8

CFD Analysis of the Use of Desert Sand as Thermal Energy Storage Medium in a Solar Powered Fluidised Bed Harvesting Unit

Mustapha Hamdan[a], Daniel Sebastia-Saez[a], Malak Hamdan[c], Harvey Arellano-Garcia[a,b*]

[a]*Dep. of Chemical and Process Eng.,University of Surrey, Guildford, GU2 7XH, UK*
[b]*LS Prozess- und Anlagentechnik, Brandenburgische Technische Universität Cottbus-Senftenberg, D-03046 Cottbus, Germany*
[c]*The Claude Littner Business School, University of West London, TW8 9GA, UK*
h.arellano-garcia@surrey.ac.uk)

Abstract

This work presents an Euler-Euler hydrodynamic and heat transfer numerical analysis of the multiphase flow involving desert sand and a continuous gas phase in a compact-size fluidised bed. The latter is part of a novel conceptual solar power design intended for domestic use. Desert sand is a highly available and unused resource with suitable thermal properties to be employed as thermal energy storage medium. It also allows for high working temperatures owing to its high resistance to agglomeration. Computational Fluid Dynamics simulations are used here to assess the heat transfer between desert sand and several proposed working fluids (including air, argon, nitrogen and carbon dioxide) to justify the design in terms of equipment dimensions and suitability of the materials used. The results show that the device can provide up to 1,031 kW when using carbon dioxide as the heat transfer fluid.

Keywords: sensible heat storage, desert sand, fluidised bed, solar energy, carbon dioxide utilization.

1. Introduction

Concentrated solar power (CSP) is a promising energy capture technology that uses optical devices to concentrate the power of the sun on to a surface and in turn generates power by means of a thermal-to-electric conversion unit (Zhang et al., 2011). Each year 885 million TWh of solar power reaches the earth surface, however, less than 0.002% of primary energy is consumed by humans (IEA, 2011). The International Energy Agency suggest that approximately 11.3% of the global electricity demand could be met by Concentrated Solar Power (CSP) by 2050 (Pramanik et al., 2017). However, the U.S. Department of Energy released a target for concentrated solar power (CSP) cycles to be more than 50% efficient by 2030 to reduce the levelized cost of energy (LCOE) to 5¢/kWh (SETO, 2018).

Concentrated solar power technology which integrates Thermal Energy Storage (TES) materials is seen as the way forward to solving the current problem of solar energy discontinuity. Thermal energy storage materials have the ability to store heat and thus enable power production in the absence of sunlight, at night or in poor weather conditions (Fernández et al., 2014). An example of TES material used currently to store energy is a binary molten salt mixture of 60 wt% $NaNO_3$ 40 wt% KNO_3(solar salt) which can currently store energy for up to 15 hours (Today, 2011). However, molten salts present a significant problem in that their use results in a high levelized cost of energy. The use of molten salts as TES materials carries with it high maintenance and operation costs due to a number of reasons: 1) highly corrosive and thus requiring expensive containment materials; 2) Molten salt must be kept heated at approximately 200°C to prevent freezing, thus, solidifying in pipes; 3) high viscosity has a negative impact of pump performance adding to LCOE. Molten salts are also costly materials and have an outlet receiver temperature below 600°C which limits the thermal-to-electric efficiency of the power cycle (Kearney et al., 2003). To overcome the current limitations of CSP technologies, it is necessary to select an alternative TES material as well as a new receiver design improving LCOE and profitability of these plants (Almendros et al., 2018).

Current CSP plants employ conventional receiver technologies that use gas or liquid continuous phase TES or HTF fluid which flow through pipes. However, temperature limitations, corrosion and costly maintenance of conventional TES materials result in high LCOE. This has led researchers to alternative TES material and CSP receiver systems. Such systems being researched include high-temperature particle receivers which use air as the HTF (Clifford et al., 2016). The natural abundance of desert sand is an interesting option for thermal energy storage especially in regions such as the GCC. There are several benefits using desert sand: 1) desert sand is a costless local material which is a key factor to reduce the LCOE of CSP systems (Schlipf et al., 2015); 2) it is a highly stable material, and therefore requires significantly cheaper containment units; 3) the sand is stable above 1000°C, resulting in higher thermal-to-electric efficiency (Ma et al., 2014).

In this study, computational fluid dynamics (CFD) will be used to model the gas/sand two-phase fluid flow in a fluidised bed system. This study will look at maximising the rate of heat transfer from sand to HTF by addressing the following. Selecting the optimum fluidising agent (HTF), based on achieving high heat transfer rates - a comparison between various fluidising agents - Air, Carbon dioxide, Argon, Nitrogen (similar densities to air and most abundant) will be performed in this work. Optimising and identifying the parameters related to the fluidised bed system. Varying the mass flowrate of the HTF to fluidise the particulate material (sand) in the fluidised bed. Air will be used to choose optimum flowrate since all other HTF's selected have similar densities to air. It should be noted that a large difference in HTF density would mean the requirement of a large difference in velocity to produce same mass flowrates for each HTF being tested – a large velocity difference would have a major impact on the fluidisation. Selecting the optimum HTF based on maximum heat transfer values between sand and the HTF.

2. Method

The conceptual design proposed in this work is depicted in Figure 1, where the flow of materials and basic equipment are shown. Figure 2 shows a schematic of the device and preliminary biphasic solid-gas flow results obtained with CFD. The thermal energy storage media (Desert sand) stores the energy from the sun gathered by means of the CSP receiver. The heat exchange between the particulate material and the working fluid (air, carbon dioxide, argon and nitrogen) would take place in the fluidised bed, which constitutes the numerical domain. Finally, the energy stored in the working fluid would be used to produce power in the energy harvesting unit. Further numerical results will be obtained to establish a comparison, in terms of hydrodynamics and heat exchange performance of the use of natural desert sand and a cost assessment to determine the best option for the gas used as the working fluid.

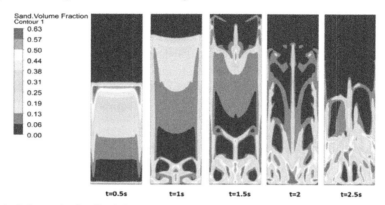

Figure 1. Schematic detail of the geometry and the solid-gas flow obtained using CFD.

The gases air, argon, nitrogen and carbon dioxide were analysed for their heat transfer characteristics to identify the optimum HTF. The four gases were selected as they are abundant in air and have similar densities. Air was used to determine the optimum velocity and thus mass flow rate. The mass flow rate was used to analyse the gases for their heat transfer performance. All the selected gases have a similar density to air, and therefore, the velocity of the gas at inlet was adjusted to keep a constant mass flowrate.

The selected velocity of air was used as a benchmark to achieve greater homogenisation of the two phases, thus reducing the variation of the flow of sand and the outlet temperatures.

This can be observed from the mass flow rate equation below.

$$\dot{m} = \rho \cdot v \cdot A \qquad \text{(Eq. 1)}$$

Where ρ is the density v is the velocity and A is the gas inlet area.

The equation used to calculate the heat transfer from the sand to the HTF is show bellow.

$$Q = \dot{m} \cdot C_P \cdot \Delta T \qquad \text{(Eq. 2)}$$

Where $\dot{m}$ is the mass flow rate, C_P is the specific heat capacity and ΔT is the change in temperature of the gas.

3. Computational Fluid Dynamics model

The Euler-Euler model is selected to treat both phases as interpenetrating continua, introducing the concept of volume fraction α (Sivier et al., 1993). The model includes an additional transport equation for the volume fraction, the value of which varies between 0 (primary phase) and 1 (secondary phase). A computational cell with a value of the volume fraction equal to 1 means, thus, that is entirely occupied by the secondary phase. Therefore, if the volume fraction in a particular computational cell is 0, that means it entirely occupied by the primary phase. Any cell with a volume fraction between 0 and 1 forms the interface. The software solves, thus, n conservation equations, which correspond to the n phases present in the model. The continuity equation for the ith phase is given by

$$\frac{\partial}{\partial t}(\alpha_i \rho_i) + \nabla \cdot (\alpha_i \rho_i \vec{v}_i) = \sum_{j=1}^{n}(\dot{m}_{ij} - \dot{m}_{ji}) + S_i, \qquad \text{(Eq. 3)}$$

where the term $\dot{m}_{ij}$ and $\dot{m}_{ji}$ account for the interphase mass transfer, and S_i is an additional mass source term that can be used to introduce the creation/consumption rate of a given species due to the existence of a chemical reaction. However, since no chemical reaction is taking place S_i is assumed zero.

The equation of the conversation of momentum for the ith phase reads

$$\frac{\partial}{\partial t}(\alpha_i \rho_i \vec{v}_i) + \nabla \cdot (\alpha_i \rho_i \vec{v}_i \vec{v}_i) = -\alpha_i \nabla p + \nabla \cdot \bar{\bar{\tau}}_i + \alpha_i \rho_i \vec{g}_i + \sum_{j=1}^{n-1} \vec{R}_{ij}, \qquad \text{(Eq. 4)}$$

where $\bar{\bar{\tau}}_i$ is the stress-strain tensor, and $\vec{R}_{ij}$ account for any other interaction between the phases. Drag interaction was accounted for by selecting the Syamlal-O'brien model and Gunn model was selected for the heat transfer between the two phases.

4. Results and discussion

The gas mass flow rate passing through the bed was therefore, modified to observe its effect on the fluidisation process, and to optimise the heat capacity of the gas at outlet conditions. The three superficial gas velocities used were $v_g = 1.5$, 1.75 and 2 m·s⁻¹, which was over five to seven times more than the minimum velocity for fluidisation. The velocities correspond to air mass flow rates of $\dot{m}_g = 0.92$, 1.07, and 1.23 kg·s⁻¹ per meter depth of the device, respectively, at $T_g = 300$ K. These three simulations have the same initial height of the packed bed $h_{bed}=0.4$ m. Figure 2a shows plots of the solid volume fraction for the different air inlet velocities after a flow time $t_{flow}= 10$ s. The effect of the gas mass flow rate on the solid distribution within the vessel is clearly shown in Figure 2a, where the greatest value of the mass flow rate gives rise to smaller accumulations of solids along the high of the vessel. The plot also shows greater average values, and therefore, greater accumulations for a mass flow rate of 0.92 kg·s⁻¹ and a less homogenous sand distribution. Figure 2b shows the air velocity profiles along the height of the device, their average value increasing with the air mass flow rate at inlet conditions as expected. The greatest effect of the inlet mass flow rate is observed in the amount of particulate material distributed along the height of the bed, with a mass flow rate of $\dot{m}_g=1.23$ kg·s⁻¹ causing the sand to occupy almost the entirety of the space available. In terms of hydrodynamics therefore, the ideal range of values for the mass flow rate lie between 1.07 and 1.23 kg·s⁻¹.

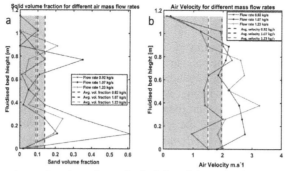

Figure 2. Solid volume fraction along the height of the vessel for all flow rates at flow time $t_{flow}=10$ s (a), the gas phase velocity (b).

Figure 3a indicates that increasing the mass flow rate will slightly decrease the outlet temperature. However, the slightly higher temperature of the lowest mass flow rate is not large enough to produce a higher power output. The power output of the device is defined as the change in enthalpy of the gas stream, which is calculated as the product between the mass flow rate, the specific capacity and the change in temperature between inlet and outlet conditions. Considering the results presented in Figure 3a, one can conclude that the reason for a greater heat capacity in the gas stream is primarily due to the flow rate and the ability of the fluidised bed to effectively transfer heat between the desert sand and the gas phase. This indicates that the proposed fluidised bed can greatly homogenise the two phases allowing the gas phase to have a stable uniform high outlet temperature. As a comparison, Figure 3b shows the transient behaviour of the power output at a constant gas mass flow rate of 1.07 kg·s⁻¹ per meter depth using different gases. Carbon dioxide is the most favourable case, with a maximum power output of 1031 kW found after pseudo-steady fluidisation conditions unfold at flow time $t_{flow}=2$ s. In this instance, with all of the four gases tested matching closely the temperature of the particulate material when exiting the device, and with the gas mass flow rate having been kept constant, the key to obtaining more usable power at outlet conditions lies in the specific heat capacity of the gas phases employed to retrieve the heat stored in the sand. The greatest power output corresponds, therefore, to carbon dioxide, which has a specific heat capacity of $C_p=1.24$ kJ·kg·K at $T_g=1073.15$ K, greater than that of nitrogen ($C_p=1.16$ kJ·kg·K), air ($C_p=1.14$ kJ·kg·K) and argon ($C_p=0.9$ kJ·kg·K).

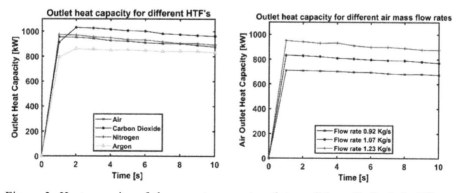

Figure 3. Heat capacity of the gas streams at outlet conditions (Left plot). Effect of different working fluids for the same gas mass flow rate (1.07 Kg/s) (right plot).

5. Conclusions

Desert sand as a particulate material offers high interface area, combined with its capability to withstand temperatures of up to 1000°C without undergoing agglomeration and subsequent degradation, makes it an attractive option to be used in thermal systems. Moreover, desert sand is highly abundant in GCC countries and has suitable thermal properties, which add to its potential as a heat storage medium. With the gas phase attaining the same temperature throughout the vessel regardless of the gas used, the better results must correspond to the gas with the highest specific heat capacity (C_p) provided the mass flow rate is kept constant. This is confirmed in Figure 3, where the highest enthalpy change corresponds to carbon dioxide, followed by nitrogen, air, and argon. From the results included in Figure 3 one can conclude that the present fluidised bed can deliver an increase in enthalpy of air at $\approx$1000 kW, with carbon dioxide offering the best results. The results herein prove the feasibility of desert sand as a suitable material for energy storage, with effective energy transfer towards a working fluid.

References

H.L. Zhang, J. Baeyens, J. Degreve, G. Caceres, 2013, Concentrated solar power plants: Review and design methodology, Renewable and Sustainable Energy Reviews 22:466-481.

IEA (International Energy Agency), Solar Energy Perspectives; 2011.

S. Pramanik and R.V. Ravikrishna, 2017, A review of concentrated solar power hybrid technologies. Applied Thermal Engineering 127, 602–637.

Solar Energy Technologies Office Funding Opportunity Announcement Supporting Research 2018.

A.G. Fernández, S. Ushak, H. Galleguillos, F.J. Pérez, 2014, Development of new molten salts with LiNO3 and Ca(NO3)2 for energy storage in CSP plants, Applied Energy, 119: 131-140.

C. Today, SENER and Torresol Energy win U.S. CSP Today awards, Renew Energy Focus 2011.

Kearney, D., Herrmann, U., Nava, P., Kelly, B., Mahoney, R., Pacheco, J., Cable, R., Potrovitza, N., Blake, D., Price, H., 2003, Assessment of a molten salt heat transfer fluid in a parabolic trough solar field. J. Solar Energy Eng. 125 (2), 170–176.

J.A. Almendros-Ibáñeza, M. Fernández-Torrijos, M. Díaz-Heras, J.F. Belmonte, C. Sobrino, 2018, A review of solar thermal energy storage in beds of particles: Packed and fluidized beds, Solar Energy.

Clifford K. Ho, 2016, A review of high-temperature particle receivers for concentrating solar power, Applied Thermal Engineering 109, 958–969.

D. Schlipf, P. Schicktanz, H. Maier, G. Schneider, 2015, Using sand and other small grained materials as heat storage medium in a packed bed HTTESS. Energy Procedia 69:1029–1038.

Z. Ma, M. Mehos, G. Glatzmaier. B. B. Sakadjian, 2015, Development of a Concentrating Solar Power System Using Fluidized-bed Technology for Thermal Energy Conversion and Solid Particles for Thermal Energy Storage. Energy Procedia 69, 1349 – 1359.

S. Sivier, E. Loth, J. Baum, and R. Löhner, 1993, Eulerian-Eulerian and Eulerian-Lagrangian methods in two phase flow. Editor: Napolitano M., Sabetta F. (eds) Thirteenth International Conference on Numerical Methods in Fluid Dynamics. Lecture Notes in Physics, 414, 473-477.

Sauro Pierucci, Flavio Manenti, Giulia Bozzano, Davide Manca (Eds.)
Proceedings of the 30th European Symposium on Computer Aided Process Engineering
(ESCAPE30), May 24-27, 2020, Milano, Italy. © 2020 Elsevier B.V. All rights reserved.
http://dx.doi.org/10.1016/B978-0-12-823377-1.50060-4

Model of Spray-Drying for Encapsulation of Natural Extracts

Andrea Bassani,[a] * Francesco Rossi,[b] Cecilia Fiorentini,[a] Guillermo D. Garrido,[a] Gintaras V. R. Reklaitis,[b] Irene Bonadies,[c] Giorgia Spigno[a]

[a]Università Cattolica del Sacro Cuore, Department for Sustainbale Food Process (DiSTAS), Via Emilia Parmense 84, 29122 Piacenza, Italy
[b]Purdue University, Forney Hall of Chemical Engineering, 480 Stadium Mall Drive, West Lafayette, IN 47907, United States.
[c]Italian National Research Council CNR, Institute for Polymers, Composites and Biomaterials (IPCB-CNR), Via Campi Flegrei 34, Comprensorio "A. Olivetti", 80078 Pozzuoli (NA), Italy
andrea.bassani@unicatt.it

Abstract

Spray drying unit operation is generally used for separating and drying a solid that cannot be mechanically dried because cannot be exposed to high-temperature atmospheres for long periods. For this reason, spray dryers are related to heat-sensitive products like food or drugs but can be also used for natural extract encapsulation in order to increase their thermal stability. In this work, this last aspect was investigated and a model of co-current spray-drying, was developed and validated. This model is based on mass, energy and momentum balances and take into account of the distribution of the particle size. An experimental campaign was performed using a laboratory scale spray dryer (Büchi Mini Spray Dryer B-290, Switzerland) to validate the model. Maltodextrin and cyclodextrin were used as carrier to encapsulate grape skin and citrus extracts respectively. Different tests were done varying the operating condition of the spray dryer like the inlet air temperature (from 120°C to 180°C) and the mass ratio between carrier and natural extract. Simulation results and experimental data showed a good agreement in terms of mass yield and outlet temperature, while the outlet moisture content show slightly difference e needs to be further investigated.

Keywords: Natural extract, Encapsulation, Spray dryer, Model.

1. Introduction

Spray drying is a technology that has been widely used since '50s in food industry for its economic convenience, flexibility and ease of use. This technology can be also used for coating very small drops of liquid or gas to form microcapsules with an external thin layer of solid (wall material) made from natural polymers (e.g. carbohydrates, proteins, fibers and gums) and the core material inside. In the case of natural extracts, typically containing bioactive compounds material, microencapsulation can give protection from oxidation, light and temperature and, at the same time, a controlled release (Gharsallaoui et al., 2007). For instance, spray-drying encapsulation could be applied to increase thermal stability of natural extracts in order to include them into (bio)plastic film before extrusion (Bassani et al., 2019). The most used technique is the encapsulation of target molecules using polysaccharides like (starch, cellulose, cyclodextrins, pectin and maltodextrin). Encapsulation spray drying process consists of three basic steps: fluid power preparation, homogenization and atomization in the drying chamber. The compounds to be encapsulated should be homogenized together with the material that surround them and then the mixture has to be sent to the spray-drier and atomized through a nozzle. The water is evaporated through the contact of the atomized material with the hot air. The particles obtained have a spherical morphology and a uniform distribution of sizes. However, a limitation of the use of spray-drying is due to the type of coating material, which must necessarily be soluble and so the choice of the coating material is a critical step in the process of encapsulation because it must ensure the stability and the quality of the final product. Another important parameter is also the inlet air temperature, which could deteriorate the encapsulated compound (Georgetti et al., 2008). The aim of this work is to develop and validate a suitable model of co-current spray-drying for natural extract encapsulation with particular reference to grape skin (Spigno et al., 2007) and citrus extract (Bassani et al., 2019). As first, experimental data was collected using a laboratory scale spray dryer and different operating condition was tested. Then the spray dryer model was developed including mass, energy and momentum balances and taking into account of the distribution of the particle size. Finally, the model simulation and the experimental results were compared.

2. Material and Methods

In this section, materials and methods concerning the experimental campaign and the model development are briefly described.

2.1. Natural extract extraction procedure

The extracts used in this study were made with Barbera grapes skin, kindly provided by different wineries from Piemonte (North Italy), while the citrus extracts are a commercial type one. For this reason, only Barbera grape skin needs an extraction procedure. The extraction was made using ethanol-water (60:40 v/v) as solvent with 1:8 (w/v) solid-to-solvent ratio at 60°C (Amendola et al., 2010).

2.2. Production of natural extract encapsulated powders trough Spray-dryer

Spray Drying process was performed with a laboratory scale spray dryer (Büchi Mini Spray Dryer B-290, Switzerland), with a 0.0007 m diameter of the nozzle. The height of the spray is equal to 0.45 m while the diameter is equal to 0.16 m. Compressed and pure air was used to disperse the liquid in fine droplets which was subsequently dried. Samples were introduced into the main chamber through a peristaltic pump. Drying air flow rate was 35 m³/h, while the its temperature varied from 120 °C to 180 °C. The feed flow rate was 4 ml/min, for each experimental trials. One disadvantage of this laboratory spray dryer is related to the angle of exit of the particles from the nozzle (assumed to be equal to 55°). Indeed, during the process, some particles end up against the wall of the spray dryer and so there is a reduction of the global mass yield of the process. For this reason, the following useful index has been defined in order to evaluate the overall yield:

$$Recovery\ yield\ (\%) = \frac{weight\ of\ the\ dried\ powder\ (g)}{Theoretical\ total\ solids\ of\ the\ feed\ (g)} \tag{1}$$

As already mentioned, maltodextrin and cyclodextrin were used as a carrier for grape skin and citrus extracts respectively. Maltodextrin, with dextrose equivalent (DE) value equal to 12, was used in three series of experiments with grape skin extracts. The first tests were done at different inlet air temperatures (120 – 150 – 180 °C) and at a constant molar ratio (dextrose equivalent/ gallic acid equivalent = DE/GAE) equal 2.5. The second tests were done at constant inlet air temperature (150°C) with different DE/GAE (0.3 - 0.6 - 1.3 - 2.5). The third tests were equal to the previous one with the only variation of the inlet air temperature (120°C). On the other hand, cyclodextrin (CD) was used just for one test, which operating condition is: inlet air temperature equal to 120°C, cyclodextrin to citrus extract ratio (CD/CIT, w/w) equal to 0.750 and 97.8% of initial humidity.

2.3. Analysis

Several analysis needs to be done in order to properly characterize both the original and the encapsulated extract. However, for this first study, only the total phenols and the moisture content were evaluated.

2.3.1. Total phenols content (TPC)

Total phenols content were determined with Folin-Ciocalteu assay and with direct reading of the absorbance at 280 nm (Vadivel et al., 2017). In both methods, total phenols were expressed as Gallic Acid Equivalents (GAE) by means of calibration curves with a Gallic acid standard.

2.3.2. Moisture content

The moisture content of the powders was determined weighing 5 g of powders in a pre-weighed ceramic crucible and dried at 105 ± 2 °C for 24 h.

2.4. Spray dying model

In this section, the model equations and the assumption made are shown. Only the main equation and parameters are presented, with the necessary modification, while the clear and in-deep description of the whole set of equations is given by Truong et al (2005).

2.4.1. Momentum balance equation

The droplet trajectory are described by equation (2) and (3), which represent axial and radial trajectory respectively, while the tangential one is neglected due to the mechanical characteristic of the spray dryer. v_p and v_a represent the velocity (m/s) of the particles and air, respectively. The axial distance from the atomizer is h (m).

$$\frac{dv_{px}}{dh} = \frac{\left[\left(1 - \frac{\rho_a}{\rho_p}\right)g - \frac{\frac{3}{4}\rho_a C_D v_R\left(v_{px} - v_{ax}\right)}{\rho_p d_p}\right]}{v_{px}} \tag{2}$$

$$\frac{dv_{pr}}{dh} = \frac{\left[-\frac{\frac{3}{4}\rho_a C_D v_R\left(v_{px} - v_{ax}\right)}{\rho_p d_p}\right]}{v_{px}} \tag{3}$$

Here ρ is the density (kg/m3), d_p is the droplet diameter (m), v_r is the relative velocity between the droplet and the air, and C_D is the drag coefficient.

2.4.2. Mass balance equation

The unsteady-state mass balance for the droplet can be stated as follows:

$$\frac{dm_p}{dh} = -\frac{\xi A_p K_p}{v_{px}}\left(P_{sv} - P_{vb}\right) \tag{4}$$

$$\frac{dY_b}{dh} = \sum_{droplets} \frac{\left(-\frac{dm_p}{dh}\right) n_{droplets}}{G} \tag{5}$$

Where m_p is the mass of the particle or droplet (kg), ξ is the relative drying rate (evaluated as reported by Truong et al (2005)), A_p is the droplet surface area (m^2), Kp is the mass-transfer coefficient (kg/(m*s*Pa), p_{vs} is the partial pressure of the surface of the droplet (Pa) and p_{vb} is the partial pressure of water vapour in the bulk air (Pa). For equation (5), Y is the gas humidity on dry basis, G is the mass flow rate of the dry air (kg/s), and $n_{droplets}$ is the flow rate of droplets (number of particle/s)

2.4.3. Energy balance equation
The unsteady-state heat balance for the droplet or particle is:

$$\frac{dT_p}{dh} = \frac{A_p H(T_g - T_p) + \left(-\frac{dm_p}{dh}\right)\Delta H_{ev}}{m_p c_{p_{mix}} v_{px}} \tag{6}$$

$$\frac{dT_g}{dh} = \sum_{droplets} \frac{A_p H(T_p - T_g) n_{droplets}}{G_{tot} m_p c_{p_{air}} v_{px}} - \frac{U_{glob} D_{spray} \pi (T_g - T_{amb})}{G_{tot} c_{p_{air}}} \tag{7}$$

where, T_p and T_g are the particle and gas temperature [K] respectively, H is the heat convection coefficient (W/(m^2*K)), ΔH_{ev} is the latent heat of water evaporation (J/kg) (Green and Perry, 2003), cp_{mix} is the specific heat capacity of the droplet that is a mixture of water, natural extract and maltodextrin or ciclodextrin. As assumption, cp_{mix} was consider as constant and equal to 4186 (J/(kg*K)). Concerning equation (7), G_{tot} is the total gas flow rate (kg/s), Cp_{air} is the air specific heat, U_{glob} is the global heat transfer coefficient and was assumed equal to 22.2 (W/(m^2*K)), T_{amb} is the ambient temperature, assumed constant and equal to 25°C, and D_{spray} is the diameter of the spray dryer.

2.4.4. Equilibrium moisture content through sorption isotherm
For the relative drying rate (ξ) evaluation it is necessary to evaluate the equilibrium moisture content of the solid. The equilibrium moisture content is a function of the relative humidity of the gas, the temperature of the gas and the nature of the solid and the liquid. The variation of the equilibrium moisture content with relative humidity at a constant temperature is called a sorption isotherm. Sorption isotherms can be correlated by using equations such as the one proposed by Ozmen and Langrish (2003).

$$X_{eq} = A exp\left(-BT ln\left(\frac{1}{\psi}\right)\right) \tag{8}$$

where X_{eq} is the equilibrium moisture content on a dry basis, T is the temperature of the gas (K), and ψ is the relative humidity of the gas. A and B are empirical constants with units and in this study A and B were evaluated as a function of the mass fraction of maltodextrin or cyclodestrix into the dry particle (ω):

$$A = 0.03315 \exp(2.92745\omega) \quad B = -0.00127786 \ln(\omega) - 0.00168899 \tag{9}$$

2.4.5. Droplet size distribution
In this study, the size of the droplets are assumed to follow a log-normal distribution. To define the mean value to be include into log-normal distribution, different equations are available for prediction of droplet size for sprays from two-fluid nozzles. The following one, reported by Green and Perry (2003), was chosen:

$$d_{50} = K_t \rho_a^{-0.325} \left(\frac{m_L}{m_L U_L + m_a U_a}\right)^{0.55} \tag{10}$$

Where d_{50} is the mass median droplet size, K_t is an empirical value equal to 0.008, m_l and m_a are the liquid feed rate and the atomization gas rate respectively, while U_l and U_a are liquid velocity and atomization gas velocity respectively. Knowing d_{50} it is possible to evaluate the mean value of log-normal distribution.

3. Results and Discussions

As first, Barbera extract had a total polyphenol content of 7.44 ± 0.55 GAE/L at 280nm, while with Folin-Ciocalteau assay, the result was 14.61 ± 0.65 GAE/L. this results are obtained through a calibration curve and are important in order to properly evaluate the inlet ratio DE/GAE previously defined. Table 1 shows the principal experimental and simulated results as function of the inlet air temperature and DE/GAE molar ration. The experimental results are reported with the related standard deviation value.

Table 1 Experimental and Simulation results of grape skin natural extract encapsulation

T_{air_in} (°C)	DE/GAE	Recovery (%)		T_{air_out} (°C)		Moisture (%)	
		exp	sim	exp	sim	exp	sim
120	2.5	80.4 ± 2.58	78.52	66 ± 1	71.79	3.48 ± 0.13	6.63
150	2.5	81.7 ± 0.65	78.52	83 ± 2	86.91	3.65 ± 0.23	5.01
180	2.5	80.5 ± 0.50	78.52	97 ± 1	101.17	3.78 ± 0.19	3.85
150	1.3	80.77 ± 8.19	80.71	83 ± 0	86.32	4.17 ± 0.23	4.73
150	0.6	83.96 ± 5.58	81.51	83 ± 0	86.15	5.35 ± 0.14	5.19
150	0.3	78.57 ± 9.75	82.05	83 ± 0	86.10	7.66 ± 0.23	7.11
120	1.3	81.36 ± 3.25	80.71	66 ± 0	71.14	5.43 ± 0.32	5.75
120	0.6	83.45 ± 7.09	81.51	66 ± 0	70.96	5.96 ± 0.26	5.76
120	0.3	80.24 ± 0.73	89.94	66 ± 0	70.89	7.58 ± 0.12	7.00

A good agreement between experimental and simulated data can be highlighted, especially regarding the percentage of the mass recovered and the outlet air temperature. At the same time, there are still slightly discrepancies regarding the outlet moisture content. For this reason, further development the model, for instance removing one of the hypotheses made, and further experimental tests will be necessary. The model was also validated by the residence time of the particles in the spray dryer and by the final distribution of the particles (Figure 1). Indeed, according to the technical manual of the spray dryer, the average residence time of the particles in the spray dryer and in the subsequent cyclone is about 1.0 second, while the average residence time evaluated by the model for spray dryer only is about 0.85 seconds. Concerning the final distribution,

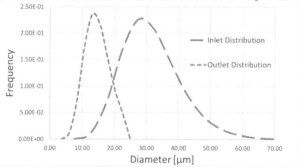

Figure 1 Size distribution of the inlet and outlet particle

Figure 1 reports the initial particle distribution and the final particle distribution. It can be noted that the final distribution is still log-normal and the highest diameter never exceeds the value of about 25 μm. This is in perfect agreement with the technical manual of the spray dryer where it is reported that the final particles have a size between 1 and 25 μm. Moreover, this model was also validated trough the simulation of the citrus extract encapsulation with cyclodextrine. Table 2 shows a good agreement between simulation experimental data. It is important to underline the fact that the commercial citrus extract was solubilized in 0.5% (w/v) solution of NaOH.

Table 2 Experimental and Simulation results of citrus natural extract encapsulation

T_{air_in} (°C)	CD/CIT	Recovery (%)		T_{air_out} (°C)		Moisture (%)	
		exp	*sim*	*exp*	*sim*	*exp*	*sim*
120	0.750	82.34 ± 0.93	89.7	64 ± 0	69.99	5.38 ± 0.03	6.11

4. Conclusions

Spray dryer technology is found to be suitable for natural extracts encapsulation with, with different carriers, such as maltodextrins or cyclodextrins. In this work, a model for natural extract encapsulation was developed and validated at different temperatures and at different ratios between natural extract and carrier. The results show a good agreement in terms of process yield and outlet temperature, while there are still slightly differences in the outlet moisture prediction. For this reason, an in-deep investigation needs to done both in terms of model and in terms of experimental data collection. Moreover, an optimization of the process could be done to obtain, for instance, the inlet temperature or the ratio between carrier and natural extract related to the highest recovery yield.

Acknowledgments

This research was financially European Union's Horizon 2020 Research and Innovation programme under grant agreement No 792261 (NewPack project).

References

D. Amendola, D. M. De Faveri, G. Spigno, 2010, Grape marc phenolics: Extraction kinetics, quality and stability of extracts, Journal of Food Engineering, 97(3), 384-392.

A. Bassani, S. Montes, E. Jubete, J. Palenzuela, A. P. Sanjuan, G. Spigno, 2019, Incorporation of Waste Orange Peels Extracts into PLA Films, Chemical Engineering Transactions, 74, 1063-1068

S. R. Georgetti, R. Casagrande, C. R. F. Souza, W. P. Oliveira, M. J. V. Fonseca, 2008, Spray drying of the soybean extract: effects on chemical properties and antioxidant activity, LWT-Food Science and Technology, 41(8), 1521-1527.

A. Gharsallaoui, G. Roudaut, O. Chambin, A. Voilley, R. Saurel, 2007, Applications of spray-drying in microencapsulation of food ingredients: An overview, Food research international, 40(9), 1107-1121

D. W. Green, R. H. Perry, 2003, Perry's Chemical Engineers' Handbook, 8[Th] edition.

L. T. A. G. Ozmen, T. A. G. Langrish, 2003, A study of the limitations to spray dryer outlet performance, Drying technology, 21(5), 895-917.

G. Spigno, L. Tramelli, D. M. De Faveri, 2007, Effects of extraction time, temperature and solvent on concentration and antioxidant activity of grape marc phenolics, Journal of food engineering, 81(1), 200-208.

V. Truong, B. R. Bhandari, T. Howes, 2005, Optimization of co-current spray drying process of sugar-rich foods. Part I—Moisture and glass transition temperature profile during drying, Journal of Food Engineering, 71(1), 55-65.

V. Vadivel, A. Moncalvo, R. Dordoni, G. Spigno, 2017, Effects of an acid/alkaline treatment on the release of antioxidants and cellulose from different agro-food wastes, Waste Management, 64, 305-314.

Sauro Pierucci, Flavio Manenti, Giulia Bozzano, Davide Manca (Eds.)
Proceedings of the 30th European Symposium on Computer Aided Process Engineering
(ESCAPE30), May 24-27, 2020, Milano, Italy. © 2020 Elsevier B.V. All rights reserved.
http://dx.doi.org/10.1016/B978-0-12-823377-1.50061-6

Modelling and Simulation of Low Pressure Carburizing Furnaces

Fatima Matamoros[a,b,*], Pierre-Alexandre Glaude[a], Roda Bounaceur[a], Hubert Monnier[b], Abderrazak M. Latifi[a]

[a]*Laboratoire Réactions et Génie des Procédés, CNRS-ENISC, Université de Lorraine, Nancy, France*
[b]*Institut National de Recherche et de Sécurité, Vandoeuvre-lès-Nancy, France*
fatima.matamoros-marin@univ-lorraine.fr

Abstract

In this paper, modelling of a low pressure carburizing furnace is developed. Acetylene is chosen as the reactive gas and its pyrolysis, described by a detailed kinetic mechanism is studied in a perfectly stirred tank reactor. Special attention is paid to the fluid-solid interactions; adsorption is described using a Langmuir approach and a first order surface reaction in acetylene is assumed. The diffusion of carbon in the steel is modelled by means of Fick's second law and solved numerically using a finite volume method. All the simulations are performed using MATLAB environment. The numerical results provide the composition of the gas phase in the reactor as well as the spatio-temporal carbon profile in the steel, and are consistent with the experimental observations.

Keywords: Modelling, simulation, carburizing, PAH.

1. Introduction

Low pressure carburizing is a thermochemical process that aims to harden the surface of metals by increasing their carbon concentration. This is done by supplying a carburizing gas in a furnace containing non-treated steel. The process is conducted at pressures far below atmospheric pressure and temperatures within the range of 900°C to 1050°C (Buchholz et al., 2010). At such temperatures however, there is pyrolysis of the reactive gas and this leads to the production of toxic compounds in the form of polycyclic aromatic hydrocarbons (PAHs). This group of organic molecules is harmful to human health and some are considered carcinogenic. The current operating procedure used in carburizing consists of a discontinuous feed of hydrocarbons. Boost stages, where carburizing gas is fed into the reactor and surface reaction takes place, are followed by diffusion stages, where an inert gas is fed into the reactor and only the diffusion of carbon into the metal takes place. The operating conditions (temperature, boost and diffusion times…) are generally determined by trial and error with the sole objective of satisfying the desired carbon profile in the steel. However, the production of toxic compounds is a major issue which has not been extensively investigated, and deserves to be addressed. A mathematical modelling of the different stages of carburizing and a subsequent optimization are therefore necessary to determine the operating conditions that not only guarantee the carbon content in the metal but also minimize the production of PAHs.

The aim of the present work is to propose a modelling of low pressure carburizing process in its entirety. A detailed gas phase mechanism of the pyrolysis of acetylene is coupled to a surface reaction and diffusion model and the numerical modelling of these different stages is described. The results of simulations using the software MATLAB are presented.

2. Model description

Low pressure carburizing process (LPC) consists of three main phenomena, presented in Figure 1. The carburizing gas, in this case acetylene, undergoes pyrolysis and simultaneous external transfer to the surface of the metal where it is adsorbed and decomposes into solid carbon. The latter then joins the crystalline lattice of iron and diffuses into the depth of the steel. Each phenomenon is described as follows.

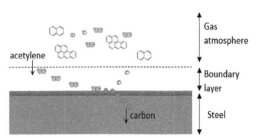

Figure 1: Phenomena occurring during LPC

2.1 Gas phase mechanism of the pyrolysis of acetylene

The mechanism describing the pyrolysis of acetylene selected for this study is the one proposed by Bensabath (2017). It was chosen because it considers the formation of the sixteen PAHs that the U.S. Environmental Protection Agency (EPA) labeled as priority pollutant PAH compounds. The mechanism consists of 1255 reactions and 363 species and some modifications were deemed necessary. First, a reduction of the mechanism carried out to lower its computational cost in view of the optimization; then, the coupling of a soot model to the homogenous reactions. Indeed, it is a consensus in the literature that PAHs are precursors to soot and therefore a soot model would allow to more correctly determine PAH production.

2.1.1. Reduction of the kinetic mechanism

The reduction was carried out with the workbench of the software Chemkin Pro by implementing a skeletal mechanism reduction. This type of reduction consists in eliminating unimportant reactions and species. The skeletal methods used are the Directed Relation Graph with Error Propagation method (DRGEP) and the Full Species Sensitivity Analysis method (FSSA). The description of these methods is not presented in this paper but can be found in Pepiot et al. (2005). The target species and the relative and absolute tolerances R and A respectively used to compute the error E (Eq.(1)) were the required inputs. Target species are the species that the skeletal mechanism should reproduce the most accurately possible when compared to the master mechanism and are represented in our case by the 16 U.S EPA PAHs. For each set j of operating conditions, error E for target species i is:

$$E_i = \frac{|x_{i,master} - x_{i,skeletal}|}{R_i \times |x_{i,master}| + A_i} \tag{1}$$

where x are molar fractions, i represents a target species and j a set of operating conditions. Error E determines whether a skeletal mechanism is acceptable. If it is lower than 1 for all j and i, then the skeletal mechanism is considered satisfactory, otherwise it is not, and another skeletal mechanism is determined. The tolerances were chosen accordingly for each target species in order to obtain the smallest skeletal mechanism possible. The ranges of conditions in which the skeletal mechanism had to be valid were set as [880-1100] °C for temperature and [300-8000] Pa for pressure. The skeletal mechanism obtained consists of 139 species and 444 reactions with the methods applied.

2.1.2. Soot model

The method of moments (MOM) with interpolative closure presented by Frenklach (2002) was deemed the best option to study particle evolution of soot in our case. This choice is based on the low computational cost of MOM compared to other methods as well as the nature of its outputs, i.e. global properties such as the total number of particles, average diameter, etc. Other methods provide more detailed results like the density of each particle class of soot (N_i in Eq. (2)) but this results in a higher computational cost. In our case however, global properties are sufficient because the focus is not on soot itself but its impact on PAHs. The MOM focuses on the determination of the moments of the particle size distribution function (PSDF). The knowledge of all the moments would allow to determine the PSDF itself but only the first few moments are calculated because they are the ones that can be physically interpreted, e.g. the 0th order moment is the total number of particles and the 1st order moment is the total mass of the particles. The rth moment and its derivative are defined as:

$$M_r = \sum_{i=1}^{\infty} m_i^r N_i \tag{2}$$

$$\frac{dM_r}{dt} = \sum_{i=1}^{\infty} m_i{}^r \frac{dN_i}{dt} = \left(\sum_{i=1}^{\infty} m_i{}^r \frac{dN_i}{dt} \right)_{nuc} + \left(\sum_{i=1}^{\infty} m_i{}^r \frac{dN_i}{dt} \right)_{coa} + \left(\sum_{i=1}^{\infty} m_i{}^r \frac{dN_i}{dt} \right)_{sur} \tag{3}$$

where N_i is the number density and m_i is the mass of particles of class (size) i. In order to determine the time evolution of each moment, different phenomena are considered: nucleation, coagulation and surface growth of soot. For each particle class, population balances are developed considering each phenomenon separately. By multiplying by m_i^r and doing the summation for all particle classes, a source term for each phenomenon in terms of moments can be established. The derivative of moment r can then be written as the summation of the source terms (Eq. (3)) (Frenklach, 2002).

2.1.3   Mass balance on gaseous phase species

The mass balance for gas species k in a continuously stirred tank reactor can be written as:

$$\rho V \frac{dY_k}{dt} = \dot{m}_{in}(Y_{kin} - Y_k) + V r_k W_k + V_P s_k W_k - Y_k (\dot{m}_{surf} + \dot{m}_{soot}) \tag{4}$$

where ρ is the mass density of the mixture, V is the volume of the reactor, Y_k is the mass fraction of species k, Y_{kin} is the inlet mass fraction of species k, $\dot{m}_{in}$ is the inlet mass flowrate, r_k and s_k are the molar production rates per unit volume of species k by gas-phase reactions and the heterogeneous reaction respectively, W_k is the molar weight of species k, V_P is the volume of the steel and $\dot{m}_{surf}$ and $\dot{m}_{soot}$ are the total mass production rates of gaseous species by the surface reaction and by soot nucleation respectively. Production of gas species by the surface reaction (s_k and $\dot{m}_{surf}$) are determined from the surface reaction rate, which is developed in the following sections.

2.2   External mass transfer

The film theory is used to model the external mass transfer of acetylene to the surface of the steel. A mass balance on acetylene leads to Eq.(5) and by considering only the flux due to molecular diffusion, Eq.(6) is obtained. At the boundary in contact with the gas phase, (z=0), the concentration of acetylene is taken equal to the acetylene concentration in the reactor. At the boundary in contact with the steel, (z=δ) the flux is assumed equal to the acetylene that is consumed by the heterogeneous reaction per unit area $\dot{m}_{C2H2}$.

$$\frac{\partial[C_2H_2]}{\partial t} + \frac{\partial F_{C_2H_2}}{\partial z} = 0 \tag{5}$$

$$\frac{\partial[C_2H_2]}{\partial t} = D_{C_2H_2}\frac{\partial^2[C_2H_2]}{\partial z^2} \tag{6}$$

$$[C_2H_2]_{z=0} = [C_2H_2]_{PSTR} \tag{7}$$

$$-D_{C2H2}\frac{\partial[C_2H_2]}{\partial z}\bigg|_{z=\delta} = \dot{m}_{C2H2} \tag{8}$$

where $[C_2H_2]$ and $[C_2H_2]_{PSTR}$ are the acetylene concentration in the reactor and the film respectively, F_{C2H2} is the acetylene flowrate per unit area in the film and D_{C2H2} is the diffusion coefficient of acetylene in the mixture.

2.3 Adsorption and surface reaction

Once the acetylene in the gas phase reaches the surface of the solid, it will adsorb and react. Ryzhov et al. (2004) describe its decomposition on the surface of iron as an adsorption phenomenon followed by dissociation with simultaneous chemisorption of the products. Surface reaction is considered irreversible, leading to solid carbon and gaseous hydrogen. This is illustrated by Eq.(9) and (10), where S represents a surface adsorption site. Adsorption, desorption and surface reaction rates are then readily deduced.

$$C_2H_{2(g)} + S \longleftrightarrow C_2H_2^* \tag{9}$$

$$C_2H_2^* + S \longrightarrow 2C^* + H_{2(g)} \tag{10}$$

$$r_{ads} = k_{ads}[C_2H_{2(g)}][S] \tag{11}$$

$$r_{des} = k_{des}[C_2H_2^*] \tag{12}$$

$$r_{surf} = k_{surf}[C_2H_2^*][S] \tag{13}$$

where k_{ads}, k_{des} and k_{surf} are the kinetic constants of adsorption, desorption and surface reaction, $[C_2H_{2(g)}]$ is the concentration of acetylene in the gas phase at the surface of steel and $[C_2H_2^*]$ and $[S]$ are the concentrations of adsorbed acetylene and unoccupied sites at the surface of the steel. By analogy with catalytic reactions, a Langmuir-Hinshelwood-Hougen-Watson methodology is adopted to study the phenomena involved at the surface. One rate limiting step is assumed, in our case this corresponds to the chemical reaction, Eq.(10), and the other step, Eq. (9), is considered at equilibrium. This means that the adsorption rate is taken equal to the desorption rate. The Langmuir constant and fractional surface coverages are defined and conservation of surface sites is applied to determine the surface reaction volumetric rate.

$$r_{surf} = k_{surf} K_{eq} C_{tot}^2 \left(\frac{1 - \theta_C}{1 + K_{eq}[C_2H_2]} \right)^2 [C_2H_2] \tag{14}$$

where K_{eq} is the Langmuir constant, C_{tot} is the total quantity of surface sites in a monolayer per unit volume and θ_C is the fractional surface coverages of carbon. Its value is deduced from the concentration of carbon at the surface of the steel; the assumption is made that any carbon atom at the surface of the steel occupies a free site.

2.4 Carbon diffusion

The diffusion of the carbon resulting from the surface reaction is modelled by means of Fick's second law in one dimension (Eq.15). Only the diffusion of carbon is considered. At the upper boundary ($x=x_0$), the flow of carbon that diffuses from the surface is supposed equal to the amount of carbon produced by the heterogeneous reaction per unit area, $\dot{m}_C$ (Eq.16). At the lower boundary ($x=x_L$) a null flux is imposed (Eq.17). Here C denotes the concentration of carbon in the steel and D is the diffusion coefficient of the carbon in austenite.

$$\frac{\partial C}{\partial t} = \frac{\partial^2 DC}{\partial x^2} \tag{15}$$

$$-D \frac{\partial C}{\partial x} \bigg|_{x=x_0} = \dot{m}_C \tag{16}$$

$$-D \frac{\partial C}{\partial x} \bigg|_{x=x_L} = 0 \tag{17}$$

3. Simulation results

The process model was implemented and solved within MATLAB environment. Only nucleation and coagulation are considered for the soot model and nucleation is taken to be the dimerization of two pyrene molecules. Fick's second law and the boundary conditions are discretized using a finite volume method. Operating temperature, number of cycles, boost and diffusion times, the dimensions of the steel and the diffusion coefficient of carbon in steel are chosen as in the studies by Zajusz et al. (2014) and Kula et al. (2005). There remain however some unknown parameters in the model that are needed to perform the simulations, i.e. K_{eq}, C_{tot} and k_{surf}. The order of magnitude of C_{tot} was determined from the maximum solubility of carbon in austenite at 920 °C and the values of K_{eq} and k_{surf} were chosen in a way to obtain the same orders of magnitude in the results as Zajusz et al. (2014).

Table 1: PAH, soot production and carbon introduced in the steel at T= 920 °C

Total PAH production	Total soot production	Carbon introduced in the steel
$4.2 \cdot 10^{-1}$ g	$1.3 \cdot 10^{-6}$ g	$3.5 \ 10^{-3}$ g

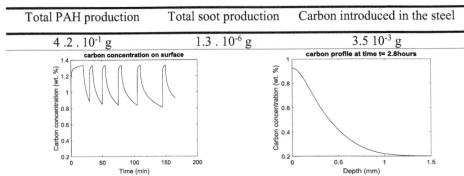

Figure 2: Results from the simulation at T= 920 °C after 6 cycles

Some of the values that will be used for experimental validation such as soot production and the quantity of carbon introduced in the steel are presented in

Table 1. The composition of the gas phase is determined during each cycle and the total mass of PAH that is produced during the process is deduced. The results of carbon profiles are presented in Figure 2 and show that the predictions of the model developed are consistent with the experimental observations. However, some parameters are still to be measured or deduced from the experimental measurements in order to improve the predictions and validate the model. The latter will then be used to optimize the design and operation of the carburizing furnace.

4. Conclusions

In this paper, modelling of low pressure carburizing furnace has been developed and simulated in the MATLAB environment. The model reproduces the correct tendencies and it represents a first step in the optimization objective. The upcoming tasks will focus on the determination of the unknown parameters as well as a refinement of the model. Indeed, the Langmuir isotherm equation assumes equilibrium between the acetylene in the gas phase and the acetylene adsorbed in the solid and it is a starting point for modelling. However, non-equilibrium between the phases will have to be considered before attempting to validate the model from experimental data.

References

D. Buchholz, R.U. Khan, S. Bajohr, R. Reimert, 2010,Computational fluid dynamics modelling of acetylene pyrolysis for vacuum carburizing of steel, Ind. Eng. Chem. Res. 49, 1130-1137.

M. Frenklach, 2002, Method of moments with interpolative closure, Chemical Engineering Science, 57, 2229-2239

M. Zajusz, K. Tkacz-Smiech, M. Danielewski, 2014, Modelling of vacuum pulse carburizing of steel, Surface & Coatings Technology, 258, 646–651.

N. M. Ryzhov, A. E. Smirnov, R.S Fakhurtdinov, L.M Mulyakaev, V.I Gromov, 2004, Special features of vacuum carburizing of heat-resistant steel in acetylene, Metal Science and Heat Treatment, Vol. 46, Nos. 5-6, 230-235.

P. Kula, R. Pietrasik, K. Dybowski, 2005, Vacuum carburizing-process optimization, Journal of Materials Processing Technology 164–165, 876–881

P. Pepiot, H. Pitsch, 2005, Systematic reduction of large chemical mechanisms, 4th Joint Meeting of the US Sections of the Combustion Institute. Vol. 2123

T. Bensabath, 2017, Approche préventive pour une réduction des Hydrocarbures Aromatiques Polycycliques (HAP) dans les fours à pyrolyse, PhD thesis, Université de Loraine, France.

Sauro Pierucci, Flavio Manenti, Giulia Bozzano, Davide Manca (Eds.)
Proceedings of the 30th European Symposium on Computer Aided Process Engineering
(ESCAPE30), May 24-27, 2020, Milano, Italy. © 2020 Elsevier B.V. All rights reserved.
http://dx.doi.org/10.1016/B978-0-12-823377-1.50062-8

Thermodynamic Analysis of Different Methanation Reactors for Biogas Upgrading

Sayed Ebrahim Hashemi[a], Kristian M. Lien[a], Sondre K. Schnell[b], Bjørn Austbø[a,*]

[a]*Department of Energy and Process Engineering, Norwegian University of Science and Technology (NTNU), NO-7491, Trondheim, Norway.*
[b]*Department of Materials Science and Engineering, Norwegian University of Science and Technology (NTNU), NO-7491, Trondheim, Norway.*
bjorn.austbo@ntnu.no

Abstract

Biomethane production from biogas can be increased by methanation of carbon dioxide with hydrogen through the Sabatier reaction. In this work, the performance of the methanation process is investigated under isothermal and adiabatic conditions for different temperature and pressure levels. The processes were modelled assuming equilibrium conditions, minimizing the Gibbs free energy. The results indicate that the exergy of heat removed from the process, and thereby the integration potential, increases with increasing temperature. The internal irreversibility is smaller and the heat integration potential larger for adiabatic reactors than for isothermal reactors.

Keywords: Biogas upgrading, Sabatier reaction, Exergy analysis, Process integration

1. Introduction

The global share of renewable energy in the transportation sector is limited to 3.3 % (REN21, 2019). High quality biomethane in liquid form, with characteristics similar to liquefied natural gas (LNG), is considered to be one alternative to fossil fuels. However, production of LBM requires upgrading biogas whereby undesired contaminants (mainly CO_2) are removed, increasing the CH_4 content of the final product. In conventional approaches, biogas is upgraded through gas separation technologies such as absorption, adsorption, and membrane separation (Kadam and Panwar, 2017). One drawback of conventional biogas upgrading technologies is that the removed CO_2, typically 25−55 mol% of the biogas (Kadam and Panwar, 2017), is emitted to the atmosphere.

Recently, application of the Sabatier reaction for biogas upgrading has gained attention (Witte et al., 2018). Here, CO_2 in the raw biogas reacts with H_2 in order to increase the CH_4 content in the final product. Depending on the CO_2 content in the raw biogas, the biomethane production can increase up to 80 % compared to common biogas upgrading technologies (Witte et al., 2018). As a Power-to-Gas concept, biomethane can be used as an energy carrier for intermittent energy sources, with hydrogen produced from excess electricity (Wang et al., 2018).

The Sabatier reaction is a catalytic reaction that is a linear combination of the CO methanation reaction (Eq. (1)) and the reverse water gas shift reaction (Eq. (2)) (Witte et al., 2018):

$$CO + 3H_2 \ \Box \ \ CH_4 + H_2O \qquad \Delta h^0_{298\,K} = -206.3 \text{ kJ/mol} \qquad (1)$$

$$CO_2 + H_2 \ \Box \ \ CO + H_2O \qquad \Delta h^0_{298\,K} = +41.2 \text{ kJ/mol} \qquad (2)$$

The Sabatier reaction is typically carried out under either isothermal or adiabatic conditions. Gao et al. (2012) conducted a detailed thermodynamic equilibrium analysis for carbon oxides methanation under isothermal conditions through minimization of Gibbs free energy, reporting results in good accordance with experimental data. Jürgensen et al. (2015) considered biogas methanation through the Sabatier reaction under equilibrium and isothermal conditions. They observed that the starting temperature for carbon formation increased with increasing pressure. Moreover, they demonstrated that the CO_2 conversion was highly influenced by the CH_4 content of biogas at pressure levels below 8 bar.

The design of isothermal reactors for the Sabatier reaction is complex and costly. Hence, a series of adiabatic reactors with intercooling is often used in practice (Walspurger et al., 2014). Since heat will be available at different temperature levels for isothermal and adiabatic conditions, the heat integration potential will also be different.

This study aims to evaluate the performance of methanation reactors for biogas upgrading running under isothermal and adiabatic conditions. In addition, potential use of available heat from the reactors is examined through exergy analysis.

2. Methodology

2.1. Model description

Process configurations for isothermal and adiabatic reactors are illustrated in Figure 1. Under isothermal conditions (Figure 1 (a)), the biogas methanation takes place in a single stage reactor at constant temperature, assuming that heat is removed at the reactor temperature. Under adiabatic conditions (Figure 1 (b)), a series of reactors with intercooling is used, and heat will be removed at higher temperature than for the isothermal case. The number of reactors was chosen such that the composition of the final product stream was the same for both designs.

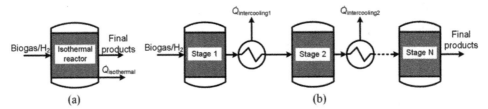

Figure 1. Methanation process configuration for (a) Single stage isothermal reactor (b) Series of adiabatic reactors with intercooling

In this study, it was assumed that equilibrium was reached in all the reactors. The two models were simulated for different temperatures and pressures with Aspen HYSYS® V9.0, using Gibbs reactors and Soave-Redlich-Kwong (SRK) equation of state. The advantage of using Gibbs reactors is that the final equilibrium composition is determined in accordance with the minimum Gibbs energy of the system without considering the equilibrium constants of the involving reactions. However, the Gibbs reactors do not provide information regarding kinetics or size of the reactors. The pressure drops within reactors and intercoolers were assumed negligible.

In order to make a reasonable comparison between isothermal and adiabatic conditions, it was assumed that the temperature after each intercooler was equal to the temperature of the feed stream, except for the last reactor, where the inlet temperature was manipulated in order to obtain the same final product as for the isothermal reactor.

The temperature of the isothermal reactor was assumed to be 10 °C above the feed stream temperature (Wang et al., 2018). The feed stream contained biogas (a mixture of

60 mol% CH_4 and 40 mol% CO_2) with a molar flow rate of 1 kmol/h, and H_2 with a flow rate four times as large the flow rate of CO_2 (stoichiometric ratio).

First, the performance of the Sabatier reaction was examined in terms of CO_2 conversion (Eq. (3)) and CH_4 yield (Eq. (4)), comparing the single stage isothermal reactor with the first stage of the adiabatic reactors:

$$X_{CO_2} = \frac{\dot{n}_{CO_2,in} - \dot{n}_{CO_2,out}}{\dot{n}_{CO_2,in}}, \tag{3}$$

$$Y_{CH_4} = \frac{\dot{n}_{CH_4,out} - \dot{n}_{CH_4,in}}{\dot{n}_{CO_2,in}}. \tag{4}$$

Here, $\dot{n}$ denotes the molar flow rate.

Second, potential use of available heat from the methanation reactors was assessed through exergy analysis, comparing the single stage isothermal reactor and the complete series of adiabatic reactors with intercooling. The exergy of material streams was calculated in accordance with the methodology described by Kotas (2012), implemented as in the work by Hashemi et al. (2019). At steady state operation, the irreversibility rate within the system can be expressed as

$$\dot{I} = \dot{E}_{x,in} - \dot{E}_{x,out} + \dot{E}_x^Q, \tag{5}$$

where $\dot{E}_{x,in}$ and $\dot{E}_{x,out}$ denotes the exergy of inlet and outlet material streams, respectively. The exergy of heat is given as

$$\dot{E}_x^Q = \dot{Q} \cdot (1 - \frac{T_0}{T}), \tag{6}$$

where $\dot{Q}$ is the amount of heat supplied (negative if removed), T_0 the ambient temperature (assumed to be 25 °C) and T the temperature at which the heat is transferred. For the intercoolers, the exergy of the heat removed is equal to the difference in exergy for the inlet and outlet material streams.

Unlike the internal irreversibilities within the methanation reactors, the exergy of the heat produced in the reactors can potentially be utilized. However, if the generated heat is not utilized, the total exergy loss in the system can be expressed as

$$\dot{E}_x^{loss} = \dot{I} - \dot{E}_x^Q \tag{7}$$

In the present study, the use of availabe heat was investigated only for temperatures at which the methanation reaction occurres.

3. Results and discussion

3.1. Isothermal vs. adiabatic (conversion performance)

Figure 2 illustrates the effects of temperature and pressure on CO_2 conversion and CH_4 yield for the isothermal reactor and the first stage of the adiabatic reactors. The CO_2 conversion is higher for the isothermal reactor than for the first stage of the adiabatic reactors. The CO_2 conversion decreases with increasing temperature, and is higher at higher pressure.

As can be seen from Figure 2, an increase in temperature reduces the CH_4 yield, while the CH_4 yield increases at higher pressure under both isothermal and adiabatic conditions. The changes in CO_2 conversion and CH_4 yield with temperature and pressure are smaller for the first stage of the adiabatic reactors than for the isothermal reactor.

The results demonstrate that optimal CO_2 conversion and CH_4 yield are obtained at lower temperature and higher pressure, which is in accordance with Le Chatelier's principle.

While the Sabatier reacion is limited by the chemical equilibrium at high temperature, it is limited by reaction kinetics at low temperature (depending on the type and quantity of the catalyst) (Wang et al., 2018). Hence, an operating temperature below 200 °C is not favorable. Moreover, the optimal operating pressure for the Sabatier reaction depends on the application of the produced CH_4 and a trade-off between extra compression work and improvements in the CO_2 conversion.

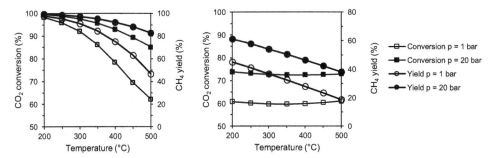

Figure 2. CO_2 conversion and CH_4 yield as functions of temperature and pressure within isothermal reactor (left) and the first stage of adiabatic reactors (right)

3.2. Isothermal vs. adiabatic (potential use of available heat)

Figure 3 demonstrates the effects of temperature and pressure on the amount of heat supplied to the isothermal reactor. The negative values illustrate exothermic reactions, where heat is removed from the reactor. The amount of heat supplied to the single stage isothermal reactor and the series of adiabatic reactors is equal since the feed and product streams are identical. The higher the pressure, the larger the heat removal from the reactor. As can be seen from Figure 3, increasing the inlet temperature reduces the heat generated within the reactor until the point at which the reaction becomes endothermic. This means that the reverse water gas shift reaction (Eq. (2)) dominates the overall reaction, producing more CO and less CH_4.

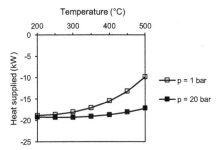

Figure 3. Heat supplied for isothermal reactor

The number of stages required under adiabatic conditions (see Figure 1 (b)) is indicated in Figure 4. The number of required stages increases with increasing feed stream temperature, while it reduces with increasing pressure.

Results from the exergy analysis for the two reactor models are given in Table 1. Since the inlet and outlet streams are the same, the total exergy loss is the same for both rector models if the heat from the processes is not utilized. However, under adiabatic conditions, the internal irreversibility rate is smaller and the exergy content of the heat is higher (due to higher temperature). Moreover, operating the methanation reactors at lower pressure and higher temperature results in lower exergy loss within the reactors. The maximum exergy of heat at fixed pressure is achieved at lower temperature for the methanation reactors running under adiabatic conditions.

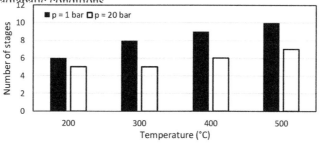

Figure 4. Required stages for adiabatic conditions as a function of temperature and pressure

As can be noticed, favourable pressure and temperature for higher CH_4 yield contradicts the reduction in the irreversibilities within the reactors. Hence, for system level process integration, the CH_4 yield must be weighed against the irreversibilities when determining the operating temperature and pressure.

Table 1 demonstrates that running the Sabatier reaction within the series of adiabatic reactors leads to the larger amounts of exergy of heat and lower irreversibilities within reactors at given temperature and pressure. This suggests that a series of adiabatic reactors could provide improved process integration potential compared to an isothermal reactor.

Table 1. Results from the exergy analysis for isothermal and adiabatic reactors

	Isothermal							
	$p = 1$ bar				$p = 20$ bar			
Temp. (°C)	$\dot{n}_{CH_4,out}$ (kg/h)	$\dot{I}$	$\dot{E}_x^Q$	$\dot{E}_x^{loss}$	$\dot{n}_{CH_4,out}$ (kg/h)	$\dot{I}$	$\dot{E}_x^Q$	$\dot{E}_x^{loss}$
		(kWh/kg CH4)				(kWh/kg CH4)		
200	15.9	0.28	-0.45	0.73	16.0	0.38	-0.46	0.84
300	15.5	0.16	-0.56	0.72	15.9	0.26	-0.59	0.84
400	14.5	0.09	-0.58	0.66	15.5	0.17	-0.67	0.84
500	12.6	0.05	-0.43	0.47	14.9	0.11	-0.69	0.80
	Adiabatic							
200	15.9	0.16	-0.57	0.73	16.0	0.21	-0.63	0.84
300	15.5	0.10	-0.62	0.72	15.9	0.15	-0.69	0.84
400	14.5	0.06	-0.60	0.66	15.5	0.11	-0.73	0.84
500	12.6	0.04	-0.43	0.47	14.9	0.08	-0.72	0.80

In order to complete the present analysis with respect to the potential use of available heat, consideration of reaction kinetics is essential, as the performance of the reactor is highly dependent on the catalyst and operating temperature.

From a practical point of view, the application of the Sabatier reaction for biogas upgrading depends on the availability of hydrogen, because the production of hydrogen is a major cost driving factor. Besides, the temperature and pressure within the reactors influence the amount of unreacted hydrogen. In this sense, operating with less hydrogen than the stoichiometric amount and operating the series of adiabatic reactors, which improves the usable exergy of heat, might benefit the economy of the overall process. However, further studies must be conducted to determine the appropriate ratio between H_2 and CO_2.

4. Conclusions

Biogas upgrading through the Sabatier reaction was examined for a single stage isothermal reactor and a series of adiabatic reactors with intercooling, with respect to conversion of CO_2 to CH_4 and the potential use of available heat from the reactors. The reactor models were simulated in Aspen HYSYS® V9.0 using Gibbs reactors. The use of available heat was evaluated by exergy analysis.

The results indicate that the performance of the single stage isothermal reactor is better than the first stage of adiabatic reactors in terms of CH_4 yield. In order to achieve the isothermal performance, a series of adiabatic reactor with intercooling is required.

On the one hand, operating the methanation reactors at higher pressure and lower temperature leads to greater CO_2 conversion and CH_4 yield. On the other hand, the total exergy loss decreases with decreasing pressure and increasing temperature. The number of adiabatic reactors required to reach the same product conditions as for the isothermal reactor increases with increasing temperature and decreasing pressure. Ideally, the internal irreversibilities would be minimized and the heat integration potential maximized if the Sabatier reaction was carried out in stages at gradually reducing temperature, keeping the process close to equilibrium all the way. The heat integration potential must, however, be balanced against reaction kinetics and equipment size.

Acknowledgments

Financial support from the Norwegian University of Science and Technology (NTNU) through the strategic research program ENERSENSE is greatly acknowledged.

References

J. Gao, Y. Wang, Y. Ping, D. Hu, G. Xu, F. Gu, F. Su, 2012, A thermodynamic analysis of methanation reactions of carbon oxides for the production of synthetic natural gas, RSC Advances, 2, 6, 2358-2368.

S.E. Hashemi, K.M. Lien, S.K. Schnell, B. Austbø, 2019, Optimization of an Absorption-Based Biogas Upgrading and Liquefaction Process, Chemical Engineering Transactions, 76, 697-702.

R. Kadam, N.L. Panwar, 2017, Recent advancement in biogas enrichment and its applications, Renewable and Sustainable Energy Reviews, 73, 892-903.

T.J. Kotas, 2012, The Exergy Method of Thermal Plant Analysis, Exergon Publishing Company, London, UK.

L. Jürgensen, E.A. Ehimen, J. Born, J.B. Holm-Nielsen, 2015, Dynamic biogas upgrading based on the Sabatier process: Thermodynamic and dynamic process simulation, Bioresource Technology, 178, 323-329.

REN21, 2019, Renewables 2019 Global Status Report, Renewables Energy Policy Network for 21st Century, accessed 14.11.2019.

S. Walspurger, G.D. Elzinga, J.W. Dijkstra, M. Sarić, W.G. Haije, 2014, Sorption enhanced methanation for substitute natural gas production: Experimental results and thermodynamic considerations, Chemical Engineering Journal, 242, 379-386.

L. Wang, M. Pérez-Fortes, H. Madi, S. Diethelm, J.V. Herle, F. Maréchal, 2018, Optimal design of solid-oxide electrolyzer based power-to-methane systems: A comprehensive comparison between steam electrolysis and co-electrolysis, Applied Energy, 211, 1060-1079.

J. Witte, J. Settino, S.M.A. Biollaz, T.J. Schildhauer, 2018, Direct catalytic methanation of biogas – Part I: New insights into biomethane production using rate-based modelling and detailed process analysis, Energy Conversion and Management, 171, 750-768.

Sauro Pierucci, Flavio Manenti, Giulia Bozzano, Davide Manca (Eds.)
Proceedings of the 30th European Symposium on Computer Aided Process Engineering
(ESCAPE30), May 24-27, 2020, Milano, Italy. © 2020 Elsevier B.V. All rights reserved.
http://dx.doi.org/10.1016/B978-0-12-823377-1.50063-X

Optimisation of Energy Consumption in a Medium-scale Reverse Osmosis Brackish Water Desalination Plant

Alanood A. Alsarayreh [a], M. A. Al-Obaidi [b], A. M. Al-Hroub [c], R. Patel [a],
I. M. Mujtaba [a]

[a] Department of Chemical of Engineering, Faculty of Engineering and Informatics.
University of Bradford.Bradford, West Yorkshire, BD7 1DP, UK
[b] Middle Technical University, Technical Institute of Baquba, Dayala – Iraq
[c] Senior Chemical Engineer, Energy and Water Directorate, Arab Potash Company,
Jordan
I.M.Mujtaba@bradford.ac.uk

Abstract

The Reverse Osmosis (RO) process has been universally employed for the production of potable water from brackish water resources. However, the RO process still operates at an elevated level of an energy consumption, in kWh per m^3 of product water, due to the use of high-pressure pumps. In this study, an earlier steady-state operation model developed by the same authors for a medium-scale RO brackish water desalination system of Arab Potash Company (APC) (Jordan) is embedded within an optimisation framework. Typically, the optimisation problem is expressed as a Nonlinear Programming problem to attain the lowest specific energy consumption (objective function), as well as optimising the decision variables of operating flow rate and pressure for a given feed concentration and temperature. Moreover, the optimisation problem has been associated with upper and lower limits of decision variables as characterised by the membrane manufacturer. Also, to quantify the high-standards of filtration process, feasible constraints of the pressure loss along the x-axis of membrane length and upper and lower bound of feed flow rate of each membrane are considered. Interestingly, detailed optimisation results have conceived the optimal operating conditions that have the potential to gain net energy saving of RO system by 35%, whilst fulfilling the need for producing high-quality water. This research has economically upgraded the RO system of APC with a substantial improvement of process performance.

Keywords: Brackish water desalination; Arab Potash Company; Reverse Osmosis process; Optimisation; Energy consumption.

1. Introduction

Fresh water is becoming rare in some regions of the world that associated with progressive people worldwide demands due to increase of population growth and change of their lifestyle. Therefore, several desalination processes were invented. In this regard, the desalination of brackish water offers a feasible solution to tackle the water shortage.

Membrane technology has been used very effectively to produce fresh water from different resources of water (Tsiourtis, 2001). Specifically, RO process is a pressure-driven process and considered as one of the commercially attractive membrane technology available for desalting brackish and seawater (Peñate and García-Rodríguez, 2012). The RO membrane has the ability to differentiate and selectively separate salts and water based on the operating conditions such as feed salinity, applied pressure, flow rate and temperature (Tsiourtis 2001). Simple design of RO process and high quality of water produced are the main reasons why it is widely accepted throughout the world compared to, for example, thermal desalination processes. However, the RO process consumes a considerable amount of energy that needs to be reduced considerably. Therefore, several studies have been carried out to minimise the specific energy consumption or the production cost, which in turn make this process more affordable. In this regard, the optimisation of the RO system has been successfully used to mitigate the energy consumption. For this, the RO process market has seen a steady increase due to a primitive advancement in RO operation that is associated with a lower energy consumption and reduced fresh water production cost (Shenvi et al., 2015). Some comments on the most successful research are reported below.

Zhu et al. (2008) minimised the energy consumption of RO membrane process via constraining the thermodynamic cross flow and feed or permeate flow rate. Results showed that lowering of osmotic pressure would limit the energy consumption The optimisation of energy consumption of two-pass RO seawater desalination unit and a single pass membrane desalination unit, by considering the goal of product recovery and salt rejection, was investigated by Zhu et al. (2009). This in turn affirmed the optimal operational conditions to lowering the energy consumption. Their studies showed that the two-pass process performs better than the single-pass RO one. Bartman et al. (2010) used an energy optimisation methodology of multiple RO system variables to estimate the optimal operating conditions that minimise the specific energy consumption. The results showed that increasing water recovery would lower the energy consumption with reduced salt rejection. Li (2010) implemented a constrained nonlinear optimisation to minimise the total energy consumption of single-stage, two-stage, and single-stage RO modules with an energy recovery device (ERD). The results showed that the two-stage module is better than one stage based on specific energy consumption and water recovery. To the best of the authors' knowledge, the lowering of the total energy consumption of RO system of APC via optimisation cannot be found in the open literature. Therefore, the current research attempts to optimise the decision variables of feed pressure and flow rate for a considered feed concentration 1098.62 ppm and temperature 25 °C to explore the lowest energy consumption.

2. Plant description and feed characteristics

Figure 1 shows the layout of BWRO (Brackish Water Reverse Osmosis) for the APC plant (with capacity 1200 m³/day and conductivity 1983.06 μs/cm). It consists of two passes with permeate and retentate reprocessing designs. The 1st pass comprises two stages with pressure vessels design (4:2). However, the 2nd pass holds two stages with pressure vessel design (2:1:1) as a sequence. The permeate of 1st pass is fed to the 2nd pass for further processing. The high-concentration stream of the 1st pass is sent to drain. However, the low-concentration streams of the 2nd pass are collected to constitute the high-quality water (salinity 2 ppm). The high-concentration stream of 2nd pass is reprocessed back to the raw feed water of the 1st pass. The feed characteristics of RO plant are 1098.62 ppm, 74 m³/h, 25 °C, and 9.22 atm of feed water salinity, flow rate, temperature, and pressure, respectively. Table 1 gives the specification of RO module.

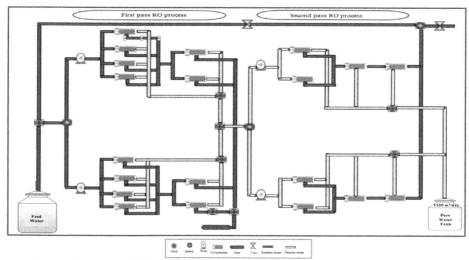

Figure1. Layout of BWRO desalination plant of APC (Adapted from Al-Obaidi et al., 2018)

Table 1. Specifications of Ro module of APC plant.

Parameter	Value
Membrane provider, brand and configuration	Toray Membrane USA Inc, TMG20D-400, spiral wound
Membrane area A (m²)	37.2
Water permeability constant (A_w) (m/atm s) at 25 °C	9.6203×10^{-7}
Salt permeability constant (B_s) (m/s) at 25 °C	1.61277×10^{-7}
Pump efficiency (η)	85%
Max. operating pressure (atm)	40.464
Max. operating temperature (°C)	45
Salt rejection (%)	99.5
Max. and Min. feed flow rate (m³/s)	0.001-0.005

3. Modelling of RO system of APC

Al-Obaidi et al. (2018) established a steady-state operation model for a medium-scale BWRO desalination system of APC. The detailed model was validated against actual data collected from the APC and then used to study the plant performance with operating conditions variation. However, this model is modified by including energy consumption correlations as shown in Table A.1 of Appendix. A.

4. Simulation of RO system of APC plant

The simulation of the specified RO plant is achieved under the base operating conditions and using the gPROMS suites. The performance indicators results are given in Table 2.

5. Optimisation of the RO system of APC plant

5.1 Problem construction

The main goal of this section is to optimise the RO system of APC, i.e., to target the objective function of minimising the specific energy consumption by forecasting the best-operating conditions (optimal values) of the process which include feed flow rate and feed operating pressure at fixed temperature and concentration. Therefore, the model of RO system is incorporated in a single optimization framework as a Non-Linear Programming (NLP) Problem with consideration of varying operating conditions within upper and lower limits which recommended by the module's manufacturer. The fixed feed water characteristics of 988.93 ppm and 25 °C of feed water salinity and temperature respectively, are considered.

5.2 Mathematical optimisation problem

Given: Feed water conditions, RO module specifications.
Optimise: The optimisation variables of feed pressure, and flow rate.
Minimise: The total energy consumption of RO system.
Subject to: Equality and inequality constraints of process model and limits of optimisation variables, respectively.
Hence, the optimisation problem is mathematically fashioned as;

$$\text{Min} \qquad\qquad E_{consumption}$$
$$Q_{f(plant)}, P_{p(plant)},$$

Subject to: Equality constraints: RO process model
              Inequality constraints:
a) lower and upper limits of feed flow rate of RO system

$$(29.04 \, \text{m}^3/\text{h}) \quad Q_{f(plant)}{}^{L} \leq Q_{f(plant)} \leq Q_{f(plant)}{}^{U} \ (154.48 \, \text{m}^3/\text{h})$$
$$(5 \, \text{atm}) \ P_{f(plant)}{}^{L} \leq P_{f(plant)} \leq P_{f(plant)}{}^{U} \ (20 \, \text{atm})$$

b) lower and upper limits of feed flow rate of each membrane module

$$(3.63 \, \text{m}^3/\text{h}) \quad Q_{f(membrane)}{}^{L} \leq Q_{f(membrane)} \leq Q_{f(membrane)}{}^{U} \ (19.31 \, \text{m}^3/\text{h})$$

5.3 Optimisation results

Table 2 displays the simulation values as the base case (not optimised) of the RO process at given feed operating (salinity and temperature). Also, the optimisation results including the performance indicators are presented in Table 2. The ratio of energy-saving of RO system is accounted by subtraction of simulated and optimised values. It can be clearly seen that the optimisation framework has entailed a gain of energy saving of 35% based on the optimum feed flow rate of 0.0171 m³/s and pressure of 7.5743 atm. Moreover, there is a considerable enhancement of water recovery (12.8 %), which contributes to improving the produced water concentration by 15.6 %. Furthermore, the produced water flow rate is enhanced by 130 % whilst at the same time reducing the retentate flow rate by 50%.

Table 2. Simulation and optimisation results at base case operating conditions (988.93 ppm and 25 °C).

Feed conditions			Optimised feed conditions	
Parameter	Value	Unit	Parameter	Value
Plant feed pressure	9.2202	atm	Optimal operating pressure	7.5743
Plant feed flow rate	0.0235	m³/s	Optimal feed flow rate	0.0171
Feed operating salinity	988.93	ppm	Feed operating salinity	988.93
Feed operating temperature	25	°C	Feed operating temperature	25
Simulation results			Optimised results	
Plant water recovery	57.205	%	Plant water recovery	64.545
Plant salt rejection	99.797	%	Plant salt rejection	99.922
Produced water flow rate	0.0135	m³/s	Produced water flow rate	0.03105
Produced water concentration	2.0052	ppm	Produced water concentration	1.7345
Retentate flow rate	0.0032	m³/s	Retentate flow rate	0.0016
Specific energy consumption	0.9977	kWh/m³	Specific energy consumption	0.6478
Energy-saving = 35%				

6 Conclusions

In this research, a single optimisation framework was developed to mitigate the total energy consumption of a medium-scale RO brackish water desalination system of APC. This is basically carried out within allowed operational limits of the operating conditions to maintain a safe process. In general, the manipulation of control variables via optimization has a positive influence on reducing the energy consumption by 35% when compared with the original simulation value of consumed energy. Also, the product water salinity has been enhanced by 15.6% to fulfill the requirements of high-quality water.

References

Al-Obaidi M.A., Alsarayreh A.A., Al-Hroub A.M., Alsadaie S., Mujtaba I.M., 2018. Performance analysis of a medium-sized industrial reverse osmosis brackish water desalination plant. Desalination, 443, 272-284.

Bartman A.R., Zhu A., Christofides P.D., Cohen Y., 2010. Minimizing energy consumption in reverse osmosis membrane desalination using optimization-based control. Journal of Process Control, 20 (10), 1261-1269.

Li M., 2010. Minimization of energy in reverse osmosis water desalination using constrained nonlinear optimization. Industrial & Engineering Chemistry Research, 49(4), 1822-1831.

Peñate B., García-Rodríguez L., 2012. Current trends and future prospects in the design of seawater reverse osmosis desalination technology. Desalination, 284, 1-8.

Shenvi S.S., Isloor A.M., Ismail A.F., 2015. A review on RO membrane technology: Developments and challenges. Desalination, 368, 10-26.

Tsiourtis N.X., 2001. Desalination and the environment. Desalination, 141(3), 223-236.

Zhu A., Christofides P.D., Cohen Y., 2008. Effect of thermodynamic restriction on energy cost optimization of RO membrane water desalination. Industrial and Engineering Chemistry Research, 48(13), 6010-6021.

Zhu A., Christofides P.D., Cohen, Y., 2009. Minimization of energy consumption for a two-pass membrane desalination: effect of energy recovery, membrane rejection and retentate recycling. Journal of Membrane Science, 339(1-2), 126-137.

APPENDIX A

Table. A.1. Mathematical model of RO system of APC

No.	Model equation	Specifications
1	$Q_p = A_{w(T)} NDP_{fb} A_m$	Total water flux (m³/s)
2	$A_{w(T)} = A_{w(25\ C)} TCF_p F_f$	Water permeability constant at 25 °C (m/s atm)
3	$TCF_p = \exp[0.0343\ (T - 25)]$ < 25 °C $TCF_p = \exp[0.0307\ (T - 25)]$ > 25 °C	Temperature correction factor of permeate
4	$NDP_{fb} = P_{fb} - P_p - \pi_b + \pi_p$	The driving pressure (atm)
5	$P_{fb} = P_f - \frac{\Delta P_{drop,E}}{2}$	The feed brine pressure (atm)
6	$\Delta P_{drop,E} = \frac{9.8692x10^{-6}\ A^* \rho_b\ U_b^2\ L}{2d_h\ Re_b^n}$	The pressure drop along the membrane element (atm)
7	$\pi_b = 0.7994\ C_b\ [1 + 0.003\ (T - 25)]$ $\pi_p = 0.7994\ C_p\ [1 + 0.003\ (T - 25)]$	The bulk and permeate osmotic pressure (atm)
8	$C_b = \frac{C_f + C_r}{2}$	The bulk salinity (kg/m³)
9	$Q_s = B_{s(T)}(C_w - C_p)$	The solute flux through the membrane (kg/m² s)
10	$B_{s(T)} = B_{s(25\ C)} TCF_s$	The solute transport parameter at operating temperature (m/s)
11	$C_w = C_p + \left(\frac{C_f + C_r}{2} - C_p\right) exp\left(\frac{Q_p/A_m}{k}\right)$	The concentration at the membrane surface (kg/m³)
12	$k = 0.664\ k_{dc}\ Re_b^{0.5}\ Sc^{0.33}\left(\frac{D_b}{d_h}\right)\left(\frac{2d_h}{L_f}\right)^{0.5}$	Mass transfer coefficient (dimensionless)
13	$Sc = \frac{\mu_b}{\rho_b\ D_b}$	Schmidt number (dimensionless)
14	$Re = \frac{\rho\ d_e J_w}{\mu}$	Reynolds number (dimensionless)
15	$Rec = \frac{Q_p}{Q_f} = \frac{(C_r - C_f)}{(C_r - C_p)}$	Total recovery (dimensionless)
16	$Rej = \frac{C_f - C_p}{C_f}$	Observed rejection (dimensionless)
17	$J_w = \frac{B_{s(T)}\ Rej_{real}}{(1 - Rej)}$	The water flux (m/s)
18	$C_p = \frac{C_f}{Rec}\ [1 - (1 - Rec)]^{(1-Rej)}$	The average permeate salinity at the permeate channel (kg/m³)
19	$C_r = C_f\ [1 - Rec]^{-Rej}$	The average retentate salinity at the permeate channel (kg/m³)
20	$E1 = \frac{\frac{Pf_{(in)(plant)}*101325*Qf_{(Raw\ water)}}{Qp_{(plant)}*\varepsilon\ punp}}{36x10^5} + \frac{\frac{Pf_{(Block\ 3)}*101325*Qf_{(Block\ 3)}}{Qp_{(plant)}*\varepsilon\ punp}}{36x10^5}$	The total plant energy consumption (kWh/m³)

Sauro Pierucci, Flavio Manenti, Giulia Bozzano, Davide Manca (Eds.)
Proceedings of the 30th European Symposium on Computer Aided Process Engineering
(ESCAPE30), May 24-27, 2020, Milano, Italy. © 2020 Elsevier B.V. All rights reserved.
http://dx.doi.org/10.1016/B978-0-12-823377-1.50064-1

Minimisation of Energy Consumption via Optimisation of a Simple Hybrid System of Multi Effect Distillation and Permeate Reprocessing Reverse Osmosis Processes for Seawater Desalination

O. M. A. Al-hotmani [a], M. A. Al-Obaidi [b], Y. M. John [a], R. Patel [a], F. Manenti [c], I. M. Mujtaba [a],*

[a] Department of Chemical Engineering, Faculty of Engineering and Informatics.
  University of Bradford. Bradford, West Yorkshire BD7 1DP, UK
[b] Middle Technical University, Technical Institute of Baquba, Baquba, Dayala - Iraq
[c] Chemical Engineering Department, Politecnico di Milano, Milan, Italy
I.M.Mujtaba@bradford.ac.uk

Abstract

Multi Effect Distillation (MED) and Reverse Osmosis (RO) processes have been expansively explored for fresh water production from seawater resources. Interestingly, the performance indicators including energy consumption of different proposed arrangements of hybrid system of MED and RO processes have been analysed in a previous study by the same authors. This in turn has explored the feasibility of a simple design of permeate reprocessing RO process and MED process of hybrid system that corresponding the lowest energy consumption compared to other experienced arrangements of hybrid system. However, this design still operated at a significantly high level of energy utilisation measured in kWh per m^3 of produced water. In this research, the lowest possible energy consumption of the chosen hybrid system is investigated via the embedment of an optimisation framework in the same author's previous operation model for the same design. Occasionally, the optimisation problem is framed as a Nonlinear Programming problem to locate the optimal control variables of the associated RO process within their upper and lower limits to achieve the main objective function. This in turn has resulted in mitigating the total energy utilisation of the hybrid system with satisfying a constraint of high-quality produced water.

Keywords: Seawater desalination, Multi Effect Distillation + Reverse Osmosis hybrid system, Permeate processing design of RO, Optimisation, Energy Consumption.

1. Introduction

Due to a continuous growth for water demand in warm areas, seawater desalination technologies have seen a surge in popularity.in providing potable water. In this regard, the MED and RO systems have been nominated as the favorable thermal and membrane processes respectively, due to their stability, high quality and product capacity. Specifically, MED process can produce salt free water from very poor seawater. Moreover, RO process has been utilised for different kinds of water including seawater, brackish water and wastewater with strong potential. Therefore, the integration of MED with a variety of industrial processes such as concentrated solar power cogeneration scheme and RO process has been investigated by some new studies (Cipollina et al., 2017; Filippini et al., 2018). Recently, Filippini et al. (2018) compared the performance of several designs of hybrid system of MED + retentate reprocessing design of RO process via a detailed model developed by the same authors. The performance or effectiveness of the hybrid system was assessed and quietly generated an improved performance compared to individual processes of multi effect distillation - thermal vacuum compressor (MED_TVC) and RO. This is followed by a novel design of a simple hybrid system of permeate reprocessing RO process integrated with MED_TVC process suggested by Al-hotmani et al. (2019). The performance metrics of this design have been compared against other proposed designs of hybrid systems of MED process and retentate reprocessing RO process of Filippini et al. (2018). This in turn has affirmed the suitability of the simple hybrid MED_TVC+ permeate reprocessing design of RO process as a superior layout. Specifically, it is concluded that this layout has attained the lowest energy consumption measured in kWh per m^3 of fresh water when compared to other configurations of hybrid systems. de Boer (2014) confirmed that both the RO and MED processes are the most energy demanding filtration processes because of the use of high-pressure pump and steam generator, respectively. However, it is believed that there is still scope to reduce the total consumption energy of the chosen hybrid design of MED_TVC and permeate reprocessing RO process proposed by Al-hotmani et al. (2019). Therefore, this work intends to solve the problem using the model developed by the same authors for this layout with an optimisation framework. This is specifically targeted at the lowest energy consumption (objective function) at an optimum control variables of the related RO process. Moreover, the optimisation has respected the upper and lower limits of the control variables with training a practical constraint of high-quality produced water.

2. Description of the simple hybrid system and feed characteristics

Figure 1 shows the projected design of a permeate reprocessing RO process integrated with MED_TVC process in a simple hybrid system. The MED system usually contains TVC section as an external steam provider, which in turn give advantages of upgrading the total energy of MED system. In this respect, the feed water is split into two parts to simultaneously feed the RO process and MED process (simple layout). The design of the RO process comprises a high pressure pump and three blocks of twenty, fifteen, and eight pressure vessels joined in parallel with 8 spiral wound modules, made by Toray, and connected in series. Of high importance is the flow rate of feed for all blocks and each module which is restricted to the acceptable limits of feed flow rate specified by the manufacturer. The high-concentration stream of the 1st block is directed to the 2nd block for advanced filtration. However, the 3rd block is used to further polish off the joined permeate streams of 1st and 2nd blocks. In this regard, the 3rd block operates at approximately similar operating pressure of the 1st block using an ERD system of 80% efficiency. This in turn would upgrade the quality of low-salinity water produced from 3rd block. Occasionally, the existence of ERD in the RO system would decrease the total energy consumption compared to RO systems without ERD. The features of produced water including its salinity and quantity are characterised by the combination of product streams of RO process and MED process. Moreover, the retentates of both MED and RO systems are blended to form the main disposed stream. The RO membrane measurements and its lower and upper constraints, water and solute transport

Minimisation of energy consumption via optimisation of a simple hybrid system of 381
multieffect distillation and permeate reprocessing reverse osmosis processes for
seawater desalination

coefficients, and the allowed control variables are given in Table 1. Also, the design parameters of Multi Effect Distillation process are presented in Table 1.

Table 1. Design and technical parameters of RO and MED_TVC processes with the operating conditions

	Parameter	Unit	Value
RO Process	Membrane supplier and brand	(-)	Toray membrane, TM820M-400/ SWRO
	Module configuration	(-)	Spiral wound
	Maximum pressure	(atm)	81.91
	Maximum and minimum feed flow rate	(m³/s)	0.00536 – 0.001
	Maximum temperature	(°C)	45
	Membrane area (A_m)	(m²)	37.2
	A_w and B_s NaCl at 25 °C	(m/s atm) and (m/s)	3.1591×10^{-7} and 1.74934×10^{-8}
	η_{pump}, $\eta_{Booster\ pump}$ and η_{ERD}	(-)	85%, 85% and 80%
MED Process	Number of stages	(-)	10
	External steam temperature / flow rate / pressure	(°C / kg/s / kPa)	70 / 8 / 1300
	Brine temperature / salinity	(°C / ppm)	40 / 6000
	Operating conditions		
	Parameter	Unit	Value
	Feed pressure of RO process	(atm)	50
	Feed flow rate of RO process	(m³/s)	0.058
	Seawater salinity	(ppm)	39000
	Seawater temperature	(°C)	25

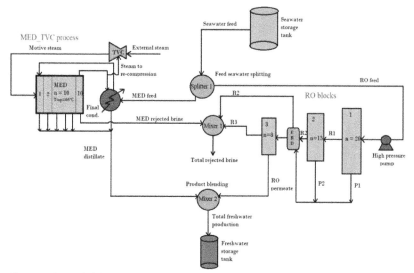

Figure 1. Simple hybrid MED_TVC and permeate reprocessing RO processes (Al-hotmani et al., 2019)

3. Modelling of the hybrid system

Al-hotmani et al. (2019) modified the model developed by Filippini et al. (2018) by incorporating a detailed set of model equations to investigate the performance indicators of permeate reprocessing RO process of the hybrid MED_TVC+RO processes.

The detailed model is included in Table 3 (APPENDIX A). The nonlinear algebraic equations of the hybrid model of MED_TVC+RO processes are tabulated in a compact form $f(x, u, v) = 0$.

4. Simulation of the hybrid system

Al-hotmani et al. (2019) simulated the hybrid system shown in Fig. 1 under the control variables of both processes (shown in Table 1). This in turn has obtained the performance results as shown in Table 2.

5. Optimisation of the hybrid system

This section aims to optimise the hybrid system shown in Fig. 1 in such a way as to minimise the total energy consumption (objective function) measured in kWh per m³ of the produced water by predicting the best control variables of the RO process. Therefore, the model established by Al-hotmani et al. (2019) is embedded in a single optimisation framework as a Non-Linear Programming (NLP) Problem using the gPROMS suites to allow the operating conditions to vary within the upper and lower limits constrained by the manufacturer as reported in Table 1 and one constraint of fresh water concentration less than 100 ppm. The seawater characteristics including salinity and temperature have been taken same as what has been considered by Al-hotmani et al. (2019) of 39000 ppm and 25 °C, respectively.

    a)   *Single objective optimisation problem*

Given: Seawater feed conditions, MED_TVC design specifications, RO design specifications (Table 1).

Optimisation variables:

    Operating conditions of RO process (pressure, feed flow rate, and temperature)

    Minimise: Total energy consumption of the hybrid system of MED+RO processes

Subject to:

    Equality (MED_TVC + RO hybrid system model of Al-hotmani et al., 2019)

    Inequality constraints (linear limits of optimisation variables)

Therefore, the mathematical description of the optimisation problem is formulated as;

    Min $E_{consumption}$

F_b, P_b, T_b

Subject to: Equality constraints: Hybrid system model: $f(x, u, v) = 0$

        Inequality constraints of Block 1 of the RO process:

$$(0.02 \text{ m}^3/\text{s}) \quad F_b^L \leq F_b \leq F_b^U \, (0.1072 \text{ m}^3/\text{s}); \quad (40 \text{ atm}) \quad P_b^L \leq P_b \leq P_b^U \, (81.91 \text{ atm});$$
$$(20 \text{ °C}) \quad T_b^L \leq T_b \leq T_b^U \quad (45 \text{ °C})$$

        Inequality constraints of each single membrane in the RO process:

$$(0.001 \text{ m}^3/\text{s}) \quad F_{b(membrane)}^L \leq F_{b(membrane)} \leq F_{b(membrane)}^U \, (0.00536 \text{ m}^3/\text{s});$$
$$(40 \text{ atm}) \quad P_b(membrane)^L \leq P_{b(membrane)} \leq P_{b(membrane)}^U \, (81.91 \text{atm});$$
$$(20 \text{ °C}) \quad T_{b(membrane)}^L \leq T_{b(membrane)} \leq T_{b(membrane)}^U \quad (45 \text{ °C})$$
$$\text{End-point constrain: } C_{p\,Hybrid\,system} \leq 100 \text{ ppm}$$

U and L are the upper and lower limits of the optimisation variables provided by the manufacturer (Table 1).

    b)   *Optimisation results*

Table 2 shows the optimisation results including the total energy consumption of the hybrid system at specified seawater concentration and temperature. In this regard, the simulation results (base case, not optimised) are also presented in Table 2. Both simulation and optimisation are compared to account the ration of energy saving. Interestingly, Table 2 shows a noticeable energy saving of 25.14% as a result of optimising the control variables of the RO process. This is basically associated with optimal values of 81.915 atm, 0.1072 m³/s, and 38.85 °C of pressure, flow rate, and temperature, respectively.

Minimisation of energy consumption via optimisation of a simple hybrid system of 383
multie ffect distillation and permeate reprocessing reverse osmosis processes for
seawater desalination

The total flow rate of fresh water of the RO process has been significantly increased from 0.0216 m³/s to 0.06726 m³/s (increase around 212%) which expresses an improvement of water flux. This has entirely enhanced the total fresh water flow rate of the hybrid system from base case of 0.08994 m³/s to 0.1355 m³/s (increase around 51%), which contributes to the decrease in energy consumption. Interestingly, increasing the feed pressure with its allowed value of the Toray membrane at an elevated temperature showed a positive contribution on the water recovery compared to the base case. Moreover, the salt concentration in the fresh water of the hybrid system has also significantly improved from 10.88 ppm to 6.13 ppm. This is already attributed to a considerable increase happened in the water recovery of the RO process.

Table 2. Simulation and optimisation results of the hybrid system and relevant processes

Parameter				Unit			Simulation results		Optimisation results
Total energy consumption (hybrid system)				(kWh/m^3)			14.296		10.702
Specific energy consumption (RO process)				(kWh/m^3)			2.622		3.301
Specific energy consumption (MED process)				(kWh/m^3)			17.988		17.988
%Water recovery% (RO process)				(-)			37.26		62.744
%Salt rejection (RO process)				(-)			99.965		99.994
Fresh water flow rate (RO process)				(m^3/s)			0.0216		0.06726
Salt concentration of the fresh water (RO process)				(ppm)			13.67		2.20
Fresh water flow rate (hybrid system)				(m^3/s)			0.08994		0.1355
Salt concentration of the fresh water (hybrid system)				(ppm)			10.88		6.13
Optimal values	Flow rate	(m^3/s)	0.1072	Pressure	(atm)	81.915	Temp.	(°C)	38.85
Energy saving = 25.14%									

6. Conclusions

A single objective problem optimisation methodology of the hybrid system of MED+RO processes was developed and introduced a reliable increase in the operating pressure, flow rate and temperature of the RO process compared to the base case of not optimised operating conditions presented by Al-hotmani et al. (2019). This in turn has confirmed the capacity of reducing the total energy consumption of the hybrid system by 25%. The noticed reduction in energy consumption is ascribed to a greater portion of high-quality produced water that meets the demands of generating high quantity of fresh water.

References

Al-hotmani O.M.A., Al-Obaidi M.A., Patel R., Mujtaba I.M., 2019. Performance analysis of a hybrid system of multi effect distillation and permeate reprocessing reverse osmosis processes for seawater desalination. Desalination, 470, 114066.

Cipollina A., Agnello M., Piacentino A., Tamburini A., Ortega B., Palenzuela P., Alarcon D., Micale G., 2017. A dynamic model for MED-TVC transient operation. Desalination, 413, 234–257

de Boer R., 2014. Vital Membrane Processes, in: de Boer, R. (Ed.), From Milk By-Products to Milk Ingredients: Upgrading the Cycle. John Wiley and Sons, Hoboken, 141–167. https://doi.org/10.1002/9781118598634.ch6

Filippini G., Al-Obaidi M.A., Manenti F., Mujtaba I.M., 2018. Performance analysis of hybrid system of multi effect distillation and reverse osmosis for seawater desalination via modeling and simulation. Desalination, 448, 21–35. Y. Brown, Year, Article or Chapter Title, etc.

APPENDIX A

Table 3. Model equation of MED process and RO process (Al-hotmani et.at. 2018)

No	Title / MED process	Unit	Equation
1	Temperature drop among effects first attempt	(°C)	$\Delta T = \dfrac{T1 - Tb}{n-1}$ or $\Delta T = \dfrac{Ts - Tb}{n}$
2	Mean temperature in the plant	(°C)	$T_{mean} = \dfrac{T1 + Tb}{2}$
3	Mean salinity	(ppm)	$x_{mean} = \dfrac{xf + xb}{2}$
4	Fraction of flashed distillate	(-)	$\propto = \dfrac{cp(T_{mean}, x_{mean})\Delta T}{\lambda(T_{mean})}$
5	Fraction of total distillate boiled in each evaporator	(-)	$\beta = \dfrac{\alpha[xb(1-\alpha)^n - xf]}{(xb - xf)[1 - (1-\alpha)^n]}$
6	Heat load in i-th effect	(kJ/s)	$Qi = D_{boiled,i-1}\lambda(Tv_{i-1})$
7	Sensible heat used in first effect	(kJ/kg)	$Q_{sensible} = Mf \displaystyle\int_{t1}^{T1} cp(T1, x1)dT$
8	Feed flowrate	(kJ/s)	$Mf = \dfrac{Ms\,\lambda(Ts)}{Q_{sensible} + Q_{latent}}$
9	Latent heat in first effect	(kJ/s)	$Q_{latent} = D1\lambda(Tv1)$
10	Rejected brine flowrate	(kg/s)	$Mb = Mf - Md$
11	Feed flow rate	(kg/s)	$Mf = Md\dfrac{xb - xf}{xb}$
12	Total distillate produced in i-th effect	(kg/s)	$D_i = D_{boiled,i} + D_{flash,i}$
13	Brine rejected in the i-th effect	(kg/s)	$B_i = B_{i-1} - D_i$
14	Mean salinity in the plant	(ppm)	$x_i = \dfrac{x_{i-1}B_{i-1}}{B_i}$
15	Feed temperature in first effect	(°C)	$t1 = tn + (n-1)\Delta t$
16	Temperature of the vapour phase in i-th effect	(°C)	$Tv = T - BPE(T, x)$
17	Driving force for heat exchange in i-th pre-heater	(°C)	$\Delta t_{\log,i} = \dfrac{\Delta t}{\log(\dfrac{Tv_i - t_{i+1}}{Tv_i - t_i})}$
18	Gained Output Ratio	(-)	$GOR = \dfrac{Md}{Ms}$
19	Specific total area	(m² s/kg)	$Atot_s = \dfrac{Atot}{Md}$
20	Specific seawater intake	(-)	$Mw_s = \dfrac{Mw}{Md}$

No	Title / RO process	Unit	Equation
1	Material balance	(m³/s)	$Q_{f(plant)} = Q_{r(plant)} + Q_{p(plant)}$
2	Mass balance	(ppm)	$Q_{f(plant)} C_{f(plant)} = Q_{r(plant)} C_{r(plant)} + Q_{p(plant)} C_{p(plant)}$
3	Retentate concentration	(ppm)	$C_{r(plant)} = \dfrac{(C_{r(Block\,2)}Q_{r(Block\,2)}) + (C_{r(Block\,3)}Q_{r(Block\,3)})}{Q_{r(plant)}}$
4	Water recovery	(-)	$Rec_{(plant)} = \dfrac{Q_{p(plant)}}{Q_{f(plant)}} \times 100$
5	Solute rejection	(-)	$Rej_{(plant)} = \dfrac{C_{f(plant)} - C_{p(plant)}}{C_{f(plant)}} \times 100$
6	Energy consumption	(kWh/m³)	$E_{s,RO} = \left\{ \dfrac{\left[\dfrac{(P_{f(plant)} \times 101325)\, Q_{f(plant)}]}{\eta_{pump}\, Q_{p(plant)}} \right]}{3600000} \right\} - \dfrac{\dfrac{(P_{r(block2)} \times 101325)\, Q_{f(block3)}\, \eta_{ERD}}{Q_{p(plant)}}}{3600000}$

Sauro Pierucci, Flavio Manenti, Giulia Bozzano, Davide Manca (Eds.)
Proceedings of the 30th European Symposium on Computer Aided Process Engineering
(ESCAPE30), May 24-27, 2020, Milano, Italy. © 2020 Elsevier B.V. All rights reserved.
http://dx.doi.org/10.1016/B978-0-12-823377-1.50065-3

Modelling and Performance Evaluation of Humidification-Dehumidification Desalination Plant with Column Packing of Various Textures

Damson Kaunga, Raj Patel, Iqbal Mujtaba*

*Department of Chemical Engineering, Faculty of Engineering and Informatics.
University of Bradford. Bradford, West Yorkshire BD7 1DP, UK*
I.M.Mujtaba@bradford.ac.uk

Abstract

In this study a detailed mechanistic model for the packed column of the humidification-dehumidification (DHD) desalination plant was developed. This model was derived by considering an individual raschig ring with porous wall within a column as control volume then used to establish the relationship of vapor transfer rate to temperature and moisture gradients. gPROMS software was used to simulate the model with second order centered finite difference as discretization method and the results compared with those from literature. It was found that the maximum vapor transfer rate corresponds with coarse-textured media at volumetric moisture content of 0.05 m^3/m^3. While the volumetric moisture content was highly influential to the isothermal vapor diffusivity which had maximum value of 1.17×10^{-5} cm^2/s it had negligible influence to the thermal vapor diffusivity that was relatively low at 4.3×10^{-8} cm^2/s for the entire range.

Keywords: Desalination, Humidification, Moisture, Diffusivity, Porous.

1. Introduction

Demand for fresh water has been increasing in many parts of the world. This has been caused by various factors including rapid growth of population, industrialization, urbanization and climate change. On the other hand, sea water or underground saline water is abundantly available in most areas where fresh water shortage persists. As demand for fresh water keeps on increasing; desalination of saline water is inevitable. A process of Humidification-Dehumidification (HDH) desalination, using solar energy is viewed by many researchers as a promising technique for small capacity fresh water production plants. The advantages of this technique over others are the ability to operate at low temperature, utilization of solar energy and the use of low level technology to operate the process (Kang, et al., 2015).

Numerous researchers (Zubair, et al., 2018) and (Kang, et al., 2015) have investigated influential factors on improving the performance and efficiency of the HDH systems. Nafey, et al (2004) investigated the effect of system configuration and air-water flow orientation on system productivity. They compared four different systems which were; air heated, water heated, air heated-water heated open loop and air heated-water heated closed loop systems. They found that the air heated-water heated closed loop system as the most effective with the highest productivity. Their findings coincided with those of Yamali & Solmus (2008) who noticed a 15% decrease of system productivity when a double-pass solar air heater for heating the air was not used.

Although considerable research has been devoted to the influential factors on HDH desalination processes, less attention has been paid to the influence of packing materials' texture on rate of evaporation in the humidifier column. Research has shown that porous media of different textures influences differently the evaporation rates (Moroi, et al., 2004) and (Brutin & Starov, 2018). Therefore, the purpose of this study is to develop and simulate a mechanistic model of the HDH desalination system. The refined model is then used to investigate performance of the system, particularly, the influence of packing materials' texture on rate of humidification in the column.

2. Description of model

2.1. Flow configuration

The flow configuration considered in this work is typical of humidifier columns of HDH plants. As shown in Figure 1, a bed of height (L) is formed by packing porous Raschig rings of random orientation in a cylindrical column of diameter (D). Saline water enters the column at the top with the flat velocity profile, flows through the packing of rings and leaves the column at the bottom while the air flows in the opposite direction. Figure 1 also shows an individual ring with internal diameter (d_i), external diameter (d_o) and porosity (e). If the saline water stream is hotter than air, then a simultaneous flow of heat and water vapor (q_v) will occur across the porous wall of the ring with thickness (t). Finally, the flowing heat and water vapor will heat and humidify the dry air passing inside the ring.

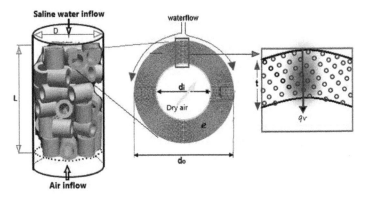

Figure 1: Flow configuration in the humidifiers' column of the HDH plant

2.2. Vapor transfer model

The water vapor diffusion can be described using a modified Fick's law, applied to porous media (Nassar & Horton, 1997) and (Philip & De Vries, 1957)

$$q_v = -D\alpha v \vartheta \nabla \rho \qquad (1)$$

Where q_v is a mass flux of vapor in porous media (kg/m²s), D a molecular diffusivity of water vapor in air (m²/s), α a tortuosity factor allowing for the extra path length (dimensionless) and v the mass-flow factor introduced to allow for the mass flow of vapor arising from the difference in boundary conditions governing the convective movement of vapor and air components. ϑ is the volumetric air content of the medium (m³ of air/m³) and ρ is the density of water vapor (kg/m³).

Vapor flux is a function of two components which are temperature gradient and moisture gradient. Therefore, equation 1 can be modified to describe water vapor movement due to both components in unsaturated, non-isothermal porous material. This is achieved by introducing the thermodynamic relationship as suggested by Edlefsen & Anderson (1943)

$$\rho = \rho_0 h = \rho_0 \exp\left(\Psi g / RT\right) \qquad (2)$$

In which ρ_0 is the density of saturated water vapour (kg/m³), h the relative humidity, g the acceleration due to gravity (m/s²), R the gas constant of water vapour (J/kg.K) and Ψ the water pressure (m) in thermodynamic equilibrium with water in the medium. This pressure depends on volumetric moisture content θ (m³/m³) and temperature T. From equation 2 the following can be deduced:

$$\nabla\rho = h\nabla\rho_0 + \rho_0\nabla h \qquad (3)$$

By differentiating wrt temperature and volumetric moisture content we obtain

$$\frac{\partial\rho}{\partial T} = h\frac{\partial\rho_0}{\partial T} + \rho_0\frac{\partial h}{\partial T} \qquad (4)$$

$$\frac{\partial\rho}{\partial\theta} = h\frac{\partial\rho_0}{\partial\theta} + \rho_0\frac{\partial h}{\partial\theta} \qquad (5)$$

Since ρ_0 is a function of T only while h is a function of θ only (Philip & De Vries, 1957) then

$$\partial h / \partial T = 0 \ and \ \ \partial\rho_0 / \partial\theta = 0$$

Equation 3 therefore becomes

$$\nabla\rho = h\frac{d\rho_0}{dT}\nabla T + \rho_0\frac{dh}{d\theta}\nabla\theta \qquad (6)$$

Equation 2 can also be used to evaluate $dh / d\theta$ in equation 6 to obtain

$$\nabla\rho = h\frac{d\rho_0}{dT}\nabla T + \frac{g\rho}{RT}\frac{d\Psi}{d\theta}\nabla\theta \qquad (7)$$

Substituting equation 7 in equation 1 we obtain an equation of the form

$$q_v\frac{p}{\rho_w} = -D_{Tv}\nabla T - D_{\theta v}\nabla\theta \qquad (8)$$

whereby, ρ_w is the density of liquid water and p the partial pressure of water vapor Equation 8 describe vapor transfer under combined moisture and temperature gradients in porous materials. From this equation two coefficients which are thermal vapor diffusivity (D_{Tv}) and isothermal vapor diffusivity ($D_{\theta v}$) are defined as

$$D_{Tv} = D\alpha v\vartheta h\frac{d\rho_0}{dT} \qquad (9)$$

$$D_{\theta v} = \frac{D\alpha v\vartheta g\rho}{\rho_w RT}\frac{d\Psi}{d\theta} \qquad (10)$$

Using the moisture retention function as proposed by Campbell (1974), the derivative of the Ψ in equation 10 is given as

$$\frac{d\Psi}{d\theta} = \frac{-\lambda\Psi_e}{\theta_s}\left(\frac{\theta}{\theta_s}\right)^{-(\lambda+1)} \qquad (11)$$

where θ_s is a saturated volumetric water content; λ and Ψ_e are dimensionless fitting parameters.

The developed model equations were simulated using a general PROcess Modelling System (gPROMs) software for an entire tube length L and Diameter D with the assumptions that, the porous media are rigid, unsaturated and inert materials, the transfer of mass and energy occurs in one-dimension only i.e across porous wall and solute movement doesn't interfere with vapor transfer. During simulation, the discretisation method used was a second order Centered Finite Difference Method (CFDM). Simulation results are shown in Figures 2 and 3.

Parameter	Value	Unit	Parameter	Value	Unit
D	2.93E-5	m²/s	p	12350	Pascal
α	0.67		h	0.6	
v	1		θ_s	0.2	m³/m³
ϑ	0.349	m³/m³	Ψ_e	-1	m
ρ_w	1000	kg/m³	λ	0.25	

Table 1: Parameters used in simulation

3. Results and discussion

A water vapor transfer rate in porous wall of Raschig ring (packed in humidifier's column) was investigated using mechanistic models developed in this study. Specifically, we have analyzed the influence of volumetric moisture content on both isothermal coefficient of vapor diffusivity and vapor flowrate.

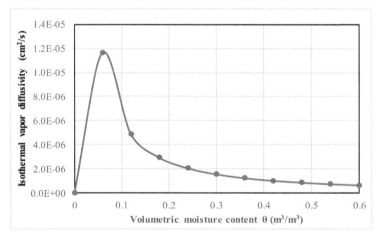

Figure 2: The influence of volumetric moisture content on Isothermal vapor diffusivity

As shown in Figure 2, the isothermal coefficient of vapor diffusivity increases initially with increasing moisture content within a porous media until a peak value (maximum point) was obtained; then a further increase in moisture content resulted into decrease of the vapor diffusivity coefficient. This maximum value occurred at moisture content of 0.05 m³/m³. On the other hand, the thermal vapor diffusivity was 4.3 x 10⁻⁸ cm²/s and constant for the entire range of moisture content.

This finding is similar to the results demonstrated by Nassar & Horton (1997) and those of Philip & De Vries (1957) who also studied the effect of texture on the point of maximum transfer rate. From their findings it is interesting to note, that, maximum point occurs at low moisture content in coarse-textured media, while in fine-textured media it occurs at relatively high moisture contents.

The influence of moisture content on vapor transfer (resulted by both temperature and moisture gradients) is shown in Figure 3. There is a clear resemblance in trend between Figures 2 and 3 which supports the observation of many other investigators (Hadley & Eisenstadt, 1955), (Srikiatden & Roberts, 2007) and (Baker, et al., 2009) that, moisture transfer under temperature gradients is relatively small in both dry and wet media compared to transfer under moisture gradients. It can also be noted that for non-porous media (such as glass raschig rings), diffusion of vapor across the wall as well as moisture content are absolutely negligible because the pore sizes are extremely small. Under such circumstances the dominant process is convective mass transfer of water vapor at the water-air interface, whereby, the description of such process is beyond the scope of the current study.

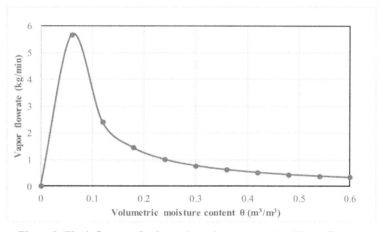

Figure 3: The influence of volumetric moisture content on Vapor flowrate

In general, the findings of this study are of particular importance in improving the performance of the humidification-dehumidification desalination process. Previous studies (Nematollahi, et al., 2013) and (Adel, 2011) has attempted to model this process using black box models, whereby, only relationship of the input and output properties are given without providing analysis of such problems as the heat and mass transfer within the packed column. This study has provided a plausible model and explanation of the classical mechanisms of vapor diffusion within porous packing under the influence of temperature gradient and moisture gradient. On the other hand, these findings can be useful in choosing appropriately the packing of an optimum texture, that could enhance optimum performance of the HDH system by improving the rate of evaporation within its column.

In order to improve the prediction accuracy of the proposed model, future research should address the contribution of convective vapor transfer taking place at the air-water interface on the outer surface of the ring; to the total vapor transfer. Moreover, it has been suggested by Nassar & Horton (1997) that for salt concentrated solution like saline water, there is flow of solute in unsaturated, non-isothermal porous material driven by moisture content, solute concentration and temperature gradients. Future research should therefore focus on investigating at what extend the flow of solute influences the vapor transfers within the media and hence for the entire humidification process within a column.

4. Conclusion

In this study we have developed a simulation model for vapor transfer within a packed column (humidifier) of the HDH system. This model was used to investigate the influence of moisture content on the rate of vapor transfer. In general, it was shown that the driving forces for vapor diffusion within a porous packing of the column are the temperature gradient and moisture gradient and two coefficients of vapor diffusivity were deduced. These were thermal vapor diffusivity and isothermal vapor diffusivity.

The volumetric moisture content was found to be highly influential to the isothermal vapor diffusivity that had maximum value of $1.17 \times 10^{-5} cm^2/s$ as well as to the total vapor flow rate. On the other hand, it had negligible influence to the thermal vapor diffusivity that was relatively low at $4.3 \times 10^{-8} cm^2/s$ for the entire range. The maximum vapor transfer rate was corresponding with volumetric moisture content of $0.05 \ m^3/m^3$. It is hoped that the findings of this study will enable designers to choose appropriately the packing of an optimum texture that could enhance optimum performance of the HDH system.

References

Adel, A. D., 2011. Pioneer Solar Water Desalination System: Experimental Testing and Numerical Simulation. *Energy Science and Technology,* 1(1), pp. 33-48.

Baker, P., Galbraith, G. & McLean, C., 2009. Temperature gradient effects on moisture transport in porous building materials. *Building Serv. Eng. Res. Technol,* 30(1), p. 37–48.

Brutin, D. & Starov, V., 2018. Recent advances in droplet wetting and evaporation. *Chem Soc Rev,* Volume 47, pp. 558--585.

Campbell, G., 1974. A simple method for determining unsaturated conductivity from moisture retention data. *Soil Science,* 117(6), pp. 311-314.

Edlefsen, N. & Anderson, A., 1943. The thermodynamics of soil moisture. *Hilgardia,* Volume 16, pp. 231-299.

Hadley, W. & Eisenstadt, R., 1955. Thermally actuated moisture migration in granular media. *Trans. Amer. Geophys. Union,* Volume 36, pp. 615-623.

Kang, H. et al., 2015. Performance of a 3-stage regenerative desalination system based on humidification-dehumidification process. *Applied Thermal Engineering,* Volume 90, pp. 182-192.

Moroi, Y., Rusdi, M. & Kubo, I., 2004. Difference in Surface Properties between Insoluble Monolayer and Adsorbed Film from Kinetics of Water Evaporation and BAM Image. *J. Phys. Chem. B,* Volume 108, pp. 6351-6358.

Nafey, A., Fath, H., El-Helaby, S. & Soliman, A., 2004. Solar desalination using humidification dehumidification processes. Part I. A numerical investigation. *Energy Conversion and Management,* Volume 45, p. 1243–1261.

Nassar, I. & Horton, R., 1997. Heat, Water, and Solute Transfer in Unsaturated Porous Media: I – Theory Development and Transport Coefficient Evaluation. *Transport in Porous Media,* Volume 27, p. 17–38.

Nematollahi, F., Rahimi, A. & Gheinani, T., 2013. Experimental and theoretical energy and exergy analysis for a solar desalination system. *Desalination,* 317(317), p. 23–31.

Philip, J. & De Vries, D., 1957. Moisture Movement in Porous Materials under Temperature Gradients. *Transactions, American Geophysical Union,* 38(2), pp. 222-232.

Srikiatden, J. & Roberts, . J., 2007. Moisture Transfer in Solid Food Materials. *International Journal of Food Properties,* Volume 10, p. 739–777.

Yamali, C. & Solmus, I., 2008. A solar desalination system using humidification–dehumidification process: experimental study and comparison with the theoretical results. *Desalination,* Volume 220, p. 538–551.

Zubair, S., Antar, M., Elmutasim, S. & Lawal, D., 2018. Performance evaluation of humidification-dehumidification (HDH) desalination systems with and without heat recovery options: An experimental and theoretical investigation. *Desalination,* p. 161–175.

Sauro Pierucci, Flavio Manenti, Giulia Bozzano, Davide Manca (Eds.)
Proceedings of the 30th European Symposium on Computer Aided Process Engineering
(ESCAPE30), May 24-27, 2020, Milano, Italy. © 2020 Elsevier B.V. All rights reserved.
http://dx.doi.org/10.1016/B978-0-12-823377-1.50066-5

Application Domain Discovery of Thermodynamic Models by Mixture of Experts Learning

Omar Péter Hamadi[a], Tamás Varga[a], János Abonyi[a,b]

[a]Department of Process Engineering, University of Pannonia, Egyetem str. 10, Veszrpém H-8200, Hungary
[b]MTA-PE Lendület Complex System Monitoring Research Group, Egyetem str. 10, Veszrpém H-8200, Hungary
hamadio@fmt.uni-pannon.hu

Abstract

The proper selection of thermodynamic models (TM) is a starting point for an accurate process simulation. It can occur in a process simulation that the proper thermodynamic model changes with the operating conditions. Therefore, the application domains for all appropriate models have to be determined and the models have to be used respectively to the domains. In this work, six TMs are investigated in case of hydrogen solubility in several n-paraffin, olefins and aromatic compounds. In petroleum industry, the most commonly used TMs are the Soave-Redlich-Kwong EOS, and the Peng-Robinson EOS. The Zudkevitch Joffee, Chao Seader and Grayson Streed models are recommended to use in case of high hydrogen content. As the first step to determine the application domains, several measurements were collected from literature, and the solubility of hydrogen was estimated with the abovementioned TMs. Based on the prediction error, a mixture of experts-based expectation maximization (EM) algorithm was used to explore the optimal combination of a set of TMs through the corresponding application domains. As multivariate Gaussian distributions with zero covariance represent the mixture-of experts, the resulted axis-parallel clusters can be easily visualized as a set of univariate normal distributions determining the suggested application regions. The results illustrate that the developed Gaussian mixture model not only significantly improves the prediction performance of the TMs, but the extracted information also supports the systematic development of the models.

Keywords: hydrogen solubility, fluid packages, Gaussian mixture model

1. Introduction

To calculate the hydrogen solubility in different mixtures even in pure components is a challenging mission. However in many processes (e.g. hydrocracking) the concentration of hydrogen in the liquid phase plays a very important role. The solubility of hydrogen is mainly depend on pressure and temperature, therefore with calculating the optimal amount of dissolved hydrogen and the softening operating conditions can help to reduce the operating cost of the process.

 One way to calculate the amount of dissolved hydrogen is the application of the appropriate thermodynamic model (TM), but the proper selection of TMs is a recurrent problem in process simulations. According to the *Aspen HYSYS Property Package Selection Assistant*, there are four possible packages to calculate the properties of hydrocarbons in case of non-vacuum conditions, these are: SRK, Peng-Robinson (PR), Chao-Seader (CS), and Grayson-Streed (GS).

The conditions of applicability of the recommended and an extra (Zudkevitch-Joffee (ZJ)) property packages are summarized in Table 1. Three of these models were developed to calculate the properties of systems with high hydrogen content, these are: ZJ (Zudkevitch and Joffe 1970) CS (Chao and Seader 1961) and GS (Torres, de Hemptinne, and Machin 2013).

Table 1 Conditions of applicability of the TMs recommended by *Aspen HYSYS Property Package Selection Assistant*

		CS	GS	PR	SRK	ZJ
T [K]		255 to 533	255 to 698	> 2	> 130	-
p [bar]		<100	<200	$<1{,}000$	<350	>10
For all hydrocarbons (except CH₄)		$0.5<T_{ri}<1.3$ $P_{mixture} <0.8$	$0.5<T_{ri}<1.3$ $P_{mixture} <0.8$	-	-	-
If CH₄ or H₂ is present:	-molal average T_r	< 0.93	< 0.93	-	-	-
	CH₄ mole fraction	<0.3	<0.3	-	-	-
	-mole fraction dissolved gases	<0.2	<0.2	-	-	-
Predicting K values for:	-Paraffinic or olefinic mixtures, liquid phase aromatic mole fraction:	< 0.5	< 0.5	-	-	-
	-Aromatic mixtures, liquid phase aromatic mole fraction:	> 0.5	> 0.5	-	-	

According to Table 1, different models are recommended to use based on the operating conditions. However, there are several domains where multiple models are suitable for modeling, and there is no pure measure to compare their goodness based on the "selection guideline". For example, every model is suitable in temperature range between 255 and 533 K and pressure range between 10 and 100 bar.

In addition not all models can be compared to each other, rather a pairwise analysis is possible (CS and GS, PR and SRK have similar characterization). Based on these considerations, one can conclude that the provided framework for the selection of proper TM is not straightforward (at least in case of predicting the hydrogen solubility), despite to the fact, that selecting the appropriate model is the first task for describing successfully the physical properties (Carlson 1996). Moreover, the available decision trees for the selection of TMs lead to several cases, when multiple models can be used (Al-Matar 2015).

The application of the proper model is not the only way to improve the prediction: if there are multiple candidates, one can take the advantage of all models and combine them into a mixture model. There are several techniques to combine multiple models e.g.: simple weighted average of the predictions of individual models or the mixture of experts approach, where the weights are the function of the feature space (Yuksel, Wilson, and Gader 2012).

As we would like to explore the application domains of the TMs, we designed a Gaussian mixture of experts model that combines the TMs, in which the products of univariate Gaussian functions representing the optimal regions of the models. The proposed generative model can be easily visualized with the distribution of the planned applications, so the developed tool highlights how the available sets of TMs should be combined for a given set of applications. According to our knowledge, this is the first work discussing how the trained Gaussian mixture of expert approach can be utilized for the determination of application domains of TMs.

In this work, we compared the aforementioned TMs calculation obtained by Aspen HYSYS to measurement data (634) from literature (Tsuji et al. 2014; Young 1981). The collected measurements consist of data on the solubility of H_2 in paraffins, olefins and aromatic compounds. The results illustrate that the developed Gaussian mixture model gives excellent prediction performance, and the proposed visualization provides interpretable information about how TMs should be applied for specific applications.

2. Gaussian mixture of thermodynamic models

The key idea of the proposed approach is that the distribution of the validation data used to represent the planned prediction tasks is approximated by a Gaussian mixture of the available TMs. In the studied specific problem the N pairs of validation data is represented as $\{(x_k, y_k)\}_{k=1}^N$, where y_k is the measured hydrogen solubility and x_k denotes the explanatory variables including molecular descriptors like the carbon number (C_n) and the number of the hydrogen atoms (H_n) and the operating conditions of the experiments (pressure and temperature). The set of the predictions of the available TMs are also represented as paired samples $\left\{ \left(x_k, \hat{y}_{k,j} \right)_{j=1}^n \right\}_{k=1}^N$ where $\hat{y}_{k,j}$ is the kth predicted hydrogen solubility by the jth thermodynamic model, hence the kth prediction error of the jth TM can be calculated as $e_{k,j} = (y_k - \hat{y}_{k,j})^2$. The identification of the model is formulated as a clustering problem in which the prediction error is used to measure the distance of the models and the validation data. The clustering is based on the Expectation Maximization algorithm that minimizes the sum of the weighted squared distances: $J = \sum_{j=1}^n \sum_{k=1}^N (u_{j,k})^m D^2(x_k, y_k, \eta_j)$, where η_j represents the parameters of the jth cluster including the jth TM. The proposed clustering algorithm can be interpreted in a probabilistic framework, the distance is inversely proportional to the $p(x_k, y_k | \eta_j)$ probability that the x_k data point belongs to the ith cluster,

$$\frac{1}{D^2(x_k, y_k, \eta_j)} = \alpha_j \frac{1}{\sqrt{2\pi\sigma_{j,l}^2}} e^{\left(-\frac{e_{k,j}^2}{2\sigma_{j,l}^2} \right)} \frac{1}{\sqrt{2\pi|\Sigma_j|}} e^{\left(-\frac{1}{2} \cdot (x_i - v_j)^T \cdot \Sigma_j^{-1} (x_i - v_j) \right)} \tag{1}$$

The first α_j term represents the a priori probability of the cluster, while second is the distance between the kth data point and the jth model. The third term defines the distance between the cluster prototype and the data in the feature space of the variables describing the applicability domain of the models represented by the mean and the covariance matrices calculated as:

$$v_j = \frac{\Sigma_i (u_{j,k})^m x_i}{\Sigma_i (u_{j,k})^m}, \Sigma_j = \frac{\Sigma_i (u_{j,k})^m (x_i - v_j)^T (x_i - v_j)}{\Sigma_i (u_{j,k})^m}, \alpha_j = \frac{\Sigma_i (u_{j,k})^m}{N} \tag{2}$$

the $u_{j,k}$ weights are updated in every iteration.

$$u_{j,k} = \frac{1}{\sum_{l=1}^n \left(D^2(x_k, y_k, \eta_j) / D^2(x_k, y_k, \eta_l) \right)^{2/(m-1)}}, \forall j, k \tag{3}$$

The Alternating Optimization (AO) of these clusters is identical to the Expectation Maximization (EM) (maximum likelihood estimation) identification of the mixture of these Gaussian models when the fuzzy weighting exponent $m = 2$.

3. Application domains of thermodynamic models

To investigate the goodness of the TMs, 634 solubility data from literature was collected. The data set contains of H_2 solubility in paraffinic (458), olefinic (49), and aromatic (127) compounds with carbon range between 1-16, 2-8 ,6-13, temperature range between 90.5-623 K, 123.15-436.15 K , 208.15-621.75 K and pressure range between 7.08-784.5 bar, 20.3-304 bar, and 20.3-507 bar respectively. In Figure 1 every data point is marked according to the smallest prediction error.

In paraffinic compounds all models are required to predict the H_2 solubility, but it can be noted, that different models dominate different, but well specified domains. However, in case of olefinic and aromatic compounds the usage of ZJ model is not recommended at all, and the application domains distributed lightly. There are a few but coupled measurements for olefinic compounds, hence it is hard to make proper conclusions. The only thing is clear that the CS GS and PR are the dominant models and the application domains mainly distributed along the carbon number and the temperature. The PR is the best approach to reproduce the measurements in aromatic compounds, but in case of lower pressure and carbon number mainly the SRK performs better.

The selection of the proper model is really challenging based on Figure 1. To determine well defined application domains, Gaussian mixture model was used. As the TMs are treated like black box models, the application domains are investigated along arbitrary chosen variables. The selection of pressure and temperature as variables is natural, but for identifying different molecule types and size, carbon number (C_n) and the number of the hydrogen atoms (H_n) in the molecules was applied.

The mean square errors for 10-fold cross-validation based training are presented in Figure 2. Despite that the linear mixed model is not suitable to determine the application domains, it is a good benchmark to compare the prediction errors. The Gaussian mixed model has better performance than the individual models, but slightly worse than the linear combination. Based on the mean square errors, the developed mixed model is a reasonable choice to investigate the application domains of the TMs.

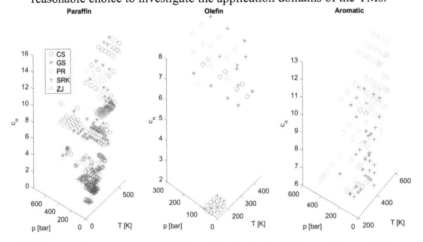

Figure 1 Different markers represents the TMs which obtained with the smallest prediction error at each investigation condition.

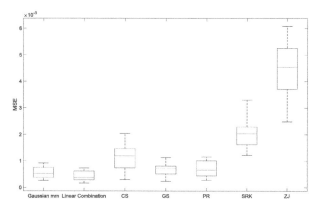

Figure 2 The mean square error of individual TMs and mixture models

In Figure 3 the distribution of the data along the variables is presented as histograms, and the calculated application domains are presented as Gaussian distributions. The multivariate distribution used by the algorithm can be obtained with multiplying the individual distributions. The height of curves represents the "probability of being appropriate" for the TMs at a specified modeling condition, moreover this height is proportion to the weights of the TMs in the mixed model. The conclusions which can be made based on Figure 3 can be divided into two main groups:

1) The ones which are confirm or at least not disprove the fluid package selection guideline:
   -   PR has the widest application domain, and dominates most of the domains of investigated variables.
   -   ZJ is recommended only in case of light hydrocarbons and extremely low temperature, but as the solubility exists in liquid phase and the light hydrocarbons have low dew point, these statements can be coupled.
   -   The performance of CS and GS are nearly the same, but in higher temperatures GS predicts better.

2) The others which are disprove some of the statements of Table 1:
   -   From those models which were developed for calculate properties in high H_2 content, only the ZJ dominates a wide range of domain.
   -   The CS performs best at extremely high pressure outside the recommended application range, but it can be the result of the lack of data in this domain.
   -   The performance of SRK is far worst then the performance of PR.

4. Conclusion

We developed a tool to explore the optimal combination of a set of thermodynamic models for a set of planned applications or validation data but it should be mentioned, that the well distributed the data is in the planned application domain, the better the exploration is. The visualization of the proposed Gaussian mixture of expert model with the distribution of the data along the variables determines the suggested application domains of TMs. The application domains of five TMs were investigated based on the hydrogen solubility in paraffinic, olefinic, and aromatic compounds. The results illustrate that the developed method not only explores how the models should be combined or under which operating conditions should be used. Next to this the resulted model gives significantly better prediction performance than the TMs which can be a good starting point of the kinetic model development of hydrocracking.

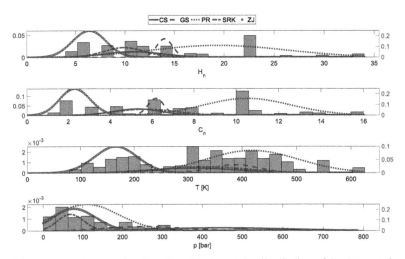

Figure 3 The proposed application domains of TMs and the distribution of the data set along the variables

Acknowledgment

We acknowledge the financial support of Széchenyi 2020 under the GINOP-2.3.2-15-2016-00053. Tamás Varga's contribution to this paper was supported by the Janos Bolyai Research Scholarship of the Hungarian Academy of Sciences.

References

Al-Matar, Ali. 2015. 'Selecting Fluid Packages (Thermodynamic Model) for HYSYS/ Aspen Plus/ ChemCAD Process Simulators'. Unpublished. https://doi.org/10.13140/RG.2.1.3461.4487.

Carlson, Eric. 1996. 'Don't Gamble with Physical Properties for Simulations'. *Chemical Engineering Progress* 92: 35–46.

Chao, K. C., and J. D. Seader. 1961. 'A General Correlation of Vapor-Liquid Equilibria in Hydrocarbon Mixtures'. *AIChE Journal* 7 (4): 598–605. https://doi.org/10.1002/aic.690070414.

Torres, R., J.-C. de Hemptinne, and I. Machin. 2013. 'Improving the Modeling of Hydrogen Solubility in Heavy Oil Cuts Using an Augmented Grayson Streed (AGS) Approach'. *Oil & Gas Science and Technology – Revue d'IFP Energies Nouvelles* 68 (2): 217–33. https://doi.org/10.2516/ogst/2012061.

Tsuji, Tomoya, Koh-hei Ohya, Taka-aki Hoshina, Toshihiko Hiaki, Koji Maeda, Hidetoshi Kuramochi, and Masahiro Osako. 2014. 'Hydrogen Solubility in Triolein, and Propane Solubility in Oleic Acid for Second Generation BDF Synthesis by Use of Hydrodeoxygenation Reaction'. *Fluid Phase Equilibria* 362 (January): 383–88. https://doi.org/10.1016/j.fluid.2013.11.006.

Young, Colin Leslie, ed. 1981. Hydrogen and Deuterium. 1st ed. Solubility Data Series, v. 5-6. Oxford ; New York: Pergamon Press.

Yuksel, S. E., J. N. Wilson, and P. D. Gader. 2012. 'Twenty Years of Mixture of Experts'. *IEEE Transactions on Neural Networks and Learning Systems* 23 (8): 1177–93. https://doi.org/10.1109/TNNLS.2012.2200299.

Zudkevitch, David, and Joseph Joffe. 1970. 'Correlation and Prediction of Vapor-Liquid Equilibria with the Redlich-Kwong Equation of State'. *AIChE Journal* 16 (1): 112–19. https://doi.org/10.1002/aic.690160122.

Sauro Pierucci, Flavio Manenti, Giulia Bozzano, Davide Manca (Eds.)
Proceedings of the 30th European Symposium on Computer Aided Process Engineering
(ESCAPE30), May 24-27, 2020, Milano, Italy. © 2020 Elsevier B.V. All rights reserved.
http://dx.doi.org/10.1016/B978-0-12-823377-1.50067-7

Kinetics Study on Removal of Cadmium from Wastewater

Haya Alyasi, Hamish R. Mackey, Gordon McKay

Division of Sustainable Development, College of Science and Engineering, Hamad Bin Khalifa University, Qatar Foundation, Qatar

gmckay@hbku.edu.qa

Abstract

Cadmium is a toxic heavy metal prevalent in the industry that frequently enters waterways through industrial effluents and stormwater runoff, posing a threat to the environment and human health. Strict water quality guidelines of 5 µg/L exist in the United States and European Union and adsorption provides an ideal treatment technology for reducing cadmium to these levels. This study utilizes nanochitosan, a natural polymer derived from seafood shell waste, as an effective cadmium adsorbent. The kinetics are studied through experimental batch tests and common kinetic models are examined to identify which is the most suitable for predicting the cadmium-nanochitosan adsorption rates by comparing the sum of the square errors and the correlation coefficient. The process is then optimized to minimize the contact time in a two-stage batch absorber system. It has been found that the Elovich kinetic model was the most suitable, followed closely by the pseudo-second-order kinetic model. The Elovich kinetic model is utilized to determine the minimum contact time necessary for a two-stage process at various initial and target cadmium concentrations with different adsorbent masses through optimization. A significant reduction in volume was found with the two-stage batch absorber compared to a one-stage process, which was accentuated when low discharge concentrations such as regulatory limits needed to be met.

Keywords: cadmium removal, contact time minimization, equilibrium and kinetic studies, nanochitosan adsorbent.

1. Introduction

Water contamination is a major concern globally because of its impact on human and environmental health and wellness. The degradation of water quality may be attributed to causes such as industrialization, farming practices, rapid urbanization, and global population growth, among other issues. Cadmium is one of the most troublesome water pollutants due to its widespread use in industry and high toxicity. The binding of cadmium with cystein-metallothionein inside the human liver leads to the development of hepatotoxicity (Jaishankar et al., 2014; Valko et al., 2016). Therefore, efficient methods for its removal are necessary.

Chitosan is a prominent, deacetylated biopolymer of chitin. On the surface, there are – OH and –NH$_2$ functional groups. The existence of these groups allows for many modifications. The usage of chitosan in heavy metal elimination from wastewater is widespread. This research utilizes nanochitosan as an active cadmium adsorbent, an organic polymer produced from seafood shell waste (Pal & Pal, 2017). Nanochitosan is an effective adsorbent for cadmium removal from water. Based on our isotherm study from our previous work (Alyasi et al., 2020), the uptake capacity of nanochitosan was 219 mg Cd/g, which is higher than most of other adsorbents studied for cadmium removal reported in the literature. This previous study used the optimization of a two stage adsorber based on adsorbent mass distribution using the isotherm data to reduce the quantity of adsorbent required to treat cadmium polluted water. Therefore, the focus of this study is on an alternate space based (time) optimization using adsorption kinetic data to minimize the total treatment time and reactor volume.

Equilibrium study outcomes are described and kinetics are investigated by laboratory batch tests and multiple kinetic designs to determine which is most appropriate for predicting adsorption rates of cadmium through nanochitosan by making comparisons between the sum of the square of the errors and the correlation coefficient. The process design is then optimized in order to reduce the contact time in a staging batch absorber process.

2. Methods and methodology

Nanochitosan was synthesized from chitosan flake purchased from Sigma-Aldrich Ltd. The synthesizing method has been explained previously (Anand et al., 2017). Analar grade cadmium nitrate was provided by Sigma-Aldrich and all solutions were made up using deionized water. A sequence of cadmium solutions with concentrations of 0.50–10.0 mmol/L was used to test equilibrium isotherms. The pH and temperature were maintained at 5.50 ± 0.05 and 22 ± 1 °C, respectively. Next, 0.50 g nanochitosan was mixed with 100 mL of aqueous Cd (II) solution by means of capped 125 mL HDPE flasks with a temperature-controlled water bath shaker at 200 rpm for 24 h. This contact period allows the adsorbent and cadmium solution to reach equilibrium.

The kinetic evaluations for Cd (II) adsorption on nanochitosan were achieved by mixing different masses of a specimen in 1.7 L of Cd (II) solution of different concentrations for 6 hours in a baffled agitated batch absorber. The impeller rate was set at 400 rpm, the temperature was maintained at 22 ± 1 °C and the pH at 5.50 ± 0.05. The details of the absorber vessel are described in preceding work (Alyasi et al., 2019).

3. Results and discussion

Analysis of the kinetic data showed that the Elovich model is the best-fit kinetic model by means of two statistical error analyses (SSE and R^2) as presented in Table 1.

Table 1: Kinetic parameters for pseudo-first order (PFO), pseudo-second order (PSO) and Elovich kinetic models.

Kinetic Parameters	PFO	Kinetic Parameters	PSO	Kinetic Parameters	Elovich
k_1 (min^{-1})	0.003	k_2 (kg/g·min)	0.016	β (mmol/g.min)	3.618
q_e (mmol/g)	1.554	q_e (mmol/g)	1.472	α (g/mmol)	0.118
R^2	0.961	R^2	0.991	R^2	0.998
SSE	0.655	SSE	0.067	SSE	0.027

Kinetic data has been utilized to determine the minimum contact time necessary for a two-stage process at various initial and target cadmium concentration (Ho & McKay, 1999). An optimization model has been developed to determine the minimum contact time needed to remove the cadmium from water based on Elovich, "best-fit kinetic model", to assist in the process treatment plant design. A significant reduction in the required adsorption time was found with the optimization process for a multi-stage batch adsorber compared to a one-stage process, which was greatly accentuated when low discharge concentrations such as regulatory limits needed to be met.

As the Elovich model is ideally suited to the kinetic data due to a lower SSE of 0.027 in comparison with two other models, the lowest contact time for a two-stage mechanism has been determined at various initial concentrations of cadmium and adsorbent mass (Ho & McKay, 1999). In order to identify the lowest possible contact time required to remove cadmium from water, a best fit kinetics model based on Elovich has been designed to help with the wastewater treatment procedure design. With the optimized method for a dual-stage batch absorber, the necessary adsorption period was significantly reduced in contrast to a one-stage system. It was significantly highlighted if low levels of discharge, such as controlling limitations, were to be achieved.

For the cadmium adsorption, a combination of the time required in both phases will attain the lowest possible cumulative contact time. The operating time at each phase can be calculated with a mass balance calculation and the kinetic parameter. Generally, the mass balance gives:

$$V(C_{n-1} - C_n) = m(q_n - q_0) \tag{1}$$

where V is the volume, C is the pollutant concentration, m is the mass of adsorbent and q is the adsorbent capacity. Subscript n and $n-1$ refer to the stage and 0 to the initial condition. The Elovich kinetic model can be written as:

$$q_t = \frac{1}{\beta}\ln(\alpha\beta) + \frac{1}{\beta}\ln t \tag{2}$$

where α is the initial rate of sorption and β is the activation energy in the context of chemisorption and the degree of surface coverage.

By combining these two equations, the mass balance equation becomes:

$$C_n = C_{n-1} - \frac{m}{V}\left(\frac{1}{\beta_n}\ln(\alpha_n\beta_n) + \frac{1}{\beta_n}\ln t_n\right) \tag{3}$$

where β and α are expressed as a function of C_o for metal ion removal onto the sorbent as follows:

$$\beta = x_\beta C_0^2 + x_\beta C_0 + x_\beta \tag{4}$$

$$\alpha = x_\alpha C_0^2 + x_\alpha C_0 + x_\alpha \tag{5}$$

In this study, nanochitosan was examined to determine the lowest possible contact times for 90%, 95% and 99% of cadmium removal using a two-stage batch method. For the simulation of contact period, cadmium doses of 1, 1.5 and 3 mmol/L were used for adsorbent mass 1.7 and 3.4 g.

Substituting Equations (5) and (4) into Equation (3) are used to calculate the total contact time for any removal percentage. The optimum contact time for the process can was then determined by setting t_1 and calculating the necessary t_2 to meet the required removal percentage using the solver optimisation function in Microsoft Excel. The final optimum was determined by plotting the time required for stage 1, stage 2 and total time. The results are shown in Figures 1 and 2.

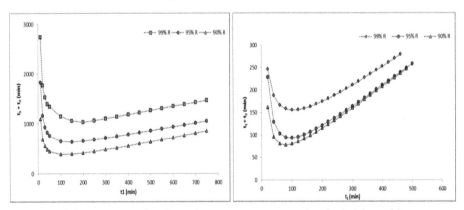

Figure 1: Minimum contact time for various percentage removal at the intial metal ion concentration 3 mmol/L and a) adsorbent mass = 1.7g b) adsorbent mass = 3.4g.

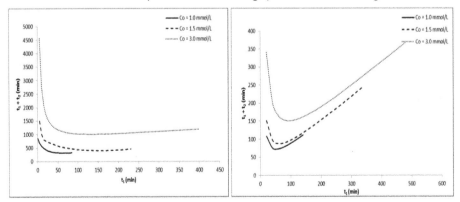

Figure 2:The total time optimisation at different initial concentrations of metal ion at removal 99% and a) adsorbent mass = 1.7g b) adsorbent mass = 3.4g.

Figure 1 shows the minimum contact time for different percentage removal at initial ion concentration 3.0 mmol/L and adsorbent mass 1.7 and 3.4 g. The optimum contact time for different removal percentage is lower for larger amount of adsorbent. For mass adsorbent 3.4 g, the minimum contact time to achieve 90% removal is 80.8 min while the minimum contact time to achieve the same removal percentage for adsorbent mass 1.7 g is 387.0 min. A large mass adsorbent provides more active site for metal ions to attach hence shorter contact time is needed.

The results from Figure 2a show that the contact time for initial concentrations 1.0 and 1.5 mmol/L is lower than initial metal ion concentration 3.0 mmol/L. This is due to the fact that at higher metal ion concentration, the adsorbent active sites are more limited and longer contact time is needed. To overcome the problem, more adsorbent mass can be used to reduce the contact time by providing more sites for the reaction. In Figure 2b, the minimum contact time for 1.0, 1.5 and 3.0 mmol/L were reduced from 312.5, 402.5 and 1031.8 min to 73.3, 90.3 and 151.2 min respectively by increasing the mass of adsorbent from 1.7 to 3.4 g.

Table 2 summarize the results obtained by using two stage batch system to achieve 90, 95 and 99% removal at different metal ion initial concentrations and adsorbent mass = 1.7g.

Table 2: Calculated minimum contact times to achieve 99%, 95% and 90% cadmium removal for different initial concentrations and 1.7g of adsorbent.

C_o (mmol L^{-1})	Minimum contact time (min) one stage absorber T	Minimum contact time (min) two stage absorber		
		Stage 1 t_1	Stage 2 t_2	T (t_1+t_2)
99% removal				
1	676.3	65.0	247.5	312.5
1.5	1609.5	155.0	247.5	402.5
3	4118.1	200.0	831.8	1031.8
95% removal				
1	520.4	60.0	149.9	209.8
1.5	1193.9	125.0	137.7	262.7
3	2967.5	150.0	490.3	640.3
90% removal				
1	374.3	50.0	86.3	136.3
1.5	821.4	80.0	90.1	170.1
3	1969.2	100.0	287.0	387.0

The results show that the contact time for stage 1 is shorter than contact time for stage 2 due to the higher activation and strong bonding. In stage 1, high initial concentration and availability of active site speed up the reaction. Therefore, a shorter contact time is needed. In stage 2, the initial concentration of metal ion has been reduced from C_0 to C_1 and the active sites available for the ions exchange have been limited. Hence, a longer contact time is needed. Figure 1 and 2 also show that the optimum point is much more defined for larger mass and lower initial concentration.

4. Conclusion

The Elovich kinetic model was observed to be the most effective and accurate kinetic model for cadmium removal using nanochitosan. Therefore, a method for optimizing the contact times required to remove cadmium from wastewater based on an Elovich kinetic model has been designed to help developing a process system in a two-stage batch adsorber system. The optimum time in stage 1 was significantly less than stage 2 and showed a strong optimal point (more sensitive design) for systems operated at larger adsorbent masses and lower pollutant concentrations. The two-stage batch absorber showed a large decrease in volume compared to a one-stage process that has been enhanced when low release levels such as regulatory limits had to be fulfilled.

Acknowledgment

One of the authors (HA) wishes to thank the Qatar National Leadership Program of the Qatar National Research Foundation for a scholarship award.

References

Alyasi, H., Mackey, H.R., Loganathan K., & McKay, G. (2020) Adsorbent minimisation in a two-stage batch adsorber for cadmium removal. *J. Ind. Eng. Chem.* 81, 153-160. doi: 10.1016/j.jiec.2019.09.003.

Alyasi, H., Mackey, H. R., & McKay, G. (2019). Removal of cadmium from waters by adsorption using nanochitosan. *Energy & Environment*, 0958305X19876191. doi: 10.1177/0958305X19876191

Anand, S., Hadi, P., Hui, C.-W., Ansari, T. A., & McKay, G. (2017). Optimisation of the Removal of Arsenate from Water using Nanochitosan. *Des. Water Treat.*, 1-9. doi: 10.5004/dwt.2017.20561

Ho, Y. S., & McKay, G. (1999). Pseudo-second order model for sorption processes. *Process Biochem, 34*, 451-465.

Jaishankar, M., Tseten, T., Anbalagan, N., Mathew, B. B., & Beeregowda, K. N. (2014). Toxicity, mechanism and health effects of some heavy metals. *Interdisciplinary toxicology, 7*(2), 60-72. doi: 10.2478/intox-2014-0009

Pal, P., & Pal, A. (2017). Modifications of Chitosan for Cadmium Removal: A Short Review. *Journal of Polymer Materials, 34*(1), 331-341.

Valko, M., Jomova, K., Rhodes, C. J., Kuča, K., & Musílek, K. (2016). Redox- and non-redox-metal-induced formation of free radicals and their role in human disease. *Archives of Toxicology, 90*(1), 1-37. doi: 10.1007/s00204-015-1579-5

Sauro Pierucci, Flavio Manenti, Giulia Bozzano, Davide Manca (Eds.)
Proceedings of the 30th European Symposium on Computer Aided Process Engineering
(ESCAPE30), May 24-27, 2020, Milano, Italy. © 2020 Elsevier B.V. All rights reserved.
http://dx.doi.org/10.1016/B978-0-12-823377-1.50068-9

Cost-Effective Processes of Solar District Heating System Based on Optimal Artificial Neural Network

Mohamed Hany Abokersh,[a] Manel Vallès,[a] Laureano Jiménez,[b] Dieter Boer,[a]

[a]Departament d'Enginyeria Mecànica, Universitat Rovira i Virgili, Av. Països Catalans 26, 43007 Tarragona, Spain

[b]Departament d'Enginyeria Química, Universitat Rovira i Virgili, Av. Països Catalans 26, 43007 Tarragona, Spain

Dieter.boer@urv.cat

Abstract

Aligning with the EU 2030 climate and energy package to achieve a share of at least 27% of renewable energies, and to improve the energy efficiency by at least 27%, the future solar district heating systems (SDHS) may enable the transition to a complete renewable society. Even though this promising tendency of the SDHS, a range of potential barriers are obstructing the wide deployment of SDHS and promoting high variation in quantifying the SDHS benefits over its lifetime. In this context, the optimization approaches are a viable option for determining the optimal structure, sizing, and operation of the SDHS. However, Meta-heuristics optimization models are computationally very expensive and have many limitations regarding the optimization process. Aligning with these challenges, this work tends to develop a robust Artificial Neural Network model based on Bayesian Optimization to solve the computational obstacle associated with heuristics optimization models for SDHS.

Keywords: Solar District Heating, Cost-effective, TRNSYS, Artificial Neural Network, Bayesian Optimization.

1. Introduction

One goal of the European Union "2030 Agenda for Sustainable Development" (European Commission, 2012) is the transition to a more efficient, and sustainable energy future that will include high shares of renewable energy in the global energy mix with major intention to cut 80% of the green emission. A promising pathway towards this vision lies in the adoption of solar district heating systems (SDHS). SDHS are placed in proximity to the energy end-use sector they serve, hence, minimizing energy transmission losses and incorporating locally available energy resources. Moreover, they typically incorporate multiple energy carriers and renewable and other efficient technologies that convert, store and deliver energy in the form of heating, cooling, and electricity or as other energy carriers (e.g., hydrogen) (Di Somma et al., 2015), which allows them to increase operational flexibility. Overall, SDHS delivers a series of economic, environmental, and technical benefits, as discussed in (Akorede et al., 2010). However, the vast quantity of combinations of available devices into a SDHS and the specific subsidies require a systematic analysis and evaluation method (Yang et al., 2015), making modeling and optimization approaches a viable option for determining the optimal structure, sizing and operation of SDHS.

During the design phase of a SDHS, several questions are answered by a quantitative analysis, which is usually performed with specific software simulation tools. However, the complexity of the system increases rapidly with the increment in the design variables. The coupling between the stochastic energy production and the energy consumption determined by the system properties makes the influences of single elements hard to estimate without the appropriate tools. In this respect, software simulation tools (TRNSYS, Modelica, EnergyPlus, etc.) offer the possibility to achieve a high level of rationalization and transparency, enabling users to make informed choices. However, in order to produce accurate results, the level of abstraction of the system description must be accurately chosen. For instance, the system parametrization must cover all relevant variables, and the resolution of the weather data used must be relevant. Thus, a significant amount of time is required for completing a simulation with the use of a detailed (e.g., first principles) model, which we will call a fine model.

This computational obstacle of SDHS simulation may be overcome by supercomputers, cloud computing, or metamodeling. Supercomputers are expensive if not managed efficiently to avoid downtime. Cloud computing is presumably a cheaper alternative. Still, if the design team wishes to perform sensitivity analysis to identify relevant inputs or interaction effects, such analysis easily requires thousands of simulations to cover the design space sufficiently. This is likely to take hours or days – even with access to cloud computers (Yang, 2011). In this work we aim to create a fast-robust machine learning technique based on an artificial neural network (ANN) to predict the performance of the SDHS with diverse outputs. This will be a bridge to introduce the disciplines of Meta-heuristics optimization in SDHS simulation models.

2. Methodology Framework

The robust machine learning framework of this study includes three sequential steps. First, a set of SDHS cases were created and simulated in TRNSYS with different decision variables for the sizing and operation of the equipment, resulting in a simulation generated database. The hyperparameters of the ANN, such as the number of hidden layers, the number of neurons per hidden layer, the activation function, etc. are often set via rules of thumb or trial and error. However, suitable hyperparameters depend on the system considered and generally cannot be determined beforehand. For this propose, the Bayesian optimization is employed to find a suitable set of hyperparameters for the prediction of the ANNs. Once the robust optimal design of the ANN is achieved, in the third step, the simulations generated data are used to train and validate the robust ANN-based model for predicting the performance of the SDHS instead of using a software simulation tool (TRNSYS).

2.1. SDHS Model in TRNSYS

The SDHS is designed to fulfill energy demands for space heating (SH) and domestic hot water (DHW) in a residential sector. Usually, these systems are designed to supply district heating for more than 100 apartments with a solar fraction of approximately 50%. The main components of the SDHS simulation model, as shown in Figure 1, are the thermal solar collector, the seasonal storage tank (SST), and the DHW storage tank (DHWT). The solar collector transfers the heat gained from the solar radiation to the storage tanks, which is then supplied to the customer on demand. The mismatching between the energy supply and demand in the daily and seasonal bases is balanced through the storage tanks. Auxiliary natural gas heaters are installed to back up the required heat demand in case the solar heating system failed to cover it. The SST based on water storage tank facilitates long-term storage of thermal energy used to cover the SH demand during the winter season with solar energy stored during a summer period. The long-term storage implies relatively large dimensions for the SST, which favors slow charging and discharging processes. On the other hand, the

DHWT is a short-term independent storage tank which is used to cover the daily DHW service at a temperature of 60°C. The proposed simulation model follows the models previously developed by Tulus et al. (Tulus et al., 2016).

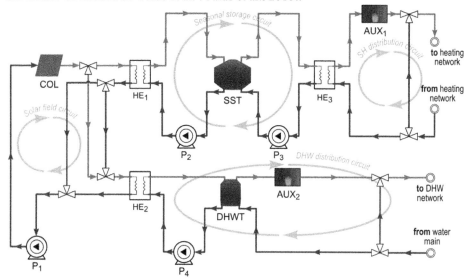

Figure 1: Process flow diagram of the SDHS simulated in TRNSYS 18

2.2. Robust ANN model approach

The robust surrogate model building process has been divided into two main steps; the model setting selection and the model convergence testing. In the first step (Step A), this study emphasizes on the model settings and its relative hyperparameters through using the Bayesian optimization approach at different training set sizes. In the second step (Step B), the convergence of the ANN model is assessed through testing the develop a surrogate model based on the optimal model settings under a wide range of training set to define the optimal sample size.

3. Results and discussion

The results of the model setting and its convergence with various training sets are summarized in this section. First, the results of Bayesian optimization are analyzed for three primary training set to define the optimal setting model. Then, the ANN performance is tested under various training sets to identify the optimal sample size with consideration for the computational model expenses.

3.1. Model Setting

The solution of Bayesian optimization is given by an interactive parallel coordinate plot to identify suitable hyperparameters settings for the reduced number of configurations in step B (see.Figure 2). The plot shows the top 20% ranked optimal solutions results comprising 500 ANN model settings where each line represents one of these optimal solutions along with the achieved coefficient of variation ($C.V$) values. The table below the interactive parallel coordinate plots shows the optimal metamodel setting that achieves the highest accuracy at step (A) training sets. In case of no agreement for selecting a certain optimal setting at different sample sizes, the histogram attached to each interactive parallel coordinate column is utilized to propose the most frequently setting at each hyperparameter. The hyperparameters, including the training function, number of layers, layer function, hidden function, and momentum mean at each training set, have the same optimal setting at different training sets, whereas the number of neurons and learning rate change at each training set. As observed from the histogram, most of the optimal results setting for the learning rate are set in a range below 0.01. Thus, the learning rate is set to 0.001 for the convergence stage (step B) to sustain the training set converge. On the other hand, the number of neurons with the size of 3, 14, and 20 are set for the convergence stage (Step B) since its optimal value is different for the training set size 64, 256, and 1024. A summary of the selected settings in the convergence stage (step B) is shown in the below table in Figure 2, where the nominated settings are highlighted.

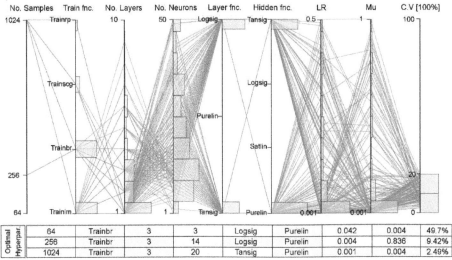

	No. Samples	Train fnc.	No. Layers	No. Neurons	Layer fnc.	Hidden fnc.	LR	Mu	C.V [100%]
Optimal Hyperpar.	64	Trainbr	3	3	Logsig	Purelin	0.042	0.004	49.7%
	256	Trainbr	3	14	Logsig	Purelin	0.004	0.836	9.42%
	1024	Trainbr	3	20	Tansig	Purelin	0.001	0.004	2.49%

Figure 2: interactive parallel coordinate plot combined with histograms are utilized to identify the optimal hypermeters setting for the ANN model in step A. The plot shows the top 20% ranked ANN model settings. The table below shows the optimal hyperparameters

Following the interactive parallel coordinate plot, a box plot (see. Figure 3) is built to show the performance of the three-training sets (64, 256, and 1024) based on the $C.V$ rank under the optimal selected hyperparameters with considering for three neurons sizes comprising 3, 14, and 20 in comparison to the default settings.

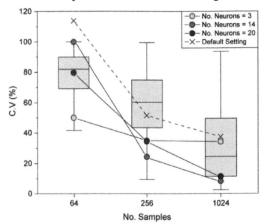

Figure 3: Box plot for the output in step A including the ANN model performance under the optimal and default settings

The box plot is characterized by the central mark and the upper and lower quartiles, which correspond to the box edge and show other optimal solutions. While the minimum and maximum optimal values are indicated at the whiskers. On the plot, the lined circles at each sample size show the results under optimal settings at a different number of neurons, whereas the cross symbols represent the results at the default settings. In general, the default setting does not yield to build accurate ANN models that approve the importance hyperparameters tuning. Moreover, fixing the number of neurons at 14 provides the most accurate results with a $C.V$ value of 24.1% and 9.2% for the 256 and 1024 training set, respectively.

3.2. Model Setting

In step B, we test the performance of the selected optimal hyperparameters at various training sizes in order to choose the most accurate ANN model with consideration for its efficiency in terms of the computational cost, as shown in Figure 4.

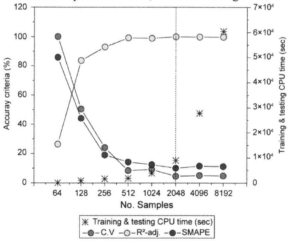

Figure 4: Convergence of accuracy criteria at various training size with consideration for its relative computational cost

In terms of the convergence, three accuracy criteria comprising the adjusted R-squared (R^2-adj), $C.V$, and Symmetric mean absolute percentage error (SMAPE) are utilized to evaluate the performance of the ANN model. The results show that the R^2-adj is a misleading criterion since most of the sample sizes excess 97%. Therefore, using $C.V$ and SMAPE can be more efficient to measure the ANN model accuracy. Increasing the sample size has a clear tendency to improve the ANN model accuracy where the highest accurate value of 4.5% and 10% was indicated in a sample size of 2048 for the $C.V$ and SMAPE criterion, respectively.

In terms of the ANN model computational cost, an exponential behavior is indicated by increasing the sample size where the CPU time at 8192 sample size is 6×10^4 sec. Comprising the model accuracy with its efficiency simultaneously, the sample size 2048 provides the highest accuracy at an affordable computational time of 8.9×10^3 sec using an Intel® Xeon® E5-2620 v4 2.10 GHz processor with 32.0 GB RAM.

4. Conclusion

Following the high computational expenses obstacles associated with the SDHS simulation, this study proposes a complete framework based on a robust ANN model to solve this computational obstacle. a summary of the robust ANN model key findings is the following:

- Relate to the ANN model settings, the hyperparameters comprising the number of hidden layers at 3, the number of neurons at 14, training function at Bayesian regularization, layer function at logsig, hidden function at purelin, learning rate at 0.001 and Momentum mean at 0.004 show the highest accurate ANN model at various training set size.
- Relate to the ANN model convergence at different training set sizes, the sample size of 2048 shows the highest accurate model prediction, where the $C.V$ criterion does not get below 4.5% for all model outputs at an affordable computational time of 8.9×10^3 sec.

In general, the proposed robust surrogate model built based on the two-model steps offers a sufficient approach for the construction of fast metamodels to overcome the computational barrier related to design space exploration, design optimization, and sensitivity analysis of heuristics optimization models.

Acknowledgment

The authors would like to acknowledge financial support from the Spanish Ministry of Economy and Competitiveness (RTI2018-093849-B-C33 (MCIU/AEI/FEDER, UE) and CTQ2016-77968 (MINECO/FEDER)) and to thank the Catalan Government for the quality accreditation given to their research group (2017 SGR 1409). This project has received funding from the European Union's Horizon 2020 research and innovation programme under the Marie Skłodowska-Curie grant agreement No. 713679 and from the Universitat Rovira i Virgili (URV).

References

Akorede, M.F., Hizam, H., Pouresmaeil, E., 2010. Distributed energy resources and benefits to the environment. Renew. Sustain. Energy Rev. 14, 724–734. https://doi.org/10.1016/j.rser.2009.10.025

Di Somma, M., Yan, B., Bianco, N., Graditi, G., Luh, P.B., Mongibello, L., Naso, V., 2015. Operation optimization of a distributed energy system considering energy costs and exergy efficiency. Energy Convers. Manag. 103, 739–751. https://doi.org/10.1016/j.enconman.2015.07.009

European Commission, 2012. Energy: Roadmap 2050, European Commissioner for Energy. https://doi.org/10.2833/10759

Klein, S.A. et al., 2004. TRNSYS Version. 18, Solar Energy Laboratory, University of Wisconsin-Madison, Website: <http://sel.me.wisc.edu/ trnsys>.

Tulus, V., Boer, D., Cabeza, L.F., Jiménez, L., Guillén-Gosálbez, G., 2016. Enhanced thermal energy supply via central solar heating plants with seasonal storage: A multi-objective optimization approach. Appl. Energy 181, 549–561. https://doi.org/10.1016/j.apenergy.2016.08.037

Yang, J., 2011. Convergence and uncertainty analyses in Monte-Carlo based sensitivity analysis. Environ. Model. Softw. 26, 444–457. https://doi.org/10.1016/j.envsoft.2010.10.007

Yang, Y., Zhang, S., Xiao, Y., 2015. Optimal design of distributed energy resource systems coupled withenergy distribution networks. Energy 85, 433–448. https://doi.org/10.1016/j.energy.2015.03.101

Sauro Pierucci, Flavio Manenti, Giulia Bozzano, Davide Manca (Eds.)
Proceedings of the 30th European Symposium on Computer Aided Process Engineering
(ESCAPE30), May 24-27, 2020, Milano, Italy. © 2020 Elsevier B.V. All rights reserved.
http://dx.doi.org/10.1016/B978-0-12-823377-1.50069-0

Packed-bed and Microchannel Reactors for the Reactive Capture of CO₂ within Power-to-Methane (P2M) Context: A Comparison

Santiago Ortiz [a], Camilo Rengifo [b], Martha Cobo [c], Manuel Figueredo [d,*]

[a] *Master in Process Design and Management. Faculty of Engineering, Universidad de La Sabana, Km. 7 Autopista Norte, Bogotá, Colombia.*

[b] *Department of Mathematics, Physics and Statistics. Faculty of Engineering, Universidad de La Sabana, Km. 7 Autopista Norte, Bogotá, Colombia.*

[a, c, d] *Energy, Materials, and Environment Laboratory. Department of Chemical Engineering, Universidad de La Sabana, Km. 7 Autopista Norte, Bogotá, Colombia.*
manuel.figueredo@unisabana.edu.co

Abstract

Carbon capture and utilization technologies have recently boomed as strategies to decrease carbon dioxide (CO_2) emissions, in which methanation (via-Sabatier process) seems to be a prominent pathway. However, CO_2 methanation involves technical challenges to be overcome, such as heat removal and high intermittency during the operation. This study assesses the operation of a packed-bed and a microreactor in the Synthetic Natural Gas (SNG) production through computational fluid dynamics modeling. The data compilation from simulations and further analysis provides valuable information about hot spots formation and CO_2 conversion under established dimensional specifications and cooling conditions. From the above configurations, microreactor configuration was the best option to control the hot spot formation without leaving aside the SNG production.

Keywords: Methanation, Microreactor, Packed–bed reactor; Hot spot formation, Computational Fluid Dynamics.

1. Introduction

Carbon Capture and Utilization (CCU) technologies such as Power-to-methane (P2M) have brought advantages to overcome the environmental issues by reducing greenhouse gas emissions. Accordingly, P2M aims to capture carbon dioxide (CO_2) and transform it into methane (CH_4) to produce Synthetic Natural Gas (SNG) by catalytic methanation (Ghaib and Ben-Fares, 2018). However, CO_2 methanation exhibits a highly exothermic nature that triggers the hot spots formation inside the reactor and, therefore, contributes to catalyst deactivation. Moreover, appropriate heat management is challenging owing to the operation intermittency that catalytic methanation units must deal under the P2M context. Consequently, maintaining the operating temperature within an ideal range without leaving aside the CH_4 production presents a technological trial (Sun et al., 2017). Several studies have tackled this technical challenge considering aspects in the reactor design (Schlereth and Hinrichsen, 2014) or by proposing optimal control strategies (Bremer and Sundmacher, 2019). In most of the cases, packed bed reactors (PBRs) have been selected as the catalytic-reaction system. Nonetheless, some alternative reaction technologies have also been proposed so far, such as microchannel reactors (Engelbrecht et al., 2017). These reactors may afford large heat- and mass-transfer rates that ease heat removal from the system due to high interfacial surface areas and short diffusion paths

(Némethné-Sóvágó and Benke, 2014). Hence, improving CCU technologies is necessary to make alternatives suchlike P2M more competitive within the electricity and fuel markets. However, their improvement will be barely accomplished without a deeper understanding of the process fundamentals. This research aims to compare the operation of a microchannel and average PBR employed for CO_2 methanation through Computational Fluid Dynamics (CFD). This study focuses on analyzing the thermal performance of both reactors owing to the importance that this matter represents within the P2M context.

2. Model formulation

2.1. Methanation reactions and kinetics

During CO_2-methanation there are multiple reactions involved. Nevertheless, for simulation, modeling purposes and available information about kinetics, only the Sabatier reaction is considered:

$$CO_2 + 4H_2 \Leftrightarrow CH_4 + 2H_2O \quad ; \quad \Delta H_R^{298K} = -164.9 \, kJ \, mol^{-1}.$$

Methanation reactions are thermodynamically favored at lower temperatures. Therefore, more active and thermally fewer sensitive catalysts should be employed. Consequently, with the purpose of including a state-of-the-art methanation catalyst, this research, employs the model proposed by Koschany et al. (2016) for Ni/SiO$_2$. It relies on a Langmuir-Hinshelwood-Hougen-Watson (LHHW) type rate equation and it is parametrized for the Sabatier reaction:

$$r_{Sab}^{intrinsic} = k \, p_{H_2}^{0.5} p_{CO_2}^{0.5} \left(1 - \frac{p_{CH_4} p_{H_2O}^2}{p_{CO_2} p_{H_2}^4 K_{eq}}\right)/DEN^2 , \tag{1}$$

$$DEN = 1 + K_{OH} \frac{p_{H_2O}}{p_{H_2}^{0.5}} + K_{H_2} p_{H_2}^{0.5} + K_{mix} p_{CO_2}^{0.5} , \tag{2}$$

where p_α accounts for the species partial pressure, k refers to the catalytic rate coefficient, and K_{eq} denotes the temperature dependent equilibrium constant, Eq.(1). Further, DEN is a dimensionless parameter determined by correlations of the adsorption constants (K_x), Eq.(2). For a detailed description about Ni/SiO$_2$ kinetic parametrization refers to Koschany et al. (2016).

2.2. Reaction systems

2.2.1. Packed-bed reactor

Regarding PBR, this study considers the simulation of one single tube part of an entire tube-bundle pilot-scale reactor employed in the methanation process. These reactors are composed by heat exchangers and reacting tubes of relatively small diameters (i.e., 1 - 5 cm) and lengths (i.e., 0.3 - 10 m) (El Sibai et al., 2015). Bremer et al. (2019) evaluated some control strategies for CO_2−methanation in PBRs, aiming to avoid distinct hot spots formation. Therefore, this study harnesses some of the reactor parameters applied in that research (close reactor dimensions, cooling and feed conditions).

2.2.2. Microreactor

A 2-D geometry of a single micro-channel was used for the CFD simulations. All micro-channels were assumed to be identical. They were established as follows: height = 190μm and length = 5cm. The microchannel model is composed of a free-fluid region together with a porous catalytic washcoat layer of 40 μm, as exemplified by Engelbrecht et al. (2017). The latter implies the coupling and computation of two sets of PDEs referring to mass-, heat- and momentum- transport in each domain.

2.3. Governing transport phenomena

Both reactors envisage a porous domain of catalytic nature, leading the reactive source to be exclusively considered within each porous region. Subsequently, governing equations through porous media concerning mass-, heat- and momentum- transport are supposed to be stationary and pseudo-homogeneous, Eqs.(3-6):

$$\frac{\mu}{\Phi}\boldsymbol{u} = \vec{\nabla} \cdot \left[-PI + \frac{\mu}{\varepsilon_p}(\nabla\boldsymbol{u} + (\nabla\boldsymbol{u})^T) \right] - \frac{\rho\varepsilon_p C_f}{\sqrt{\Phi}}\boldsymbol{u}|\boldsymbol{u}| \quad , \tag{3}$$

$$\vec{\nabla} \cdot (\varepsilon_p \rho \boldsymbol{u}) = 0 \quad , \tag{4}$$

$$\frac{\partial \rho_\propto}{\partial t} = -\boldsymbol{u} \cdot \vec{\nabla}\rho_\propto + D_\propto^{eff}(\nabla^2\rho_\propto) + (1-\varepsilon)M_\propto \, v_{\propto_{Sab}} \, r_{Sab}^{eff} \quad , \tag{5}$$

$$(\rho C_p)^{eff} \frac{\partial T}{\partial t} = -\sum_\propto (\rho_\propto C_{p_\propto})\boldsymbol{u} \cdot \vec{\nabla}T + \lambda^{eff}(\nabla^2 T) - (1-\varepsilon)(\Delta_R H_{Sab})r_{Sab}^{eff} \quad . \tag{6}$$

Momentum transport was modeled with the Brinkman-Forchheimer extended Darcy equation, Eqs.(3-4); where μ denotes the dynamic viscosity, $\boldsymbol{u}$ the fluid velocity, ρ the fluid's density ($\rho_\propto$ for single component density), P the total pressure, Φ the porous permeability, ε_p the bed porosity, and C_f the dimensionless friction coefficient as a function of ε_p. Likewise, mass- and heat- transfer are computed through Eq.(5) and Eq.(6), respectively. These models include mass ($D_\propto^{eff}$) and heat (λ^{eff}) dispersion effective coefficients as well as temperature-dependent thermo-physical properties obtained by polynomial correlations referred to as NASA format. Further, the resistance effects in the solid and void regions of the catalyst are quantified through an effectiveness factor (η):

$$r_{Sab}^{eff} = \eta \, r_{Sab}^{intrinsic} \quad . \tag{7}$$

This factor exclusively contemplates intraparticle (internal) temperature-dependent diffusion resistances, and its calculation procedure was proposed by Kiewidt and Thöming (2015). Finally, flow through the free channel (fluid region) within the microreactor is described by the stationary, incompressible Navier-Stokes equations:

$$\rho(\boldsymbol{u} \cdot \nabla)\boldsymbol{u} = -\nabla \cdot [-pI + \mu(\nabla\boldsymbol{u})] \quad , \tag{8}$$

$$\nabla \cdot \boldsymbol{u} = 0 \quad . \tag{9}$$

Herein, the gradient operator $\vec{\nabla}$ accounts for the vector $\frac{\partial}{\partial x}\hat{i} + \frac{\partial}{\partial z}\hat{j}$, which provides a two (2) dimensional notation for the model spatial distribution.

3. Computational and simulation aspects

The commercial software COMSOL Multiphysics® was employed to couple and solve the reacting-flow model for each case. 3D simulations no longer reflected different results from 2D simulations, so all the simulations were performed over 2D symmetric domains to reduce computational effort. Furthermore, grid independence was achieved above fine grids for both 2D geometries. PBR and microreactor meshes consist of 101966 and 79318 free-triangular elements, respectively. In addition, methanation simulations were developed in both cases by feeding a stoichiometric gas mixture of H_2/CO_2 (ratio of 4:1) at 400 K and 5 bar. These operating conditions have been found to be favorable for the SNG production and process profitability (Ghaib and Ben-Fares, 2018). Lastly, each porous media is assumed to be loaded with spherical particles of catalyst Ni/SiO₂.

4. Results and discussion

This section presents the CFD modeling results of both PBR and microreactor used for CO_2 methanation, together with the appropriate comparative discussion. The reactor axial (relative) position z was normalized with respect to the total length L. Besides, the CO_2 is given by Eq.(10), where ρ_{CO_2} is the CO_2 mass concentration, g/m^3.

$$X_{CO_2} = \frac{\rho_{CO_2}|in - \Sigma \rho_{CO_2}|_{z/L=1}}{\rho_{CO_2}|in}. \qquad (10)$$

4.1. Effect of coolant temperature on CO_2 conversion

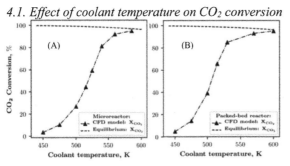

Figure 1. Effect of the CJ temperature on CO_2 conversion for microreactor (A) and PBR (B).

As a point of reference, the maximum achievable conversion, based on a thermodynamic analysis, was carried out in AspenPlus™. This evaluation was developed at 5 bar, at the coolant temperature. The Peng-Robinson package was used to model the gas mixture. Figure 1 shows that regardless the reaction exothermic nature (thermodynamically limited at higher temperatures), the higher the temperature of the Cooling Jacket (CJ), the higher the CO_2 conversion. Therefore, at low temperatures (< 500 K), the Ni/SiO_2 is not active enough to convert more than 45 % of reagent into SNG in any of the reactors with such dimensions and catalytic features. Still, an increment on the jacket temperature chemically activates the system until it is thermodynamically limited. Nevertheless, unlike the microreactor, in the PBR, higher coolant temperatures are required to achieve conversions close to equilibrium.

4.2. Effect of coolant temperature on Hot spot formation

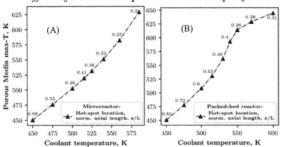

Figure 2: Effect of the CJ temperature on the hot spot max-T (with location) for microreactor (A) and PBR (B).

As a result of the chemical activation caused by temperature increment in the CJ, the formation of hot spots is also triggered. Figure 2 presents the temperature of the hottest spots inside each reactor. This analysis was performed over the axial coordinate (symmetric plane for the PBR) and along the porous-fluid media interface (referring to the microreactor). The rise of the coolant temperature has not only a direct impact on the max-temperature reached by the system (hot spot), but also its axial location. Each marker-text indicates the axial position (normalized, z/L) where the hot spot max-T occurs. The location of the hot spot approaches the reactor entrance as the coolant temperature increases ascribed to speeded activation effects resulting from heat-transfer from wall in each case. In other words, the residence time required to attain a precise conversion becomes shorter. Otherwise, when comparing both reactors, the hot spots temperature within the PBR (Figure 2A) exceeds

Packed-bed and Microchannel Reactors for the Reactive Capture of CO$_2$
within Power-to-Methane (P2M) Context: A Comparison
413

the microreactor (Figure 2B), despite the wall temperature is the same. At first glance, this disparity should represent an improvement in reaction kinetics within the PBR. However, the space-times required to reach certain conversions in this reactor are "delayed". This affair may be better understood by inspecting the effectiveness factor as discussed in the following section.

4.3. Study case comparison

4.3.1. Hot spot formation

A heterogeneous catalytic system is susceptible to the wall temperature when it comes to an exothermic reaction since hot spots are unavoidable. Figure 3 depicts the isothermal contours of both microreactor and PBR when CJ operates at 588K. It can be appreciated that even though the max-T reached in both cases differ by about 15 degrees, the

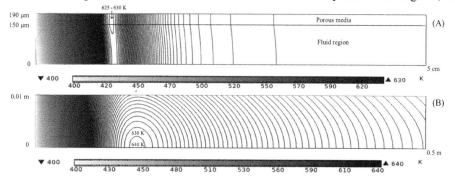

Figure 3: Isothermal contours of microreactor (A) and PBR (B), with a stochiometric gas feed (H2:CO2, 4:1) at 400 K, 5 bar, and a constant wall temperature of 588 K.

thermally affected area is greater within the PBR. It means that the energy dispersion in the packed-bed suffers a higher transfer resistance than in the microreactor due to reactor dimensions, leading energy removal to be less efficient. Therefore, the radial temperature profile is no longer negligible in the PBR. Besides, the role of the free-fluid region is also relevant within the microreactor owing to the provision of a convective energy dispersion, which decreases the energy accumulation in a specific location inside this reactor. Moreover, note that within the later, this accumulation of energy is mainly located at the porous media. Unlike the PBR, where the energy is concentrated at the furthest site from the wall (the symmetric plane).

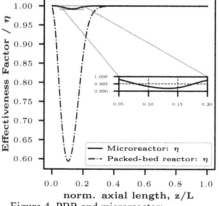

Figure 4. PBR and microreactor: Effectiveness factor (η) comparison.

4.3.2. Effectiveness factor involvement

The solid-fluid interaction in heterogeneous processes is associated with transfer resistances at catalyst level, which can be accounted through the Effectiveness Factor (EF). Figure 4 compares the PBR and microreactor EFs from the study case in section 4.3.1. In both cases, it is shown that the formation of the hot spot concurs with the lowest EF. Notwithstanding, the hot spot presence implies a catalytic rate peak regardless of a drop in the EF, pointing that, there is a thermal effect prevailing over other factors (transfer-resistances, heat removal, and the EF itself). The EF reached higher values in the microreactor because catalyst particle size was about 330 times smaller (0.002 m / 6 µm) than in PBR, which causes an almost negligible effect on the transport-resistances (catalyst internal diffusion). Therefore, regardless the formation of more extensive hot spots in the PBR, said reactor had longer residence time than microreactors.

5. Conclusions and Outlook

This work compares the operation (under the criteria of hot spots formation) of a microreactor and PBR to produce SNG from H_2 and CO_2 by CFD modeling. This approach represents a sharp insight to better understand the integration between the transport processes and the intrinsic chemistry of CO_2 methanation. Simulations showed the direct relation between cooling jacket temperature and hot spots formation (max-T and its location). Indeed, the exemplified microreactor allows both more efficient heat removal and conversions closer to the equilibrium. On the other hand, PBR must be operated under stricter cooling strategies to avoid larger hot spots, while affecting the SNG production. Efficient heat-removal strategies are key point on the CO_2 methanation to maintain a suitable balance between kinetic and thermodynamic limitations, as well as a techno-economic feasibility that warrants the operability of the process. Moreover, results showed the relevance of involving the EF calculation as it becomes substantial to determine the effective reaction rate within the system. Lastly, this study represents a first step analysis in the search for a suitable reactor technology. However, additional variables should be incorporated into the sensibility evaluation to boost methanation systems with P2M applications.

References

J. Bremer and K. Sundmacher, 2019. Operation range extension via hot-spot control for catalytic CO_2 methanation reactors. Reaction Chemistry and Engineering, 4(6), 1019–1037.

A. El Sibai, L. Rihko-Struckmann and K. Sundmacher, 2015. Synthetic Methane from CO_2: Dynamic Optimization of the Sabatier Process for Power-to-Gas Applications. Computer Aided Chemical Engineering (Vol. 37).

N. Engelbrecht, S. Chiuta, R. C. Everson, H. W. J. P. Neomagus and D. G. Bessarabov, 2017. Experimentation and CFD modelling of a microchannel reactor for carbon dioxide methanation. Chemical Engineering Journal, 313, 847–857.

K. Ghaib and F.-Z. Ben-Fares, 2018. Power-to-Methane: A state-of-the-art review. Renewable and Sustainable Energy Reviews, 81(June 2017), 433–446.

L. Kiewidt and J. Thöming, 2015. Predicting optimal temperature profiles in single-stage fixed-bed reactors for CO_2-methanation. Chemical Engineering Science, 132, 59–71.

F. Koschany, D. Schlereth and O. Hinrichsen, 2016. On the kinetics of the methanation of carbon dioxide on coprecipitated $NiAl(O)_x$. Applied Catalysis B: Environmental, 181, 504–516.

J. Némethné-Sóvágó and M. Benke, 2014. Microreactors: a new concept for chemical synthesis and technological feasibility. Materials Science and Engineering, 39(2), 89–101.

D. Schlereth and O. Hinrichsen, 2014. A fixed-bed reactor modeling study on the methanation of CO_2. Chemical Engineering Research and Design, 92(4), 702–712.

D. Sun, F. M. Khan and D. S. A. Simakov, 2017. Heat removal and catalyst deactivation in a Sabatier reactor for chemical fixation of CO_2 : Simulation-based analysis. Chemical Engineering Journal, 329, 165–177.

Sauro Pierucci, Flavio Manenti, Giulia Bozzano, Davide Manca (Eds.)
Proceedings of the 30th European Symposium on Computer Aided Process Engineering
(ESCAPE30), May 24-27, 2020, Milano, Italy. © 2020 Elsevier B.V. All rights reserved.
http://dx.doi.org/10.1016/B978-0-12-823377-1.50070-7

Design and Eco-techno-economic Analyses of SOFC /Gas Turbine Hybrid Systems Accounting for Long-Term Degradation

Haoxiang Lai,[a] Nor Farida Harun,[b] David Tucker,[b] and Thomas A. Adams II[a*]

[a] *McMaster University, Department of Chemical Engineering, Hamilton, ON, Canada*
[b] *US Department of Energy, National Energy Technology Laboratory, Morgantown, WV, USA*
tadams@mcmaster.ca

Abstract

Solid oxide fuel cells (SOFCs) are a promising next-generation technology for power production from fossil fuels. Because they convert chemical energy into electricity electrochemically, they are generally more efficient than combustion-based power plants due to the thermodynamic limitations of combustion cycles, and accordingly, have lower carbon intensities. However, one of the major drawbacks of SOFCs is that they degrade over time, and the degradation rate varies with different operating conditions. When operated in constant power mode (the most common way of baseload power production), the degradation rate is fast such that the lifetime of the SOFC stack is around one tenth of that when in constant voltage mode (in which the power output from SOFC stack decreases). To achieve baseload power production and a long lifetime simultaneously, one potential solution is to integrate SOFC stack (operated in constant voltage mode) with a gas turbine (GT) in a SOFC/GT hybrid system. As the SOFC stack degrades, the power produced from GT increases over time by using the increasing heating value of the unspent fuel from the SOFC exhaust. We performed an eco-technoeconomic analysis (eTEA) of the SOFC/GT concept with degradation in comparison with the SOFC standalone system. The results of model simulations showed that, with certain operating conditions, the SOFC/GT hybrid system was around 36% more efficient than the SOFC standalone system, and also had about 18 times longer lifetime. On a 550 MW scale and 30-year-lifetime, SOFC/GT hybrid system can reduce the levelized cost of electricity (LCOE) by around 80 % as well as CO_2 emission by around 27 %, compared to the SOFC standalone system. The results show that SOFC/GT hybrids are a promising near-term approach because existing SOFC technology can be used directly while both avoiding short cell lifetimes and still getting near-baseload performance.

Keywords: Solid oxide fuel cell, SOFC/GT hybrid, eco-technoeconomic analysis

1. Introduction

Solid oxide fuel cells (SOFCs) produce power electrochemically, which is more efficient than conventional combustion-based power production processes such as coal power plants (Adams et al., 2013). By using coal-based syngas (a mixture of mainly CO and H_2) as a fuel source, SOFCs generate electricity through electrochemical reactions shown in Figure 1. However, one of the main drawbacks of SOFCs (and SOFC stacks) is that they can degrade over time in a variety of ways, including accruing damage to the anode, cathode, interconnects, and other cell or stack components. SOFCs are most

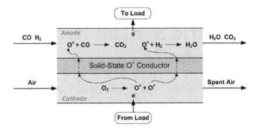

Figure 1. Simple schematic of a SOFC. Reproduced from (Nease and Adams, 2014).

commonly used in constant power mode, in which the fuel flow rate and current density are increased over time to counteract the degradation effects and yield a constant power output. However, higher flow rates cause the degradation rates to grow even faster, resulting in a lifetime potentially as short as 1.5 years (Tucker et al., 2014).

Recent research has found that by operating in constant voltage mode, along with some other operating strategies, SOFC lifetime can greatly increase to as long as 13-14 years (Tucker et al., 2014). However, the power produced decays over time, and in fact, the fuel utilization (the percentage of fuel oxidized in the anode) decays as well. This means that the anode exhaust has a large and increasingly unused heating value. The solution is to use this anode exhaust as a fuel for a gas turbine (GT), creating the SOFC/GT hybrid system (Tucker et al., 2012). The system is designed such that as the SOFC decays in power production while operating in constant voltage mode, the GT turbine increases in power production over time as the anode exhaust heating value increases. The efficiency of the GT changes during its life as well depending on the anode exhaust conditions. The net effect is that the total system power decays slowly over time, and is suitable for baseload grid-power generation in the long term. It is also more efficient than a standalone GT system.

In this work, we present an eco-technoeconomic analysis (eTEA) of the SOFC/GT concept with degradation considered. Dynamic Matlab Simulink models of the SOFC which considers degradation effects were coupled with Aspen Plus steady-state models of the balance of plant in a pseudo-steady approach. This enables the simulation of the gradual degradation of the plant over a 14 year lifetime. This simulation was used to compute key performance indicators like levelized cost of electricity, greenhouse gas emissions, efficiency, and dynamic performance curves for power, current, voltage, fuel utilization, etc. These are used in turn to quantify the trade-offs between standalone SOFC, standalone GT, and SOFC/GT hybrid systems on a power production scale of 550 MW for a lifetime of 30 years.

2. Methodology

The proposed SOFC standalone system consists of two main components: a SOFC stack with a post combustor, and an upstream syngas production and clean-up process (Figure 2). The upstream syngas process provides clean syngas as the fuel source to the SOFC anode, and it includes a coal gasifier (producing syngas from coal), an air separation unit (providing oxygen for the gasifier), scrubber (removing HCl from syngas), water-gas shift reactor (converting CO and H_2O to CO_2 and H_2, also converting COS and H_2O to CO_2 and H_2S), and a Selexol process (a solvent-based H_2S removal process). The

SOFC is operated at near atmospheric pressure, and so cathode air is provided through a blower and then preheated by the gas exhaust from the post-combustion. Similarly, the

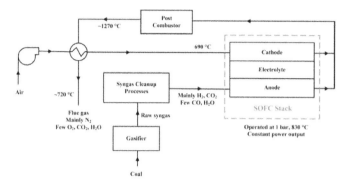

Figure 2. Process flow diagram of SOFC standalone system.

proposed SOFC/GT hybrid system consists of three main components: a SOFC stack with a post combustor, upstream syngas production and clean-up process, and a gas turbine (including a compressor and a recuperator) (Figure 3). The SOFC stack section and the upstream syngas process are the same as in the SOFC standalone system, except that the SOFC stack is operated at 4 bar. The hybrid system also has cold air bypass streams to control the cathode inlet temperature and the gas turbine inlet temperature. In these two proposed systems, models of SOFC stack and post combustor were developed in Matlab Simulink R2017a in a prior work (Zaccaria et al., 2016), and were coupled with steady-state models of the balance-of-the-plant developed in Aspen Plus V10. Because the time scale of degradation is slow, a pseudo-steady-state approach with a weekly time step was used. The models were connected through Aspen Simulation Workbook (add-in application in Microsoft Excel) and macro scripts developed in Microsoft Excel VBA (Visual Basic for Applications). The dynamic model in Simulink considers the spatial degradation over the axial length of the cells over time based on factors such as fuel composition, fuel rate, humidity, utilization, current, voltage, and other factors. The Aspen Plus models were developed using the Peng-Robinson equation of state (EOS) with the Boston-Mathias modification (PR-BM) with a few exceptions: the NBC/NRC steam tables were used for pure water streams, the Electrolyte-NRTL method with Henry coefficients and electrolyte chemistry specification obtained from the AP065 databank was used for streams consisting of mostly CO_2 and H_2O near the critical point, and the Redlich-Kwong-Soave EOS with predictive Holderbraum mixing rules was used for streams consisting of mostly CO_2 and H_2O below the critical point. Since the heating value of the gas turbine inlet stream increased over time as the fuel cells degraded, a gas turbine efficiency curve was considered in the model which accounts for off-design turbine operating conditions. This curve uses propriatary data from the turbine manufacturer (Siemens) for the selected turbine (SGT6-9000HL) and so cannot be released for intellectual property reasons.

3. Results and Discussions

The simulation results of the SOFC standalone system are shown in Figure 4. Figure 4 (a) shows the dynamic performance of the SOFC stack. The power production and fuel utilization were kept as 550 MW and 80 %, respectively. The voltage dropped from the initial condition of around 0.8 V, and the current density increased from 0.5 A/cm². The average temperature of the SOFC stack was maintained at around 830 °C. With the

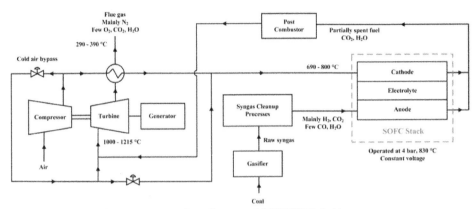

Figure 3. Process flow diagram of SOFC/GT hybrid system.

above operating conditions, the lifetime of the SOFC in the standalone system was around 3132 hours (which is around 19 weeks) before catastrophic breakage was predicted. Figure 4 (b) shows the replacement of SOFC stack every 19 weeks throughout the lifetime of 30 years. The SOFC stack efficiency was defined as the power output from the SOFC stack over the low heating value (LHV) of the portion of the fuel that was consumed by the SOFC stack. The net efficiency was calculated as the net power produced by the system over the LHV of the coal entering the system. The efficiency dropped as SOFC degraded because the stack produced the same amount of power by consuming an increasing amount of fuel. The SOFC standalone plant has a high value of waste heat (flue gas stream in Figure 2) that can be used in a steam bottoming cycle for extra power production, which would alternatively increase the net efficiency of the system. Such combined cycles were not considered in this work.

The dynamic performance of the SOFC stack in the hybrid system can be seen in Figure 5 (a). The SOFC stack was operated in constant voltage mode so that the lifetime of the SOFC stack increased. Although the simulation predicted that catastrophic SOFC breakdown would not occur until about 14 years of use, a practical regular replacement time of 351 weeks (or 6.7 years or 58968 hours) was selected because at this point, the fuel utilization dropped to 25 % from 80 % at the beginning of life. The power output from the SOFC stack decreased to 150 MW which is around 37.5 % of its initial capacity (400 MW) as the fuel utilization dropped to 25 %. Accordingly, the current density dropped from 0.5 A/cm² to around 0.19 A/cm². Further optimization studies would be needed to determine an optimal replacement time of the SOFC stack in the hybrid system. The spatial average temperature of the stack was regulated at 830 °C. Figure 5 (b) shows that the power load shifted from the SOFC stack to the GT as the SOFCs degraded, so that the net power was essentially constant at 550 MW. The GT was designed such that its maximum power capacity would be reached at the end of the lifetime of 351 weeks. As such, the GT efficiency increased over time as the GT operation gradually moves closer to peak design performance. The net efficiency of the whole system decreased gradually over time since the power load was being shifted from a more efficient component SOFC stack to the less efficient GT. Similar to the standalone system, the waste heat could also be captured and used for extra power production in a steam cycle, but this was not considered in this analysis. However, the quality, temperature, and exergetic value of the waste heat in the hybrid system is lower than that of the standalone system.

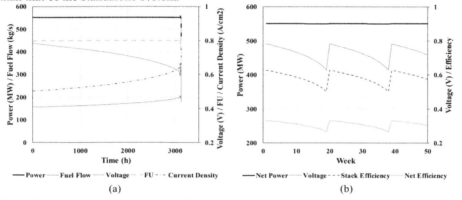

Figure 4. System performance curves of (a) the SOFC stack in SOFC standalone plant and (b) the SOFC standalone plant.

Table 1 summarizes the key parameters for the eco-technoeconomic comparison between the SOFC standalone plant and the SOFC/GT hybrid plant. The costs of the plants were estimated based on literature (Adams et al., 2017; James et al., 2019). SOFC stacks were purchased and replaced in a cycle of 19 weeks for SOFC standalone plant, and in a cycle of 351 weeks for SOFC/GT hybrid plant over the 30-year-lifetime. The first year capital cost of SOFC standalone plant was higher than SOFC/GT hybrid plant, because three SOFC stacks with a capacity of 550 MW were needed in the standalone plant while only one stack with a capacity of 400 MW was needed in the hybrid plant. The SOFC/GT hybrid plant has higher efficiency, lower costs, and lower greenhouse gas emission than the SOFC standalone plant over the 30-year-lifetime. The levelized cost of electricity (LCOE) of SOFC/GT hybrid plant was computed as \$85/MWh, which is around 20 % of the LCOE of SOFC standalone plant. The CO_2 emissions of the hybrid plant was calculated as 493 kg/MWh, which is around 27 % lower than that of the standalone plant.

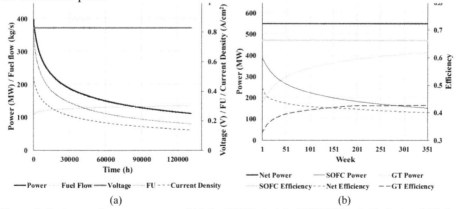

Figure 5. System performance curves of (a) the SOFC stack in SOFC/GT hybrid plant and (b) the SOFC/GT hybrid plant.

Table 1. Key performance indicators of SOFC standalone plant and SOFC/GT hybrid plant.

	SOFC Standalone Plant	SOFC/GT Hybrid Plant
SOFC Stack Efficiency (LHV)	57.9 %	66.2 %
Overall Plant Efficiency (LHV)	30.7 %	41.8 %
First year Capital Cost ($ Million)	$7,216	$4,129
Average Annual SOFC Replacement Cost ($ Million)	$3,048	$109
Annual Material, Operating and Maintenance Cost ($ Million)	$421	$398
LCOE ($/MWh)	$426	$85
CO_2 Emission (kg/MWh)	673	493

4. Conclusion

The proposed SOFC standalone plant and SOFC/GT hybrid plant were modelled and simulated with a pseudo-steady-state approach. By utilizing the simulation results, the eco-technoeconomic analysis showed that the SOFC/GT hybrid plant is more efficient with less cost compared to SOFC standalone plant. The overall plant efficiency of the hybrid plant was found to be 41.8 % which was around 36 % more efficient than the standalone plant. The hybrid plant had an LCOE of $85/MWh, and was around 80 % lower than the LCOE of the standalone plant. The CO_2 emission from the hybrid plant was also 27 % lower compared to the standalone plant. Therefore, the SOFC/GT hybrid was found to be a promising near-term approach for baseload power production in comparison with SOFC standalone system. Alternative designs with steam cycles will be analysed and included in future work.

References

T. A. Adams, L. Hoseinzade, P. B. Madabhushi, and I. J. Okeke. "Comparison of CO2 capture approaches for fossil-based power generation: review and meta-study." Processes 5, no. 3 (2017): 44.

T. A. Adams, J. Nease, D. Tucker, and P. I. Barton, "Energy Conversion with Solid Oxide Fuel Cell Systems: A Review of Concepts and Outlooks for the Short- and Long-Term," Ind. Eng. Chem. Res., vol. 52, no. 9, pp. 3089–3111, Mar. 2013.

R. James, A. Zoelle, D. Keairns, M. Turner, M. Woods, and N. Kuehn, "Cost and Performance Baseline for Fossil Energy Plants Volume 1: Bituminous Coal and Natural Gas to Electricity", Sept. 2019. NETL-PUB-22638

J. Nease and T. A. Adams, "Coal-fuelled systems for peaking power with 100% CO2 capture through integration of solid oxide fuel cells with compressed air energy storage," J. Power Sources, vol. 251, pp. 92–107, Apr. 2014.

D. Tucker, M. Abreu-Sepulveda, and N. F. Harun, "SOFC Lifetime Assessment in Gas Turbine Hybrid Power Systems," J. Fuel Cell Sci. Technol., vol. 11, no. 5, pp. 051008-051008-7, Aug. 2014.

D. Tucker, J. VanOsdol, E. Liese, L. Lawson, S. Zitney, R. Gemmen, J. C. Ford, and C. Haynes, "Evaluation of methods for thermal management in a coal-based SOFC turbine hybrid through numerical simulation." Journal of Fuel Cell Science and Technology 9, no. 4 (2012): 041004.

V. Zaccaria, D. Tucker, and A. Traverso, "A distributed real-time model of degradation in a solid oxide fuel cell, part I: Model characterization," J. Power Sources, vol. 311, pp. 175–181, Apr. 2016.

Sauro Pierucci, Flavio Manenti, Giulia Bozzano, Davide Manca (Eds.)
Proceedings of the 30th European Symposium on Computer Aided Process Engineering
(ESCAPE30), May 24-27, 2020, Milano, Italy. © 2020 Elsevier B.V. All rights reserved.
http://dx.doi.org/10.1016/B978-0-12-823377-1.50071-9

Analysis of the Effect of the Ceramic Membrane Module Based on Ebsilon Software on Water Recovery of Flue Gas from Coal-fired Power Plants

Chao Jiang, Chenhui Jia, Pei Liu, Zheng Li

State Key Lab of Power Systems, Department of Energy and Power Engineering,
Tsinghua University, Beijing 100084, China
liu_pei@tsinghua.edu.cn

Abstract

In this paper, the mechanism of flue gas desulfurization and membrane module water recycling was studied, based on Ebsilon software modeling of the thermal system of coal-fired power plant unit, under different operation conditions on the basis of this study membrane module set mode for water recycling effect, the results show that the membrane module placed in front of the desulfurization tower can effectively reduce the temperature of flue gas, recover heat and reduce the water consumption in the desulfurization process; the membrane module placed behind the desulfurization tower, it can recover the desulfurization process of flue gas absorption of water effective. The results provide support and guidance for the practical application of flue gas moisture recovery in coal-fired power plants.

Keywords: water recovery, Ebsilon software, setting mode

1. Introduction

Coal-fired power generation is China's main source of electricity. By the end of 2017, China's total installed capacity of power generation was 1.77 billion kilowatts, of which 0.98 billion kilowatts were coal-fired, accounting for 55.2 %. Coal-fired power generation uses and consumes a lot of water. In 2017, China's water consumption for coal-fired power generation was 5.187 billion m^3, accounting for 17.7 % of the country's industrial water consumption. The uneven distribution of water resources in China and the reverse spatial distribution of water resources and fossil energy lead to the prominent contradiction between regional supply and demand of water resources in China. Therefore, it is of great significance for coal-fired power plants to save water consumption.

According to the different functions of water in each subsystem or equipment, the water system of the coal-fired power plant can be roughly divided into 7 subsystems (Li,2011). For the air-cooled coal-fired power plant, the water consumption of the desulfurization system accounts for 38.40 %, which is the main water consumption point of this power plant. At present, more than 90 % of coal-fired power plants in China adopt the limestone-gypsum wet desulfurization process. The main water consumption of the system includes Gas and liquid water carried away by flue gas in desulfurization tower; Free water and crystal water contained in the reaction product gypsum; Discharge of desulfurization wastewater.

Table 1 shows the water consumption of the desulfurization system of a 2×300 MW coal-fired power plant as an example.

Table 1 The water consumption of the desulfurization system of a 2×300MW coal-fired power plant

Consumption	Water Consumption （t/h）	Proportion （%）
Evaporated Water	106.16	90.80
Liquid Water in Flue Gas	0.15	0.13
Free Water in Gypsum	2.02	1.73
Crystal Water in Gypsum	4.24	3.62
Desulfurization Waste Water	4.35	3.72

Table 1 shows that the gaseous water taken away by the flue gas after the absorption tower, namely the evaporation loss, accounts for 90.80 % of the system's water consumption and it is the most important water consumption point in the desulfurization process. The flue gas will contain trace sulfuric acid vapor, so that the flue gas dew point temperature increases, contact with the heating surface will condense and form sulfuric acid solution corrosion heating surface. On the other hand, desulfurization wastewater contains a lot of waste liquid of chloride and fluoride. To maintain the material balance of the slurry circulation system of the desulfurization unit, prevent the desulfurization equipment from being corroded and ensure the quality of gypsum. Therefore, recovery and effective treatment of water in the flue gas of coal-fired power plants is necessary. (Ma et al.,2017).

The main methods of recovering water vapor from flue gas are condensation, drying and composite membrane. The condensation method separates water from flue gas by lowering the temperature of flue gas below the dew point temperature (Xiong et al.,2017). The absorption method is based on the water vapor pressure difference between the flue gas and the desiccant solution as the driving force (Wang et al.,2016). The principle of composite membrane is to separate water and gas by driving differential pressure and using mixed gas components to have different adsorption capacity and permeation rate to water vapor on the membrane surface.

Compared with the other two methods, the composite membrane method can recycle the moisture in the flue gas with higher efficiency and quality (Gao et al.,2019). This project will mainly adopt the composite membrane method to research the moisture recovery of flue gas.

2. Methodology

2.1. Water absorption mechanism of desulfurization tower

There are many kinds of desulphurization processes. The most widely used process is selected in this research. The basic process flow is as in Figure 1.

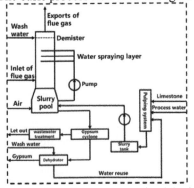

Figure 1 Schematic diagram of limestone - gypsum desulphurization system

The flue gas enters the lower part of the desulfurization absorption column under the action of the booster fan after being dusted by the dust collector. In the rising process, it comes into full contact with the falling limestone slurry sprayed by the spray. SO_2 in the flue gas is absorbed by the slurry and falls into the slurry pool at the bottom of the column. This is a complex process of heat and mass transfer accompanied by chemical reactions. This project mainly simulates the evaporation of water accompanying the heat transfer process, so the following assumptions are made:

(a) the flue gas passes through the absorber quickly, and the reaction process between flue gas and slurry is adiabatic.

(b) the heat transfer process in the tower is rapid and complete;

(c) the kinetic energy of flue gas inlet and outlet are ignored;

(d) the heat change of slurry entering and leaving the tower was ignored.

At this time, the thermal process of the hot flue gas in the absorption tower is similar to adiabatic humidification process, the enthalpy value of the flue gas in the tower is unchanged, the moisture content increases continuously, and it is saturated when it leaves the tower, given by Eq. (1)

$$h_i = h_o \tag{1}$$

Where h_i and h_o are the specific enthalpy of the flue gas inlet and outlet absorption towers respectively.

Therefore, the enthalpy value can be obtained from the state parameters of the flue gas entering the tower, and then other state parameters such as temperature and moisture content of the flue gas can be obtained. The calculation steps are shown in Figure 2.

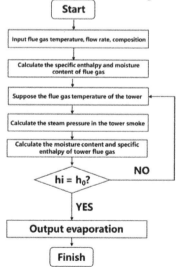

Figure 2 Calculation diagram of evaporation water in the desulfurization process

This model is used to analyze the characteristics of the process of flue gas desulfurization and water absorption, and to simulate and compare the results under different conditions such as flue gas inlet temperature and flue gas flow, as shown in Figure 3.

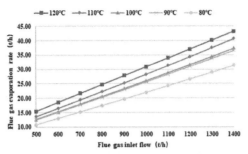

Figure 3 The variation of evaporation water with flue gas flow and inlet temperature in the desulfurization process

The results show that the desulfurization process of evaporation of water with the flue gas flow rate increases, the flue gas flow rate, water evaporation increases with flue gas inlet temperature increased significantly, therefore in flue gas desulfurization absorption tower set before the membrane module was carried out on the water and flue gas waste heat recovery is necessary, it can reduce the consumption of water in the desulfurization process.

2.2. Ceramic membrane module

The membrane module used in the water recovery system of coal-fired units are a ceramic composite membrane, and the ceramic membrane bundle is arranged in a cross row, and perpendicular to the flue gas flow direction, with cooling water inside. The ceramic-composite film is highly selective. When the smoke flows through the surface of the ceramic film, the water vapor condenses and condenses into water on the ceramic film wall. Under the action of the vapor pressure difference, the condensate water in the ceramic film enters the ceramic film tube, and nitrogen, sulfur dioxide, and other substances are blocked outside the film tube. The latent heat released by the condensation of steam and the sensible heat released by the flue gas is carried away by the cooling water to complete the process of mass transfer and heat transfer.

According to the flue gas water recovery system, the relevant research team（Gao et al.,2019）used the established membrane module mechanism model to analyze the water recovery and recovery rate under different flue gas flow, flue gas temperature, and other conditions, and the conclusions were as follows:

With the increase of flue gas flow in a certain range, the water recovery volume increases, but the water recovery efficiency decreases. When the flue gas flow exceeds a certain value, all the membrane tubes in the membrane assembly are close to full load, and the water recovery tends to be stable. As the temperature of the flue gas increases, the temperature difference between the flue gas and the condensed water increases, the heat exchange is enhanced, and more water vapor in the flue gas condenses into water and is recycled, so the amount of water recycling increases and the recovery rate increases. The influence of temperature on water recovery decreases with the increase of flue gas flow.

3. Analysis results and discussion

According to this unit 6 typical design conditions, Ebsilon software was used to model the thermal system of a 330MW coal-fired unit. The main component characteristics and leading factors of the system were determined by the dominant factor method, and the main component models of heat exchanger, pipeline, steam turbine unit and water pump were established respectively, and the overall variable condition simulation was realized, as shown in Figure 4.

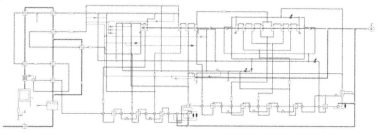

Figure 4 The thermal system of a 330MW coal-fired unit based on Ebsilon software

The simulation results were compared with the design values, and the average error of each measurement point was less than 1 %. The simulation results of the model were accurate. Through this model, the physical parameters of flue gas in the tail flue can be obtained under the actual operating conditions, and then the water recovery effect can be simulated and evaluated under different Settings of the membrane components.

Under different working conditions, the setting mode of the membrane module was used to simulate the water recovery effect in the flue gas. The setting mode of the membrane module was as follows: (a) No membrane module; (b) Set membrane module only in the flue in front of the desulfurization tower; (c) Set membrane module only in the flue behind the desulfurization tower; (d) Set membrane modules in the flue both in front of and behind the desulfurization tower, as shown in Figure 5, and results are shown in Figure6.

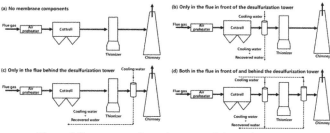

Figure 5 Four types of membrane module settings

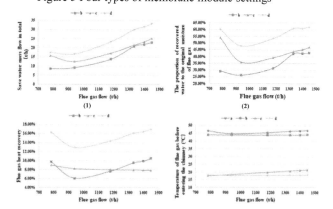

Figure 6 Effects of different types of membrane components on flue gas water recovery and heat recovery

As shown in Figure 6, although the water recovered by placing the membrane module before the desulfurization tower is not as much as that after the desulfurization tower, it can greatly reduce the temperature of flue gas entering the desulfurization tower, thus reducing the absorption of flue gas during the desulfurization process. After placing the membrane assembly in the desulfurization tower, more moisture can be recovered from the flue gas and the temperature of the flue gas outlet can be reduced. In addition, the membrane module is set in front of the desulfurized tower and behind the desulfurized tower to maximize the water recovery and heat recovery in the flue gas. Therefore, it is necessary to set up the membrane assembly before and after the desulfurization tower in the actual operation of the coal-fired power plant.

4. Conclusions

This work based on the existing water recovery technology on the basis of investigation and the key parts of the mechanism analysis and modeling, and combined with the actual situation of coal-fired power plants, coal-fired units were built based on Ebsilon software system and combustion system of variable working condition model, analysis of membrane module in all operating conditions, and the effects of different settings of flue gas water recycling. The results provide support and guidance for the practical application of membrane modules in the recovery of flue gas water in coal-fired power plants.

Acknowledgment

The authors gratefully acknowledge the support by The National Key Research and Development of China (2018YFB0604301) and the Phase III Collaboration between BP and Tsinghua University.

References

Li, Y., 2011. Water Consumption Calculation Model and Water-saving Analysis of Thermal Power Plant（in Chinese）, Master's degree dissertation, Tsinghua University, 17-21.

Ma, S., Chai, J., Jiao, K., Ma, L., Zhu, S., Wu, K., 2017. Environmental influence and countermeasures for high humidity flue gas discharging from power plants, Renew. Sustain. Energy Rev. 73, 225-235.

Xiong, Y., Tan, H., Wang, Y., Xu, W., Mikulcic, H., Duic, N., 2017. Pilot-scale study on water and latent heat recovery from flue gas using fluorine plastic heat exchangers, J. Clean. Prod. 161, 1416-1422.

Wang, Z., Zhang, X., Li, Z., 2016. Evaluation of a flue gas driven open absorption system for heat and water recovery from fossil flue boilers, Energy Convers. Manag. 128, 57-65.

Gao, D., Li, Z., Zhang, H., Chen, H., Cheng, C., Liang, K., 2019. Moisture and latent heat recovery from flue gas by nonporous organic membranes, J. Clean. Prod. 225, 1065-1078.

Gao, D., Li, Z., Zhang, H., Chen, H., Wang, L., Liu, H., 2019. The investigation of desulphurization and water recovery from flue gas using a ceramic composite membrane, Int J Energy Res., 43,1747‐1759.

Sauro Pierucci, Flavio Manenti, Giulia Bozzano, Davide Manca (Eds.)
Proceedings of the 30th European Symposium on Computer Aided Process Engineering
(ESCAPE30), May 24-27, 2020, Milano, Italy. © 2020 Elsevier B.V. All rights reserved.
http://dx.doi.org/10.1016/B978-0-12-823377-1.50072-0

Multi-objective Optimization under Uncertainty of Novel CHPC Process

Daniele Previtali[a], Francesco Rossi[b], Gintaras Reklaitis[b], Flavio Manenti*[a]

[a] Politecnico di Milano, Dipartimento di Chimica, Materiali e Ingegneria Chimica

"G.Natta", Piazza Leonardo da Vinci 32, 20133 Milano, Italy

[b] Purdue University, Forney Hall of Chemical Engineering, 480 Stadium Mall Drive, West Lafayette, IN 47907-2100, United States

flavio.manenti@polimi.it

Abstract

Combined Heat and Power (CHP) and biomethane upgrading plants are the two main processes that use biogas in Europe. The first converts biogas into electric energy and heat while the second consist of the purification of methane, via removal of other components, and its injection into the national natural gas distribution grid. They both are considered to be green technologies but the overall carbon balance is positive for both processes. Use of biogas as raw material in chemical synthesis allows to fix carbon in the chemical molecule and avoid its release as carbon dioxide. This is the basic idea of Combined Heat Power and Chemical plants (CHPC). Starting from biogas, CHPC produces methanol, a valuable and important building block for industrial chemistry. In this work we optimized the entire process by using multiple objective functions (economics and environmental) and considering the uncertainty of the feed composition. The results of mono-objective optimization show that the CHPC plant can be economically feasible with a net consumption of CO_2. Multiple objective optimization identified the operating conditions in which payback time is reasonable and CO_2 balance negative. Optimization under uncertainty allowed to design a more flexible and realistic process which can accommodate the variations in inlet biogas composition.

Keywords: biogas, CHPC, optimization, process simulation.

1. Introduction

Biogas is a mixture of methane (CH_4) and carbon dioxide (CO_2), produced by anaerobic digestion of organic matter (sewage, manure, organic/agricultural waste, etc.). It is considered a renewable energy source with zero carbon emissions. Biogas is usually used as fuel in Combined Heat and Power (CHP) plant to produce heat and electricity or is upgraded to bio-methane, via removal of CO_2 and other impurities, which then can be injected into the natural gas distribution grid. In Europe, the electrical energy production from biogas increased from 4,778 MWe in 2011 to 10,532 MWe in 2017, while the biomethane production rose from 752 GWh in 2011 to 19,352 GWh in 2017 (EBA, 2018). Although these two technologies for energy production (thermal and/or electrical) may be considered green since the organic matter comes from fixed atmospheric CO_2, the overall carbon emissions are not zero, if all of the processing steps needed to produce feedstocks, biogas and its use are taken into account. The impact of CHP can be improved (Hijazi et al., 2016) but it is important also to evaluate alternative uses of biogas, which can lead to no carbon emissions like the novel concept of the Combined Heat, Power and Chemical (CHPC) plant (Previtali et al., 2018). A CHPC plant converts biogas into bio-methanol (MeOH) such that at least part of the carbon of the biogas feedstock is not released back into the atmosphere as CO_2. Methanol is a widely used chemical with an annual world production of about 100 Mt [Alvarado, 2016], which is used as solvent and building-block to produce other chemicals, like dimethyl ether, acetic acid and formaldehyde. This chemical conversion process takes place in two principal unit operations, namely a reformer and a methanol synthesis reactor, the first of which converts biogas into syngas while the second transforms syngas into methanol. Compared to most conventional biogas conversion processes, CHPC plants offer lower environmental impact and generate a valuable chemical. Therefore, it is important to investigate the optimal design, optimal operating conditions and flexibility of this novel type of chemical process. The principal sources of uncertainty, considered in this analysis, will consist of the variations in the biogas feedstock composition. This aspect is extremely important due to the intrinsic variations of biogas composition which result from different biomass feedstocks and processing time (Herout et al., 2011). In this work we developed C++ models of each process unit (compressors, membranes, heat exchangers, reformers, plug flow reactors, etc.) and combined these models into a simulation which represent the entire CHPC process. The C++ implementation enables the efficient execution of the stochastic optimization computations. The model is validated by comparing results with PRO/II®, a well-recognized process simulation software by AVEVA (former Schneider Electric). Finally, using stochastic optimization and uncertainty quantification techniques, we establish robust optimal operating conditions and assess the degree of flexibility, offered by this new chemical process. All the optimization tasks are carried out using both conventional economic optimization and multi-objective optimization methods, which allows us to consider both economic and environmental impact indicators.

2. Materials and Methods

The CHCP process which converts biogas to methanol, is shown in Figure 1.

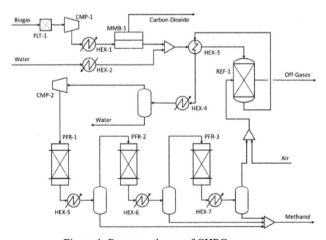

Figure 1. Process scheme of CHPC process

Biogas fed to the CHPC plant and is compressed up to about 15 bar by compressor CMP-1. We assumed that the only components in biogas are CH_4 (60%), H_2S (200ppm) and CO_2 (the remaining, about 40%); in other words, methane and carbon dioxide are the main components while although H_2S composition is small it cannot be neglected due to its important poisoning effects on reformer and methanol catalysts. The FLT-1 unit is an activated carbon filter for H_2S removal. This kind of guard bed is able to remove also other impurities (ammonia, siloxane…) but in this study its sizing is directly determined by the H_2S concentration and flowrate. Heat exchanger HEX-1 cools the purified biogas before processing in the membrane MMB-1. The biogas is partially upgraded to increase the methane fraction, since too high of a CO_2 content causes the production of a syngas with a low methanol module number which, in the PFRs, facilitates the reverse Water Gas Shift (rWGS) reaction favouring production of CO and H_2O instead of methanol (Bozzano, 2016). Steam is added before heat exchanger HEX-3 where the mixture is preheated recovering heat from the products of the reformer REF-1. The reformer is simulated as an equilibrium reactor since products can be considered to exit at the thermodynamic equilibria. Hot produced syngas is sent to the preheater HEX-3 to recover part of the sensible heat and then to the condenser HEX-4 where water is removed. Syngas is sent to compressor CMP-2 which increases the pressure up to 40 bar. The outlet of the third reactor is mixed with air (5% of oxygen in excess) and burned to provide heat for REF-1. The combustion can be considered to occur at the equilibria; a Gibbs reactor simulates the hot side of the reformer REF-1. The heat duty produced by combustion of off-gases sustains the reforming reactions. The CHPC process was modelled using C++ code. The Object-Oriented Programming (OOP) paradigm allows implementation of a general framework which is able to model several plant configurations. Each equipment is coded as a class with a standardized structure. Inputs and outputs are divided as Model Parameters, Manipulated Variables and State Variables. Model Parameters are the design variables associated with each equipment, such as the internal diameter of heat exchanger tubes, volume of a PFR, area of membranes, thermal coefficients of building materials. The manipulated Variables are operating conditions and parameters that can be adjust for the equipment its design like flowrate of heat exchanger coolant or heating medium, power of compressor or temperature, pressure, composition and flowrate of feed streams. Redlich-Kwong-Soave equation of state is the thermodynamic model implemented (Soave, 1972). The binary parameters for each compound were extracted from the PRO/II® 10.0 database. Functions for estimation of liquid and vapor properties such as the density, specific heat capacity, vaporization enthalpy, vapor liquid equilibria, thermal conductivity and viscosity, are available in PRO/II® 10.0 and online from the NIST database. Usually all these properties are described by complicated functions and, since they are called numerous times during each iteration, they can lead to high computational time. Use of simplified correlations, usually a second-degree function, facilitates computational efficiency. Re-regression and code cleanness are mandatory steps to keep the program execution as fast as possible; this is particularly important for the Thermopackage class which is the most frequently called class during the execution of the entire program. BzzMath library (Buzzi-Ferraris, 2012) routines were used to solve Non-Linear Systems, Differential Algebraic Equations, Ordinary and Differential Equations and to conduct the minimizations. The final software, called BigSQRT, was tested comparing the technical results with the those obtained with PRO/II®. Guthrie's method was used to estimate capital costs (Guthrie, 1969, Guthrie et al, 1974). Capital expenses (CAPEX) are estimated considering three main parameters: equipment type, characteristic dimension (power for pumps, area for heat exchanger…), operating pressure and material of construction. The life-time of the plant is 10 years according with

Turton (Turton et al., 2012). Operating expenses (OPEX) considered include cooling water, electricity, steam, catalysts and maintenance. The environmental footprint is calculated considering the impact due to equipment construction (steel production, manufacturing, welding…) as well as that one due to consumables such as (steam, electricity, heat, catalysts…). The Carbon footprint, or global warming according with IPCC, was the only indicator considered (IPCC, 2013), implementation of more complex models like ReCiPe or ILCD was considered overly complex and unnecessary for this work. Environmental data and impacts for secondary data were extracted from Ecoinvent 3.1 database. The CHPC process was optimized with respect to two different criteria: a mono-objective and a multi-objective. Mono-objective optimization minimizes an economic function (payback time), an environmental function (carbon footprint) or both, using a traditional economic function in which CO_2 emissions are weighted by a carbon tax. The Multi-objective optimization is based on using the utopian point method instead of the more traditional one based on a Pareto-curve. The latter method produces a series of points, a curve (grey line in Figure 2), in which the improvement of one criterion (payback time) causes the deterioration of the other (carbon footprint). This method is not an actual optimization since does not produce an optimal point, rather several optimal points. Moreover, the computational effort is high due to the high number of points that must be calculated.

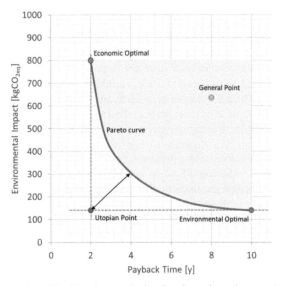

Figure 2. Scheme of multi-objective optimization based on the utopian point method

Multi-objective optimization based on the utopian point method allows faster optimization and leads to a single solution. The utopian point (red point) is defined by the optimal results of each mono-objective optimization (green and blue points), the result of multi-objective optimization is the point on the pareto curve at which the distance z is minimum. Optimization was done also considering uncertainty on inlet biogas composition, an annual variation of methane (55 – 65 %vol), carbon dioxide (33 – 43 %vol) and hydrogen sulphide (150 – 300 ppm) was assumed. Traditional mono-objective optimization was run also with PRO/II® in order to compare the robustness and the speed of the two optimization approaches.

3. Results and Discussion

Thermodynamic properties of pure components were found to be equal to those calculated with PRO/II® (average difference lower than 1%) while for mixtures the average error is slightly higher but acceptable (lower than 5%). Other calculated properties like dew/bubble point temperature and pressure can be considered equal (average difference lower than 2%). Simulation of single unit like heat exchanger, flash, compressor, equilibrium and plug flow reactor, H_2S filter and membrane gives similar results. Calculated duties, outlet compositions, flowrates, temperatures and pressures have an average error lower than 5%. Relative errors of composition can be higher for some components, up to 50% – 70%, but in those limited cases the difference is due to substances with a very low concentration, which means that the error can be considered negligible. BigSQRT is about 10 times faster than PRO/II®, the average computational time of 1 iteration is 0.2 sec compared to 2.2 sec for the latter. Optimizations were run varying several parameters: power of compressors CMP-1 and CMP2, area of heat exchangers HEX-1, HEX-2, HEX-3, HEX-4, HEX-5, HEX-6, HEX-7, temperature of equilibrium reactor REF-1, length of PFRs PFR-1, PFR-2, PFR-3, area of membrane MMB-1, volume of filter FLT-1. Robustness of BigSQRT is higher than PRO/II®, starting from the same initial conditions the first one can reach better terminal points. Optimized results obtained with BigSQRT were verified by using the calculated optimal parameters as input to PRO/II®.

Table 1. Results of different optimization

Optimization function	CAPEX [M\$]	OPEX [M\$/y]	Payback [y]	Net Present Value [M\$]	CO_2 emissions [tonCO$_{2eq}$/ y]
Economic	4.78	0.59	6.06	2.22	7,195
Environmental	4.33	0.35	9.96	-0.47	5,507
Eco – Environmental	4.65	0.92	10.85	-0.78	7,142
Eco – Environmental (MultiObjective)	4.61	0.51	6.81	1.78	6,636

Economic optimization results in a payback time of 6.06 years; while minimizing the overall CO_2 emissions (without considering the stored carbon dioxide as methanol) the carbon footprint can be decreased up to 24% but with a payback time of 10 years (Table 1). An initial eco-economical optimization was done considering a carbon tax of 70€ per tons of CO_2 but this kind of optimization may give misleading results since the result is strictly dependent on the selected value of the carbon tax. The Eco-Environmental optimization using multi-objective function was performed setting 6.06 years of payback and 5,507 tonCO$_{2eq}$/y as utopian point. The multi-objective optimization shows that the operating parameters can be optimized to obtain a good balance between environmental impact and economics. Considering uncertainty, both payback time and CO_2 emissions increase to 7.74 years and 7,812 tonCO$_{2eq}$/y respectively. Variations in biogas composition cause higher CAPEX and OPEX, the first is due to the need to oversize the design of some equipment like H_2S filter, membrane, reactors and compressors while, higher OPEX are mainly caused by a higher consumption of catalysts and higher pressure in the methanol synthesis section. Although these results seem worse that those obtained without considering uncertainty, the latter cannot be considered reliable since they are based on the assumption that biogas composition is always the same. Using a different inlet biogas composition of (CH_4 56%, H_2S 230ppm and remaining CO_2) and the operating parameters obtained with the optimization without uncertainty, the methanol production decreases and so the resulting payback time to 8,93 years, while with operating parameters optimized considering uncertainty the payback time increase only to 8.18 years. This is due to the plant design which in the first case is optimized for only one biogas composition, namely the average value. Variations in feed composition cannot be considered negligible since they lead to important differences in process design that can only be evaluated with optimization under uncertainty.

4. Conclusions

Optimization of processes that use bio-feedstock as raw material can be challenging because traditional methods can lead to misleading results. The CHPC is a novel process which converts biogas into methanol. In this work we developed a software tool for optimizing the design of the CHPC process in order to minimize environmental impact and payback time. Several methods were considered, the results of the optimization under uncertainty showed that the results can be significantly influenced by variations of biogas composition. Payback times and environmental impacts that are too optimistic could be obtained if optimization under uncertainty is not performed. The CHPC process does offer a promising payback time and its carbon footprint, under some conditions, may be negative. Future work will be focussed on improvements to the stochastic optimization.

References

Alvarado M., (2016). The changing face of the global methanol industry, HIS Chemical Bulletin (Issue 3, pp. 10-11)

Bozzano G., Manenti F., (2016), Efficient methanol synthesis: Perspectives, technologies and optimization strategies, Progress in Energy and Combustion Science, 56, 71-105.

Buzzi-Ferraris G, Manenti F. BzzMath: Library Overview and Recent Advances in Numerical Methods. vol. 30. Elsevier B.V.; 2012. doi:10.1016/b978-0-444-59520-1.50121-4.

EBA Annual Statistical Report (2018), European Biogas Association

Previtali D., Vita A., Bassani A., Italiano C., Furtado Amaral A., Pirola C., Pino L., Palella A., Manenti F., (2018). Methanol Synthesis: a Distributed Production Concept Based on Biogas Plants, Chemical Engineering Transactions, 65, 409-414.

Guthrie K.M., 1969, Capital cost estimating, Chemical Engineering, 76, 114-142

Guthrie, K.M. Eds., 1974, Process Plant Estimating, Evaluation and Control, Craffsman Book Company, Solana Beach, USA

Herout, M., Maľaťák, J., Kučera, L., & Dlabaja, T. (2011). Biogas composition depending on the type of plant biomass used. Research in Agricultural Engineering, 57(4), 137-143.

Hijazi O., Munro S., Zerhusen B., Effenberger M. (2016). Review of life cycle assessment for biogas production in Europe Renewable and Sustainable Energy Reviews (Vol. 54, pp. 1291–1300)

IPCC. Climate Change 2013 2013. http://www.climatechange2013.org/

Rossi, F., Manenti, F., Buzzi-Ferraris, G., & Reklaitis, G. (2017). Stochastic NMPC/DRTO of Batch Operations: Batch-to-Batch Dynamic Identification of the Optimal Description of Model Uncertainty. In Computer Aided Chemical Engineering (Vol. 40, pp. 2251-2256). Elsevier.

Soave, G., (1972) Equilibrium constants from a modified Redlich-Kwong equation of state, Chemical Engineering Science, (Vol. 27, pp. 1197-)

Turton R, Bailie RC, Whiting WB, Shaeiwitz JA. (2012) Analysis, Synthesis, and Design of Chemical Processes. Fourth Edi. Pearson Education, Inc.

Sauro Pierucci, Flavio Manenti, Giulia Bozzano, Davide Manca (Eds.)
Proceedings of the 30th European Symposium on Computer Aided Process Engineering
(ESCAPE30), May 24-27, 2020, Milano, Italy. © 2020 Elsevier B.V. All rights reserved.
http://dx.doi.org/10.1016/B978-0-12-823377-1.50073-2

Multi-objective Dynamic Optimisation of Ampicillin Batch Crystallisation

Antonios Dafnomilis[a], Samir Diab[b], Alistair D. Rodman[b], Andreas G. Boudouvis,[a] Dimitrios I. Gerogiorgis[b*]

[a] *School of Chemical Engineering, National Technical University of Athens, Athens 15780, Greece*
[b] *Institute for Materials and Processes (IMP), School of Engineering, University of Edinburgh, The Kings Buildings, Edinburgh, EH9 3FB, United Kingdom*
D.Gerogiorgis@ed.ac.uk

Abstract

Ampicillin is a key β-lactam antibiotic listed as a World Health Organisation (WHO) *Essential Medicine*. Crystallisation is a unit operation of paramount importance in pharmaceutical manufacturing, whose design and operation are essential in controlling process yield and important product quality attributes, such as mean product crystal size (MCS) and size distribution width. A published model for the solubility of ampicillin as a function of pH as well as growth and nucleation kinetics is used towards the simulation and optimisation of its batch crystallisation. This study performs multi-objective dynamic optimisation of the batch crystallisation of ampicillin to establish optimal pH trajectories for different production objectives, including maximising the mean crystal size whilst minimising the size distribution width subject to various yield constraints. Trade-offs between different product quality attributes are thus quantified, visualised and discussed.

Keywords: Multi-objective dynamic optimisation; batch crystallisation; ampicillin.

1. Introduction

Ampicillin is a broad-spectrum, semi-synthetic β-lactam antibiotic, used to treat various bacterial infections such as urinary and respiratory tract infections, being one of the ten most consumed antibiotics worldwide (Hamed et al., 2015). The β-lactam family of antibiotics are typically delivered orally and hence crystallisation is an essential unit operation in the production of these drugs, including ampicillin. The design and optimisation of crystallisation processes for efficient antibiotic production is important for its lean and agile manufacturing. The final size, shape and form of crystalline products are essential in pharmaceutical manufacturing as these product quality attributes influence downstream operations as well as the bioavailability of the crystalline product. Significant efforts in the development of batch crystallisation processes for their design and control have furthered pharmaceutical crystallisation significantly (Gao et al., 2017). Process modelling and optimisation studies performed before laborious, expensive experimental campaigns can elucidate optimal batch crystallisation manipulations (e.g. temperature, pH, antisolvent dosing) profiles, thus allowing for significant R&D time and cost savings.

The batch crystallisation of ampicillin via pH manipulation has been demonstrated in the literature, including a model with detailed kinetics and solubility behaviour as a function of pH (Encarnación-Gómez et al., 2016). Dynamic optimisation of pH-profiles for ampicillin batch crystallisation may establish improved operating policies for improved process performances vs. straightforward linear pH variations demonstrated in the literature thus far. This study implements the described ampicillin batch crystallisation model for dynamic optimisation of pH manipulation profiles to optimise product quality attributes subject to different operational and performance constraints. First, the published dynamic model for batch crystallisation is described in detail. The formulation of a dynamic optimisation problem with pH as the manipulated variable is described, with different case studies corresponding to experimental demonstrations. Optimisation results for different considered cases are presented in detail, followed by a critical comparison regarding trade-offs between process performance and key product quality attributes.

2. Batch Crystallisation Model

The ampicillin batch crystallisation model describes the antibiotic's aqueous solubility vs. pH, nucleation and growth kinetics and population and mass balance equations, the simultaneous solution of which describes the crystallisation process (Encarnación-Gómez et al., 2016). It is assumed that all considered processes are isothermal at $T = 25\ °C$, crystallisation is only induced via pH-variation and that pH variation in mixtures are instantaneous upon the implemented manipulation. The solubility of ampicillin as a function of pH is described using the extended Pitzer model (de Pessôa Filho et al., 2008) in Eqs. 1–2, where constants ε, σ, pK_{A1} and pK_{A2} are taken from the literature (Encarnación-Gómez et al., 2016), k_B = Boltzmann constant, N_A = Avogadro number, ρ = ampicillin density and the isoelectric point (pI) and its corresponding solubility ($S(pI)$) are regressed in previous work (Dafnomilis et al., 2019)

$$\log\frac{S(pH)}{S(pI)} = pI - pH + \log\left[\frac{1 + 10^{pH-pK_{A1}}}{1 + 10^{pI-pK_{A1}}}\right] + \log\left[\frac{1 + 10^{pH-pK_{A2}}}{1 + 10^{pI-pK_{A2}}}\right] + \frac{2}{\ln 10}\lambda[S(pI) \\ - S(pH)] \tag{1}$$

$$\lambda = \frac{2\pi\sigma^3 N_A\rho}{3}\left(1 - \frac{\varepsilon}{k_B T}\right) \tag{2}$$

Crystallisation kinetics are described by Eqs. 3–7, where J = overall nucleation rate, G = linear growth rate, M = suspension density, SS = supersaturation (all of which are a function of time, t), and parameters k_B, B_0, b, s, k_G and g are found in the literature (Encarnación-Gómez et al., 2016). The population balance in a batch crystalliser is described by Eq. 8, where n = the population density function, L = characteristic crystal length (assuming linear 1D growth), complimented by the boundary (Eq. 9) and initial (Eq. 10) conditions, corresponding to the population density of nuclei at t and that of seeds (n_0), respectively. The solute mass balance across the liquid and solid phases is described by Eq. 11, where the ampicillin concentration, $[Amp]$, removed from solution via crystallisation and contributes to the suspension density (M).

$$G(t) = k_G\,(SS(t) - 1)^g \tag{3}$$

$$J(t) = B_1(t) + B_2(t) \tag{4}$$

$$B_1(t) = k_{B1}\exp\left(-\frac{B_0}{\ln(SS(t)^2)}\right) \tag{5}$$

$$B_2(t) = k_{B2}\,M(t)^b\,(SS(t) - 1)^s \tag{6}$$

$$SS(t) = \frac{[Amp](t)}{S(t)} \tag{7}$$

$$\frac{\partial n(t, L)}{\partial t} = -\frac{\partial\big(G(t)n(t, L)\big)}{\partial L} \tag{8}$$

$$n(t, 0) = \frac{J(t)}{G(t)} \tag{9}$$

$$n(0, L) = n_0 \tag{10}$$

$$\frac{d[Amp]}{dt} = -\frac{dM}{dt} \tag{11}$$

3. Dynamic Optimisation Problem Formulation

This study considers the dynamic optimisation of the batch seeded crystallisation of ampicillin by manipulation of the pH trajectory over the batch duration. Generally, large Mean Crystal Sizes (*MCS*) and narrow size distributions (i.e., low *STD* or *CV*) are desired. Here, we maximise *MCS* while minimising *STD* by considering the objective function as a weighted sum of *MCS* and *STD* (Eq. 12), with associated weights W_{STD} and W_{MCS}. Imposed constraints on the problem are defined as follows. The first constraint (Eq. 13) ensures sufficient supersaturation at the beginning of the batch. The second constraint (Eq. 14) ensures the pH is not too low (causing ampicillin degradation) or high (forming undesirable non-trihydrate ampicillin polymorphs); ampicillin has limited chemical stability at pH $\leq$ 5, below which degradation products are formed, and undesired non-trihydrate polymorphs are formed at pH > 8 (Bezerra et al., 2018). The third constraint (Eq. 15) ensures that a minimum of a target amount of ampicillin is crystallised from solution at the end of the batch duration, t_f. The fourth constraint (Eq. 16) ensures sufficient *SS* is maintained. We consider W_{STD} = 1.0, W_{MCS} = 1.5 and the number of equispaced time discretisation intervals in the time domain, N = 30. The number of state variable collocation points, K_x = 3, and the initialisation pH profile is constant $pH(t)$ = 7, unless stated otherwise in Section 4; the effects of varying W_i on the objective function and values of N have been considered and analysed previously (Dafnomilis et al., 2019).

$$\min_{pH(t),t_f} f(x, t_f) = W_{STD}STD - W_{MCS}MCS \tag{12}$$

$$7 \leq pH(t_0) \tag{13}$$

$$5.5 \leq pH(t) \leq 8.0 \tag{14}$$

$$[Amp](t_f) \leq [Amp]_{target} \tag{15}$$

$$1 < SS(t) \tag{16}$$

The optimisation problem is solved using orthogonal collocation on finite elements via the DynOpt package in MATLAB (Čižniar et al., 2005), which has been used in previous work for the optimisation of biochemical process control trajectories (Rodman and Gerogiorgis, 2019). We compare dynamic optimisation results for different cases of seed loading. Table 1 summarises parameters considered for each case, corresponding to three (experimentally demonstrated already) seeded ampicillin crystallisation cases. The target crystallisation yields are comparable with experiments (Encarnación-Gómez et al., 2016).

Table 1: Dynamic optimisation problem cases considered.

Case	1	2	3
Seeding (wt%)	1.8	3.0	15.0
$[Amp](t_f)$ (g kg^{-1})	{6.8, 8.0}	{6.8, 8.0}	{6.9, 9.0}
Yield (%)	{39.8, 29.2}	{39.8, 29.2}	{46.4, 52.1}
t_f (min)	250	350	1,500

4. Results and Discussion

Optimal *pH*, nucleation, growth, *SS* and *MCS* profiles for different cases and yields are shown in Fig. 1. For lower crystallisation yields, the general pH manipulation is a drop near the beginning of the batch, followed by an increase and then a drop towards the end; this results in high *SS* at the start, followed by a decrease and then an increase towards the end. The initial high *SS* promotes nucleation; the subsequent lower supersaturation allows nuclei to grow to attain high *MCS* as per the defined objective function. The final increase in *SS* allows further nucleation to increase the yield to meet the target yield. This

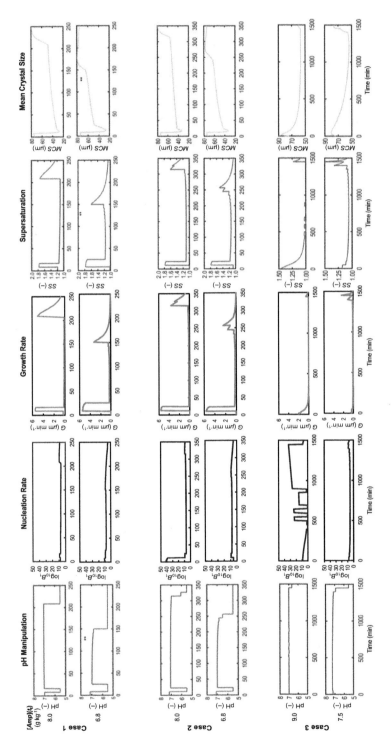

Figure 1: Optimal trajectories for all cases; $N = 30$; $K_x = 3$; initialised at $pH(t) = 7$.

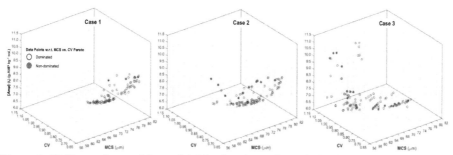

Figure 2: 3D Pareto front of the multiobjective dynamic optimisation problem (all cases).

results in *MCS* profiles which drop at the start (as nuclei form, the average *MCS* decreases) followed by an increase (due to growth dominating). As the target crystallisation yield is increased, the resulting optimal profiles change. The final decrease in pH in order to enhance the yield occurs earlier; this is due to the need to crystallise more nuclei in order to meet the target yield. As a consequence, *MCS* profiles begin to gradually decrease due to the formation of nuclei, although are approximately the same as for lower yields. Lower W_{MCS} values result in similar forms of pH manipulation and state trajectories, with more drastic pH drops resulting in more nucleation, and thus lower final *MCS* values, as *MCS* is given less importance in the objective function (Dafnomilis et al., 2019). As the seed loading is increased, the pH drop towards the end of the batch duration is observed later. For higher seed loading; the yield is enhanced as fewer nuclei are needed to meet the target yield. In all cases, a pH drop is only implemented towards the end of the batch duration, as growth is more important than generating new nuclei.

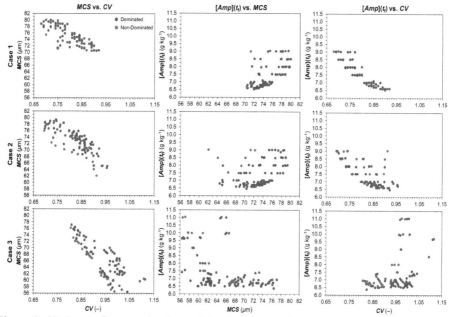

Figure 3: 2D Pareto front projections of the dynamic optimisation problem.

Pareto fronts of $[Amp](t_f)$ vs. *MCS* and *CV* are shown in Figs. 2 and 3 to quantify and visualise production trade-offs. For lower seed loadings, the attained *MCS* and *CV* are higher and lower, respectively, than for higher loading. For Case 3, there is not as evident a trade-off between yield and *MCS* or *CV*. Investigating the effect of intermediate seed loadings and dynamic seeding policies will further elucidate process improvements. While experimental values of *CV* for different seeded cases are not provided in the literature (Encarnación-Gómez et al., 2016), computed *MCS* values attained via dynamic optimisation of pH profiles in this study are higher than reported values, illustrating the benefit of the implemented framework for batch crystallisation process improvements.

5. Conclusions

This study implemented dynamic optimisation for the batch crystallisation of ampicillin via pH control. The dynamic batch crystallisation model encompasses ampicillin solubility behaviour as a function of pH, growth and nucleation kinetics as a function of crystallisation pH, population balances (using the method of moments to reduce their complexity) and solute mass balances. The optimal pH manipulation trajectory varies with target crystallisation yield and considered seed loading. Optimal pH profiles are such that high supersaturation is generated at the start of the batch run in order to meet the target crystallisation yield followed by lower supersaturation to promote growth and minimise the size distribution width. Illustrations of Pareto fronts of target yield vs. product quality attributes (*MCS* and *CV*) show evident trade-offs between the crystallisation performance and desired product size distribution properties. Future work will consider seed loading as a dynamic control variable to further optimise dynamic control profiles to meet different production specifications of ampicillin production.

Acknowledgements

The authors acknowledge the support of the Engineering and Physical Sciences Research Council (EPSRC)/IAA, the Japan Society for the Promotion of Science, the Great Britain Sasakawa and Nagai Foundations and the Royal Academy of Engineering (RAEng). We are grateful for recent support by the Erasmus+ Student/Teaching Exchange Programme (A.D., A.B., D.G.) and a completed Eric Birse Charitable Trust PhD Fellowship (A.R.).

References

I.M. Bezerra, L.C. Moreira, O. Chiavone-Filho and S. Mattedi, 2018, Effect of different variables in the solubility of ampicillin and corresponding solid phase, *Fluid Phase Equilib.*, 459, 18–29.

M. Čižniar, M. Fikar and M.A. Latifi, 2005, MATLAB Dynamic optimisation code DynOpt. User's guide, *KIRP FCHPT STU Bratislava*.

A.D. Dafnomilis, S. Diab, A.D. Rodman, A.G. Boudouvis and D.I. Gerogiorgis, 2019, Multi-objective dynamic optimization of ampicillin crystallization: sensitivity analysis of attainable performance vs. product quality constraints, *Ind. Eng. Chem. Res.*, 58, 40, 18756–18771.

L.G. Encarnación-Gómez, A.S. Bommarius and R.W. Rousseau, 2016, Crystallization kinetics of ampicillin using online monitoring tools and robust parameter estimation, *Ind. Eng. Chem. Res.*, 55, 7, 2153–2162.

Z. Gao, S. Rohani, J. Gong and J. Wang, 2017, Recent developments in the crystallization process: toward the pharmaceutical industry, *Engineering*, 3, 3, 343–353.

R.B. Hamed, J.R. Gomez-Castellanos, L. Henry, C. Ducho, M.A. McDonough and C.J. Schofield, 2013, The enzymes of β-lactam biosynthesis, *Nat. Prod. Rep.*, 30, 1, 21–107.

P.A. de Pessôa Filho and G. Maurer, 2008, An extension of the Pitzer equation for the excess Gibbs energy of aqueous electrolyte to polyelectrolyte solutions, *Fluid Phase Equilib.*, 269, 25–35.

A.D. Rodman and D.I. Gerogiorgis, 2019, An investigation of initialisation strategies for dynamic temperature optimisation in beer fermentation, *Comput. Chem. Eng.*, 124, 43–61.

Sauro Pierucci, Flavio Manenti, Giulia Bozzano, Davide Manca (Eds.)
Proceedings of the 30th European Symposium on Computer Aided Process Engineering
(ESCAPE30), May 24-27, 2020, Milano, Italy. © 2020 Elsevier B.V. All rights reserved.
http://dx.doi.org/10.1016/B978-0-12-823377-1.50074-4

Reliability Estimation for Sensor Networks in Chemical Plants using Monte Carlo Methods

José Hernández[a], Carolina Salto[b], Gabriela Minetti[b], Mercedes Carnero[a],
Mabel Sánchez[c]

[a] *Grupo de Optimización Facultad de Ingeniería – Universidad Nacional de Río Cuarto*
[b] *Lab. de Investigación en Sistemas Inteligentes-Universidad Nacional de La Pampa*
[c] *Universidad Nacional del Sur (UNS-CONICET), (8000) Bahía Blanca, Argentina*
jlh@ing.unrc.edu.ar

Abstract

The aim of this work is to analyze and determine an efficient and flexible resolution methodology to address the design of a minimum cost instrument network subject to restrictions over a set of key variables. In this sense, a Monte Carlo Simulation method is proposes to evaluate the reliability of the network defined as the probability of continuing to observe the keys variables when the instruments fails according to a given failure model. This is a powerful technique to model this stochastic behavior of systems and components. The optimization engine chosen is a heuristic, Simulated Annealing, which has shown to have a good performance for this kind of problems. Industrial examples of increasing complexity are provided to show the efficiency of the algorithms.

Keywords: sensor network, combinatorial optimization, reliability, metaheuristics.

1. Introduction

In a chemical plant, having a knowledge of the process state at any time is absolutely crucial with impact on aspects such as economic, control, energy efficiency or safety. In other words, the monitoring of the plant must be guaranteed. The information is collected by sensors distributed throughout the plant, responsible for measuring and transmitting the values of magnitudes such as flows, temperature, humidity, pressure, etc. The set of devices used in the measurement is called the sensor network (SN, Sensor Network). The SN design systematically made by formulating an optimization problem called Sensor Network Design Problem (SNDP), which is a discrete optimization problem. The design of sensor networks in process plants can be stated in a general way as a strategy whose objective is to reach a certain degree of estimability for a set of key process variables, while a certain quality is required on these estimates. In general, the number of variables that are involved in these problems for a real work scenario is quite large and the formulation can be more or less complex depending on the performance criteria and the restrictions set imposed on it. The optimal design of instrumentation networks in chemical plants involves two fundamental aspects. The first one is associated to the different formulations in terms of performance functions to optimize, and restrictions imposed. The second aspect is related to the choice of the resolution methodology. Although exact methods have been presented for this purpose, (Zhang and Chmielewski, 2017), there is today a more or less generalized consensus that the methods encompassed within metaheuristic techniques are the ones that provide the possibility to solve problems more real that can involve hundreds of variables while offering greater flexibility and shorter computation times, (Carnero et al., 2018, He et al., 2014).

The aim of this work is to analyze and determine an efficient and flexible resolution methodology to address the design of a minimum cost instrument network subject to restrictions over a set of key variables.

In literature, there can be found works that have addressed the problem of sensor network design where the reliability associated with the instrument system to be installed is considered as a fundamental performance criterion. Kotecha et.al (2008), proposed an explicit Mixed Integer Nonlinear Programming (MINLP) optimization framework, based on cut sets, for the design of sensor network which maximizes the network reliability for the non redundant case, in linear systems.

This means that the number of sensors is known in advance, which simplifies the optimization problem to be solved and allows to express and calculate in relatively simple way the reliability associated with the sensor network. On the other hand, Wang et al, (2007) show a procedure for the design of a sensor network that uses the graph theory and takes the reliability objective and cost constraint into account for small instances.

In the case of designing more general sensor networks that involve the observability of only a set of variables, in a redundant instrumentation system, the calculation of the reliability associated with any variable implies determining all possible ways of estimate it, a task that becomes impracticable as the number of variables grows.

This work proposes to use a Monte Carlo Simulation method, MS, to evaluate the reliability of the network defined as the probability of continuing to observe the keys variables when the instruments faults according to a given failure model. This is a powerful technique to model this stochastic behavior of systems and components. The optimization engine chosen is a trajectory heuristic, Simulated Annealing, SA.

The rest of this article is organized as follows. In Section 2 the SNDP is described. Section 3 introduces and explains the approach proposed in this work. Section 4 refers to the experimental analysis and the methodology used. Then, a study and analysis of the results obtained are presented. Finally, the main conclusions and future lines of research are drawn in Section 5.

2. Problem Formulation

The SNDP is summarized as a discrete optimization problem of finding the minimum cost network that satisfies estimability, precision and reliability constraints. Formally, an SNDP solution has to satisfy these constraints for a set of key variable estimates, as stated by Eq(1), where $\mathbf{q}$ is an n-dimensional vector of binary variables such that $q_i = 1$ if variable i is measured, and $q_i = 0$ otherwise, $\mathbf{c}^\mathsf{T}$ is the cost vector; $\hat{\sigma}_k$ is the estimate standard deviation of the k-th variable contained in S_σ after a data reconciliation procedure is applied, and E_l stands for the degree of estimability of the l-th variable included in S_E Furthermore, S_σ , S_R and S_E are the set of key process variables with requirements in precision, reliability and ability to be estimated, respectively.

$$
\begin{aligned}
\min \quad & \mathbf{c}^\mathsf{T}\mathbf{q} \\
\text{s.t.} \quad & \\
& \hat{\sigma}_k(\mathbf{q}) \leq \sigma_k^*(\mathbf{q}) && \forall\, k \in S_\sigma \\
& R_i(t,\mathbf{q}) \geq R_i^*(t,\mathbf{q}) && \forall\, i \in S_R \\
& E_l(\mathbf{q}) \geq 1 && \forall\, l \in S_E \\
& \mathbf{q} \in \{0,1\}^n
\end{aligned}
\tag{1}
$$

Precision and estimation constraints are evaluated using a matrix-oriented data reconciliation algorithm.

2.1. Exact reliability computation

To determine the reliability associated to each variable, two cases must be considered according to whether or not the variable is measured directly. If a variable is measure, then its reliability simply coincides with the reliability of the instrument with which it is measured. Otherwise, it is necessary to know all the possible alternatives of calculating through the balance equations where this variable appears.

Kotecha et al. (2007) proposed an expression that uses the concept of cut sets for evaluation of reliability. It is possible to demonstrate that, given a process flowsheet, all the ways of estimating a variable correspond to the determination of the set, C^i of all possible cut sets where such variable appears. If $\#C^i$ is the cardinal of the C^i set, then the reliability associated with the i-th variable is given by:

$$R_i(t,\mathbf{q}) = q_i R_i(t) + (1-q_i) \sum_{k=1}^{\#C^i} \left(\prod_{\substack{j \in C_k^i \\ j \neq i}} R_j(t) \right) \qquad \text{con} \quad i = 1:n \qquad (2)$$

If the sensor network is a minimum sensors one, then each unmeasured variable belongs to a single cut set, where the rest of the intervening variables are measured and the $\#C^i$ is equal to one. However, in the case of general sensor networks, where observability is required on a set of key variables and redundancy that ensures a certain level of reliability on them, $\#C^i$ constitutes a true bottleneck for the calculation of this expression. The number of cut sets where the considered variable appears grows exponentially with the increase in the size of the problem. For this reason this methodology is only applicable to plants with a small number of variables and balance equations.

2.2. Simulation approach to evaluate the variable relialibity

As it is known evaluation of reliability in engineering systems of different types is a complex task that presents, for example, the difficulties above mentioned. For this reason, other alternative estimation methods appear, such as MS methods. In this context, let $R_i(t,\mathbf{q})$ the probability of random event A defined as:

A = {continue observing at the time t the ith key variable included in S_R, when the implemented instrumentation network fails according to a given model}.

If a model for the fault associated with each installed instrument is available, then the occurrence of event A can be computed simulation a number of tests, N, enough large, so that relative frequency of occurrence of A, f_A, differs of $R_i(t,\mathbf{q})$ an arbitrarily small number ε. The above can be expressed in terms of the probability, Pr, as follows:

$$\Pr\left(|f_A - R_i(t,\mathbf{q})| \leq \varepsilon \right) \geq 1 - \delta \quad \text{then} \quad N \geq \frac{1}{4}\left(\frac{1}{\delta \varepsilon^2} \right) \qquad (2)$$

Where δ is a confidence level. Although the number of trials necessary to achieve adequate convergence must be large with its consequently high computation time, this technique can be applied to any type of process system.

3. Hybrid Simulated Annealing Algorithm

In this section, a brief description of SA and its variants is introduced. After that, the Hybrid Simulated Annealing, HSA, to optimize the cost instrumentation in chemical plants is explained and how the SA variants are adapted the HSA.

3.1. Simulated Annealing Algorithm

SA is a well-studied trajectory-based metaheuristic used to address discrete and, to a lesser extent, continuous optimization problems. The SA algorithm simulates the energy changes in a system subjected to a cooling process until it converges to an equilibrium state, where the physical material states correspond to problem solutions, the energy of a state to cost of a solution, and the temperature to a control parameter. At the beginning SA accepts solutions with high cost values under a certain probability in order to explore the search space and to escape from local optima. During the annealing process this probability decreases according to temperature cooling; intensifying the search and reducing the exploration in order to exploit a restricted area of a search space. SA evolves by a sequence of transitions between states and these transitions are generated by transition probabilities. Consequently, SA can be mathematically modeled by Markov chains, where a sequence of chains is generated by a transition probability, which is calculated involving the current temperature. Most of the search components of SA are fixed in function of the problem to be solved. Consequently, the search space, cost (evaluation) function, perturbation operator, and local search are directly related to the problem. The main search components, which are variable during the process, are the initial temperature, T^0, the temperature through their annealing schedules, and the Markov chain length, *MCL*, (Talbi, 2009). The most known cooling process in the literature are proportional, exponential and logarithmic schemes. Furthermore, a random schedule is considered (Bermúdez, et al., 2019). *MCL*, the number of required transitions to reach the equilibrium state at each temperature can be either static or adaptive. At the first case, it is calculated before the search starts.

3.2. Hybrid Simulated Annealing Algorithm for SNDP

In Hernández et al. (2019) an adapted and hybridized SA algorithm to solve the SNDP in chemical plants has been proposed. SA works as main heuristic with a subordinated ad-hoc local search, inspired in Tabu Search with strategic oscillation technique, SOTS, giving rise to the Hybrid Simulated Annealing (HSA_SOTS) algorithm. The hybridization in HSA_SOTS is applied in two levels: in the first one to generate an initial solution, and in the second level to improve the solution during the annealing process.

The perturbation scheme of the current solution is carried out through a certain swapping number of measured variables to unmeasured ones and vice versa in order to generate a candidate solution q_2 from q_0. Furthermore, the temperature is updated using the geometric criterion (Du and Swamy, 2016).

4. Experiments and results

In this section, two examples of increasing size are presented for stationary state process plants which are represented by lineal equations. However, the proposed methodology is applicable even when balances by components or non-linear systems are considered. Case 1 corresponds to a simplified hydrodealkylation plant, HAD, which due to its reduced dimension, it allows to implement not only a method for exact calculus of key variables reliability but also a simulation method based. Process graph is constituted by 8 nodes and 14 edges. Case 2 corresponds to the flowsheet of a Steam Metering Network plant, SMN, which has been wildly used in literature as an example of medium size. It consists of 28 flows and 11 equations of mass balance

The standard deviation of flow meters is 2%, 2.5%, of the corresponding true flow rates for case studies 1and 2, respectively.

In all cases, it is considered that for a proposed instrumentation system, reliability of each variable is evaluated to time $t=2$ years.

Furthermore, it is estimated that the time of life of each sensor is modeled with a Weibull distribution, whose instant rate of failure is constant and it has a medium time up to the specific failure for each sensor μ_i. Table1 shows the complexity of the set of constraints imposed for Case Studies 1 and 2.

The interested readers can gain access to the file containing information about the case studies, from https://www.ing.unrc.edu.ar/archivos/sndp_cases.doc. In this file, process flowsheet, purchase cost, precision and μ_i data for the set of sensors are available.

Table 1: Constraints for case studies

Case Study	Constraints
1	$E_I \geq 1$ for streams 3 4 8 10 12 $\quad R(t)_4^* = 0.8 \;\; R(t)_8^* = 0.8 \;\; R(t)_{10}^* = 0.8$ $\sigma_3^* = 0.7 \;\; \sigma_8^* = 0.15 \;\; \sigma_{12}^* = 0.40$
2	$E_I \geq 1$ for streams 2 4 8 12 17 21 23 25 27 28 $R(t)_8^* = 0.7 \;\; R(t)_{12}^* = 0.65 \;\; R(t)_{23}^* = 0.8 \;\; R(t)_{27}^* = 0.80$ $\hat{\sigma}_4^* = 2.2 \;\; \sigma_8^* = 3.28 \;\; \sigma_{12}^* = 1.54 \;\; \sigma_{27}^* = 1.41 \;\; \sigma_{28}^* = 1.44$

The set of parameters used to carry out the optimization with HSA_SOTS, as well as the simulation experiments, are shown in Table 2. Because of the stochastic nature of the algorithms, 30 independent runs of each instance were performed to gather meaningful experimental data.

Table 2: Parameter setting

Parameter	HAS_SOTS	Parameter	MS
T^0	900	N	25000
CL	30	ε	0.01
PSO	0.005	δ	0.01

Tables 3 and 4 reports the best attained solutions for the case studies. These are expressed in terms of the set of measured variables, the standard deviation of their estimates after the data reconciliation procedure is done, the reliability obtained and the total instrumentation cost. For comparative purposes, it should be noted that the cost is expressed in units of generic cost, CU. In addition, the reliability evaluated using an exact method is shown for the first design analyzed. In this smaller instance, it can be seen that the value reached by MS estimates $R_i(t)$ with an error of less than 0.3%.

Table 3: Optimization Results for Case 1

Best Solution	Standard deviation	Reliability Exact Method	Reliability Simulation Method	Cost [CU]
1,2,4,5,7-11,13	$\sigma_3 = 0.32$ $\sigma_8 = 0.136$ $\sigma_{12} = 0.238$	$R(t)_4 = 0.8150$ $R(t)_8 = 0.8150$ $R(t)_{10} = 0.8150$	$R(t)_4 = 0.8115$ $R(t)_8 = 0.8129$ $R(t)_{10} = 0.8115$	623222

Table 4: Optimization results for Case 2

Best Solution	Standard deviation	Reliability		Cost [U]
1 2 4-7 9-11 13 16 17 19-24 26-28	$\sigma_4 = 2,06 \;\; \sigma_8 = 1,5$ $\sigma_{12} = 0.09 \;\; \sigma_{27} = 1.2$ $\sigma_{28} = 1.44$	$R(t)_8 = 0.7421$ $R(t)_{23} = 0.8369$	$R(t)_{12} = 0.6921$ $R(t)_{27} = 0.8723$	1086.10

The design analyzed in case 2 has a high specification degree. Consequently the best solution found involves placing a set of 22 instruments. The variance of the reliability estimation is also calculated. The maximum value obtained is 4.10^{-5} for $R(t)_{27}$.

5. Conclusions

This work presents an analysis on the behavior of two particular simulations technique for the SNDP resolution. The first, HSA_SOTS a simulation optimization technique is performed for search the optimum solutions to SNDP problem which is formulated as a combinatorial optimization problem and includes the selection and determination of the number of process variables that must be measured to achieve the specific state of knowledge about the plant. The second, MS, a mechanism for the simulation of a failure scenarios, is used with the aim of evaluating the key variables reliability. Besides, the variance of the estimator is also returned, which is a measure of the quality of the estimate reached. MS is analyzed and discussed, as well as their performance in two industrials example of increasing size and complexity. The simulation results for the reliability calculation are coincident with the one obtained when an exact method is applied for the small size instance. In the second design analyzed, a high precision reliability estimation was obtained. The simulation tool proposed is a flexible and scalable one to solve other formulations of SNDP. However, for large plants with high reliability restrictions, generating samples of failure scenarios that lead to the non-observability of a key variable can result in a very large number of trials with the consequent increase in computational effort. This suggests, in these cases, the need to parallelize the proposed tool.

References

Bermudez C., Salto C., Minetti G. 2019, "Solving the Multi-Period Water Distribution Network Design Problem with a Hybrid Simulated Anealling". In: Pesado P., Aciti C. (eds) Computer Science – CACIC 2018. CACIC 2018. Communications in Computer and Information Science, vol 995. Springer, Cham.

Carnero, M., Hernández, J.L., Sánchez, M. 2018, "Optimal sensor location in chemical plants using the estimation of distribution algorithms". Ind. & Eng. Chem. Res. doi.org/10.1021/acs.iecr.8b01680.

Du Ke-Lin, Swamy M. N. S. (Ed), Search and Optimization by Metaheuristics, Techniques and Algorithms Inspired by Nature, Springer International Publishing, Switzerland (2016)

He, Y.J., Ma, Z.F. 2014, "Optimal Design of Linear Sensor Networks for Process Plants: A Multi-Objective Ant Colony Optimization Approach". Chemometrics and Intelligent Laboratory Systems, 135, 37-47, 2014.

Hernandez J., Salto C., Minetti G., Carnero M., Sanchez M.C., Hybrid Simulated Annealing for Optimal Cost Instrumentation in Chemical Plants, Chemical Engineering Transactions, 74, 709-714 (2019)

Kotecha PR, Bhushan M, Gudi RD. 2007, Constrained programming based robust sensor network design. Ind. Eng. Chem. Res.; 46, 5985-99.

Kotecha PR, Bhushan M, Gudi RD. 2007, Constrained programming based robust sensor network design. Ind. Eng. Chem. Res.; 46, 5985-99.

Kotecha, P., Bhushan, M., Gudi, R., Keshari, M. 2008, "A duality based framework for Integrating reliability and precision for sensor network design". Journal of Process Control, 18(2):189 – 201.

Talbi E. G., 2009, Metaheuristics: From Design to Implementation, Wiley.

Xu Wang, Gang Rong, Jianlie Li. "A New Approach To Design Reliable General Sensor Network on the Basis of Graph Theory". Ind. Eng. Chem. Res., 46, 2520-2525, 2007.

Zhang, Jin and Donald J. Chmielewski, 2017 "Profit-based Sensor Network Design using the Generalized Benders Decomposition." American Control Conference, (ACC) 3894-3899.

Sauro Pierucci, Flavio Manenti, Giulia Bozzano, Davide Manca (Eds.)
Proceedings of the 30th European Symposium on Computer Aided Process Engineering
(ESCAPE30), May 24-27, 2020, Milano, Italy. © 2020 Elsevier B.V. All rights reserved.
http://dx.doi.org/10.1016/B978-0-12-823377-1.50075-6

Low Temperature Applications for CO_2 Capture in Hydrogen Production

Donghoi Kim,[a] David Berstad,[b] Rahul Anantharaman,[b] Julian Straus,[b] Thijs A. Peters,[c] Truls Gundersen[a*]

[a]Department of Energy and Process Engineering, Norwegian University of Science and Technology (NTNU), Trondheim 7491, Norway
[b]SINTEF Energy Research, Trondheim 7465, Norway
[c]SINTEF Industry, Oslo 0314, Norway
Truls.gundersen@ntnu.no

Abstract

The recent development of the protonic membrane reformer (PMR) technology allows an energy efficient hydrogen production from natural gas. To liquefy and separate CO_2 from the retentate gas of the PMR, various low temperature processes are modelled and compared. The optimization results indicate that the single mixed refrigerant based process gives the smallest power consumption and fewest number of units. The cascade and the self-liquefaction processes can be considered as alternatives when the retentate gas is rich and lean in CO_2 respectively.

Keywords: Low temperature separation, CO_2 capture, hydrogen production, CO_2 liquefaction.

1. Introduction

Due to the increasing demand for clean fuels, hydrogen has been considered a promising energy carrier since it does not emit CO_2 after combustion. However, current hydrogen production relies on fossil fuels (98% of world H_2 production), thus emitting a large amount of carbon dioxide (IEA, 2019). Nevertheless, in the short/mid-term perspective, fossil fuel based hydrogen production is expected to increase before the transition to environmentally friendly hydrogen production like water electrolysis using renewable energy sources is completed (Voldsund et al., 2016). Thus, it is essential to develop efficient CO_2 capture processes for hydrocarbon based H_2 production.

Natural gas is the main fossil fuel to produce hydrogen, accounting for over 70% of total production (IEA, 2019). Such a hydrocarbon mixture is transformed into hydrogen and carbon dioxide by steam reforming (SR) and water gas shift (WGS). Then, CO_2 and other impurities are removed from the shifted syngas to produce pure hydrogen. Thus, the hydrogen production system consists of multiple sub-processes. As an alternative, SR and WGS stages can be replaced by the protonic membrane reformer (PMR) technology (Malerød-Fjeld et al., 2017). The PMR acts as a combined reactor and separator, where natural gas and electricity are consumed to produce a CO_2 rich stream with impurities and electrochemically compressed pure hydrogen separated through the membrane. The net endothermic chemical reaction is balanced with the heat evolved from the galvanic operation of the membrane reformer, resulting in higher overall energy efficiency compared to conventional hydrogen production processes. Therefore, the PMR system can be an attractive technology for efficient hydrocarbon based H_2 production.

The retentate gas from the PMR has a relatively high fraction of CO_2, which makes cryogenic separation technologies promising options to achieve a high CO_2 capture rate with reasonable energy consumption (Berstad et al., 2013a) and cost (Berstad et al., 2014). Applicable cryogenic CO_2 separation processes are flashing-based and external refrigeration-based. Thus, this paper suggests various types of cryogenic processes that are applied to the PMR based hydrogen production system. This work also performs a comparative evaluation of the cryogenic processes by conducting optimization work based on thermodynamic efficiency. Besides, the results from sensitivity analysis with different compositions of the retentate gas are analyzed to evaluate the operational flexibility of the CO_2 separation processes.

2. Background

After dehydration, the retentate gas from the PMR typically contains CO_2, CO, CH_4, and H_2 (Malerød-Fjeld et al., 2017). For the separation of carbon dioxide from a PMR based H_2 production system, the retentate gas can be compressed and cooled to sub-ambient temperatures using compressors and external refrigeration. Then, a part of CO_2 can be condensed to liquid phase and removed by a phase separator. During this process, the pressure and temperature of the retentate gas at the inlet of the phase separator decide the performance of CO_2 separation such as CO_2 capture rate and CO_2 mole fraction in the liquid CO_2.

Figure 1 shows the performance of such a CO_2 separation system with the dehyrated retentate gas having around 55 mol% CO_2 as obtained at a hydrogen recovery factor (HRF) of near 91%. As seen in Figure 1, the CO_2 capture rate (CCR) increases with higher pressures and lower temperatures. In this case, however, energy consumption for the CO_2 capture system will also be larger due to the increased compression and refrigeration duties. In addition, higher pressure levels result in lower CO_2 mole fraction in the liquid CO_2, which is not ideal for CO_2 transport and storage. Although lowering the temperature is beneficial to have higher CCR and CO_2 mole fraction for a given pressure, the lower bound of the temperature level is limited by CO_2 freezing temperature. Therefore, optimal pressure and temperature levels of the retentate gas are required to have an energy efficient CO_2 separation system for the PMR, while achieving high CCR and CO_2 mole fraction in the captured CO_2.

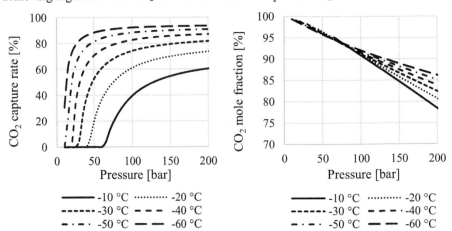

Figure 1. CO_2 capture rate (left) and CO_2 mole fraction in liquefied CO_2 (right) versus the retentate gas pressure with varying temperature at phase separator inlet.

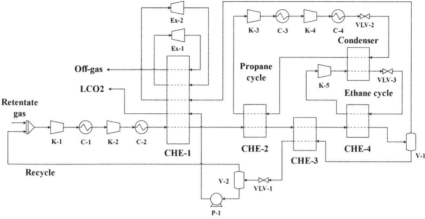

Figure 2. Cascade CO₂ liquefaction system (Berstad et al., 2013b).

3. CO₂ liquefaction processes

This CO_2 capture system is varying depending on the selection of refrigeration process. Berstad et al. (2013b) suggested a cascade type of CO_2 liquefaction process using pure component refrigerants such as propane and ethane. As shown in Figure 2, the retentate gas is pressurized through multi-stage compression and cooled mainly by the propane and ethane refrigeration cycles. Then, the retentate gas is separated into a CO_2 rich liquid stream and an H_2 rich vapor stream by phase separator V-1. The liquid stream gives the cold duty to heat exchanger CHE-3 to reduce the load of the external refrigeration cycles. The warmed liquid is then throttled to remove impurities through a flash gas. This flash gas is recycled for further purification. The purified CO_2 rich liquid is pumped to high pressure before it delivers cold duty for heat exchanger CHE-1.

The H_2 rich vapor stream from phase separator V-1 also precools the retentate gas from the compressors. The warmed H_2 rich vapor from CHE-1 can still supply refrigeration duty for heat exchanger CHE-1 by being depressurized through two gas expanders, which produce low temperature streams. The power produced from the expanders is also an extra benefit to reduce the total power consumption of this liquefaction process. The H_2 rich stream depressurized to the operating pressure of the PMR through the expanders (Off-gas) is then returned to the membrane reformer to maximize the overall HRF.

The cascade system using two pure component refrigerants can be replaced by a single mixed refrigerant (SMR) process, thus having a simpler configuration as seen in Figure 3. Compared to the cascade system, the CO_2 rich liquid from phase separator V-1 in the SMR based process is used not for liquefaction but precooling of the compressed retentate gas. Therefore, only one gas expander is required to supply enough cold duty to heat exchanger CHE-1, reducing the capital cost of this system.

The CO_2 liquefaction and separation can be performed without any external refrigerants as seen in Figure 4. A part of the refrigeration duty of this self-liquefaction system is produced by Joule-Thomson (JT) throttling of the CO_2 rich liquid stream and the H_2 rich vapor from phase separator V-1. Besides, this process heavily relies on the two gas expanders in order to generate sufficient amounts of refrigeration for the system.

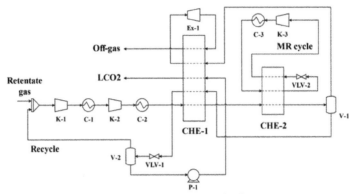

Figure 3. Single mixed refrigerant (SMR) CO$_2$ liquefaction system.

However, the retentate gas has to be compressed to very high pressure in order to have a large enough refrigeration from JT throttling and gas expanders, requiring a larger number of compression stages. Moreover, this high pressure feed gas results in low CO$_2$ fraction in the captured CO$_2$. Thus, the self-liquefaction process uses an additional phase separation for the partially condensed retentate gas from the precooling heat exchanger (CHE-1) in order to increase the purity of the captured CO$_2$.

4. Design basis and optimization

The three CO$_2$ liquefaction processes were simulated in Aspen HYSYS. The retentate gas from the PMR was assumed to be dehydrated. For case studies, the composition of the retentate gas was varied from CO$_2$ lean to CO$_2$ rich gas (Table 1) in order to evaluate the efficiency changes of the processes. These cases represent an HRF of 79.3, 91.4, and 97.8, respectively. Other design specifications are listed in Table 2. Optimization of the systems was also conducted by a particle swarm optimization algorithm in Matlab, connected to Aspen HYSYS. The objective function is minimizing specific power consumption for 1kg of liquid CO$_2$ (LCO2) production. Outlet pressure levels of compressors, expanders, and JT valves were set as variables. Outlet temperature levels of heat exchangers were also varied. The molar flow rates and compositions were also variables for the cascade and the SMR process. The mixed refrigerant of the SMR process is composed of CH$_4$, C$_2$H$_6$, C$_3$H$_8$, and C$_4$H$_{10}$.

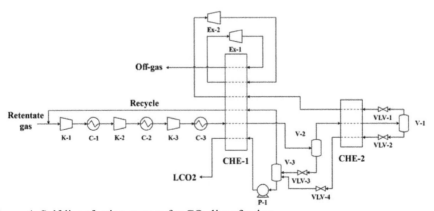

Figure 4. Self-liquefaction system for CO$_2$ liquefaction.

Table 1. Dehydrated PMR retentate composition (Malerød-Fjeld et al., 2017).

Component	Mole fraction [-]		
	CO$_2$ lean case	Base case	CO$_2$ rich case
Methane	0.0082	0.0012	0.0000
Carbon monoxide	0.2369	0.2072	0.1028
Carbon dioxide	0.3321	0.5491	0.8200
Hydrogen	0.4228	0.2425	0.0772

The minimum temperature difference of heat exchangers and minimum superheating of compressor inlet were set to 3 K. In order to avoid solid formation, the temperature of all the streams was constrained to be 3 K warmer than its CO$_2$ freezing temperature. Higher than 95 mol% of CO$_2$ and lower than 0.5 vol% of CO in the liquefied CO$_2$ were product specifications (Harkin et al., 2017), also satisfying 70, 85, and 95 % of CO$_2$ capture rate for CO$_2$ lean, base, and CO$_2$ rich cases respectively.

5. Results

The optimization results in Table 3 indicate that the SMR process is the most energy efficient process to liquefy CO$_2$ from the base case retentate gas. The cascade system only requires a marginally larger energy consumption compared to the SMR process since the two gas expanders allow a smaller overall temperature difference in the precooling part (CHE-1), indicating better heat integration. However, the cascade system has larger temperature differences in heat exchangers operating at low temperatures than the SMR process, resulting in larger entropy generation and reduced overall thermodynamic efficiency. The composition of the mixed refrigerant in the SMR system can be manipulated to have a better temperature match with the retentate gas. The self-liquefaction system shows the largest power consumption due to its inherent low efficiency, requiring a considerable increase in the retentate gas pressure level and thus compression work. However, the high pressure feed gas results in a warmer operating temperature for CO$_2$ separation, thus a larger temperature margin to CO$_2$ freeze-out.

When the feed gas is lean in CO$_2$, the cascade process consumes slightly less power than the SMR process. Due to the increased impurities, the retentate gas has to be flashed more. This results in a larger amount of flash gases, which is more favorable for CO$_2$ liquefaction systems having two gas expanders to produce refrigeration duty and work. However, the self-liquefaction process will also have significantly increased recycle stream and compression work, thus giving the largest power consumption. For the CO$_2$ rich case, the SMR process has noticeably smaller power consumption than the cascade system because of less impurities in the feed gas and flash gases in the processes, resulting in a reduced influence of the expanders on the process efficiency.

Table 2. Simulation conditions and assumptions.

Property	Value	Unit	Property	Value	Unit
Feed temperature	25	°C	Equation of state	PR	-
Feed pressure	10	bar	Δp in heat exchangers	2% of p$_{in}$	-
Feed flow rate	200	kmol/h	Compressor efficiency*	80	%
Off-gas pressure	25	bar	Pump efficiency*	75	%
LCO2 pressure	150	bar	Expander efficiency *	85	%

*Isentropic efficiency

Table 3. Specific power consumption with the temperature and pressure levels at the first phase separator (V-1).

Process	Cascade			SMR			Self-liquefaction		
	Power	T	p	Power	T	p	Power	T	p
	MJ/kgCO_2	°C	bar	MJ/kgCO_2	°C	bar	MJ/kgCO_2	°C	bar
CO_2 lean	0.781	-55.6	68.5	0.786	-55.6	64.7	0.993	-46.9	169.2
base	0.460	-55.2	64.6	0.455	-55.5	56.1	0.555	-45.8	160.4
CO_2 rich	0.337	-54.0	50.3	0.316	-54.7	40.3	0.470	-40.0	125.4

6. Conclusions

In this paper, different low temperature processes for CO_2 liquefaction and separation from a membrane retentate gas were compared. Considering the overall efficiency with changes in CO_2 fraction of the feed gas, the SMR process gives the highest energy efficiency. This process also has the smallest number of units compared to other processes, which may give a smaller capital cost than other systems. When the feed gas is lean in CO_2, the cascade process will be an alternative option to the SMR system. The self-liquefaction process can be considered if the feed gas is rich in CO_2 and no external refrigerant is accessible. Thus, proper process selection for CO_2 liquefaction will depend on the feed gas conditions and other design criteria such as cost.

Acknowledgements

This publication has been produced within the CLIMIT-KPN MACH-2 project (294629) with support from the NCCS Centre, performed under the Norwegian research program Centres for Environment-friendly Energy Research (FME). The authors acknowledge the following partners for their contributions: Aker Solutions, ANSALDO Energia, CoorsTek Membrane Sciences, Equinor, EMGS, Gassco, KROHNE, Larvik Shipping, Norcem, Norwegian Oil and Gas, Quad Geometrics, Shell, TOTAL, and the Research Council of Norway (257579).

References

International Energy Agency (IEA), 2019, The future of hydrogen. Available from https://www.iea.org/hydrogen2019/.

M. Voldsund, K. Jordal, R. Anantharaman, 2016, Hydrogen production with CO_2 capture, International Journal of Hydrogen Energy, 41, 9, 4969-4992.

H. Malerød-Fjeld, D. Clark, I, Yuste-Tirados, R. Zanón, D. Catalán-Martinez, D. Beeaff, S.H. Morejudo, P.K. Vestre, T. Norby, R. Haugsrud, J.M. Serra, C. Kjølseth, 2017, Thermo-electrochemical production of compressed hydrogen from methane with near-zero energy loss, Nature Energy, 2, 12, 923-931.

D. Berstad, R. Anantharaman, P. Nekså, 2013a, Low-temperature CO2 capture technologies – Applications and potential, International Journal of Refrigeration, 36, 5, 1403-1416.

D. Berstad, R. Anantharaman, P. Nekså, 2013b, Low-temperature CCS from an IGCC Power Plant and Comparison with Physical Solvents, Energy Procedia, 37, 2204-2211.

D. Berstad, S. Roussanaly, G. Skaugen, R. Anantharaman, P. Nekså, K. Jordal, 2014, Energy and Cost Evaluation of A Low-temperature CO2 Capture Unit for IGCC plants, Energy Procedia, 63, 2031-2036.

T. Harkin, I. Filby, H. Sick, D. Manderson, R. Ashton, 2017, Development of a CO2 Specification for a CCS Hub Network, Energy Procedia, 114, 6708-6720.

Sauro Pierucci, Flavio Manenti, Giulia Bozzano, Davide Manca (Eds.)
Proceedings of the 30th European Symposium on Computer Aided Process Engineering
(ESCAPE30), May 24-27, 2020, Milano, Italy. © 2020 Elsevier B.V. All rights reserved.
http://dx.doi.org/10.1016/B978-0-12-823377-1.50076-8

Development and Application of Simulation-based Methods for Engineering Optimization Under Uncertainty

Atli Freyr Magnússon, Resul Al, Gürkan Sin

Process and Systems Engineering Center (PROSYS), Department of Chemical and Biochemical Engineering, Technical University of Denmark, Building 227, 2800 Kgs, Lyngby, Denmark

Abstract

This study presents a methodology that combines Monte Carlo methods for uncertainty propagation along with modern stochastic programming methods for optimization of chemical engineering process models. The aim is to integrate uncertainty information of model parameters directly into optimization workflow. Successful implementation will give statistically strong optimum designs that do not require the use of safety factors that could compromise the cost competitiveness of the process design. Assuming that uncertainty behaves as random disturbances, Monte Carlo sampling techniques of model parameters uncertainty are used to quantify disturbances effects in model output. The resulting information is then used in a surrogate assisted optimization approach designed specifically for stochastic simulations. The surrogate methods used are the developed Stochastic Kriging methods along with a novel infill criterion. This work will also include an Artificial Neural Network alternative approach. The methodology is applied to two distillation flowsheets built in *Aspen Plus*. Both proposed methods showcase superior results to a traditional SQP in a case study. Stochastic Kriging approach showcases superior results when optimizing a two-column distillation loop of a DIPE + IPA + 2MEt system, showcasing three times lower cost evaluation compared to other methods while respecting propagation of uncertainty. This work demonstrates the applicability of simulation-based optimization for engineering designs under uncertainty.

Keywords: Kriging, optimization, uncertainty, process simulators, artificial neural networks

1. Introduction

Process optimization is an important tool in chemical engineering to ensure that process designs remain cost competitive while upholding specifications. Many mathematical programming techniques exist and are applied in process optimization. Process optimization is usually performed on a deterministic model where the selected model parameters are put in place with no assumed disturbances. In reality most model parameters in process models are subject to varying degrees of uncertainty. Variety of studies have showcased that uncertainties in model parameters can have great impact on reliability and sensitivity of the model as well as the propagation of uncertainties in the model outputs (Frutiger et al. (2017)). While optimization under uncertainty has been performed in bioprocess design by Morales-Rodriguez et al. (2012), the prospect remains a challenge and is rarely conducted in chemical engineering practice. One possible reason is the lack of a concise and reliable methodology that engineers can apply directly to their process models.

Recently Wang and Ierapetritou (2018) developed a novel robust method of optimizing stochastic simulations using a surrogate assisted optimization method (SAO). SAO are attractive to chemical engineering research field due being a global and derivative free optimization solver that are highly efficient for time consuming simulations making them prime candidates when applied directly to process simulators like SimSci PRO\II or Aspen Plus. This method uses a Stochastic Kriging meta-model developed by Ankenman et al. (2010) to assist in exploiting and exploring the design space. Their newly developed Feasibility-enhanced Expected Improvement (FEI) infill criterion is used to select new input points to improve meta-model accuracy iteratively until the computational budget runs out and the optimum is reported. In this study a Monte Carlo based methodology is presented on optimizing process design variables while integrating the effects of model parameter uncertainties during the optimization workflow. The methods are showcased by applying them on a case studies developed in the commercial process simulation software Aspen Plus. The Stochastic Kriging approach is considered along with an Artificial Neural Network (ANN) approach, whose performances will be compared along with a Sequential Quadratic Programming (SQP) optimization algorithm built into the Aspen Plus software.

2. Surrogate Assisted Optimization

Surrogate Assisted Optimization (SAO) methods are best utilized in computationally intensive tasks. The basis of all SAO methods is to create a simple meta-model to capture input-output correlations of a complex model. These meta-models are mathematically well defined and easy to compute so they can be used to exploit and explore the input space.

Meta-models are not always reliable and can have significant errors if not enough data exists in areas of interest. To improve reliability more data is supplied to the meta-model where the optimum point is likely to be located. Promising candidates are identified using an infill criterion or acquisition function which use meta-model predictions as the input. Thus, SAO methods are an iterative sequence where a meta-model accuracy is continuously improved in areas of interest via rigorous simulations of new infill points generated by the acquisition function. A common acquisition function that provides a decent balance between exploring and exploiting is the Expected Improvement (EI) method by Jones (1998).

2.1. Stochastic Kriging approach

Wang and Ierapetritou (2018) coupled their novel Feasibility-enhanced Expected Improvement (FEI) to a Stochastic Kriging (SK) meta-model for optimization which will be referred to as SK-FEI. SK was developed by Ankenman et al. (2010) and is an extension of ordinary Kriging which are popular meta-models in SAO methods. SK attempts to account for randomness by incorporating an intrinsic noise factor based on the measured variance of model outputs. For run j the SK model predicts a following output

$$y_j = \alpha_0 + M(\mathbf{x}) + \grave{o}_j \tag{1}$$

Where α_0 is a constant capturing the surface trend, M is a Gaussian process with mean 0 and variance modelled using spatial correlation functions of already visited input points and $\grave{o}_j$ is a random noise of observation j estimated using measured variances.

FEI is an extension of the traditional EI approach. The modifications are done to make the algorithm more efficient at solving optimization problems that have imposed non-linear constraints which are the most common types of problem in process optimization. This was accomplished by including a feasibility factor that actively tries improving knowledge of the feasible region i.e. where the non-linear constraints are met. Furthermore, randomness of a stochastic simulation is accounted for by assuming that process variance can be explained by a numerical function $\sigma^2 = V(\mathbf{x})$ which are fitted using another meta-model and by reducing focus on areas with large predicted $V(\mathbf{x})$. For further details the reader is referred to the Wang and Ierapetritou (2018) original paper.

2.2. Artificial Neural Network approach

This work will also attempt to introduce a SAO approach using ANN. This is to provide alternatives to SK which are known to cause computational issues as amount of data grows due to inversion of a correlation matrix. ANN are known to be exceptional at function fitting and interests in this technology is rapidly growing. ANN is constructed like a biological brain system where information from the input is fed forward through neurons in hidden layers in order to produce an output

Traditional EI family of methods do not work with ANN meta-models as they require an increased error approximation in unexplored regions which is provided by Kriging models but not ANN. In order to solve optimization problems under uncertainty the assumption that process variance can be described by a function $V(\mathbf{x})$ is repeated. Two ANN models are then fitted to each stochastic output, one predicts the mean value and one predicts the variance. These models are then coupled to an extension to the classic Probability of Improvement (PI) for non-linear constraints used by Carpio et al. (2018) which is as follows

$$cPI(\mathbf{x}) = PI(\mathbf{x})\prod_{i=1}^{m} PC_i\mathbf{x} \tag{2}$$

Where $PI(\mathbf{x})$ is the probability that x is an improvement in the objective function for an already established $\mathbf{x}_{min}$ and $PC_i(\mathbf{x})$ is the probability that x upholds the constraint for output *i*. This approach will be further referred to as ANN-cPI.

3. Monte Carlo based optimization strategy

Current proposal of optimization under uncertainty only works if the process can be treated as a stochastic simulation. This can be achieved using a Monte Carlo based method of uncertainty analysis. The Monte Carlo method recommended by Sin et al. (2009) can be summarized in four steps

1. Define input parameters and distribution
2. Sample from defined distribution using a random number generator
3. Perform the simulations with the generated samples
4. Statistical analysis and interpretation of the results

Monte Carlo simulations provide information of mean and measured variance which can then be used to generate SK and ANN models for optimization. If a commercial process simulator is used to build the model it is recommended to follow the procedure of Jones et al. (2019) who utilized Monte Carlo simulations to perform uncertainty and sensitivity analysis on a *PRO\II* simulation using Component Object Model (COM) interface that allows communication between process simulators and numerical software. Before optimization starts it is important to decide on how to distribute the computational budget. Currently one must decide on initial sample size (*N*) in which to create a working initial meta-model, number of Monte Carlo Simulations (*m*) per sample point xi and number of iterations (*n*) in which the acquisition function is to generate new sample points. The total computational budget i.e. number of times the objective and constraint functions are evaluated respectively then becomes

$$M = (N + n)m \tag{3}$$

This computational budget is used to determine the stopping criterion of the optimization workflow as randomization factors prevent the use of any reliable convergence criterion. The optimization workflow is then:

1. **Initial Sampling** Generate *N* number of initial samples. To improve the reliability of the meta-model the initial samples should be randomized and space-filling thus the recommended approach is to use Latin Hypercube Sampling (LHS).

2. **Monte Carlo Simulations** Sample point x_i is sampled *m* times in the original model or process simulations to get mean and variance for each sample point.

3. **Dataset evaluation** The results of the Monte Carlo Simulations are used to identify the current strongest sample point subject to minimizing the objective function and constraints. To account for uncertainty, one should factor in the measured standard deviation as well. Example for this work is to use confidence intervals for measured mean values.

$$y_{min,f} = min(y_f(\mathbf{x}) + \frac{z}{\sqrt{m}} s_f(\mathbf{x})) \tag{4}$$

$$x \in \chi$$

Where *s* is measured standard deviation from Monte Carlo simulations, subscripts *f* and *g* denote objective and constraint values respectively and *z* is the standard score used in statistics. For this work *z* was set to 1.96 in both cases. χ is the set of all previously visited sample points ensuring that reported optimum has been rigorously simulated.

4. **Computational budget check** If total number of simulations has exceeded *M* then the optimization is terminated and result of step 3 is reported as the optimum. Else Step 5 is executed.

5. **Fit Surrogate model** Using the measured means and standard deviations from Monte Carlo simulations a surrogate model is fit to the outputs of the objective function and constraint functions to predict stochastic responses of unvisited **x**.

6. **Maximize infill** Depending on the surrogate model either cPI or FEI acquisition functions should be maximized to generate the next sample point $\mathbf{x}_{infill}$ Since cPI and FEI are deterministic functions one should set up a traditional global solver. This work saw good success using a Particle Swarm Optimization (PSO) algorithm. The generated $\mathbf{x}_{infill}$ is then sent to step 2.

4. Case Studies

The applications of the current strategy are demonstrated on a case study. A distillation network separating DiIsoPropyl-Ether (DIPE) and IsoPropyl Alcohol (IPA) using a pressure swing and a 2-MethoxyEthanol (2MEt) as a solvent.

The process model is developed in the process simulator *Aspen Plus* v10. *MATLAB* 2018b is used to generate the Monte Carlo samples and run the optimization algorithm. *MATLAB* and *Aspen Plus* are interconnected using COM interface, SK models are built using the ooDACE toolbox (Couckuyt et al. (2014)) and ANN models are trained using *MATLAB* Neural Network toolbox. For comparison purposes, the models are also solved deterministically i.e. neglecting uncertainty using Aspen's built in optimizer which by default uses an SQP approach.

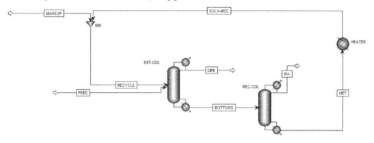

Figure 1:Aspen Plus flowsheet of the extractive distillation process

The flowsheet is depicted in figure 1. This process entails a pressure swing distillation with a solvent of 2MEt to break the azeotrope of DIPE and IPA. The feed consists of 100 *kmol/h* of 25 mol% IPA and 75 mol% DIPE at 1.42 bar and 55 °C. The primary column consists of 67 theoretical stages with the feed entering on stage 56 and the 2MEt solvent enters at stage 29. The primary column produces pure DIPE in the distillate, while the bottoms is sent to a secondary recovery column to recover the solvent for recycle as well as pure IPA.

The goal is to optimize the operational parameters *distillate rate* and *reflux ratio* of the two columns in the flowsheet in order to drive operating costs down while keeping DIPE and IPA purity over 95% on a mass basis. The operating costs associated with the process is the energy requirements of the two columns as well as the solvent makeup required. To that end the following formula is adopted for cost estimation

$$C = 180V_{2MEt} + 0.048\sum Q_H + 0.0013\sum \| Q_C \| \qquad (5)$$

Where V_{2MEt} is the volume flow of the solvent in *L/h* while Q_H and Q_C are the heat duties of the reboilers and condenser respectively. Uncertainties in the process model stem from the thermodynamic method used. For this work NRTL method is used. The parameters of NRTL are based on regression of experimental data. Correlation control in the sampling step is used by utilizing the multivariate normal distribution (Kotz et al. (2005)). For comparison purposes both SK-FEI and ANN-cPI will be provided the same computational budget of *(N, m, n) = (40,100,100)*. This simulation is adapted from works of Burger and Schwarz (2018) whose paper will provide all simulation details and input uncertainties of the NRTL parameters. The optimization results are shown in table 1. In terms of constraints, no algorithm violated the non-linear constraints imposed on the problem. However, SQP results are on the constraint boundary of 95% mass fraction of DIPE. Uncertainty analysis concluded that the product purities are not sensitive to uncertainties of the NRTL parameters for the selected operating parameters. These results could be cause for alarm, nonetheless. ANN-cPI and SK-FEI are both well within the non-linear constraints with no risks of not fulfilling product specifications.

Table 1: Reported optimum design variables and results

	SQP	SK-FEI	ANN-cPI
Extractive Column Distillate Rate ($kmol/h$)	81.71	79.76	80.27
Recovery Column Distillate Rate ($kmol/h$)	18.29	20.44	20.36
Extractive Column Reflux Ratio	1.78	1.78	3.34
Recovery Column Reflux Ratio	3.14	2.34	1.32
Cost Evaluation (USD/h)	10447.97 ± 2.68	3045.42 ± 2.94	9319.99 ± 4.14
DIPE Mass Fraction	0.950	0.964	0.960
IPA Mass Fraction	0.953	0.988	0.960

Cost wise SK-FEI showcases the best performance, tripling the cost efficiency compared to the design proposed by the ANN-cPI algorithm. This is likely due to ANN-cPI lacks proper balance between exploiting and exploring for a global optimization and needs further development before it can be reliably applied to optimize process models under uncertainty.

5. Conclusions

This study presented an optimization strategy for engineering system subject to model uncertainties using Monte Carlo simulation approaches combined with new novel methods in stochastic programming. The methodology was applied to a case study developed in *Aspen Plus* process simulator to minimize the cost of running a distillation method of a DIPE-IPA-2MEtsystem subject to product specifications. Two SAO approaches were considered, both methods show superior results to a traditional SQP algorithm while accounting for the uncertainty effects in the workflow. The proposed ANN method is an attempt to provide alternatives to Kriging based methods, but direct comparison showcases it to be underdeveloped, more research is required to improve robustness. This study showcases that the SK-FEI approach can reliably solve optimization problems in a commercial process simulator under uncertainty.

References

B. Ankenman, B. L. Nelson, J. Staum,2010. Stochastic Kriging for Simulation Metamodeling. Operations Research 58 (2), 371–382.

L. Burger, C. Schwarz,2018. Sensitivity of process design to phase equilibrium uncertainty: Study of the isopropanol + DIPE + 2-methoxyethanol system. Fluid Phase Equilibria 458, 234–242.

R. R. Carpio, R. C. Giordano, A. R. Secchi, oct 2018. Enhanced surrogate assisted framework for constrained global optimization of expensive black-box functions. Computers & Chemical Engineering 118, 91–102.

I. Couckuyt, T. Dhaene, P. Demeester, 10 2014. ooDACE toolbox: A flexible object-oriented kriging implementation. Journal of Machine Learning Research 15, 3183–3186.

J. Frutiger, I. Bell, J. P. O'Connell, K. Kroenlein, J. Abildskov, G. Sin, 2017. Uncertainty assessment of equations of state with application to an organic Rankine cycle. Molecular Physics 115 (9-12), 1225–1244.

D. Jones, 1998. Efficient global optimization of expensive black-box functions. Journal of Global Optimization 13 (4).

M. N. Jones, J. Frutiger, N. G. Ince, G. Sin, 2019. The Monte Carlo driven and machine learning enhanced process simulator. Computers & Chemical Engineering 125, 324–338.

S. Kotz, N. Balakrishnan, N. L. Johnson, 2005. Continuous Multivariate Distributions, Models and Applications: Second Edition. Vol. 1. John Wiley and Sons Inc.

R. Morales-Rodriguez, A. S. Meyer, K. V. Gernaey, G. Sin, 2012. A framework for model-based optimization of bioprocesses under uncertainty: Lignocellulosic ethanol production case. Computers & Chemical Engineering 42, 115–129.

G. Sin, K. V. Gernaey, A. E. Lantz, 2009. Good modeling practice for PAT applications: Propagation of input uncertainty and sensitivity analysis. Biotechnology Progress 25 (4), 1043–1053.

Z. Wang, M. Ierapetritou, oct 2018. Constrained optimization of black-box stochastic systems using a novel feasibility enhanced Kriging-based method. Computers & Chemical Engineering 118, 210–22

Sauro Pierucci, Flavio Manenti, Giulia Bozzano, Davide Manca (Eds.)
Proceedings of the 30th European Symposium on Computer Aided Process Engineering
(ESCAPE30), May 24-27, 2020, Milano, Italy. © 2020 Elsevier B.V. All rights reserved.
http://dx.doi.org/10.1016/B978-0-12-823377-1.50077-X

An Application of Computer Vision for Optimal Sensor Placement in Drop Printing

Andrew J. Radcliffe,* Gintaras V. Reklaitis

Purdue University, Forney Hall of Chemical Engineering, 480 Stadium Mall Drive, West Lafayette, IN 47907-2100, United States
aradcli@purdue.edu

Abstract

The use of imaging technologies in the process industries has the potential to provide state, dynamic, statistical or modal information that cannot otherwise be obtained from systems which limit or invalidate the use of physical property and spectroscopic measurement methods for real-time acquisition. To extract the desired information, computer vision techniques can be used to reduce the high-dimensional image data to the salient features, which can then be employed for modelling, optimization, and control purposes. This work applies such an approach to determine the optimal placement of a high-resolution camera for online quantification of drops printed in a slurry-based additive manufacturing process for pharmaceuticals. Systematic selection requires a model of drop instability, which, due to stochastic effects introduced by particles, must be based on real data with sufficient temporal discretization to capture the event dynamics. Thus, high-speed imaging was utilized to generate representative videos, and computer vision algorithms were employed to automate extraction of the coupled temporal evolution of object shape and position, and to detect and recognize breakup and coalescence events. The resultant data were subsequently employed to determine the image sensor and fiber-optic placements that maximize measurement information acquired by online acquisition system. Results are presented for drop printing slurries at 15 distinct ink formulations – spanning several particle size distributions and particle loadings – which are comprised of a set of 250,000 images.

Keywords: add three to five keywords here, separated with a comma.

1. Introduction

Drop printing serves as an important component of widely varied manufacturing processes, encompassing examples from semi-conductors, pharmaceuticals and biomaterials – essentially, anywhere precision deposition of material is required. In such applications, drops serve as the source of a critical chemical component themselves, or as a liquid binder, the patterning of which on the substrate enables creation of two-/three-dimensional structures. Consequently, in order to control the drop formation/deposition, online monitoring of the generated drops is desirable; this would be best achieved by high-speed imaging due to the small timescales involved, but economic and practical considerations encourage the use of a normal camera to capture one image of each emergent drop. In this context, placement of the online imaging system in relation to the printing nozzle determines what can be extracted and inferred from the resultant images, thus, it is important to optimize the arrangement of the camera, flashbulb & fiber-optic sensor (camera trigger) so as to maximize the information about each drop.

Previously work by colleagues (Hirshfield et al. 2015) designed a system for online image acquisition that considered the optics, using the system geometry to select lens and camera y-axis placements that maximize the depth of field for objects emerging from the nozzle; this incorporated an actuation system based on a fiber-optic sensor positioned at the same z-height as the center of the imaged area. The position of these two components will be selected by the user; for well-behaved inks (i.e. ideal fluids), a trial and error approach can affect a suitable measurement, with errors as low as 0.33% (Hirshfield et al. 2015). However, for cases in which printing exhibits non-ideal effects – multiple satellite droplets, variability in trajectory, non-deterministic events (breakup, coalescence) – the captured images can be quite different (Figure 1, Inset #1, 2, 3), despite apparent uniformity of drop volume at the eventual point of deposition. Consequently, it becomes difficult to even arrive at a satisfactory result, or to be convinced that such a placement captures the maximum amount of information.

In the pharmaceutical manufacturing process considered here, the printed drops contain the active drug compound, thus, the images obtained by the online acquisition system enable model-based estimates of the product content; maximizing the information contained in the captured images through optimization of component placement with respect to drop formation phenomena reduces uncertainty in the model structures and in the product content predictions. This work focuses on non-Brownian particle inks, which motivate the use of a data-driven approach due to the substantial non-idealities involved– high particle loading, distributed particle size, non-spherical shape. High-speed imaging of drop printing across a range of operating conditions and ink formulations is used to record the dynamics from the incipience of flow to the eventual stabilization of the drop(s) after detachment. Then, computer vision algorithms are applied to each image sequence to extract the total lifetime of each drop: dynamic evolution of position and shape; non-deterministic events and spatiotemporal location thereof; parent-child relations with other drop(s). With this information, particle-driven effects on detachment, trajectory and events can thus be accounted for.

2. Problem Description

2.1. Components of Online Image Acquisition System

In order to formulate the problem, one must first define the geometry and adjustable components of the online imaging system. From the previous work, camera and lens are fixed, thus leaving the position of the camera and fiber-optic sensor as the only variables. The camera is to be placed at some z-position below the nozzle orifice so as to capture a single image for each drop; the fiber-optic sensor consists of a light beam, which when interrupted by the drop triggers the acquisition of the image. The high-resolution camera captures an area with dimensions H, W, which is effectively constant due to the fixed distance between the lens and drop paths. The high-speed camera captures a substantially larger actual area; with the actual sizes and known conversion factors (real length per pixel), the potential positions of the area captured by the online camera can be superimposed onto the images from the high-speed videos, as shown in Figure 1.

2.2. Feasible camera, fiber-optic sensor placements

Given the geometry (Figure 1) thus defined, and the total imaged area from the high-speed sequences, one can then define the set of feasible camera positions as $\mathbf{Z} = \{ \zeta \; \forall \; z_{Box,L} \mid z_{Box,L} = (z_{nozzle} + H), \dots, z_{limit} \}$, in which a single camera position encompasses the set of points: $\zeta = \{ z_{Box,L} - j \mid j = 1, \dots, H \}$. As the area imaged by the online camera covers 90% of the x-axis, the problem can justifiably be simplified by fixing the camera box x-position at the centerline. Feasible positions of the fiber-optic sensor for each ζ are constrained to be $z_{FbOp} \leq z_{Box,L}$, though, given the configuration in which interruption of the fiber-optic signal is exactly coincident with the camera trigger, one can further limit the feasible points to $z_{FbOp} \in \zeta$, as image acquisition, triggered at some position outside the camera box is readily identifiable as leading to suboptimal results. The former, more lenient constraint could be used if one considers adding a time delay between the fiber-optic signal interrupt and image acquisition.

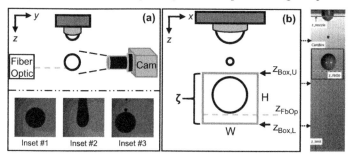

Figure 1. (a): Side-view of online image acquisition setup. (b): Scene as observed by camera

2.3. Objective function

With the feasible sensor placements defined, consider the following scenario in which a drop is printed: mechanical actuator induces pressure wave, fluid is emitted from the nozzle, and after thinning of the liquid thread, one or more drops detach; thereafter, these drops deform, and potentially undergo breakup or coalescence. Let us assume that the operating conditions and ink formulation are such that per actuation event, one large drop ("primary drop") is formed, with the possibility of one or more smaller drops ("satellites"). The system can acquire one image per actuation event, given limitations on the flashbulb frequency and online camera, and the volume of fluid deposited will be estimated using an object detection and segmentation algorithm (Radcliffe & Reklaitis, 2019) to extract the diameter for each object, $D(z)$, which, assuming axial symmetry, is used to compute: $V_{Drop} = (\pi/4) \int D(z)^2 dz$. For the purposes of online process monitoring in the pharmaceutical manufacturing process, as accurate as possible estimate of drop volume is desired; as illustrated by Figure 1, there is considerable uncertainty as to whether the acquired image contains representative information of the deposited volume (e.g. Inset #2, 3), due to differing detachment phenomena, and the potential for satellite drops. Thus, the optimal camera placement and fiber-optic sensor position are the ζ, z_{FbOp} that maximize the observed drop volume – either across a range of conditions (if ζ, z_{FbOp} are to be fixed henceforth), or, for each operating condition/ink formulation, provided the flexibility exists to make automatic adjustments in response to process changes. Noting that the volume computed from the image is proportional to the area, the objective function can be defined based on the area of the object(s) of interest inside the box, normalized to the total area of said object(s), evaluated at the instant of image acquisition – that is, the point at which the lowermost drop interrupts the fiber-optic signal. If only the primary drop is considered, the object function can be defined as the sum across p sequences, as shown in Eq. (1):

$$f(\zeta, z_{FbOp}) = \sum_p \left(\frac{A_{obj,in}}{A_{obj}} \right)_p \tag{1}$$

In which the total area of the object, A_{obj}, is defined as in Eq. (2):

$$A_{obj} = \int_{z_L}^{z_U} D(z)dz = \sum_j D(z_j)\Delta z, \qquad \{\forall j : z_j \in ID_{Primary}\} \tag{2}$$

wherein the limits on the integral are the respective lower/upper boundaries of the primary object. The area of the object inside the camera box, $A_{obj,in}$, is evaluated analogously, with the limits on the integral such that only the area contained within ζ contributes, illustrated in Figure 2; the index set is then: $\{\forall j : z_j \in ID_{Primary} \cap z_j \in \zeta\}$.

This serves as a reasonable approximation for cases in which the primary drop is much larger than the satellite drops. However, given the detailed information, one can more rigorously re-define the objective function for multiple drops (Figure 2) as the sum of areas of all objects inside the camera box, normalized by the total areas of all objects both inside/outside, as shown in Eq (3):

$$F(\zeta, z_{FbOp}) = \sum_p \left(\frac{\sum_{\widetilde{ID}(p)} A_{obj,in,ID}}{\sum_{\widetilde{ID}(p)} A_{obj,ID}} \right)_p \tag{3}$$

With the object-specific event information extracted by the computer vision algorithms, one is able to make an important distinction in terms of the objects and their eventual fates: Eq.(3) should be evaluated for all objects that do not merge with the nozzle, thus, $\widetilde{ID}$ is the subset of all object identities, ID, that satisfy this condition. The reasoning for this is straightforward: through the objects detach, they do not actually contribute to the deposited volume, hence, they should be excluded from the set of objects over which the multi-drop objective function is evaluated. A further note on the definition of what precisely constitutes an object – $A_{obj,in,ID}$ or $A_{obj,ID}$ – is warranted. Consider a case in which the camera box is positioned as close to the nozzle as possible: when the fluid filament begins to form, it then extends into the box, and may perhaps trigger image acquisition before the drop detaches. If the area in the camera box were simply the apparent area, this would result in objective functions that favour being close to the nozzle – as perhaps more volume is extended from the nozzle than actually forms a drop. This problem can be elegantly dealt with utilizing the object-specific events construction inherent to the CV algorithms, therefore enabling one to evaluate the objective function for all dynamically instantiated objects active at a given spatiotemporal point, while excluding persistent objects (i.e. fluid attached to nozzle). This enables consideration of the full range of possible $\zeta's$ without the need to artificially set an upper bound so as to exclude contributions from the nozzle-attached filament. The convenience of the object-oriented perspective is that it permits us to specify in the objective function the high-level criterion that "valid" area within the camera box must belong to a free liquid fragment (nozzle-attached filament can be present, but its contribution is always zero), and to easily re-define subsets of objects to evaluate Eq. (3).

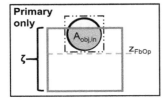 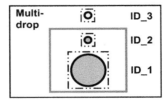

Figure 2. Illustration of contributions to objective function: area inside and total areas

2.4. Solution Method

From the definitions of the objective functions, it can be readily inferred that a gradient-based method may not be preferable. As one expects that a range of ζ, z_{FbOp} are likely to yield quite similar objective function values, a derivative free method is selected; the classic formulation of the particle swarm optimization algorithm, using 50 particles and 150 generations is used to obtain solutions. An additional advantage for the problems posed here is due to the shape of the objective function (obtained by exhaustive evaluations for p sequences at one set of operating conditions), which resembles a plateau with very steep slopes along the boundary where z_{FbOp} is very near to $z_{Box,L} + H$. Intuitively, this must be the case: as one allows more of the drop area to enter the imaged box, the function changes rapidly.

3. Results: Primary drop, Multi-drop, Primary drop + Interaction partners

The solution to the optimization problem yields a set ζ, parameterized by $z_{Box,L}$, which comprises the camera box positions and a z_{FbOp} which constitutes the location of the fiber-optic sensor. Results are presented in this section for the cases involving only the primary drop, multiple drops, and a third case that takes further advantage of the vent information which pertains to the parent-child relations of the objects. In this third case, the primary object and its interaction partners form a subset of the objects, therefore, by replacing $\widetilde{ID}$, one can evaluate the respective objective function (Eq.(3) directly.

The solutions obtained indicate that when only the primary drop is considered in the objective function, multiple optimal solutions exist, as shown in Figure 3 by the light gray dots, at which points (ζ, z_{FbOp}) the objective function is essentially equal. Including the extra drops in the objective function – multi-drop form, $F(\zeta, z_{FbOp})$ – has a dramatic effect (black dots, Figure 3), in that solutions are then essentially limited to one location which has strong dependence on the satellite drop trajectories. In the third case (dark gray dots, Figure 3), which considers all the events and drop-drop interactions, but limited to the perspective of the primary drop and its interaction partners; the optimal placements are nearly equal – around $z_{FbOp} \approx 400$, which corresponds to a physical distance approximately 4 drop diameters from the nozzle, essentially in the middle of the potential placements.

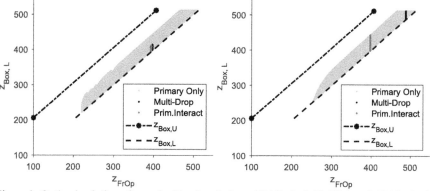

Figure 3. Optimal solutions for each objective. Left: μ-APAP, Φ=0.22; Right: sf-APAP, Φ=0.28

Closer inspect of the primary-only objective function evaluated on all points in the feasible region indicates larger gain as one moves away from the nozzle orifice, but, from

≈225 onward, the gain levels off rapidly with respect to camera placement, akin to a plateau. With respect to fiber-optic placement, generally the closer it is to the upper limit of the camera box, the lower the objective function value – which fits with intuition.

4. Discussion

The difference in the placements for the primary-only and multi-drop objective function fits with intuition – for a single object, there should be many camera/sensor placements that enable one to capture the entire volume of the primary drop across all the sequences at a given condition. Coincidentally, this is why it is easy to select by trial and error a camera/sensor position capable of capturing the whole deposited volume when the fluid properties yield a single drop per actuation event. On the other hand, the placement for the primary+interaction and full multi-drop cases yield very specific regions which are respectively far from many of the points that are potential optima for the primary drop. There are only a few possible ζ, z_{FbOp} that maximize the objective function; this results from the variability in the spatiotemporal events (particularly those that involve the primary drop) which lead to satellite drop formation. Comparison of the two conditions shown in Figure 3 indicates a significant difference in the placements between them for the multi-drop case; in the μ-APAP set, the placement is nearly the same as the primary+interaction, whereas in the sf-APAP set, the multi-drop placement is notably farther from the nozzle, and from the primary + interaction. This is due to the difference in the volumes of the satellite drops, as their contribution is proportionate – μ-APAP generally produced smaller satellites, but sf-APAP yielded larger satellites whose volume more significant, hence the shift to a position which was able to achieve approximately 1% greater imaged volume by their inclusion.

5. Conclusion

The optimization problem posed here becomes particularly important when one expects to have multiple droplets which undergo breakup or coalescence, as exemplified by the severely restricted regions which contain optima obtained for the primary+ and multi-drop cases. As these images provide a critical process measurement, minimizing uncertainty at the point of acquisition improves predictions from any models that subsequently make use of this information. Though trial and error enables one to guess the conditions when only the primary drop is considered, the treatment presented here demonstrates that some information would inherently be missing. What enables us to approach this problem despite the marked stochastic effects is the use of a data-driven approach which utilizes computer vision to extract object-specific and event type information, from a large number of images – 250,000+ - for real data obtained by high-speed imaging. This provides clear guidance on placements for the complex (multiple drops) scenarios regularly encountered when working with non-ideal inks.

References

L. Hirshfield, E. Icten, A. Giridhar, Z.K. Nagy, G.V. Reklaitis, 2015, "Real-Time Process Management Strategy for Dropwise Additive Manufacturing of Pharmaceutical Products", J. Pharm. Innov., 10, 2, 140-155
A.J. Radcliffe, G.V. Reklaitis, 2019, "Dynamic Object Tracking, Event Detectino and Recognition for High-speed Imaging of Drop Formation Phenomena", Intl. J. Comput. Vis. (in review at time of submission)

Sauro Pierucci, Flavio Manenti, Giulia Bozzano, Davide Manca (Eds.)
Proceedings of the 30th European Symposium on Computer Aided Process Engineering
(ESCAPE30), May 24-27, 2020, Milano, Italy. © 2020 Elsevier B.V. All rights reserved.
http://dx.doi.org/10.1016/B978-0-12-823377-1.50078-1

Livestock Production Planning with Batch-lines in the Agriculture Industry

Brenno C. Menezes,[a,*] Jeffrey D. Kelly,[b] Tareq Al-Ansari[a,c]

[a]*Division of Engineering Management and Decision Sciences, College of Science and Engineering, Hamad Bin Khalifa University, Qatar Foundation, Doha, Qatar*

[b]*Industrial Algorithms Ltd., 15 St. Andrews Road, Toronto M1P 4C3, Canada*

[c]*Division of Sustainable Development, College of Science and Engineering, Hamad Bin Khalifa University, Qatar Foundation, Doha, Qatar*

bmenezes@hbku.edu.qa

Abstract

With the expansion of the global population coupled with the improving quality of life in developing countries, an increasing demand of food for humans and feed for livestock are expected. Therefore, global pressures and food security issues encourage research, development and deployment of alternatives to improve the performance of the production of livestock and crops in the agriculture industry. Considering such environment, we propose a production planning optimization to be applied in livestock growth (of fish, poultry, pork, cattle, etc.) that considers the necessary feed (ration, vitamins, etc.) and number of animals (from the hatchery) to be placed into appropriate spaces (cages) or facilities (farms) for their proper growth. In the proposed livestock planning model, the placed animals are grown considering the assigned unit-places as batch-processes with limited capacity and variate time-of-growing of the livestock batches. For complex animals such as gallinaceous, swine, caprine and bovine (cattle) species, they are separated by gender to reduce the competition for feed and have comparable time-of-growth (within a range) among the live entities. The results show the batch-lines (batch-processes in lines) of production per gender and time-of-growth to be sequenced and assigned to maintain stable feed amounts in number of individuals and weights to the food processing plant.

Keywords: Livestock planning, Batch process, Feed-to-food, Agriculture industry.

1. Introduction

The increase in the costs of feed inputs and more expensive management of livestock and crops along with higher demands of food outputs and reducing farming resources have been pushing a move in academia and industry in the recent years in researching, developing and deploying novel apparatus and operations in the agriculture field. The expected outcome from this so-called precise farming aims to a) increase the reliability of farming decisions and operations (Anbuselvan et al., 2014); b) reduce inputs such as raw materials, assigned spaces and low-skilled labor; and c) improve livestock and crop yields and qualities. The multidisciplinary expertise in both fundamental and applied sciences for advanced operations in agricultural systems counts on pervasive sensing and actuation, automated decisions, advanced analytics, autonomous machinery and embedded computer control (Muangprathub et al., 2019) as the elements for smart manufacturing and high-performance logistics in this field.

In such context, considering accurate engineering management by the utilization of decision sciences in the agriculture industry (an automated decision element), a livestock production planning is proposed for the growth of fish, poultry, pork, goat, cattle, etc., whereby the number of male and female to be placed in spaces (cages) or facilities (farms) for the proper animal growth is addressed using batch-processes. The needs of separation by gender is more prominent in complex animals as gallinaceous, swine, caprine and bovine species to reduce the male and female competition among the live entities in the assigned spaces. In such model, although the average time of the life growth of each specie is well-known, two issues that conduce to the spread of the time-of-growing of the animals in different assigned places are acknowledged. The fundamental one is to circumvent congestion during the livestock slaughter or harvesting procedures that would drive to infeasible management of the animals in the slaughtering houses during the pre-slaughter handling (immobilization), stunning (to render the animal unconscious) and slaughtering per se. Such over handling may also cause mismanagement in the additional stages of separation of the animal parts and their packing and stocking in the industrial processing plants. The secondary matter to distribute the time-of-growth of the animals, considered as a virtuous side effect of the primary one, is to reduce the impact of the genetics differences. Within the same caged, assigned or placed group-to-grow, there are animals requiring lower time-of-growing (when compared to the average time to grow) and are those that demand longer time before the slaughtering or butchery assignment and further packing, freeze-stocking and selling to the market.

2. Problem statement

Batch-processes with a variate time-of-growing for the animal batches are proposed in the livestock planning model to determine the sequence and amounts of the types (per time-of-growing) of batch-processes in-line to be processed (the batch-lines) in the plant. Availability of the cages or free-range spaces to grow is controlled in the pool of cages. The network in Figure 1 shows a unitary livestock production system constructed in the unit-operation-port-state superstructure (UOPSS) from Kelly (2005) and its objects are defined as: a) unit-operations m for sources and sinks ($\diamond$), tanks or inventories ($\triangle$), batch-processes ($\square$) and continuous-processes ($\boxtimes$) and b) the connectivity involving arrows ($\rightarrow$), inlet-port-states i ($\bigcirc$) and outlet-port-states j ($\otimes$). Unit-operations and arrows have binary y and continuous x variables and the ports as process yields or qualities.

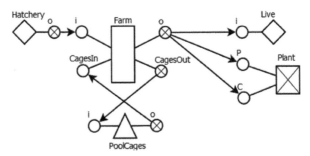

Figure 1. Unitary livestock production system.

Brunaud et al. (2020) demonstrate that the UOPSS formulation is computational superior to STN (Kondili et al., 1993; Shah et al., 1993) and RTN (Pantelides, 1994) in complex scheduling cases tested from the chemical production industry using batch processes, reducing large-scale problems from quarter of hours to seconds. See Kelly and Menezes (2019) for more details on the UOPSS and other large-scale examples.

3. Mathematical formulation

In the mixed-integer linear (MILP) problem (P), the objective function (1) maximizes the outputs of the livestock production $x_{j,i,t}$ (to the plant and as live entities) by discounting the feed costs of the animal batches with inventory or holdup $xh_{m,t}$ ($m \in M_{Farm}$). The semi-continuous constraints of the unit-operations m for the plant are controlled by $x^L_{m,t} y_{m,t} \leq x_{m,t} \leq x^U_{m,t} y_{m,t}$. For the batch-process farm, $xh_{m,t}$ is taken when the unit-operation m starts up ($zu_{m,t}= 1$) considering the respective bounds ($xh^L_{m,t} zsu_{m,t} \leq xh_{m,t} \leq xh^u_{m,t} zsu_{m,t}$). The arrows or connecting-flows from out- to in-port-states, are bounded as $x^L_{j,i,t} y_{j,i,t} \leq x_{j,i,t} \leq x^U_{j,i,t} y_{j,i,t}$. In Eqs. (2) to (9), $j \in J_{up}$ and $i \in I_{do}$ represent, respectively, up and downstream ports of other unit-operations. For $x \in \mathbb{R}^+$, $y \in \{0,1\}$ and $zsu_{m,t} \in [0,1]$:

$$(P) \; Min \; Z = \sum_t \left[\sum_{ji \in JI_{Plant}} \left(pr_P \, x_{j,i_p,t} + pr_C \, x_{j,i_p,t} \right) + \sum_{ji \in JI_{Live}} pr_L \, x_{j,i,t} \right.$$
$$\left. - \sum_{m \in M_{Farm}} c_F \, xh_{m,t} \right] \qquad s.t. \tag{1}$$

$$\frac{1}{x^U_{m,t}} \sum_{j \in J_{up}} x_{j,i,t} \leq y_{m,t} \leq \frac{1}{x^L_{m,t}} \sum_{j \in J_{up}} x_{j,i,t} \quad \forall \, (i,m) \in (M_{Live}, M_{Plant}), t \tag{2}$$

$$\frac{1}{x^U_{m,t}} \sum_{i \in I_{do}} x_{j,i,t} \leq y_{m,t} \leq \frac{1}{x^L_{m,t}} \sum_{i \in I_{do}} x_{j,i,t} \quad \forall \, (m,j) \in M_{Hatchry}, t \tag{3}$$

$$\sum_{tt<t} r_{j,tt} \, xh_{m,t} \geq \sum_{i \in I_{do}} x_{j,i,t} \quad \forall \, (m,j) \in M_{Farm}, t \tag{4}$$

$$\frac{1}{r^U_{i,t}} \sum_{j \in J_{up}} x_{j,i,t} \leq x_{m,t} \leq \frac{1}{r^L_{i,t}} \sum_{j \in J_{up}} x_{j,i,t} \quad \forall \, (i,m) \in (M_{Live}, M_{Plant}), t \tag{5}$$

$$\frac{1}{r^U_{j,t}} \sum_{i \in I_{do}} x_{j,i,t} \leq x_{m,t} \leq \frac{1}{r^L_{j,t}} \sum_{i \in I_{do}} x_{j,i,t} \quad \forall \, (m,j) \in M_{Hatchry}, t \tag{6}$$

$$\frac{1}{r^U_{i,t}} \sum_{j \in J_{up}} x_{j,i,t} \leq xh_{m,t} \leq \frac{1}{r^L_{i,t}} \sum_{j \in J_{up}} x_{j,i,t} \quad \forall \, (m,j) \in M_{Farm}, t \tag{7}$$

$$\frac{1}{r^U_{j,t}} \sum_{i \in I_{do}} x_{j,i,t} \leq xh_{m,t} \leq \frac{1}{r^L_{j,t}} \sum_{i \in I_{do}} x_{j,i,t} \quad \forall \, (m,j) \in M_{Farm}, t \tag{8}$$

$$xh_{m,t} = xh_{m,t-1} + \sum_{j' \in J_{up}} x_{j',i,t} - \sum_{i' \in I_{do}} x_{j,i',t} \quad \forall \, (i,m,j) \in M_{Cages}, t \tag{9}$$

$$y_{m',t} + y_{m,t} \leq y_{j,i,t} \quad \forall \, (m',j,i,m), t \tag{10}$$

$$\sum_{tt<t} zsu_{m',tt} + y_{m,t} \leq y_{j,i,t} \quad \forall \, (m',j,i,m), t \tag{11}$$

Equations (2) and (3) represent, respectively, the sum of the arrows leaving from the out-port-states j (or splitters) and arriving in the in-port-states i (or mixers) and their summation must be between the bounds of the unit-operation m connected to them. These constraints can be considered semi-continuous constraints for the summation of the flows in- and out- of a port connected to a unit-operation or more specifically to the setup or binary variable of the unit-operation. The production from the farm are controlled by Eq. (4) with the proposition of considering them as a batch-process with a decaying plot $r_{j,tt}$. Equations (5) to (8) consider bounds on yields, both inverse ($r_{i,t}^L$ and $r_{i,t}^U$) in the in-port-states i and direct ($r_{j,t}^L$ and $r_{j,t}^U$) in the out-port-states j, since the unit-operations m can have more than one stream arriving in or leaving from their connected ports. Equations (7) and (8) are related to yields of the batch-process, when occurs the starts up, i.e, $zsu_{m,t} = 1$, its holdup $xh_{m,t}$ is taken at this moment to start the animal creation.

The quantity balance of the inventory or holdup for unit-operations of tanks is defined in Eq. (9) and manages the availability of the cages. Equations (10) and (11) are the structural transition constraints to facilitate the setup $y_{m,t}$ or startup $zsu_{m,t}$ of different unit-operations interconnected by out-port-states j and in-port-states i. If the setup of unit-operations m and m' are true in Eq. (10), then the setup variable $y_{j,i,t}$ of the arrow stream between them are implicitly turned-on. In Eq. (11), the setup variable of m' is replaced by the summation of the startups as the farm cages are treated as batch-processes. These logic valid cuts reduce the tree search in branch-and-bound methods. Other constraints to model the run-length or uptime of the batch-processes and the sequence-dependency can be found in Kelly and Zyngier (2007).

4. Results

The livestock planning model in Figure 2 applied for a gallinaceous species is constructed considering the male growing from 16 to 20-months and the female from 13 to 17-months. The optimization for the proposed MILP in Figure 2 for 52-weeks as time-horizon with 1-week time-step gives 20,959 K USD of profit for the planning growth. The problem is solved in 45 seconds with GUROBI 9.0 and > 3600 seconds with CPLEX 12.10 both at 1.0% of MILP relaxation gap using an Intel Core i7 machine at 3.4 GHz (8 threads) with 64 GB of RAM. There are 16,888 constraints (4,613 equality) for 5,895 continuous variables and 4,704 binary variables with 5,986 degrees-of-freedom in the problem (variables minus equality constraints).

The Gantt chart in Figure 3 shows the startups of the animal growth in cages considering the different types of time-of-growing batches for male (16 to 20-months) and female (13 to 17-months). The different types of batch-processes representing the male and female types of cages can be started up continuously or in-line since the batch is initialized by using the available resource cages (of any type of time-of-growing or gender) taken from the PoolCages inventories.

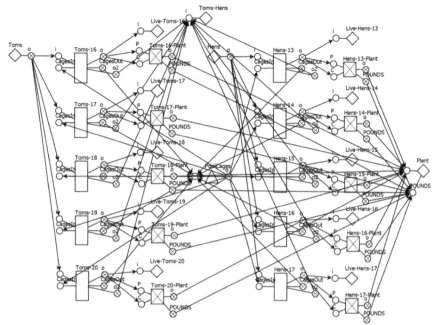

Figure 2. Livestock production planning considering variate time-of-growing of male (toms) and female (hens) cages.

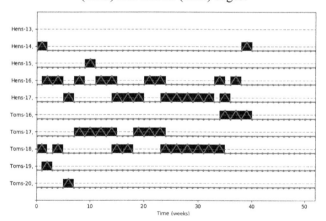

Figure 3. Startups of the male and female procreation cages considering the variate time-of-growing batches.

The Gantt chart in Figure 4 shows the PoolCages object that represents the inventory of cages to start the livestock production. The inventory upper bound is two cages ready for the procreation to be initialized per week. The formulation uses inventories to control the resources of cages in the out-port-states of the PoolCages inventory for the batch startups (see Figure 2 the PoolCages object). It may be considered as the capacity of workers or machinery limits to be modeled in a problem.

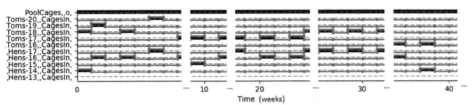

Figure 4. PoolCages release of the male and female cages and time-of-growing batches.

5. Conclusions

The livestock planning approach using batch-lines to manage animal procreation is an effective tool to improve overall gains and avoid mismanagement in the agriculture industry. When planning the livestock growth by distributing its time-of-growing in the different cages, the uncertainties and bottlenecks related to the production (from the management/processing) and from the hatchery (incubator or breeding locations), are reduced or mitigated. The high-performance management of livestock demonstrated in this work is mandatory to face higher demands of food outputs and reducing farming resources as well as in the global competitiveness of the new industrial efficiency age.

References

S. Anbuselvan, S. Arunkumar, G. Guhan, K. Muruganantham, T. Rajesh, 2014, Optimization of Productivity in Agro Industries Using Reliability Centered Maintenance, International Journal of Technology and Engineering System, 6 (2), 203-208.

B. Brunaud, S. Amaran, S. Bury, J. Wassick, I.E. Grossmann, 2020, Batch Scheduling with Quality-Based Changeovers, Computer and Chemical Engineering, Computers and Chemical Engineering, 132, 106617.

J.D. Kelly, 2005, The Unit-Operation-Stock Superstructure (UOSS) and the Quantity-Logic-Quality Paradigm (QLQP) for Production Scheduling in The Process Industries, In Multidisciplinary International Scheduling Conference Proceedings: New York, United States, 327-333.

J. D. Kelly, D. Zyngier, 2007, An Improved MILP Modeling of Sequence-Dependent Switchovers for Discrete-Time Scheduling Problems, Industrial and Engineering Chemistry Research., 46, 4964-4973.

J.D. Kelly, B.C. Menezes, 2019, Industrial Modeling and Programming Language (IMPL) for Off- and On-Line Optimization and Estimation Applications. In: Fathi M., Khakifirooz M., Pardalos P. (eds) Optimization in Large Scale Problems. Springer Optimization and Its Applications, 152, 75-96.

E. Kondili, C.C. Pantelides, R.W.H. Sargent, 1993, A General Algorithm for Short-Term Scheduling Of Batch Operations – I MILP Formulation, Computers and Chemical Engineering, 17, 211-227.

J. Muangprathub, N. Boonnam, S. Kajornkasirat, N. Lekbangpong, A. Wanichsombat, P. Nillaor, 2019, IoT and Agriculture Data Analysis for Smart Farm, Computers and Electronics in Agriculture, 156, 467-474.

N. Shah, C.C. Pantelides, R.W.H. Sargent, 1993, A General Algorithm for Short-Term Scheduling of Batch Operations – II. Computational Issues. Computers and Chemical Engineering, 17, 229-244.

C.C. Pantelides. Unified Frameworks for the Optimal Process Planning and Scheduling. Proceedings on the Second Conference on Foundations of Computer Aided Operations. 1994, 253-274.

Sauro Pierucci, Flavio Manenti, Giulia Bozzano, Davide Manca (Eds.)
Proceedings of the 30th European Symposium on Computer Aided Process Engineering
(ESCAPE30), May 24-27, 2020, Milano, Italy. © 2020 Elsevier B.V. All rights reserved.
http://dx.doi.org/10.1016/B978-0-12-823377-1.50079-3

Ethanol Reforming: Setting up Performance Target

Shahid H Ansari, Baraka C Sempuga, Xinying Liu

Institut of Development of Energy for African Sustainability, University of South Africa, Private Bag X6, Florida, 0710, Johannesburg, South Africa
liux@unisa.ac.za

Abstract

Process Synthesis techniques and Attainable region principles were used to determine the target of ethanol reforming to hydrogen from a material, energy and work balance point of view. From a material balance point of view, 100% hydrogen efficiency, defined as the fraction of hydrogen in the feed that is converted into the desired product (H_2), can be achieved by partial oxidation at the ratio of ethanol to oxygen of 1 : 1.5, producing H_2 and CO_2. However, the process releases a significant amount of energy and work potential, which might not be economically recovered especially for small scale applications. Co-feeding water is one of the ways to recover this energy by producing more H_2. We, therefore, look at the ultimate energy target for the process, which is considered to be at the point where ΔH across the process is zero. In order to achieve this water and oxygen must be fed to the process at ratios of 1:1.77 and 1: 0.62 respectively. This increases H_2 production by 59%. However, the process will still have a significant amount of work potential indicated by the negative change in Gibbs free energy across the process. When work balance target of $\Delta G = 0$ was considered, we can show that the hydrogen production can be increased up to 87%. However, the process will require heat to be supplied. If a low cost heat source is available, such as solar or waste heat from other processes, then a maximum of 187% selectivity of H_2 based on ethanol can be achieved. For a fully energy integrated process, at $\Delta G = 0$ the process does not require high quality heat for it to proceed. Therefore, at this point any source of heat at a temperature high enough to enable heat flow at any point in the process will be sufficient to drive the process. We consider this to be the ultimate target for ethanol reforming, which not only enables to conserve the chemical potential of ethanol but also provides an opportunity to store additional external energy in the form of H_2. The feasibility of these targets were validated by Aspen Plus simulation.

Keywords: Ethanol autothermal reforming, Process Target, Gibbs free energy minimization, Hydrogen production, Tail gas

1. Introduction

Hydrogen fuel cell technologies has big potential to be used in vehicle or portable power plants as a clean energy supply solution. But there are challenges in its implementation such that currently most of the hydrogen is produced from fossil fuel such as natural gas or coal, which are not renewable, while the hydrogen produced from water electrolysis by using renewable power is still expensive. Furthermore, if hydrogen is produced from a big hydrogen plant, it still needs to be transported to the user end and stored at the user end, which raised concerns of its safety. It would be a good option to study the potential of using liquid fuel, which are easy to be stored and transported as a feed stock for on-site hydrogen production in vehicle or hydrogen filling station (Di Marcoberardino 2017). Among various ethanol to hydrogen processes studied, ethanol autothermal reforming, which is a combination of the exothermic ethanol partial oxidation process and endothermic ethanol steam reforming process, is most suited for mobile application as it doesn't require external heat load (Hou 2015). Furthermore, ethanol water mixture can be used in the autothermal reforming process, thus the high energy cost paid to remove all water in the ethanol production by distillation and zeolite adsorption can be saved (Deluga 2004).

To achieve thermal neutral, for every mol of ethanol, 1.78 mole of water and 0.61 mole of Oxygen is needed (Graschinsky 2012), to produce 4.78 mole of hydrogen. But there is still a significant amount of work as indicated by the negative change in the free energy across the process. To utilize this work, a work balanced target at $\Delta G = 0$ was considered and analyzed by targeting techniques.

2. Method

The targeting technique employs three basic tools namely the mass, energy and work (entropy) balance to determine a feasible region from which a design target for the process can be set. It starts by first identifying the major components of the process and ignores the components in smaller quantities and the impurities. This is done to simply the analysis while extracting the essential information that does not require the details, which will be included at a later stage of design. The major components that were considered here are C_2H_6O, H_2, CO_2, H_2O, CO, CH_4, O_2. From these components, we can derive the following independent material balances using the method by (Yin, 2010)

$$
\begin{aligned}
C_2H_6O + 0.5O_2 &\Rightarrow 3H_2 + 2CO \dots\dots\dots E_1 \\
CO_2 + H_2 &\Rightarrow CO + H_2O \dots\dots\dots\dots E_2 \\
CH_4 + 2O_2 &\Rightarrow CO_2 + 2H_2O \dots\dots\dots E_3 \\
H_2 + 0.5O_2 &\Rightarrow H_2O \dots\dots\dots\dots\dots E_4
\end{aligned}
\tag{1}
$$

Note that these are not necessarily the actual reactions occurring in the process, they are simply material balances representing all achievable outcome from the process. Each component can then be written in terms of extent as $N_i = \sum_{i,j}' v_{ij} E_j$.

The constraints set by the energy and work balances are also included. These are expressed as follows:

$$
\begin{aligned}
\Delta H_P &= \sum_i N_i \Delta \hat{H}_i(T_O) \\
\Delta G_P &= \sum_i N_i \Delta \hat{G}_i(T_O)
\end{aligned}
\tag{2}
$$

ΔH_P represents the net energy requirement of the process and ΔG_P is the change in the Gibbs free energy and represents the work requirement (or work potential) of the process.

In other words, ΔG_P represents the portion of the energy equivalent to mechanical work that must be supplied (positive) or removed (negative) from the process.

3. Results and Discussion

It can be shown that the process has four degrees of freedom representing four possible targets that can be set simultaneously. In order to explore these targets, we used a linear programming approach to determine the feasible regions. Two cases are considered namely $\Delta Hp = 0$ for an energy neutral process and $\Delta Gp = 0$ for a work neutral process. Figure 1 shows the feasible regions obtained by plotting the oxygen fed to the process versus the hydrogen production at $\Delta Hp = 0$ per mole of ethanol fed. The negative number of moles indicates that the component is a feed while the positive number indicates that the component is a product. The feasible region is considered to be where H_2, CO_2, CO, CH_4 are products and O_2 is feed. H_2O is allowed to be either feed or products. It is clear from Figure 1 that the maximum H_2 production occurs at zero CH_4 and CO produced. At this point $\Delta Gp < 0$, this means that the process should proceed with less effort. It also means that the process has the potential to do work, which can be recovered by applying an appropriate process configuration. Therefore, the ultimate H_2 production target for an autothermal ethanol reformer is about 4.77 per mole of ethanol.

$$C_2H_6O + 1.77H_2O + 0.62O_2 \Rightarrow 4.77H_2 + 2CO_2 \quad \Delta G = -195 \text{ kJ}; \Delta H = 0 \text{ kJ} \quad (3)$$

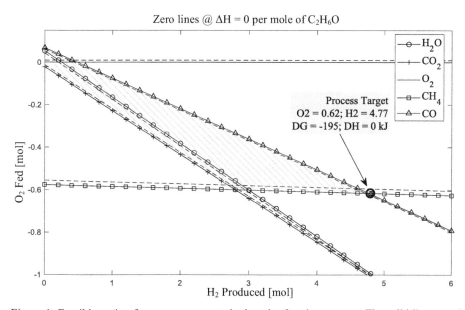

Figure 1: Feasible region for an energy neutral ethanol reforming process. The solid lines are the boundaries indicating zero moles of the components. The dashed lines indicate the side where the components are net products. The ultimate hydrogen production target is 4.77 moles per mole of C_2H_6O.

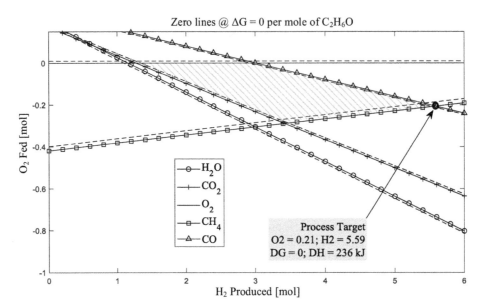

Figure 2: Feasible region for a work neutral ethanol reforming process. The solid lines are the boundaries indicating zero moles of the components. The dashed lines indicate the side where the components are net products. The ultimate hydrogen production target is 5.59 moles per mole of C_2H_6O

Figure 2 shows the feasible region for a work neutral process ($\Delta Gp = 0$). The maximum hydrogen production also occurs at zero CH_4 and CO produced. However, at this point $\Delta Hp > 0$. This means that energy in the form of heat must be supplied to the process from an external source. The significance of a work neutral process is that the chemical potential of the feed material is fully conserved when they are converted into products (Sempuga and Yao, 2017). Consequently, the energy that must be supplied can be in the form of heat and can be at any temperature that enables the flow of energy from an external source to the process, not necessarily higher than the actual reforming temperature. This target represents the limit of performance for any ethanol reforming process contrary to what is considered to be the limit set by an auto thermal reformer (Graschinsky 2012). The H_2 production target at this limit is 5.59 per mole of ethanol.

$$C_2H_6O + 2.59H_2O + 0.21O_2 \Rightarrow 5.59H_2 + 2CO_2 \quad \Delta G = 0 \text{ kJ}; \Delta H = 236 \text{ kJ} \quad (4)$$

This target provides a means for improving the hydrogen production of an auto thermal reformer by up to 17%, if a source of low cost energy is available, which is likely the case in the actually application environmental such as in the vehicle. For a fully energy integrated process, at $\Delta G = 0$ the process does not require high quality heat for it to proceed. Therefore, at this point any source of heat at a temperature high enough to enable heat flow at any point in the process will be sufficient to drive the process. For example, one of the efficient ways of supplying the energy to the process is by generating steam using any heat source at low temperature but high enough to produce the steam (above 100°C at 1atm) and feed the steam that carries the required amount of energy into the process.

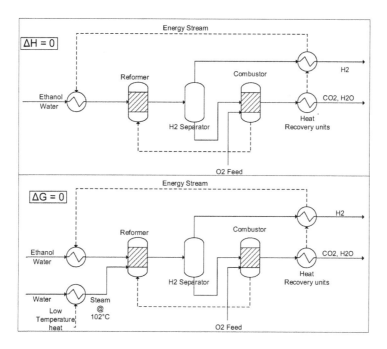

Figure 3: Flow diagram for the Aspen Plus simulations at $\Delta H = 0$ and $\Delta G = 0$

Simulations in Aspen Plus ® were conducted to explore how the targets in (3) and (4) can be achieved. The flow sheets are shown in figure 3. The main assumptions taken in the simulation are: 1) the reforming reaction reaches equilibrium and therefore an equilibrium reactor (RGibbs) was used to simulate the reaction. 2) Pure H_2 can be recovered from the product stream at the reactor temperature therefore; a perfect separator was used to selectively remove H_2 from the other products. The latter assumption is possible in a membrane reactor, which can separate out H_2 during the reaction.

For the $\Delta H = 0$ process, the feed stream containing ethanol and water is pre-heated and fed to membrane reactor. The temperature in the reactor is set to between 500°C and 1000°C. The membrane process, which selectively removes H_2 from the reactor, is simulated by multistage equilibrium reactors with hydrogen separation between stages. The energy required in the reformers is supplied by burning the tail gas from the reformer after H_2 has be separated out. For this purpose, a stoichiometric reactor (Rstoic) was used. The combustion is assumed to occur at the same temperature as the reactor. Heat integration is done between the feed stream and the product streams from the combustor. A temperature approach of 10°C is considered in the heat integration process.

The flowsheet of the $\Delta G = 0$ process is the same as that of $\Delta H = 0$ except for the additional steam generated from an external source of energy and fed to the reactor. The stream brings in the additional energy required to reach the target H_2 at $\Delta G = 0$. In the current simulation it assumed that external heat is available to generate steam and 102°C and 1bar from a stream of liquid water at 25°C.

The simulation results show that for the $\Delta H = 0$ process the H_2 production target of 4.77/mole of ethanol at an oxygen to ethanol ratio of 0.62 : 1 can be achieved over the temperature range 500 - 1000°C. The water to ethanol feed ratio varies depending on the reaction temperature, the minimum feed ratio 4.40 : 1 occurs at 700°C. If we consider recycling the water, then the net water to ethanol feed ratio is constant over the temperature range and is 1.77 : 1; this is the same as the target water feed ratio in (3).

The simulation results for the $\Delta G = 0$ process show that the H_2 production target of 5.59/mole of ethanol at an oxygen to ethanol ratio of 0.21 : 1 can be achieved over the temperature range 500 - 1000°C. The water to ethanol feed ratio also varies depending on the reaction temperature, the minimum feed ratio 9.01 : 1 occurs at 620°C. If we consider recycling the water, then the net water to ethanol feed ratio is constant over the temperature range and is 2.59 : 1; this is the same as the target water feed ratio in (4).

4. Conclusions

By conducting work balance target analysis, we found that hydrogen production of the ethanol to hydrogen process can be increased up to 87% compared to ethanol partial oxidation process and 17% more compared to the target of the energy neutral process, with less oxygen required and more water tolerated in the feed. Although external heat is needed, a low cost heat can be utilized in a fully energy integrated process operated at $\Delta G = 0$. We consider this to be the ultimate target for ethanol reforming, which not only enables to conserve the chemical potential of ethanol but also provides an opportunity to store additional external energy in the form of H_2.

Acknowledgement

The authors would like to acknowledge the University of South Africa (UNISA) and the financial support from National Research Foundation (NRF) with grant numbers 95983 and 113648.

References

G a Deluga, J R Salge, L D Schmide, X E Verykios, 2004, Reneable hydrogen from ethanol by autothermal reforming, Sciences, 303, 993-997

C Graschinsky, P Giunta, N Amadeo, M Laborde, 2012, Thermodynamic analysis of hydrogen production by autothermal reforming of ethanol, International Journal of Hydrogn Energy, 37 (13), 10118-10124

T Hou, S Zhang, Y Chen, D Wang, 2015, W Cai, Hydrogn production from ethanol reforming: Catalysts and reaction mechanism, Reneable and Sustainable Energy Reviews, 44, 132-148

G Di Marcoberardino, M Binotti, G Manzolini, J L Viviente, A Arratibel, L Roses, F Gallucci, 2017, Achievements of European projects on membrane reactor for hydrogen production, Journla of Cleaner Production, 161, 1442-1450

B C Sempuga and Y Yao, 2017, CO_2 hydrogenation from a process synthesis perspective: Setting up process targets', Journal of CO_2 Utilization, 20, 34–42.

Yin, F., 2010, A simple method for finding independent reactions, Chemical Engineering Communications, 83 (1), 117–127.

Sauro Pierucci, Flavio Manenti, Giulia Bozzano, Davide Manca (Eds.)
Proceedings of the 30th European Symposium on Computer Aided Process Engineering
(ESCAPE30), May 24-27, 2020, Milano, Italy. © 2020 Elsevier B.V. All rights reserved.
http://dx.doi.org/10.1016/B978-0-12-823377-1.50080-X

Thermodynamic Framework for Cryogenic Carbon Capture

Laura A. Pellegrini,[a*] Giorgia De Guido,[a] Stefania Ingrosso[b]

[a]*Dipartimento di Chimica, Materiali e Ingegneria Chimica "G. Natta", Politecnico di Milano, Piazza Leonardo da Vinci 32, I-20133 Milan, Italy*
[b]*SAIPEM S.p.A., via Martiri di Cefalonia 67, I-20097 San Donato Milanese (MI), Italy*
laura.pellegrini@polimi.it

Abstract

Carbon dioxide capture and storage (CCS) is an important option for climate change mitigation and it has been extensively analysed in recent years to face the climate challenge. A portion of the emitted CO_2 comes from fossil fuel power plants. Several post-combustion technologies are available for separating CO_2 from the flue gases produced by the combustion of fossil fuels. In recent years, low-temperature/cryogenic technologies have been investigated for this purpose, which rely on the fact that CO_2 can be separated out of flue gas by freezing it out. As a consequence, when dealing with the design of this type of processes, it is of paramount importance to be able to satisfactorily predict the thermodynamic phase behaviour of the system of interest, which involves equilibrium conditions also in the presence of solid CO_2.

The classical approach for phase equilibria calculations involving a solid phase is based on the equality of components' fugacities in the different phases and on the use of an expression for the fugacity of the freezing component in the solid phase that can be derived by relating it to its fugacity in the vapor phase following a proper thermodynamic cycle. This work compares the predictions for solid-vapor equilibria (SVE) conditions of a flue gas mixture that are obtained using such a classical approach with those obtained using the RGibbs calculation block available in the Aspen Plus® process simulator. The latter one enables SVE calculations by minimizing the Gibbs energy. The obtained results are useful for determining suitable operating conditions for the separation process, depending on the desired level of CO_2 recovery to be achieved.

Keywords: CO_2, carbon capture, solid-vapor equilibria, cryogenic gas separation, flue gas

1. Introduction

Climate change represents a serious challenge the world has to face today. At the 21st Conference held in Paris in 2015, Parties in the United Nations Framework Convention on Climate Change reached an agreement to combat this issue and to accelerate and intensify the actions and investments needed for a sustainable low carbon future. In this context, CCS techniques have been extensively studied in recent years as a mitigation option for reducing anthropogenic CO_2 emissions into the atmosphere.
Different technologies are currently available for CO_2 removal from flue gases, including chemical (De Guido et al., 2018) and physical absorption, adsorption (Gutierrez-Ortega et al., 2017), permeation through membranes (Leimbrink et al., 2015) and low-temperature or commonly referred to as "cryogenic" separation. Recently, a great attention has been devoted to cryogenic separation methods for application not

only to natural gas purification (De Guido et al., 2015) and biogas upgrading (Pellegrini et al., 2017), but also to nitrogen rejection (De Guido et al., 2019) and CO_2 capture from flue gas. When this last application is considered, the separation process aims at reducing the flue gas temperature from ambient to a low temperature range at which CO_2 freezes out and can be removed from the main gas stream in a solid phase. The advantages of this technology can be summarized as follows: liquid CO_2 is directly produced, thus making it relatively easy to be stored or to be used for Enhanced Oil Recovery; the use of solvents is avoided (Sipöcz et al., 2013). Certainly, a major disadvantage consists in the large amount of energy required for refrigeration. However, literature works have proved that the use of low-temperature technologies for natural gas purification becomes less energy demanding at CO_2 concentrations higher than 8-9 mol% (Langè et al., 2015).

Clodic et al. (Clodic et al., 2005) proposed a cryogenic technology for CO_2 separation from the flue gases for a conventional pulverized coal-fired power boiler, which is based on CO_2 frosting (anti-sublimation) and defrosting at atmospheric pressure in a low-temperature evaporator. Baxter et al. (Baxter et al., 2009) proposed the CCC™ (Cryogenic CO_2 Capture™) technology, which uses a phase change (*i.e.*, desublimation) to separate CO_2 from exhaust or process gases. Tuinier et al. (Tuinier et al., 2010) developed a novel post-combustion CO_2 capture process concept, based on cryogenic CO_2 freeze-out in dynamically operated packed beds. Song et al. (Song et al., 2012) developed a novel cryogenic CO_2 capture system based on the use of Stirling coolers, which is able to condense and separate CO_2 from flue gas according to differences in condensation and desublimation.

The increased interest in this type of processes requires a proper tool to be available for the correct prediction of phase equilibria also involving the solid phase. In this work, a method based on a classical approach is presented and results are compared with those found in the literature and the ones that can be obtained using a tool available in a commercial process simulator. These results are exploited to establish the suitable operating conditions for CO_2 separation from flue gas by a cryogenic separation method.

2. Methods

2.1. Proposed thermodynamic approach for SVE calculations

In this work, a classical approach has been used (it will be referred to as "proposed approach" in the following) to solve a two-phase solid-vapor equilibrium (SVE) problem for a flue gas mixture having the following composition: 14.0 mol% CO_2, 83.0 mol% N_2, and 3.0 mol% O_2. Since the number and type of phases present at equilibrium are not known *a-priori*, the choice of studying SVE conditions for the system of interest has to be considered as an assumption based on the type of components the system consists of. The SVE problem has been solved assigning the pressure and recovery of CO_2 with the aim of plotting the equilibrium temperature curve as a function of pressure for each recovery level. In particular, three values have been chosen for that (*i.e.*, 90 %, 95 % and 99 %) for comparison of the results obtained in this work with those presented in the literature (Baxter et al., 2009).

The recovery of CO_2 in the solid phase (*REC*) is calculated according to Eq. (1):

$$REC = \frac{S \cdot x_{CO_2}^S}{F \cdot z_{CO_2}} = \frac{S}{F \cdot z_{CO_2}} \tag{1}$$

In Eq. (1), $x_{CO_2}^S$, which denotes the molar fraction of CO_2 in the solid phase, has been set equal to one since the solid phase is assumed to consist of pure CO_2. Moreover, in Eq. (1) F and S denote the molar flow rates, respectively, of the feed stream and of the solid phase, and z_{CO_2} refers to the molar fraction of CO_2 in the feed stream (*i.e.*, 0.14).

By combining Eq. (1) with the material balances on the species involved in the investigated system, it is possible to get the composition of the vapor phase at equilibrium for each case study (*i.e.*, each pair of pressure and CO_2 recovery). The SVE calculation is based on the equality of fugacity of each *i*-th component in the two considered phases (*i.e.*, solid and vapor), and Eq. (2) holds:

$$\hat{f}_i^S(T,P,\underline{x}^S) = \hat{f}_i^V(T,P,\underline{x}^V) \tag{2}$$

Since CO_2 is the only species to be present in both phases at equilibrium, Eq. (2) can be rewritten, according to the classical method, as Eq. (3), where $\phi_{CO_2}^V$ is the fugacity coefficient of pure CO_2 in the vapor phase evaluated at the sublimation pressure, $P_{CO_2}^{subl}$, and equilibrium temperature, T, and $\hat{\phi}_{CO_2}^V$ is the fugacity coefficient of CO_2 in the vapor mixture evaluated at the equilibrium temperature, at the given pressure, P, of the system and composition.

$$\phi_{CO_2}^V(T,P_{CO_2}^{subl}(T)) \cdot P_{CO_2}^{subl}(T) \cdot \exp\left(\frac{v_{CO_2}^S \cdot (P - P_{CO_2}^{subl}(T))}{RT}\right) = P \cdot x_{CO_2}^V \cdot \hat{\phi}_{CO_2}^V(T,P,\underline{x}^V) \tag{3}$$

The two fugacity coefficients in Eq. (3) have been calculated using the Peng-Robinson Equation of State (Peng and Robinson, 1976). As for the binary interaction parameters, the values have been taken from the Aspen Hysys® V9.0 database (AspenTech, 2016a). Therefore, Eq. (3) can be solved in the unknown temperature, at given pressure and CO_2 recovery. The solid molar volume, $v_{CO_2}^S$, in the Poynting correction term has been assumed to be constant and equal to 0.0282 m³/kmol. As for the sublimation pressure, $P_{CO_2}^{subl}$, it has been computed using the expression proposed by Jensen et al. (Jensen et al., 2015) and reported in Eq. (4), where $P_{CO_2}^{subl}$ is in Pa and T in K.

$$P_{CO_2}^{subl}(T) = \exp\left(57.52 - \frac{3992.84}{T} - 4.9003 \cdot \ln(T) + 2.415 \cdot 10^{-15} T^6 + \frac{8125.6}{T^2}\right) \tag{4}$$

2.2. Thermodynamic approach available in the process simulator

The RGibbs reactor is the only calculation block available in Aspen Plus® V9.0 (AspenTech, 2016b) that is able to solve a system involving phase equilibria also in the presence of a solid phase (Schach et al., 2011). It uses Gibbs energy minimization techniques, instead of methods based on the equality of fugacities of each component in each phase. The system is considered at equilibrium when the distribution of the components corresponds to the minimum of the Gibbs energy (subject to atom balance constraints). According to the literature from Aspen Technology, this method can be used for any number of phases and components and always yields stable solutions. Since the RGibbs cannot handle phase equilibria between solid and fluid phases of a component directly (*e.g.*, CO_2-dry ice equilibria), it is necessary to identify the solid component as a different one. The Peng-Robinson Equation of State (Peng and

Robinson, 1976) has been used as property method and the values of the standard solid heat of formation and of the standard solid Gibbs free energy of formation have been specified.

3. Results and discussion

Before solving the SVE problem investigated in this work with the proposed approach, the reliability of Eq. (4) in predicting the CO_2 sublimation pressure has been checked. Results are shown in the parity plot in Fig. 1. They suggest a good agreement between calculated and experimental values (Fernández-Fassnacht and Del Río, 1984; Levenson, 1974), with an average absolute deviation of 23.6 %.

Fig. 2 illustrates the results obtained using the proposed approach (dashed line), which are compared with those obtained using the RGibbs tool available in Aspen Plus® V9.0 (dotted lines) and with those available in the literature (Baxter et al., 2009) (solid line). In Fig. 2, the symbols refer to the points of the curves where each approach registers a maximum. The proposed approach is about 2 degrees more conservative in correspondence of the value of pressure where the maximum is found in the literature and is in good agreement with the results obtained using the RGibbs tool.

As a general result, it is possible to state that, for achieving a higher recovery at a given pressure, it is necessary to operate the process at a lower temperature. Moreover, the maximum trend the curves in Fig. 2 exhibit suggests that, if a certain CO_2 recovery is desired, the process can be operated at a higher temperature at increasing pressure and viceversa for pressures up to the labelled maximum point. Beyond the labelled points in Fig. 2, higher pressures and lower temperatures are required to achieve the same CO_2 recovery in the solid phase, both of which would make the CO_2 separation process more energy-intensive. Therefore, for each curve in Fig. 2, the portion up to the labelled point is the one corresponding to the operating conditions of interest for the process, which aims at separating CO_2 from a flue gas mixture by desublimation.

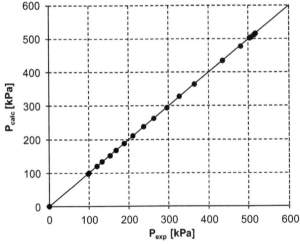

Figure 1. Parity plot for CO_2 sublimation pressure. Experimental data have been taken from the literature (Fernández-Fassnacht and Del Río, 1984; Levenson, 1974) and cover the temperature range 69.7-216.6 K; calculated values have been obtained using Eq. (4).

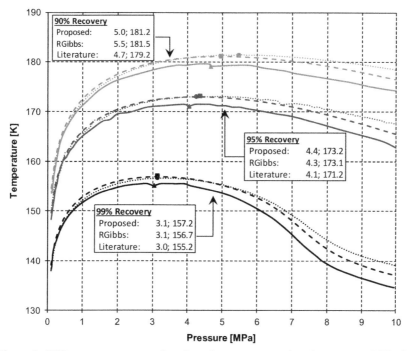

Figure 2. SVE temperatures as a function of pressure at assigned recovery of CO_2 in the solid phase. Comparison between the results obtained using: the proposed approach (dashed line), the RGibbs tool of Aspen Plus® V9.0 (AspenTech, 2016b) (dotted line), and the ones presented in the literature (Baxter et al., 2009) (solid line). The different colors refer to different CO_2 recovery values: 90 % (light grey); 95 % (grey); 99 % (black). For each curve, the symbols (square: proposed approach; circle: RGibbs; triangle: literature) refer to the values in the text box that correspond to the pressure at which each approach registers the maximum temperature.

4. Conclusions

Low-temperature or cryogenic technologies for CO_2 capture from flue gases have received great attention in the last years to cope with the disadvantages of conventionally adopted technologies mainly based on absorption. Since these novel separation methods are operated at conditions where CO_2 freezes out, it is important to have a tool capable of satisfactorily predicting phase equilibria in the presence of a solid phase, which is not always taken into account in phase equilibria calculations. This is important for a correct process design.

In this work, a calculation method is proposed for this purpose and the obtained results are compared with those of a calculation block available in a commercial process simulator, based on a different approach. The good agreement suggests that the proposed method can be used to design the CO_2 separation process.

In particular, for achieving 99 % recovery of CO_2 in the solid phase, temperatures of about 140 K have to be reached at atmospheric pressure or higher temperatures (up to about 155 K) at increasing pressures up to about 3 MPa. Above this pressure value, due to the maximum trend exhibited by the temperature-pressure curve at fixed CO_2 recovery, the process should be operated at lower temperatures, which is disadvantageous since this makes it more energy-intensive.

For an improved analysis, an advanced phase equilibria calculation method has been developed in the framework of a joint project between the GASP group of Politecnico di Milano and Saipem S.p.A. and implemented in the "SLVEcalc" tool. The advanced model takes into account the phase stability analysis (Gupta, 1990) for the identification of the type of phases present at equilibrium and will be the subject of a future work.

References

AspenTech, 2016a. Aspen Hysys®. AspenTech, Burlington (MA), United States.

AspenTech, 2016b. Aspen Plus®. AspenTech, Burlington (MA), United States.

L. Baxter, A. Baxter, S. Burt, 2009. Cryogenic CO_2 capture as a cost-effective CO_2 capture process, International Pittsburgh Coal Conference, Pittsburgh, USA.

D. Clodic, R. El Hitti, M. Younes, A. Bill, F. Casier, 2005. CO_2 capture by anti-sublimation Thermo-economic process evaluation, 4th Annual Conference on Carbon Capture and Sequestration. National Energy Technology Laboratory Alexandria (VA) USA, pp. 2-5.

G. De Guido, M. Compagnoni, L.A. Pellegrini, I. Rossetti, 2018. Mature versus emerging technologies for CO_2 capture in power plants: Key open issues in post-combustion amine scrubbing and in chemical looping combustion. Frontiers of Chemical Science and Engineering 12, 315-325.

G. De Guido, S. Langè, L.A. Pellegrini, 2015. Refrigeration cycles in low-temperature distillation processes for the purification of natural gas. Journal of Natural Gas Science and Engineering 27, 887-900.

G. De Guido, F. Messinetti, E. Spatolisano, 2019. Cryogenic nitrogen rejection schemes: analysis of their tolerance to CO_2. Industrial & Engineering Chemistry Research 58, 17475-17488.

E. Fernández-Fassnacht, F. Del Río, 1984. The vapour pressure of CO_2 from 194 to 243 K. The Journal of Chemical Thermodynamics 16, 469-474.

A.K. Gupta, 1990. Steady state simulation of chemical processes. Chemical and Petroleum Engineering, University of Calgary.

A. Gutierrez-Ortega, J. Menacho, R. Gonzalez-Olmos, R. Nomen, J. Sempere, 2017. Numerical simulation of fixed bed for CO_2 capture in a fossil fuel emission points by Pressure Swing Adsorption system, Computer Aided Chemical Engineering. Elsevier, pp. 415-420.

M.J. Jensen, C.S. Russell, D. Bergeson, C.D. Hoeger, D.J. Frankman, C.S. Bence, L.L. Baxter, 2015. Prediction and validation of external cooling loop cryogenic carbon capture (CCC-ECL) for full-scale coal-fired power plant retrofit. International Journal of Greenhouse Gas Control 42, 200-212.

S. Langè, L.A. Pellegrini, P. Vergani, M. Lo Savio, 2015. Energy and Economic Analysis of a New Low-Temperature Distillation Process for the Upgrading of High-CO_2 Content Natural Gas Streams. Industrial & Engineering Chemistry Research 54, 9770-9782.

M. Leimbrink, A.-K. Kunze, D. Hellmann, A. Górak, M. Skiborowski, 2015. Conceptual Design of Post-Combustion CO_2 Capture Processes-Packed Columns and Membrane Technologies, Computer Aided Chemical Engineering. Elsevier, pp. 1223-1228.

L. Levenson, 1974. Sublimation rates and vapor pressure of H_2O, CO_2, N_2O and Xe. Journal of Chemical & Engineering Data 19, 107-110.

L.A. Pellegrini, G. De Guido, S. Langé, 2017. Biogas to liquefied biomethane via cryogenic upgrading technologies. Renewable Energy 124, 75-83.

D.-Y. Peng, D.B. Robinson, 1976. A new two-constant equation of state. Industrial & Engineering Chemistry Fundamentals 15, 59-64.

M.-O. Schach, B. Oyarzún, H. Schramm, R. Schneider, J.-U. Repke, 2011. Feasibility study of CO_2 capture by anti-sublimation. Energy Procedia 4, 1403-1410.

N. Sipöcz, A. Hernandez-Nogales, M.A. Gonzalez-Salazar, R. Shisler, V. Lissianski, 2013. Low temperature CO_2 capture for near-term applications. Energy Procedia 37, 1228-1238.

C.-F. Song, Y. Kitamura, S.-H. Li, K. Ogasawara, 2012. Design of a cryogenic CO_2 capture system based on Stirling coolers. International Journal of Greenhouse Gas Control 7, 107-114.

M. Tuinier, M. van Sint Annaland, G.J. Kramer, J. Kuipers, 2010. Cryogenic CO_2 capture using dynamically operated packed beds. Chemical Engineering Science 65, 114-119.

Sauro Pierucci, Flavio Manenti, Giulia Bozzano, Davide Manca (Eds.)
Proceedings of the 30th European Symposium on Computer Aided Process Engineering
(ESCAPE30), May 24-27, 2020, Milano, Italy. © 2020 Elsevier B.V. All rights reserved.
http://dx.doi.org/10.1016/B978-0-12-823377-1.50081-1

Investigation of a Hybrid Approach to Find all Solutions of Nonlinear Equation Systems

Saskia Bublitz*, Erik Esche, Jens-Uwe Repke

*Technische Universität Berlin, Chair of Process Dynamics and Operation,
Str. del 17. Juni 135, 10623 Berlin, Germany*
saskia.bublitz@tu-berlin.de

Abstract

We examine a novel procedure to solve nonlinear systems without manual initialization and apply it on the model of a Methanol-Water distillation process. The approach starts with a reduction of user-defined variable bounds by a box reduction procedure based on interval arithmetic. Secondly, the narrowed search space is sampled to finally start a numerical solver from the most promising initial points. For our tested example, we could find a solution with MATLAB's fsolve function and the TNC solver from the python package SciPy.

Keywords: box reduction, interval arithmetic, sampling, multi-start

1. Motivation

Numerically solving nonlinear systems, as they frequently appear in chemical process models, is still quite challenging. While local solvers combined with line search or trust region methods as described by Deuflhard (2011) work well on Lipschitz-continuous solution spaces, there is still no generally applicable procedure in place to find good initial values for them. Global optimization methods, such as described by Floudas (2000), adequately find all solutions of small systems for a given set of function terms. Nevertheless, they are *a priori* not applicable to all types of systems and especially large systems of equations. Constraint propagation methods based on expression trees or directed graphs as detailed in Moore et. al. (2009) are designed to find all solutions of a problem but are computationally intractable for large systems (Schnepper & Stadtherr, 1996). Therefore, we suggest a hybrid approach consisting of box reduction, sampling, and multi-start that tries to avoid the individual flaws of these methods.

2. Solution Approach: Box Reduction and Multi-start

The initial bounds of iteration variables from a process model span a certain multi-dimensional solution space called a *box*. Box volumes of large equation systems are mostly enormous in case tight variable bounds are not at hand. Besides, they often contain singular points that cause failure of derivative-based solvers. Hence, we develop a box reduction algorithm that lowers the initial volume down to tighter solution enclosures by interval bisection and removes singular points by interval nesting. This may result in multiple multi-dimensional boxes as possible solution space.

On the reduced box(es), a Hammersley low-discrepancy sequence is applied to generate pseudo-random sample points. Nevertheless, the point-density (number of points per box volume) in reduced boxes of large systems can still be relatively low.

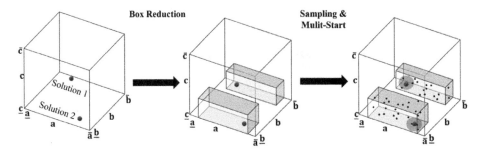

Figure 1. Hybrid approach sketched for a three-dimensional system with two actual solutions.

Hence, the chance that the majority of points does not converge in finite time is still quite high. This makes a direct multi-start very inefficient. Therefore, the residual of the nonlinear equation system at each sample point is tested before a numerical equation solver is only applied on a predefined number of promising candidate points, i.e., those with the lowest residuals. The Newton-type solvers applied are MATLAB's fsolve function (MATLAB, 2019) and TNC from the python package SciPy (Jones et. al. 2001). Both box reduction and multi-start procedure are parallelized using the python package multiprocessing (McKerns, 2011).

The box reduction algorithm tries to reduce an interval x in functions of the form:

$$f(x, y) = 0 \tag{1}$$

with y being intervals of other variables that stay constant in one reduction step. Eq. (1) is reformulated into an x-dependent part $g(x, y)$ and an x-independent part $b(y)$:

$$g(x, y) = b(y) \tag{2}$$

The algorithm matches the interval $g(x, y)$ as tightly as possible to the interval $b(y)$. The interval functions are evaluated by interval arithmetic. Here, the python package mmpath (Johannsson, 2013) is employed for these operations. In the linear case with a constant interval or scalar a:

$$g(x, y) = a(y) \cdot x = b(y), \tag{3}$$

the Gauss-Seidl Operator Γ (Montanher et. al., 2017) is applied to calculate the reduced interval $x^{(1)}$ from the initial $x^{(0)}$:

$$x^{(1)} = \Gamma\big(b, a, x^{(0)}\big) = b \backslash a \cap x^{(0)} \tag{4}$$

Three cases for $b \backslash a \cap x^{(0)}$ can occur:

1. $x^{(1)} = \emptyset$: no solution (the user has to reconsider the initial bounds of x)
2. $x^{(1)} \subseteq x^{(0)} \wedge x^{(1)} = \{x_1^{(1)}, x_2^{(1)}\}$: two reduced intervals (branching)
3. $x^{(1)} \subseteq x^{(0)}$: one interval

In case the intersection is empty, there cannot be a solution in $x^{(0)}$. Branching occurs when a contains positive and negative values ($\underline{a} < 0 < \bar{a}$). Referring to general interval arithmetic, a division of b by a results in an unbounded interval and information is lost

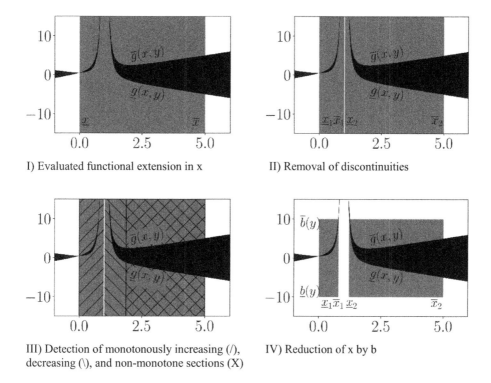

I) Evaluated functional extension in x

II) Removal of discontinuities

III) Detection of monotonously increasing (/), decreasing (\\), and non-monotone sections (X)

IV) Reduction of x by b

Figure 2. Scheme of INES applied on a function g(x, y) for an initial interval $x = [0, 5]$ and a right-hand side interval $b = [-10, 10]$.

about maximum negative values and minimum positive values. The Gauss-Seidl Operator retains these bounds by bisecting the interval into a negative interval bounded from above and a positive interval bounded from below. In the third case, the initial interval is reduced or remains constant, if it is already a subset of $b\backslash a$.

Intervals in nonlinear functions are reduced by our three-step interval nesting procedure (INES). First, the discontinuous functions terms $g(x, y)$ are divided into continuous parts by bisection at the discontinuity. The procedure stops as soon as the width of the interval around the discontinuity is below a pre-defined tolerance or bisection lasts too long.

All continuous, non-monotone functions are sorted into increasing, decreasing, and apparently non-monotone sections. Through interval bisection and nesting the sub-intervals are checked regarding their first derivatives of $g(x, y)$ being ≥ 0 (monotonously increasing) or ≤ 0 (monotonously decreasing). The non-monotone intervals are further processed until the remaining interval width is below a pre-defined tolerance or the latter cannot be reduced in case of apparently non-monotone intervals. They occur whenever the derivative includes positive and negative values at certain points within x.

In the last step, INES intersects all monotone, continuous functions with $b(y)$. Two cases exist: one solution interval or no solution. If a solution exists, the algorithm proceeds with bisecting x to find a tighter enclosure $g(x, y)$ for $b(y)$. If $b(y)$ contains $g(x, y)$ no reduction of x is possible. All remaining, apparently non-monotone and discontinuous intervals are separated into subintervals, for which $g(x,y)$ is directly evaluated and checked for intersections with $b(y)$.

Figure 2 shows the stepwise reduction with INES for the function:

$$g(x,y) = y \cdot x + \frac{0.5}{(1-x)^2} = b(y) \tag{5}$$

with initial bounds $x = [0,5]$ and $y = [-1,1]$. The interval x is reduced to the sub-intervals $[0,0.785]$ and $[1.2,5]$.

In multi-dimensional systems, the box reduction algorithm is applied on all iteration variables separately. The algorithm reduces each variable's bounds by analysing all equations it appears in. Once this is completed for all variables the procedure is repeated on the reduced set of boxes. The algorithm terminates, when the intervals cannot be further reduced or the maximum number of iteration steps is reached. Since the key task of the box reduction algorithm is to remove discontinuities and to find better solution enclosures, and not the solution itself, we choose the maximum number of iteration steps to be 10 at most. Whenever interval branching occurs, the resulting boxes are iterated independently.

The success of the k-th box reduction of an n-dimensional system is measured by the dimensionless hypercubic length $l^{(k)}$:

$$l^{(k)} = \sqrt[n]{\prod_{i=1}^{n} \frac{\sum_{j=1}^{m_i} w(x_{i,j}^{(k)})}{w(x_i^{(0)})}} , \tag{6}$$

wherein $w(x_{ji}^{(k)})$ is the width of the j-th interval that results from branching $x_i^{(0)}$. The quantity ranges from 0 (solution(s) found) to 1 (no reduction). All solved variables $(\sum_{j=1}^{m_i} w(x_{i,j}^{(k)}) = 0)$ are removed from the box.

3. Case Study

3.1. Process Model

The presented hybrid approach is tested on a steady-state model for a methanol-water-distillation column consisting of ten equilibrium trays, a total condenser, and a partial reboiler. The model has been implemented in MOSAICmodeling (Esche et. al., 2016).

3.2. Initialization of Variable Bounds

Our hybrid approach requires some carefully chosen initial bounds based on the range of validity of the process model. Otherwise interval branching can occur. If k intervals decompose each into two sub intervals, the number of boxes n grows by 2^k. This increases the processing time greatly. Besides, interval bounds cannot be reduced at all occasionally if other variable bounds are chosen too loose.

Since the mixture is zeotropic minimum and maximum values of pure component data is used to initialize the bounds of stream enthalpies, tray temperatures and pressures.

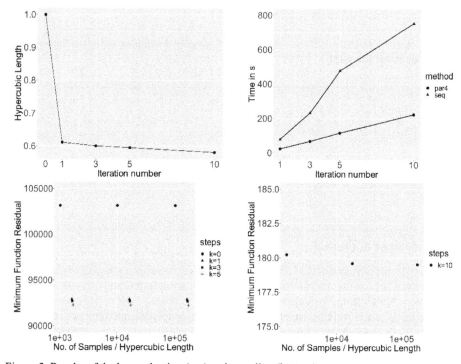

Figure 3. Results of the box reduction (top) and sampling (bottom)

Flowrates range from zero to the user-specified feed flow rate, for the bottom and distillate stream. Upper bounds for the internal streams are roughly overestimated by the user-specified reflux ratio. Their lower bounds equal 0. The initial intervals of the mole fractions range from 0 to 1.

3.3. Analysis

After initialization, 1, 3, 5, or 10 reduction steps were performed and the corresponding hypercubic lengths of the reduced boxes were computed as given in Fig. 3. The method works efficiently for the first iteration step and after that stagnates as shown. Since the purpose is to remove discontinuities and reduce bounds rather than solving the system, higher number of reduction steps are not tested. Within 10 reduction steps no branching occurs. Through parallelization of the procedure CPU time is greatly decreased as shown here for using 4 processors (par4) instead of one (seq).

For the initial box (k=0) and each reduced box 1.0E3, 1.0E4 and 1.0E5 samples are generated. As can be seen from Fig. 3 no great reduction in function residuals can be achieved if the number of samples is increased in the constant box volumes. Hence, only the five samples with the lowest residual out of 1.0E3 generated samples for the different box volumes are passed to Newton-type solvers. The function residuals of the samples after 10 box reduction steps decrease by almost 3 orders of magnitude in comparison to the other cases (Fig. 3, bottom right).

The function tolerance of the solvers was set to 1.0E-7 and the maximum iteration number to 10^5. Tab. 1 shows the results of both solvers for all tested box reduction steps.

Table 1 Results from Multi-Start procedure

Box reduction steps	Number of converged samples out of the 5 best for	
	MATLAB	TNC
0	0	0
1	0	0
3	0	1
5	0	1
10	1	3

4. Conclusions & Outlook

A solution to the investigated Methanol-Water distillation column is successfully found by the hybrid approach presented in this contribution without passing any initial guess to the problem highlighting the capabilities compared to usual solution based on manually obtained initial guesses. In future research we will apply this method on more challenging problems such as separation processes of multicomponent and / or azeotropic mixtures and full process models with recycle streams. Through tests on the presented process model and further unit operations such as a flash, a heat exchanger and a reactor three bottlenecks were identified that can further improve the performance of this approach. Firstly, the equation formulation has a great influence on the box reduction efficiency and reformulations should hence be investigated. Secondly, complex values should be filtered the same way as discontinuities. Currently, the box reduction algorithm lets variable intervals unchanged whenever complex values occur. Finally, the test results show that the procedure greatly under- and overestimates bounds for fugacity coefficients by conventional interval arithmetic due to interval dependency (Moore, 2009). This problem can be solved by applying INES on the righthand side of Eq. (2) as well to identify its monotonous continuous y intervals and to determine tighter bounds for $b(y)$.

References

C.A. Floudas, 2000, Deterministic Global Optimization, Springer-Science-Business Media

C.A. Schnepper, M.A. Stadtherr, 1996, Robust Process Simulation using Interval Methods, Computers & Chemical Engineering, 20, 2, 187-199

E. Esche, C. Hoffmann, M. Ilner, D. Müller, S. Fillinger, G. Tolksdorf, H. Bonart, G. Wozny, J.-U. Repke, 2016, MOSAIC, Chemie Ingenieur Technik,89, 5, 1522-2640

E. Jones, T. Oliphant, P. Petersion & others, 2001, SciPy: Open Source Scientific Tools for Python

F. Johansson, 2013, mpmath: a Python library for arbitary-precision floating-point arithmetic, version: 1.1.0., http://mpmath.org/

M. M. McKerns, L. Strand, T. Sullivan, A. Fang, M. A. G. Aivazis, 2011, Building a framework for predictve science, version: 0.70, Proceedings of 10th Pyhton in Science Conference, 67-78

MATLAB, 2019, The MathWorks Inc., version 7.10.0 (2019b)

P. Deuflhard, 2011, Newton Methods for Nonlinear Problems, Springer

R. E. Moore, R. Baker Kearfott, M.J. Cloud, 2009, Introduction to Interval Analysis, SIAM, 7-40

T. Montanher, F. Domes, H. Schichl, A. Neumaier, 2017, Using interval unions to solve linear systems of equations with uncertainties, BIT Numerical Mathematics, 57, 3, 901-926

Sauro Pierucci, Flavio Manenti, Giulia Bozzano, Davide Manca (Eds.)
Proceedings of the 30ᵗʰ European Symposium on Computer Aided Process Engineering
(ESCAPE30), May 24-27, 2020, Milano, Italy. © 2020 Elsevier B.V. All rights reserved.
http://dx.doi.org/10.1016/B978-0-12-823377-1.50082-3

Fast and Accurate Simulation of Simulated Moving Bed Chromatographic Processes with Linear Adsorption Isotherms

Rojiar Pishkari,[b,*] and Achim Kienle[a,b]

ᵃ Max Planck Institute for Dynamics of Complex Technical Systems, Sandtorstrasse 1, 39106 Magdeburg, Germany

ᵇ Otto von Guericke University Magdeburg, Universitätplatz 2, 39106 Magdeburg
Pishkari@mpi-magdeburg.mpg.de

Abstract

In this paper, we propose a new fast and accurate simulation method for highly efficient chromatographic columns with linear adsorption isotherms. The method is based on an analytical solution of the underlying partial differential equations using the method of characteristics, which describes the propagation of selected concentration values. The method is exact. The discretization of the concentrations is only used for the representation of the solution and the evaluation of the coupling conditions between the different columns. Application is demonstrated for binary 4-zone and ternary 8-zone SMB processes with center-cut separation. It is shown, that the computational effort can be reduced by more than factor 100 compared to the popular discrete cell model.

Keywords: Simulated moving bed chromatography, simulation, method of characteristics, cell model.

1. Introduction

Simulated moving bed (SMB) processes are an advanced technology for continuous chromatographic separations (Schmidt Traub et al., 2012). The main advantage is an increased productivity and a reduced solvent consumption compared to conventional batch processes. A standard configuration for a binary separation process is shown in Figure 1a. It consists of four chromatographic columns representing the four zones of the process. They are connected to a ring. The component with the higher affinity to the solid phase located in the columns is obtained at the extract, while the component with the lower affinity to the solid phase, i.e. the higher affinity to the fluid phase, is obtained at the raffinate. The counter-current flow of the solid phase which is essential for continuous operation is simulated by cyclic switching of the in- and outlets in direction of fluid flow or by switching the columns in the opposite direction.

In practice, besides binary separation processes, often ternary separation problems play an important role in isolating an intermediate adsorbing component from a complex mixture. This type of process is also termed as a center-cut separation. For center-cut separation problems various options are available including a cascade of two binary separation processes, as well as eight or nine zone SMB processes (Nicolaos et al., 2001, Kessler et al., 2006). Focus in this contribution, is on an eight zone process with raffinate recycle as illustrated in Figure 1b. It is worth noting that with this configuration a fraction of pure intermediate B can be obtained in the extract 2 flow, but not all three product flows can be obtained as pure components (Nicolaos et al., 2001). For example, the raffinate 2 product may also contain some amount of component B.

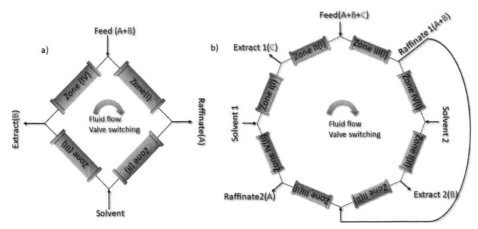

Figure 1. Schematic illustration of SMB system. (a) 4-zone SMB. (b) 8-zone SMB.

The conceptual process design of SMB processes is based on the true moving bed analogon using triangle theory (Migliorini et al., 1998) or standing wave theory (Ma et al., 1997). Numerical simulation of the simulated moving bed process can be applied to further optimize the separation. For this purpose, some discretization using well known finite difference, finite volume, or finite element schemes can be used. Due to the presence of steep concentration fronts this may require a large number of grid points leading to a considerable computational effort, in particular, when a large number of simulations is required, for example during optimization. For this purpose, we propose an alternative approach based on an analytical solution which is possible for linear adsorption isotherms using the method of characteristics.

In 1995, an analytical solution for binary SMB process was proposed by (Zhong et al., 1995) using a set of algebraic equation to calculate the concentration profiles assuming linear adsorption isotherm and highly efficient columns. Although the present approach is based on the same principles it is more flexible, much easier to implement and is therefore readily extended to more complex process configurations like the ternary center-cut separation considered in this paper.

2. Model description

The model of the SMB plants shown in Figure 1 consists of the models of the chromatographic columns, the material balances of the in- and outlet ports and the switching conditions. The chromatographic columns can be described by the well-known equilibrium dispersion model.

$$\varepsilon \frac{\partial c_i}{\partial t} + (1 - \varepsilon) \frac{\partial q_i}{\partial t} + \varepsilon v \frac{\partial c_i}{\partial z} = D_{ax} \varepsilon \frac{\partial^2 c_i}{\partial z^2} \tag{1}$$

Therein, ε is the volume fraction of the fluid phase, v the interstitial velocity and D_{ax} an apparent dispersion coefficient, which lumps together all effects contributing to band broadening. Moreover, c_i is the concentration of component 'i' in the fluid phase and q_i

the corresponding concentration in the solid phase. Since the model assumes thermodynamic equilibrium between both phases, q_i is directly related to the fluid phase composition by the adsorption isotherm. In the following focus is on linear isotherms according to

$$q_i = H_i c_i \qquad (2)$$

with Henry coefficient H_i.

For highly efficient columns, axial dispersion can be neglected in a first step, leading to a system of first order partial differential equations.

$$\frac{\partial c_i}{\partial t} + \frac{(1-\varepsilon)}{\varepsilon}\frac{\partial q_i}{\partial t} + v\frac{\partial c_i}{\partial z} = 0 \qquad (3)$$

Together with the adsorption isotherm Eq. (2), this represents a set of linear decoupled transport equations, where every concentration value of component 'i' is transported with the corresponding constant characteristic velocity.

$$w_i = \frac{dz}{dt} = \frac{v}{(1+\frac{1-\varepsilon}{\varepsilon}H_i)} \qquad (4)$$

3. Analytical solution

For simulating the SMB processes shown in Figure 1, the analytical solution which is obtained from Eq. (4) is implemented in discrete form, i.e. the initial profile of each component in each column is discretized and put into a matrix form according to

$$\begin{bmatrix} concentration\ value\ 1 & concentration\ value\ 2 & ... & concentration\ value\ n \\ position\ value\ 1 & position\ value\ 2 & ... & position\ value\ n \end{bmatrix} \qquad (5)$$

In the multicomponent case, the corresponding concentration profiles are put together in a multi-dimensional tensor form and the positions for each component are calculated using its specific propagation velocity.

In the remainder, 100 spatial grid points are used for this purpose. Further, time is also discretized. In particular, 100 time steps per switching interval are used in this study. For the calculation of the concentration profiles in the next time step, first, new positions are calculated for the concentration values in Eq. (5) using Eq. (4) according to:

$$new\ position = old\ position + w_i dt \qquad (6)$$

Afterwards, the concentration vector is rearranged. Concentration values with positions beyond the actual column length are removed, and the remaining values are shifted to the right. Then node balances at the entrance of the columns are evaluated and resulting values are propagated into the column to fill the gaps in the concentration vector from the left. For this purpose, it is important to calculate at which exact intermediate time point the concentration values have left the previous column, which is again simply done by application of Eq. (4) according to:

$$intermediate\ time\ point = old\ time\ point + (column\ length - old\ position)/w_i \qquad (7)$$

Corresponding node balances are evaluated at this time point and the propagation into the subsequent column for the remaining time of this interval is determined. In this way, the solution is exact. Discretization is done only for the graphical representation of the solution. Accuracy is not affected.

4. Numerical solution (cell model)

For comparison with the analytical approach, a simple numerical solution is applied using the popular cell model. This corresponds to a 1st order finite volume discretization of Eq. (3) on an equidistant grid assuming piecewise constant profiles. From the physical point of view, the continuous column is replaced by a discrete series of stirred tanks. The material balance of component 'i' at cell 'j' is then

$$V_{cell} \frac{d}{dt}(\varepsilon c_i + (1 - \varepsilon)H_i c_i) = q(c_{i,j-1} - c_{i,j}) \tag{8}$$

with the cell volume $V_{cell} = \frac{V_{col}}{n}$ and the volumetric flow rate $q = \varepsilon A_{col} v$. Therein, n is the number of cells per column.

The resulting system of ordinary differential equations is solved numerically in MATLAB using the integrator ode45. For this purpose, node balances are directly included in the material balances of the corresponding cells.

5. Results

In this section, application is demonstrated for the binary and the ternary processes presented in Figure 1. Model parameters and column properties used in this simulation study are given in Table 1.

Table 1. Model parameters and column properties

Parameter	(4-zone SMB)	(8-zone SMB)
Number of the column	4	8
Column dimensions	100[mm]	100[mm]
Column porosity	0.75	0.75
Henry constant A	5	1.1
Henry constant B	7.5	1.7
Henry constant C	-	2.5
Switching time	100[s]	654[s]
Feed concentration A	2 [gr/L]	2 [gr/L]
Feed concentration B	3 [gr/L]	3 [gr/L]
Feed concentration C	-	4 [gr/L]

Table 2. Dimensionless flow rates

4-zone SMB			
m_I	m_{II}	m_{III}	m_{IV}
7.5	4.5	7.7	5.0
8-zone SMB			
$m_{I(1)}$	$m_{II(1)}$	$m_{III(1)}$	$m_{IV(1)}$
2.55	1.57	2.19	0.86
$m_{I(2)}$	$m_{II(2)}$	$m_{III(2)}$	$m_{IV(2)}$
1.82	1.22	2.55	1.01

Optimal operating conditions for the binary true moving bed analogon to Figure 1a follows in the linear case directly from the Henry coefficients of the two components using triangle theory (Migliorini et al., 1998). To account for numerical dispersion in the discrete model and prevent breakthrough, some safety margins were introduced. The operating conditions for the ternary process in Figure 1b were taken from (Kessler et al.,

2006) Operating conditions in terms of m-values are given in Table 2. These m-values are related to the fluid flow rate and the switching time in the following way.

$$m_k = \frac{Q_k T_{sw} - \varepsilon V_{col}}{(1-\varepsilon)V_{col}} \tag{9}$$

Figure 2 shows the internal concentration profiles during start up at the end of each cycle for the binary and the ternary SMB processes shown in Figure 1. The left diagrams show the numerical solution using the cell model.

To achieve steeps fronts as predicted by the equilibrium model a large number of 1,000 cells per column is required. The right column shows the corresponding solution using the analytical approach described above. The arrows at the bottom of each of the diagrams indicate the positions of the in- and outlet streams as indicated in Figure 1. 'F' stands for feed, 'R' for raffinate and 'E' for extract. The numerical and analytical solutions in Figure 2 show good agreement. Minor differences are due to the numerical dispersion introduced by the cell model in the left diagrams. It could be reduced by a further increase of the number of grid points or by using some more advanced discretization of the underlying partial differential equations as briefly mentioned above.

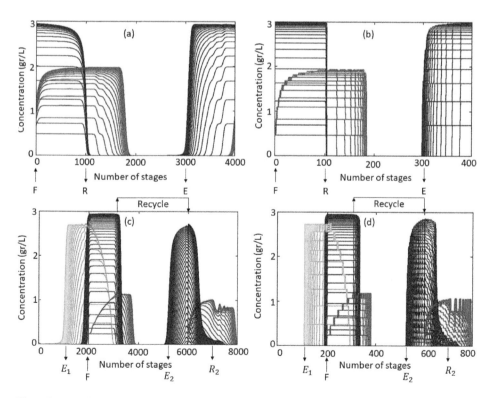

Figure 2. Internal concentration profiles of (a) Binary mixture inside 4-zone SMB using cell model with 1000 grid points (b) Binary mixture inside 4-zone SMB using analytical model. (c) Ternary mixture inside 8-zone SMB using cell model with 1000 grid points (d) Ternary mixture inside 8-zone SMB using analytical model.

Corresponding computation times are shown in Table 3, the analytical model is about 400 times faster than the cell model in the 4-zone SMB simulation and 800 times faster in the 8-zone SMB simulation. It is worth noting, the computational time of the numerical solution is further increasing drastically if an implicit integration scheme like ode 15s in MATLAB is used.

Table 3. Computational times for 4- and 8-zone configuration using cell and analytical model

Model	Cell model		Analytical model
No of grid points	100	1,000	-
4-zone SMB	2.80 (s)	167.34 (s)	0.34 (s)
8-zone SMB	10.00 (s)	689.46 (s)	0.77 (s)

6. Conclusion

In this paper, a fast and accurate method for the simulation of chromatographic columns with linear adsorption isotherms using the ideal equilibrium model was presented. It is most suitable for highly efficient chromatographic columns with negligible axial dispersion and steep concentration fronts. It outperforms standard approaches based on the popular cell model.

An application was demonstrated for binary and ternary SMB processes with center-cut separations. However, the method can be easily applied to other process configurations and will be used in the future for rigorous optimization and evaluation of alternative process schemes for ternary center-cut separations.

References

A. Nicolaos, M. Laurence, P. Gotteland, R.M. Nicoud, M. Bailly, 2001, Application of the equilibrium theory to ternary moving bed configurations (4+4, 5+4, 8 and 9 zones) II. Langmuir case. Journal of Chromatography A. 908(1-2): p. 87-109.

C. Migliorini, M. Mazzotti, M. Morbidelli, 1998, Continuous chromatographic separation through simulated moving beds under linear and nonlinear conditions. Journal of Chromatography A, 827, 161–173.

G. Zhong, G. Guiochon, 1996, Analytical Solution for the linear ideal model of simulated moving bed chromatography. Chemical Engineering Science. 51, 4307–4319.

H. Schmidt-Traub, M. Schulte, and A. Seidel-Morgenstern, 2012, Preparative chromatography, 2nd completely revised and enlarged edition.

L.C. Keßler, A. Seidel-Morgenstern, 2006, Theoretical study of multicomponent continuous countercurrent chromatography based on connected 4-zone units. Journal of ChromatographyA, 1126, 323–337.

Z. Ma, N.-H. L. Wang, 1997, Standing wave analysis of smb chromatography: linear systems, AIChE 20 J. 43, 2488-2508.

Sauro Pierucci, Flavio Manenti, Giulia Bozzano, Davide Manca (Eds.)
Proceedings of the 30th European Symposium on Computer Aided Process Engineering
(ESCAPE30), May 24-27, 2020, Milano, Italy. © 2020 Elsevier B.V. All rights reserved.
http://dx.doi.org/10.1016/B978-0-12-823377-1.50083-5

Efficient Parameterization of a Surrogate Model of Molecular Interactions in Crystals

David H. Bowskill,[a] Isaac J. Sugden,[a] Neil George,[b] Adam Keates,[b] Jennifer Webb,[b] Constantinos C. Pantelides,[a] Claire S. Adjiman[a*]

[a]*Department of Chemical Engineering, Centre for Process Systems Engineering, Imperial College London, London, SW7 2AZ, United Kingdom*
[b]*Process Studies Group, Syngenta, Jealott's Hill International Research Centre, Bracknell, Berkshire, RG42 6EY, United Kingdom*
c.adjiman@imperial.ac.uk

Abstract

We propose a surrogate model for lattice energy that allows the accurate prediction of the crystal structures formed by a given molecule and their relative stability ranking. The model is derived from a combination of isolated-molecule quantum mechanical calculations and a relatively small number of more expensive solid-state DFT-D computations. The surrogate model provides an effective mechanism for refining the crystal structure landscape predicted by current Crystal Structure Prediction methodologies. Applied to the agrochemical Chlorothalonil, the approach is shown to be highly accurate whilst reducing the computational costs by approximately a factor of 20 compared to refinement of all structures using solid-state DFT.

Keywords: Crystal Structure Prediction, Parameter Estimation, DFT-D

1. Introduction

The material properties of crystalline solid materials are dependent on both the molecular compound and the arrangement of molecules in a 3-dimensional lattice. This is especially important due to the prevalence of polymorphism, whereby different stable structures may be observed depending on crystallization temperature, pressure and composition. Furthermore, kinetic barriers can result in the synthesis of metastable polymorphs (Bernstein, et al., 1999). There are well-recorded cases where failure to identify the most stable polymorph of a substance during product development has led to major operational disasters when a more stable form has appeared during production (Bauer, et al., 2001). Understanding the crystallization behaviour and relative stability of the polymorphs of an active ingredient is therefore critical for the pharmaceutical and agrochemical industries, where many products involve crystalline solids.

Crystal Structure Prediction aims to predict all possible polymorphs of a compound given only the molecular connectivity diagram as input. Observable crystal structures of a given compound are assumed to be local minima at, or close to, the global minimum in the Gibbs free energy of the crystal. For practical reasons, this is often approximated as low-lying minima in the lattice energy, U^{latt} (Day, 2011). Thus, the output of a CSP investigation is a list of crystal structures ranked in order of increasing U^{latt}. These putative structures can be compared to known polymorphs to assess the risk of more stable, as yet unsynthesized, polymorphs appearing, or to rationalize observed polymorphic behaviour (Price, et al., 2016).

One current approach to modelling crystalline energies makes use of hybrid *ab initio*/empirical models. These combine tailor-made potentials (derived from quantum mechanical calculations on isolated molecules) for the intramolecular and electrostatic contributions to the lattice energy, with transferable empirical potentials for the remaining contributions, in particular those arising from repulsive/dispersive interactions. Such empirical potentials have previously been derived using training sets containing experimental data of many diverse compounds (Gatsiou, et al., 2018; Pyzer-Knapp, et al., 2016). However, the transferable component can often lack the accuracy required for CSP to be effective. An alternative is to derive a tailor-made force field (TMFF) of all interactions for the particular system of interest using the results of solid-state DFT-D calculations (Neumann, 2008). However, whilst accurate, this approach requires a large number of computationally very expensive solid-state DFT-D calculations.

Here we seek to achieve the accuracy of solid-state DFT-D at a fraction of the cost. This is achieved by deriving a surrogate lattice energy model from a small number of DFT-D calculations. The surrogate model can then be used to refine and re-rank the large sets of structures typically generated by existing CSP methodologies. The proposed methodology is presented in Section 2 of this paper. Section 3 illustrates its application to predicting the polymorphs of Chlorothalonil, a polymorphic agrochemical.

2. Methodology

2.1. Surrogate lattice energy model
Our surrogate lattice energy model is of the form:

$$U^{latt}(\boldsymbol{\theta}, \boldsymbol{p}) = \Delta U^{intra}(\boldsymbol{\theta}) + U^{elec}(\boldsymbol{\theta}) + U^{resid}(\boldsymbol{\theta}, \boldsymbol{p}) \tag{1}$$

where $\boldsymbol{\theta}$ represents the crystal structure in terms of the lattice lengths and angles of the unit cell, and positions of all atoms in the asymmetric unit. The first two terms on the right-hand side represent the contributions of intramolecular and intermolecular electrostatic interactions; as in well-established CSP methodologies, those are derived from quantum mechanical calculations on isolated molecules (Pantelides, et al., 2014). The last, "residual", term attempts to capture all the effects, such as dispersive/repulsive interactions and induction, that are not already accounted for by the first two terms. This last term includes a set of parameters $\boldsymbol{p}$ that can be adjusted to match the predictions of a more accurate but computationally much more expensive model such as DFT-D.

In principle, there are many possible algebraic forms for the residual term, including some based on standard machine learning methodologies, such as artificial neural networks. For the purposes of this paper, we choose one that is based on the standard Buckingham potential for repulsive/dispersive interactions:

$$U^{resid}(\boldsymbol{\theta}, \boldsymbol{p}) \equiv \sum_{ij} A_{ij} \exp\left(-r_{ij} \Big/ B_{ij}\right) - \frac{C_{ij}}{r_{ij}^6} \tag{2}$$

where the parameters $\boldsymbol{p} \equiv \{A_{ij}, B_{ij}, C_{ij}\}$ describe the interactions between atoms i and j, and $r_{ij}(\boldsymbol{\theta})$ is the corresponding interatomic distance in the crystal lattice.

2.2. Deriving the surrogate lattice energy model
The proposed methodology is intended to be applied as a final refinement step to a crystal structure landscape determined by standard CSP techniques. This landscape consists of a minimum lattice energy structure and all other structures identified within, typically, 5-

20 kJ/mol above the minimum. Overall, this may involve several hundreds or thousands of structures.

As illustrated in Figure 1, our methodology selects a small subset of *NS* structures out of the *N* structures in the initial landscape (Step 1). The lattice energy of each of these *NS* structures is then minimized using an accurate solid-state DFT-D model (Step 2). The lattice energies and crystal geometries determined at Step 2 are then used to estimate the surrogate model parameters p (Step 3). Finally, the surrogate model is used to re-optimize the energy/geometry of all *N* structures in the original landscape (Step 4), which results in the final crystal structure landscape.

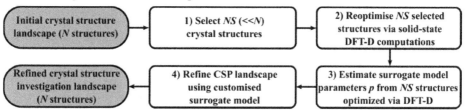

Figure 1: Flowchart of proposed methodology

2.3. Estimation of surrogate model parameters

The accurate DFT-D calculations applied at Step 2 to each selected crystal structure s generate the minimized lattice energy U_s^{ref}, and the corresponding crystal structure geometry in terms of the unit cell lattice parameters l_s^{ref}, and the relative fractional coordinate positions δx_s^{ref} for all atomic sites within the asymmetric unit. These "reference" data are collectively denoted as a_s^{ref}.

At Step 3, the parameters p are adjusted so that the corresponding *NS* crystal structures properties a_s derived via lattice energy minimization using the surrogate model match as closely as possible the reference data a_s^{ref}. This is achieved via the solution of a weighted nonlinear least squares optimization problem:

$$\min_{p \in [p^L, p^U]} \sum_{s=1}^{NS} \| a_s(p) - a_s^{ref} \|^2 \tag{3}$$

where p^L and p^U denote lower and upper bounds on the parameters p, and $\|.\|$ denotes a weighted square norm. The weights are selected so that the objective function measures the *relative* deviations in U_s and l_s, and the *absolute* deviations in δx_s, and also scales with the number of elements in each of the vectors l_s and δx_s.

2.4. Numerical considerations

The parameter estimation problem is a bilevel optimization problem since the vector $a(p)$ at a given p needs to be determined by minimization of the lattice energy (cf. Eq. (1)). Thus, each evaluation of the objective function in Eq. (3) requires *NS* minimizations.

The parameter estimation problem is solved for each initial parameter vector using a specialized unconstrained nonlinear residual least squares solver, nl2sol (Dennis Jr, et al., 1981). A smooth penalty function is included in the objective function to constrain allowable parameter values between p^L and p^U, and line searches are also constrained to keep the parameter values within these bounds. The gradients of the objective function are obtained using second-order centered finite differences.

Over the space of parameter values, the objective function is non-convex, exhibits discontinuities and its evaluation is subject to numerical instabilities due to the complexity of the lattice energy minimization code used. Due to these characteristics, a multistart global optimization approach is employed, whereby multiple initial parameter vectors $p^{[0]}$ lying between p^L and p^U are generated using low-discrepancy Sobol' sequences (Bratley & Fox, 1988). A distributed computing implementation has been developed so that optimizations from different starting points can be run simultaneously. The set of parameters p resulting in the lowest objective function value among all runs is selected and used to refine the crystal structure landscape in Step 4 of the methodology.

3. Application to Chlorothalonil

To test the effectiveness of the proposed approach, we carry out a case study on the agrochemical fungicide Chlorothalonil (m-$C_6(CN)_2Cl_4$). There are currently two experimentally identified polymorphs with one molecule in the asymmetric unit (Z'=1): Form I, the most stable known polymorph at ambient conditions, and Form II, a metastable form which is stabilized at higher temperatures through structural disorder.

An initial CSP investigation is carried out in Z'=1 space using the CSP methodology presented by Pantelides, et al. (2014) and related publications. It is assumed that the intramolecular energy contributions are negligible, and the molecule's conformation is fixed to its gas-phase conformation, as calculated via an isolated-molecule quantum mechanical calculation. The latter also allows the determination of point charges located at atomic sites that are used to describe intermolecular electrostatic interactions. Intermolecular repulsive/dispersive interactions are described via an empirical potential of the form given by Eq. (2) with transferable parameters (Gatsiou, et al., 2018).

This initial CSP study results in a ranked set of candidate structures. The 92 structures identified with lattice energies within 8 kJ/mol of the global minimum are shown in Figure 2 (left). They include the experimentally known Forms I & II, with energetic rankings of 6th and 60th, respectively. However, five structures are predicted to be lower in energy, and thus more stable, than either of the experimental forms. This suggests that a more stable crystal, yet unidentified, form may exist, something which, in practice, could have serious technical and financial implications.

On the other hand, as the energy difference between Form I and the global minimum structure is small (0.72 kJ/mol), the use of more accurate DFT-D calculations could well lead to a different conclusion. However, applying DFT-D calculations directly to all structures in the landscape would be prohibitively expensive. Instead, we apply the methodology described in Section 2. At Step 1, we select NS=5 structures out of the 92 structures in the landscape, as indicated by the blue circles in Figure 2 (left). The selection is performed randomly, except that, in order to test the robustness of the methodology, the lowest-energy structures and the two experimental forms are excluded.

At Step 2, each of these 5 structures is optimized using DFT-D calculations, using a large basis set and a tight convergence tolerance. These are particularly expensive calculations, taking between 5,000 to 15,000 CPU h per structure.

Step 3 derives the surrogate lattice energy model by determining the parameters in the residual term U^{resid} (cf. Eq. (2)) that describe the interactions between Carbon, Nitrogen, and Chlorine atoms. Here we decide to fix B_{ij} at the values used by the empirical potential (Gatsiou, et al., 2018) employed in the initial CSP study, and refit all A_{ij} and C_{ij}

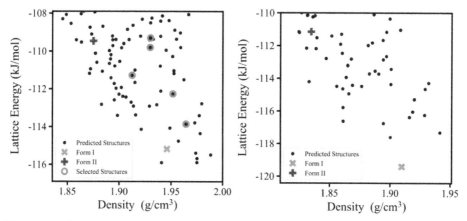

Figure 2: Lattice energy landscape for Chlorothalonil using transferable parameters (left), and using customized parameters (right). Each point corresponds to the energy and density of a predicted structure. Experimental Forms I & II are marked with crosses on the plots. The five structures randomly selected for refinement using solid-state DFT-D are also highlighted.

parameters. This includes the explicit fitting of all cross-interactions, resulting in a total of 12 parameters. The parameter estimation makes use of the reference data determined at Step 2, comprising 5 lattice energy values and 225 data points relating to crystal structure geometry. The estimation is repeated using 1,000 different sets of initial guesses generated via Sobol' sequences, with each such calculation taking between 1 and 2 hours on a single computer core. The parameter values leading to the lowest value of the objective function computed via Eq. (3) are incorporated in the surrogate model. Compared to the original transferable potential parameters (Gatsiou, et al., 2018), they reduce the geometric deviation ($RMSD_{15}$) from the DFT-D data by approximately 45%, and the absolute mean deviation in energy from 1.61 kJ/mol to 0.57 kJ/mol.

Finally, in Step 4, we minimize the lattice energy of all 92 structures in the original crystal structure landscape using the surrogate model. This takes approximately 1 CPU h, and results in the landscape shown in Figure 2 (right). Form I & II of Chlorothalonil are now ranked as 1st and 44th on the landscape, respectively, indicating a clear improvement in the model's prediction in line with known experimental information. Moreover, Form I is predicted to be 1.8 kJ/mol more stable than the second most stable predicted structure. From a practical perspective, this provides a much higher degree of confidence that the most stable crystal structure has already been identified experimentally, while reducing the overall computational cost of refining the landscape by approximately 94% compared to refinement of the whole landscape using solid-state DFT-D.

4. Concluding remarks

The mathematical form of the surrogate lattice energy model proposed in this paper is, in fact, identical to that of the hybrid *ab initio*/empirical models used in many current CSP methodologies. This is a deliberate choice as the current approaches have proven quite successful in identifying all putative solid forms, and in producing reasonable predictions of their geometries. Their main deficiency is in predicting the correct relative energetic ranking of these forms. This is something that more accurate techniques based on solid-state DFT-D computations are capable of correcting. However, the application of these computations to landscapes involving large numbers of structures is prohibitively expensive, especially in the case of the more complex molecules of interest to the pharmaceutical industry.

The novel aspect of our proposed methodology is in the way in which the parameters in the term described by Eq. (2) are obtained. Current methodologies attempt to derive a generally applicable ("transferable") potential for each type of pairwise atom-atom by fitting the parameters to a number of experimental data. Notwithstanding the obvious attractions of transferability, this approach suffers from a number of deficiencies, e.g. the relative lack of experimentally-measured energetic data such as sublimation energies, the difficulty of accurately relating the latter to theoretically predicted lattice energies, and, ultimately, the fact that experimental data from completely different systems may not be particularly relevant to the system that is currently under investigation. In contrast, our approach derives a customized parameterization for the system of interest using high-accuracy data from DFT-D computations. Unlike techniques that derive tailor-made force fields (TMFF) entirely from such computations, the number of the latter is kept to a minimum by the fact that the first two terms of the proposed surrogate model (cf. Eq. (1)) already capture a significant part of the lattice energy while being derived from much cheaper isolated-molecule quantum mechanical calculations.

Acknowledgements

The authors gratefully acknowledge funding from the United Kingdom's Engineering and Physical Sciences Research Council (EPSRC) (EP/M507878/1), and Syngenta. We are also grateful for access to computational resources from the High-Performance Computing Cluster at Imperial College London.

References

J. Bauer, S. Spanton, R. Henry, J. Quick, W. Dziki, W. Porter, J. Morris, 2001, Ritonavir: an extraordinary example of conformational polymorphism, *Pharmaceutical research,* 18, 6, 859-866

J. Bernstien, R. J. Davey, J.-O. Henck, 1999, Concomitant Polymorphs, *Angewandte Chemie International Edition,* 38, 23, 3440-3461

P. Bratley, B. L. Fox, 1988, Algorithm 659: Implementing Sobol's quasirandom sequence generator, *ACM Transactions on Mathematical Software (TOMS),* 14, 1, 88-100

G. M. Day, 2011, Current approaches to predicting molecular organic crystal structures, *Crystallography Reviews,* 17, 1, 3-52

J. E. Dennis Jr, D. M. Gay, R. E. Welsch,1981, Algorithm 573: NL2SOL—an adaptive nonlinear least-squares algorithm [E4], *ACM Transactions on Mathematical Software (TOMS),* 7 3, 369-383

C.-A. Gatsiou, C. S. Adjiman, C. C. Pantelides, 2018, Repulsion-dispersion parameters for the modelling of organic molecular crystals containing N, O, S and Cl, *Faraday discussions,* 211, 297-323

M. A. Neumann, 2008, Tailor-made force fields for crystal-structure prediction, *The Journal of Physical Chemistry B,* 112, 32, 9810-9829

C. C. Pantelides, C. S. Adjiman, A. V. Kazantsev, 2014, General computational algorithms for ab initio crystal structure prediction for organic molecules, *Prediction and Calculation of Crystal Structures,* Springer, 25-58

S. L. Price, D. E. Braun, S. M. Reutzel-Edens, 2016, Can computed crystal energy landscapes help understand pharmaceutical solids?, *Chemical Communications,* 52, 44, 7065-7077

E. O. Pyzer-Knapp, H. P. G. Thompson, G. M. Day, 2016, An optimized intermolecular force field for hydrogen-bonded organic molecular crystals using atomic multipole electrostatics, *Acta Crystallographica Section B: Structural Science, Crystal Engineering and Materials,* 72, 4, 477-487

Sauro Pierucci, Flavio Manenti, Giulia Bozzano, Davide Manca (Eds.)
Proceedings of the 30th European Symposium on Computer Aided Process Engineering
(ESCAPE30), May 24-27, 2020, Milano, Italy. © 2020 Elsevier B.V. All rights reserved.
http://dx.doi.org/10.1016/B978-0-12-823377-1.50084-7

Computational Fluid Dynamics Simulation of CO_2 Methanation in a Fixed-bed Profile Reactor

Steffen Flaischlen[a,b,*], Jan Martin[a,b], Bjarne Kreitz[a,b], Thomas Turek[a,b], Gregor D. Wehinger[a,b]

aInstitute of Chemical and Electrochemical Process Engineering, Clausthal University of Technology, Leibnizstr. 17, 38678 Clausthal-Zellerfeld, Germany
bResearch Center Energy Storage Technologies (EST), Clausthal University of Technology, Am Stollen 19A, 38640 Goslar, Germany
flaischlen@icvt.tu-clausthal

Abstract

In this contribution, we present a detailed three-dimensional computational fluid dynamics (CFD) model of a fixed-bed reactor processing the catalytic CO_2 methanation reaction. Due to the small tube-to-particle-diameter ratio, particle-resolved CFD simulations are carried out, since they can locally account for transport phenomena, i.e. momentum, heat, and mass transfer. In addition to the interstitial flow simulation, three-dimensional diffusion plus reaction is modelled inside the catalytic pellets. The comparison in terms of axial temperature with a one-dimensional model shows the discrepancy between the models. Additional CFD simulations with different pellet shapes show that the shape has little influence on the heat transfer in these slender fixed-bed arrangements. Experimental results of axial concentration profiles will further validate the CFD model.

Keywords: Methanation, Computational Fluid Dynamics (CFD), Particle-resolved CFD, Fixed-bed reactors

1. Introduction

In the context of the energy transition to renewable energies, energy storage is a key stone. The surplus energy can be used for the electrolysis of water into hydrogen and oxygen. However, the storage of hydrogen is challenging due to reactivity, diffusivity and corrosion. This is why the hydrogen obtained is further converted into methane with carbon dioxide in the methanation process. The advantage is the storage and use of the existing natural gas infrastructure, since methane is the key component. For the catalytic methanation of CO_2, fixed-bed reactors are typically used in which the particles are coated or impregnated with the active catalytic component, e.g. nickel, ruthenium and palladium. Due to the exothermic reaction, the use of small tube diameters is necessary to increase the cooling surface area. Another process engineering aspect is to maintain a low pressure drop. While small particle diameters lead to higher pressure drops, the methanation reaction is realized in fixed-bed reactors with a small tube-to-particle diameter ratio D/d_p. The simplest catalyst particle geometry is the sphere, but over the years, various complex geometries have been developed to increase the surface area and to reduce the pressure drop. For the prediction of the reaction process, the use of computer-aided models is the state of the art. For the development of more comprehensive models, a better understanding of the underlying kinetics is important. In addition, the effect of model assumptions and uncertainties should be quantified wherever possible. Since the porosity in fixed-bed reactors with small D/d_p is highly local dependent, the assumption of a plug flow behavior is not very precise. Therefore, particle-resolved computational fluid dynamic (CFD) simulations are used, where every particle in the bed is described with the three dimensional discretization (Jurtz et al. 2019). To get a better insight into the process occurring in the bed, axial temperature and concentration profiles are measured in a special reactor setup. The obtained detailed experimental data allow a critical validation of the detailed CFD model.

2. Methods

2.1. Experimental Setup of the Profile Reactor

The profile reactor is a special research reactor developed and distributed by REACNOSTICS GmbH (Hamburg, Germany), which enables the user to obtain axial temperature and concentration profiles. A capillary is inserted in the center of the bed. This is an advantage over traditional fixed-bed reactors in which only data can be obtained before and after the bed. The capillary can be used in two ways. First, it is possible to place a thermocouple inside. The temperature sensor is in contact with the gas flowing through the reactor through a small opening in one position. In the second mode, a small portion of the gas in the reactor is sucked through the capillary for concentration measurement by gas chromatography. Both temperature and concentration measurement can be carried out simultaneously. The bed is positioned on a movable carriage, which changes the position of the small capillary hole. With one movement of the carriage, it is possible to perform the measurement at different axial positions of the fixed bed. The bed is located in a heated isothermal zone. The experimental setup of the profile reactor is shown in Figure 1 (A).

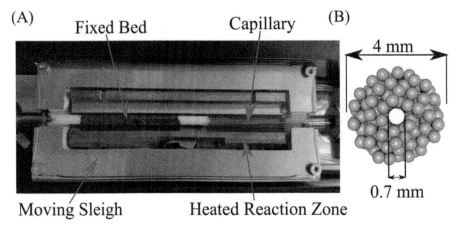

Figure 1: (A) Parts of the profile reactor (B) Dimensions of the fixed-bed.

The fixed bed in the heating zone has a length up to 60 mm, a tube diameter $D = 4$ mm, the capillary diameter $d_c = 0.7$ mm, and the particle diameter $d_p = 0.5$ mm (Figure 1 (B)). The resulting tube-to-particle diameter is $D/d_p < 10$, where particle resolved CFD simulations should be applied.

2.2. Numerical Setup for synthetic fixed-beds

Before applying fixed-bed CFD simulations, it is necessary to obtain an input geometry. Different methods are known, but the most common are the Discrete Element Method (DEM) and the Rigid Body Approach (RBA). In this contribution, the RBA is used with the open source video animation software Blender. Boccardo et al. (2014) first published this approach of using RBA for the synthetic generation of fixed-beds. The results of Flaischlen and Wehinger (2019) showed the advantages of RBA over the classical DEM, especially for non-spherical pellets and in terms of simulation time. The beds consisted of 1000 to 1500 particles and required some hours for packing generation. In the case of the profile reactor, the total number of particles for a bed height of 60 mm is about 6,000. While the simulation time scales with the number of particles, more precisely the number of particle contacts, the simulation time is very high. Therefore, a smaller number of particles is used for the model development. This leads to shorter bed generation times and faster CFD simulations as the number of mesh cells also increases with the number of particles.

2.3. Numerical Setup for CFD Simulations

The complexity of the CFD simulations is increased stepwise. In a first step, only heat transfer investigations are carried out in which no chemical reaction is taken into account. Nitrogen flows through the reactor and the wall temperature is set to a constant value. The particles are described with a solid model and a fixed thermal conductivity in the range of a typical porous Ni catalyst. The boundary conditions for the heat transfer simulation are summarized in Tab. 1.

Tab. 1: Boundary conditions of CFD simulations for heat transfer studies.

	Heat Transfer	*Methanation*	
Velocity Inlet /m s^{-1}	0.3421	0.3421	
Inlet Temperature /°C	25	281.85	
Wall Temperature /°C	250	281.85	
Capillary Wall Temperature	*Adiabatic*	*Adiabatic*	
Solid Thermal Conductivity /W m^{-1} K^{-1}	0.3	0.3	
Pellet Diameter /mm	0.6	0.524	
Number of Pellets	450	450	
Bed Height /mm	6.184	6.184	
Mole Fraction	$N_2 = 1$	$H_2 = 0.8, CO_2 = 0.1$	
Pellet Dimensions	*Spheres*	*Cylinders*	*Rings*
Diameter /mm	0.6	0.524	0.524
Height /mm	–	0.524	0.524
Inner Diameter /mm	–	–	0.210

In the next step, the methanation reaction is included in the CFD pellet model. The reaction kinetics from Koschany et al. (2016) describe the CO₂ methanation with a Langmuir-Hinshelwood-Hougon-Watson approach. Due to the small pore size of the porous catalyst, convection is assumed to be negligible and hence only diffusion is the transport mechanism inside the catalyst pellets. In the CFD simulations, only the values for temperature and mole fractions are exchanged via an internal table across the gas-solid interface. This guarantees that no momentum is transferred into the particle region and hence, the velocity inside the pellets is exactly zero. This is similar to the method of co-simulations described in Wehinger et al. (2017) with the advantage that all models are contained in only one CFD simulation.

3. Results

3.1. Porosity and Velocity Profile

As already mentioned, wall effects have a large influence on heat and mass transfer in small D/d_p fixed-bed arrangements. The capillary has additional wall effect leads to an even severe situation. This can be shown with the centroid representation, where the midpoint of every spherical particle is projected to the x-y plane (Figure 2 (A)).

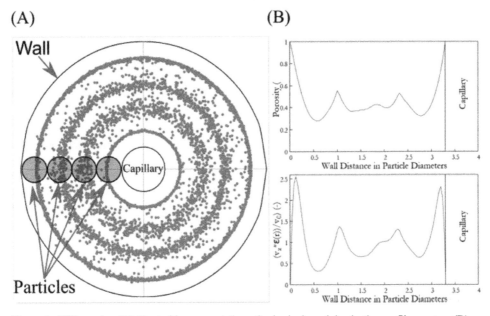

Figure 2: CFD results. (A) Centroid representation of spherical particles in the profile reactor. (B) Radial porosity and normalized velocity profile. Volume flow is $4.167 \cdot 10^{-6}$ m³ s⁻¹.

The centroids are grouped in concentric circles with a clear structure. This is in contrast to a random distribution of the particles in the bed. The bed structure can also be represented by the radial porosity profile, where the porosity is averaged in the axial and azimuth direction (Figure 2 (B) top). The shape of the curve is almost mirrored at the wall distance of approx. 1.7. Irregularities are due to the convex shape of the capillary. Taking the flow simulation into account, it can be seen that the radial velocity profile follows the porosity profile. The velocity peak close to the wall is larger, since the cross section at this position is larger than at the capillary. The results show the difference to other models where the flow is modeled under the plug flow assumption.

3.2. Heat Transfer

The first step of the heat transfer CFD simulations is to compare the performance of different particle shapes, i.e. spheres, cylinders, and rings. The results for the simulation with the boundary conditions from Tab. 1 are shown in Figure 3. It can be observed that the particle shape has only little influence on the heat transfer in the fixed bed. Nevertheless, heat transfer from the wall to the fluid is intensified with particles inserted in comparison to the empty tube.

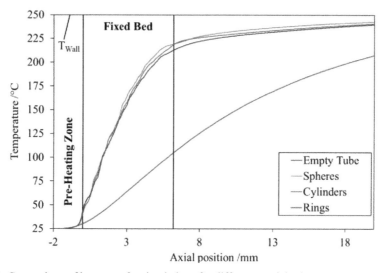

Figure 3: Comparison of heat transfer simulations for different particle shapes.

Figure 4 shows the axial temperature profile of the 3D particle-resolved CFD model and a 1D heterogeneous model. The increase of temperature of the 1D model is much steeper and the wall temperature is reached at the end of the bed. The difference between the two models can be attributed to the strong wall channeling effects and hence to a reduced radial mixing, which is not accounted for in the 1D model.

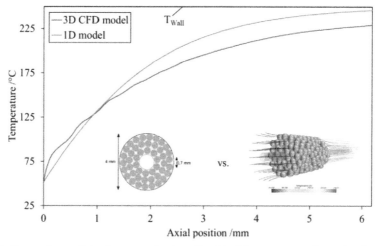

Figure 4: Comparison of the heat transfer in a fixed-bed between one-dimensional and three-dimensional models

3.3. Methanation of CO₂

Figure 5 shows a fixed-bed reactor consisting of rings under catalytic reaction conditions. The results show the conversion of carbon dioxide and hydrogen into methane. The largest mole fractions occurring inside the rings which are close to the capillary (Figure 5 (A)). The velocity inside the porous catalyst pellets is zero (Figure 5 (B)).

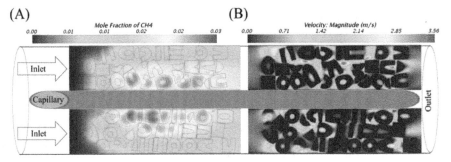

Figure 5: (A) Methanation reaction in the profile reactor with ring particle shape (B) Velocity in the reactor and the pellets.

This shows the complex interplay between local kinetics and local transport phenomena. In the next step, we compare quantitatively axial experimental concentration profiles with the CFD model.

4. Conclusion

This study shows clearly that the profile reactor is highly influenced by wall effects, both at the reactor wall and at the capillary, which makes it necessary to apply particle-resolved CFD simulations. The comparison between the detailed CFD model and the 1D heterogeneous model for heat transfer shows a significant difference in the axial temperature profile. With the particle-resolved CFD simulation approach, different particle shapes can be studied. The reaction model of Koschany et al. (2016) can be included in the simulation and preliminary results show a locally varying conversion of CO_2 and H_2 into CH_4. With a fully validated CFD model, the reactor performance can be improved by analyzing the simulation results, which have a nearly unlimited level of detail.

References

Boccardo, G., Del Plato, L., Marchisio, D., Augier, F., Haroun, Y., Ferre, D., & Icardi, M. (2014, June). Pore-scale simulation of fluid flow in packed-bed reactors via rigid-body simulations and CFD. In *Conference proceedings. SINTEF-NTNU.*

Flaischlen, S., & Wehinger, G. D. (2019). Synthetic Packed-Bed Generation for CFD Simulations: Blender vs. STAR-CCM+. *ChemEngineering, 3*(2), 52.

Jurtz, N., Kraume, M., & Wehinger, G. D. (2019). Advances in fixed-bed reactor modeling using particle-resolved computational fluid dynamics (CFD). *Reviews in Chemical Engineering, 35*(2), 139-190.

Koschany, F., Schlereth, D., & Hinrichsen, O. (2016). On the kinetics of the methanation of carbon dioxide on coprecipitated NiAl (O) x. *Applied Catalysis B: Environmental, 181*, 504-516.

Wehinger, G. D., Klippel, F., & Kraume, M. (2017). Modeling pore processes for particle-resolved CFD simulations of catalytic fixed-bed reactors. *Computers & Chemical Engineering, 101*, 11-22.

Sauro Pierucci, Flavio Manenti, Giulia Bozzano, Davide Manca (Eds.)
Proceedings of the 30th European Symposium on Computer Aided Process Engineering
(ESCAPE30), May 24-27, 2020, Milano, Italy. © 2020 Elsevier B.V. All rights reserved.
http://dx.doi.org/10.1016/B978-0-12-823377-1.50085-9

Data-Driven Approach for Predictive Modeling of By-Product Formation in Methanol Synthesis

Tibor Svitnic[a], Nga T. Q. Do[a]*, Timm Schuhmann[b], Thomas Renner[a],
Stéphane Haag[a], Evrim Örs[a],*

*a AIR LIQUIDE Forschung und Entwicklung GmbH, Frankfurt Innovation Campus,
Gwinnerstrasse 27-33, Frankfurt am Main, Germany*

*b AIR LIQUIDE Global E&C Solutions Germany GmbH,
Olof-Palme-Strasse 35,60439, Frankfurt am Main, Germany*
ngathiquynh.do@airliquide.com; evrim.oers@airliquide.com

Abstract

In this work, the application of a novel data-driven approach for predictive modeling of by-product formation in methanol (MeOH) synthesis is demonstrated. Due to the number of by-products present in MeOH synthesis, building reliable first-principles models for each by-product is very complex and time consuming. The total by-products of MeOH synthesis are classified into 5 main groups, namely alcohols, esters, ketones, ethers and paraffins, where alcohol and ester groups are usually predominant. In the data preparation phase, a collection of more than 900 experimental points for each individual from test campaigns conducted at a pilot plant was preprocessed using Python™. This cleaned dataset was used for model development in proprietary software JMP® via neural networks, where special care was taken to ensure a representative training vs. test set distribution, avoidance of overfitting, as well as the physical interpretability of data-driven models. The resulting predictive models have a very good generalization behavior covering the wide range of operating conditions, e.g. the alcohol predictive model has an R^2 value of 0.96, and 66.4% of experimental data points are predicted with ±15% accuracy. While a further refinement of the model can be possible through physical considerations, the integration of the model within the MeOH process design workflow is recommended. Moreover, the approach can be extended to other chemical processes.

Keywords: By-products, Methanol, Neural Networks, Predictive Modeling.

1. Introduction

To understand, design and optimize a chemical process, an engineer conventionally uses physical modelling, however practical limitations caused by high computational effort and time can be associated with this first-principles approach. Moreover the designer may not have the complete knowledge of physico-chemical relationship of input-output variables in the system. On the other side, with the rise of artificial intelligence and machine learning techniques in chemical engineering (Venkatasubramanian, 2019), data-driven modeling approach gains increasing interest. McBride and Sundmacher (2019) summarize the various computational methodologies and applications of data-driven approach in different disciplines of chemical engineering. While reduction of model complexity, faster solutions and easier deployment options constitute the primary advantages of data-driven modeling, an integrated approach with process know-how is required for developing reliable applications with this approach. As mentioned by

Asprion et al. (2019), there is growing effort for the corresponding hybrid modeling within chemical and process engineering community.

As for the industrial aspect, digital transformation is a key driver for businesses in all sectors, including process industry (Les Echos, 2019). While the deployment of digital tools primarily targets to achieve operational excellence, the corresponding applications range from plant economic performance monitoring and predictive asset maintenance, to advanced process control and real time optimization (OSIsoft, 2019). Prior work on catalyst deactivation (Örs et al., 2018) and ash fusion behavior prediction (Sasi et al., 2018) demonstrate the potential of data-driven methodologies in H_2/Syngas production. Regarding the further development of novel digital solutions for process industry (especially based on artificial intelligence), collaboration projects with academia represent a strong enhancer for business (chemie.de, 2019).

Methanol (MeOH) is one of the value molecules for convenient energy carrier and for chemical storage. Nowadays, MeOH is synthesized from syngas generated from several carbon-containing feedstocks including natural gas and coal. The reactors are imbedded with $Cu/ZnO/Al_2O_3$ catalyst and operated usually from 50 to 100 bar and 200-300 °C (Bozzano et al., 2016). In the context of energy transition and global warming, an efficient and flexible MeOH process to additionally deal with unconventional gas i.e. stranded gas, biomass syngas, unused syngas capacities and CO_2 rich gases are required. The efforts in this regards can be seen in several works and projects (i3upgrade, 2017), (Haag et al, 2019), (Do et al., 2019). The variety of syngas precursor, resulting in diversity of reactor inlet compositions compared to conventional design, can be challenging for not only reactor design but also for the separation section. Therefore, the ability to predict catalyst performance (Bonilla, 2017) and by-product formation are key for designing new technologies and offering commercial guarantees.

Considering the high number of by-products in methanol synthesis loop, it is a challenge to build first-principles models for each component. The total by-products of MeOH synthesis can be classified into 5 main categories based on similar functional groups in each molecule, namely alcohols, esters, ketones, ethers and paraffins, where the alcohol group is usually predominant. There is effort in literature to build up models for major by-products nonetheless they are limited in prediction due to the narrow range of experimental data and different reactor systems (Wu et al., 2017). In this work, we demonstrate the predictive model of individual by-products group and total by-products in MeOH synthesis depending on the operating conditions following a data-driven approach. While the current design of the methanol distillation unit is able to meet required methanol grade, an integrated implementation of the by-product model with first-principles model may lead to further improvement.

2. Computational Methodology

2.1. Data collection and preparation

The methodology applied for the development of a data-driven model for the by-products formation consists of several steps. First, the measured data of the by-products formation was consolidated into one dataset. This covers different test campaigns carried out at the methanol synthesis pilot plant in the last 10 years, and is finally comprised of ca. 900 data points for each of the by-product groups. The detail of the pilot plant can be referred in the work of Do et al. (2019). The collected data points represent only the water cooled reactor unit at the pilot unit. The measured compositions for individual by-products were grouped into 5 categories based on their similar chemical characteristics (Figure 1). The dataset was cleaned to only include points satisfying the mass balance closure criterion.

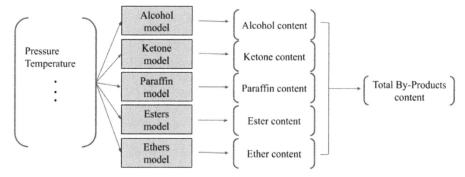

Figure 1: Schematic representation of modeling input and output variables

From the set of all measured process variables, a subset of relevant features were selected as model input. This selection step requires process know-how and technical understanding, considering not only the pilot plant of concern, but also applicability at commercial scale. The selected model input includes process variables such as temperature, pressure, etc. (Figure 1). Furthermore, since the model input and target variables are of significantly different order of magnitude, a normalization procedure was implemented to avoid potential problems in model development such as transfer function saturation and non-homogeneous weight and bias values (Sasi et al., 2018).

2.2. Model development

The cleaned and scaled data was randomly split into training and blind test sets, where 70% of the data was used for model training and the remaining 30% to evaluate the predictive capabilities of the developed model on data points that the model has never seen before. The statistical representability of both sets was checked by comparing the means, standard deviations and visually inspecting the histograms of all model variables. To ensure a systematic and reusable computational workflow, the consolidated dataset was imported into Python™ where the abovementioned steps were implemented.

Following input selection and training/test set distribution, the data was imported into JMP® for model development. The selected model structure in JMP® was neural networks with 1 hidden layer. For each by-product group, several models were built based on the training dataset following the K-fold cross-validation feature with k=5, and compared based on their performance metrics, namely R^2 and RMSE. After a thorough screening, the number of nodes was determined by reaching the best model performance while keeping model complexity as low as possible. Additionally, to integrate the model selection phase with physical interpretability, sensitivity analyses were carried out. This helped to prevent potential overfitting via eliminating models which show a physically unexplainable response (such as unsmooth and/or with several local extrema). That is, even though a model structure was observed to yield better results based on performance metrics, it was disregarded if its sensitivity analysis showed poor response.

After careful execution of all these steps of computational methodology, a final set of models for each by-product group was selected and combined into a total by-product prediction model as shown in Figure 1.

3. Results and Discussion

In this part, the modeling results of the two most dominant by-product groups (alcohols and esters), will be illustrated, as well as the total by-products. Table 1 shows selected computational performance metrics, R^2 and NRMSE (normalized root mean squared error). Note that the NRMSE is calculated via dividing the RMSE by the overall range of the corresponding variable. The comparable values among training, test and all data points indicate the appropriate data splitting and statistical representativeness of the training and test data distribution. Also note that no training and test metrics are tabulated for the total by-product model, since it was not constructed following the model development steps and is a post-processed summation of prediction results based on individual by-product models. It can be concluded that the models have not undergone overfitting and the generalization capability is good for the whole set of data points.

Table 1: Performance metrics of the developed by-product formation models

	Alcohol Model		**Ester Model**		**Total By-Product Model**	
Dataset	NRMSE (%)	R^2 (%)	NRMSE (%)	R^2 (%)	NRMSE (%)	R^2 (%)
Training	3.04	95.82	1.61	95.81	-	-
Testing	2.87	96.34	1.59	96.35	-	-
All Data Points	2.99	95.98	1.61	95.97	1.86	97.44

3.1. Prediction of Selected Individual Groups: Alcohols and Esters

The prediction of both alcohol and ester formation showed best performance for a 4-node neural network structure. Figure 2 shows the parity plot of the measured and predicted values after normalization for alcohols (a) and esters (b). The results indicate that 66.4% and 70.0% of all the predicted points for alcohols and esters respectively fall within 15% deviation interval (dashed lines in Figure 2). The performance metrics shown in Table 1 are calculated based on alcohol and ester model results illustrated in Figure 2. For instance the R^2 value of 95.82 refers to the accuracy of alcohol model considering the training dataset, i.e. the data points depicted with circles in Figure 2.a.

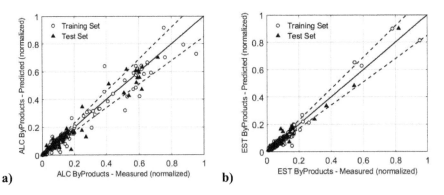

a)   b)

Figure 2: Normalized parity plot of alcohol (a) and ester (b) by-product models, dashed lines indicate 15% deviation from perfect prediction

In order to ensure physical interpretability of the developed models, sensitivity analyses of the finally selected alcohol model prediction showed smooth response (Figure 3). Note that for each single sensitivity plot, only one variable was altered and all others were kept constant at their mean values. At this condition, the sensitivity analysis indicates a proportional relationship of higher alcohol by-product formation with the temperature. This agrees with the process know-how and literature (Wu et al., 2017). Similarly, the decrease of higher alcohol formation (i.e. C_2+) at higher pressure can be ascribed to better carbon efficiency favoring the main product. This analysis denotes the importance of optimal operating conditions in order to reduce the forming of higher alcohols.

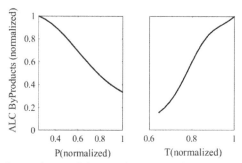

Figure 3: Sensitivity analyses of the alcohol by-product model (P = pressure, T = temperature)

3.2. Total By-Products Model

The total by-product model is the sum of all individual groups and 80.2% of the predicted data points fall within the 15% deviation interval (dashed line in Figure 4). The accuracy of the total by-products model approaches the values of alcohols and esters group model, which is logical since their quantities dominate the whole by-products spectrum. Similar to Figure 2, the performance metrics for total by-products shown in Table 1 are calculated based on prediction results depicted in Figure 4.

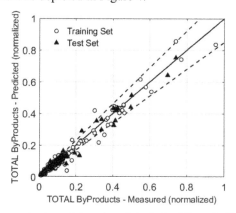

Figure 4: Total by-product model parity plot, dashed lines indicate 15% deviation

4. Conclusion and Outlook

In this work, the application of a data-driven approach for the development of a predictive model of by-product formation in MeOH synthesis process is demonstrated. Two representative groups and total by-product models have been shown. It is observed that the resulting predictive models have a very good generalization behavior covering the wide range of operating conditions. The sensitivity analysis shows the dependency of by-products formation based on input variables allowing physical interpretability. This data-driven approach is promising for every process in which data can be exploited but is too complex to construct a first-principles model. The main challenges are the need of collecting sufficiently large and reliable data to develop the model. Finally, model update, validation and improvement for different scenarios are key to increase the reliability of the model and to adapt it for further applications.

References

N. Asprion, R. Böttcher, R. Pack, M. Stavrou, J. Höller, J. Schwientek, M. Bortz, 2019, Gray-box Modeling for the Optimization of Chemical Processes, Chem. Ing. Tech. 91(3): 305–313.

A. Bonilla, 2017, Catalyst Deactivation Estimation in Methanol Synthesis and Medium Temperature Shift Processes, M.Sc. thesis, Process Dynamics and Operations Group, TU Dortmund, Germany.

G. Bozzano, F. Manenti, 2016, Efficient methanol synthesis: perspectives, technologies and optimization strategies, Prog. Energy Combust. Sci. 56: 71–105.

Chemie.de, 2019, 17 Mio. EUR für die künstliche Intelligenz in Prozessindustrie, https://www.chemie.de/news/1162875/17-mio-eur-fuer-die-kuenstliche-intelligenz-in-der-prozessindustrie.html?pk_campaign=ca0259&WT.mc_id=ca0259

N. T. Q. Do, S. Haag, V. Gronemann, T. Schuhmann, T. Oelmann, M. Gorny, H. Schwarz, S. Werner, S. J. Reitmeier, S. Gebert, A. Reitzmann, 2019, Layer Management for Methanol Process, DGMK Circular Economy - A Fresh View on Petrochemistry, ISBN 978-3-941721-98-2.

Les Echos, 2019, eCAC40: chez Air Liquide, Le numérique a changé d'échelle, https://business.lesechos.fr/directions-generales/strategie/transformation/ 0602026569459-ecac40-chez-air-liquide-le-numerique-a-change-d-echelle-332389.php

S. Haag, F. Castillo-Welter, T. Schuhmann, B. A. Williams, T. Oelmann, A. Günther, M. Gorny, 2019, How to Convert CO_2 to Green Methanol. Oil and Gas Magazine, 46 edition, Issue 2.

i3upgrade, 2017, Integrated and intelligent upgrade of carbon sources through hydrogen addition for the steel industry, https://www.i3upgrade.eu/

K. McBride, K. Sundmacher, 2019, Overview of Surrogate Modeling in Chemical Process Engineering, Chem. Ing. Tech., 91(3): 228-239.

E. Örs, R. Schmidt, M. Mighani, K. Dabhadkar, K. Ingale, N. Sahinidis, 2018, Data Science Applied to the Monitoring of Catalyst Deactivation, Presentation at SFGP Big Data and Process Engineering Thematic Day, Paris (available on demand).

OSIsoft, 2019, How Air Liquide leverages on PI technologies to optimize its operations - SIO.Optim program, Presentation at PI World Conference, San Francisco, https://www.osisoft.com/presentations/how-air-liquide-leverages-on-pi-technologies-to-optimize-its-operations---sio-optim-program/

T. Sasi, M. Mighani, E. Örs, R. Tawani, M. Gräbner, 2018, Prediction of ash fusion behavior from coal ash composition for entrained-flow gasification, Fuel Processing Technology, 176: 64-75.

V. Venkatasubramanian, 2019, The promise of artificial intelligence in chemical engineering: Is it here, finally?, AIChE J.; 65(2):466–78.

Z. Wu, M. Qin, Y. Liu, H. L. Fang, 2017, Prediction of Major Impurities during MeOH Synthesis over a $Cu/ZnO/Al_2O_3$ Catalyst, Ind. Eng. Chem. Res., 56, 49: 14430-14436.

Sauro Pierucci, Flavio Manenti, Giulia Bozzano, Davide Manca (Eds.)
Proceedings of the 30th European Symposium on Computer Aided Process Engineering
(ESCAPE30), May 24-27, 2020, Milano, Italy. © 2020 Elsevier B.V. All rights reserved.
http://dx.doi.org/10.1016/B978-0-12-823377-1.50086-0

Modeling of The Solid Oxide Fuel Cell Considering H2 and CO Electrochemical Reactions

Jia-Lin Kang[a*], Chien-Chien Wang[b], Po-Hsun Chang[b], David Shan-Hill Wong[b],
Shi-Shang Jang[b], Chun-Hsiu Wang[c]

[a] *Department of Chemical and Material Engineering, National Yunlin, University of
Science and Technology, Yunlin, 64002, Taiwan, ROC*

[b] *Department of Chemical Engineering, National Tsing Hua University,
Hsinchu, 30013, Taiwan, ROC*

[c] *Green Energy & System Integration Research & Development Department, China*

Steel Corporation, Kaohsiung 81233, Taiwan, ROC

jlkang@yuntech.edu.tw

Abstract

this study presented a competitive electrochemical mechanism of the hydrogen and carbon monoxide to describe the real electrochemical reactions in SOFC. The SOFC models employed the competitive electrochemical mechanism was validated with a variety of fuels as the feedstocks, such as methane, mixing gas of H2 and CO, blast furnace gas (BFG), and coke oven gas (COG), via pilot-scale SOFC modules of 1 kW and 50 kW. The models were implemented on Aspen Custom Modeler platform to simulate steady-state results. Further, the SOFC of the 50 kW pilot simulation considering the whole pilot process including pre-reformers, heat exchangers, and fuel recycling. The results showed the SOFC employed the competitive electrochemical mechanism has the better performances of the power generation and voltage predictions regardless of the what fuel used in SOFC of the 1 kW scale, compared to the SOFC only employed hydrogen electrochemical mechanism. The mean voltage error of the SOFC with the competitive electrochemical mechanism using various fuels was 1.52%. the minimum error was 0.73% using COG as the feedstock. The validation of the SOFC model of the 50 kW scale showed that only a 5% error with the experiment in steady-state and 6.91% error in transition.

Keywords: solid oxide fuel cell, electrochemical reaction, pilot-scale validation, Aspen simulation

1. Introduction

Most Solid Oxide Fuel Cell (SOFC) studies (Aguiar et al., 2004; Debenedetti and Vayenas, 1983; Nikooyeh et al., 2007; Stiller et al., 2005) employed only the hydrogen electrochemical reaction to predict power generation regardless of the fuel resources used, which contains methane and carbon monoxide. However, in fact, the pure CO or the CO produced by CH4 can directly conduct electrochemical reactions to generate power. Especially when the SOFC scales up, the CO electrochemical reaction becomes more significant. Suwanwarangkul (Suwanwarangkul et al., 2006) established a 2D-SOFC model for syngas (H2, H2O, CO, and CO2). The model could demonstrate the effects of the electrochemical reaction of using hydrogen and carbon monoxide. The result suggested that CO should be considered as a useful fuel for SOFCs. Andersson(Andersson et al., 2013) also stated that both CO and H2 were considered as electrochemical reactants within the anode. They also found that the activation polarization for the electrochemical reaction with hydrogen as a reactant and the one with carbon monoxide as reactant did not correspond to the same current density. Hence, the authors suggested that these two electrochemical reactions should be treated as two individual ones in parallel current density. As the above two studies mentioned, the use of CO as the electrochemical reactants was necessary. However, regarding an electrochemical reaction of the SOFC considering H2 and CO as reactants, there were few studies discussed. Furthermore, how to determine the voltages of these two electrochemical reactions is a big issue if considering H2 and CO electrochemical reactions in a SOFC. Thus, the purpose of this study was to present a competitive electrochemical mechanism of the H2 and CO to describe the real electrochemical reactions in SOFC. The SOFC models employed the competitive electrochemical mechanism was validated with a variety of fuels as the feedstocks, such as methane, mixing gas of H2 and CO, blast furnace gas (BFG), and coke oven gas (COG), via pilot-scale SOFC modules of 1 kW and 50 kW.

2. Modeling of SOFC

The developed SOFC model in this study was based on a cell of the SOFC, which was modified from Aguiar et al. (2004). Figure 1 shows the structure of a SOFC cell.

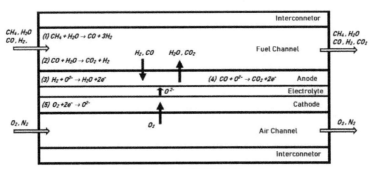

Figure 1 Schematic of SOFC Structure

2.1. Chemical Reactions

Table 1 shows the reactions considered in the SOFC model. The use of methane as a fuel is accompanied by the methane steam reforming reaction (MSRR) and a water gas shift reaction (WGSR). Carbon monoxide (CO) and hydrogen (H₂) are produced as elements of power generation during the reaction. The reaction rate of the MSRR(Aguiar et al., 2004) was shown as following:

$$r_{MSRR} = k_{MSRR} p_{CH_4} e^{-\frac{E_a}{RT}} \tag{1}$$

where k_{MSRR} represents the reaction rate constant of MSRR; p_{CH_4} represents the partial pressure of methane; Ea represents the activation energy; R represents the ideal gas coefficient. The activation energy of Ea = 82 kJ mol⁻¹ and the reaction rate constant of k_{MSRR} = 4274 mol s⁻¹ m⁻² bar⁻¹, has been adopted.

The reaction rate of the WGSR(Haberman and Young, 2004) is expressed in the below:

$$r_{WGS} = k_{0,WGSR} \times e^{-\frac{E_a}{RT}} \times p_{CO} \left(1 - \frac{p_{CO_2} p_{H_2} / p_{CO} p_{H_2O}}{K_{eq,WGSR}} \right) \tag{2}$$

$$K_{eq,WGSR} = e^{(-0.2935Z^3 + 0.6351Z^2 + 4.1788Z + 0.3169)} \tag{3}$$

$$Z = \frac{1000}{T} - 1 \tag{4}$$

where k_{WGSR} represents the reaction rate constant of the WGSR; $K_{eq,WGSR}$ represents the equilibrium reaction rate constant of the WGSR; p_i represent partial pressure of the i spices. The activation energy, Ea is 103.191 kJ mol^{-1} and the reaction rate constant, k_{MSRR} is 1.71×10^8 mol s^{-1} m^{-3} bar^{-1}. The reaction rates of the overall oxidation reactions of hydrogen, R_v and carbon monoxide, R_{vii} are shown as following:

$$R_v = \frac{j_{H_2}}{2F} \tag{5}$$

$$R_{vii} = \frac{j_{CO}}{2F} \tag{6}$$

where j_{H_2} and j_{CO} are the current used by hydrogen and carbon monoxide, respectively; F represents Faraday constant. The reaction rate of the Oxygen reduction reaction, R_{iv}:

$$R_{iv} = \frac{j_{H_2} + j_{CO}}{2F} \tag{7}$$

Table 1 Chemical Reactions of SOFC

Reaction	Mechanism	Standard reaction heat
(i) Methane steam reforming reaction	$CH_4 + H_2O \Leftrightarrow CO + 3H_2$	$\Delta H° = 205.81$ kJ/mol
(ii) Water gas-shift reaction	$CO + H_2O \Leftrightarrow CO_2 + H_2$	$\Delta H° = -41.16$ kJ/mol
(iii) Hydrogen oxidation reaction at (+)	$H_2 + O^{2-} \rightarrow H_2O + 2e^-$	
(iv) Oxygen reduction reaction at (-)	$\frac{1}{2}O_2 + 2e^- \rightarrow O^{2-}$	
(v) Overall hydrogen oxidation in a cell	$H_2 + \frac{1}{2}O_2 \rightarrow H_2O$	$\Delta H° = -241.82$ kJ/mol
(iv) Carbon monoxide oxidation reaction at (+)	$CO + O^{2-} \rightarrow CO_2 + 2e^-$	
(vii) Overall carbon monoxide reaction in a cell	$CO + \frac{1}{2}O_2 \rightarrow CO_2$	$\Delta H° = -282.98$ kJ/mol

2.2. Electrochemical reaction

The open-circuit potential of the H2 and CO are shown as follows:

$$U_{H_2/O_2}^{OCP} = U_{H_2/O_2}^0 - \frac{\Re T}{2F} ln \left(\frac{p_{H_2O}}{p_{H_2}p_{O_2}^{1/2}} \right) \tag{8}$$

$$U_{CO/O_2}^{OCP} = U_{CO/O_2}^0 - \frac{\Re T}{2F} ln \left(\frac{p_{CO_2}}{p_{CO}p_{O_2}^{1/2}} \right) \tag{9}$$

where U^{OCP} represents open-circuit potential; $U_{H_2}^0$ and U_{CO}^0 represents H2 and CO reduction potentials at standard conditions; $\Re$ represents the ideal gas constant; T represents the temperature of SOFC; F represents Faraday constant; p_i represent the partial pressure of i spices. The output voltage, U of the SOFC is shown as below:

$$U = U_{H_2/O_2}^{OCP} - \left(\eta_{Ohm} + \eta_{conc,anode,H_2} + \eta_{conc,cathode} + \eta_{act,anode,H_2} + \eta_{act,cathode} \right)$$
$$= U_{CO/O_2}^{OCP} - \left(\eta_{Ohm} + \eta_{conc,anode,CO} + \eta_{conc,cathode} + \eta_{act,anode,CO} + \eta_{act,cathode} \right) \tag{10}$$

where η_{Ohm} represents Ohmic loss; η_{conc} represents the concentration overvoltage loss at anode and cathode; η_{act} represents the active overvoltage loss at anode and cathode. Ohmic loss, η_{Ohm} is estimated by the following equations:

$$\eta_{Ohm} = jR_{Ohm} \tag{11}$$

$$R_{Ohm} = \frac{\tau_{anode}}{\sigma_{anode}} + \frac{\tau_{electrolyte}}{\sigma_{electrolyte}} + \frac{\tau_{cathode}}{\sigma_{cathode}} + R_i \tag{12}$$

where j represents the current density; R_{Ohm} represents Ohmic resistance; τ_i represent the thickness of i layer in SOFC; σ_i represent the conductivity of i layer; R_i represents Interconnect resistance. The concentration overvoltage losses of the anode and cathode are shown as below:

$$\eta_{conc,anode,H_2} = \frac{\Re T}{2F} ln \left(\frac{p_{H_2O,TPB}p_{H_2,f}}{p_{H_2O,f}p_{H_2,TPB}} \right) \tag{13}$$

$$\eta_{conc,anode,CO} = \frac{\Re T}{2F} ln \left(\frac{p_{CO_2,TPB}p_{CO,f}}{p_{CO_2,f}p_{CO,TPB}} \right) \tag{14}$$

$$\eta_{conc,cathode} = \frac{\Re T}{4F} \ln\left(\frac{p_{O_2,a}}{p_{O_2,TPB}}\right) \tag{15}$$

where $p_{i,TPB}$ represent the partial pressures of i specie at three-phase boundaries. The partial pressures at three-phase boundaries are calculated as follows:

$$p_{H_2,TPB} = p_{H_2,f} - \frac{\Re T \tau_{anode}}{2F\overline{D}_{eff,anode}} j \tag{16}$$

$$p_{CO,TPB} = p_{CO,f} - \frac{\Re T \tau_{anode}}{2F\overline{D}_{eff,anode}} j \tag{17}$$

$$p_{H_2O,TPB} = p_{H_2O,f} + \frac{\Re T \tau_{anode}}{2F\overline{D}_{eff,anode}} j \tag{18}$$

$$p_{CO_2,TPB} = p_{CO_2,f} + \frac{\Re T \tau_{anode}}{2F\overline{D}_{eff,anode}} j \tag{19}$$

$$p_{O_2,TPB} = P - (P - p_{O_2,a})exp\left(\frac{\Re T \tau_{cathode}}{4F D_{eff,cathode} P} j\right) \tag{20}$$

where $D_{eff,i}$ represent the effective diffusivities of i species. In this study, $D_{eff,i}$ were assumed as constants evaluating at 1073K of the temperature of SOFC. The active overvoltage loss, η_{act} at the anode and cathode can be expressed as follows:

$$j_{0,electrode} = \frac{\Re T}{nF} k_{electrode} exp\left(\frac{E_{electrode}}{\Re T}\right) \tag{21}$$

$$j_{H_2} = j_{0,anode,H_2}\left[\frac{p_{H_2,TPB}}{p_{H_2,f}} exp\left(\frac{\alpha nF}{\Re T}\eta_{act,electrode}\right) - \frac{p_{H_2O,TPB}}{p_{H_2O,f}} exp\left(-\frac{(1-\alpha)nF}{\Re T}\eta_{act,electrode}\right)\right] \tag{22}$$

$$j_{CO} = j_{0,anode,CO}\left[\frac{p_{CO,TPB}}{p_{CO,f}} exp\left(\frac{\alpha nF}{\Re T}\eta_{act,electrode}\right) - \frac{p_{CO_2,TPB}}{p_{CO_2,f}} exp\left(-\frac{(1-\alpha)nF}{\Re T}\eta_{act,electrode}\right)\right] \tag{23}$$

$$j = j_{H_2} + j_{CO}$$

$$j = j_{0,cathode}\left[exp\left(\frac{\alpha nF}{\Re T}\eta_{act,cathode}\right) - exp\left(-\frac{(1-\alpha)nF}{\Re T}\eta_{act,cathode}\right)\right] \tag{24}$$

where $k_{electrode}$ represents Electrode reaction constant; $E_{electrode}$ represents Electrode activation energy; n represents the number of electrons; α represents the Transfer coefficient.

2.3. A Cell Specification and Material Properties
The Material Properties of Electrons were obtained from Aguiar et al. (2004). The specification of a cell of the SOFC is shown in Table 2.

Table 2 Specification of SOFC

Specification	Value
Cell Length, L	0.15 m
Cell Width, W	0.12 m
Cell height, H	0.12 m
Channel height, $h_f \cdot h_a$,	0.001 m
Anode thickness, τ_{anode}	10^{-6} m
Cathode thickness, $\tau_{cathode}$	10^{-6} m
Electrolyte thickness, $\tau_{electrolyte}$	$150*10^{-6}$ m
Interconnect thickness, τ_I	$150*10^{-6}$ m

The SOFC models of 1 kW and 50kW scales were implemented on Aspen Custom Modeler platform. The SOFC of the 50 kW pilot simulation considering the whole pilot process, including pre-reformers, heat exchangers, and fuel recycling.

3. Results and Discussions

3.1. Adjusting and Validation of 1 kW SOFC model
The experimental data of the 1 kW SOFC were obtained from China Steel Corporation (CSC). Figure 2 shows the agreements between the experimental data from various fuel sources and predictions from the competitive H2+CO electrochemical mechanism and the single H2 electrochemical mechanism, using H2 + CO as a fuel source and BFG. As Figure 2(a) shows, the SOFC model using the single H2 electrochemical

mechanism underestimated the output voltage, while the SOFC model using the competitive electrochemical mechanism significantly corrected the predicted performance with experimental voltage data. The average error of using the single H2 electrochemical mechanism and using the competitive electrochemical mechanism was 2.63% and 0.98 %, respectively. In Figure 2(b), the SOFC model using the competitive electrochemical mechanism obtained much more accuracy of the prediction than the model using the single H2 electrochemical mechanism. The average errors of the single and competitive electrochemical mechanisms were 5.78% and 1.60%, respectively. As Figure 2(c) shows, the average error of the voltage can be improved from 2.12% to 0.73%. Hence, using the competitive H2+CO electrochemical mechanism can obtain more accuracy of the output voltage of the SOFC with various fuel sources.

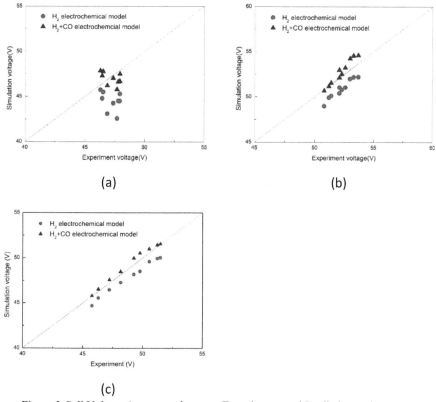

Figure 2 Cell Voltage Agreement between Experiments and Predictions using
(a)H2+CO, (b) BFG, and (c) COG as the feeding fuel in Steady State

3.2. Steady State Validation of 50 kW SOFC Plant Test

The real plant data of the 50 kW SOFC were also obtained from CSC. The fuel source was CH4. The fuel source would go through a pre-former to product a certain amount of H2 and CO with a part of CH4, and then going into the 50 kW SOFC to generate electricity. Figure 3 shows the voltage agreement between experiments and predictions of the 50 kW SOFC. As the figure shows, the SOFC model can predict the output voltage in the 50 kW pilot-scale SOFC system. The average error of the voltage was 4.61%.

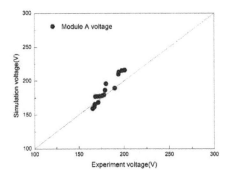

Figure 3 Cell Voltage Agreement between Experiments and Predictions in Steady State

4. Conclusions

In the study, we presented a competitive electrochemical mechanism of the H2 and CO to correct the prediction of the output voltage of SOFCs. The results showed the SOFC employed the competitive electrochemical mechanism has the better performances of the power generation and voltage predictions regardless of the what fuel used in SOFC of the 1 kW scale, compared to the SOFC only employed the single hydrogen electrochemical mechanism. The mean voltage error of the SOFC with the competitive electrochemical mechanism using various fuels was 1.52%. the minimum error was 0.73% using COG as the feedstock. The validation of the SOFC model of the 50 kW scale showed that only a 5% error with the experiment in steady-state and 6.91% error in transition.

References

Aguiar, P., Adjiman, C., & Brandon, N. P. (2004). Anode-supported intermediate temperature direct internal reforming solid oxide fuel cell. I: model-based steady-state performance. *Journal of Power Sources, 138*(1-2), 120-136.

Andersson, M., Yuan, J., & Sundén, B. (2013). SOFC modeling considering hydrogen and carbon monoxide as electrochemical reactants. *Journal of Power Sources, 232*, 42-54.

Debenedetti, P., & Vayenas, C. (1983). Steady-state analysis of high temperature fuel cells. *Chemical Engineering Science, 38*(11), 1817-1829.

Haberman, B., & Young, J. (2004). Three-dimensional simulation of chemically reacting gas flows in the porous support structure of an integrated-planar solid oxide fuel cell. *International Journal of Heat and Mass Transfer, 47*(17-18), 3617-3629.

Nikooyeh, K., Jeje, A. A., & Hill, J. M. (2007). 3D modeling of anode-supported planar SOFC with internal reforming of methane. *Journal of Power Sources, 171*(2), 601-609.

Stiller, C., Thorud, B., Seljebø, S., Mathisen, Ø., Karoliussen, H., & Bolland, O. (2005). Finite-volume modeling and hybrid-cycle performance of planar and tubular solid oxide fuel cells. *Journal of Power Sources, 141*(2), 227-240.

Suwanwarangkul, R., Croiset, E., Entchev, E., Charojrochkul, S., Pritzker, M., Fowler, M., . . . Mahaudom, H. (2006). Experimental and modeling study of solid oxide fuel cell operating with syngas fuel. *Journal of Power Sources, 161*(1), 308-322.

Sauro Pierucci, Flavio Manenti, Giulia Bozzano, Davide Manca (Eds.)
Proceedings of the 30th European Symposium on Computer Aided Process Engineering
(ESCAPE30), May 24-27, 2020, Milano, Italy. © 2020 Elsevier B.V. All rights reserved.
http://dx.doi.org/10.1016/B978-0-12-823377-1.50087-2

Design Optimization of C3MR Natural Gas Liquefaction Process

Pavan Kumar Veldandi , Sunjay Kurian

Connected Products, Industrial Operations Group, Cognizant Technology Solutions, Hyderabad-500008,India
Pavan.veldandi@cognizant.com

Abstract

Liquefied Natural Gas plants are energy intensive processes. In order to reduce their energy consumption, optimization is an often-sought step in process design. But it is less common for real existing plants. This is especially laborious for plant operators when they need to work with design simulation software in conjunction myriad of other tools to evaluate equipment adequacy for new HMB or use a dynamic simulation software in steady state mode with an optimizer linked.

The novelty of this paper is to showcase how intuitive open modelling with right specifications and in-built optimizers can be the right tool for both Process Designs as well as for re-optimizing/debottlenecking for real plants. This study uses AVEVA SimCentral Simulation Platform to develop the optimized design and real plant model within same simulation.

The process design was created with specifications that reflect the process design objectives and then optimized for compressor power by varying refrigerant compositions and compression pressure. This becomes the basis for the real plant studies like similar optimization for a changed natural gas feed. This is where real plant operators can save efforts by working with a steady state pressure solved network simulation which obeys the equipment limitations. Since this is a steady state simulation the transient to steady state is not a concern, hence time/effort is saved when operators can simplify the simulation by simply swapping detailed controls for simple specifications in open modelling environment.

Keywords: C3MR Process, Energy Optimization, Mixed Refrigerant Composition

1. Introduction

Natural Gas Liquefaction plants are energy intensive processes. With growing demand of Liquefied Natural Gas (LNG), it is important to review the simulation solutions available to process designers and operators to find optimized solutions.

Several studies discuss about optimization different aspects of LNG process design and operation. Among studies in design optimization, it is important to note that Abbas et al. [1] studied the design optimization of LNG mixed-refrigerant processes to conclude that the most effective operation optimisation objective function is the minimisation of the major operating cost, being compressor power. The other flavour of optimization studies is like the energy and cost optimization done by M Wang et al. [2] which considered a minimization of the CAPEX and OPEX. This paper reviews existing optimization studies and suggests the combined use of flexible specifications, multiple modes and optimizers to help process designers and operators.

When process designers begin design simulations, they use a sequential modular based simulator which forces design to detail refrigerant flowrate which is often an unknown. This unknown then becomes part of an optimization objective. The process design should focus on objectives like liquefaction temperature and should allow the refrigerant flowrate to be calculated based on heat balance. This was achieved with ease in AVEVA SimCentral Simulation Platform Process (design) mode. With the simulation with true process objectives, designers can run the optimization for compression power as an objective as suggested by Abbas Ali et al. [1]. As this design becomes a real plant, there is a common need for operators to optimize for changed natural gas feeds based on changing market conditions. This is where the same Process mode simulation was be updated to FluidFlow (steady state pressure solve network) mode which will reflect real plants. The key here is that simulation gets set to equipment sizes that were calculated in design. The complexity with detailed controls can be mimics with specifications like liquefaction product temperature can be specified / maintained by letting the expansion valve position be calculated by simulation. With all appropriate controls mimicked correctly and equipment sizes set, operators can identify new optimums for compression power by varying mixed refrigerant compositions and compressor outlet pressure. Husnil et al.(2014)[3] proposed a new Control structure synthesis for operational optimization of mixed refrigerant processes.

2. Process Description

Figure 1 shows the propane pre-cooled C3MR NG liquefaction process. Propane pre-cooling refrigeration process is not modelled as part of this study, it is assumed that natural gas is precooled and available at -36.3°C. The natural gas is pre-cooled and subcooled to -160°C with two rigorously modelled spiral wound exchangers that exchange heat with mixed refrigerant (MR). The MR cycle is compressed in two compressor stages with an intercooler and an aftercooler. The after cooler outlet (2-phase) is separated as MRV (mixed refrigerant vapor) and MRL (mixed refrigerant liquid) before entering the spiral wound exchangers and then back. The design objectives of simulation model are given in Table 1.

Table 1. Process objectives

Natural gas liquefaction objectives			
Feed Pressure (bar)	61.70	Composition (fraction)	
Feed Temperature (°C)	-32.70	Nitrogen	0.05
Product Temperature (°C)	-160.00	Methane	0.87
		Ethane	0.05
		Propane	0.02

3. Process (design) simulation and optimization

Table 2 gives the specifications/flowsheet equations that help to set up the design simulation with design target objectives and calculate unknowns on the refrigeration/compression system:

The natural gas cooler and subcooling unit are modelled with spiral wound heat exchangers with discretization of heat transfer by splitting (5 times) the heat transfer across the tube lengths. These spiral wound heat exchangers are set with area and heat transfer coefficient. With above updates, the simulation can be solved with an initial mixed refrigerant composition. See Figure 1 for a preview of simulation.

Table 2. Setting simulation with process design objectives

Variable	Changes done	Justification
Mixed refrigerant flow	Flow is commonly specified in sequential solve simulator, but it is made calculated here.	Flow is best identified based on heat balance
Cryogenic exchanger outlet i.e. mixed refrigerant to compressor suction drum	Vapor fraction set to above dew point.	Dew point specification will avoid liquid in compressor suction drum.
Liquefied Natural Gas to storage - target temperature	Product temperature is generally a calculated variable, but it set as specified here to 160 C.	Natural gas heat balance to calculate required refrigerant flow.
Expansion valve pressure drop	Pressure drop is made calculated.	Liquefied natural gas target temperature should calculated expansion valve pressure drop.
Compression ratio per stage.	Flowsheet equation setting both stages with equal compression ratio.	Compression system is defined by desired outlet pressure.
Mixed refrigerant N2 composition	N2 composition set as calculated. Total refrigerant composition is summed to 1 with a flowsheet equation.	Specified composition of C1, C2 and C3 should defined N2 composition.

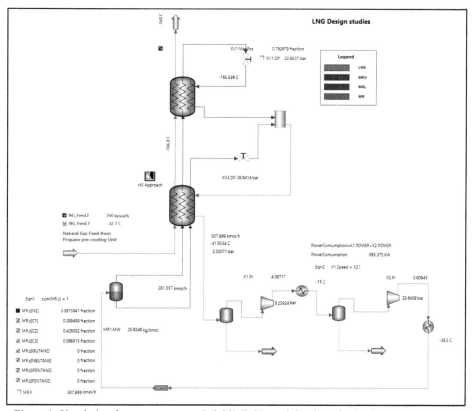

Figure 1. Simulation for propane precooled C3MR Natural Gas liquefaction Process

Table 3. Summary of design optimization of mixed refrigerant composition and compression outlet pressure

	Optimization setting	Bounds	Base	Optimized
Composition (fraction)				
Nitrogen	Dependent	0-100%	0.10	0.08
Methane	Independent	0-100%	0.40	0.39
Ethane	Independent	0-100%	0.30	0.40
Propane	Independent	0-100%	0.20	0.13
Compressor 2nd stage outlet pressure (bar)	Independent	0-100%	62.10	33.67
Compression power consumption (kW)	Objective function		1351	1044
Mixed Refrigerant flow (kmol/h)	Dependent	Positive values	397	474
Compression suction drum vapor fraction	Dependent	Above dew point	1	1

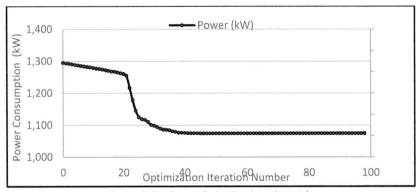

Figure 2. Design optimization iteration path

The optimization achieved a 22% reduction in power consumption as shown in Figure2.

Table 4. Simplifying detailed controls

Variable	Changes done	Justification
Natural gas flow	Natural flow is specified instead of pressure	Flow is expected to maintained by product flow control valve.
Compressor outlet pressure	Both stages speed is set to be same with a flowsheet equation assuming that it run by same rotor.	Controlling compressor in simulation can done via speed/outlet pressure.
Liquefied natural gas temperature to storage – target temperature	Liquefied natural gas temperature is assumed to be maintained by letting simulation calculate expansion valve position.	Natural gas heat balance to calculate required refrigerant flow.
Mixed refrigerant drum separation level	Level in drum is specified instead of position of the mixed refrigerant liquid expansion valve.	Level in drum is assumed to be maintained by control that maintains the mixed refrigerant liquid expansion valve.

Table 5. Natural gas feed changes in pressure solve network

Natural Gas			Mixed Refrigerant		
	Desi gn	Feed Changed		Desig n	Feed Changed
Feed Pressure (bar)	61.70	61.84	Power Consumption (kW)	1044. 22	1038.85
Feed Temperature (°C)	- 32.70	-32.70	Mixed Refrigerant flowrate (kmol/h)	473.9 7	470.70
Product Temperature (°C)	- 160.0 0	-160.00			
Composition (fraction)			Composition (fraction)		
Nitrogen	0.05	0.06	Nitrogen	0.08	0.08
Methane	0.87	0.80	Methane	0.39	0.39
Ethane	0.05	0.10	Ethane	0.40	0.40
Propane	0.02	0.03	Propane	0.13	0.13
i-Butane	0.00	0.01			
n-Butane	0.00	0.01			
i-Pentane	0.00	0.00			
n-Pentane	0.00	0.00			

4. Real plant (pressure solved network) optimization

Real plant can be modelled with steady state pressure solve network called Fluid Flow mode.

The above design Process (design) simulation was switched to Fluid Flow mode (steady state pressure solve network) with the design equipment sizes. This is generally when operator can now use the same process design simulation for his operational needs.

Since FluidFlow is a pressure solve network with steady state, detailed controls were replaced with specifications to simplify the real plant simulation as given in Table 4.

Table 6: Summary of real plant optimization of mixed refrigerant composition and compression speed

	Optimization setting	Bounds	Base	Optimiz ed
Composition (fraction)				
Nitrogen	Dependent	0-100%	0.08	0.10
Methane	Independent	0-50%	0.39	0.39
Ethane	Independent	0-50%	0.40	0.43
Propane	Independent	0-50%	0.13	0.09
Compressor 2nd stage outlet pressure (bar)	Dependent		33.87	29.64
Compressor speed (rpm)	Independent	3000 - 4200 rpm	3600.0 0	3582.15
Power Consumption (kW)	Objective function		1039	895
Mixed Refrigerant flow (kmol/h)	Dependent	Positive values	471	508
Compression suction drum vapor fraction	Dependent	Above dew point	1	1

4.1. Natural Gas Composition change case study

The fluid flow mode model has been tested for fidelity by varying the Natural Gas feed composition as shown in Table 5Now with "Feed Changed" case as the starting point in fluid flow mode, the optimization problem has been run again to yield below results given in Table 6.

The optimization achieved a 14% reduction in power consumption as shown in Figure 3.

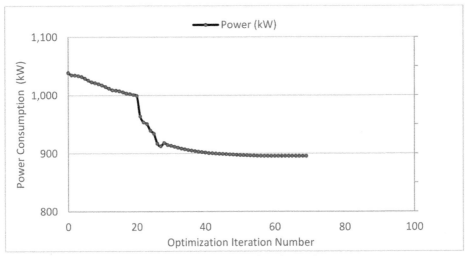

Figure 3. Real optimization iteration path

5. Conclusion

In this work the C3MR Natural Gas liquefaction process has been modeled using Aveva SimCentral Simulation platform for process design as well as operations. The design simulation was successfully set to work with process objectives instead of unknowns of refrigeration cycle. Now the compressor power consumption is minimized by optimizing mixed refrigerant composition and compressor outlet pressure. It is found that the compressor power can be reduced by 22% for design. Further this simulation was successfully moved to a simplified (no controls) pressure driven network steady state simulation. Operators can now use this simulation to identify optimized solutions for changes in natural gas feed composition. In this case the optimizer reduced the compressor power consumption by 14%.

References

1. Hatcher, Prue & Khalilpour, Kaveh & Abbas, Ali. (2012). Optimization of LNG mixed refrigerant process considering operation and design objectives. Computers & Chemical Engineering. 41. 123–133. 10.1016/j.compchemeng.2012.03.005.
2. Mengyu Wang, Rajab Khalilpour, Ali Abbas (2014). Thermodynamic and economic optimization of LNG mixed refrigerant processes.
3. Yuli Amalia Husnil Moonyong Lee,(2014), Control structure synthesis for operational optimization of mixed refrigerant processes for liquefied natural gas plant, Vol 60, No. 7 2428- 2441. 10.1002/aic.14430

Sauro Pierucci, Flavio Manenti, Giulia Bozzano, Davide Manca (Eds.)
Proceedings of the 30th European Symposium on Computer Aided Process Engineering
(ESCAPE30), May 24-27, 2020, Milano, Italy. © 2020 Elsevier B.V. All rights reserved.
http://dx.doi.org/10.1016/B978-0-12-823377-1.50088-4

A Practical Application of Simulation-based Surrogate Modeling for Prereformer Reactor

Robin Schmidt, Amélie Chattot, Amal Bouchrit, Moein Mighani, Evrim Örs*

AIR LIQUIDE Forschung und Entwicklung GmbH, Frankfurt Innovation Campus, Gwinnerstrasse 27-33, Frankfurt am Main, Germany
evrim.oers@airliquide.com

Abstract

In this work, a practical example of surrogate modeling in process engineering is demonstrated in the field of hydrogen production: Modeling of a prereformer reactor. The main motivation is to show the potential of this approach for performance increase of simulations in process design and operation optimization. In a first step, sample points were generated following a computational design of experiments procedure. A prereformer reactor model was built in Aspen Plus®, and corresponding simulation results were collected based on the sample points. The resulting dataset, i.e. sample points and simulation outputs, were used for surrogate model development for the reactor outlet temperature and concentrations, via built-in artificial neural networks (ANN) feature of JMP®. It was observed that resulting surrogate models, with a single layer ANN of 100 hidden nodes, satisfied the expected accuracy limits, e.g. the outlet temperature was predicted with an RMSE of less than 0.04 °C. The predictive behavior of the models was also examined via a blind test set, and the speedup in computation was shown. While this study constitutes a successful proof-of-concept, further improvements are possible via e.g. customization of model development, employment of adaptive sampling methodology.

Keywords: Surrogate, Data-Driven, Neural Networks, Prereformer, Hydrogen

1. Introduction

In engineering practice, one uses physical modeling approach to understand, design and optimize a process. Nonetheless, this first-principles approach can be limited requiring a substantial computational effort and time, and the physico-chemical relationship of input-output variables may not always be accessible to the designer. On the other hand, data-driven modeling approach, i.e. a mapping of input and output variables, gains increasing interest in chemical engineering with the rise of artificial intelligence and machine learning techniques (Venkatasubramanian, 2019). Various applications of this approach employing different computational methodologies can be found in multiple disciplines of chemical engineering, where simulation-based surrogate modeling constitutes a key branch (McBride and Sundmacher, 2019), (Nentwich and Engell, 2019). Along with its advantageous aspects such as reducing the model complexity and allowing faster solutions and deployment options, surrogate modeling also requires an integrated approach with process know-how for developing reliable applications. The corresponding hybrid modeling is therefore being addressed more and more by the academic chemical and process engineering community (Asprion et al., 2019).

From an industrial perspective, digitalization is becoming more and more an integral part of business in all sectors, including process industry (Les Echos, 2019). The digital solutions usually target to achieve operational excellence, where the applications primarily consist of plant economic performance monitoring, predictive asset maintenance, real time optimization (OSIsoft, 2019) and advanced process control. Prior work on catalyst deactivation modeling (Schmidt et al., 2017) and ash fusion behavior prediction (Sasi et al., 2018) are exemplary in H_2/Syngas production field. It is also notable that collaboration projects with academia constitute a key driver for business in exploiting the increasing digitalization trend, especially regarding development of novel AI-based solutions for process industry (chemie.de, 2019).

In this work, focusing on the extension of abovementioned activities with faster and accurate modeling strategies, we conduct a proof-of-concept study concentrating on one unit operation, namely a prereformer reactor as a key component of H_2/Syngas production plants offered and operated by Air Liquide. We describe an approach to illustrate the employment of surrogate models as an enabler for faster computation of first-principles models. Moreover, their integration with optimization procedures can significantly reduce the computational effort in process design and operation. Finally, allowing an explicit mathematical formula, surrogate models based on process simulator results may lead to easily deployable solutions.

2. Prereformer Reactor Simulation

To illustrate the potential of surrogate modeling, an industrial prereformer reactor was selected. From process aspect, a prereformer is frequently used in H_2/Syngas production plants and targets to convert heavy hydrocarbons (C2+) into methane irreversibly. This allows a better heat utilization in the plant by achieving higher preheating temperature for natural gas (NG) as feedstock. Furthermore, it enables the processing of heavy feedstock's, such as naphtha, refinery off-gases, via preventing coke deposition on the subsequent reforming catalyst.

In this work, carbon formation and heavy hydrocarbons were neglected for demonstration purpose and the dry inlet gas is considered a NG containing CO and CO_2 (e.g. originating from refinery-off gas). With these assumptions, only steam methane reforming (SMR) and water gas shift (WGS) reactions are required to describe chemical conversion:

$$\text{SMR}: \ CH_4 + H_2O \leftrightarrow CO + 3\,H_2 \qquad \Delta H = 206.2\,\text{kJ/mol} \qquad (1)$$

$$\text{WGS}: \ CO + H_2O \leftrightarrow H_2 + CO_2 \qquad \Delta H = -41.2\,\text{kJ/mol} \qquad (2)$$

The amount of reaction can be expressed by the reaction extent ξ_{SMR} and ξ_{WGS} in mol/h.

The steam-to-carbon ratio *S/C*, which is a parameter varied independent from the dry inlet gas composition to determine the steam amount, is defined as:

$$S\,/\,C = x_{H_2O} \big/ x_{CH_4} \qquad (3)$$

with the mole fraction of methane x_{CH_4} and steam x_{H_2O}. Based on the dry gas composition and steam-to-carbon ratio *S/C*, wet compositions are calculated:

$$x_i = x_{i,\text{dry}} \big/ (1 + x_{CH_4,\text{dry}} \cdot S\,/\,C) \qquad (4)$$

Other parameters describing the process are the inlet temperature T_{in}, inlet pressure p_{in}, the pressure drop over the reactor Δp and the approach temperatures for the two reactions $T_{ap,SMR}$ and $T_{ap,WGS}$. Due to the fact that we use an adiabatic reactor the molar flow rate has no influence on the resulting outlet temperature, pressure or gas compositions, hence the total inlet flow was set at 100 mol/h.

The outlet of the prereformer is fully described if we predict the T_{out}, p_{out} and flow rates of all components. A possible solution strategy is to predict the outlet temperature and the two extents of reaction, ξ_{SMR} and ξ_{WGS}.

The outlet flow rates of all components are then calculated using ξ_j:

$$\dot{n}_{i,out} = \dot{n}_{i,in} + \sum_j v_{i,j} \cdot \xi_j \tag{5}$$

with the stoichiometric number v, and the indices j for reactions and i for components.

The outlet pressure is calculated directly from the inputs as:

$$p_{out} = p_{in} + \Delta p \tag{6}$$

Based on these conditions, a prereformer simulation in Aspen V9 using Peng-Robinson equation of state was built as a data generator for the surrogate model development.

3. Computational Methodology

3.1. Data Generation using Design of Experiments

For this application, a training dataset with 100,000 sample points was generated. To construct the design of experiments (DoE), input variables were divided into two groups and their ranges were determined considering wide operating conditions as follows:

i) Dry gas composition: x_{CH_4} [0.44, 0.98], x_{CO} [0.00, 0.12], x_{H_2} [0.00, 0.12],

                            x_{CO_2} [0.00, 0.12], x_{N_2} [0.00, 0.20]

ii) Process conditions: T_{in} [350, 600] °C, p_{in} [10, 50] barg, Δp [0, 5] bar,

                         $T_{ap,SMR}$ [-50, 50] °C, $T_{ap,WGS}$ [-50, 50] °C, S/C [1, 3]

For both of these variable groups, a separate design was created using JMP 14 software and the two sets were combined. A space filling latin hypercube design with 25,000 runs was generated for the process conditions ii), which was followed by 10,000 runs using a space filling mixture design for the dry gas composition i). Consequently 100,000 data points were created by random combinations of both variable groups.

The test set consists of 10,000 points. Data generation differs slightly from the training set, conducted this time in Matlab. For the dry gas compositions, a grid sampling using 0.5 % steps was implemented. Among the resulting 397,169 possible gas mixtures, 10,000 points were randomly selected. As for the operating variables, we randomly selected 10,000 points within the variable ranges. Finally both groups were combined.

The simulation results were calculated in Aspen and stored in Excel. After accounting for the convergence of Aspen, the training and test sets contained 99,982 and 9,993 data points, respectively. While both sets cover the same range for model input variables, their statistical representativeness was ensured by randomness.

3.2. Model Development

The selected model structure in JMP 14 was artificial neural networks (ANN) with one hidden layer, where the K-fold cross validation method was employed with k=4. As a preliminary investigation, the model training was conducted using 25, 50 and 100 nodes, and resulting RMSE values were observed. In addition to RMSE, the model robustness was also monitored via observing the fraction of predicted outcomes within a specified error range. All three target variables, i.e. the outlet temperature and the two extents of reaction, were modeled using all input variables following a multi-input single-output (MISO) structure. It is notable that, thanks to the prediction of the extents of reaction, the mass balance around the reactor is ensured to be closed.

4. Results and Discussion

As mentioned earlier, in order to have a full description of the prereformer reactor outlet, the outlet temperature, and the two extents of reaction for SMR and WGS are to be predicted. However, in this section, the reactor outlet concentrations are presented to allow a more tangible interpretation of the results, since the extents are relatively harder to be interpreted as they are intermediate variables by nature.

4.1. Model Selection

In this part, modeling results illustrating both accuracy and robustness are tabulated. Table 1 focuses on the model accuracy with RMSE values. It can be seen that the training accuracy is significantly improved with increasing number of nodes, therefore the 100-nodes model is chosen for further investigation. It is observed that RMSE values for test set are also comparable with the training results, showing a good predictive behavior. Considering test set, the largest error is in H_2 concentration prediction with 0.0056 %-points, which can be considered as an acceptable deviation for a practical application.

Table 1: Model accuracy - RMSE values for outlet temperature and compositions

Number of nodes	T_{out} (° C)	CH4 (pp)	CO (pp)	CO2 (pp)	H2 (pp)	H2O (pp)	N2 (pp)
25 (Train)	0.0867	0.0034	0.0036	0.0037	0.0080	0.0065	0.0003
50 (Train)	0.0463	0.0016	0.0017	0.0016	0.0035	0.0028	0.0001
100 (Train)	0.0326	0.0014	0.0010	0.0010	0.0029	0.0023	0.0001
100 (Test)	0.0345	0.0027	0.0010	0.0015	0.0056	0.0042	0.0001

Table 2 concentrates on the robustness of the selected 100-node model, tabulating the fraction of data points predicted within a specific error range. For instance, the temperature is predicted for 99.90 % of the test dataset with an error less than 0.3 °C. The most significant error is observed in H_2 (as in Table 1), which can be explained by the error propagation of ξ_{SMR} on the amount of H_2 produced (i.e. $v_{H_2} = 3$ for SMR reaction).

Table 2: Model robustness - Fraction of data points within specified error range

	Outlet Temperature		x_{CO}		x_{H2}	
Criteria	< 0.3 K	< 0.1 K	< 0.02 pp	< 0.01 pp	< 0.02 pp	< 0.01 pp
100 (Train)	99.97	98.07	100.00	99.97	99.89	98.79
100 (Test)	99.90	98.17	100.00	99.99	99.86	98.82

4.2. Modeling Results : Outlet Temperature and Concentrations

In this section, first the residual plot of the outlet temperature model based on the selected 100-node ANN is depicted, both for training (Figure 1.a) and test sets (Figure 1.b). It can be seen that the residual distribution has no systematic dependency, and that the predictive capability of the outlet temperature model is very good.

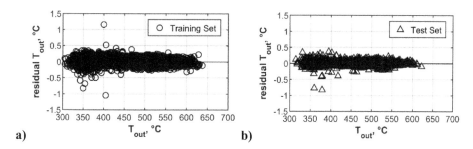

a)   b)

Figure 1: Residual values for outlet temperature - training (a) and test set (b)

Figure 2 shows the residual plot for x_{CO}^{out} values as a representative outlet concentration. Similar to outlet temperature, it can be seen that the prediction capability of the x_{CO}^{out} model is good, with no systematic deviation.

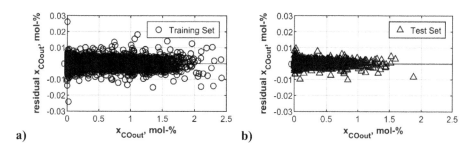

a)   b)

Figure 2: Residual values for x_{CO}^{out} - training (a) and test set (b)

Although a good overall prediction capability is achieved and the closing of mass balance is ensured, one deficit of the current model is that the predicted CO outlet concentration can be negative. This has been observed for 0.11 % of data points in the test set.

4.3. Computing Time

Based on the computing time measurements throughout this study, a comparable call in Aspen (avoiding the communication overhead) for a bunch of 100 simulations takes 0.54 seconds, whereas a function call based on a non-optimal implementation of the resulting 100-nodes ANN in Matlab takes 0.00014 seconds on average. It can be concluded with this preliminary investigation that a speed-up of ca. 40 was reached.

5. Conclusion and Outlook

In this work we showed a practical application of surrogate modeling for a prereformer reactor, based on the results of an Aspen Plus flowsheet simulation. Three ANN models with single layer were developed to predict the target variables, i.e. the outlet temperature and the extents of the two reactions, namely SMR and WGS. This modeling strategy enabled to fully describe the reactor outlet conditions including gas compositions with a high accuracy and less computing time. The work showed the potential of surrogate modeling to achieve improved performance for process simulations in design and operation optimization problems. Further improvements to increase model quality are possible via e.g. customization of model development, and adaptive sampling methodology. It is also anticipated to use other machine learning methods, e.g. Kriging, as well as to extend the modeled unit operations and to combine them for efficient deployment of applications, such as data reconciliation, and real-time optimization.

References

N. Asprion, R. Böttcher, R. Pack, M. Stavrou, J. Höller, J. Schwientek, M. Bortz, 2019, Gray-box Modeling for the Optimization of Chemical Processes, Chem. Ing. Tech.. 91(3): 305–313.

Chemie.de, 2019, 17 Mio. EUR für die künstliche Intelligenz in Prozessindustrie, https://www.chemie.de/news/1162875/17-mio-eur-fuer-die-kuenstliche-intelligenz-in-der-prozessindustrie.html?pk_campaign=ca0259&WT.mc_id=ca0259

Les Echos, 2019, eCAC40: chez Air Liquide, Le numérique a changé d'échelle, https://business.lesechos.fr/directions-generales/strategie/transformation/0602026569459-ecac40-chez-air-liquide-le-numerique-a-change-d-echelle-332389.php

K. McBride, K. Sundmacher, 2019, Overview of Surrogate Modeling in Chemical Process Engineering, Chem. Ing. Tech., 91(3): 228-239.

C. Nentwich, S. Engell, 2019, Surrogate modeling of phase equilibrium calculations using adaptive sampling, Computers and Chemical Engineering, pp. 204-217.

OSIsoft, 2019, How Air Liquide leverages on PI technologies to optimize its operations - SIO.Optim program, Presentation at PI World Conference, San Francisco, https://www.osisoft.com/presentations/how-air-liquide-leverages-on-pi-technologies-to-optimize-its-operations---sio-optim-program/

R. Schmidt, E. Örs, A. Chattot, 2017, Prediction of Catalyst Lifetime: Example MT-Shift Reactor, Presentation at 50. Jahrestreffen Deutscher Katalytiker, Weimar (available on demand).

T. Sasi, M. Mighani, E. Örs, R. Tawani, M. Gräbner, 2018, Prediction of ash fusion behavior from coal ash composition for entrained-flow gasification, Fuel Processing Technology, 176: 64-75.

V. Venkatasubramanian, 2019, The promise of artificial intelligence in chemical engineering: Is it here, finally?, AIChE J., 65(2):466–78.

Sauro Pierucci, Flavio Manenti, Giulia Bozzano, Davide Manca (Eds.)
Proceedings of the 30th European Symposium on Computer Aided Process Engineering
(ESCAPE30), May 24-27, 2020, Milano, Italy. © 2020 Elsevier B.V. All rights reserved.
http://dx.doi.org/10.1016/B978-0-12-823377-1.50089-6

Development of a Microkinetic Model for the CO_2 Methanation with an Automated Reaction Mechanism Generator

Bjarne Kreitz[a,b,*], Gregor D. Wehinger[a], C. Franklin Goldsmith[b], Thomas Turek[a]

[a] Institute of Chemical and Electrochemical Engineering, Clausthal University of Technology, Leibnizstr. 17, 38678 Clausthal-Zellerfeld, Germany
[b] School of Engineering, Brown University, 184 Hope Street, RI 02912 Providence, USA
kreitz@icvt.tu-clausthal.de

Abstract

The automated reaction mechanism generator (RMG) is used to investigate the methanation of CO_2 on the Ni(111) and Ni(211) surface. Linear scaling relations are applied for the thermochemistry of the adsorbates, which are compared to state-of-the-art electronic structure calculations and show a reasonable predictability. RMG discovers nearly the same amount of species and reactions for both facets. However, a reaction path analysis in a reactor simulation shows that the reaction pathways on both surfaces differ significantly, which is caused by the difference in the binding energy of the adsorbates. Reactor simulations reveal a lower methane production rate compared to experiments obtained in a Berty reactor with a Ni/Al_2O_3 catalyst, which is a result of a high surface coverage with CO^* and demands, therefore, the inclusion of a coverage dependent heat of formation of the adsorbates.

Keywords: Methanation, Microkinetic modeling, Rate-based algorithm

1. Introduction

The hydrogenation of carbon dioxide with hydrogen to methane in the Power-to-Gas process is a crucial method to tackle the requirements of long-term energy storage and the production of sustainable natural gas (Götz et al., 2016). The knowledge of the kinetics of all elementary steps of the methanation mechanism, the microkinetics, is the key to develop more active catalysts and to describe the transient operation of the reactor, which is caused by the volatile feed supply. Simulation studies have shown that drastic variations in the hot-spot temperature and productivity are possible during dynamic operation (Kreitz et al., 2019a).

However, the theoretical construction of a microkinetic model from scratch is a long process, requiring substantial computational resources to determine binding energies and to elucidate the pathway with the lowest energy barrier on a crystal facet. An alternative approach is the automated reaction mechanism generation (Gao et al., 2016). This is a promising method for the fast creation of microkinetic models by relying on databases and parameter estimation methods (Gao et al., 2016). RMG has extensively and successfully been used for the development of gas-phase mechanisms. In the work of Goldsmith and West (2017), a functionality for heterogeneously catalyzed reactions was added to RMG, which is denoted as RMG-Cat. This extension to heterogeneous systems is based on scaling relations for the thermochemistry of the adsorbates and the reaction rate expressions (Mazeau et al. 2019). Goldsmith and West (2107) showed that RMG-Cat could rediscover a mechanism for dry reforming of methane as predicted by sophisticated experiments.

In this study, we use RMG-Cat to determine the mechanism of the CO_2 methanation for the Ni(111) and Ni(211) surface, which are discussed as the active facets for the methanation reaction (Andersson et al., 2008). The microkinetics are evaluated in a Berty reactor model and compared to experimental results.

2. Methods

RMG-Cat determines the mechanism based on reaction libraries and the estimation of thermodynamic properties of the adsorbates (Goldsmith and West, 2017). Specific rules for the evaluation of reaction rates are assigned to the reaction families, such as Brønsted-Evans-Polanyi (BEP) relations, for the determination of activation energies. Thermodynamic properties of the adsorbates depend on the metal surface and are therefore computed with linear scaling relations (Abild-Pedersen et al., 2007). The thermochemistry of unknown species can be automatically estimated by the method proposed by Goldsmith (2012), which enables the algorithm to consider all possible reactions and intermediates. For the generation of a mechanism, it is necessary to specify the temperature T, pressure p, active surface area a, the surface site density Γ the initial mole fractions of the educts x^0 and binding energies for C, H, and O for linear scaling relations. Moreover, it is necessary to specify starting species for the core mechanism. RMG-Cat estimates all possible reactions between the core species and evaluates the rates in a batch reactor simulation. If a generated species exceeds a certain threshold, this species is included in the core mechanism along with the reaction through which it is formed. Other species and reactions are discarded and stored in an edge mechanism. With the new species in the core, RMG-Cat starts over again and predicts new reactions and species. This loop breaks when a previously defined termination criterion, e.g. reaction time or conversion (X) of a reactant, is reached. Table 1 shows the input parameters for RMG-Cat, which are used for the generation of the microkinetic model.

Table 1: Parameters used for the generation of the methanation mechanism for both Ni facets with RMG-Cat.

Parameter	Value
$T\,/\,K$	573
$p\,/\,bar$	1
$\Gamma\,/\,mol\;cm^{-2}$	$2.9 \cdot 10^{-9}$
$x_{H_2}^0\,/-$	0.8
$x_{CO_2}^0\,/-$	0.2
$X_{CO_2}\,/-$	0.8
$a\,/\,m^{-1}$	$1 \cdot 10^5$

Density functional theory (DFT) calculations for the adsorbates on the Ni surface are calculated with the Vienna ab-initio Simulation Package (Kresse, Furthmüller, 1996a, Kresse, Furthmüller, 1996b) in the Atomic Simulation Environment using plane-wave pseudopotentials. The single-point energy for the Ni(111) [Ni(211)] surface is computed for a p(3x3) [p(1x3)] supercell with 4 [12] layers of Ni atoms where the 2 [6] top layers are relaxed together with the adsorbate with a cut-off energy of 400 eV and the usage of the RPBE exchange-correlation functional. The Brillouin zone is sampled with a (3x3x1) [(4x3x1)] Monkhorst-Pack mesh and the structure is relaxed until all forces are below 0.02 eV A^{-1}. Thermodynamic properties for the adsorbates are calculated based on the harmonic oscillator approximation. Further details can be found in the work of Blondal et al. (2019). The model generation is assisted by steady-state and transient methanation experiments carried out in a Berty reactor with an 11 wt.-% Ni/Al$_2$O$_3$ catalyst. For details on the setup, refer to previous work (Kreitz et al., 2019b). Generated microkinetics are evaluated in a reactor model of the Berty reactor, which is implemented in Cantera and based on the governing equations of an isothermal continuously stirred tank reactor (CSTR).

3. Results and Discussion

Binding energies obtained from the DFT calculations in Table 2 are in good agreement with literature values (Catapan et al., 2012, Blaylock et al., 2009). The binding energies of H and O remain merely unchanged by the facet, but carbon binds stronger to the Ni catalyst in the 4-fold hollow site on the (211) surface. Additional DFT calculations for various adsorbates on the (111) surface are performed to determine if the linear scaling relations work accordingly. For the (211) facet, additional adsorbates are computed based on literature values (Andersen et al., 2017, Medford et al., 2014).

Table 2: Zero-point corrected binding energies for C, O, and H on Ni(111) and Ni(211) with adsorption position in brackets and referenced according to Blondal et al. (2019).

	Ni(111)	Ni(211)
C	- 6.44 eV (hcp)	- 7.33eV (4f)
H	- 2.76 eV (fcc)	- 2.76 eV (bridge)
O	- 4.70 eV (fcc)	- 4.88 eV (bridge)

Thermodynamic properties of the adsorbate are scaled from a Pt(111) and a Pt(211) database with the binding energies from Table 2. The Pt(111) database is based on the work of Blondal et al. (2019), while the Pt(211) database is created from the work of Medford et al. (2014) and Andersen et al. (2017). The results of the linear scaling predictions are displayed in Figure 1 in the form of a parity plot for the standard heat of formation ($\Delta_f H$) of the adsorbates.

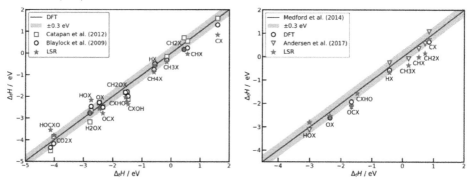

Figure 1: Parity plot of the standard heat of formation of the adsorbates predicted by linear scaling relations for Ni(111) and Ni(211) and the values calculated from the DFT calculations.

The scaling based on the (111) surface is relatively accurate, with a mean absolute error (MAE) of 0.41 eV to the heat of formation from the DFT calculation and 0.22 eV to the values from Blaylock et al. (2009). Values from Blaylock et al. (2009) and Catapan et al. (2012) are also depicted to illustrate that there is also a distinct difference between the DFT calculations, which is caused by the different pseudopotentials and exchange-correlation functionals. For the thermochemistry of the (211) surface, the values from Medford et al. (2014) are arbitrarily chosen as the reference, which results in a MAE of 0.33 eV. In conclusion, RMG-Cat can accurately estimate the thermochemistry of the adsorbates of the investigated Ni facets.

For the conditions mentioned in Table 1, RMG-Cat discovers 28 [27] species and 47 [38] reactions for the Ni(111) [Ni(211)] facet. The model generation takes approx. 2 min on an Intel i7-8565U processor. In the edge mechanism, RMG-Cat stores an additional 55 species and 76 reactions. The mechanism contains 15 [15] reactions from a library for steam reforming on Ni from Delgado et al. (2015) and the rest of the reactions is determined from reaction families such as dissociation (7 [8]) , van-der-Waals adsorption (5 [5]), and abstraction reactions (18 [11]). Two [one] reactions are discovered from a newly implemented family for the dissociation of a molecule in the "beta" position, which considers the formation of COH^* from CO^* since it is discussed as the rate-limiting step by Andersson et al. (2008), with BEP parameters from Sutton and Vlachos (2015). The generated microkinetic model is evaluated with a model of the Berty reactor. Figure 2 shows a reaction path analysis of this model when tracking carbon.

Ni(111)

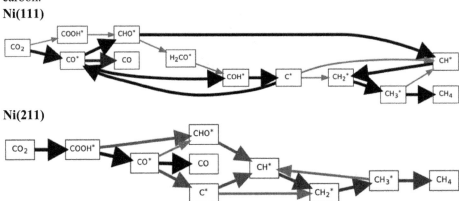

Ni(211)

Figure 2: Reaction path analysis for the steady-state CO_2 methanation on the Ni(111) (upper) and Ni(211) (lower) surface. The thickness of the arrow illustrates the reaction rate. The reaction path analysis is conducted with a model of the Berty reactor in Cantera. *Conditions: T=400 °C, p=5 bar, m_{cat}=0.3 g, a_{cat}=10 m² g⁻¹, V=299 mL$_N$ min⁻¹, V_R=88 mL.*

On the Ni(111) facet CO_2 adsorbs via a dissociative adsorption and CO^* is further hydrogenated to CHO^* and COH^*. The unassisted dissociation of CO^* to surface carbon does not proceed with a sufficient rate at these conditions. It is interesting to note that COH^* decomposes to C^*, which is then again oxidized to CO^*. Carbon monoxide also desorbs in significant amounts from the surface, which is contradictory to the experiment because the Ni/Al$_2$O$_3$ catalyst shows a high selectivity towards methane. The dominant pathway at these conditions passes over CHO^*, which undergoes an O^* abstraction reaction. The methylene species is further hydrogenated to methane. A carboxyl route ($COOH^*$) contributes only to a small extent to the overall rate on the (111) surface. However, CO_2 adsorbs with the assistance of hydrogen on Ni(211) and forms COOH*, which dissociates to OH* and CO*. On the (211) surface, CO* dissociates to C*, because of a reduced activation energy for the dissociation by the stepped surface. Figure 3 (a) compares the methane yield from steady-state experiments to the simulation results, obtained from a model of the Berty reactor with the generated microkinetics, and the corresponding equilibrium yield.

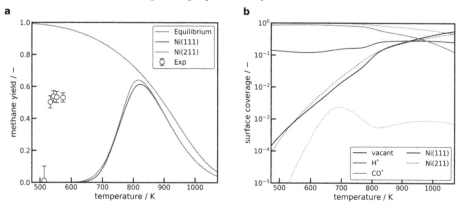

Figure 3: (a) Comparison of the steady-state results from the Berty reactor simulations with the generated microkinetic models for the two surfaces and experimental data from an 11 wt.-% Ni/Al$_2$O$_3$ catalyst. (b) Simulated steady-state surface coverages of the most abundant adsorbates. *Conditions:* $p=5$ bar, $m_{cat}=0.3$ g, $a_{cat}=10$ m^2 g^{-1}, $V=299$ mL$_N$ min^{-1}, $V_R=88$ mL, *Feed:* $x_{CO_2}=13.81$ %, $x_{H_2}=55.25$ %, $x_{He}=7.69$ %, $x_{Ar}=23.2$ %.

At a temperature of 573 K, a methane yield of 53 % is measured in the experiment. The microkinetic model, however, shows a low yield, with a methane production only at temperatures above 650 K. At lower temperatures, the most abundant adsorbate on the (111) facet is CO*, which prohibits H$_2$ from adsorbing. This results in an extremely low reaction rate and the hydrogen deficiency leads to a formation of CO, as shown in the reaction path analysis. At high temperatures, does the CO* coverage decrease, which allows the H* concentration to increase, resulting in a high methane formation rate. An H* covered (211) surface is predicted due to an estimated lower CO* binding energy. This surface needs further investigation because of the sparsely populated thermochemical database. The comparison to the calculated equilibrium composition shows that the predicted methane yield does not exceed the thermodynamic limit, which indicates a thermodynamic consistent microkinetic model. For the improvement of the microkinetics, it is necessary to include coverage effects, e.g. coverage dependent heat of formation of the adsorbates, to increase the low-temperature reaction rates (Lausche et al., 2013).

Conclusions

It was shown that generating a microkinetic model for the CO$_2$ methanation with RMG-Cat is possible and results in a mechanism, which is in good agreement with mechanisms discussed in the literature. The usage of the generated microkinetics in a model of the Berty reactor results in a low CH$_4$ formation rate. Analysis of the results reveals that the surface is mostly covered by one species (CO*, H*) at low temperatures. Consequently, coverage effects need to be considered to bridge the gap between experiments and simulation. In future work, sensitivity analysis will be applied to the generated mechanism to explore the most important elementary reactions, for which rate parameters can then be refined based on transition-state theory calculations.

Acknowledgments

Bjarne Kreitz gratefully acknowledges financial support from the German academic exchange service (DAAD) for a research stay at Brown University in the group of Franklin Goldsmith.

References

F. Abild-Pedersen; J. Greeley, F. Studt, J. Rossmeisl, T. R. Munter, P. G. Moses, E. Skúlason, T. Bligaard, J. K. Nørskov, 2007, Scaling properties of adsorption energies for hydrogen-containing molecules on transition-metal surfaces, Phys. Rev. Lett., 99, 1, 16105

M. Andersen, C. P. Plaisance, K. Reuter, 2017, Assessment of mean-field microkinetic models for CO methanation on stepped metal surfaces using accelerated kinetic Monte Carlo, J. Chem. Phys., 147, 15, 152705

M. P. Andersson, F. Abild-Pedersen, I. N. Remediakis, T. Bligaard, G. Jones, J. Engæk, O. Lytken, S. Horch, J. H. Nielsen, J. Sehested, J. R. Rostrup-Nielsen, J. K. Nørskov, I. Chorkendorff, (2008), Structure sensitivity of the methanation reaction: H_2-induced CO dissociation on nickel surfaces, J. Catal., 255, 6-19

D. W. Blaylock, T. Ogura, W. H. Green, G. J. O. Beran, 2009, Computational Investigation of Thermochemistry and Kinetics of Steam Methane Reforming on Ni(111) under Realistic Conditions, J. Phys. Chem. C, 113, 12, 4898–4908

K. Blondal, J. Jelic, E. Mazeau, F. Studt, R. H. West, C. F. Goldsmith, 2019, Computer-Generated Kinetics for Coupled Heterogeneous/Homogeneous Systems: A Case Study in Catalytic Combustion of Methane on Platinum, Ind. Eng. Chem. Res., 58, 38, 17682–17691

R. C. Catapan, A. A. M. Oliveira, Y. Chen, D. G. Vlachos, 2012, DFT Study of the Water–Gas Shift Reaction and Coke Formation on Ni(111) and Ni(211) Surfaces, J. Phys. Chem. C, 116, 38, 20281–20291

K. Delgado, L. Maier, S. Tischer, A. Zellner, H. Stotz, O. Deutschmann, 2015, Surface Reaction Kinetics of Steam- and CO_2-Reforming as Well as Oxidation of Methane over Nickel-Based Catalysts, Catalysts, 5, 2, 871–904

W. C. Gao, J. W. Allen, W. H. Green, R. H. West, 2016, Reaction Mechanism Generator: Automatic construction of chemical kinetic mechanisms, Comput. Phys. Commun., 203, 212–225

C. F. Goldsmith, 2012, Estimating the Thermochemistry of Adsorbates Based Upon Gas-Phase Properties, Top. Catal., 55, 5-6, 366–375

C. F. Goldsmith, R. H. West, 2017, Automatic Generation of Microkinetic Mechanisms for Heterogeneous Catalysis, J. Phys. Chem. C, 121, 18, 9970–9981

M. Götz, J. Lefebvre, F. Mörs, A. McDaniel Koch, F. Graf, S. Bajohr, R. Reimert, T. Kolb, 2016, Renewable Power-to-Gas: A technological and economic review. Renew. Energy, 85, 1371–1390

A. C. Lausche, A. J. Medford, T. S. Khan, Y. Xu, T. Bligaard, F. Abild-Pedersen, J. K. Nørskov, F. Studt, 2013, On the effect of coverage-dependent adsorbate-adsorbate interactions for the CO methanation on transition metal surfaces, J. Catal., 307, 275-282

E. Mazeau, P. Satupte, K. Blondal, C. F. Goldsmith, R. H. West, 2019, Catalytic Partial Oxidation of Methane Using Linear Scaling Relationships and Sensitivity Analysis in RMG, submitted to ChemSystemsChem

A. J. Medford, A. C. Lausche, F. Abild-Pedersen, B. Temel, N. C. Schjødt, J K. Nørskov, F. Studt, 2014, Activity and Selectivity Trends in Synthesis Gas Conversion to Higher Alcohols, Top. Catal., 57, 1-4, 135–142

B. Kreitz, G. D. Wehinger, T. Turek, 2019a, Dynamic simulation of the CO_2 methanation in a micro-structured fixed-bed reactor, Chem. Eng. Sci., 195, 541-552

B. Kreitz, J. Friedland, R. Güttel, G. D. Wehinger, T. Turek, 2019b, Dynamic Methanation of CO_2 - Effect of Concentration Forcing, Chem. Ing. Tech., 166, 4, 276

G. Kresse, J. Furthmüller, 1996a, Efficient iterative schemes for ab initio total-energy calculations using a plane-wave basis set, Phys. Rev. B: Condens. Matter, 54, 16, 11169–11186

G. Kresse, J. Furthmüller, 1996b, Efficiency of ab-initio total energy calculations for metals and semiconductors using a plane-wave basis set. Comput. Mater. Sci., 6, 1, 15–50

J. E. Sutton, D. G. Vlachos, 2015, Ethanol Activation on Closed-Packed Surfaces, Ind. Eng. Chem. Res., 54, 16, 4213–4225

Sauro Pierucci, Flavio Manenti, Giulia Bozzano, Davide Manca (Eds.)
Proceedings of the 30th European Symposium on Computer Aided Process Engineering
(ESCAPE30), May 24-27, 2020, Milano, Italy. © 2020 Elsevier B.V. All rights reserved.
http://dx.doi.org/10.1016/B978-0-12-823377-1.50090-2

Custom-made Temporomandibular Joint Mechanical Simulation: Different Fixation Pattern

Anita G. Mazzocco,[a*] André L. Jardini,[b] Elifas L. Nunes,[c] Rubens Maciel Filho[a,b]

[a]University of Campinas (Unicamp), Campinas, ZP: 13083-852, SP, Brazil [b]National Institute of Biofabrication (INCT BIOFABRIS), Campinas, ZP: 13083-852, SP, Brazil
[c]Medical School, São Paulo State University (Unesp), Botucatu, ZP: 18618-687, SP, Brazil
anitagaia.mazzocco@gmail.com

Abstract

Nowadays Computed Aided Design (CAD) and additive manufacture technologies are widely used in orthopedic field. These technologies allow to build anatomic 3D model in CAD software from tomographic data and then to fabricate a replacement device matching patient specific anatomy. Temporomandibular joint (TMJ) is small size joint and its replacement surgery is complicated and requires specialized surgeons. Thus CAD allows surgery planning and custom-made TMJ prosthesis developing. This study shows a pre-operative step that is to simulate physiological mechanical loading of TMJ replacement device in Ansys software with the purpose of testing device mechanical resistance and verifying osseointegration. Correct fitting is the primary stability which is necessary for osseointegration process to take place and so replacement device gain long-term stability. Therefore different pattern of screw fixation are tested and the effect in terms of strain and stress generated is evaluated to predict post-implant mechanical behaviour.

Keywords: temporomandibular joint, custom-made, computer aided design, mechanical simulation, Ansys.

1. Introduction

Medical imaging was used initially for diagnostic purposes, nowadays with the advent of Computer Aided Design (CAD) technology and 3d printing, the health care is revolutionizing. Thus, Computed Tomography (CT) and Magnetic Resonance Imaging (MRI) provide detailed anatomic images to be processed with CAD software to create a three-dimensional computational model. This model allows surgeons to see patient anatomy in more concrete way and to plan and simulate surgery, not only in virtual view but also on physical 3d printed model (Altobelli et al. 1993; Liu et al., 2006). In orthopedics field, additive manufacturing provides customized surgical instrument, intraoperative guidance and custom-made implant production (Eltorai et al., 2015). Temporomandibular Joint (TMJ) is characterized by complex kinematics, small dimensions and difficult surgery that needs specialized surgeon. Thus, CAD and 3D printing technologies can be considered a relevant approach to investigate better replacement solutions. TMJ replacement device is developed to mimics TMJ in function and form, so it has to be able to withstand bite loading, imitate joint kinematics, be biocompatible and be osseointegrated in surrounding anatomical structure. To osseointegration occur, primary stability is necessary, so correct fitting during surgery is a requisite for long-term stability. This study aims to analyze the effect on mechanical behavior of TMJ custom-made prosthesis, manufactured from tomographic data, of five different pattern of screw fixation, by Finite Element Analysis (FEA).

2. Materials and methods

FEA is performed using Ansys Workbench (Swanson Analysis, Canonsburg, PA, USA), TMJ mandible model is constructed by CT-data and TMJ condylar prosthesis is created by SolidWorks (Dassault Systèmes, SolidWorks Corporation) and Magics (Materialise, Belgium). Mandible finite element model is composed by linear tetrahedral elements and condylar prosthesis by linear hexagonal element. Whole model is formed by 40030 nodes and 187931 elements. Mandible is modeled as cortical bone characterized by isotropic and linear elastic material (Hsu et al. 2011) with 13 GPa elastic modulus and 0.3 Poisson ratio. TMJ condylar replacement device is implanted on the right mandibular ramus. Since we want to simulate a prosthesis manufactured with 3d printing, the material used is a titanium alloy (Ti6Al4V) and properties derived from mechanical characterization of Ti6Al4V ELI produced by DMLS (Direct Metal Laser Sintering) technology (Longhitano et al. 2018). Thus, condylar prosthesis properties are 110 GPa of elastic modulus and 0.3 Poisson ratio. Fixation system is composed by five cylindrical screw of 2.7 mm diameter, made with commercial Ti6Al4V ELI (120 GPa elastic modulus and 0.3 Poisson ratio).

2.1. Muscular force and boundary conditions

FEA realizes a static structural analysis of TMJ replacement system subjected to bite loading to calculate mechanical response in terms of stress and strain produced. Thus, bite loading is simulated applying muscular force of six masticatory muscle on virtual model. The model is fully constrained at condyle extremities and vertical movement, along z axis, is blocked at incisors (Huang et al. 2015). Screw contact is modeled as bonded to simulate bi-cortical locking fixation system and bone-implant contact as frictional with a friction coefficient of 0.3 (Shirazi-Adl et al., 1993). Muscular forces magnitude and directions are shown in Table 1 and they derive from validated model (Korioth and Hannam 1994; Huang et al. 2015). In this study unilateral bite on Right Molar (RMOL) and Left Molar (LMOL) is simulated blocking the movement respectively on right and left molar. Figure 1.A shows whole finite element model and the number of screw positions. The different fixation pattern tested are the following: Pattern 1) 1, 2, 5, 9, 10; Pattern 2) 1, 2, 4, 7, 10; Pattern 3) 1, 3, 6, 9, 10; Pattern 4) 2, 3, 4, 7, 10; Pattern 5) 1, 2, 3, 7, 10.

Table 1. Muscular Forces. The following values refer to forces applied to right mandibular ramus; the corresponding forces on left are obtained by inverting x-direction forces.

	RMOL			LMOL		
	Fx	Fy	Fz	Fx	Fy	Fz
Superficial Masseter	-28.38	-57.44	121.32	-23.65	-47.87	101.10
Deep Masseter	-32.08	21.03	44.53	-26.73	17.53	37.11
Medial Pterygoid	71.36	-54.62	116.14	50.97	-39.02	82.96
Anterior Temporal	-17.19	-5.07	113.96	-13.65	-4.03	90.54
Middle Temporal	-13.94	31.55	52.81	-14.16	32.03	53.61
Posterior Temporal	-9.28	38.14	21.14	-6.13	25.21	13.98

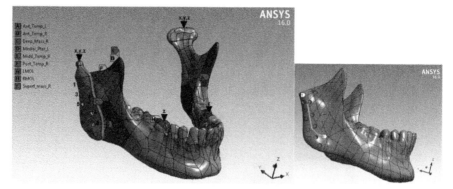

Figure 1. A) Finite Element Model with muscular forces and boundary conditions; and screw position number. B) Control line: Ansys collects strain variations on this control line from 1 to 2.

3. Result and discussion

The aim of this study is to analyze how different positions of fixation screws influence mechanical behavior of TMJ replacement subjected to right and left unilateral bite. Thus, results collected in Ansys are equivalent Von Mises stress on TMJ condylar prosthesis and distribution of minimum principal elastic strain on mandibular bone. According to previous studies (Van Loon et al. 1998; Huang et al. 2015; Mazzocco et al. 2019), unilateral bites are more critical loading cases than bilateral bite. Unilateral bite causes an overloading on contralateral side, also called balancing side, of about two times clenching side. Results of equivalent stress calculated on TMJ condylar prosthesis shows that maximum stress in LMOL case are about four times greater than maximum stress in RMOL (Fig. 2-3), moreover, distribution of strain collected in LMOL is almost twice the RMOL (Fig. 3-4). Distribution of stress on prosthesis in all cases simulated does not reach material yield stress (Ackland et al., 2015) and presents that maximum occurs at first screw holes: in RMOL, stress is concentrated on positions number 1-5, instead in LMOL simulation it is concentrated on position screws 1-3. Both in RMOL and LMOL cases, Pattern 1 generates the minor loading of 42.5 MPa and 182.7 MPa, respectively. The major loading in case of bite on working side (RMOL) is found with Pattern 3, instead in case of bite on balancing side (LMOL) Pattern 4 produces major stress.

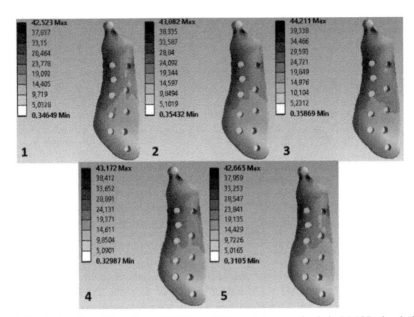

Figure 2. Equivalent Von Mises Stress [MPa] on TMJ condylar prosthesis in RMOL simulation.

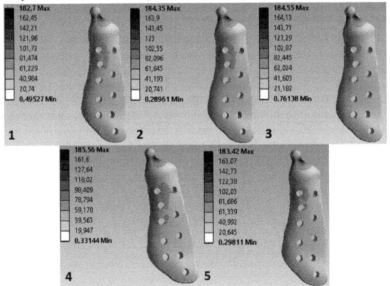

Figure 3. Equivalent Von Mises Stress [MPa] on TMJ condylar prosthesis in LMOL simulation.
Distribution of Minimum Principal Elastic Strain in case of RMOL (Fig. 4) on
mandibular bone in contact with prosthesis shows that closest to condyle resection
Pattern 1, Pattern 2 and Pattern 3 present the smallest strain peak of 1.1e-4 mm/mm.
These patterns are characterized by initial screws fixed on positions 1 and 2. Pattern 3
produces two strain peaks of 1.95e-4 and 1.6e-4 mm/mm caused by screws 1 and 3;
Pattern 4 (without any screw in position 1) presents major initial strain of 2.3e-4
mm/mm. In Pattern 3 and Pattern 5, the strain increase at 10 mm from point 1 of control
line is caused by screw number 6 and 7 without any screw fixed in position 4 or 5.
Unlike RMOL, Figure 4 shows maximum strain occurring at 10 mm on control line of

4e-4 mm/mm. This maximum is reached by Pattern 3 and Pattern 5, probably due to the absence of screw in position 4, 5. Similarly to RMOL, Pattern 4 produces the largest strain of 2.7e-4 mm/mm closest to condyle resection.

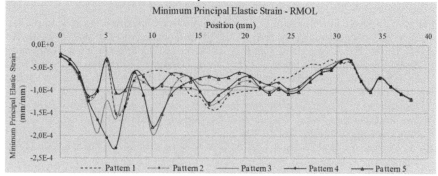

Figure 4. Minimum Principal Elastic Strain collected on control line in RMOL simulation.

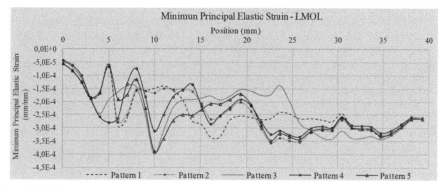

Figure 5. Minimum Principal Elastic Strain collected on control line in LMOL simulation.

4. Conclusion

Literature of FEA of TMJ fixation screw offers the following findings: minimum of three staggered screws provides stable fixation and good strain distribution (Hsu et al., 2011), and maximum stresses occurred at the first screw hole closest to condyle resection (Kashi et al., 2010). According to results collected, this study reveals that to solve overload problem on the first screw it should require to insert a screw laterally to the first one than inferiorly and that staggered distribution of screw is preferable because it distributes strain along bone. Thus, considering that TMJ prosthesis does not run any failure risk and therefore focusing on strain distribution, Pattern 2 can be considered biomechanically the best. Moreover, Roberts theory (Roberts et al., 2004) of bone remodeling explains that dynamic loading included within 0.2–2.5e-3 mm/mm produces bone remodeling and if strain peaks are lowest than 0.2e-3 mm/mm bone undergoes atrophy and if strain peaks exceed 2.5e-3 mm/mm it undergoes bone hypertrophy. Considering that mastication cycle by which TMJ is physiologically loaded, is a combination of bilateral and unilateral bite and that LMOL result are included in remodeling range, it might be considered that in this study TMJ replacement with fixation Pattern 2 should undergo osseointegration in mandibular bone.

This FEA result shows how CAD technology is considered revolutionizing the medical field because it allows planning a customized surgery decreasing the risk of TMJ replacement failure and optimizing the surgery time.

References

Altobelli, D. E., Kikinis, R., Mulliken, J. B., Cline, H., Lorensen, W., Jolesz, F. (1993), *Computer-Assisted Three-Dimensional Planning in Craniofacial Surgery*. Plastic and Reconstructive Surgery, 92 (4): 576–77.

Eltorai, A. E., Nguyen, E., Daniels, A. H. (2015), *Three-Dimensional Printing in Orthopedic Surgery*. Orthopedics, 38 (11): 684–87, DOI: https://doi.org/10.3928/01477447-20151016-

Hsu, J. T., Huang, H. L., Tsai, M. T., Fuh, L. J., Tu, M. G. (2011), *Effect of Screw Fixation on Temporomandibular Joint Condylar Prosthesis*. J Oral Maxillofac Surg, 69 (5): 1320–28. DOI: https://doi.org/10.1016/j.joms.2010.05.074.

Huang, H. L., Su, K. C., Fuh, L. J., Chen, M. Y., Wu, J., Tsai, M. T., Hsu, J. T. (2015). *Biomechanical Analysis of a Temporomandibular Joint Condylar Prosthesis during Various Clenching Tasks*. J Craniomaxillofac Surg, 43 (7): 1194–1201. DOI: https://doi.org/10.1016/j.jcms.2015.04.016.

Kashi, A., Chowdhury, A. R., Saha, S. (2010) *Finite element analysis of a TMJ implant,* J Dent Res, 89(3): p. 241-5.

Korioth, T. W., Hannam, A. G., (1994). *Deformation of the Human Mandible during Simulated Tooth Clenching*. J Dent Res 73 (1): 56–66. DOI: https://doi.org/10.1177/00220345940730010801.

Liu, Q., Leu, M. C., Schmitt, S. M., (2006) *Rapid Prototyping in Dentistry: Technology and Application*. The International Journal of Advanced Manufacturing Technology 29 (3): 317–35. DOI: https://doi.org/10.1007/s00170-005-2523-2.

Longhitano, G. A., Larosa, M. A., Jardini, A. L., de Carvalho Zavaglia, C. A., Filippini Ierardi, M. C., (2018) *Correlation between Microstructures and Mechanical Properties under Tensile and Compression Tests of Heat-Treated Ti-6Al–4V ELI Alloy Produced by Additive Manufacturing for Biomedical Applications*. Journal of Materials Processing Technology 252: 202–10. DOI: https://doi.org/10.1016/j.jmatprotec.2017.09.022.

Loon, J. P., Otten, V. E., Falkenstrom, C. H., de Bont, L. G., Verkerke, G. J. (1998) *Loading of a Unilateral Temporomandibular Joint Prosthesis: A Three-Dimensional Mathematical Study*. J Dent Res 77 (11): 1939–47. DOI:https://doi.org/10.1177/00220345980770111201.

Mazzocco, A. G., Jardini, A. L., Nunes, E. L., Maciel Filho, R. (2019) *Custom-Made Temporomandibular Joint Prosthesis: Computer Aided Modeling and Finite Elements Analysis*. Chemical Engineering Transactions. DOI: https://doi.org/http://dx.doi.org/10.3303/CET1974249.

Roberts, W. E., Huja, S., Roberts, J. A., (2004) *Bone modeling: biomechanics, molecular mechanisms, and clinical perspectives*, Seminars in Orthodontics, 10, 2, 123-161.

Shirazi-Adl, A., Dammak, M., Paiement G. (1993) *Experimental Determination of Friction Characteristics at the Trabecular Bone/Porous-Coated Metal Interface in Cementless Implants*. J Biomed Mater Res 27 (2): 167–75. DOI:https://doi.org/10.1002/jbm.820270205.

Sauro Pierucci, Flavio Manenti, Giulia Bozzano, Davide Manca (Eds.)
Proceedings of the 30th European Symposium on Computer Aided Process Engineering
(ESCAPE30), May 24-27, 2020, Milano, Italy. © 2020 Elsevier B.V. All rights reserved.
http://dx.doi.org/10.1016/B978-0-12-823377-1.50091-4

Cluster Analysis of Crude Oils based on Physicochemical Properties

Andre Sancho,[a,b] Jorge C. Ribeiro,[b] Marco S. Reis,[c] Fernando G. Martins[a*]

[a]LEPABE, Chemical Engineering Dpt., Faculty of Eng.University of Porto, Portugal

[b]Petrogal SA, Laboratory of Matosinhos Refinery, Rua Belchior Robles, 4452-852 Leça da Palmeira, Matosinhos

[c]CIEPQPF, Department of Chemical Engineering, University of Coimbra, Rua Sílvio Lima, 3030-790 Coimbra, Portugal

fgm@fe.up.pt

Abstract

The physicochemical properties of the crude oils can vary significantly, depending on their sources. While cheaper crude oils are desirable, the selection and blending operations should also take into consideration the potential operational problems on the downstream processing units. Cluster analysis is a data science technique that groups observations based on their similarity. By clustering crude oils based on their properties, it is expected that observations within a cluster will present similar behavior in the refining process. In this work, a data set from Galp's refineries containing 418 observations, with 9 properties, from 38 different sources was used. K-means clustering was applied after preprocessing and good results were obtained by selecting both 3 and 8 clusters, with only 0.7% and 3.7%, respectively, being placed in different clusters than the one with the highest family representation. This method also identified some observations with abnormal properties such as iron content. These results show the potential of grouping crudes based on their properties and the capability of finding potential outliers. This work allows the refineries to know how similar different sources are, potentially improving the task of formulating crude oil blends.

Keywords: crude oil; cluster analysis; k-means

1. Introduction

Crude oils are composed mostly by different organic components, containing also metals, sulfur, nitrogen and oxygen (Silva et al., 2011). The amount of each component in crude oil varies, depending on the crude geographic source and on the petroleum reservoir itself, causing crude oils to have physicochemical properties within a wide range of values. It is of economic interest to process cheaper crude oils, but these contain more impurities, which can cause operational problems on the downstream processing units.

With the increasing amount of data available in the industry, the use of data science techniques to extract additional knowledge is becoming popular (Hassani and Silva, 2018). Cluster analysis is an unsupervised method that groups information in clusters, where a cluster is a group of observations that are similar to each other and dissimilar to those in other clusters. By grouping crude oils based on their physicochemical properties using cluster analysis, it is expected that crude oils within a cluster will present similar behavior during the refining process.

2. Background

Crude oils are typically characterized based on their API gravity and sulfur content. Lighter crude oils tend to produce products with high added value, but are generally more expensive, while heavier crudes tend to be cheaper, but have more impurities. Depending on the amount of sulfur content, a crude can be considered "sweet" or "sour", with the latter requiring more intense treatment in the refining process. More recently, advanced characterization techniques such as near-infrared spectroscopy (Falla et al., 2006), nuclear magnetic resonance spectroscopy (Masili et al., 2012) and gas chromatography (El Nady et al., 2014) have also been used to successfully determine physicochemical properties of crude oils.

Cluster Analysis is used in a wide range of fields, including the chemical industry. However, applying cluster analysis to crude oils has been done scarcely, and usually confined to the use of techniques such as dendogram (Onojake et al., 2015) and swarm particle clustering (Ferreira et al., 2017) to compare against the typical crude classification based on the density.

3. Methods

The data set used in the present work was composed by the crudes processed in Matosinhos and Sines refineries of Galp in the last years, containing 418 observations from 38 different crude oils sources (here designated by families), and with the following measured properties: API; sulfur content; pour point; acidity; CCR content; nickel content; vanadium content; iron content; vanadium-nickel ratio. The data set was firstly preprocessed using the following techniques:

- For "less than" entries, the inequality values were assumed;

- For "more than" entries, the values were replaced using the mean based on observations of the crude oils from the same family that have higher values. If there are no higher values, the inequality values were assumed;

- Zero values were replaced by the lower detection limits;

- A mean value imputation technique was applied to missing values using the crude oils from the same family.

While the purpose of cluster analysis is to group observations in different groups, which implies that they have different properties from each other, outliers can worsen the results of centroid based clustering by shifting the kernel of the clusters in order to be accommodated. Typical outlier detection tools such as box plot with standard deviations, while good for univariate problems, are not adequate for multivariate data. Thus, the Mahalanobis (1936) distance was applied for this purpose as a multivariate metric that also takes into account the correlation between properties. The last preprocessing technique implemented was standardization by z-scores.

Cluster analysis was performed using the k-means clustering method (Lloyd, 1982), available in the scikit-learn library for *python*, and the silhouette score (Rousseeuw, 1987) was used as the internal validation metric to determine the best number of clusters for both low and high discrimination.

While the clusters are determined by k-means, typically, it is of interest to visualize graphically the results. This however is a challenging task for high dimensional data, and while it is always possible to do pairwise plots, each alone cannot show all the variables' interactions. So, a data reduction technique to project this high dimensional data to 2D was needed. For this, the uniform manifold approximation and projection, UMAP, (McInnes et al., 2018) technique was chosen and applied.

4. Results

4.1. Outlier Detection

Figure 1 shows the violin plot of the data set, and presents the cutoff point determined by the Mahalanobis distance. 10 observations were considered outliers and excluded from the data set.

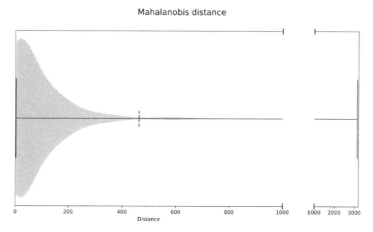

Figure 1: Mahalanobis distance for the crude oils data.

4.2. Cluster Analysis

The optimal number of clusters was selected based on the mean silhouette value, giving high values for 3 and 8 clusters. Thus, these were the selected number of clusters, corresponding to a low and high discriminant power.

The crude oils distributions for 3 and 8 clusters were analyzed by families and are shown on Table 1 and Table 2, respectively. It was verified that only 0.7% and 3.7%, for 3 and 8 clusters, respectively, were placed in different clusters than the one where it is found the highest representation of observations from the same crude oil family. As an example, the crude oil family XU (Table 1), composed by 14 different observations, had all but one of its observations allocated to cluster A for the 3 clusters case.

To visualize the high dimensional data, UMAP was applied to the data set and as a post-processing step, the observations were colored based on the clustering results. Figure 2 and Figure 3 show the data projection for 3 and 8 clusters, respectively, where the different crude oils cluster are displayed by the datapoint shape.

Table 1: Crude oil distribution (3 clusters).

A	187	B	132	C	89
CQ	58	BQ	3	CE	1
FC	4	CL	34	CF	3
GU	16	EV	2	DD	42
JF	65	FS	1	EF	3
NV	1	HU	1	GE	1
OV	24	MG	1	HF	1
XU	13	OI	33	IM	2
ZC	5	RJ	1	IV	2
ZS	1	RX	49	LU	1
		SE	2	ON	1
		SW	1	RF	4
		UV	1	SW	1
		XJ	3	UM	7
				XU	1
				YC	19

Table 2: Crude oil distribution (8 clusters).

A	77	B	65	C	108	D	26	E	86	F	29	G	8	H	9
CQ	58	CL	33	BQ	3	FC	4	JF	63	DD	2	CE	1	CL	1
JF	1	EV	1	CF	3	GU	16	OV	23	EF	3	UM	7	EV	1
ON	1	OI	31	DD	40	NV	1			HF	1			JF	1
RJ	1			FS	1	ZC	5			IV	1			OI	2
SW	1			GE	1					RF	3			OV	1
XU	14			HU	1					YC	19			RF	1
ZS	1			IM	2									RX	2
				IV	1										
				LU	1										
				MG	1										
				RX	47										
				SE	2										
				SW	1										
				UV	1										
				XJ	3										

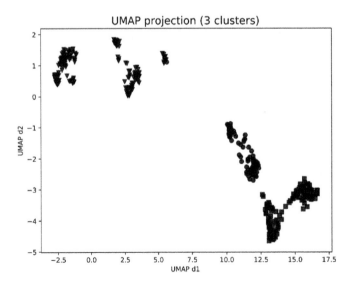

Figure 2: UMAP projection (3 clusters).

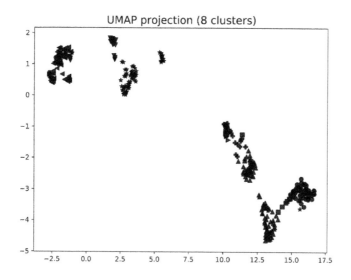

Figure 3: UMAP projection (8 clusters).

5. Discussion

The results show that the crude oils properties data is highly clusterable, and that, with few exceptions, crude oils from the same family are clustered together. After a closer look into the observations placed on different clusters, it was noted that they have some abnormal properties, when compared to the rest of the family members.

When comparing the crude families in both 3 and 8 clusters, it was found that the 8 clusters are primarily subclusters of the former. This behavior is beneficial and helps to further understand the relationships between clusters.

In the case of 8 clusters, one of them was composed solely by observations with abnormally higher amounts of iron when compared to the rest of their families. This is shown in Figure 4, for crude of the family RX.

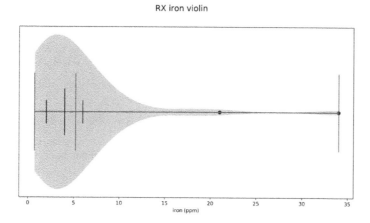

Figure 4: Violin plot for the RX crude family.

6. Conclusions

These findings demonstrate the potential of grouping crude oils based on their physicochemical properties. The k-means method gave good results for 3 and 8 clusters, with most of the observations of each family being allocated to the same cluster. It was also shown the capability of detecting crude oils with abnormal properties. The 8 clusters correspond to a further subdivision of the crude oils groups for 3 clusters, with one cluster being composed by observations with rather abnormal properties.

The information about the clusters can be very usefully in the plant management, namely: i) to improve the refining operations, where operating conditions and challenges can be associated to each cluster; ii) to predict the behavior of a crude oil that is being processed the first time and; iii) to help in the decision-making of the crude oils to be processed, by formulating a blend that will fall in a desired cluster or to prevent the blending of certain crude oils that are allocated to incompatible clusters.

References

Silva, S. L., Silva, A. M., Ribeiro, J. C., Martins, F. G., Da Silva, F. A., & Silva, C. M. (2011). Chromatographic and spectroscopic analysis of heavy crude oil mixtures with emphasis in nuclear magnetic resonance spectroscopy: A review. Analytica Chimica Acta, 707(1-2), 18-37.

Hassani, H., & Silva, E. S. (2018). Big Data: a big opportunity for the petroleum and petrochemical industry. OPEC Energy Review, 42(1), 74-89.

Falla, F. S., Larini, C., Le Roux, G. A. C., Quina, F. H., Moro, L. F. L., & Nascimento, C. A. O. D. (2006). Characterization of crude petroleum by NIR. *Journal of petroleum science and engineering, 51*(1-2), 127-137.

Masili, A., Puligheddu, S., Sassu, L., Scano, P., & Lai, A. (2012). Prediction of physical–chemical properties of crude oils by 1H NMR analysis of neat samples and chemometrics. *Magnetic Resonance in Chemistry, 50*(11), 729-738.

El Nady, M. M., Harb, F. M., & Mohamed, N. S. (2014). Biomarker characteristics of crude oils from Ashrafi and GH oilfields in the Gulf of Suez, Egypt: An implication to source input and paleoenvironmental assessments. *Egyptian Journal of Petroleum, 23*(4), 455-459.

Onojake, M. C., Abrakasa, S., & Osuji, L. C. (2015). Chemometric representation of molecular marker data of some Niger Delta crude oils. *Egyptian Journal of Petroleum, 24*(2), 139-143.

Ferreira, F., Ciodaro, T., de Seixas, J. M., Xavier, G., & Torres, A. (2017). Clustering Crude Oil Samples Using Swarm Intelligence. XIII Brazilian Congress on Computational Intelligence.

Mahalanobis, P. C. (1936). On the generalized distance in statistics. *Proceedings of the National Institute of Sciences (Calcutta)*, 2:49-55.

Lloyd, S. (1982). Least squares quantization in PCM. IEEE transactions on information theory, 28(2), 129-137.

Rousseeuw, P. J. (1987). Silhouettes: a graphical aid to the interpretation and validation of cluster analysis. Journal of computational and applied mathematics, 20, 53-65.

McInnes, L., Healy, J., & Melville, J. (2018). Umap: Uniform manifold approximation and projection for dimension reduction. *arXiv preprint arXiv:1802.03426.*

Sauro Pierucci, Flavio Manenti, Giulia Bozzano, Davide Manca (Eds.)
Proceedings of the 30th European Symposium on Computer Aided Process Engineering
(ESCAPE30), May 24-27, 2020, Milano, Italy. © 2020 Elsevier B.V. All rights reserved.
http://dx.doi.org/10.1016/B978-0-12-823377-1.50092-6

Optimization and Control of a Rainwater Detention and Harvesting Tank

Qiao Yan Soh,[*] Edward O'Dwyer, Salvador Acha, Nilay Shah

Center for Process Systems Engineering, Department of Chemical Engineering, Imperial College London, London SW7 2AZ, UK
qiaoyan.soh13@imperial.ac.uk

Abstract

Decentralized rainwater detention tanks are usually implemented as a method for reducing rainfall runoff volumes entering centralized reservoirs and treatment plants, but these systems also provide the opportunity for harvesting and locally treating rainwater such that local demand for potable water can be reduced. Here we evaluate the effectiveness of real time control strategies in a detention and harvesting system as a primary step towards future-proofing existing urban drainage infrastructure against increased rainfall loads. The implementation of control strategies has allowed for a four-fold increase in harvested water yield and shows promise in reducing the tank capacities necessary in handling high rainfall intensities.

Keywords: Real-time Control, Rainwater harvesting, Urban Water Management

1. Introduction

Stormwater management systems play a crucial part in maintaining sanitation and livability in an urban environment by efficiently removing excess water from population centers. However, once the infrastructure for these systems has been built, these stormwater management strategies have remained largely unchanged and modifications typically relied on increasing the physical capacities of the system. Spatial constraints faced in well-established cities have spurred researchers to look to alternative methods for improving existing stormwater management infrastructure, resulting in a steady increase in literature in recent years focusing on real-time control (RTC) methods applied to urban water systems.

RTC methods in application to urban drainage systems have been around since the 1960s [2], but only in the last decade after rapid developments in control strategies have RTC methods become more feasible to implement in practice. Exploiting reduced costs in sophisticated sensor and communication systems that are now available, Bartos et al., 2018 developed a platform for more autonomous management of water systems in cities [1]. This has been implemented in a 4 km² watershed in Ann Arbor, Michigan by Wong et al. 2018 for flood mitigation and flow reduction purposes [6]. Rohrer and Armitage, 2017 have also used stormwater detention ponds in Cape Town, South Africa to demonstrate the rainwater harvesting potential of these systems, and the potential of RTC strategies in improving water yield without significant impacts to the flood mitigation performance [4]. A comprehensive review on the use of Model Predictive Control (MPC) strategies on urban drainage systems was presented by Lund et al., 2018, discussing the strategies and challenges faced by researchers in developing MPC systems into mature technology for this use case, highlighting the rate of innovation from cross-disciplinary teams over the globe [3].

This paper presents a comparative analysis of rule-based and proportional controllers in achieving improved system performances in terms of maximizing rainwater harvested and minimizing stress in a stormwater detention and harvesting tank. The system and a case study are presented in Section 2.1, where a base configuration is used to determine the impact of the control strategies outlined in Section 2.2. The results are discussed in Section 3, with further work and conclusions discussed in Section 4.

2. Methods

2.1. Tank system set up and working principles

The system explored in this paper is a three-tank water harvesting and detention system, shown in Figure 1. Rainwater enters the system through a first tank that acts as a separation filter, directing flow towards either the detention or the harvesting tanks. Water is held within the detention tank to ensure that rainfall runoff is efficiently collected but also discharged into the public drain network at a suitable rate. The harvesting tank is used to collect cleaner water that can be used to satisfy non-potable water demands in the residential estate. To reduce sedimentation and pollutants, water can only be directed into the harvesting tank 10 minutes after the start of the rain event.

This demand is satisfied through a pumped treatment system from the harvesting tank source, allowing improved water use efficiency in the urban environment as well as reducing costs associated with purchasing potable water. However, the local water demand is not necessary in achieving a representative study of the effects of implementing control strategies, and henceforth the harvesting tank will be treated as a collection tank.

The water tank is modelled using equations of motion derived from mass balances for each individual tank. Explicitly, the state dynamic equations for each tank j with area A_j and water levels H_j, follow Equations (1-3) where Q_k is the flowrate between the tanks through orifice or weir k.

$$A_s \frac{dH_s}{dt} = Q_{in}(t) - Q_1(t) - Q_2(t) - Q_3(t) \tag{1}$$

$$A_d \frac{dH_d}{dt} = Q_1(t) + Q_3(t) - Q_{out}(t) \tag{2}$$

$$A_h \frac{dH_h}{dt} = Q_2(t) \tag{3}$$

The discharge rate at each tank can be modelled as an orifice or a weir, introducing nonlinearities into the model. For a small, sharp edged orifice with an area a and a rectangular weir of length L, these can be derived from Bernoulli's principle[6] to follow Equations (4) and (5) respectively for a water level H above the orifice opening or weir height. The additional parameters are the discharge coefficient C_d, and gravitational constant g.

$$Q_{orifice}(t) = C_d\, a\, \sqrt{2gH(t)} \tag{4}$$

$$Q_{weir}(t) = \frac{2}{3} C_d\, L\, \sqrt{2g}\, H(t)^{\frac{3}{2}} \tag{5}$$

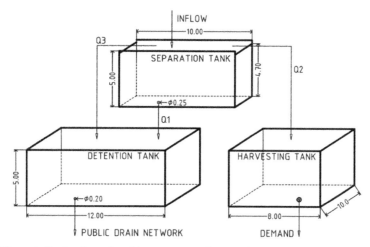

Figure 1: Tank schematic with parameter values used in the base configuration

2.1.1. Case Study

A base configuration was developed such that the constraints and fill rules are satisfied in a passive, uncontrolled system, and is used to evaluate the impact of each control strategy implementation. This can also be used as a simulation framework for determining a suitable strategy for the purposes of retrofitting an existing tank. In this configuration, $Q_1(t)$ and $Q_{out}(t)$ are modelled as small orifices, and $Q_2(t)$ and $Q_3(t)$ are weirs, and the parameter values used are as shown in Figure 1.

In developing suitable tank configurations for evaluation, the maximum depth allowable is defined to be 5 m. The case study area is based on a residential estate of 4.53 ha, and a detention tank servicing the entire estate would require a volume of 1250 m³ with an allowable public drain discharge rate of 1.34 m³/s.

2.2. Implemented Control Strategies

The passive, uncontrolled tank response was first determined to provide a baseline for evaluating the control strategies. In this section, the simulations consider the implementation of a control valve located at the orifice between the separation and detention tanks, adjusting $Q_1(t)$ only.

2.2.1. Rule-based Controller

The rule-based controllers implemented acts to open or close the valve based on the value of one or more monitored parameters. More specifically, these are the time elapsed since the start of the rain event, and tank water levels. The first strategy monitors the elapsed time such that cleaner runoff can be collected into the harvesting tank as soon as possible, where the valve leading to the detention tank is closed when harvesting can start taking place. The second strategy opens the same valve when the water level in the separation tank is close to capacity to prevent surface overflows.

A tuned rule-based controller for the base configuration was also implemented, monitoring time elapsed to ensure cleaner harvested water, as well as the harvesting tank water levels such that water can be discharged into the detention tank as quickly as possible once the harvesting tank is full.

2.2.2. Proportional Controller

The proportional controller adjusts the flowrate by changing the orifice area, calculated as a function of an error signal $\varepsilon(t)$, which is measured as the difference between the observed and desired ("set point") tank levels [5]. The desired system behavior over the course of a rainfall event can be represented by a setpoint profile, $H_{sp}(t)$ and the control action $u(t)$ follows Equation (6), with proportional gain K.

$$u(t) = K \times \varepsilon(t) = K(H(t) - H_{sp}(t)) \qquad (6)$$

The controller gain K is designed such that the orifice is fully open when the tank level exceeds a user-specified tank level. The separation tank set point profile $H_{sp}(t)$ implemented is a rectangular function that always minimizes the water level, except after the first 10 minutes of the event for a period sufficiently long for the harvesting tank to fill up completely. During this period, the water level is set just below the harvesting outlet height to ensure that there is no system overflow, as the controller action would result in a steady state offset above the new desired set point level.

2.3. Optimal Strategy

An idealized benchmark was developed to determine the most optimal performance achievable by the system. For the rainfall profile outlined above, an optimal strategy for a tank with the same volume configuration was determined for comparison purposes with the assumption that the flow rate between each tank can be fully controlled, such that these are only dependent on the volume of water available in the source tank. This was formulated as an LP problem and solved with GAMS [8]. The optimization objective was to maximize the amount of rainwater harvested, whilst maintaining a balance between minimizing the amount of water discharged into the public drain network and minimizing the use of the separation and detention tank volumes such that the system is able to handle a second rainfall event. Under this problem formulation, the optimal strategy can maximize the flow rates between each tank to the value allowable to enhance the system performance in each of the desired goals, outlined in the next section.

2.4. Rainfall input

The existing stormwater detention tanks are designed using a 10-year design storm with an average intensity of 193 mm/h. The Modified Rational Method assumes that the inflow hydrograph with the highest peak intensity is an event with a duration equal to the time of concentration of the catchment, which is the maximum time required for water to flow to the outlet from the furthest point in the catchment. Hence, in this study we seek to utilize the rainfall profile used in designing the systems, which corresponds to a 10-minute event with a peak inflow rate of 2.24 m^3/s.

3. Results

3.1. Key Performance Indicators

There are four key quantitative measures used to evaluate the system performance under the influence of each control strategy:

- Water harvesting potential, indicated by total amount of rainfall collected in the harvesting tank
- Risk of surface pooling, characterized by the ratio of the time-averaged water level in the separation tank after the rainfall event, and the maximum separation tank height.
- Tank size reduction, represented by the unused separation and detention tank capacities in the base configuration
- Public drain network integration, as indicated by the maximum public drain discharge rate.

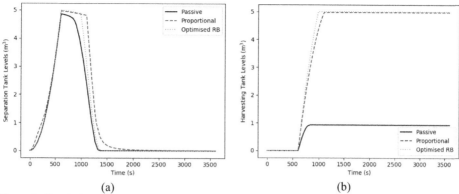

(a)   (b)

Figure 2: Simulation results for the passive system baseline and optimized controlled systems for (a) Separation tank levels and (b) Harvesting tank levels.

3.2. Results and discussion

The response of the system and the impacts of the rule-based and proportional control strategies were evaluated for the 10-minute high intensity storm, over the course of an hour by which it would reach system steady state. Figure 2 shows the simulation results for the rule-based and proportional controllers in comparison to the equivalent passive system. The ideal separation tank performance should always minimize the water level but hold the water level close to the harvesting orifice when this element is desired.

To increase the harvested yield, both the rule-based and P-control approaches were designed to maintain a high separation tank water level to ensure that the water height was near the harvesting outlet. This in turn would tend to increase the pooling risk relative to the passive approach. This could be improved through optimizing the tank configuration for each control strategy. By virtue of requiring less water to pass through the detention tank route with a higher amount of water harvested, the tank capacity required to deal with a high intensity storm can be significantly lowered when there is a higher degree of control over the flow of water within the system.

Figure 3 shows the performance of each single-event control strategy with a control valve implemented at the primary separation to detention tank outlet only. The harvested yields are significantly increased in all the control strategies implemented, with the lowest performing control strategy demonstrating a 4.35-fold increase in the harvested yield.

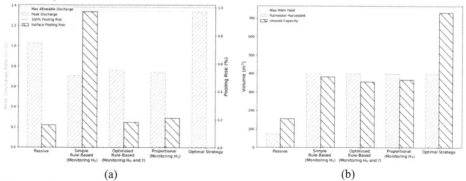

(a)   (b)

Figure 3: Results of implemented control strategies in achieving desired KPIs of (a) Minimizing discharge rates and pooling risk and (b) Maximizing unused capacities and harvested water yield

Under the optimal strategy the controller utilizes the peak allowable discharge such that the system can maximize the amount of rainwater harvested, whilst draining the separation tank to achieve negligible pooling risk and high unused capacity in the separation and detention tanks.

4. Conclusion

The simulations show significant improvements to the stormwater management system in all the performance measures, demonstrating that simple retrofitting of actuators and controllers within a tank allows it to be more adaptable to change. However, for the implementations to be effective, expertise in the systems operations may be required in order to achieve an optimized controller with a suitable set point profile.

In cases where the tank configuration can be altered and further optimized, the system has the potential to handle much higher intensity rainstorms with the same volume capacity. However, further analyses should be taken to evaluate such an operation strategy on the downstream public drain network.

This study serves as a primary step towards future-proofing existing urban drainage infrastructure. The full potential of utilizing control strategies in this context can be realized with further work focusing on the system response towards longer, more extreme events and optimizing the control strategies in consideration of water demand profiles. A significant area of study could look at the potential of reducing the required tank volume using a virtual tank and combining the detention and harvesting tanks.

Acknowledgement

This research is supported by the Singapore Ministry of National Development and the National Research Foundation, Prime Minister's Office under the Land and Liveability National Innovation Challenge (L2 NIC) Research Programme (L2 NIC Award No. L2NICTDF1-2017-3). Any opinions, findings, and conclusions or recommendations expressed in this material are those of the author(s) and do not reflect the views of the Singapore Ministry of National Development and National Research Foundation, Prime Minister's Office, Singapore.

References

[1]   Bartos, M., Wong, B., & Kerkez, B. (2018). Open storm: A complete framework for sensing and control of urban watersheds. Environmental Science: Water Research and Technology, 4(3), 346–358. https://doi.org/10.1039/c7ew00374a

[2]   García, L., Barreiro-gomez, J., Escobar, E., Téllez, D., Quijano, N., & Ocampo-martinez, C. (2015). Modeling and real-time control of urban drainage systems: A review. 85, 120–132. https://doi.org/10.1016/j.advwatres.2015.08.007

[3]   Lund, N. S. V., Falk, A. K. V., Borup, M., Madsen, H., & Steen Mikkelsen, P. (2018). Model predictive control of urban drainage systems: A review and perspective towards smart real-time water management. Critical Reviews in Environmental Science and Technology, 48(3), 279–339. https://doi.org/10.1080/10643389.2018.1455484

[4]   Rohrer, A. R., & Armitage, N. P. (2017). Improving the viability of stormwater harvesting through rudimentary real time control. Water (Switzerland), 9(6). https://doi.org/10.3390/w9060371

[5]   Ogunnaike, B.A. and Ray, W.H., 1994. Process dynamics, modeling, and control (Vol. 1). New York: Oxford University Press.

[6]   Streeter, Victor L., Bedford, K. W, and Wylie, E. Benjamin. Fluid Mechanics. 9th ed. Boston: McGraw-Hill, 1998. Print.

[7]   Wong, B. P., & Kerkez, B. (2018). Real- Time Control of Urban Headwater Catchments Through Linear Feedback: Performance, Analysis, and Site Selection. Water Resources Research, 54(10), 7309–7330. https://doi.org/10.1029/2018WR02265

[8]   GAMS Development Corporation. General Algebraic Modeling System (GAMS) Release 27.1.0, Fairfax, VA, USA, 2019.

Sauro Pierucci, Flavio Manenti, Giulia Bozzano, Davide Manca (Eds.)
Proceedings of the 30th European Symposium on Computer Aided Process Engineering
(ESCAPE30), May 24-27, 2020, Milano, Italy. © 2020 Elsevier B.V. All rights reserved.
http://dx.doi.org/10.1016/B978-0-12-823377-1.50093-8

Modelling and Simulation of Methanol Production and Conversion into Various Chemical Intermediates and Products

Letitia Petrescu[*], Stefan-Cristian Galusnyak, Dora-Andreea Chisalita,

Calin-Cristian Cormos

Babes-Bolyai University, Faculty of Chemistry and Chemical Engineering, Arany Janos 11, Postal code: RO-400028, Cluj-Napoca, Romania
letitiapetrescu@chem.ubbcluj.ro

Abstract

The present work is focused on process modeling and simulation of methanol production and conversion into various chemical intermediates and final products. Methanol synthesis is achieved by chemical reaction between CO_2 and H_2, this method being considered an important method for carbon dioxide valorization. The main advantages of this route are the reduction of greenhouse gas emissions and production of one valuable chemical, methanol. A productivity of 500 kmols/h of methanol was set in the present study. Methanol is furthermore converted into useful intermediates and products such as: *1)* acetic acid, *2)* dimethyl carbonate (DMC), *3)* formalin *4)* dimethyl ether (DME) *5)* biodiesel and *6)* methyl tert-butil ether (MTBE). The proposed design models were validated using data from the scientific literature. Purities higher than 99% for methanol and methanol derived products were achieved in all cases. The designs under investigation are compared from technical and environmental point of view leading to the conclusion that biodiesel and MTBE productions are the most convenient routes for methanol valorization.

Keywords: Methanol production; Methanol valorisation; CO_2 valorisation; Process design; Environmental evaluation.

1. Introduction

Nowadays methanol is considered to be an essential chemical for our society. It has applications in two important sectors: chemical industry and transportation sector. Each day, nearly 200,000 tons of methanol are used as raw-material for the production of various chemicals or as a transportation fuel. On one hand, in the chemical industry, formaldehyde, methyl tert-butil ether (MTBE), acetic acid, dimethyl ether (DME), TAME (tert-amyl methyl ether), biodiesel, DMT (dimethyl terephthalate), MMA (methyl metacrylate), dimethyl carbonate (DMC) are relevant products derived from methanol (Simões et al., 2013). On the other hand, methanol is considered to be a low-emission fuel. The NO_x emissions from methanol are approximately 45% of those from conventional fuels while the SO_x emissions are approximately 8% of those from conventional fuels per unit energy. The emissions reductions are due to the fact that methanol results in lower emissions during the combustion phase (IMO, 2016).

Methanol demand is continuously increasing due to its multiple ways of valorisation, the demand increase is supposed to expand more in the future (Jarvis and Samsatli, 2018). Methanol can be produced using several technologies and feed stocks (e.g. natural gas, coal and biomass) (Dalena et al., 2018). Most of the methanol produced industrially today is derived from syngas, a gaseous mixture of CO and H_2, most of it being produced from natural gas (Simões et al., 2013). Natural gas is converted to syngas using steam in the well-known reforming technology. Furthermore, syngas reacts over a $CuO/ZnO/Al_2O_3$ catalyst at 250-300°C and 10 MPa to produce methanol and water (Jarvis and Samsatli, 2018).

In recent years, several research groups and studies have considered methanol synthesis through CO_2 hydrogenation (Jarvis and Samsatli, 2018), the process belonging to the carbon dioxide utilization (CCU) topic. According to Dalena and co-authors methanol production from CO_2 offers at least two significant advantages: i) the overcoming of CO_2 sequestration and ii) mitigation of greenhouse gas effect through an efficient CO_2 recycling (Dalena et al, 2018). Figure 1 presents a simplified flow-diagram of methanol synthesis and methanol derived products considered in the present study. The novelty of the work consists on the comparison of various routes for methanol valorisation this comparison being based on technical and environmental key performance indicators.

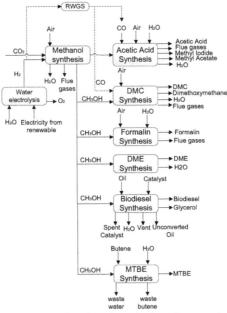

Figure 1. Conceptual configuration of methanol synthesis and conversion into various chemicals

2. Plants configurations & models assumptions

The cases investigated in the present paper are presented in Table 1.

Table 1. Case studies description

Name	Description
Case 1	Methanol production from CO_2 and H_2 coupled with Acetic Acid production
Case 2	Methanol production from CO_2 and H_2 coupled with DMC production
Case 3	Methanol production from CO_2 and H_2 coupled with formalin production
Case 4	Methanol production from CO_2 and H_2 coupled with DME production
Case 5	Methanol production from CO_2 and H_2 coupled with biodiesel production
Case 6	Methanol production from CO_2 and H_2 coupled with MTBE production

Each case under investigation can be divided in two sections. The first section is a common section and refers to the methanol production process, described in detail in the next paragraphs. The second section is not common any more, being different in terms of raw - materials, units operations and reactions involved for each case under investigation (see Table 2). Figure 2 presents the methanol production process from CO_2 and H_2.

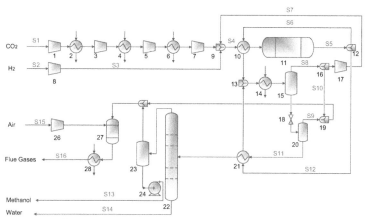

Figure 2. Process flow diagram for methanol production

The CO_2 feed, S1, is compressed to 78 atm, through a four-stage compressor with intermediate cooling. The H_2 feed stream, S2, is compressed also up to 78 atm using a compressor (Unit 8). The raw-materials streams are mixed with recycled stream (S7), heated up in heat exchanger (Unit 10) and sent to the plug flow rector, Unit 11, where the following reactions occur at 210°C:

$$CO_2 + 3H_2 \rightarrow CH_3OH + H_2O \tag{1}$$
$$CO_2 + H_2 \rightarrow CO + H_2O \tag{2}$$

The output stream of the reactor is divided into two streams: S6 is used to heat the reactor feed through the heat exchanger (Unit 10) and Stream 12 is used to preheat the column feed through the heat exchanger (Unit 21). After this thermal integration, the streams are mixed and cooled to 35°C in Unit 14. The liquid and gaseous phases are separated in the flash (Unit 15). Part of the gas stream from Unit 15 is compressed and recycled to the reactor. After a second gas-liquid separation in Unit 20, S11 stream containing methanol and water; the mass concentration of methanol being 63%, was obtained. This mixture is preheated in the heat exchanger (Unit 21) using the heat of the residual gas reactor. Then, the stream is fed to the distillation column (Unit 22). Liquid methanol is produced in S13 (wt. methanol 99.80%) (Prez-Fortes et al., 2016).

Table 2. Evaluated case studies and main design assumptions

Modeling and simulation details and main design assumptions
Raw-materials: methanol, H_2, CO_2, water; *Main product*: Acetic Acid; *By-products*: wastewater, Methyl Iodide, Methyl Acetate, Flue gases; *Thermodynamic package used*: SRK; *Units operations*: 3 reactors, 2 distillation columns, 5 separators, 6 compressors, 6 pumps, 11 HE, 6 mixers, 4 dividers

Case1

Case 1(cont.)

Reactions involved:

$$CH_3OH + CO \rightarrow CH_3COOH \tag{3}$$

$$CH_3COOH + CH_3OH \rightarrow CH_3COOCH_3 + 2H_2O \tag{4}$$

$$CO + H_2O \rightarrow CO_2 + H_2 \tag{5}$$

Assumptions: reactor thermal mode adiabatic, reactor pressure 30 atm; off-gas treatment column 35 stages, methanol recovery 96%; acetic acid purification column 50 stages, RR 3.54; pumps efficiencies 80%; compressors efficiencies 75%; HE min ΔT 10˚C.

Case 2

Raw-materials: methanol, H_2, CO_2, air; *Main product*: DMC; *By-products*: dimethoxymethane, Water, Flue gases; *Thermodynamic package used*: PSRK; *Units operations*: 3 reactors, 3 distillation columns, 5 separators, 4 compressors, 3 pumps, 4 HE, 5 mixers, 1 divider

Reactions involved:

$$CO_2 + H_2 \rightarrow CO + H_2O \tag{6}$$

$$4CH_3COOH + 2CO + O_2 \rightarrow 2C_3H_6O_3 + 2H_2O \tag{7}$$

$$4CH_3COOH + 2CO \rightarrow 2C_3H_8O_2 + O_2 \tag{8}$$

Assumptions: reactor thermal mode-isothermal, reactor pressure 20 atm; methanol recovery column 30 stages, methanol recovery 99%; DMC purification column 45 stages; pumps efficiencies 80%; compressors efficiencies 75%; HE min ΔT 10˚C.

Case 3

Raw-materials: methanol, air, water; *Main product*: formaldehyde; *By-products*: off gases *Thermodynamic package used*: SRK; *Units operations*: 1 reactor, 2 pumps, 4 HE, 2 mixers, 1 compressor, 1 absorber, 1 distillation column

Reactions involved:

$$CH_3OH + \tfrac{1}{2}O_2 \rightarrow CH_2O + H_2O \tag{9}$$

$$CH_3OH \rightarrow CH_2O + H_2 \tag{10}$$

Assumptions: reactor thermal mode isothermal, reactor pressure 1.83 atm; absorber 20 stages; formaldehyde separation column 20 stages; pumps efficiencies 80%; compressors efficiencies 75%; HE min ΔT 10˚C.

Case 4

Raw-materials: methanol; *Main product*: DME; *By-products*: wastewater; *Thermodynamic package used*: SRK; *Units operations*: 1 reactor, 1 pump, 4 HE, 1 valve, 2 distillation columns

Reaction involved:

$$2CH_3OH \rightarrow C_2H_6O + H_2O \tag{11}$$

Assumptions: reactor thermal mode isothermal, reactor pressure 14.5 atm; DME separation column 24 stages, RR 0.35, bottom product temperature 153˚C; pumps efficiencies 80%; compressors efficiencies 75%; HE min ΔT 10˚C.

Case 5

Raw-materials: methanol, oil, catalyst (NaOH), water, H_3PO_4; *Main product*: biodiesel; *By-products*: glycerol, vent, unconverted oil, Na_3PO_4; *Thermodynamic package used*: SRK; *Units operations*: 2 reactors, 4 mixers, 4 pumps, 2 HE, 3 distillation columns, 1 extractor

Reactions involved:

$$C_{57}H_{104}O_6 + CH_3OH \leftrightarrow C_{39}H_{72}O_5 + C_{19}H_{36}O_2 \tag{12}$$

$$C_{39}H_{72}O_5 + CH_3OH \leftrightarrow C_{21}H_{40}O_4 + C_{19}H_{36}O_2 \tag{13}$$

$$C_{21}H_{40}O_4 + CH_3OH \leftrightarrow C_3H_8O_3 + C_{19}H_{36}O_2 \tag{14}$$

$$3NaOH + H_3PO_4 \rightarrow Na_3PO_4 + 3H_2O \tag{15}$$

Assumptions: biodiesel reactor thermal mode-isothermal (60˚C); catalyst neutralization reactor thermal mode - isothermal (60˚C); extractor stages 4; biodiesel distillation column

Case 5

10 stages, RR 4, bottom product temperature 382˚C; glycerol distillation column RR 2, bottom product temperature 112˚C; pumps efficiencies 80%; compressors efficiencies 75%; HE min ΔT 10˚C.

	Raw-materials: methanol, butylene, water; *Main product*: MTBE; *By-products*: wastewater, waste butylene; *Thermodynamic package used*: SRK; *Units operations*: 1 reactor, 1 absorber, 2 distillation columns, 2 mixers, 3 pumps, 2 valves, 1HE

Case 6

Reaction involved:

$$CH_3OH \quad + \quad C_4H_8 \quad \rightarrow \quad C_5H_{12}O \tag{16}$$

Assumptions: reactor mode isothermal (130°C) reactor pressure 30 atm; MTBE column 72 stages; RR 1.62; methanol absorber 5 stages; methanol separation column 42 stages, RR 3.44; pumps efficiencies 80%; compressors efficiencies 75%, HE min ΔT 10°C.

HE - heat exchanger, RR - reflux ratio, SRK - Soave Redlich Kwong, PSRK – Predictive Soave Redlich Kwong

3. Results and discussions

All evaluated cases were modelled, simulated and validated (Turton et al., 2008) using ChemCAD process simulation software. The validation differences between the literature results and those obtained from the simulations were below 2%. Once the models were validated they were scaled-up to the same quantity of methanol used (e.g. 500 kmols/h). The mass and energy balances from the simulation were used to calculate technical and environmental indicators. For environmental impact Waste Reduction (WAR) Algorithm, developed by US EPA, was applied (EPA, 2019). The WAR methodology is not a complete LCA tool since it is focused only on the manufacturing aspect without considering the upstream (i.e. raw-materials supply chain) and downstream processes. The technical indicators obtained are summarized in Table 3. Electricity to run the machineries was considered under electricity consumption.

Table 3. Technical comparison between investigated cases

Parameter	Unit	Case 1	Case 2	Case 3	Case 4	Case 5	Case 6
Methanol used	t/h	16	16	16	16	16	16
Product Name	-	AceticAcid	DMC	Formalin	DME	Biodiesel	MTBE
Product Rate	t/h	25.52	18.06	37.35	11.46	143.48	36.31
Product Purity	%	100	99.58	32.38	99.44	99.99	99.92
El.consumption	kW$_e$	6,056.65	6,630.74	6,878.66	5,822.59	5,859.21	5,907.90

It can be noticed from Table 3 that starting from the same quantity of methanol different quantities of products are obtained. The highest quantities of products are obtained in Case 5 followed by Case 3. Purities of methanol derived products are higher than 99%, except Case 3. Formalin obtained in Case 3 represents a diluted solution of formaldehyde (wt. 32.38%). Another issue with Case 3 is the fact that it has the highest electricity consumption among all cases under investigation. Methanol conversion into biodiesel (Case 5) and MTBE (Case 6) seem to be more profitable compared to other cases due to high quantity of products obtained, high purities and low energy consumption. The environmental indicators obtained are reported in Table 4. Those indicators consider: the inputs and the outputs streams from the chemical process as well as from the energy generation process related to the chemical process and the toxicity of the substances involved. Considering the indicators reported in Table 4, the most environmentally friendly designs are Case 2 and Case 4 having the lowest emissions to air, water and soil. For instance, for Case 2, six of nine impact indicators (i.e. AP, ATP, TTP, ODP, HTPE. HTPI) have the lowest values in the above mentioned scenario. On the other hand Case 2 and Case 4 are not so advantageous from a technical point of view (see Table 3). Even if the purities of the products obtained are high, their flow-rates are relatively low (e.g. 18.06 tons/h in Case 2 and 11.46 tons/h in Case 4). Case 5 and Case 6 have a medium environmental impact and good technical performance.

Table 4. Environmental comparison between investigated cases

Parameter	Units	Case 1	Case 2	Case 3	Case 4	Case 5	Case 6
GWP	PEI/h	12.4	6.74	5.95	8.00	5.25	36.2
AP	PEI/h	130	143	148	125	126	127
PCOP	PEI/h	5,510	1370	38,300	2,840	14,800	8,210
ATP	PEI/h	180	11.8	206	6.35	86.40	27
TTP	PEI/h	44,000	623	5,890	214	5,950	4,640
ODP $* 10^5$	PEI/h	4.43	4.85	5.03	4.26	4.28	4.32
HTPE	PEI/h	315	0.59	3,200	0.29	1800	51.5
HTPI	PEI/h	44,000	623	5,890	214	5,950	4,640
Total Impact	PEI/h	94,200	2,780	53,600	3,410	28,700	17,700

GWP - Global Warming Potential, AP - Acidification Potential, PCOP - Photochemical Oxidation Potential, ATP - Aquatic Toxicity Potential, TTP - Terrestrial Toxicity Potential, HTPE - Human Toxicity Potential by Exposure, HTPI - Human Toxicity Potential by Ingestion, ODP - Ozone Depletion Potential, PEI - Potential Environmental Impact

4. Conclusions

The present paper evaluates methanol production from CO_2 and H_2 and its conversion into various chemicals. Technical and environmental indicators were calculated and compared for the evaluated cases. A quantity of 143.48 t/h of biodiesel with a purity of 99.44% and 36.31 t/h of MTBE with a purity of 99.92% were obtained starting from 16 t/h of methanol. These two products have a medium environmental impact, lower than the environmental impact of methanol transformation into acetic acid or formalin (e.g. 28,700 PEI/h in biodiesel production and 17,700 PEI/h for MTBE vs. 94,200 PEI/h for acetic acid and 53,600 PEI/h for formalin) but higher than the impact of methanol conversion into DMC and DME. Even if DMC and DME processes are more environmental friendly they are not so convenient from technical point of view. The technical and environmental evaluations lead to the conclusion that methanol conversion into biodiesel and MTBE are the most convenient solutions from technical and environmental point of view.

Acknowledgement

This work was supported by CONVERGE Project, European Union's Horizon 2020 research and innovation programme under grant agreement No. 818135.

References

F. Dalena, A. Senatore, M. Basile, S. Knani, A. Basile, A. Iulianelli, 2018. Advances in Methanol Production and Utilization, with Particular Emphasis toward Hydrogen Generation via Membrane Reactor Technology, Membranes 8, 98, 1-27

IMO, 2016. Methanol as marine fuel: Environmental benefits, technology readiness, and economic feasibility. http://www.imo.org (las accessed January 2020)

EPA, 2019. https://www.epa.gov/chemical-research (last accessed November 2019)

S. M. Jarvis, S. Samsatli, 2018. Technologies and infrastructures underpinning future CO_2 value chains: A comprehensive review and comparative analysis, Renewable and Sustainable Energy Reviews, 85, 46-68

M. Prez-Fortes, J. Schoneberger, A. Boulamanti, E. Tzimas, 2016. Methanol synthesis using captured CO_2 as raw material :Techno-economic and environmental assessment, Applied Energy, 161, 718-732

É. Simões, Van-Dal, C. Bouallou, 2013. Design and simulation of a methanol production plant from CO_2 hydrogenation, Journal of Cleaner Production 57, 38-45.

R. Turton, R.C. Bailie, W.B. Whiting, A. Shaeiwitz, 2008. Analysis, Syinthesis, and Design of Chemical Processes, Perason Education.

Sauro Pierucci, Flavio Manenti, Giulia Bozzano, Davide Manca (Eds.)
Proceedings of the 30th European Symposium on Computer Aided Process Engineering
(ESCAPE30), May 24-27, 2020, Milano, Italy. © 2020 Elsevier B.V. All rights reserved.
http://dx.doi.org/10.1016/B978-0-12-823377-1.50094-X

Evaluating the Existing Protocol for LNG Bunkering Operations

Aruna Coimbatore Meenakshi Sundaram, Iftekhar Abubakar Karimi

Department of Chemical & Biomolecular Engineering, National University of Singapore, 4 Engineerign Drive 4, 117585, Singapore

Abstract

IMO 2020, a regulation mandated by the International Maritime Organization, demands an 80% reduction in NOx emissions and limits Sulphur to 1000 ppm in fuels used for maritime transportation. This forces the need for a cleaner and sustainable fuel for the ocean-going ships to reduce the emissions generated by the conventional Heavy Fuel Oil (HFO). Liquefied Natural Gas (LNG) turns out to be a promising and long-term solution that complies with the new set of emission standards, but the technology to use LNG for ships is still underdeveloped. The cryogenic nature of LNG demands a special infrastructure and protocol for LNG bunkering operations. However, the procedures suggested in the literature seem to be mere concepts/ideas proposed without detailed quantitative evaluation. In this study, a comprehensive evaluation of the existing LNG bunkering protocol was conducted using a Unisim Dynamic Simulation (DS) model of the LNG bunkering system. The major pitfalls identified in the current protocol are a) the time taken for inerting and purging processes, b) GHG emissions (methane/CO2) released from frequent inerting and purging operations, c) high cost of inerting gas and d) improper pressure management resulting in increased Boil-Off Gas (BOG) generation. These shortcomings will have a major impact on the safety and operating cost of an LNG bunkering system, especially for busy bunkering ports/facilities.

Keywords: LNG, Bunkering, Marine Fuel, IMO 2020

Introduction

Heavy Fuel Oil (HFO), the traditionally used bunker fuel for maritime transportation is accompanied with significant amount of Sulphur and particulate matter emissions. To reduce the emissions from these ocean-going ships, the International Maritime Organization (IMO) enforced a new regulation, IMO2020 from 1st January 2020 (Seas, 2008). This forced many shipping companies and regulatory bodies to come up with a solution that can comply with the new set of standards. Several alternatives such as the use of (a) HFO with a scrubber, (b) Marine Diesel Oil (MDO) with lower Sulphur content and (c) an alternative fuel like Liquefied Natural Gas (LNG) were suggested. Critical evaluation of these alternatives showed that the scrubber installation cost and the scrubbed waste disposal are problematic for HFO and the cost of producing low Sulphur MDO is very high. On the other hand, LNG (primarily methane) is the cheapest low-carbon intensive fossil fuel available today and hence turned out to be the most promising and long-term solution (Danish Maritime Authority, 2012).

Unlike HFO, LNG is stored and transported in heavily vacuum-insulated large tanks under cryogenic conditions (about 1.2 atm and 113 K) (Han and Lim, 2012). Thus, LNG demands special treatments and procedures during transfer. Hence, developing a reliable and safe bunkering procedure is essential for global standardization of LNG transfer operations. The process of transferring LNG from one vessel to another as a marine fuel is termed as LNG bunkering and can be performed in any of three modes: Truck-to-Ship (TTS), Shore-to-Ship (PTS) or Ship-to-Ship (STS), based on the location of the bunkering facility and the volume of fuel to be transferred (DNV GL, 2017).

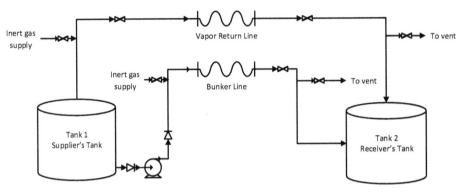

Figure 1: LNG Bunkering System

American Bureau of Shipping (ABS, 2014) suggested a protocol for LNG bunkering operations. According to this protocol, a bunkering system consists of two LNG tanks on the supplier and receiver end irrespective of the mode of transfer (shown in Figure 1). The process begins by connecting the two LNG tanks with a flexible, cryogenic bunker hose. The first step is *Pre-Inerting* (shown in Figure 2) where the moisture/air in the hose is removed using an inert gas like nitrogen to bring the air vol% below the flammability limits of methane (5-15 vol%). Once the hose has been inerted with nitrogen, a small amount of LNG is used to purge/flush out the nitrogen in the hose to avoid nitrogen contamination in the receiver's LNG tank. This *Purging* process will also ensure that the hose is cooled down to LNG temperature without causing mechanical stress or fractures in the bunkering hose. On completion of purging, *Filling* commences wherein the actual transfer of LNG from the supplier to the receiver tank takes place. Once the required filling level has been achieved, the valves leading to the supplier LNG tank is closed while the valve going to the receiver's tank is opened and closed multiple times until the LNG in the hose is pressurized and forced towards the receiver's tank, to ensure complete *Draining* of LNG from the hose. Before disconnecting the hose, the traces of methane vapors left in the hose is removed by *Post-Inerting* using nitrogen. This completes the LNG bunkering process and the hose is disconnected.

Figure 2: Step-by-Step LNG Bunkering Procedure

Despite the insulation, heat ingress into the LNG tanks are unavoidable, and it causes LNG to vaporize. These LNG vapors called Boil-Off Gas (BOG) occupies more volume than LNG itself causing an increase in tank operating pressure. In some systems, the use of a Vapor Return Line (VRL) (Figure 1), additional flexible cryogenic hose identical to a bunker hose that connects the vapor outlets of the two tanks was suggested to maintain a constant pressure difference between the two tanks by allowing bidirectional flow of vapors from one vessel to the other.

Though the protocol describes the complete step-by-step process, it lacks several technical and operational details such as the time taken for each step, the source of nitrogen used for inerting, the amount of methane or LNG vapors emitted during the inerting and purging operations and the applicability of the suggested protocol to various modes of bunkering. Literature show that many industrial experts and shipping companies are focused on the construction of LNG fueled ships (Danish Maritime Authority, 2012) and the safety issues in handling LNG (EMSA, 2017) (Vandebroek and Berghmans, 2012). But least attention has been given to the development of LNG bunkering procedure. Thus, in this paper a quantitative evaluation of the suggested LNG bunkering protocol will be presented using a dynamic simulation model.

Methodology

The cryogenic and flammable nature of LNG does not allow for experimentation. Thus, a simulation model for the LNG Bunkering system was developed using a well-known process simulator, Unisim®. The Unisim Dynamic Simulation (DS) uses a pressure flow solver to compute the system dynamics as a function of time. The DS model was constructed using the bunkering system outline provided in Figure 1 with a Peng-Robinson fluid package.

Table 1: Bunkering System Parameters (DNV-GL, 2014)

Parameters	Truck-to-Ship	Shore-to-Ship	Ship-to-Ship
Tank 1 Volume (m^3)	1500	4000	7500
Tank 2 Volume (m^3)	500	1500	3000
Tank 1 Pressure (barg)	2.8	2.8	2.8
Tank 2 Pressure (barg)	5.8	5.8	5.8
Tank 1 Temperature (˚C)	-147	-147	-147
Tank 2 Temperature (˚C)	-134.5	-134.5	-134.5
Tank 1 Level (%)	90	90	90
Tank 2 Level (%)	20	20	20
Pipe length (in)	4	8	10
VRL length (in)	2	4	4
Transfer rate (m^3/s)	75	200	400

The most important component in the DS model for LNG bunkering process is the simulation of an LNG tank. Though these process simulators have an inbuilt tank module, they do not allow providing separate heat leak rates for the tank wall, roof and top. On the contrary, these heat leaks are the major reason for the vaporization of LNG resulting in BOG generation and tank pressurization. Hence to compute the BOG generation rate accurately, a corrected LNG tank model suggested by (Khan et al., 2019) was employed.

For the system parameters such as flowrate, tank size, hose size etc., literature provides a range of values suitable for each mode of bunkering. Hence an arbitrary value in the suggested range was chosen for this study (see Table 1) to develop the DS model for all three modes of bunkering with and without the presence of VRL.

Following the model development, a step-by-step bunkering process was carried out using an Event Scheduler available in Unisim DS. The Event Scheduler treats each bunkering step as an event and enables us to provide a set of instructions/actions to be performed for each event along with a set of conditions to mark the end of that event. Once the condition(s) is(are) satisfied, the event scheduler switches the simulation from one event to another by executing the set of actions provided. For example, a reduction in air vol% from 100% to less than 3% in the bunkering hose indicate the completion of pre-inerting and commencement of purging process. After providing necessary conditions and actions for all the steps, the entire sequence of events was executed at once to compute the time taken for each step. The same procedure was followed for all the three modes of bunkering (both with and without VRL).

Results & Discussion

In this study, the missing information in the existing LNG bunkering protocol were computed using the developed DS model. Firstly, the time taken for each mode of transfer was computed (shown in Table 2). Though in literature the use of VRL was suggested, they failed to consider the additional inerting and purging required for the VRL. Here, the bunkering time computed in the presence of a VRL is indicated by the numbers within the parentheses in Table 2. Thus, from table 2 we conclude that the inerting and purging processes contribute to the maximum % of the total bunkering time.

Table 2: LNG Bunkering Timeline (min)

Steps	Truck-to-Ship	Shore-to-Ship	Ship-to-Ship
Pre-inerting	8 (14)	14 (29)	19 (39)
Purging	7 (12)	12 (21)	16 (29)
Filling	62 (259)	70 (292)	75 (292)
Draining	29 (26)	48 (43)	81 (54)
Post-Inerting	8 (14)	14 (29)	19 (39)
Total Time (min)	114 (325)	158 (414)	210 (453)

Secondly, the nitrogen source for inerting was not mentioned in the current protocol. From the DS model, the nitrogen requirement for inerting was computed to be approximately 7.5 kg, 18 kg and 28 kg for TTS, PTS and STS respectively without VRL and 12 kg, 27 kg and 42 kg with VRL for one bunkering process. While the cost of nitrogen is directly proportional to the amount of nitrogen required, the current protocol will suffer from high inerting cost in the absence of a nitrogen generation unit. On the other hand, installing a nitrogen generation unit will increase both the capital and operating cost. Thus, in either case inerting processes will increase the operating cost of LNG bunkering system.

Another important issue to be addressed is the methane emissions. Though the use of LNG can eliminate the Sulphur and NOx emissions, the current protocol emits significant amount of methane during the purging and inerting processes. The amount of methane emitted per bunkering process was computed to be 11 kg, 28 kg and 52 kg for TTS, PTS and STS respectively without VRL and 15 kg, 40 kg and 80 kg with VRL. Published literature does not indicate the presence of any Incineration Unit (IU) that can convert the methane vapors to CO_2 before releasing to the atmosphere. In the absence of an IU, direct release of methane to the atmosphere can worsen the situation as methane is a more potent greenhouse gas (GHG) compared to CO_2. An IU installation in the bunkering port will still result in carbon emissions to the atmosphere.

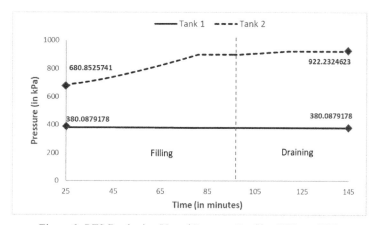

Figure 3: PTS Bunkering Vessel Pressure Profiles Without VRL

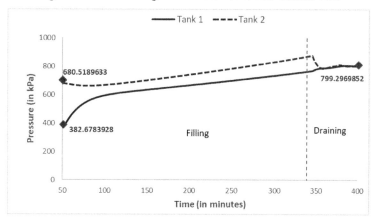

Figure 4: PTS Bunkering Vessel Pressure Profiles With VRL

BOG generation from LNG tanks will also result in methane emissions in the absence of an IU. Further, improper planning and management of LNG delivery can result in significant amount of BOG generation and tank pressurization. Figure 3 and Figure 4 show the tank pressure profiles obtained during filling and draining stages of a Shore-to-Ship LNG bunkering system with both the absence and presence of VRL respectively. The dotted and continuous lines represent the pressure profiles of receiver and supplier tank respectively. The tank relief valve pressure was set to 1000 kPa for both the tanks in the DS model. The event scheduler condition was programmed to stop the filling process if the pressure in either tanks exceeded 900 kPa to ensure safe operation. In the absence of a VRL, it was noted that the pressure difference between the two tanks increased continuously due to excess BOG generation (shown in Figure 4). As a result, the filling was stopped by the scheduler when the receiver vessel liquid % reached 35% tank level in all three modes. On the other hand, in the presence of a VRL, 85% filling level was achieved by maintaining a constant pressure difference (shown in Figure 5) between the two tanks allowing the excess BOG to flow from one vessel to the other through VRL ensuring a smooth transfer process. During the draining process, the pressure of the two vessels almost became equal for a system with VRL (after t=342 min in Figure 5). Clearly, the presence of a VRL is mandatory to maintain a constant pressure difference between the two tanks and manage the BOG generated during the bunkering operation.

In brief, the evaluation of the existing bunkering protocol informs us that the current protocol has been proposed without much quantitative analysis on the time, cost, BOG generation and emissions. The several shortcomings associated with the current protocol, as discussed above, will definitely affect the operational safety of a bunkering port and inhibit the standardization of the procedure for worldwide operation.

Conclusion

The step-by-step LNG bunkering procedure suggested by ABS was simulated using Unisim Dynamic Simulation. The simulation results concluded that the inerting and purging operations waste a lot of material and are also time consuming. Additionally, purging operations release LNG vapors to the atmosphere which leads to loss of LNG/methane which is 2600 times more potent than carbon dioxide as a GHG. Further, in the absence of a VRL, a large pressure difference was observed between the two tanks directly impacting the filling rate and preventing the system from attaining the required filling level. Thus, the presence of VRL is mandatory to maintain a constant pressure difference between the two tanks to enable smooth transfer process. But, this in turn will result in increased time, cost and emissions as the inerting and purging process are performed for both bunkering and vapor return line. The effect of these issues will be manifold for busy bunkering ports which receive around 200-300 ships per day, as the cost, emissions, and time taken are directly proportional to the number of bunkering operations conducted at a facility. Undoubtedly, a better LNG bunkering system that is operationally safe, economically viable and environment-friendly must be designed in the future for worldwide standardization of LNG bunkering procedure.

References

ABS, 2014, LNG Bunkering: Technical and Operational Advisory 68.
Danish Maritime Authority, 2012, North European LNG Infrastructure Project- A feasibilty study for an LNG filling station infrastructure and test of recommendations.
DNV-GL, 2014, Liquefied Natural Gas (LNG) Bunkering Study.
DNV GL, 2017, Gas as a Marine Fuel.
EMSA, 2017, Guidance on LNG Bunkering to Port Authorities and Administration.
Han, C., Lim, Y., 2012, LNG Processing: From Liquefaction to Storage, Comput. Aided Chem. Eng. 31, 99–106.
Khan, M.S., Effendy, S., Karimi, I.A., Wazwaz, A., 2019, Improving design and operation at LNG regasification terminals through a corrected storage tank model. Appl. Therm. Eng. 149, 344–353.
Seas, N., 2008, Maritime Gas Fuel Logistics, Transportation.
Vandebroek, L., Berghmans, J., 2012, Safety aspects of the use of LNG for marine propulsion. Procedia Eng. 45, 21–26.

Sauro Pierucci, Flavio Manenti, Giulia Bozzano, Davide Manca (Eds.)
Proceedings of the 30th European Symposium on Computer Aided Process Engineering
(ESCAPE30), May 24-27, 2020, Milano, Italy. © 2020 Elsevier B.V. All rights reserved.
http://dx.doi.org/10.1016/B978-0-12-823377-1.50095-1

A Recycle Model of Spent Liquor in Pre-treatment of Lignocellulosic Biomass

Franco Mangone*, Soledad Gutiérrez

Chemical and Process Systems Engineering Group – Chemical Engineering Institute - Engineering School – Universidad de la República, Julio Herrera y Reissig 565, PC 11300, Montevideo, Uruguay

Abstract

The pre-treatment of lignocellulosic biomass to produce valuable products is one of the key steps of the process, due to the high costs involved. In most typical methods, biomass is treated with a water solution of either mineral or organic acids, caustic soda or organic solvents. The high costs associated with supply of these chemicals and energy requirements make the pre-treatment step a bottleneck in the development of cost-effective bioprocesses. In order to save water, chemicals and energy, a strategy that decouples liquid and solid residence time is proposed. A sequential re-use strategy of the spent liquor has been proposed recently by many authors, independently. It consists in retaining part of the liquor for the subsequent batch, instead of utilizing a fresh liquid mixture. This causes the conditions in every batch cycle to be different, which is a hindrance to effective overall process integration, because it is difficult to include such operation in a general process flowsheet. However, we observe that after several batches have occurred, cycles reach a stationary condition in the sense that initial and final conditions do not change. The presented model describes the behaviour of the cyclic re-use of spent liquor as a function of decision variables such as *removed spent liquor (r)* and *cycle time (t_c)*. For a series of first order reactions, it will be shown that the cyclic condition can be obtained analytically without needing to simulate every preceding stage.

Keywords: sequential, batch, re-use, pre-treatment, biorefinery.

1. Introduction

Pre-treatment of lignocellulosic biomass is a key step in preparation for its conversion to valuable products. Several alternatives exist for this purpose. Some examples are dilute acid pre-treatment, organosolv, steam explosion, and water-solvent fractionation (Davis et al., 2018). The main drawback associated with these processes are their high energy and chemicals related costs – most of them operate at high temperatures and pressures, and some need the addition of solvents or water which incur in additional costs.

In order to develop cost-effective processes, alternatives or enhancements to these technologies need to be proposed. Recently, the strategy of re-utilizing part of the spent liquor from one batch as solvent for the next one has been proposed by different authors (Chen et al. 2018, Park et al. 2018, Vergara et al. 2019). This strategy generates both energy and chemical savings, because the amount of fresh reposition liquid required for each batch (including solvents) is reduced, while also retaining some of the energy from the spent liquor in the form of higher temperatures. Also, more concentrated solutions of valuable sugars released from lignocellulosic biomass are obtained, thus reducing the downstream handling costs (concentration steps).

However, a framework for the design and integration of these kind of batch recycle strategies has not yet been developed, as suggested in the revised literature. The present work will focus on a case-study which will serve as a basis for the development of such framework.

2. Kinetic Model

A diluted acid pretreatment was selected for the case-study. In this process, lignocellulosic biomass is submerged in a diluted sulfuric acid solution, and then heated to temperatures higher than 100°C. Because of this, a fraction of cellulose, hemicelluloses, and acid-soluble lignin are hydrolyzed. The remaining solid is washed and then usually undergoes a hydrolysis step, while the spent liquor can be treated to remove lignin, converting it into a sugar-rich solution.

The hydrolysis of both cellulose and hemicelluloses yields a plethora of 5 and 6 carbon sugars. Oligomer formation is neglected, as suggested by various authors (Aguilar et al., 2002; Guerra-Rodríguez et al. 2012). Also, 5 and 6-carbon sugars will be modeled as xylose and glucose, respectively. Taking this into account, the following kinetic model can be used to represent the system (Aguilar et al., 2002):

$$Gn \xrightarrow{k_1} G \xrightarrow{k_2} Gd$$

$$Xn \xrightarrow{k_3} X \xrightarrow{k_4} Xd$$

Where *Gn*, *G*, and *Gd* represent glucan, glucose and glucose decomposition products, respectively; similarly, *Xn*, *X*, and *Xd* represent xylan, xylose and xylose decomposition products. The main decomposition products of glucose and xylose are hydroximethylfurfural (HMF) and furfural.

This set of chemical reactions occurring in a batch reactor yield a set of ordinary differential equations, whose solution represents the evolution in time of the species present in the broth. The solution is of the form:

$$C_{Gn} = C_{Gn,0} \cdot e^{-k_1 t} \tag{1}$$

$$C_G = C_{G,0} \cdot e^{-k_2 t} + C_{Gn,0} \cdot \frac{k_1}{k_2 - k_1} (e^{-k_1 t} - e^{-k_2 t}) \tag{2}$$

$$C_{Gd} = C_{Gd,0} + C_{G,0} \cdot (1 - e^{-k_2 t}) + C_{Gn,0} \cdot \frac{k_1 \cdot k_2}{k_2 - k_1} \left(\frac{1 - e^{-k_1 t}}{k_1} - \frac{1 - e^{-k_2 t}}{k_2} \right) \tag{3}$$

$$C_{Xn} = C_{Xn,0} \cdot e^{-k_3 t} \tag{4}$$

$$C_X = C_{X,0} \cdot e^{-k_3 t} + C_{Xn,0} \cdot \frac{k_3}{k_4 - k_3} (e^{-k_3 t} - e^{-k_4 t}) \tag{5}$$

$$C_{Xd} = C_{Xd,0} + C_{X,0} \cdot (1 - e^{-k_3 t}) + C_{Xn,0} \cdot \frac{k_3 \cdot k_4}{k_4 - k_3} \left(\frac{1 - e^{-k_3 t}}{k_3} - \frac{1 - e^{-k_4 t}}{k_4} \right) \tag{6}$$

Where C_j represents the concentration of species j at time t, and $C_{j,0}$ is the concentration of said species at the start of the cycle. For simplicity, it can be observed that every equation can be written in the following form:

$$C_i = \sum_j C_{j,0} \cdot a_{i,j}(t) \tag{7}$$

Where $a_{i,j}(t)$ is a coefficient that is a function of t.

3. Cyclic behavior

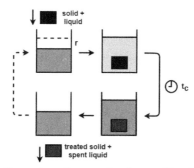

Figure 1– Operation diagram for the reutilization process.

Once the evolution during a single cycle has been deduced, the next step is to model the transition to one cycle to the next. It is assumed that any change is performed instantly, although a time evolution could also be formulated. Figure 1 shows schematically how the cyclic operation works.

The operations that take place between cycles correspond to the removal of the treated solid, alongside a portion r of the total volume of liquid. Then, a new solid is loaded, and enough reposition liquid is added to ensure that the initial liquid volume is the same as in the last cycle. This causes the initial concentration of polymers (glucan, xylan) to be the same for every cycle, since they are contained in the solid. The calculation of polymer concentration is detailed in Aguilar et al., 2002. At the same time, the concentration of monomers and decomposition products will experiment a dilution process, since this species are not added with the reposition. Thus, the process could be described as follows:

$$C_{Gn,0}^{k+1} = C_{Gn,in} \tag{8}$$

$$C_{G,0}^{k+1} = r \cdot C_{G,f}^{k} \tag{9}$$

$$C_{Gd,0}^{k+1} = r \cdot C_{Gd,f}^{k} \tag{10}$$

$$C_{Xn,0}^{k+1} = C_{Xn,in} \tag{11}$$

$$C_{X,0}^{k+1} = r \cdot C_{X,f}^{k} \tag{12}$$

$$C_{Xd,0}^{k+1} = r \cdot C_{Xd,f}^{k} \tag{13}$$

Where the supraindex k represents the cycle number. This set of equations will be denominated *handling functions*. This sequential operation is expected to reach a stationary condition after several cycles. An intuitive approach to understand this is that as the solution concentrates from cycle to cycle, the liquor removal step will remove more and more dissolved species (because of high concentrations); thus, at some point, the removed material will be equal to the generated species during the reaction step. Furthermore, it is assumed that after a large time t has passed, the concentrations will reach a "stationary condition", in the sense that the initial and final conditions for subsequent batches will be the same. One way to formulate that observation is by imposing the following:

$$C_{j,f}{}^{k+1} = C_{j,f}{}^{k} = C_{j,f}{}^{\infty} \tag{14}$$

Which states that the concentration at the end of cycles k and $k+1$ must be the same for a given species j. With Eq. 14, it is possible to find the initial and final concentrations for the stationary condition mentioned earlier, which will be called the *invariant cycle* (IC). This IC will have an *invariant initial condition* (IIC), and an *invariant final condition* (IFC).

The analytical procedure for the IC condition is rather straightforward:

1. Take the final condition for cycle k, for any given species j.

2. Apply the *handling functions* described in equations 8 to 13. A new initial condition will be obtained.

3. Apply the time evolution described by equations 1 to 6. A new final condition will be obtained.

4. Impose the condition described in equation 14. Operate to find and expression for $C_{j,f}{}^{\infty}$, the IFCs.

5. Find the IICs by applying the *handling functions* again, to the values found in the previous point.

This results in the expressions shown below:

$$C_{Gn,f}{}^{\infty} = C_{Gn,in} \cdot a_{Gn,Gn} \tag{15}$$

$$C_{G,f}{}^{\infty} = \frac{C_{Gn,in} \cdot a_{G,Gn}}{1 - r \cdot a_{G,G}} \tag{16}$$

$$C_{Gd,f}{}^{\infty} = \frac{C_{Gn,in} \cdot a_{Gd,Gn} + r \cdot C_{G,f}{}^{\infty} \cdot a_{Gd,G}}{1 - r \cdot a_{Gd,Gd}} \tag{17}$$

$$C_{Xn,f}{}^{\infty} = C_{Xn,in} \cdot a_{Xn,Xn} \tag{18}$$

$$C_{X,f}{}^{\infty} = \frac{C_{Xn,in} \cdot a_{X,Xn}}{1 - r \cdot a_{X,X}} \tag{19}$$

$$C_{Xd,f}{}^{\infty} = \frac{C_{Xn,in} \cdot a_{Xd,Xn} + r \cdot C_{X,f}{}^{\infty} \cdot a_{Xd,X}}{1 - r \cdot a_{Xd,Xd}} \tag{20}$$

These values are shown in Figure 2 as dashed lines, plotted alongside a simulation of several cycles of operation. The obtained expressions are an accurate representation of the initial and final conditions of the invariant cycle.

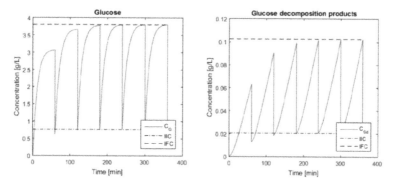

Figure 2 – Stationary condition reached after a few cycles for glucose and its decomposition products.

3.1. Inspecting the solution

Upon inspection, the expressions obtained in equations 15 to 20 do not depend on the initial conditions of the system. That is, given two different initial conditions, eventually the exact same IC will be reached. Importantly then, what determines the IC is not the selected initial condition, but rather the operative parameters governing the cyclic behavior, such as the cycle time t_c. Figure 3 shows this principle in action, where two different initial conditions are chosen for the glucose decomposition products.

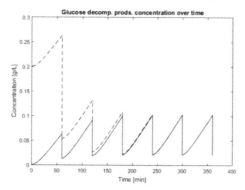

Figure 3 – Two different initial conditions reaching the same IC for glucose decomposition products.

4. Invariant-cycle-oriented design

In practice, the first few cycles will resemble a continuous reactor startup, since subsequent cycles will have different initial conditions. But after enough time, the IC condition will be *the only* operative condition. Thus, the IC is what should be incorporated for equipment and process design, utilizing the results from equations 15 to 20. However, the advantages of this approach are not immediately obvious.

In the presented system, operating with this reutilization strategy allows for reduction of liquid reposition costs, and heating utilities. Also, the concentrated spent liquor could be utilized for fermentation purposes after adequate treatment. Usually, this liquid must be concentrated prior to further usage - and because of the reutilization scheme, the liquid will naturally be more concentrated even before being treated. This means that lower concentration utilities will be needed, which in turn means lower overall costs.

All the previously mentioned points, however, are not independent from the selected downstream process. Integration is key for the design of the reutilization strategy. In this sense, having explicit, analytical expressions for the IC (Eq. 15 to 20) could allow for optimization opportunities, by manipulating decision variables such as the cycle time t_c, the reposition factor r, or the solid to liquid ratio. As an example, higher values of r cause the initial concentrations to resemble the reposition concentrations more strongly. Taking it to an extreme, when $r = 1$, then the initial concentrations of the IC will be *exactly* the ones from the reposition. This is in fact the case of standard batch operation, where no liquor is reutilized from cycle to cycle.

5. Conclusions and future work

IC conditions could potentially appear in various operation types, the obvious example being the cyclic batch operations. Other examples could include more complex cyclic operations (for instance, Sequential Batch Reactors in the context of wastewater treatment), as well as integration of discrete and continuous flows. This work presents a first approach to a simple case, to illustrate how the methodology works.

Nevertheless, cases may and will arise in which analytical solutions are not attainable, and at that point, a deeper understanding of the IC phenomenon will be needed. It is in this regard that further developments need to be made. Questions such as existence of the IC, or its unicity should be addressed. This has deep implications, connecting to the stability of the solutions and how it interacts with the sequential operation.

Lastly, algorithms may be developed where analytical solutions are not possible, to allow for process integration even in complex operation schemes.

References

R. Aguilar, J.A. Ramirez, G. Garrote, M. Vázquez, 2002, "Kinetic dtudy of the acid hydrolysisof sugar cane bagasse", Journal of Food Engineering, 55, 309-318.

X. Chen, E. Kuhn, N. Nagle, R. Nelson, L. Tao, N. Crawford, M. Tucker, 2018, "Recycling of Dilute Deacetylation Black Liquor to Enable Efficient Recovery and Reuse of Spent Chemicals and Biomass Pretreatment Waste", Frontiers in Energy Research.

R. Davis, N. Grundl, L. Tao, M. J. Biddy, E.C.D. Tan, G.T. Beckham, D. Humbird, D.N. Thompson, M.S. Roni, 2018, "Process Design and Economics for the Conversion of Lignocellulosic Biomass to Hydrocarbon Fuels and Coproducts: 2018 Biochemical Design Case Update".

E. Guerra-Rodriguez, O. M. Portilla-Rivera, L. Jarquín-Enríquez, J. A. Ramírez, Manuel Vázquez, 2012, "Acid hydrolisis of wheat straw: A kinetic study", Biomass and Bioenergy, 36, 346-355.

Y.C. Park, T.H. Kim, J.S. Kim, 2018, "Flow-Through Pretreatment of Corn Stover by Recycling Organosolv to Reduce Waste Solvent", Energies, 11.

P. Vergara, F. García-Ochoa, M. Lardero, S. Gutiérrez, J.C. Villar, 2019, "Liquor re-use strategy in lignocellulosic biomass fractionation with ethanol-water mixtures", Bioresource Technology, 280, 396-403.

Sauro Pierucci, Flavio Manenti, Giulia Bozzano, Davide Manca (Eds.)
Proceedings of the 30th European Symposium on Computer Aided Process Engineering
(ESCAPE30), May 24-27, 2020, Milano, Italy. © 2020 Elsevier B.V. All rights reserved.
http://dx.doi.org/10.1016/B978-0-12-823377-1.50096-3

Promo – a Multi-disciplinary Process Modelling Suite

Heinz A Preisig

Dept of Chemical Engineering, Norwegian University of Science and Technology, Trondheim, Norway

Heinz.Preisig@chemeng.ntnu.no

Abstract

Multi-disciplinary, multi-scale simulations are in demand as computing becomes increasingly available and the different disciplines' problem solutions become mature and broadly applicable. Material modelling has taken a lead in the subject and ProMo is one of the possible solutions to the still very intrinsic problem of supporting the process of sketching a process as a topology to an integrated solution solving multi-faceted problems that require bits and pieces from various knowledge domains. ProMo coupled with the open platform of MoDeNa provide an integrated solutions.

Keywords: simulation, ontology, computational engineering

1. Concepts

Modelling of chemical/biological processes is intrinsically a multi-scale, and not at least, a multi-disciplinary task. It incorporates the macroscopic scale of the process, the intrinsic smaller elements that make up the process, the description of the process-enabling control layer and not at least the description of all the materials in that make up the process and are being processed. Often one requires a finer granular model for individual processes where it is necessary to include a minimal level of detail to capture the larger-scale behaviour. Capturing the behaviour of the involved materials is nearly always a major challenge. It is either macroscopic models of generic nature fitted to experimental data or increasingly the option of using molecular modelling or related techniques, such as reported by Klamt (2018) to estimate the physical properties of the involved materials. Mixtures represent one of the main challenges. Experimental data are either difficult to obtain or very expensive to generate.

Multi-scale modelling and consequent simulation are seen as a difficult subject. It requires input from several disciplines' information that requires several specialists. The Framework 7 MoDeNa project (MoDeNa 2016) is a nice demonstration where polyurethane foam was modelled from quantum to mechanical properties. The project used quantum chemistry to model the chemical reactions and molecular modelling for physical properties of the polymer system and the gas phase. On top came several layers of mesoscopic models that yield beyond other things the viscosity for the combined evolving polymer and gas bubbles. At last, computational fluid mechanics reconstructed the growth of the foam in a cylinder that corresponded to the standardised laboratory experiments. The whole is followed by a mechanical analysis, which again stretches the length scales from the molecular level to the mesoscopic structures to the macroscopic mechanical properties of the foam product. The project demonstrates the multi-scale, multi-disciplinary aspect of such a process nicely.

Several of the large companies have established multi-disciplinary modelling groups who have the task to meet these challenges. ProMo is one possible answer as it is the multi-disciplinary aspect that is approached in ProMo: models to be built on the foundation of discipline-specific ontologies.

The ProMo environment grew out of an earlier development, which started in the mid 1980ties with the modelling of life support systems for NASA and eventually resulted in a software package we called Modeller, currently maintained by Mobatec BV (NL). ProMo is ontology-based and enabling the integration of different disciplines' models generically.

2. **Approach**

ProMo is a pure mathematical modelling tool, which consists of several components that support three classes of users: The first class makes it possible for the expert to capture the domain-specific knowledge in the form of mathematical equations. The second class of users utilises the captured knowledge by using the defined entity models as standard building blocks. The third using the final product to explore the issues defined for the associated case.

2.1. The Expert

The overall philosophy is to build models from principle components, entity models, which describes the conceptional basic units in the discipline.

In physics, depending on the scale, this may be a model for an electron, an atom or a molecule if one requires molecular information or it may be a unit cell if one describes a continuous material. It is the purpose of the model that determines on what level to model and to what level of detail, thus the fundamental granularity of the models to be constructed using the entity models captured in the respective ontology.

The process starts with generating a tree of what later is linked mathematical model ontologies. It reflects the structure of the disciplines. In physics, the tree on the top level typically reflects the fact that one conceptionally distinguishes between continuum models and particulate models. Within the continuum, one has the two classes of phases, namely fluids and solids and fluids split into liquids and gases, for example. On how to structure this tree is up to the experts but may also be taken from the European Material Modelling Council's EMMO, which stands for European Material Modelling Ontology. The EMMO is an attempt to standardise primarily the language, which is used to describe models. Thus defines a taxonometry/syntax that serve the purpose of establishing in the next step the mathematical entity models.

2.2. The Translator

In the broadest sense, a translator is a person who translates a given problem into a solver for the given case. Previously, we would use the term "modeller", though this would also include the expert's activity, namely the definition of the entity models.

2.2.1. Topology

The translator is building the application process model by composing the topology of the process model using the canvas of a graphical tool. The graphical language is purposely kept simple leaning on to the representation introduced in the past (Elve & Preisig 2017). The process begins by utilising the entity models taken from ProMo's initial model library. Each of these entity models is equipped with the graphical symbol.

The translator can choose from whatever ontologies are being made available to him. For example, there is an ontology for physical processes, an ontology that captures the physical property computations based on energy functions constructed from equations of states. An ontology capturing controllers provides the means to construct process models with controllers. An ontology that captures the ecology-related measures or techno-economical measures provides the means to add performance measures. Ontologies may also provide the information of linking in external programs that solve a particular problem, such as molecular dynamics codes, or computational fluid dynamics code.

The constructed topology can be saved either in pieces or as a whole to establish a composite model, which though is stored as an extension to the initial entity model library.

2.2.2. Case

This block building process is followed by an instantiation procedure, where constants and initial conditions are equipped with numerical values and assumptions can be introduced, allowing for the simplification of the build unit model. The initialisation section may also add order-of-magnitude assumptions requiring a model reduction in order to maintain a proper unit model.

2.2.3. Cases of Cases

The so-constructed unit model can then be placed into the extended entity model library where it awaits further use in an even more complex model. The building process is thus recursive, including all disciplines at all times.

2.2.4. Task Factory

The last element in the sequence is the generation of the actual code, a process that is done fully automatically except for instantiating the numerical solver. Here one may choose between different alternatives but also the settings of the parameters controlling the performance of the numerical solver. This approach is applicable if one solves essentially a set of equations that are properly instantiated and structured.

If the model includes the use of external programs, then two things need to happen. The first is the above, namely the parts that are to be solved as sets of equations must be coupled with an appropriate numerical solver, which applies to each cluster of equations. Key is that the tasks are not independent. They have built-in sections that are devoted to the interaction with the other tasks. The overall problem is then represented as a workflow. It is executed in what is currently called an Open System Platform or an Orchestrator, of which the MoDeNa (2016) and the Symphony (Ashibon et al 2015) are examples.

2.3. The User

The term "digital twin" is lately used for a simulation of a specified system. One may project the idea into the "digital twin" that it is meant to behave the same way as the modelled system, where "behave" relates to input/output behaviour: if I tickle it on this point, it does respond in a particular way, kind of thought.

If one allows for "tuning knops" allowing for changing the behaviour and allows for modifying the quantities that relate to defining the operating conditions, then the "digital twin" is to replace the real-world object with a virtual, computational experiment. Driving force to establish a "digital twin" is costs, ability to cover a wide range of operating conditions, experimentation with design parameters, consequently quite obviously also optimisation an many other attractive possibilities to "play" with the system.

One of the objectives of ProMo is to produce stand-alone digital twins, thus allowing to use it in isolation, out in the plant, or without a network, thereby avoiding all issues about protecting data and other commercial interests.

3. The Challenges

The project has to respond to many challenges. Not at least a social one: anything new is different, and anything different is not what people know. Indeed, this also applies to the theoretical background required to get a complete insight into the definition of patterns that are generic enough to capture the multi-disciplinary, and consequently multi scientific language, problems. It requires a high level of abstraction, while for the users, the interfaces must be simple, self-explainable, nice to look at and not at least functional.

Interoperability of the different parts is a key technical issue. The developments in the Web-based community is moving fast and generates increasingly more facilities to raise the level of abstraction to improve interoperability. Technologies like the semantic network, REST and other efforts move towards a more structured approach to the problem. To mention one of the currently hot issues is to collect data from a distributed set of databases, each of which has a different structure though with related contents.

ProMo implements model reduction technology, thereby removing the effects of some typical assumptions, like order-of-magnitude assumptions often in their core being time-scale assumptions. Pressure dynamics being event-dynamic requires rather sophisticated splitting of the process topology into two (Pujan & Preisig 2020), a slow one for the mass & energy dynamics and one for the pressure/velocity distribution of the fluids in the plant. Othe assumptions lead to overdetermined equation systems because it introduces an algebraic relation between fundamental state variables, therefore requiring a reduction of the state space. A common assumption of the latter type is a constant volume assumption for a multi-phase control volume.

A specific challenge is the design of the input language for the input language. The introduction of explicit naming of the dimensions and associating them with index sets, provided an elegant and efficient solution that certainly is a compromise to the intrinsic, domain-specific terminologies and symbolisms.

3.1. Workflows

When approaching multi-scale modelling and simulation problems, it becomes necessary to enable the use of external programs. It is common that different disciplines generate their own solutions, and it is certainly not productive to re-invent the wheel by mapping the equations into the ontology, define simulation cases and solve them using a numerical solver. Instead, one needs to enable the construction of a workflow, which logically couples different computing activities together. The cited MoDeNa project is an illustrative example. In the ontology, external solutions appear as input/output functions with well-defined interfaces to the calling and receiving code. ProMo represents and handles interfaces such that they are mapped into a data model ontology, which in turn can be used to generate automatically the code pieces that realise the interfaces. The MoDeNa orchestrator, an Open System Platform, executes the workflow using the defined logics, models and external solvers. Obviously, to execute a workflow, one must have access to the required external codes, which for commercial tools implies having licences for their use.

4. Architecture

ProMo utilises existing ontologies. Specifically the EMMO, European Material Modelling Ontology, is used to describe the physical parts. It introduces the nomenclature, taxonometry of the physics world seen from the material modelling side. ProMo is though not limited to EMMO, but currently also used control in order to enable the simulation of plants. We plan to extend this in the near future to the techno-economic domain, life-cycle analysis and other relevant subject. Figure 1 shows the current arrangements.

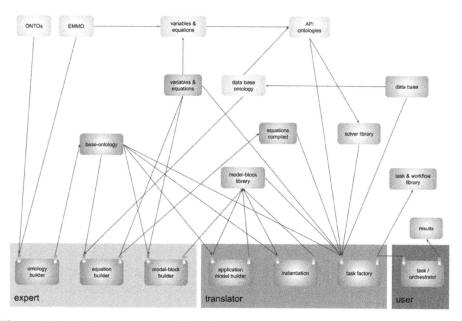

Figure 1: ProMo's components and functionalities

The yellowish boxes are OWL-based ontologies generated and maintained by Protege or from the software using python's "owlready" package. The variable/equations ontology is the core object of interest. It represents a super bipartite graph of variables and equations, where the "super" indicates that a variable may be computed by more then one expression. The latter requirement becomes obvious if one thinks of issues like computing the chemical potential for different phases. The task builder uses a type of reasoner, as they are termed in the internet-related jargon. The reasoner is tailored to process super bipartite graphs. ProMo's equation editor insists of building the equation system systematically, as reported earlier (Preisig 2010), which addresses also very important the indexing issue. The process is preceded by defining the index sets and the object required to capture the topology, thus the incidence matrices. In the equation editor, one starts with defining the constants, the initial conditions of the state equations. One then follows the scheme of defining the integrals of the differential states, followed by the differential balances. Those are defined by giving the flows and the kinetics, latter representing the internal change, of the balance equations. Finally one requires to close the loop and define the material properties and geometry. The material properties is of particular interest. We favour the idea to use the canonical energy surfaces and the configuration space as defined in the contact geometry theory (Arnold 1989). The specific models for the materials, including mixtures then come in as equation of states and properties are canonical derivatives.

5. Conclusions

ProMo as the principle modelling tool combined with the MoDeNa's composer develop into a powerful tool to model a wide range of processes. The ontology-based approach yields a compact and effective representation of multi-disciplinary model components, which in the continuation can be utilised to build recursively more an more complex models. Equation systems are constructed systematically satisfying stringent consistency conditions resulting in a lower-triagonal multi-bipartite graph, which allows for systematic handling in the task and workflow builder. Particularly, it should be noticed, that a given equation only appears once in contrast to what the standard approach is in block-based modelling tools, both on chemical engineering but also in other domains.

The future looks bright: we have the algebra to generate reduced-order models thereby implementing time-scale and other order-of-magnitude assumptions systematically. This then removes all a priori checks on the equations usually done, like degree of freedom and differential index. Scale integration has no real limits beyond not being able to compute it. ProMo allows to do derivations in the sense that starting with generic equations like the conservation of fundamental extensive quantities, one can generate simplified models through the implementation of assumptions and constraints combined with model reduction. The technology can be extended to include the development of solution algorithms. Here the feature of automatic compilation in any target language is a key.

6. References

Arnold, V I, **1989**, Contact geometry: The geometrical method of Gibbs's thermodynamics, in Proc. Gibbs Symp (new Haven, CT), 163-179

Elve, A T & Preisig, H A, **2017**, Graph-based mathematical modelling – concepts, FOCAPO/CPC

Hashibon, A.; Rasp, T.; Franklin, N.; Tziakos, I.; Pinte, D.; Dadvand, P.; Roig, C.; Mattila, K.; Puurtinen, T.; Hiltunen, K.; Roman-Perez, G.; Garcia, G.; Adler, J. 2015 Common universal data structures (CUDS) and vocabulary in the SimPhoNy integrated framework , INTOP, Workshop of the European Multi-Scale Modelling Cluster EUMMC - Interoperability in MultiscaleModelling of Nano-Enabled Materials, 3, **2015**, Jyväskylä/Finland

Klamt, A. **2018** The COSMO and COSMO-RS solvation models WIREs Comp Mol Sci, 8, 1-11 MoDeNa, **2016,** http://modena.units.it, accessed 11/2019

H.A. Preisig, **2014**, A Graph Approach to Representing the Pressure Distribution in Complex Plants, Comput. Aided Chem. Eng., 33, 865-870

Preisig, H A **2010**, Constructing and maintaining proper process models. Comp & Chem Eng 34(9) 1543-1555

Pujan, R & Preisig, Heinz A, **2020**, Systematic modelling of flow and pressure distribution in a complex tank, Comp Aided Chem Eng, this volume

Sauro Pierucci, Flavio Manenti, Giulia Bozzano, Davide Manca (Eds.)
Proceedings of the 30th European Symposium on Computer Aided Process Engineering
(ESCAPE30), May 24-27, 2020, Milano, Italy. © 2020 Elsevier B.V. All rights reserved.
http://dx.doi.org/10.1016/B978-0-12-823377-1.50097-5

Performance Evaluation of Solid Oxide Fuel Cell Coupling to Biogas Tri-reforming with Installation of Hydrogen-Selective Membrane Separator

Saebea D.[a,b*],Soisuwan S.[a,b],Patcharavorachot Y.[c]

aDepartment of Chemical Engineering, Faculty of Engineering, Burapha University, Chonburi 20131, Thailand
bReasearch Unit of Developing technology and Innovation of Alternative Energy for Industries, Burapha University, Chonburi 20131, Thailand
cDepartment of Chemical Engineering, Faculty of Engineering, King Mongkut's Institute of Technology Ladkrabang, Bangkok 10520, Thailand

Abstract

Due to high CO_2 composition in biogas, hydrogen concentration produced from the biogas reforming process is low, which has negative effect on the SOFC efficiency. Therefore, aims of this study are to improve and analyze the performance of solid oxide fuel cell (SOFC) integrated with hydrogen production from tri-reforming process of biogas coupling to hydrogen-selective membrane separator. The simulation results show that the increase of pressure increases the hydrogen separation in Pd/Ag membrane separator. The Pd/Ag membrane separator can separate hydrogen of 47.5 %, at 8 bar. When comparing the integrated system of SOFC and biogas tri-reforming without/with installing hydrogen-selective membrane separator, the efficiency of system with coupling to hydrogen-selective membrane separator is higher than that without coupling to hydrogen-selective membrane separator about 13-14.7 %.

Keywords: Solid oxide fuel cell; Hydrogen-selective membrane separator; Tri-reforming process; Biogas

1. Introduction

Solid oxide fuel cell (SOFC) is interesting device for electricity generation of large scale. It is operated at high temperatures. It has high electrical efficiency, fuel flexibility, and high efficiency system from using high-grade heat of exhaust (Saebea et al., 2018), compared to other types of fuel cell. Hydrogen as fuel is required for SOFC operation to product the electricity via the electrochemical reaction. Generally, hydrogen is mainly produced from fossil resources, i.e., steam reforming of natural gas, fraction of petroleum refining process, and coal gasification (Cruz et al., 2018). To reduce the environmental problem and enhance energy security, the utilization of sustainable and environment-friendly resources to substitute fossil resources has been concerned. Biogas has been considerably received attention because it can be produced through anaerobic digestion from different feedstocks such as seeds, crop residues, woody crops, and agricultural wastes (Ithnin and Hashim, 2019).

There are various reforming processes of hydrocarbon production. The main compositions of raw biogas are methane (40-70%) and carbon dioxide (30-60 %) (Gao et al., 2018). Thus, the biogas can produce hydrogen via the dry reforming in order not to separate CO_2 and to utilize CO_2 as main composition of biogas. However, the dry reforming is also strongly endothermic reaction and lower hydrogen yield than the steam reforming. To overcome these problems, the tri-reforming is interesting for hydrogen production derived from biogas due to including advantages of steam reforming, partial oxidation, and dry reforming.

Many researchers have been focused on the instillation of increased purified hydrogen process in the SOFC system. The instillation of hydrogen purification process can be improved the SOFC performance. There are various technologies of hydrogen purification. Pd/Ag membrane separator shows an interesting technology for hydrogen purification due to its large solubility of hydrogen over a wide temperature range (Sharma et al., 2017). The installation of Pd/Ag membrane separator after biogas tri-reforming can increase the hydrogen concentration in syngas. However, the suitability of installation of membrane separator for the combined system of SOFC and tri-reforming should be studied. This work aims to study the combined system between SOFC and biogas tri-reforming with/without installing Pd/Ag membrane separator. The effect of pressure on the membrane separation and SOFC electrical efficiency is firstly investigated. Then, the performance of biogas-fuelled SOFC systems with and without installing Pd/Ag membrane separator is compared.

2. Process description

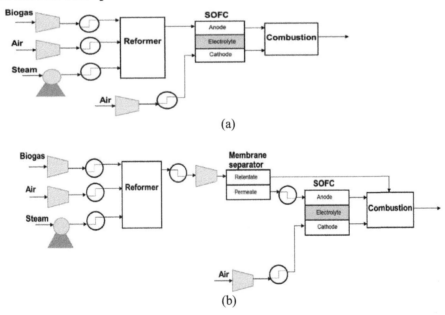

(a)

(b)

Figure 1: Schematic diagram of the integrated system (a) without and (b) with coupling to hydrogen-selective membrane separator.

The treated biogas is considered as feedstock. Biogas contains 60 %CH_4 and 40 %CO_2. Figure 1(a) shows the integrated systems between SOFC and reformer without coupling to hydrogen-selective membrane separator. From Figure 1(a), the biogas and air are compressed while water is pumped. They are heated at 873 K and fed to the mixer. In tri-reforming process, the syngas is produced from conversion of biogas with steam reforming, partial oxidation, and dry reforming reactions. The reactions of biogas tri-reforming were reported by Saebea et al. (2019). Then, the syngas is heated and introduced to the fuel channel of SOFC. Meanwhile the compressed air is heated and sent to SOFC at the air channel. The electricity is produced from SOFC via the electrochemical reaction. Figure 1(b) shows the retrofitted system with adding the hydrogen-selective membrane separator between the tri-reforming unit and SOFC. In the integrated systems between SOFC and reformer with coupling to hydrogen-selective membrane separator, the temperature of syngas from reformer is decreased at the suitable condition of hydrogen-selective membrane separator. It is fed to the retentate side of the membrane separator. H_2 from the retentate side permeates through membrane to the permeate side. Subsequently, H_2 from the permeate side is compressed and heated at the operating temperature of SOFC. The exhausted gas from the retentate side of the membrane separator is sent to the combustor.

2.1 *SOFC model*

SOFC can produce the electrical power via the electrochemical reaction. In the cathode side, oxygen ion is produced from the reduction reaction. Oxygen ion diffuses from the cathode to the anode through electrolyze and reacts with hydrogen via the oxidation reaction. Consequently, the electrons are produced and flows to external circuit. This is the generation of the electricity. The SOFC electrical power can be calculated as follows:

$$P_{sofc} = V \times I \tag{1}$$

where I is the current density and V is the operating voltage. The operating voltage can be evaluated from the reversible voltage (Eq. (2)) subtracted by three main internal voltage losses, i.e., ohmic overpotential (η_{ohmic}), activation overpotentials (η_{act}), and concentration overpotentials (η_{conc}), as shown in Eqs.(3)-(5).

$$E^{OCV} = E^0 - \frac{RT}{2F} \ln(\frac{P_{H_2O}}{P_{H_2} P_{O_2}^{0.5}}) \tag{2}$$

$$\eta_{ohm} = iR_{ohm} \tag{3}$$

$$\eta_{act} = \frac{RT}{F} \sinh^{-1}\left(\frac{i}{2i_{0,a}}\right) + \frac{RT}{F} \sinh^{-1}\left(\frac{i}{2i_{0,c}}\right) \tag{4}$$

$$\eta_{conc,anode} = \frac{RT}{2F} \ln\left(\frac{P_{H_2O,TPB} P_{H_2,f}}{P_{H_2O,f} P_{H_2,TPB}}\right) + \frac{RT}{4F} \ln\left(\frac{P_{O_2,a}}{P_{O_2,TPB}}\right) \tag{5}$$

where $p_{i,}$ is the partial pressure of H_2, H_2O and O_2 at air and fuel channels; $p_{i,TPB}$ is the partial pressure of gases at triple phase boundary; R_{ohm} is the internal electrical resistance; $i_{0,a}$ and $i_{0,c}$ are the exchange current density pre-exponential factors of the anode and cathode respectively. The electrochemical parameters can refer from Saebea et al. (2018).

2.2 *Hydrogen-selective membrane separator model*

Pd/Ag composite membrane is used as hydrogen-selective membrane in separator. H_2 flux is the amount of H_2 diffusing through membrane as follows:

$$J_{H_2} = P_i \cdot \frac{A}{L} \cdot \left(\left(P_r \cdot X_{H_2,r(ave)} \right) - \left(P_p \cdot X_{H_2,p} \right) \right) \tag{6}$$

Gas flux is function of the membrane permeability (Pi), the membrane thickness (L), and the gas concentration. P_r and P_p are pressure at retentate side and permeate side, respectively. $X_{i,r(ave)}$ is average mole fraction of species i at the feed side. $X_{i,p}$ is mole fraction of species i at the permeate side. The membrane permeability depends on the temperature can be explained by Arrhenius equation.

$$X_{i,r(ave)} = Q_0 \exp\left(\frac{-Ea}{RT} \right) \tag{7}$$

Q_0 is pre-exponential factor; and Ea is the activation energy for permeation. Q_0 and Ea are 2.06×10^{-8} mol/m.s.Pa$^{0.5}$ and Ea = 2.59×10^3 kJ/mol, respectively (Faizal et al, 2015). SOFC electrical efficiency (η_{el}) and the thermal efficiency (η_{th}) are calculated by using the following expression;

$$\text{SOFC electrical efficiency} = \frac{P_{sofc}}{\dot{n}_{H_2} LHV_{H_2} + \dot{n}_{CO} LHV_{CO} + \dot{n}_{CH_4} LHV_{CH_4}} \tag{8}$$

$$\text{Thermal efficiency} = \frac{Q_{rec} - Q_{use}}{\dot{n}_i LHV_i} \tag{9}$$

where $\dot{n}_i$ is the molar flow rate of species i at inlet; LHV_i is the lower heating value; Q_{use} is the overall thermal energy consumption in the system; and Q_{rec} is the thermal energy obtained from the combustion referring to 100 °C.

3. Results and discussion

3.1. *Effect of pressure on hydrogen-selective membrane separator*

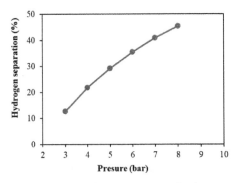

Figure 2: Effect of operating pressure on hydrogen separation.

The operating pressure of system has a direct effect on the retentane pressure of hydrogen-selective membrane separator. Figure 2 shows the effect of various retentate pressures in the range of 3-8 bar on the percentage of hydrogen separation, at 623 K. The membrane area and thickness are specified at 5,200 m² and 200 μm, respectively. From Figure 2, it indicates that the separation of hydrogen from syngas increases with increasing the retentane pressure. At pressure of 8 bar, Pd/Ag membrane separator can separate hydrogen of 47.5 %. This can be explained that the increase of retentate pressure results in enhancing the difference of pressure between retentate and permeate sides, leading to the rise of driving force of hydrogen flux and diffusing hydrogen through membrane.

3.2. Comparison of systems without/with H2 selective-membrane separator

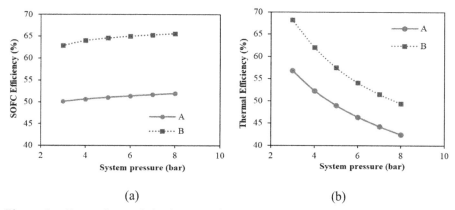

(a)   (b)

Figure 3: Comparison of the integrated system of SOFC and tri-reforming without coupling to hydrogen-selective membrane separator (System A) and that with coupling to hydrogen-selective membrane separator (System B) at various operating pressures (a) SOFC efficiency and (b) thermal efficiency.

The integrated systems of SOFC and tri-reforming without or with coupling to hydrogen-selective membrane separator at various operating pressures in the range of 3 to 8 bar are compared. The biogas tri-reforming process and SOFC of both systems are operated at the same condition. SOFC was operated at the fuel utilization of 75 %, air ratio of 8.5, and temperature 1073 K. For the system with hydrogen-selective membrane separator, the membrane was fixed at area of 5,500 m² and temperature of 623 K. Figure 3(a) indicates the SOFC with coupling to hydrogen-selective membrane separator can increase the SOFC efficiency about 13-14.7 %, compared with system without coupling to hydrogen-selective membrane separator. This is because the fuel fed to SOFC in system with coupling to hydrogen-selective membrane separator has rather high hydrogen purity. The increase of hydrogen concentration in the gas input to SOFC results in the enhancement of SOFC power density. The increment of system pressure has a more effect on the increase of efficiency of system with coupling to hydrogen-selective membrane separator than that without coupling to hydrogen-selective membrane separator, as shown in Figure 3(a). It can be explained that the increasing in the operating pressure has a positive effect on both membrane separator and SOFC. Meanwhile, the increase of pressure has a minor influence on SOFC efficiency under operation at high pressure. From 3(b), the thermal efficiency of both systems reduces with incresing pressure. When comparing both systems, the thermal efficiency of system coupling to Pd/Ag membrane separator is higher than that without coupling to Pd/Ag membrane separator.

4. Conclusions

In this work, the integrated system SOFC and biogas tri-reforming without/with coupling to Pd/Ag membrane separator were investigated and compared. The hydrogen permeability of Pd/Ag membrane separator at various pressures was firstly studied. The increase of retentate pressure enhances the hydrogen permeability of Pd/Ag membrane separator specified membrane area of 5,200 m^2 and 200 μm. At pressure of 8 bar, the hydrogen permeability is highest of 47.5 %. Moreover, the SOFC efficiency of the integrated system of SOFC and biogas tri-reforming without/with coupling Pd/Ag membrane separator increases whereas thermal efficiency of both systems reduces with increasing the pressure. When comparing the both systems, the electrical and thermal efficiencies of the integrated system with coupling to the Pd/Ag membrane separator are higher than that without coupling to the Pd/Ag membrane separator.

Acknowledgments

Support from the Thailand Research Fund and the Office of the Higher Education Commission (MRG6280043) and Burapha University is gratefully acknowledged.

References

P. L. Cruz, Z. Navas-Anguita, D. Iribarren, J. Dufour, 2018, Exergy analysis of hydrogen production via biogas dry reforming. International Journal of Hydrogen Energy, 43, 1168-11695.

H. M. Faizal. Y. Kawasaki, T. Yokomori, T. Ueda, 2015, Experimental and theoretical investigation on hydrogen permeation with flat sheet Pd/Ag membrane for hydrogen mixture with various inlet H_2 mole fractions and species. Separation and Purification Technology, 149, 208–215.

N. H. C. Ithnin, H. Hashim, 2019. Predictive modelling for biogas generation from palm oil mill effluent (POME). Chemical Engineering transaction, 72, 313-318.

Y. Gao, J. Jiang, Y. Meng, F. Yan, A. Aihemaiti, 2018, A review of recent developments in hydrogen production via biogas dry reforming. Energy Conversion and Management, 171, 133-135.

D. Saebea, S. Authayanun, Y. Patcharavorachot, N. Chatrattanawet, A. Arpornwichanop, 2018, Electrochemical performance assessment of lowtemperature solid oxide fuel cell with YSZ-based and SDC-based electrolytes. International Journal of Hydrogen Energy, 43, 921-931.

D. Saebea, S. Authayanun, A. Arpornwichanop, 2019, Process simulation of bio-dimethyl ether synthesis from tri-reforming of biogas: CO_2 utilization. Energy, 175, 36-45.

D. Saebea, S. Authayanun, Y. Patcharavorachot, A. Arpornwichanop, 2018, Performance evaluation of biogas-fed solid oxide fuel cell system coupling with CO_2-selective membrane separator. Chemical Engineering transaction, 70, 1963-1968.

R. Sharma, A. Kumar, R. K. Upadhyay, 2017, Performance comparison of methanol steam reforming integrated to Pd/Ag membrane: Membrane reformer vs. membrane separator. Separation and Purification Technology, 183, 194–203.

Sauro Pierucci, Flavio Manenti, Giulia Bozzano, Davide Manca (Eds.)
Proceedings of the 30th European Symposium on Computer Aided Process Engineering
(ESCAPE30), May 24-27, 2020, Milano, Italy. © 2020 Elsevier B.V. All rights reserved.
http://dx.doi.org/10.1016/B978-0-12-823377-1.50098-7

A Grain-Scale Study of Swelling Composite Porous Media Made of Fibres and Particles

Tommaso Santagata[a], Roberto Solimene[b]*, Gilberto Aprea[c], Piero Salatino[a]

[a]*Dipartimento di Ingegneria Chimica, dei Materiali e della Produzione Industriale, Università degli Studi di Napoli Federico II, P.le Tecchio, Napoli, Italy*
[b]*Istituto di Ricerche sulla Combustione, Consiglio Nazionale delle Ricerche, P.le Tecchio, Napoli, Italy*
[c]*Fater S.p.A., Via Alessandro Volta, 10, Pescara, Italy*
solimene@irc.cnr.it

Abstract

A numerical study based on the discrete element method (DEM) is presented for the characterization of morphological properties of absorbent hygiene products (AHP) relevant to their performance. The model was developed in YADE, an open source software focused on DEM. The simulations reproduce the samples as they were granular beds. The code allows an easily tuning of relevant numerical and physical parameters. A series of preliminary estimations has been necessary to faithfully represent a realistic AHP sample. The results of the DEM computational experiments have been compared to the values obtained from physical experiments reported in literature.

Keywords: porous media, swelling, absorbent hygiene products, SAP, DEM.

1. Introduction

In the field of absorbent porous media, a high demand for accurate and reliable measurements strongly drives the scientific community to take the knowledge further. Many permeable objects show a change in their domain sizes while fluids pass across them. This phenomenon can affect clay soils used in agricultural or urban activities (Aksu et al., 2015), wood and other materials employed as building material (Karoglou et al., 2005), absorbent hygiene products (AHPs) such as diapers and pads (DeVane et al., 2016; Diersch et al., 2010; Diersch et al., 2011), foods (Datta, 2007) or printer paper (Masoodi and Pillai, 2010). Among them all, an improvement in the characterization and prediction of AHPs' properties might immediately result in a considerable upgrading in daily living conditions for many people.

The latest AHPs are made of two components: the cellulose fibre matrix (fluff), which acts as a carrier material for the liquid, and the super absorbent polymer (SAP) particles, which is the absorbent and swelling material. SAP is a partially cross-linked polyelectrolyte, which can retain the water through the solvation of the free end-parts of the polymer chains. While the polymers chains absorb water molecules, the particle of SAP swells up to reach the size where the equilibrium of internal and external forces (cross-links forces and interphase polymer–solvent forces, respectively) is guaranteed. SAP particles change their stiffness during the process, passing from the sugar-like hardness of the dry state to a gel softness at a high liquid uptake (Zohuriaan-Mehr and Kabiri, 2008).

A good prediction of the performances of these products is essential to avoid gel-blocking and loss of liquid, due to too high or too low SAP amount, respectively (Buchholz and

Graham, 1997). Numerical simulations of absorbent pads may effectively speed up the design of AHPs, reducing the number of tests conducted on these materials. Since a representation of the fluid in a realistic pore scale would not be affordable because of the high computational costs, several simplified models were born in the last decades, to represent the fluid intrusion inside the porous material (Diersch et al., 2011). One of the coarsest methods is to consider the whole sample as a single porous block, considering spatial averaged properties in the whole domain. For instance, the porosity and the permeability are evaluated from the local liquid uptake of the material in each point of the domain. However, to resolve the mass and momentum balances of the liquid, the constitutive equations of the materials need to be determined through the experiments, which significantly increase the modelling effort (Diersch et al., 2010).

Although the analysis of porous materials at the pore scale must be avoided for large domains, the study of a representative elementary volume (REV) (Bear, 1988) at this scale may considerably increment the knowledge on the investigated sample. In this study we performed several simulations at the REV scale with the discrete element method (DEM) (Cundall and Strack, 1979) to obtain the constitutive equation of the higher scales' method. The exploited technique allows to literally assemble the sample by adding the constituents of the composite material. To have a realistic representation of the physical sample, many parameters at the REV scale need to be defined, such as the sizes and the shape of the particles.

2. Model description

The model developed here is a DEM model in which the two phases, SAP particles and fluff, are treated as two interacting granular phases. While the SAP phase is actually a granular phase, the same cannot be said for the fluff phase, which is composed by a very intricated fibrous net. Then, it is necessary to consider a granular phase, whose bulk properties resemble those of the fluff.

Heyden (2000) has studied the mechanical properties of fluff exploited in AHP products through numerical simulations in which a periodic cubic domain made of cellulose fibres is studied. Many parameters have been investigated, such as the fibres bulk density or the interactions between the fibres, and the results are shown in terms of stiffness and Poisson's ratio of the ensemble. Among the long list of results obtained by Heyden (2000), in the present model the properties of the fluff phase considered are reported in Table 1.

The stiffness of the SAP particles decreases with the liquid uptake (Zohuriaan-Mehr and Kabiri, 2008). While a dry SAP particle is conventionally represented as a sugar-like granule, and so it is quite hard, during the water absorption the mechanical properties change, and they become softer and softer. In the work of Sweijen et al. (2017a), the mechanical properties of SAP particles were related to the liquid uptake as shown in the following equation:

$$E = 2(1+v)G = 2(1+v)\frac{\beta}{Q^{\frac{1}{3}}} \tag{1}$$

where G is the shear modulus, v is the Poisson's ratio, Q is the liquid uptake, expressed as mass of liquid absorbed per mass of polymer, and β is related to the shear modulus at the maximum swelling extent and it depends on the specific polymer. The Poisson's ratio used here is $v_{SAP}=0.5$, typical of non-deformable materials.

Table 1 Values extracted from Heyden (2000) and exploited in the present work.

Cell size (mm)	Number of fibres per cell	Cross section area of the fibre (μm^2)	Porosity	Interactions among fibres
1	250	250	0.96	1

The liquid uptake of SAP particles was modelled in the time domain by means of a constant swelling rate of the absorbent material. In order to dynamically represent the liquid uptake, Sweijen et al. (2017b) developed a model in terms of radial coordinates adopting a water diffusion coefficient inside the SAP particles of $D=10^{-3}$–10^{-4} cm^2/min. In the present study, however, a higher value of the diffusion is requested, to speed up the simulations. In order to reduce the forces exerted on particles due to a so fast swelling, a high damping factor on contact force components is implemented. Being the interaction of the granular phases during the SAP swelling a quasi-static phenomenon, this artifice brings stability to the simulation, without compromising the quality of model outcomes. For more information regarding the usage of the damping factor in DEM simulations, the reader is referred to the website of the YADE software, where a large bibliography is quoted (Šmilauer and Chareyre, 2015).

3. General scheme of the simulations

Two assemblies of particles of two different sizes are generated in a parallelepiped domain. The size of the cross-section area is the characteristic length of the REV considered. The height of the box is much longer than the characteristic length, to generate two assemblies of non-overlapping particles, avoiding many numerical issues. The number of the spheres are calculated to have a determined basis weight of the two granular phases.

The particles fall driven by gravity and they deposit at the bottom of the domain. Once the unbalanced force of the particles ensemble is below 0.001 (Šmilauer and Chareyre, 2015), the deposition is considered completed and the result is an uncompressed granular material, with SAP particles and fluff pseudo-particles well-mixed. At this point, a plate with no thickness is generated above the particles.

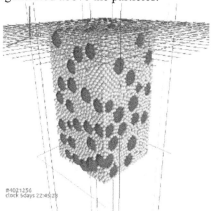

Figure 1 A generic simulated sample. The green (lightest) particles are the fluff pseudo-particles, the red (darkest) ones are the SAP particles.

While it moves downwards, it compresses the granular bed below. The compression is calculated as the ratio between the sum of the forces acting on the plate and the cross-section area of the domain. At the desired value of compression, the plate stops and the initial thickness and porosity of the sample are registered.

At the end of the compression, the SAP particles are allowed to swell, in a very controlled way. During the swelling of the SAP particles, the size of the whole sample is blocked by the domain walls and the plate above the granular bed, as shown in Figure 2. The volumetric growth of the particles increases the sum of the forces exerted on the plate above, and so the compression value of the sample. The considered swelling step conventionally corresponds to a liquid uptake of 1 g/g. Then, the plate slowly moves upwards to relax the sample and to bring back the compression value to the desired value. Therefore, the plate stops and a new swelling step starts with the same procedure. The algorithm goes on until the maximum liquid uptake of SAP particles is obtained. For each absorption level, the porosity and the thickness of the granular bed are registered. The results are shown in plots comparing these two quantities with the uptake of the liquid by SAP particles (Santagata et al.; 2019).

4. Preliminary simulations on fluff pseudo-particles

Before simulating realistic materials, we performed a convergence analysis on the size of the sample and of the fluff pseudo-particles and a sensitivity analysis on Young's modulus of the fluff pseudo-particles. Heyden (2010) reported that varying the bulk density, and so the porosity, for a given value of the interaction between fibres, has an effect on Young's modulus of the sample. Considering the void space between the granules (η), the porosity of the fluff pseudo-particles must be lower than the desired value (ε_{eq}=0.96-0.92, Table 1). With η=0.36 as the void fraction of a face-centred cubic structure, the fluff pseudo-particle intrinsic porosity was set at ε_f=0.9.

The results of the preliminary evaluations are summarized in Table 2. The size of the fluff grains and of the domain (REV) guarantees an error below 10 % respect to the ideal case (infinitesimal grains and infinitive domain, respectively). No relevant differences were observed varying the Young's modulus around the value reported by Heyden (2010).

5. Simulation of realistic absorbent layers

Once all model parameters are defined, the simulation results can be compared with the experimental values, to validate the model against the experiments. Some previously analysed absorbent pads were considered as a benchmark (Santagata et al.; 2019).

Table 2 Parameters obtained from the preliminary simulations.

Fluff pseudo-particle porosity	Fluff pseudo-particle radius (µm)	Young's modulus (kPa)	Domain (REV) size (mm)
0.9	100	200	4

Table 3 Properties of the different composite materials considered as a benchmark.

Label	Basis weight	SFR	Initial thickness	Initial porosity
1	502 g/m^2	0.67	3.31 mm	0.886
2	569 g/m^2	0.89	3.72 mm	0.889
3	669 g/m^2	1.22	4.22 mm	0.888
4	803 g/m^2	1.67	4.22 mm	0.868

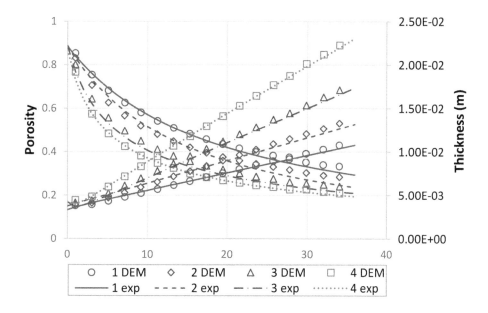

Figure 2 Porosity and thickness values from DEM and lab experiments. The properties of the investigated samples are listed in Table 3.

In Figure 2 the variables porosity and thickness are plotted against the liquid uptake of SAP particles. The basis weights and the initial thickness and porosity of these composite materials are reported in Table 3. The results of simulations carried out on the investigated samples show an excellent agreement with the experimental results, as shown in Figure 2. For each of the three samples, both the thickness and the porosity trends with the increasing liquid uptake are well predicted.

6. Conclusions

A DEM model of absorption in swelling porous media relevant to absorbent hygiene products is presented. The sample is described as a granular bed of two different granular matters: the super absorbent polymer (SAP) particles and the fluff pseudo-particles. Only uniform distributions are considered, for each phase. The water absorption of SAP particle is simulated increasing the size and decreasing the elastic modulus of the grains. The fluff pseudo-particles do not change in size or in mechanical properties during the absorption of liquid. The compression of the simulated samples is imposed and mimics the conventional body weight on absorbent products. The porosity and the thickness of the swollen samples are evaluated against the liquid uptake.

The parameters needed for DEM modelling were taken from both literature and preliminary simulations. A sensibility analysis on the size and the stiffness of the fluff pseudo-particles has been done. The size of the domain considered and the estimation of the REV have been evaluated as well.

The model has been validated against experimental results. The investigated samples have different compositions of SAP and fluff and express different changes in porosity and thickness. For all the four investigated samples, a remarkable agreement between the experiments and the DEM results is achieved. Further estimations and comparisons on many more samples are required to confirm the predictability of the model. Altogether, the model developed in the present study has the potential to effectively predict the volume averaged properties of porous swelling media and may lead to a deeper knowledge of morphological modifications occurring in similarly soft and swelling materials.

References

I. Aksu, E. Bazilevskaya, Z.T. Karpyn,.2015, Swelling of clay minerals in unconsolidated porous media and its impact on permeability, GeoResJ., 7, 1–13

J. Bear, Dynamics of fluids in porous media, 1988, Dover Publications, Inc., Mineola, NY

R.H. Brooks, A.T. Corey, 1966, Properties of porous media affecting fluid flow, J. Irrig. Drain. Div., 92, 2, 61–90

F.L. Buchholz, A.T. Graham, 1997, Modern superabsorbent polymer technology, Wiley-VCH, Boca Raton, FL

P.A Cundall, O.D.L. Strack, 1979, A discrete numerical model for granular assemblies, Geotechnique, 29, 1, 47–65

A.K. Datta, 2007, Porous media approaches to studying simultaneous heat and mass transfer in food processes. I: Problem formulations, J. Food Eng., 80, 1, 80–95

R.H. DeVane, 2016, The Procter and Gamble Company: Current State and Future Needs in Materials Modeling, Materials Research for Manufacturing, Springer series in Material Science, 224, 303–328

H.-J.G. Diersch, V. Clausnitzer, V. Myrnyy, R. Rosati, M. Schmidt, H. Beruda, B.J.. Ehrnsperger, R. Virgilio, 2010, Modeling Unsaturated Flow in Absorbent Swelling Porous Media: Part 1. Theory, Transp. Porous Media, 83, 3, 437–464

H.-J.G. Diersch, V. Clausnitzer, V. Myrnyy, R. Rosati, M. Schmidt, H. Beruda, B.J.. Ehrnsperger, R. Virgilio, 2011, Modeling Unsaturated Flow in Absorbent Swelling Porous Media: Part 2. Numerical Simulation, Transp. Porous Media, 86, 3, 753–776

M.T. Van Genuchten, 1980, A closed form equation for predicting the hydraulic conductivity of unsaturated soils, Soil. Sci. Soc. Am. J., 44, 892–898

S. Heyden, 2000, Network modelling for the evaluation of mechanical properties of cellulose fibre fluff, Lund University

M. Karoglou, A. Moropoulou, A. Giakoumaki, M.K. Krokida, 2005, Capillary rise kinetics of some building materials, J. Colloid Interface Sci., 284, 1, 260–264

R. Masoodi, K.M. Pillai, 2010, Darcy's law-based model for wicking in paper-like swelling porous media, AIChE J., 56, 9, 2257–2267

T. Santagata, R. Solimene, G. Aprea, P. Salatino, Modelling and experimental characterization of unsaturated flow in absorbent and swelling porous media – Part 2: Material characterization, *submitted to Chem Eng J.*

V. Šmilauer, B. Chareyre, 2015, DEM Formulation, Yade Documentation 2nd ed.

T. Sweijen, B. Chareyre, S.M. Hassanizadeh, N.K. Karadimitriou, 2017a, Grain scale modelling of swelling granular materials; application to super absorbent polymers, Powder Technol., 318, 411-422

T. Sweijen, C.J. van Duijin, S.M. Hassanizadeh, 2017b, A model for diffusion of water into a swelling particle with a free boundary: Application to a super absorbent polymer particle, Chem. Eng. Sci., 172, 407–413

M.J. Zohuriaan-Mehr, K. Kabiri, 2008, Superabsorbent polymer materials: a review, Iran. Polym. J., 17, 6,451–477

Sauro Pierucci, Flavio Manenti, Giulia Bozzano, Davide Manca (Eds.)
Proceedings of the 30th European Symposium on Computer Aided Process Engineering
(ESCAPE30), May 24-27, 2020, Milano, Italy. © 2020 Elsevier B.V. All rights reserved.
http://dx.doi.org/10.1016/B978-0-12-823377-1.50099-9

Assessing the Sensitivity of Technical Performance of three Ethanol Production Processes based on the Fermentation of Steel Manufacturing Offgas, Syngas and a 3:1 Mixture Between H_2 and CO_2

Eduardo Almeida Benalcázar [a,b], Henk Noorman[b,c], Rubens Maciel Filho[a], John Posada[b]

[a] *Department of Product and Process Development, Faculty of Chemical Engineering, State University of Campinas, Av. Albert Einstein 500, 13083-852, Campinas – SP, Brazil.*
[b] *Department of Biotechnology, Faculty of Applied Sciences, Delft University of Technology, Van der Maasweg 9, 2629 HZ, Delft, the Netherlands.*
[c] *DSM Biotechnology Center, A. Fleminglaan 1, 2613 AX, Delft, the Netherlands.*

Abstract

This study assesses the sensitivity of the technical, environmental and economic performance of three ethanol production process based on the fermentation of three gas mixtures: i) CO-rich flue gas from steel manufacturing, ii) biomass-based syngas with a H_2/CO ratio of 2 and iii) a 3:1 combination between H_2 and CO_2. The sensitivity analysis is based on stochastic bioreactor simulations constructed by randomly generated combinations of eight parameters that command the fermentation process i.e., temperature, pressure, gas feed dilution with an inert components, ethanol concentration, height of the liquid column, mass transfer coefficients, superficial gas velocity and, acetic acid co-production.

The sensitivity analysis identified that the bioreactor technical performance is highly sensitive to variations on pressure, liquid column height and the mass transfer coefficients. The pressure mainly improves mass transfer and consequently ethanol productivity whereas liquid column height improves the gas residence time and consequently the efficiency in the gas utilization. The trend was common for the three gas supply options. The results suggested that in order to produce an optimal bioreactor design, there are options to optimize the productivity and the gas utilization simultaneously.

The results from the sensitivity analysis may help guiding a subsequent multi-objective process optimization study.

Keywords: ethanol, syngas fermentation, sensitivity analysis, stochastic simulation.

1. Introduction

Prevention of global warming is currently pushing global policy-making towards the reduction of CO_2 emissions, which are mostly derived from the combustion of fossil fuels (Boden et al., 2013). Lignocellulosic biomass is seen as an alternative sources of fuels and chemicals that during their life cycle may result in lower carbon emissions (Liu et al., 2017). These feedstocks are abundant and renewable and can be thermochemically converted into gas mixtures containing mainly CO, H_2, CO_2 (Heidenreich and Foscolo,

2015; Matsakas et al., 2017). The gas is commonly referred as syngas and can be used as feedstock for fermentations (Kundiyana et al., 2010).

Only limited details about the industrial process performance have been made public. What has been reported is that microbial selectivity for ethanol falls around 95 % and that gas utilization overpasses 90 % (Simpson, 2018); additionally, it is argued that the exist an energy surplus generated from the based fermentation of syngas (Handler et al., 2016). Moreover, the claims that ethanol concentration in the fermentation media could be held above 50 g/L and overhead pressure should not overpass 3 atm (Li et al., 2017; Trevethick et al., n.d.) have been patented.

In consequence, a mathematical model was developed and reported elsewhere [Almeida, forthcoming] to simulate ethanol production in a bubble column bioreactor fed by CO, H_2 and CO_2 mixtures. That model is used to quantify the sensitivity of the bioreactor technical performance to certain parameters that command the fermentation step. The assessment is applied to three different gas feed compositions.

2. Methodology

2.1. Process configurations

The three process configurations which have been considered in this study differ on the gas production processes: CO-rich BOF offgas from the steel-manufacturing process; *ii)* a 3:1 mixture between H_2 and CO_2, and *iii)* syngas with a H_2/CO ratio of 2.

The fermentation process consists on a bubble column bioreactor fed by the gas mixture. The ethanol produced inside the fermentor is at all times given two possible exit routes *i.e. i)* pre-concentrated along the offgas, where it is subsequently condensed and recovered from by flash separation, and *ii)* along a liquid broth outflow. Acetic acid, also exits the bioreactor along the liquid outflow. The alcohol is distilled out of the two streams by atmospheric distillation and finally dehydrated. The unconsumed gas is here treated as waste and combusted before being released into the atmosphere, as proposed by Handler et al, 2016 (Handler et al., 2016).

2.2. Simulation of the fermentation processes

The simulation of the bioreactor uses a model previously presented elsewhere [Almeida, forthcoming]; therefore, only the basic structure of such model is introduced here.

2.2.1. Simulation of the fermentations of BOF offgas and the H_2/CO_2 mixture

The fermentation model for these two cases is formed by *i)* a black-box model of the main reactions carried out by acetogenic bacteria and *ii)* a mass transfer model of the large bubble column bioreactor. The stoichiometry of the microbial metabolic reaction is constructed by the combination of the catabolic and anabolic reactions.

Ethanol and acetic acid are the products of catabolism, thermodynamically powered by the uptake of the electron donors, CO and H_2. Cells are produced during anabolism. The Gibbs free energy harvested from the electron donors (CO and H_2) during catabolism powers cells. The uptake of CO and H_2 are assumed to follow hyperbolic kinetics. The maximum uptake rate of the electron donors is estimated using thermodynamics (Heijnen, 2013).

Mass transfer in the bioreactor is simulated assuming the process operates in continuous mode at steady-state (Heijnen and van't Riet, 1984; van't Riet and Tramper, 1991). Mass transfer is driven by the energy input provided by the gas sparging [42]. A system of non-linear equations formed by the mass balances is solved by a constrained optimization of the volumetric ethanol productivity (R_{et}).

Assessing the sensitivity of technical performance of three ethanol production   591
processes based on the fermentation of steel manufacturing offgas, syngas and
a 3:1 mixture between H2 and CO2

2.2.2. Simulation of the fermentation of biomass-derived syngas

Since the black-box model of microbial reactions is only able to simulate the consumption of either CO or H_2, the simulation of biomass-derived syngas (BDS) consumption is done indirectly adding the mass and energy streams contributions from CO fermentation (the BOF offgas case) and H_2/CO_2 fermentation cases. The H_2/CO ratio in syngas is assumed to be 2.

2.3. Process assessment and performance indicators

The ethanol production processes are evaluated from the perspective of the bioreactor technical performance through the ethanol volumetric productivity (R_{et}) and gas utilization (U_S), defined as the percent change on the gas molar flow rate of electron donors across the fermentor.

2.4. Stochastic simulation of the bioreactor

The operation of the bioreactor is simulated under 5000 randomly generated combinations of eight input parameters, which are considered to command the bioreactor performance *i.e., i)* process temperature (T), *ii)* top reactor pressure (p_t), *iii)* gas feed dilution (f_{Dil}), *iv)* maximum ethanol concentration (C_{et}^{max}), *v)* liquid column height (h_L), *vi)* mass transfer coefficient factor (f_{k_La}), *vii)* acetic acid production factor (f_{Ac^-}) and *viii)* the pressure-corrected superficial gas velocity (v_{sG}^c). See Table 1.

Table 1 Maximum and minimum values used the input parameters in the stochastic bioreactor simulation

Input parameter	T [°C]	p_t [atm]	f_{Dil} [%vol.]	C_{et}^{max} [g/L]	h_L [m]	f_{k_La} [-]	f_{Ac^-} [%]	v_{sG}^c [m/s]
Minimum value	27	0.5	0	30	8	0.5	0	0.07
Maximum value	67	3.5	45	120	64	2.0	0.15	0.14

2.5. Sensitivity analysis

The sensitivity of bioreactor and overall process performance indicators (or output parameters - OP) is evaluated using standardized regression coefficients since it offers "a good approximation to a global sensitivity with affordable computational demand" (Morales-Rodriguez et al., 2012), and allows establishing a hierarchical classification of the model IP's according to the level of impact on a determined OP. This method implies that process performance has a linear relation with each input parameter (IP). The reliability of the regression coefficients is evaluated using coefficients of determination (R^2).

3. Results and discussion

3.1. Distribution trends in the performance indicators

The distribution of the bioreactor performance indicators corroborates previous observations suggesting that the fermentation of H_2-rich gases may lead to higher productivity and gas utilization than the fermentation of CO-rich gases (Noorman and Heijnen, 2017) (Almeida et al., forthcoming) (see Figure 1). The observation is sustained on the fact that H_2 mass transfer to the liquid is faster than CO transfer; since mass transfer is linearly related for bioreactor productivity, then a higher mass transfer rate means higher productivity. Similarly, a higher productivity means than the gas consumption inside the bioreactor is more efficient, and therefore, gas utilization is higher.

Since BDS fermentation is simulated using the respective contributions of CO and H_2/CO_2 fermentations, then it is reasonable that bioreactor performance lies between the performances obtained for BOF offgas and H_2/CO_2 fermentations. In addition, as the H_2/CO ratio in the syngas is 2, then the performance of the syngas fermentor falls closer to that of the H_2/CO_2 fermentor than to the CO fermentor.

By comparing bioreactor performances with other study (Almeida et al., forthcoming) there is a high probability that gas utilization may be improved far more than bioreactor productivity. This observation is based on the fact that while the median gas utilization

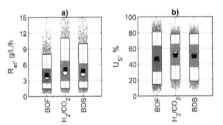

Figure 1 Boxplots summarizing the distribution of a) ethanol productivity and b) gas utilization. On the boxplots: the colored vertical rectangles represent the extension of the 25th and 75th percentiles; the white vertical rectangles represent the extension of the 5th and 95th percentiles; the small colored dots represent the outliers; the white circles represent the median values; and the black square boxes represent the mean values.

values are 45 and 53 % for CO and H_2/CO_2 fermentations, respectively, the median ethanol productivities are 3.7 and 4.5 g/h/L for CO and H_2/CO_2 fermentations, respectively. However, this observation does not necessarily suggest that productivity cannot be further increased, as there is a 25 % probability (see 25th and 75th percentiles in Figure 1) that R_{et} may increase to 5.3, 6.8 and 6.2 g/L/h for BOF offgas, H_2/CO_2 and BDS fermentations, respectively. In addition, there is a 5 % probability (see 5th and 95th percentiles in Figure 1) that R_{et} may be further improved to 8, 11 and 10 g/L/h for the same three gas supply options. That would be an improvement between 2 and 2.5 times from a previous report (Almeida et al., forthcoming).

Similarly, gas utilization in the bioreactor could be as high as 63, 66 and 65 % for BOF offgas, H_2/CO_2 and BDS fermentations, respectively with a 25 % probability. Gas utilization could climb to 82, 78 and 79 % for the same gas supply options with a 5 % probability. It is therefore, more probable that the BOF offgas fermentation case has a better gas utilization than the fermentation of H_2-rich gases.

In addition, although it may be encouraging to see that gas utilization could surpass 90 % as previously reported by LanzaTech, such achievement is highly unlikely with the proposed bioreactor configuration as there is only a 5 % probability that U_S may increase beyond 80 % (see Figure 1).

3.2. Sensitivity analysis by the standardized regression coefficients

Table 2 shows the standardized regression coefficients (β_{IP_i}) of ethanol volumetric productivity and gas utilization in the bioreactor. The value of R^2 is also included in Table 2 to show which OP's had an acceptable linear relation with all the IP's.

The relation between R_{et} and U_S and all the IP's is acceptably linear for the three gas supply cases. Remarkably, the IP's hierarchical classification is also common for these two OP's in three gas supply cases. Considering that the sign of the β_{IP_i} indicates whether the influence of each IP on one OP is positive or negative, R_{et} may be largely improved by p_t and the f_{k_La} and in a lower level of influence by the v_{sG}^c. On the other hand, the most detrimental IP for R_{et} is the gas feed dilution. According to [Almeida, forthcoming],

Assessing the sensitivity of technical performance of three ethanol production 593
processes based on the fermentation of steel manufacturing offgas, syngas and
a 3:1 mixture between H2 and CO2

these four IP's are deeply related to the rate of mass transfer in the bioreactor. f_{k_La} and v^c_{sG} determine the value of the mass transfer coefficients while p_t and f_{Dil} determine the value of the partial pressures of the electron donors in the gas phase and therefore their saturation concentrations in the liquid phase and thus, their driving forces for mass transfer. While increases in p_t will widen the mass transfer driving force, increases in dilution will shrink the driving force.

Table 2 Standardized regression coefficients (β_{IP_i}) relating the model outputs with each input parameter

OP	Gas supply case	IP								R^2
		T	p_t	f_{Dil}	C_{et}^{max}	h_L	f_{k_La}	f_{Ac^-}	v^c_{sG}	
R_{et}	BOF	0.13	0.57	-0.36	0.02	0.14	0.54	-0.06	0.32	0.90
	H$_2$/CO$_2$	0.07	0.61	-0.43	0.00	0.07	0.45	-0.05	0.28	0.86
	BDS	0.09	0.60	-0.41	0.00	0.09	0.48	-0.05	0.29	0.88
U_S	BOF	0.18	-0.05	0.01	0.01	0.77	0.55	0.00	-0.13	0.95
	H$_2$/CO$_2$	0.11	0.15	-0.04	0.01	0.77	0.54	0.00	-0.13	0.92
	BDS	0.14	0.08	-0.02	0.01	0.78	0.55	0.00	-0.13	0.95

Gas utilization, in turn may be mostly improved by h_L, f_{k_La} and T, while v^c_{sG} will be slightly detrimental. The sensitivity of U_S to h_L is remarkably high as the β_{IP_i} is the closest to one, the maximum possible value. This relation is due to the fact that as the liquid column height increases, so does the residence time of the gas inside the bioreactor. On the other hand, v^c_{sG} offers the opposite effect: as the gas velocity through the bioreactor increases, the residence time decreases. In addition, the influence of f_{k_La} and T over U_S could be regarded as a side effect of their positive influence over R_{et}, which means that the mass transfer increases, the gas consumption is more efficient.

The influence of ethanol concentration over R_{et} and U_S is negligible according the estimated β_{IP_i}; the lack of mathematical connection between this IP and the two specified OP's (Almeida et al., forthcoming) might be the cause of this negligible influence of C_{et}^{max} over bioreactor performance. Thus, regarding the fact that possible inhibition by ethanol is not considered by the electron uptake kinetic expressions in the black-box model of microbial reactions, the negligible influence of C_{et}^{max} might be somewhat underestimated. The similarity between the sensitivities for the three gas supply cases is caused by the fact that the operation of the bioreactor does not differ significantly when either CO or H$_2$ are the electron donors (Almeida et al., forthcoming). However, the intensity of such sensitivities differ between the three cases. For example, BOF offgas fermentation R_{et} is the most benefited indicator when the mass transfer coefficient factor increases. Similarly, due to the inhibition of CO at high partial pressures, the bioreactor pressure has a negative effect over gas consumption in the BOF offgas case while pressure is mostly beneficial for the fermentation of H$_2$-rich gases.

4. Conclusions

The present study showed that ethanol volumetric productivity could be as high as 8, 11 and 10 g/L/h for the fermentation of BOF offgas, H$_2$/CO$_2$ and biomass-derived syngas, respectively. This increase may be achieved by a combination of high mass transfer coefficients, high top bioreactor pressure and large gas flow rates across the bioreactor.

These three IP's improve mass transfer rates and therefore ethanol productivity. In addition, the dilution of the gas feed is to be avoided since it has the most negative effect over productivity. The IP's that increase the productivity also have a positive impact on gas utilization. However, gas utilization may be mainly improved by tall bioreactors where the residence times are higher.

References

Boden, T., Andres, R., Marland, G., 2013. Global, Regional, and National Fossil-Fuel CO2 Emissions (1751 - 2010) (V. 2013). https://doi.org/10.3334/CDIAC/00001_V2013

Handler, R.M., Shonnard, D.R., Griffing, E.M., Lai, A., Palou-Rivera, I., 2016. Life Cycle Assessments of Ethanol Production via Gas Fermentation: Anticipated Greenhouse Gas Emissions for Cellulosic and Waste Gas Feedstocks. Industrial & Engineering Chemistry Research 55, 3253–3261. https://doi.org/10.1021/acs.iecr.5b03215

Heidenreich, S., Foscolo, P.U., 2015. New concepts in biomass gasification. Progress in Energy and Combustion Science 46, 72–95. https://doi.org/10.1016/j.pecs.2014.06.002

Heijnen, J., 2013. A thermodynamic approach to predict black box model parameters for microbial growth, in: Biothermodynamics. EPFL Press, Switzerland.

Heijnen, J.J., van't Riet, K., 1984. Mass transfer, mixing and heat transfer phenomena in low viscosity bubble column reactors. The Chemical Engineering Journal 28, B21–B42. https://doi.org/10.1016/0300-9467(84)85025-X

Kundiyana, D.K., Huhnke, R.L., Wilkins, M.R., 2010. Syngas fermentation in a 100-L pilot scale fermentor: Design and process considerations. Journal of Bioscience and Bioengineering 109, 492–498. https://doi.org/10.1016/j.jbiosc.2009.10.022

Li, X., Cossey, B.J., Trevethick, S.R., 2017. Fermentation Of Gaseous Substrates. US 9,617,509 B2.

Liu, W., Zhang, Z., Xie, X., Yu, Z., von Gadow, K., Xu, J., Zhao, S., Yang, Y., 2017. Analysis of the Global Warming Potential of Biogenic CO2 Emission in Life Cycle Assessments. Scientific Reports 7. https://doi.org/10.1038/srep39857

Matsakas, L., Gao, Q., Jansson, S., Rova, U., Christakopoulos, P., 2017. Green conversion of municipal solid wastes into fuels and chemicals. Electronic Journal of Biotechnology 26, 69–83. https://doi.org/10.1016/j.ejbt.2017.01.004

Morales-Rodriguez, R., Meyer, A.S., Gernaey, K.V., Sin, G., 2012. A framework for model-based optimization of bioprocesses under uncertainty: Lignocellulosic ethanol production case. Computers & Chemical Engineering 42, 115–129. https://doi.org/10.1016/j.compchemeng.2011.12.004

Noorman, H.J., Heijnen, J.J., 2017. Biochemical engineering's grand adventure. Chemical Engineering Science 170, 677–693. https://doi.org/10.1016/j.ces.2016.12.065

Simpson, S.D., 2018. CCU-Now: fuels and chemicals from Waste.

Trevethick, S.R., Bromley, J.C., Waters, G.W., Kopke, M., Tran, L., Jensen, R.O., n.d. Multistage Bioreactor Processes. US 9834792 B2.

van't Riet, K., Tramper, J., 1991. Basic bioreactor design. M. Dekker, New York.

Sauro Pierucci, Flavio Manenti, Giulia Bozzano, Davide Manca (Eds.)
Proceedings of the 30th European Symposium on Computer Aided Process Engineering
(ESCAPE30), May 24-27, 2020, Milano, Italy. © 2020 Elsevier B.V. All rights reserved.
http://dx.doi.org/10.1016/B978-0-12-823377-1.50100-2

Techno-economic and Environmental Assessment of Electrofuels: a Case Study of Gasoline Production using a PEM Electrolyser

Diego Freire Ordóñez [a,*], Gonzalo Guillén-Gosálbez [b]

[a] *Department of Chemical Engineering, Imperial College London, South Kensington, London, SW7 2AZ, UK*

[b] *Institute for Chemical and Bioengineering, Department of Chemistry and Applied Biosciences, ETH Zürich, Vladimir-Prelog-Weg 1, 8093, Zürich, Switzerland*
dmf15@ic.ac.uk

Abstract

This work assesses, technically, economically and environmentally, the production of a liquid electrofuel, with the potential to replace conventional petrol. A conceptual design of a Power-to-Liquids process, which considers wind electricity and captured CO_2, was taken as a starting point for developing a process model in the commercial software Aspen Plus. The flowsheet includes water electrolysis, and the reverse water-gas shift (rWGS), Fischer-Tropsch (FT) and hydrocracking (HC) processes. The environmental impact assessment (EIA) of the process was conducted by means of the SimaPro 8 software, following a cradle-to-gate scope and the ReCiPe 2016 LCA damage model. The economic analysis was carried out in Aspen Process Economic Analyzer, after including the quoted costs for the electrolyser and reactors. We found that under current market conditions, the production cost of the electrofuel is higher than that of petrol in the UK for 2018 (10.03 USD/GGE and 1.71 USD/gal, respectively). However, the produced fuel shows better environmental performance than conventional gasoline in all three categories at the endpoint level (Human health, Ecosystems and Resources), which should become a major driver for its widespread adoption.

Keywords: Electrofuel production, Techno-economic assessment, Environmental Impact assessment, Sensitivity analysis, Uncertainty analysis

1. Introduction

Transportation is known as one as the most demanding consumers of energy in Europe and around the world. Nowadays, most of the fuels utilised for transportation are produced from fossil feedstocks. This makes this sector one of the main contributors to global warming, being responsible at present for more than 20% of the emissions of greenhouse gases (Brynolf *et al.*, 2018). In this context, electrofuels based on CO_2 have gained increasing significance during the last years. An electrofuel can be defined as a carbon-based fuel, ideally neutral concerning greenhouse gas emissions, that is obtained from carbon dioxide and water, employing renewable electricity as the primary source of energy (Ridjan *et al.*, 2016; Brynolf *et al.*, 2018). Hence, these fuels are regarded as a viable alternative to address climate change and energy security of supply (Schemme *et al.*, 2017), while contributing to overcome the problems associated with the intermittency of renewable sources.

In this work, we propose an integrated approach to evaluate techno-economically and environmentally a production process to obtain liquid fuel with similar properties to that of conventional petrol. The methodology followed through this case study provides a solid base that can be replicated to assess and compare the integral performance of other Power-to-Liquid (PtL) and Power-to-Gas (PtG) processes.

2. Methodology

2.1. Model description

A simulation model was run in Aspen Plus, based on a previous conceptual process design (König *et al.*, 2015), which is illustrated in Fig. 1.

2.1.1. Hydrogen Production

Wind power is utilised to produce hydrogen through water electrolysis. A PEM (Polymer Exchange Membrane) electrolyser was simulated based on a previous study (Michailos *et al.*, 2019), and incorporated in the original flowsheet. This type of electrolyser was considered due to its maturity (high TRL) and current market availability (Schmidt *et al.*, 2017).

2.1.2. Carbon dioxide capture

Post-combustion capture of carbon dioxide from flue gas streams was considered as main carbon source. The capturing process was not simulated, but rather its environmental impacts were retrieved from a previous study (Iribarren *et al.*, 2013).

2.1.3. Syngas Production

The reduction of carbon dioxide (CO_2) to carbon monoxide (CO) is achieved through the reverse water-gas shift reaction (rWGS):

$$CO_2 + H_2 \leftrightarrow CO + H_2O \qquad \Delta H = 41.2 \, kJ/mol \tag{1}$$

For this study, it was considered a nickel-based catalyst, with Al_2O_3 as base support material (Frazier *et al.*, 2015)

2.1.4. Fischer-Tropsch (FT) synthesis

The FT process comprises a set of polymerisation chemical reactions through which liquid hydrocarbons can be obtained from syngas. In this study, a cobalt-based catalyst (Jungbluth *et al.*, 2007) was employed since it is widely used in FT industrial applications. The products of the Fischer-Tropsch synthesis are FT gases and FT waxes.

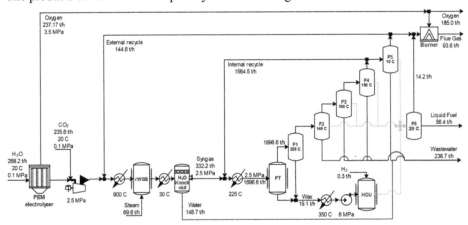

Figure 1. Process flowsheet

2.1.5. Hydrocracking Process
Hydrocracking is a catalytic cracking method supported by high partial hydrogen pressure by which hydrocarbon chains are rearranged and broken, and hydrogen is added to aromatics and olefins to produce naphthenes and alkanes (Viswanathan, 2017). A platinum-based catalyst (Calemma *et al.*, 2010) was considered because of high hydrogenation/dehydrogenation activity for heavy hydrocarbon cracking.

2.1.6. Separation and upgrading of products
The FT gas and the product from hydrocracking are separated in flash drums, thereby exploiting the different volatilities of the products (Fig. 1)

2.2. Economic Analysis
The CAPEX and OPEX of the flowsheet were estimated using the results from Aspen Process Economic Analyzer, after including the quoted costs for the electrolyser and reactors. The latter were obtained by applying Eq. (2), with information retrieved from several sources (Albrecht *et al.*, 2017; Dimitriou *et al.*, 2015; Hoseinzade and Adams, 2019; Keith *et al.*, 2018; Michailos *et al.*, 2019; Posdziech *et al.*, 2019; Wind Power Offshore, 2018). All costs, including raw materials, utilities, products and equipment, were updated to 2018, except for the PEM electrolyser that was projected for 2020. Two main scenarios were analysed; one considering the wind power cost for the electrolyser to be free and the other with a cost of 0.0744 USD/kWh, which was the reported cost in the UK for 2018.

$$PC = PC_{ref} \cdot \left(\frac{S}{S_{ref}} \right)^D \cdot \left(\frac{CEPCI_{2018}}{CEPCI_{ref}} \right) \tag{2}$$

Each case study was also evaluated with and without heat integration, which was regarded through energy targeting in the composite curves of the process. Finally, a sensitivity analysis was performed on the main CAPEX and OPEX variables along with a Monte Carlo-based uncertainty analysis. For the latter, a normal distribution with a standard deviation of 20% was assumed for the uncertain parameters. Both analyses were applied to the case study in which a non-zero cost of electricity was evaluated.

2.3. Environmental Impact Assessment (EIA)
In general terms, an Environmental Impact Assessment (EIA) is a standard methodology to evaluate and mitigate the negative consequences caused by a project on its operation area and surroundings.

In this study, an EIA was conducted based on a cradle-to-gate approach and the life cycle impact model ReCiPe 2016, through the commercial software SimaPro. In addition, an uncertainty analysis was performed through a Monte Carlo Assessment. The life cycle assessment of the PEM electrolyser was not included in this analysis since its construction is considered to have negligible influence compared to the electrolysis process itself (Bareiß *et al.*, 2019). The inventory data were retrieved from the previous simulation.

3. Results and Discussion

The results of the annualised costs and the net production costs for this case study are shown in Fig. 2 and Fig. 3. It can be seen that the estimated net production cost (NPC) of the electrofuel, assuming a zero-cost for the electricity from wind power, is 2.84 USD/GGE without heat integration and 2.58 USD/GGE after applying heat integration through pinch analysis.

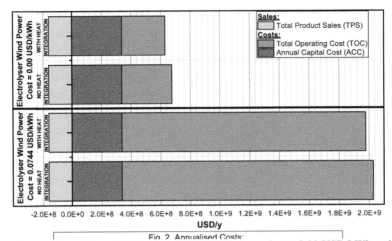

Figure 2. Annualised Costs; Wind Power Cost for the electrolyser: 0.00 USD/kWh and 0.0744 USD/kWh

On the other hand, when including the actual cost of the electricity from wind power, the NPC is 10.28 USD/GGE without heat integration and 10.03 USD/GGE after heat integration. In all cases, the results show that the production cost of the electrofuel is higher than that of the conventional petrol in the UK, which is approximately 1.71 USD/gal (Open Government License v3.0, 2018).

As expected, it can be seen from the sensitivity analysis (Fig. 4) that the operating costs have more influence than the capital costs on the net production cost of the fuel, especially the costs of the electricity from wind power as and CO_2, and the revenue from a potential sale of oxygen. Therefore, these three variables were considered for the uncertainty estimation through the Monte Carlo simulation, whose results showed a minimum NPC of 4.53 USD/GGE and a maximum NPC of 14.91 USD/GGE.

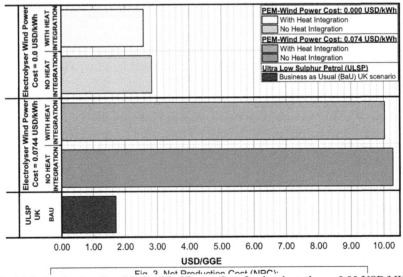

Fig. 3. Net Production Cost (NPC); Wind Power Cost for the electrolyser: 0.00 USD/kWh and 0.0744 USD/kWh

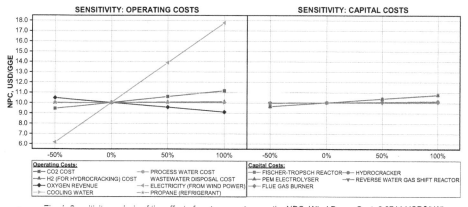

Fig. 4. Sensitivity analysis of cost parameters on the NPC; Wind Power Cost: 0.0744 USD/kWh

From the life cycle inventory (LCI) analysis at the endpoint level (Fig. 5), it can be observed that the environmental performance of the electrofuel is better than that of conventional petrol, in all three categories. However, there is high uncertainty in the results of the electrofuel since most inputs for the analysis come from the simulation of a conceptual design rather than from measurements from operating processes.

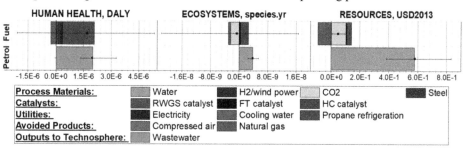

Fig. 5. ReCiPe 2016 LCI analysis at the endpoint level including absolute uncertainties

4. Conclusion

Here we carried out an economic and environmental assessment of an electrofuel using process simulation, LCA and uncertainty analysis. Under the actual market conditions, the production of the electrofuel based on the studied process would not be economically viable since its net production cost would be around 10.03 USD/GGE while the production cost of gasoline in the UK is currently around 1.71 USD/gal. However, it can be noted the potential benefits of the produced fuel from an environmental point of view. According to the results of the ReCiPe 2016 LCI analysis at the endpoint level, it can be concluded that the obtained electrofuel would have lower environmental impact compared to conventional petrol in all three categories of the analysis (Human health, Ecosystems, and Resources). This is particularly clear in the "Resources" category, for which there would be approximately 90% less impact in comparison to gasoline.

Hence, as the renewable electricity and carbon capture costs are expected to fall, and taxes on CO_2 emissions are anticipated to be applied in the coming years, the production of electrofuels may be regarded as a promising alternative to decarbonise the transportation sector.

References

F. Albrecht, D. König, N. Baucks and R.-U. Dietrich (2017), "A standardized methodology for the techno-economic evaluation of alternative fuels – A case study", *Fuel*, Vol. 194, pp. 511–526.

K. Bareiß, C. de La Rua, M. Möckl and T. Hamacher (2019), "Life cycle assessment of hydrogen from proton exchange membrane water electrolysis in future energy systems", *Applied Energy*, Vol. 237, pp. 862–872.

S. Brynolf, M. Taljegard, M. Grahn and J. Hansson (2018), "Electrofuels for the transport sector. A review of production costs", *Renewable and Sustainable Energy Reviews*, Vol. 81, pp. 1887–1905.

V. Calemma, C. Gambaro, W. Parker, R. Carbone, R. Giardino and P. Scorletti (2010), "Middle distillates from hydrocracking of FT waxes: Composition, characteristics and emission properties", *Catalysis Today*, Vol. 149 No. 1-2, pp. 40–46.

I. Dimitriou, P. García-Gutiérrez, R. Elder, R. Cuéllar-Franca, A. Azapagic and R. Allen (2015), "Carbon dioxide utilisation for production of transport fuels. Process and economic analysis", *Energy & Environmental Science*, Vol. 8 No. 6, pp. 1775–1789.

R. Frazier, E. Jin and A. Kumar (2015), "Life Cycle Assessment of Biochar versus Metal Catalysts Used in Syngas Cleaning", *Energies*, Vol. 8 No. 1, pp. 621–644.

L. Hoseinzade and T. Adams (2019), "Techno-economic and environmental analyses of a novel, sustainable process for production of liquid fuels using helium heat transfer", *Applied Energy*, Vol. 236, pp. 850–866.

D. Iribarren, F. Petrakopoulou and J. Dufour (2013), "Environmental and thermodynamic evaluation of CO2 capture, transport and storage with and without enhanced resource recovery", *Energy*, Vol. 50, pp. 477–485.

N. Jungbluth, R. Frischknecht, Faist Emmenegger, M., Steiner, R. and M. Tuchschmid (2007), "Life Cycle Assessment of BTL-fuel production: Inventory Analysis. Deliverable: D 5.2.7.".

D. Keith, G. Holmes, D. St. Angelo and K. Heidel (2018), "A Process for Capturing CO2 from the Atmosphere", *Joule*, Vol. 2 No. 8, pp. 1573–1594.

D. König, M. Freiberg, R.-U. Dietrich and A. Wörner (2015), "Techno-economic study of the storage of fluctuating renewable energy in liquid hydrocarbons", *Fuel*, Vol. 159, pp. 289–297.

S. Michailos, S. McCord, V. Sick, G. Stokes and P. Styring (2019), "Dimethyl ether synthesis via captured CO2 hydrogenation within the power to liquids concept. A techno-economic assessment", *Energy Conversion and Management*, Vol. 184, pp. 262–276.

Open Government License v3.0 (2018), "Weekly road fuel prices. Statistical data set", available at: https://www.gov.uk/government/statistical-data-sets/oil-and-petroleum-products-weekly-statistics (accessed 2 August 2019).

O. Posdziech, K. Schwarze and J. Brabandt (2019), "Efficient hydrogen production for industry and electricity storage via high-temperature electrolysis", *International Journal of Hydrogen Energy*, Vol. 44 No. 35, pp. 19089–19101.

I. Ridjan, B. Mathiesen and D. Connolly (2016), "Terminology used for renewable liquid and gaseous fuels based on the conversion of electricity. a review", *Journal of Cleaner Production*, Vol. 112, pp. 3709–3720.

S. Schemme, R. Samsun, R. Peters and D. Stolten (2017), "Power-to-fuel as a key to sustainable transport systems – An analysis of diesel fuels produced from CO2 and renewable electricity", *Fuel*, Vol. 205, pp. 198–221.

O. Schmidt, A. Gambhir, I. Staffell, A. Hawkes, J. Nelson and S. Few (2017), "Future cost and performance of water electrolysis: An expert elicitation study", *International Journal of Hydrogen Energy*, Vol. 42 No. 52, pp. 30470–30492.

B. Viswanathan (2017), *Energy sources: Fundamentals of chemical conversion processes and applications*, Elsevier, Amsterdam, Boston.

Wind Power Offshore (2018), "UK offshore capped at €63/MWh for next auction", available at: https://www.windpoweroffshore.com/article/1519177/uk-offshore-capped-%E2%82%AC63-mwh-next-auction (accessed 15 June 2019).

Sauro Pierucci, Flavio Manenti, Giulia Bozzano, Davide Manca (Eds.)
Proceedings of the 30th European Symposium on Computer Aided Process Engineering
(ESCAPE30), May 24-27, 2020, Milano, Italy. © 2020 Elsevier B.V. All rights reserved.
http://dx.doi.org/10.1016/B978-0-12-823377-1.50101-4

Dynamic Simulation of Chemical Looping Combustion in Packed Bed Reactors

Vlad C. Sandu, Calin C. Cormos, Ana-Maria Cormos*

Babes-Bolyai University, Faculty of Chemistry and Chemical Engineering, Arany Janos 11, Postal code: RO-400028, Cluj-Napoca, Romania
cani@chem.ubbcluj.ro

Abstract

Chemical looping combustion (CLC) is a promising energy conversion technology for fossil fuel combustion with inherent carbon dioxide separation and minimum energy and cost penalties for CO_2 capture. Designing and setting the optimum operating conditions for the CLC reactors are important steps to be taken before implementing the process on an industrial scale. In this work, a dynamic mathematical model has been developed to simulate packed bed reactors used in a methane-based chemical looping combustion process with iron-based oxygen carrier. The air and fuel reactor models were interconnected with the models describing the purge steps of the process to highlight the dynamic behaviour of the entire process. The developed model was used to predict (in space and time): gas flow profile, gas composition distribution, behaviour of oxygen carrier and temperature profiles inside the air and fuel reactors. The simulation results of the 1D model had been compared with the experimental data published in the literature. The model developed is able to describe the process very accurately, for a wide range of gas flow rates. Increasing the flowrate by 20% of the base value lead to a shorter time in which the process achieved stationarity by approximately 300 s (for oxidation step). During the reduction step, the reaction rate decreases very fast at a solid conversion above 85%.

Keywords: Flexible energy conversion systems, Carbon Capture and Storage (CCS), Chemical looping combustion, Packed bed reactors, Dynamic modelling and simulation.

1. Introduction

There are numerous methods for reducing greenhouse gas emissions (mainly CO_2) into the atmosphere, such as decreasing the global energy consumption by increasing the efficiency of energy consumption, or turning to alternative energy sources (wind or solar energy). However, since most of the world's electric energy comes from fossil fuel-based power plants, which produce a large amount of CO_2, carbon capture and storage (CCS) technologies seem to be a viable solution, with the potential to reduce CO_2 emissions by 90%.

Chemical looping combustion (CLC) is a promising energy conversion technology for fossil fuel combustion with inherent carbon dioxide separation and minimum energy losses. In CLC, oxygen is brought into contact with the fuel through an oxygen carrier (OC) material, a metal oxide that can alternately be oxidized and reduced. An interconnected fluidized bed system has often been used (Chisalita and Cormos 2018). The main drawbacks of the concept for fluidized reactors are related to the transport of the OC (Adanez et al., 2012). In a recent work, Noorman et al. (2011) proposed a reactor concept based on packed bed reactor technology, in which the solids are stationary and are alternately exposed to reducing and oxidizing conditions via periodic switching of the gas feed streams. The advantages of reactor concepts based on packed bed reactor technology are that the separation of gas and particles is intrinsically avoided, the reactor design can be much more compact, and they allow for better utilization of the OC. A purge step can be used in between the oxidation and reduction steps in order to avoid formation of explosive mixtures and to provide a better use of the heat produced during oxidation (usually an exothermic process) in reduction step (usually endothermic).

Setting the optimum operating conditions for the CLC reactors are important steps to be taken before implementing the process on an industrial scale. In this work, a dynamic mathematical model was developed in MATLAB/Simulink to simulate a packed bed reactor used in alternating steps for a methane-based CLC process with an iron-based OC. The steps studied in a full cycle were reduction of oxygen carrier, purge, OC oxidation of oxygen carrier, purge. A graphical representation of the dynamic CLC reactor is presented Figure 1. Although a single reactor was considered, it will be referred to as a fuel reactor during the reduction step and air reactor during the oxidation step.

The OC considered was activated ilmenite, an iron/titan oxide. Furthermore, this work assumed only iron-based OC, with the simplified oxidation and reduction reactions presented in Eqs. (1-3). The ferric component was Fe_2O_3, while the ferrous one was represented by FeO.

Initially, methane gas enters fuel reactor, filled with the iron-based OC, where Eq. 1 takes place. After the oxygen from the carrier is exhausted, the inflow of methane is stopped and a purge step takes place with a CO_2 stream to remove the unreacted methane. Subsequently, a stream of air enters the air reactor during the regeneration step, in which the oxidation reaction (Eq. 2) takes place. Finally, after the iron-based OC is regenerated, another purge step with CO_2 is required to clear the unreacted oxygen and provide a better use of the heat produced during oxidation.

$$4Fe_2O_3 + CH_4 \rightarrow 8FeO + CO_2 + 2H_2O \tag{1}$$

$$4FeO + O_2 \rightarrow 2Fe_2O_3 \tag{2}$$

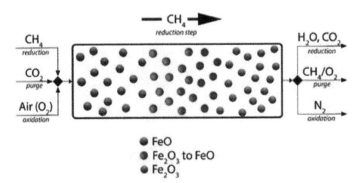

Figure 1. Process diagram during the reduction step, when CH₄ reacts with Fe₂O₃ leaving behind inactive FeO.

2. Model development

This paper is evaluating the dynamic simulation of methane-based CLC with an iron-based OC in a packed bed reactor running in alternating combustion/regeneration steps. The mass and energy balance equations for the packed bed reactor, together with the equations that describe the kinetics model and heat transfer processes were implemented in MATLAB/Simulink. After development, the air and fuel reactor models were interconnected with models describing the purge steps of the process to highlight the dynamic behaviour of the entire process.

2.1. Reactor model parameters and assumptions

The following assumptions are defined for the reactor mathematical model:
1) The solid (iron-based OC) is stationary;
2) Plug flow model for gas phase velocity profile;
3) Non-porous solid particles of spherical shape and uniform initial radius;
4) Reaction takes place inside the solid pellet.

Process and model parameters are presented in Table 1:

Table 1. Reactor model parameters used in the dynamic CLC reactor model

Parameter	Value	Parameter	Value
Reactor length, m	0.93	Solid mass, kg	3
Reactor diameter, m	0.035	O_2 concentration, kmol m^{-3}	0.003
Particle diameter, m	0.002	CH_4 concentration, kmol m^{-3}	0.016
Work pressure, atm	1.2	Air density, kg m^{-3}	0.4841
Temperature, K	873÷1073	CH_4 density, kg m^{-3}	0.263
Air flow rate, L min^{-1}	40	CH_4 flow rate, L min^{-1}	200

2.2. Reactor model equations

The reactor is mathematically represented by the following set of equations:
a) Total mass balance for the fuel and air reactor:

$$\frac{\partial m_s}{\partial t} = w_p \cdot nM_{O_2} \tag{3}$$

$$\frac{\partial F_g}{\partial t} = -w_g \cdot \frac{\partial F_g}{\partial z} + w_p \cdot \frac{w_g \cdot nM_{O_2}}{dz} \tag{4}$$

b) Component mass balance for the fuel and air reactor:

$$\frac{\partial m_{FeO}}{\partial t} = w_p \cdot nM_{FeO} \tag{5}$$

$$\frac{\partial m_{Fe_2O_3}}{\partial t} = w_p \cdot nM_{Fe_2O_3} \tag{6}$$

$$\frac{\partial F_{O_2}}{\partial t} = -w_g \cdot \frac{\partial F_{O_2}}{\partial z} + w_p \cdot \frac{w_g \cdot nM_{O_2}}{dz} \tag{7}$$

$$\frac{\partial F_{CH_4}}{\partial t} = -w_g \cdot \frac{\partial F_{CH_4}}{\partial z} + w_p \cdot \frac{w_g \cdot nM_{CH_4}}{dz} \tag{8}$$

$$\frac{\partial F_{CO_2}}{\partial t} = -w_g \cdot \frac{\partial F_{CO_2}}{\partial z} + w_p \cdot \frac{w_g \cdot nM_{CO_2}}{dz} \tag{9}$$

$$\frac{\partial F_{H_2O}}{\partial t} = -w_g \cdot \frac{\partial F_{H_2O}}{\partial z} + w_p \cdot \frac{w_g \cdot nM_{H_2O}}{dz} \tag{10}$$

where w_g was gas velocity, w_p was process velocity, m_i, F_i, M_i and n_i were mass, mass flow rate, molar mass and stoichiometric coefficient of component i, respectively. Eqs. (5, 6) took place in both reactors, Eq. (7) took place in the air reactor, while Eqs. (8-10) described the component mass balances for the fuel reactor.

2.3. Reactor model kinetics

A mixed kinetic model was used to describe the CLC process, accounting for both homogeneous and heterogeneous models. The model assumed a uniform initial solid particle radius and that the reaction took place inside the pellet, based on the shrinking core model (Abad et al., 2011). As the process velocity was directly proportional to the reaction rate and the mass transfer resistance in the gas film and diffusion inside the pellet were not considered, the reaction rate for the oxidation reaction was:

$$\frac{dn_{Fe_2O_3}}{dt} = 2.776 \cdot e^{\frac{-3.06712 \cdot 10^3}{T}} \cdot m_{FeO}^{\frac{2}{3}} \cdot m_p^{\frac{1}{3}} \cdot C_{O_2} \tag{11}$$

and for the reduction reaction:

$$\frac{dn_{FeO}}{dt} = 8.957 \cdot 10^4 \cdot e^{\frac{-1.62617 \cdot 10^4}{T}} \cdot m_{Fe_2O_3}^{\frac{2}{3}} \cdot m_p^{\frac{1}{3}} \cdot C_{CH_4} \tag{12}$$

where $mFeO$ and mFe_2O_3 represented the masses for iron (II) and (III) oxide respectively, C_{CO2} and C_{CH4} were the concentrations for oxygen and methane.

3. Results and discussions

Figure 2 shows the breakthrough curves for O_2 during oxidation and for CH_4 and CO_2 during reduction. Using different flow rate values for each gas, breakthrough times were close, with around 1000 s for the oxidation step and 1500 s for the reduction step, in accordance with literature (Gallucci et al. 2015, Zhang et al., 2018). Figure 3 shows three full cycles, highlighting the dynamic nature of the CLC reactor with alternating operation of the fuel and air reactors. Figure 4 presents the consumption of the solid reactants in time for the oxidation (Left) and reduction (Right) steps at different axial positions inside the reactor. Figure 5 presents the temperature variation in time for the solid during the oxidation step. The temperature increased by around 250 K, in line with literature (Gallucci et al. 2015).

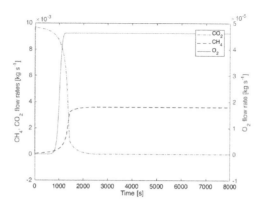

Figure 2. Flow rate profiles for CH₄, CO₂ in fuel reactor and for O₂ in air reactor.

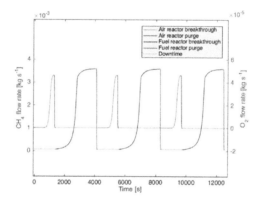

Figure 3. CH₄ and O₂ flow rates during three full cycles for the CLC reactor.

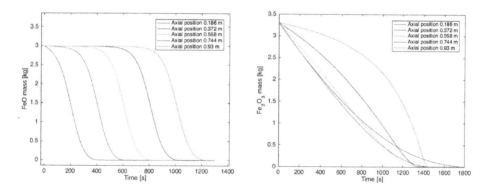

Figure 4. FeO mass (Left) and Fe₂O₃ mass (Right) as functions of time at different axial positions in the reactor during oxidation and reduction, respectively.

Finally (Figure 6), a sensitivity analysis was done for flow rate during the oxidation step, studying the time necessary for the system to reach a steady state. Increasing the flow rate by 20% led to less time required for the system to stabilize (83% of the initial time), while decreasing flow rate by 20% yielded a longer time for the system to reach stationarity (125% of initial time).

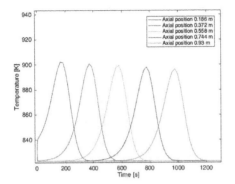
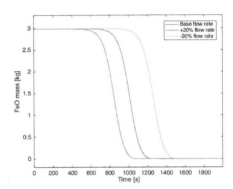

Figure 5. Temperature of the solid (FeO) during oxidation step at three different axial.

Figure 6. - FeO mass profiles during oxidation step for different flow rates

4. Conclusions

A mathematical model for a packed bed reactor used alternately in a methane-based CLC process with iron-based OC was developed. The developed model was used to predict (in space and time) the gas flow profile, velocity distribution, gas composition distribution, behaviour of OC and temperature profiles inside the air and fuel reactors. The MATLAB/Simulink model predictions were in line with published literature data. Changes to the oxygen flowrate had a high impact over the total time required to reach the complete conversion of the solid. A flow rate increase of the air stream by 20% showed the system reached a stationary state in less time by 200 seconds, while the decrease by 20% in air flow rate determined a longer time to reach steady state by 300 seconds.

References

A. Abad, J. Adánez, A. Cuadrat, F. García-Labiano, P. Gayán, L.F. de Diego, 2011, Kinetics of redox reactions of ilmenite for chemical-looping combustion, Chem. Eng. Sci., 66, 4, 689–702.

J. Adanez, A. Abad, F. Garcia-Labiano, P. Gayan, L.F. De Diego, 2012, Progress in chemical-looping combustion and reforming technologies, Prog. Energy Combust. Sci., 38, 2, 215–282.

D.A. Chisalita, A.M. Cormos, 2018, Dynamic simulation of fluidized bed chemical looping combustion process with iron based oxygen carrier, Fuel, 214, October 2017, 436–445.

F. Gallucci, H.P. Hamers, M. van Zanten, M. van Sint Annaland, 2015, Experimental demonstration of chemical-looping combustion of syngas in packed bed reactors with ilmenite, Chem. Eng. J., 274, 156–168.

S. Noorman, F. Gallucci, M. Van Sint Annaland, J.A.M. Kuipers, 2011, Experimental investigation of chemical-looping combustion in packed beds: A parametric study, Ind. Eng. Chem. Res., 50, 4, 1968–1980.

J.M. Parker, 2014, CFD model for the simulation of chemical looping combustion, Powder Technol., 265, 47–53.

H. Zhang, X. Liu, H. Hong, H. Jin, 2018, Characteristics of a 10kW honeycomb reactor for natural gas fueled chemical-looping combustion, Appl. Energ., 213, 285-292.

Sauro Pierucci, Flavio Manenti, Giulia Bozzano, Davide Manca (Eds.)
Proceedings of the 30th European Symposium on Computer Aided Process Engineering
(ESCAPE30), May 24-27, 2020, Milano, Italy. © 2020 Elsevier B.V. All rights reserved.
http://dx.doi.org/10.1016/B978-0-12-823377-1.50102-6

Life Cycle Analysis of Phenol - Formaldehyde Resins Substituted with Lignin

Olivia A. Perederic[a], Aikaterini Mountraki[b], Electra Papadopoulou[c], John M. Woodley[a], Georgios M. Kontogeorgis[a]*

[a]*Department of Chemical and Biochemical Engineering, Technical University of Denmark, DK-2800 Kgs. Lyngby, Denmark*
[b]*Department of Engineering, Aarhus Univeristy, DK-8200 Aarhus, Denmark*
[c]*CHIMAR HELLAS SA, GR-57001, Thermi-Thessaloniki, Greece*

Abstract

Phenol-formaldehyde (PF) resins are widely used in wood-based applications by reason of their heat and water resistance, high mechanical strength and chemical stability. Challenges regarding the environmental impact of petroleum-based resources lead to an increased interest of developing new resins where components such as phenol are replaced with renewable materials. This work evaluates the environmental impact of phenol-formaldehyde resins using an organosolv lignin as phenol replacement. Two life cycle analysis (LCA) boundaries (i.e. Cradle-to-Gate, Gate-to-Gate) are studied for PF resin having different substitution levels of phenol: 0%, 40% and 100%. The LC Soft (ICAS) is used for the LCA, which provides information regarding the carbon footprint (CF), fifteen environmental impact categories (e.g.: soil, water, air, human toxicity) and the life cycle inventory (LCI) contribution. The results show improvements for all environmental impact categories for the lignin substituted resins compared to PF resin, confirming the significant role of lignin. Moreover, the impact of the raw materials (Cradle-to-Gate) is significantly higher than the impact of the production process (Gate-to-Gate).

Keywords: PF resin, LPF resin, LCA, LCI

1. Introduction

The PF resins are considerably used for the production of wood-based panels as they provide water resistance, mechanical strength, chemical and thermal stability (1). The PF resins are produced from the reaction of phenol and formaldehyde under alkaline conditions. Phenol is mainly produced by petroleum, yet the environmental impact of products can be reduced when replacing the fossil-based compounds with renewable ones. Under this current trend, new alternatives, which are capable to maintain the original properties of the product, are investigated. One alternative to PF resins is the lignin-PF resins, where phenol is replaced by lignin in different amounts. Lignin is a natural wood component, which proves to be a very good additive for different polymers and adhesives (2,3). Lignin can be sourced from different biomass pretreatment processes (i.e. thermal, kraft, organosolv). The advantage of organosolv lignin is that the process has lower environmental impact compared to other pulping processes (e.g. no waste streams are generated in organosolv process, while liquid waste stream and gaseous releases result from the kraft process), and the lignin product can be obtained in higher purity and with better properties (e.g.: low molecular weight, smaller particle with better dispersity, higher reactivity, etc.) compared to the lignin resulted from other processes(4). Advanced processes for lignin extraction, such as ionic liquids extraction (5), deep eutectic solvent mixtures or other type of solvents (6) can have better extraction performances, but issues like solvent recovery and cost, together with lignin characteristics might be a limiting condition of using these methods at the industrial scale. LCA studies show that the use of kraft lignin as phenolic substitute for PF resins has better environmental profile (7). However, the use of organosolv lignin is not thoroughly studied in the literature. The aim of this work is to evaluate the environmental impact of the resin production process when phenol is replaced by an organosolv lignin.

2. Methodology

2.1. Goal, scope definition, function, and functional unit

This work is a comparative LCA study among different productions of resins. The aim is to evaluate the environmental impact of the production process, of the raw materials, and of the composition of the resins when phenol is replaced by lignin. The production is postulated to be part of a real-life lignocellulosic biorefinery, the CIMV biorefinery (Compagnie Industrielle de la Matière Végétale) (8,9). It is experimentally verified that CIMV lignin can successfully substitute phenol for the production of PF resins, while maintaining the properties of the final product (10). It is postulated that the production of all resins is at an industrial level. The resin production process consists of two main process sections: reaction and cooling. The process output is 32.2 t/h of resin. The function of the study is the synthesis and cooling of the product. The selected functional unit (FU) of the product is 1 kg of resin (solution), which is representative for industrial scale production. The LC Soft (ICAS) (11) is used for the LCA, which provides information regarding the carbon footprint (CF), the LCI contribution, and fifteen environmental impact categories.

2.2. System description and boundaries

Two case studies with different LCA boundaries are evaluated: (A) Gate-to-Gate, considering only the impact of the resin production process, and (B) Cradle-to-Gate, considering also the impact of the production of raw materials, without taking into account the impact of transportation. Three different ratios for the substitution of phenol by lignin are studied for each case study: 100% phenol-formaldehyde (PF), 60% phenol 40% lignin-formaldehyde (LPF), and 100% lignin-formaldehyde (LF). The assessment of cradle-to-grave is a challenge, since there are different applications of the final product and not enough data is available for the product after the production stage. A representation of the system boundary for the selected case studies is showed in Figure 1.

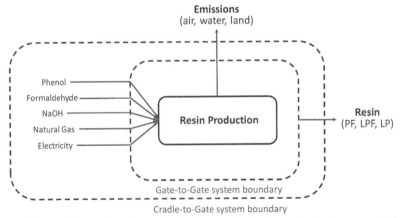

Figure 1. System boundary with Input and Output streams for the two case studies.

The reaction section for the resin production consists in mixing the raw materials in a batch reactor (12,13). The reaction takes place at 1 atm and 90 °C for a period of 8 hours. Then, the product is cooled down at 25 °C with cooling water (Ts=15 °C, Tt=22 °C). The heating is provided by low pressure steam (p=4 bar). The raw materials are: phenol 95% wt. solution, formaldehyde 37% wt. solution, sodium hydroxide (NaOH) 50% wt. solution, and organosolv lignin with 5% water content. The three different resins use the materials in following ratios:

- *PF resin*: lignin:phenol=0:1 (wt.); formaldehyde: phenol = 2.25:1 (mol fr.); formaldehyde:NaOH = 6.3:1 (mol fr.), phenol (95% wt.) flowrate = 11773 kg/h;
- *LPF resin*: lignin:phenol=2:3 (wt.); formaldehyde:phenol=3.75:1 (mol fr.); formaldehyde:NaOH= 6.3:1 (mol fr.), lignin (5% wt. humidity) flowrate = 5121 kg/h;
- *LF resin*: lignin:phenol=1:0 (wt.); formaldehyde:lignin=2.25:1 (wt. fr.), formaldehyde:NaOH = 4.7:1 (wt. fr.); lignin (5% wt. humidity) flowrate =12803 kg/h.

2.3. Data collection

The data for the analysis comes from the industry, simulation results of the industrial process, the literature, and the LC soft.

- *Industrial and simulation data*: this data provides the main information regarding process mass and energy balance (i.e. stream and equipment data,) which accounts for stream and equipment table data in LC Soft. The data is provided by Chimar (14) and Mountraki et al. (12) for PF resin. The stream data for LPF and LF resin is calculated from PF resin data, based on mass ratio substitution of phenol with lignin, while the equipment data (Table 1) is assumed to be the same for all the three resins.
- *Literature data*: emissions of the industrial process, that were not taken into account within the process simulation and could not be provided from the industry, were collected from the work of Wilson (2010) (15). The emission data used for the analysis is presented in Table 2.
- *LC Soft database*: provides all the data for chemicals and utilities used in the LC models. The data from LC Soft comes from various databases and literature.
- *Data excluded from the study*: raw materials transportation; miscellaneous materials; resources for equipment, facilities, infrastructure, support activities and personnel (materials, waste, and utilities).

The environmental impact assessment is performed with LC Soft from ICAS (11). The analysis provides information regarding carbon footprint (CF) and 15 impact categories regarding soil, water, air, and human toxicity, as well as LCI contribution. The data for each of the case studies, as implemented in LC Soft, is presented in Table 1, regarding the equipment data, and in Table 2, regarding the emission data. The emission data is adapted from Wilson (2010) (15) by considering the phenol emissions for the lignin resin (LPF) proportional with the amount of phenol available in the resin. No phenol emissions are considered for LF resin. It is assumed that the organosolv lignin has no emissions and that it is produced from wheat straw.

Table 1. Process and equipment data used for LCA for 1 kg of resin[a].

Type of unit	Duty, kW	Activity	Energy source
Emissions control[b]	0.09	Electric usage	Electricity, at grid
Process electricity[b]	0.22	Electric usage	Electricity, natural gas, at power plant
Reactor	0.21	Heating	Natural gas, combusted in industrial equipment
Heat Exchanger	0.20	Cooling	Chilled water, engine-driven chiller using natural gas

[a] Same equipment data is used for all three resins and for all case studies.
[b] Data adapted from (15)

Table 2. Plant emissions to air as undefined source for 1 kg of resin[a]

Resin	PF	LPF[b]	LF[b]
VOC[c], kg	2.89E-05	2.89E-05	2.89E-05
Formaldehyde (HAP), kg	6.69E-06	6.69E-06	6.69E-06
Phenol (HAP), kg	2.04E-06	1.22E-06	0.00E+00
Particulate, kg	2.31E-06	2.31E-06	2.31E-06

[a] Values adapted from Wilson (2010) (15)
[b] LPF resin considers 60% of the phenol emission from FP production; LF has zero phenol emissions
[c] The volatile organic compounds (VOC) are defined/assumed as benzene emissions.

3. Results and discussion

Table 3 presents the carbon footprint of the production process of the three resins. Since it is considered that all three resins have the same utility consumption, the carbon foot print of their process is similar, and it is the same for both case studies. The total carbon footprint for the production of 1 kg of resin is 0.072 g CO_2.

Table 3. Carbon footprint results for the resins production process.

Type of unit	Carbon Footprint (CO_2 eq.)
Emission control	0
Process electricity	1.81e-05
Reactor	2.02e-02
Heat Exchanger	5.22e-02
Total	7.24e-02

The environmental impact is evaluated through several indicators that cover different areas such as environmental effects (e.g. GWP, PCOP), human toxicity (e.g. HTPI, HTPE aquatic and terrestrial ecotoxicity effects and which importance is treated equally in this work. The complete list of indicators and the results for the two case studies are presented in Table 4. The results from the two case studies show the importance of a complete analysis of a process, and the impact of the raw materials. The environmental impact of the resin production (case A Gate-to-Gate) contribution is only 1% within the lifecycle of the product (case B Cradle-to-Gate), an exception is given by the global warming potential (GWP), where the production accounts for 2% for PF resin, and 3% for LPF and LF resins within the product lifecycle. In case study B (Cradle-to-Gate), the results for all three resins show significant improvements in all environmental impact indicators for the lignin-based resins. LPF resin show an improved performance for all indicators compared to PF resin, while LF resin shows the best performance across all environmental impact indicators. The LPF resin shows an average drop of 11% in all the impact categories when compared to PF resin. The highest drop is estimated for the aquatic potential (AP, H^+ eq.) indicator (19%), while the lowest value drop is estimated for the non-renewable resources (MJ eq) (8.5%). When comparing the results for LF resin to those of PF resin, the average drop over all the environmental indicators is 25%. The best performances are achieved for the AP indicator (i.e. 42% lower values), while the smallest variation is estimated for the non-renewable resources (i.e. 18%). The results show potential of future improvement if the energetic requirements for the processing of the raw materials and the resins can be provided by renewable resources.

The LCI contribution comprises of a list of 190 chemicals, where the top contributors are represented by CO_2 emissions in the air, which results from different parts of the product life cycle, and fuel emissions (e.g. natural gas, oil) in the ground. The complete LCI results can be provided upon request.

Table 4. Environmental impact generated for the production of 1 kg of resin.

Indicator [a]	Unit	Case study A Gate-to-Gate			Case study B Cradle-to-Gate		
		PF	LPF	LF	PF	LPF	LF
HTPI	1/LD50	2.12E-05	2.12E-05	2.12E-05	3.85E-03	3.51E-03	3.10E-03
HTPE	1/TWA	3.83E-07	3.83E-07	3.83E-07	6.17E-05	5.56E-05	4.83E-05
ATP	$1/LC_{50}$	1.32E-05	1.32E-05	1.32E-05	2.00E-03	1.79E-03	1.54E-03
GWP	CO_2 eq	7.24E-02	7.24E-02	7.24E-02	3.13E+00	2.69E+00	2.18E+00
ODP	CFC-11 eq	7.26E-12	7.26E-12	7.26E-12	1.03E-09	9.16E-10	7.77E-10
PCOP	C_2H_2 eq.	4.07E-05	4.07E-05	4.07E-05	5.31E-03	4.66E-03	3.88E-03
AP	H^+ eq	3.45E-03	3.45E-03	3.45E-03	6.48E-01	5.23E-01	3.75E-01
HTC	kg benzen eq	4.93E-05	4.93E-05	4.93E-05	6.86E-03	6.07E-03	5.13E-03
HTNC	kg toluen eq	1.23E+00	1.23E+00	1.23E+00	1.78E+02	1.58E+02	1.34E+02
ET	kg 2,4-D eq	3.06E-03	3.06E-03	3.06E-03	4.44E-01	3.94E-01	3.36E-01
Non-renewable, fossil	MJ eq	3.37E-01	3.37E-01	3.37E-01	6.47E+01	5.92E+01	5.28E+01
Photochemical Ozone Formation	kg NMVOC eq	1.79E-06	1.79E-06	1.79E-06	3.14E-04	2.85E-04	2.51E-04
Marine eutrophication	kg N eq	1.16E-05	1.16E-05	1.16E-05	1.32E-03	1.13E-03	9.06E-04
Terrestrial eutrophication	molc N eq	1.30E-04	1.30E-04	1.30E-04	1.48E-02	1.27E-02	1.02E-02
Particulate matter	kg PM2.5 eq	1.19E-06	1.19E-06	1.19E-06	2.00E-04	1.81E-04	1.59E-04

[a] HTPI – human toxicity potential by ingestion, HTPE – human toxicity by exposure, ATP – aquatic toxicity potential, GWP – global warming potential, ODP - ozone depletion potential, PCOP – photochemical oxidation potential, AP – acidification potential, HTC – human toxicity carcinogenic, HTNC - human toxicity non-carcinogenic, ET - fresh water ecotoxicity.

4. Conclusion

This work is a comparative LCA study among different resins productions in order to provide an overview of the impact of different factors (e.g. raw materials, resin composition) in the production of the phenol-aldehyde resins. The paper highlights the importance of replacing fossil fuels derived materials with ones derived from renewable sources. The life cycle analysis is performed for the production of three different phenol substitution ratios by an organosolv lignin (0% as PF, 40% as LPF, and 100% as LF) for two different system boundaries (case study A: Gate-to-Gate and case study B: Cradle-to-Gate). The results show that the impact of the raw materials is significantly higher than the impact of the production process. The LPF and LF resins presented lower values for all the environmental impact indicators compared to the PF resin, showing that the organosolv lignin has a positive impact in replacing the phenol within this type of resins. Further studies should include a detailed evaluation of the process parameters at industrial level for the three resins together with the impact of using renewable resources in other areas of the process (e.g. utilities, fuels, transportation, etc.).

Acknowledgments

This work has received funding from European Union's Horizon 2020 research and innovation programme under Marie Skłodowska-Curie RISE action, grant agreement No 778332, project RENESENG II.

References

1. W. Qiao, S. Li, F. Xu. Preparation and Characterization of a Phenol-formaldehyde Resin Adhesive Obtained from Bio-ethanol Production Residue. Polym Polym Compos. 2016;24(2):99–105.

2. V. Mimini, E. Sykacek, S.N.A. Hashim, J. Holzweber, H. Hettegger, K. Fackler, A. Potthast, N. Mundigler, T. Rosenau. Compatibility of Kraft Lignin, Organosolv Lignin and Lignosulfonate with PLA in 3D Printing. J Wood Chem Technol. 2019;39(1):14–30.

3. J. Lima García, G. Pans, C. Phanopoulos. Use of lignin in polyurethane-based structural wood adhesives. J Adhes. 2018;94(10):814–28.

4. J. Banoub, G.H Delmas Jr., N. Joly, G. Mackenzie, N. Cachet, B. Benjelloun- Mlayah, M. Delmas. A critique on the structural analysis of lignins and application of novel tandem mass spectrometric strategies to determine lignin sequencing. Journal of Mass Spectrometry, 2015; 50(1), pp.5-48.

5. X. Zhu, C. Peng, H. Chen, Q. Chen, Z.K. Zhao, Q. Zheng Q, H. Xie. Opportunities of Ionic Liquids for Lignin Utilization from Biorefinery. ChemistrySelect. 2018;3(27):7945–62.

6. D. Tian, R.P. Chandra, J.S. Lee, C. Lu, J.N. Saddler. A comparison of various lignin-extraction methods to enhance the accessibility and ease of enzymatic hydrolysis of the cellulosic component of steam-pretreated poplar. Biotechnol Biofuels. 2017;10(1):1–10.

7. E. Bernier, C. Lavigne, P.Y. Robidoux. Life cycle assessment of kraft lignin for polymer applications. Int J Life Cycle Assess. 2013;18(2):520–8.

8. J. Snelders, E. Dornez, B. Benjelloun-Mlayah, W.J.J. Huijgen, P.J. de Wild, R.J.A. Gosselink, J. Gerritsma, C.M. Courtin. Biorefining of wheat straw using an acetic and formic acid based organosolv fractionation process. Bioresour Technol. 2014;156:275–82

9. COMPAGNIE INDUSTRIELLE DE LA MATIERE VEGETAL (CIMV) [Internet]. Available from: www.cimv.fr/

10. N. Tachon, B. Benjelloun-Mlayah, M. Delmas. Organosolv wheat straw lignin as a phenol substitute for green phenolic resins. BioResources, 2016;11(3), 5797-5815.

11. S. Kalakul, P. Malakul, K. Siemanond, R. Gani. Integration of life cycle assessment software with tools for economic and sustainability analyses and process simulation for sustainable process design. J Clean Prod. 2014;71:98–109.

12. A. Mountraki, K. Pyrgakis, A. Nikolakopoulos, B. Benjelloun-Mlayah, A. Kokosis. D5.5: Process Designs and Flowsheet Models: CIMV and the BIOCORE pilots; 2013, report no: D5.5 FP7-241566.

13. B. Pang, S. Yang, W. Fang, T.Q. Yuan, D.S. Argyropoulos, R.C. Sun. Structure-property relationships for technical lignins for the production of lignin-phenol-formaldehyde resins. Ind Crops Prod. 2017;108:316-326.

14. Chimar Hellas [Internet]. Available from: www.chimarhellas.com

15. J.B. Wilson. Life-cycle inventory of formaldehyde-based resins used in wood composites in terms of resources, emissions, energy and carbon. Wood Fiber Sci. 2010;42(SUPPL. 1):125–43.

Sauro Pierucci, Flavio Manenti, Giulia Bozzano, Davide Manca (Eds.)
Proceedings of the 30th European Symposium on Computer Aided Process Engineering
(ESCAPE30), May 24-27, 2020, Milano, Italy. © 2020 Elsevier B.V. All rights reserved.
http://dx.doi.org/10.1016/B978-0-12-823377-1.50103-8

Transport Model of Fluids Injected in a Landfill Polluted with Lindane Wastes

David Lorenzo[a*], Aurora Sanots[a], Carmen M. Domínguez[a], Joaquín Guadaño[b],
Jorge Gómez[b], Jesús Fernández[c]

[a] Chemical Engineering and Materials Department. Universidad Complutense de
Madrid. Spain
[b] EMGRISA, Empresa Para la Gestión de Residuos Industriales, S.A., Madrid,
Spain. [c] Department of Rural Development and sustainability, Government of Aragon,
Spain.
dlorenzo@ucm.es

Abstract

Dense non-aqueous phase liquids (DNAPLs) are ubiquitous environmental problem
causing contamination of soil and groundwater. The remediation strategies, such us in
situ chemical oxidation (ISCO), need a good preliminary characterization of injected
chemicals transport within the subsoil in order to select an adequate injection-extraction
strategy and calculate both the chemical dosage and the contact time required.

In this work, the flow was studied in a polluted site located in Sabiñanigo (Spain) where
a DNAPL generated by lindane production process was dumped as production waste. The
flow was studied using a tracer step experiment injecting a constant flow rate of tap water
with bromide. Analysis of the groundwater samples composition of tracer with time
obtained was accomplished at several monitoring wells being used to propose a transport
model, which was implemented in gPROMS. The experimental data were used to fit a
dispersion coefficient to depend on the velocity of the fluid. The transport model was
validated with a second step tracer experiment, carried out at lower flowrate. Besides, the
transport model obtained has been used to predict the oxidant (persulfate) concentration
profiles from the injection point, considering different flow rates in an ISCO treatment.

Keywords: Landfill, Tracer step experiment, Advection-Dispersion model, Anisotropy,
ISCO.

1. Introduction

Many industrial activities have produced the emission and spills of dangerous substances
that greatly impact the quality of soil and particularly groundwater. This is the case of
Sabiñanigo, Spain, where a factory synthesized lindane (with insecticidal properties),
generating a high amount of solid and liquid wastes of a mixture of isomers of
hexachlorocyclohexane (HCH) (Vijgen et al., 2011). These mixtures were dumped in a
non-controlled way at Sardas landfill. The liquid waste has formed a Dense Non-Aqueous
Phase Liquid (DNAPL) composed by 30 different chlorinated organic compounds
(COCs). This phase has progressively migrated through the subsurface (density-driven)
reaching high depths and polluting the soil and groundwater (Santos et al., 2018).

The most suitable remediation strategies are those based on in situ treatments, such us:
Enhanced Surfactant Product Recovery (ESPR), with the injection of a surfactant solution
to facilitate the DNAPL extraction (Wu et al., 2016); in situ chemical oxidation (ISCO),
injecting an oxidant (persulfate for instance) to abate the COCs (Santos et al., 2017), or

the simultaneous injection of a surfactant with an oxidant (S-ISCO) (Dahal et al., 2016). All these technologies need a good preliminary characterization of injected chemicals transport within the subsoil in order to select an adequate injection-extraction strategy.

For small-scale injection points, the local flow can be influenced by the nature of the dispersion of the solute, such as its anisotropy. However, the transport of the injected substances is frequently described only by an isotropic advective flow (plug flow). Nevertheless, dispersion, as well as anisotropy, can have a remarkable contribution to the transport of the injected chemicals (Vasco et al., 2018). To characterize more accurately the transport of the injected fluids in the subsurface, the use of tracers, such us bromide, has been applied (Aggelopoulos and Tsakiroglou, 2007). Bromide as a conservative tracer has been used in this work to study the flow of the injected fluid proposing and validating a transport model. Besides, the model was used to predict the oxidant (persulfate) concentration profiles from the injection point, considering different flow rates in an ISCO treatment.

2. Experimental

Two step tracer experiments have been carried out using bromide in a test cell built ad hoc in the alluvium of the Sardas landfill. The bromide concentration at several monitoring wells was measured to obtain profiles vs. time. The first experiment (STE-1) was used to propose the transport model and the second (STE-2), which was carried out 1 month after the STE-1, was employed to validate it.

A tracer aqueous solution of bromide of 120 mg/L was injected (zero time) through flexible PVC 1-inch hose (Tiger Flex) by using an electric transfer pump. In STE-1 a flow rate of 3.9 m3/h of the tracer aqueous solution was delivered at the well PS14B at a depth of 14.5 m (thus, in the gravel-sand layer) during 5.1 h. In STE-2, a flow rate of 0.6 m³/h of the tracer solution was injected at the same well and depth (PS14B, 14.5 m) but during 8.33 h. The cell test built can be conceptualized by the scheme shown in Figure 1. Monitoring wells PS14, PS14C, and PS14D were periodically sampled at a depth of 14.5 m in both step tracer experiments with a Mini-Typhoon® DTW 40ft12V electric. After purging, a volume of about 200 mL was sampled and bromide concentration was measured, using an ionic chromatograph (Metrohm 761 Compact IC) with anionic chemical suppression coupled with a conductivity detector.

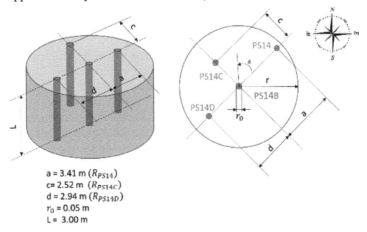

$a = 3.41$ m (R_{PS14})
$c = 2.52$ m (R_{PS14C})
$d = 2.94$ m (R_{PS14D})
$r_0 = 0.05$ m
$L = 3.00$ m

Figure 1. Scheme of the cell test.

3. Results and discussion.

The bromide concentration profiles measured in PS14, PS14C and PS14D wells are given in Figure 2. As can be seen, a rise in the bromide concentration is noted in all the wells shortly after the tracer injection began. Bromide ions were first detected in PS14C, then in PS14D and finally in PS14, accordingly with the distance between the wells and the injection point (Figure 1). If the advective flow was the only contribution to the bromide transport in the alluvium, a step for bromide concentration should be obtained at each monitoring well (show as solid line in Figure 2a, and calculated using Eq. (1)) at the corresponding time. However, the response of the tracer measured with time at each well suggests that the flow in the alluvial groundwater during the injection cannot be described only by advection, but dispersion of the fluid injected should be also considered.

$$
t_{PF} = \frac{\pi L \varepsilon_L R_{well}^2}{Q_{inj}}
\tag{1}
$$

Since the plug flow model from the injection point has been ruled out, the Advection-Dispersion Model has been tested with STE-1 data. This model explains the transport of a conservative solute in the subsurface by the advection-dispersion equation shown in Eq. (2) (Aggelopoulos and Tsakiroglou, 2007).

$$
\frac{\partial C_j}{\partial t} + \nabla \cdot \left(u_i C_j\right) = \nabla \cdot \left(D_T \cdot \nabla C_j\right)
\tag{2}
$$

where u_i is the interstitial velocity, D_T is the dispersion coefficient tensor, and C_j is the concentration of the compound j.

To solve the Eq. (2) the following assumptions have been used: i) The axial dispersion has been considered negligible because the gravel–sand layer is confined between two low-permeability layers; ii) The liquid flow has been assumed as a steady incompressible flow of a liquid with a constant density. As the injected fluid is non-compressible, the interstitial velocity at any distance in the length (r) from PS14 to the corresponding well in the direction θ can be calculated as:

$$
u_i\left(r, \theta_{well}\right) = \frac{u_0\left(\theta_{well}\right) r_0}{r} = \frac{Qa_{well}}{r}
\tag{3}
$$

where r is the radial distance in length from PS14B to the well and $u_0(\theta_{well})$, the interstitial velocity at the wall of the injection point (r_0) in the direction from PS14B to the well (θ). The possibility of anisotropy in the injected fluid flow having a different direction θ relative to the injection point has been considered in Eq.(3) . Furthermore, as $u_o(\theta_{well})$ depends linearly on the flow rate Q, $u_i(r,\theta_{well})$ can be expressed as a function of a defined parameter a_{well}, as given in Eq. (3).Taking into account these assumptions, the tracer mass balance shown in Eq. (2) can be simplified to Eq. (4).

$$
-\frac{Qa_{well}dC_{Br}}{r dr} + D_T(r)\left[\left(\frac{d^2C_{Br}}{dr^2}\right) + \frac{1}{r}\frac{dC_{Br}}{dr}\right] = \frac{dC_{Br}}{dt}
\tag{4}
$$

The boundary and initial conditions used to solve Eq.(2) are the following:

$$C_{Br} = 0 \therefore t = 0, r > r_0 \; ; \; C_{Br} = C_{Br,inj} \therefore t \geq 0, r = r_0 \; ; \; \frac{dC_{Br}}{dt} = 0 \therefore t \geq 0, r = R \qquad (5)$$

The dispersion radial coefficient $D_T(r)$ has been described in the literature as a function of the interstitial velocity, according to Eq. (6) (Gunn, 1987). The effective diffusivity D_{eff}

of the solute in the subsurface corresponds to the molecular diffusion Dm ($7.26 \cdot 10^{-6}$ m^2/h for bromide) of the solute corrected by the porosity and tortuosity of the porous media. Therefore, a negligible contribution of D_{eff} was expected in Eq. (6).

$$D_T(r) = D \cdot u_{i,well}(r) + D_{eff} \qquad (6)$$

The problem was compounded by non-linear and partial equations, which were solved using DASOLV algorithm available in gPROMS. To estimate the coefficients D, and a_{well}, the bromide concentration (C_{Br}) vs. time obtained at each well during the tracer step experiment STE-1 (Figure 4) have been fitted to the model in Eqs. (4) to (6) using a

gPROMS tool. The estimated values for STE-1 are summarized in Table 1. Predicted values have been plotted as dashed lines in Figure 2.

Table 1. Parameter estimated of Eqs. (4) to (6) to the experimental C_{Br} in Figure 2.

Well	a'$_{well}$ ± CI[a], m^{-1}	Standard Deviation	D[b] ± CI[a], m	Standard Deviation	SQR, m^2
PS14	$0.162 \pm 4.0 \cdot 10^{-4}$	$1.8 \cdot 10^{-4}$			
PS14D	$0.244 \pm 6.2 \cdot 10^{-4}$	$2.7 \cdot 10^{-4}$	12.29 ± 0.018	0.0087	43.93
PS14C	$0.427 \pm 1.3 \cdot 10^{-4}$	$5.5 \cdot 10^{-4}$			
[a] Confidence interval at 95%. [b] Deff estimated= 10-5 m2/h.					

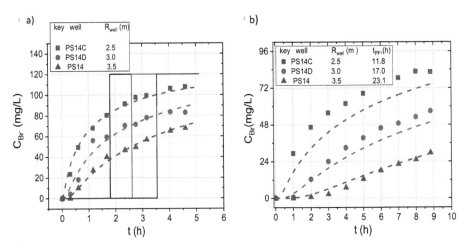

Figure 2. Bromide concentration measured at each monitoring well during the tracer step experiment a) STE-1 Q=3.9 m³/h and b) STE-2. Q=0.5 m³/h using $C_{Br,0}$ =120 mg/L. Symbols depict the experimental values. Dashed lines depict the bromide concentration using Eqs. (4) to (6) and parameters in Table 1. Continuous lines depict the simulated bromide concentration profiles with time in Eq. (1) (effective porosity of the soil 0.12).

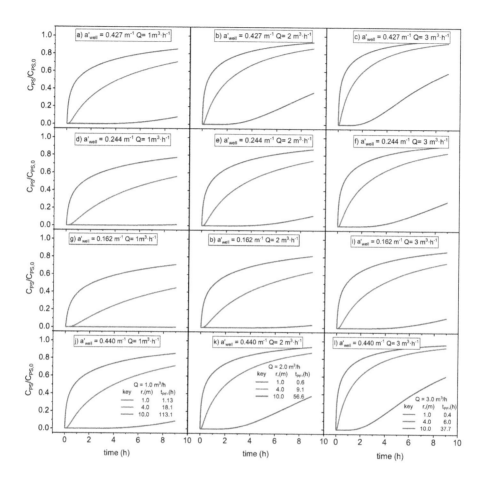

Figure 3. Simulated values of persulfate concentration ratios ($C_{PS}/C_{PS,0}$) using Eqs. (4) to (6) at different injection flow rates, Q. Porosity ε_L=0.12. The legend also indicates the required time for $C_{PS,0}$=1 calculated with Eq. (7) in only advective flow, named as t_{FP}.

The model proposed in Eqs. (4) to (6) and the parameters summarized in Table 4 were used to predict the bromide concentration profiles in STE-2 bromide was injected at Q=0.6 m³/h in PS14B during 8.3 h. The values predicted by the model are in good agreement with the experimental data in both experiments (STE-1, Figure 2a and STE-2, Figure 2b) .Moreover, The advection-dispersion has been used to predict the radial profiles of the oxidant injected in PS14B during the injection period in an ISCO treatment using Persulfate (PS). In Figure 2, the dimensionless profiles of persulfate ($C_{PS}/C_{PS,0}$) vs. time has been predicted at several injection flows rates and at several distances from the injection point (PS14B) As can be seen, a high dispersion of the injected persulfate is predicted. These profiles could be compared with those expected considering only advective flow (from Eq. (1), named as t_{PF}) have been included in the legend of Figure 2. If only advective flow were used to interpret the persulfate profiles obtained in an oxidant injection event, erroneous conclusion would be obtained.

4. Conclusions

Upon analyzing the tracer profiles at the three monitoring wells located around the injection point, it was found that the injected flow exhibited no isotropy in any direction from the injection point. A model that includes the advective and dispersive components, as well as the anisotropy of the flow, has been developed to describe the transport of the injected substances. The dispersion coefficient obtained depended linearly on the interstitial velocity. For the directions considered from the injection point, the model developed can be used to predict the concentration of the injected substances with time at other flow rates. The advection-dispersion model obtained was used to predict the oxidant profiles during the injection event in an ISCO application.

Acknowledgments

The authors acknowledge the financial support from the Comunidad Autonoma de Madrid, project CARESOIL (S2018/EMT-4317) and from the Spanish Ministry of Economy, Industry and Competitiveness, projects CTM2016-77151-C2-1-R.

References

C.A Aggelopoulos, C.D. Tsakiroglou, 2007, The longitudinal dispersion coefficient of soils as related to the variability of local permeability, Water Air Soil Poll.,185, 223-237.

G. Dahal, J. Holcomb, D. Socci, 2016, Surfactant-Oxidant Co-Application for Soil and Groundwater Remediation, Rem. J. Environ. Cleanup Costs Tech. Techni. 26, 101-108.

D.J. Gunn, 1987, Axial and radial dispersion in fixed beds, Chem.Eng. Sci. 42, 363-373.

A. Santos, J. Fernandez, J. Guadano, D. Lorenzo, A. Romero, 2018, Chlorinated organic compounds in liquid wastes (DNAPL) from lindane production dumped in landfills in Sabinanigo (Spain), Environ. Poll. 242, 1616-1624.

A. Santos, J. Fernandez, L. Perez, S. Rodriguez, C. Dominguez., M. Lominchar, D. Lorenzo, A. Romero, 2017, Abatement of chlorinated compounds in groundwater contaminated by HCH wastes using ISCO with alkali activated persulfate, Sci. Total Environ., 615, 1070-1077.

D.W. Vasco, S.R. Pride, C. Zahasky, S. M. Benson, 2018, Calculating Trajectories Associated with Solute Transport in a Heterogeneous Medium, Wat. Resources Res.54, 6890-6908.

B. Wu, H. Y. Li, X.M. Du, L. R. Zhong, B. Yang, P. Du, Q.B. Gu, F. S. Li, 2016, Correlation between DNAPL distribution area and dissolved concentration in surfactant enhanced aquifer remediation effluent: A two-dimensional flow cell study, Chemosphere 144, 2142-2149.

Sauro Pierucci, Flavio Manenti, Giulia Bozzano, Davide Manca (Eds.)
Proceedings of the 30th European Symposium on Computer Aided Process Engineering
(ESCAPE30), May 24-27, 2020, Milano, Italy. © 2020 Elsevier B.V. All rights reserved.
http://dx.doi.org/10.1016/B978-0-12-823377-1.50104-X

Modeling and Optimization for Short-term Scheduling of Plastic Bag Plants

Myrian Santos-Torres[a,b]*, J. Alberto Bandoni[b], M. Susana Moreno[b]

[a]*Escuela Superior Politécnica del Litoral, ESPOL, Facultad de Ciencias Naturales y Matemáticas, Campus Gustavo Galindo, km 30.5 Vía Perimetral, P.O. BOX 09-01-5863,Guayaquil, Ecuador.*

[b]*Planta Piloto de Ingeniería Química - PLAPIQUI (Universidad Nacional del Sur-CONICET), Camino La Carrindanga km 7, 8000 Bahía Blanca, Argentina*
mgsantos@espol.edu.ec

Abstract

This work presents a mixed-integer nonlinear programming (MINLP) formulation for the short-term scheduling of a multistage multiproduct batch facility producing different types of plastic bags. Given a number of customer orders that must be satisfied at specific due dates, the proposed model is able to determine the optimal assignment of orders to units and the sequence of orders on each unit at every processing stage. In contrast to previous works, it allows calculating both the processing rate of each equipment and the processing time of each product as a function of the bag's parameters. Also, the number and diameter of film rolls obtained in the extrusion step as well as the product quality are accounted for in the model. Two alternative performance criteria are used. The first minimizes the delay in the delivery (tardiness) of all orders in the scheduling horizon while the second minimizes the total time required for processing all the orders (makespan). The model efficiency has been evaluated using real data from a plant located in the city of Guayaquil, Ecuador. The results demonstrate the improvements obtained with the proposed model when compared to the actual situation in the company.

Keywords: short-term scheduling, optimization, MINLP model, batch plant, plastic bag.

1. Introduction

Plastic bags are everyday objects that facilitate people's lifestyle. In industry, innumerable types of bags are made according to their purpose, for example, to transport goods, keep fresh food for a certain time, protect products from harmful pollutants, etc. Therefore, plastic bags are versatile products that, despite environmental concerns due to their slow biodegradability, are still in demand.

High- and low-density polyethylene and linear low-density polyethylene are the polymers mostly used in the production of plastic bags. Here, the most important operation in the process is the film blowing to obtain the plastic film in the extruder. This process is followed by the printing, converting, and packaging stages (Gopura and Jayawardene, 2009). In the converting stage, there are units that perform varied tasks such as cutting, drilling, and sealing.

Generally, polyethylene bags are manufactured in batch facilities with multiple stages each having several units running in parallel. In this kind of industry, several production orders can be processed in the same unit at each stage of the process so the plant manager must decide where, when, and how to process them in order to avoid delays in delivering the products to the customers. Given the combinatorial nature of this problem, the best way to solve it is to use optimization-based computational tools that allow the short-term scheduling of the process operations, increasing both the productivity and profitability as well as the level of service offered to the customers.

In literature, there are few papers specifically dedicated to plastic bag production plants. Leung (2009) proposed an MINLP model to optimize the production scheduling at a plastics compounding plant considering only the extrusion stage and incorporating product quality constraints into the formulation. Then, Gopura and Jayawardene (2009) developed a simulation model to improve the production time in the plastic bag manufacturing process. Nevertheless, there are many mathematical modeling proposals for the treatment of short-term scheduling problems in similar plants. Méndez et al. (2000) posed a continuous-time MILP model for the short-term scheduling of single-stage batch plant with parallel units. They considered multiple product orders with different due-dates and accounted for sequence-dependent setups. The assignment and sequencing decisions were handled separately. Later, Gupta and Karimi (2003) improved this model by considering a multistage problem and using two-index discrete decision variables allowing to achieve a reduction in the number of binary and solve industrial-size problems in reasonable times. A. Merchan et al (2016) proposed four different discrete-time MIP models for production scheduling problems in multistage facilities.

Considering previous contributions, in this work an MINLP model is proposed for the short-term scheduling of a multistage batch plant that produces different types of plastic bags. The formulation determines, in an optimal way, the sequencing of the production orders of plastic bags and their assignment to units in different stages of the process, as well as the processing rate of each unit and processing time of each order considering product quality constraints.

2. Problem Definition

Figure 1 shows a generalized scheme of the plastic bag production plant consisting of S processing stages (i.e. extrusion, printing, and converting stages), where I customer orders must be processed in U production units over a specified scheduling horizon H. At each processing stage s, there is a number of units U_s, and each unit u processes a certain set I_u of production orders. Since the plant produces both printed and unprinted bags, there are orders that do not go through all the processing stages. For this reason, a subset I_s is defined which indicates the orders i that are processed in stage s.

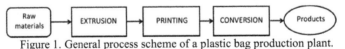

Figure 1. General process scheme of a plastic bag production plant.

Each order i specifies the product (i.e., a type of bag) to be manufactured according to the specifications requested by customers where the $m \in M_i$, raw materials and $a \in A_i$ additives are indicated and, if it is a bag printed, the $k \in K_i$ types of printing inks used. In addition, the length Lb_i, width Ab_i, and thickness Eb_i of a bag, the width Ar_i and thickness Er_i of a film roll, the number of bags Nb_i, and the percentages of raw materials PM_{mi} and additives PA_{ai} used in each order i are problem data. For each order i, several parameters are defined: the weight of a bag Qb_i as the product between the volume (Lb_i x Ab_i x Eb_i) and the density De_i, the weight of one meter of film roll Qm_i as the product between the area (Ar_i x Er_i) and the density De_i, and the total extruded weight QT_i as the product between the weight of the bag Qb_i and the total number of bags Nb_i requested by the customer.

The quantity of raw material of an order MP_{mi} is defined as the product between the percentage of raw materials PM_{mi} and the total extruded weight QT_i; while the quantity of additives of an order AD_{ai} is determined by the product between the percentage of additives PA_{ai} and the total extruded weight QT_i. All orders must be delivered in a given deadline dd_i, usually 7 days.

The basic data for the processing units are the maximum production capacity CAP_u, the change time of a film roll TCr_u, and the maximum permissible weight of a roll $PTMAX$ obtained in the first processing stage s_1 (extrusion).

The main assumptions for these types of problem are summarized below:

1. There are a fixed number of units in each processing stage that operate in parallel.
2. The processing units at each stage are not identical, as they vary by brand, model, serial number and year of manufacture, type of raw material (extrusion), number of colors (printing) and type of bag (conversion).
3. A unit cannot process more than one order at a time and an order cannot be processed by more than one unit at the same time.
4. There are no restrictions on resources, labor or materials during the orders production.
5. Unlimited intermediate storage is available after each processing stage.

The main goal of the problem is to find the detailed program of the plant operations that determines: (1) the assignment of orders to a specific unit in each processing stage, (2) the processing sequence of orders in each unit available, (3) the production time of a bag, (4) the processing rate of an order in each unit, (5) the start and end times of processing each order in all stages, (6) the number, (7) diameter and (8) weight of each film roll in the extrusion stage, (9) the quality indexes, and (10) the energy consumption in the plant.

3. Mathematical formulation

The optimization model for the short-term scheduling of the plastic bag production process can be represented mathematically through: (a) binary variables associated to the assignment of orders to units, W_{iu}, and to the sequencing of orders in a stage, X_{ijs}, and an integer variable related to the number of film rolls for each order i, Nr_i; (b) a set of different operational constraints in terms of continuous and discrete variables and, (c) two objective functions that consist in minimizing either the delay in the delivery of all orders, TD, or the makespan, MK. For space reasons, only some problem constraints are presented, mostly those nonlinear due to the multiplication between variables, for example, Tb_{ius} by Pr_{ius}.

$$Tb_{ius}\, Pr_{ius} = (1+DEX)Lb_i\, W_{iu} \qquad \forall i \in I_s, \forall u \in U_s, s=1 \tag{1}$$

$$Tb_{ius}\, Pr_{ius} = Filb_i\, Lb_i\, W_{iu} \qquad \forall i \in I_s, \forall u \in U_s, s=2 \tag{2}$$

$$Tb_{ius}\, Pr_{ius} = Lb_i\, W_{iu} \qquad \forall i \in I_s, \forall u \in U_s, s=3 \tag{3}$$

$$TT_{ius} = Tb_{ius}\, Nb_i \qquad \forall i \in I_s, \forall u \in U_s, \forall s \in S \tag{4}$$

$$Qp_{iu} = Pr_{ius}\, Qm_i \qquad \forall i \in I_s, \forall u \in U_s, \forall s \in S \tag{5}$$

$$Qr_i = \frac{\pi\, Ar_i}{4}\left(Dr_i^2 - DEM^2\right)De_i \qquad \forall i \in I_s, s=1 \tag{6}$$

$$Qr_i \leq PTMAX \qquad \forall i \in I \tag{7}$$

$$QT_i = Qr_i\, Nr_i \qquad \forall i \in I \tag{8}$$

$$TTC_{iu} = Nr_i\, TCr_u \qquad \forall i \in I_u, u \in U \tag{9}$$

$$MVR_{iu} = 28.8 + 0.0857Nt_u - 0.0812(Qp_{iu} \ 60) \qquad \forall i \in I_1, u \in U_1 \tag{10}$$

$$IMP_{iu} = 14.5 - 0.012Nt_u + 0.0150(Qp_{iu} \ 60) \qquad \forall i \in I_1, u \in U_1 \tag{11}$$

$$D_i \geq TS_{is} + \sum_{u \in U_s}(TT_{ius} + TTC_{iu}) \ dd_i \qquad \forall i \in I_s \tag{12}$$

$$MK \geq TF_{is} \qquad \forall i \in I_s, s = 3 \tag{13}$$

$$MinTD = \sum_i D_i \tag{14}$$

$$MinMK \tag{15}$$

Eqs. (1), (2) and (3) calculate the time required to process a bag of the order i in a unit u at each stage s in terms of the length of the bag and the processing rate of the order in the unit at that stage. The parameter DEX in Eq. (1) represents the waste percentage in the extrusion stage and $Filb_i$ in Eq. (2) denotes the bag printing factor. Eq. (4) specifies the total time for processing the order i in unit u TT_{ius} based on the time Tb_{ius} and the required number of bags Nb_i. Eq. (5) determines the production capacity of order i in unit u Qp_{iu} based on the processing rate and the weight of one meter of film roll, Qm_i.

Eq. (6) calculates the weight of a film roll of order i Qr_i made in the first stage in terms of the volume of the cylindrical roll and the density of the material to be processed. In this expression, Dr_i is the diameter of the film roll of order i and DEM is the diameter of the reel bobbin. Since each extruder u can handle a maximum roll diameter, the variable Qr_i can be constrained to be lower than an upper limit $PTMAX$ as stated in Eq. (7). The number of film rolls Nr_i is obtained in Eq. (8) while the total time for changing all the rolls of order i in unit u TTC_{iu} is determined in Eq. (9), where TCr_u is the change time of a film roll in unit u.

Eqs. (10) and (11) introduce the quality constraints. In case of plastic bags, there are two main quality control measures known as melt volumetric flow rate MVR and impact dart test IMP. These measurements depend on processing rate of the extruder Pr_{ius} and the screw rotating speed N_u, which in turn affect the production time of the orders.

In Eq. (12) the tardiness of order i D_i is calculated as the positive difference between the actual completion time of an order i and its deadline for delivery while in Eq. (13) the makespan MK is defined as the total time required for the completion of a series of orders. Eqs. (14) and (15) establish the objective functions of this problem which are the total tardiness TD (commonly used as an optimization criterion for a production scheduling, defined as the sum of the delay of all orders) and the makespan MK.

The remaining constraints used in this problem are mentioned below:

1. Assignment of orders to units at each stage
2. Each unit can process only one order first.
3. Each order i can have at most one direct preceding order j.
4. Each order i can have at most one successive direct order j.
5. Sequencing of consecutive orders in the same unit at each stage.
6. Relationship between start times of an order in consecutive stages.
7. Relationship between start times of consecutive orders in the same stage.
8. Relationship between restrictions 1 and 3 mentioned above.
9. Determination of the final execution time of orders at each stage.

4. Case Study: Results

The results of a real case study of a plastic bag plant in Ecuador are presented below. This plant operates 24 hours per day during 7 days a week with two daily shifts of 12 h each. Table 1 shows the main data required by the model for this particular case.

Table 1. Data for the case study

Order	Nb_i	dd_i (min)	Lb_i (m)	Qm_i (kg)	Ar_i (m)	$Filb_i$	De_i (kg/m^3)
i_1	125,000	10,080	1.8288	0.016	0.8128	0	1,900.28
i_2	100,000	10,080	1.8288	0.016	0.8128	0	1,900.28
i_3	50,000	10,080	1.3462	0.05	0.9652	0.96	1,845.97
i_4	50,000	10,080	1.3462	0.05	0.9652	0	1,845.97
i_5	50,000	10,080	1.2319	0.072	1.0287	0	1,845.97
i_6	50,000	10,080	1.3462	0.05	0.9652	0.96	1,845.97
i_7	250,000	10,080	0.254	0.048	0.8128	0.94	1,845.97
i_8	250,000	10,080	0.254	0.048	0.8128	0.94	1,845.97
i_9	400,000	10,080	0.5334	0.028	0.9652	0.48	1,900.28
i_{10}	200,000	10,080	0.5715	0.046	0.9525	0.44	1,900.28

Other required data are: (i) the waste percentage in the extrusion, $DEX = 5\%$, (ii) the diameter of the bobbin $DEM = 0.1$ m, (iii) maximum weight allowed in each extruder, $PTMAX = 180$ kg, (iv) the change time of a film roll in each unit $TCr_u = 0.3 - 3$ min.
The processing of orders in different stages is as follows: (a) Stage 1: orders 1 and 2 can be processed in units 6 and 7; orders 3 to 6 in units 1, 2, 3 and 5; orders 7 and 8 in units 2, 3 and 5; and orders 9 and 10 in unit 4; (b) Stage 2: orders 3 and 6 in units 9 and 10; orders 7 and 8 in units 8 to 10; orders 9 and 10 in unit 8; (c) Stage 3: orders 1 and 2 in units 19 and 20; orders 3 and 6 in units 11 to 14; orders 4 and 5 in units 11 to 15; orders 7 and 8 in units 16 and 17; and orders 9 and 10 in unit 18.

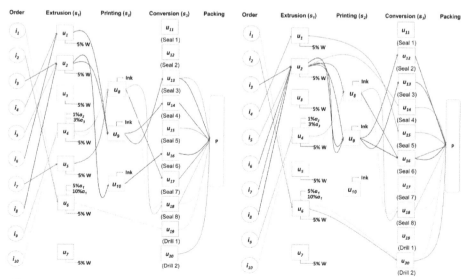

Figure 2. Optimal assignment of orders to units, tardiness minimization.

Figure 3. Optimal assignment of orders to units, makespan minimization.

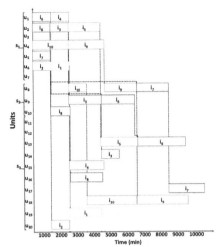

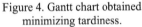

Figure 4. Gantt chart obtained
minimizing tardiness.

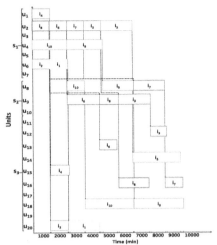

Figure 5. Gantt chart obtained
minimizing makespan.

The model was implemented in GAMS 24.1.3 and solved using BARON code for both objectives. The formulation involves 777 continuous and 220 binary variables in 1,511 constraints. The optimal solution $TD = 0$ min was obtained in 1016 s for minimizing the tardiness and $MK = 9,829$ min was obtained in 543 s for the makespan in an Intel (R) Core (TM) i7-6,500CPU. Figs. 2 and 3 show the processing path of the different production orders for the minimization of tardiness and makespan, respectively. Figs. 4 and 5 present the Gantt charts of these optimal solutions, showing the sequencing and assignment of each order to a unit at each processing stage. In addition, it is observed that all orders are delivered on time during a horizon of one week, but when minimizing makespan only 13 units are used and the solution is obtained in less CPU time than tardiness.

5. Conclusions

An MINLP model was presented for optimizing the short-term scheduling of a plastic bag plant located in Ecuador. The model captures the main operational considerations of this type of plant while verifying restrictions on unit and product quality. The results obtained by the model were compared with the actual data from the plant for the case study where some orders were delivered late. By using the model solution with zero tardiness can be obtained. Therefore, the model is a tool that allows improving the plant scheduling activity and minimizing the production times.

References

1. Gopura, R.A.C.R; Jayawardane T.S.S, (2009) "A Study on a Poly-Bag Manufacturing System Preliminary Analysis and Simulation". DOI: 10.1109/ICIINFS.2009.5429802, 4, 1-5.
2. Gupta, S; Karimi I.A. An Improved MILP Formulation for Scheduling Multiproduct, Multistage Batch Plants. Ind. Eng. Chem. Res. 2003, 42, 2365-2380.
3. Leung, Michelle, (2009). "Production Scheduling Optimization of a Plastics Compounding Plant with Quality Constraints". Master's Thesis. Chemical Engineering Department. Waterloo University, Ontario, Canada, 32-44.
4. Mendez, C.A.; Henning, G.P.; Cerdá, J. Optimal Scheduling of Batch Plants Satisfying Multiple Product Orders with Different Due Dates. Computers and Chemical Engineering, 2000, 24, 2223–2245.
5. Merchan, Andres et al; (2016) "Discrete-Time MIP Methods for Production Scheduling in Multistage Facilities". Computer Aided Process Engineering. Elsevier, DOI: 10.1016/B978-0-444-63428-3.50065-5.

Sauro Pierucci, Flavio Manenti, Giulia Bozzano, Davide Manca (Eds.)
Proceedings of the 30th European Symposium on Computer Aided Process Engineering
(ESCAPE30), May 24-27, 2020, Milano, Italy. © 2020 Elsevier B.V. All rights reserved.
http://dx.doi.org/10.1016/B978-0-12-823377-1.50105-1

Analysis of an Industrial Adsorption Process based on Ammonia Chemisorption: Modeling and Simulation

Cristian Cardenas[a,b,*], Stéphanie Marsteau[b], Léa Sigot[a], Cécile Vallières[a], Abderrazak M. Latifi[a]

[a]*Laboratoire Réactions et Génie des Procédés, CNRS-ENSIC, Université de Lorraine, Nancy, France*
[b]*Insitut National de Recherche et de Sécurité, Vandoeuvre-Lès-Nancy, France*
cristian-geovanny.cardenas-sarabia@univ-lorraine.fr

Abstract

In this study, a one-dimensional first principles model was developed to simulate an ammonia adsorption process. It is described by the mass balance equations, thermodynamic and transport properties. In order to build the adsorption process model, we started with experimental measurements of adsorption isotherms of ammonia on a doped activated carbon. A procedure was developed in order to assess the estimability of the unknown parameters involved in the Sips adsorption isotherm model. The estimable parameters were identified from the experimental data of ammonia adsorption equilibrium at 288, 303 and 313 K. The values of the parameters considered as non-estimable are fixed from one of our previous studies. In addition, we used experimental breakthrough curves to predict the kinetics of adsorption. The mass transfer coefficient K_{LDF} and axial dispersion coefficient D_{ax} were identified from the experimental breakthrough curves for different gas flow rates. The adsorption model was implemented and solved within COMSOL Multiphysics. The predicted model results using the fitted parameters exhibit a good agreement with the experimental measurements.

Keywords: Air purification boxes, ammonia adsorption, experimental analysis, modeling, simulation.

1. Introduction

Gaseous ammonia emission is one of the major concerns in composting or methanization organic waste facilities. Ammonia causes chronic respiratory diseases such as asthma, chronic bronchitis to workers when occupational exposure is too high. The French labour authorities (Courtois and Cadou, 2016) have set an occupational exposure limit for ammonia at 10 ppm. Mechanic machines used in composting and methanization plants often operate in an atmosphere where the ambient ammonia concentration is above this limit value. The cabins of these machines are then equipped with purification boxes to limit driver exposure. The boxes are composed of two separation phases in series. A filter that separates solid particles and/or aerosols and a doped activated carbon bed that removes ammonia by adsorption. The objective of the present paper is to analyze and model the adsorption process of ammonia. The model developed is a first principles model considering all the phenomena involved in the process. More specifically, it consists of momentum and mass balance equations, along with relations for the prediction of adsorption isotherms and kinetics.

2. Ammonia adsorption isotherms

For the adsorption process model development, experimental adsorption isotherms of ammonia on a doped activated carbon in a temperature range of 288–313 K at ammonia concentrations up to 1600 ppm were determined with a thermo-gravimetric analyzer from Setaram Instrumentation (SETSYS TAG). The ammonia adsorption capacity was thus evaluated from the mass gained by the sample at various ammonia concentrations. The whole experiences represent thirty equilibrium adsorption measurements.

2.1. Adsorption isotherms

In order to accurately describe the ammonia adsorption phenomenon on the doped activated carbon, the well-known Sips' adsorption model was used. This semi-empirical equation considers the interactions between the adsorbate molecules and the adsorbing surface with a heterogeneity factor, and is written as (Bedel, 2017):

$$q_e = \frac{q_m (bc)^{\frac{1}{s}}}{1 + (bc)^{\frac{1}{s}}} \tag{1}$$

with the maximum amount adsorbed:

$$q_m = q_{m0} \exp\left[\chi \left(1 - \frac{T}{T_0}\right) \right] \tag{2}$$

equilibrium constant:

$$b = b_0 \exp\left[\frac{Q}{R T_0} \left(\frac{T_0}{T} - 1\right) \right] \tag{3}$$

and heterogeneity factors:

$$\frac{1}{s} = \frac{1}{s_0} + \alpha \left(1 - \frac{T}{T_0}\right) \tag{4}$$

where α, χ are constants, q_{m0} is the maximum amount adsorbed at the reference temperature (mol.kg^{-1}), b_0 is the equilibrium constant at the reference temperature (m^3.mol^{-1}), s_0 the Sips heterogeneity factor at the reference temperature, T and T_0 are the operation and reference temperatures respectively (K), Q is the adsorption heat (J.mol^{-1}), and R is the ideal gas constant (J.mol^{-1}K^{-1}).

The isotherm equation (Eq.1) involves therefore six unknown parameters that should be deduced from experimental measurements.

2.2. Global parameter estimability analysis and identification

A preliminary step in the development of a reliable mathematical model, before the problem of parameter identification, is to evaluate the structural identifiability and estimability of the model parameters. The objective is to determine the most estimable parameters from the available measurements and possibly to design appropriate experiments to determine the less estimable ones.

The estimability algorithm used in this work is the same as the one developed by Yao et al. (2003) and used in Lei et al. (2013) and Bedel et al. (2017). The main difference here is that the sensitivity coefficient matrix is based on global sensitivities (Saltelli et al., 2006) rather than local ones. Moreover, the choice of the estimability threshold value which defines the limit between estimable and non-estimatable parameters, is still arbitrary and depends on the studied process. In this work, it is set equal to 0.04 as in Yao et al. (2003) and gives a good idea about the actual sensitivity of the isotherm models to the unknown parameters. However, it should be noted that there are more advanced and sophisticated methods in the literature (Eghtesadi and McAuley, 2014).

2.2.1. Parameters estimability analysis results

The estimability analysis algorithm using the orthogonalization algorithm described by (Yao et al. 2003) was applied to the ammonia adsorption models on doped activated carbon and led to the following estimability order : $b_0 > \chi > Q/RT_0 > q_{m0} > s_0 > \alpha$. It is noteworthy that the last parameter α is non estimable based on the available experimental measurements. Therefore, its value was taken from one of our previous studies and set equal to **0.17** (Bedel, 2017).

2.2.2. Parameters identification

The five most estimable parameters are then identified from the available experimental measurements using the COMSOL optimizer. The results are presented in Table 1 as well as the 95% confidence intevals (CI) and the correlation matrix. The accuracy of the parameters is consistent with the values reported in the literature works.

Table 1. Values of the identified parameters for the Sips model

| θ | Value | 95% CI | Correlation matrix | | | | |
			q_{m0}	b_0	s_0	Q/RT_0	χ
q_{m0}	2.83	±0.23	1				
b_0	152.39	±48.53	-0.85	1			
s_0	1.69	±0.26	-0.58	0.21	1		
Q/RT_0	8.72	±5.77	0.75	-0.82	-0.29	1	
χ	1.58	±1.24	-0.74	0.70	0.24	-0.92	1

Figure 1 compares the predictions of Sips model to the adsorption equilibrium measurements.

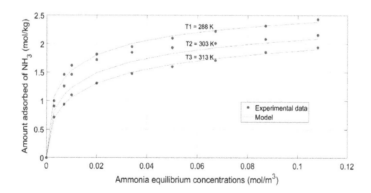

Figure 1. Comparison of Sips prediction model and experimental isotherms

The comparison exhibits a good agreement in the range of temperature and ammonia concentrations considered. The identified Sips isotherm will be used later in the modeling of the adsorption process.

3. Ammonia process experimental rig

In this section, the dynamic adsorption of ammonia in a packed column with doped activated carbon particles is studied experimentally.

3.1. Experimental set-up

The ammonia adsorption experimental set-up is presented in Figure 2. The studied gas is realized by mixing compressed dry air and bottles of pure ammonia by the use of two calibrated mass flowmeters. A small column is used to mix NH_3 and air before entering the adsorption column. The height and diameter of the column are 40 cm and 32 cm respectively. The doped activated carbon particles used without any pre-treatment. Temperature, pressure and humidity sensors are placed upstream and downstream of the adsorption column. A calibrated PID sensor is used to measure the ammonia concentration at the column exit. All the sensors are connected to an acquisition module.

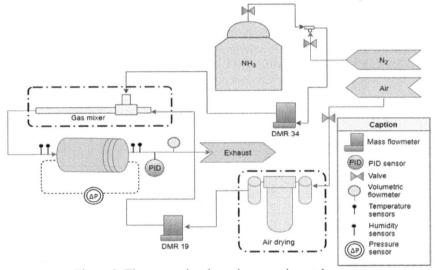

Figure 2. The ammonia adsorption experimental set-up

3.2. Experimental procedure

The adsorption column is filled with 22 g of doped activated carbon particles. The air from air network is dried in a silica gel column before entering the adsorption column. The adsorption column is kept under dry air until the column stabilizes in temperature (23°C) and a relative humidity (5%). A mixture of 1000 ppm NH_3 and air is then produced and fed the adsorption column. Three experiments were carried out at 6.9, 4.3 and 2.2 L.min^{-1}. Each experiment was repeated three times to check the reproducibility of the results.

4. Ammonia adsorption process modeling

In this section, the objective is to develop a mathematical model that accurately predicts the experimental measurements.

4.1. Model assumptions

The process model developed is based on the following assumptions: the gaseous mixture obeys the ideal gas law; the pressure drop is neglected, only ammonia is adsorbed; the resistance of mass transfer in the gas phase is negligible and the kinetics of mass transfer within a particle is approximated by the linear driving force (LDF) model; the gas phase is in equilibrium with the adsorbent; the adsorbent is considered as a homogeneous phase; the column temperature as well as the physical properties of the adsorbent are assumed to be constant.

4.2. Model Equations

The model developed is a one-dimensional first principles model. It is described by the mass balance equations, thermodynamic and transport properties. The mass balance for ammonia can be written as:

$$\frac{\partial c}{\partial t} - D_{ax}\frac{\partial^2 c}{\partial z^2} + \frac{\partial(vc)}{\partial z} = -\frac{1-\varepsilon_b}{\varepsilon_b}\frac{\partial q}{\partial t} \tag{5}$$

where c and q are the gas phase and the adsorbed phase concentrations of the adsorbate respectively (mol.m^{-3}), v is the interstitial velocity (m.s^{-1}) and D_{ax} is the axial dispersion coefficient (m^2.s^{-1}), ε_b is the bed void fraction.

The kinetics of mass transfer is approximated by the LDF equation as:

$$\frac{\partial q}{\partial t} = K_{LDF}\left(q_e - q\right) \tag{6}$$

where K_{LDF} is the overall mass transfer coefficient (s^{-1}) and q_e is the amount of adsorbed component at equilibrium (mol.m^{-3}).

The initial conditions of the variables are given as:
  - For $0 \leq z \leq L$, $t = 0$: $c = 0$, $q = 0$,
and the boundary conditions are expressed as:
  - For $t > 0$, $z = 0$: $c = c_{in}$, $q = 0$ and $z = L$: $\partial c/\partial z = 0$.

The values of the model constants are given in Table 2.

Table 2. Model constants

Parameter	Value	Unit
Solid density, ρ_p	2044.7	kg.m^{-3}
Bed density, ρ_b	675.4	kg.m^{-3}
Bed porosity, ε_b	0.67	-

The only parameters whose values are not determined are the axial dispersion coefficient D_{ax} and the material transfer kinetics K_{LDF}. These two parameters will be identified from experimental breakthrough curves.

4.3. Results and discussion

The adsorption model was implemented and solved within COMSOL Multiphysics. The identified values of K_{LDF} and D_{ax} are presented in Table 3.

Table 3. Identified values of the parameters of the ammonia adsorption process

v, (m.s^{-1})	K_{LDF}, (s^{-1})	D_{ax}, (m^2.s^{-1})
0.19	5.98E-04	0.0083
0.12	5.38E-04	0.0077
0.06	3.90E-04	0.0059

Their magnitudes are consistent with the values determined in similar operating conditions in literature (Knox et al, 2016). The predicted model results using the fitted parameters exhibit a good agreement with the experimental data (Figure 3).

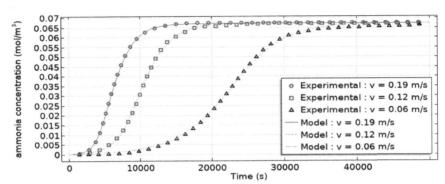

Figure 3. Comparison of predicted NH_3 breakthrough curves with experimental data

This agreement points out the accuracy of the model predictions. The resulting identified model will be further used in optimal design and operation of the ammonia adsorption process.

5. Conclusions

A procedure was developed in order to assess the estimability of the unknown parameters involved in the Sips adsorption isotherm model of ammonia on a doped activated carbon. The estimable parameters were identified from the equilibrium experimental data at 288, 303 and 313 K. The values of the parameters considered as non-estimable are fixed from literature or previous studies. A one-dimensional model was developed to simulate a column used for ammonia adsorption. The model predictions computed using the fitted parameters were in good agreement compared to the experimental measurements. This work demonstrated that it was possible to estimate the axial dispersion coefficient and the mass transfer coefficient from experimental breakthrough curves using a one-dimensional model.

References

S. Bedel, C. Vallières, M. A. Latifi, 2017, Parameters estimability analysis and identification for adsorption equilibrium models of carbon dioxide, Adsorption, 23(2-3), 373-380.

B. Courtois, S. Cadou, 2016, Valeurs limites d'exposition professionnelle aux agents chimiques en France, Institut National de Recherche et de Sécurité, ED 984, 14.

Z. Eghtesadi, K. B. McAuley, 2014, Mean square error-based method for parameter ranking and selection to obtain accurate predictions at specified operating conditions, Industrial & Engineering Chemistry Research, 53(14), 6033-6046.

J. C. Knox, A. D. Ebner, M. D LeVan, R. F. Coker, J. A. Ritter, 2016, Limitations of breakthrough curve analysis in fixed-bed adsorption, Industrial & engineering chemistry research, 55(16), 4734-4748.

M. Lei, C. Vallières, G. Grévillot, M. A. Latifi, 2013, Thermal swing adsorption process for carbon dioxide capture and recovery: modeling, simulation, parameters estimability, and identification, Industrial & Engineering Chemistry Research, 52(22), 7526-7533.

B. F. Lund, B. A. Foss, 2008, Parameter ranking by orthogonalization-Applied to nonlinear mechanistic models. Automatica, 44(1), 278-281.

A. Saltelli, M. Ratto, S. Tarantola, F Campolongo, E. Commission, 2006, Sensitivity analysis practices: Strategies for model-based inference, Reliability Engineering & System Safety, 91(10-11), 1109-1125.

K. Z. Yao, B. M. Shaw, B. Kou, K. B. McAuley, D. W. Bacon, 2003, Modeling ethylene/butene copolymerization with multi-site catalysts: parameter estimability and experimental design, Polymer Reaction Engineering, 11(3), 563-588.

Sauro Pierucci, Flavio Manenti, Giulia Bozzano, Davide Manca (Eds.)
Proceedings of the 30th European Symposium on Computer Aided Process Engineering
(ESCAPE30), May 24-27, 2020, Milano, Italy. © 2020 Elsevier B.V. All rights reserved.
http://dx.doi.org/10.1016/B978-0-12-823377-1.50106-3

Propagation of Parametric Uncertainty in a Conceptually Designed Bioethanol Production Process

Dilara B. Yıldız,[a] Nihat A. Sayar[a*]

Marmara University, Faculty of Engineering, Department of Bioengineering, Göztepe Campus, 34722, Kadikoy, Istanbul, Turkey

alpagu.sayar@marmara.edu.tr

Abstract

Understanding the propagation of parametric uncertainty in model-based computer simulations of conceptually designed bioprocesses and their metamodels is a critical step in improving the utilization and usefulness of such models. Generally, the number of design and operational parameters to be identified, calculated or assumed is very high. However, uncertainty analyses of these parameters usually focus on a selected few. The aim of this paper is to analyse the effect of increasing the number of uncertain parameters on the uncertainty of the metrics of interest acquired from the simulations and metamodels generated to relate these metrics to the uncertain parameters. The results indicate that overall uncertainty in simulated process metrics stabilises after a certain number of uncertain parameters is reached regardless of the characteristics of parametric uncertainty. However, metamodeling options such as sampling method, number of samples used, and type of metamodels used have direct effects on how the overall uncertainty can be represented by these metamodels. A demonstrative analysis is offered on a bioethanol production process model as a case study. In conclusion, the findings in this paper highlight the importance of the workflow followed in generating metamodels of bioprocess simulations under uncertainty.

Keywords: Parametric uncertainty, Kriging, bioethanol production

1. Introduction

Model-based simulations of conceptually designed bioprocesses are important tools esp. during the early techno-economic evaluation of process alternatives. The designs are generally implemented in specialized software such as SuperPro Designer or Aspen Plus. The number of design and operational parameters to be specified in such implementations of industrially relevant bioprocesses is in the order of several hundred. In the early stages of design and development, the values of most of these parameters can only be assumed. Only a critical few are obtained experimentally or calculated as development targets. Nevertheless, there is considerable uncertainty associated with the values used in the early simulations. Therefore, uncertainty analysis regarding these techno-economic parameters can be considered an important tool. Efficient workflows to facilitate such analyses have been developed (Morales-Rodriguez et al., 2012). However, in most examples of uncertainty analysis, only a selected few uncertain parameters are examined. Hence, it is important to understand the effects of increasing the number of uncertain parameters on the propagation of uncertainty into simulated process metrics (Bernardo, 2016).

Uncertainty analysis workflow involves the characterization and quantification of parametric uncertainty by probability density functions (pdfs) for the uncertain parameters followed by sampling from these distributions and propagating the uncertainty into process metrics by simulating the samples. Depending on the number of uncertain parameters involved and sampling preferences (such as sampling type and number of samples), the resulting number of simulations to be performed can be high and computationally expensive. Therefore, it may be practically preferable to generate metamodels, which describe the behavior of the simulated process metrics in the design space created by the selected uncertain parameters, to be used in subsequent tasks like optimization under uncertainty. Consequently, it is also important to understand the relationship between the uncertainty analysis workflow and subsequent metamodeling.

It is the aim of this paper to analyze the effects of the number of uncertain parameters selected as well as uncertainty analysis workflow and metamodeling preferences such as types of pdfs used to characterize parametric uncertainty, type of sampling, number of samples used and type of metamodels on the propagation of parametric uncertainty into uncertainty in simulated process metrics and their metamodels. The analysis is demonstrated on a case study involving the production of second-generation bioethanol from a lignocellulosic feedstock (hazelnut husk).

2. Propagation of uncertainty

2.1. Lignocellulosic bioethanol production process

In a previously proposed process model, hazelnut husk was used as the lignocellulosic feedstock for a bioethanol production process (Sayar et al., 2019). Figure 1 shows the process flow diagram of this process, where hazelnut husk is steam-pretreated in a reaction vessel and cooled down before a lignocellulolytic enzyme mixture is fed into the hydrolysis vessel. The hydrolysate is then used for fermentation. Crude fermentation product (including bioethanol) is filtered through microfiltration and this filtrate is then distilled for final product recovery. Over 500 design and operational parameters were specified and 15 of these are selected for analysis in this paper.

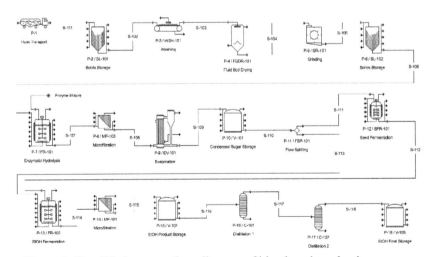

Figure 1: Simplified process flow diagram of bioethanol production process

2.2. Propagation of uncertainty into simulated process metrics

Propagation of parametric uncertainty into simulated process metrics entails the steps of uncertainty analysis. The first step is the characterization of parametric uncertainty in the selected uncertain parameters. Ideally, each uncertain parameter should be described by an appropriate pdf. In this paper, uniform and normal distributions were used as examples similar to that has been suggested by Gargalo et al. (2016). Table 1 provides the 15 selected parameters and their distribution parameters for both cases.

Table 1: Selected uncertain parameters and their uncertainty characterization

	Parameter	Uniform Distribution		Normal Distribution	
		Min Value	Max Value	Mean	Std Dev.
1	Throughput	180000	360000	270000	30000
2	Selling price	1	1.5	1.25	0.075
3	Enzyme loading	1/1000	2.5/1000	0.00175	0.0005
4	Cellulose-Glucose conversion	0.75	0.99	0.87	0.035
5	Hemicellulose–xylose conversion	0.75	0.99	0.87	0.035
6	Glucose-EtOH conversion	0.75	0.96	0.855	0.03
7	Xylose-EtOH conversion	0.75	0.96	0.855	0.03
8	Enzyme price	1	3	2	0.255
9	Peptone price	1	3	2	0.255
10	Yeast ext. price	1	3	2	0.255
11	Steam price	3	5	4	0.355
12	Electricity price	0.07	0.09	0.08	0.0058
13	Water price	0.1	0.03	0.2	0.015
14	Hazelnut husk price	0	0.005	0.0025	0.000125
15	Labor	15	30	22.5	2.25

At fifteen steps, the effect of increasing the number of uncertain parameters (from 1 to 15) was analyzed by performing Monte Carlo simulations of important process metrics (unit cost -UC- and net present value -NPV-). Sampling from the distributions were performed using Halton (HS), Sobol (SS), and Latin hypercube sampling (LHS) methods (Garud et al., 2018). With each sampling method, three sets with 25, 100, and 250 samples were generated. UC and NPV were simulated for each set using SuperPro Designer platform. Each step was repeated 30 times to represent the stochastic nature of the sampling methods. Resulting UC and NPV values (30 values for each case) were fitted to a normal distribution characterized by a mean and a standard deviation. The standard deviation obtained was considered as the measure of uncertainty in the simulated process metric. Figure 2 shows the change in the standard deviation of process metrics as a function of increasing number of uncertain parameters (NUP) for 100-sample cases.

Overall, propagation of parametric uncertainty into the selected process metrics seems to stabilize after a certain NUP is reached in all cases; although critical NUP differs for UC and NPV depending on the type of distribution used. However, these results support the hypothesis that overall metric uncertainty can be approximated by analyzing the propagation of uncertainty from a few selected uncertain parameters. Previous works on biorefineries show similar effects of parametric uncertainty on economic process metrics such as NPV and EBITDA (Chaeli et al., 2014). The results from 25 and 250 sample cases reinforce this finding (data not shown). The effect of the type of distribution used is clear from Figure 2. This means that it's an important task to identify the appropriate distribution for each selected parameter.

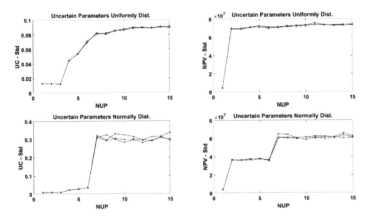

Figure 2: Propagation of parametric uncertainty as a function of NUP (HS: circle; SS: square; LHS: diamond)

2.3. Metamodeling under uncertainty

Simpler surrogate models are often used to represent computationally expensive simulations in modeling, feasibility analysis, and optimization (Bhosekar and Ierapetritou, 2018). Amongst the commonly used types of metamodels are conventional low-order polynomial models and Gaussian process-based Kriging (Kleijnen, 2017). It is important to evaluate how different types of metamodels perform under parametric uncertainty. In order to perform such an evaluation, each set of simulations detailed in the previous section were used to train metamodels using i) low-order polynomial models (LOP - quadratic), and ii) Kriging. Each resulting case is identified by its NUP (1-15), type of distribution used (Uniform, Normal), sampling method (HS, SS, LHS), number of samples (25, 100, 250), and metamodel type (LOP, Kriging).

The resulting metamodels were tested against one of 15 separate validation datasets (depending on the NUP involved). Many measures of goodness-of-fit such as root mean square error or mean absolute error (MAE) can be used for this evaluation. MAE between the simulated validation dataset values and metamodel predictions was used for the following analyses.

Each boxplot in Figure 3 illustrates a case as described above and summarizes the evaluation of 30 metamodels (one metamodel generated per repetition to represent the stochastic nature of sampling) generated under the stated preferences. Gaussian process-based Kriging can be seen to perform much better compared to conventional low-order polynomial models (LOP). It is also observed that for the Kriging models, the overall variability of model goodness-of-fit is similar for 10 and 15 uncertain parameter cases compared to 5 uncertain parameter case where variability is much lower. If these results are considered together with Figure 2 (bottom row), it can be argued that the elevated variability in model goodness-of-fit for higher NUP is due to propagated parametric uncertainty rather than the inadequacy of the models. Findings are very similar for both process metrics (UC and NPV). The analysis shown is for normally distributed uncertain parameters, sampled using LHS with 100 samples. Other cases support these general findings (data not shown).

Figure 4 shows the comparison of sampling methods for a selected case (normally distributed uncertain parameters, 100-sample sets, modelled by Kriging). In this case, HS seems to give the best results overall. The differences are qualitatively the same for both process metrics although slightly more pronounced for NPV. The difference between the sampling methods diminishes for increased NUP. Results in other cases do not correlate exactly with this case. The most significant commonality is the fact that increased NUP seems to reduce the difference between sampling methods. The combined effect of sampling method and number of samples should be considered.

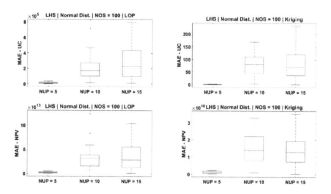

Figure 3: Effect of NUP on the propagation of metric uncertainty into metamodels

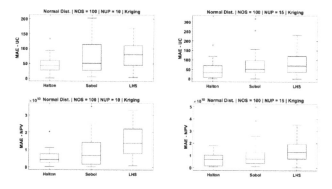

Figure 4: Effect of sampling method on the propagation of metric uncertainty into metamodels

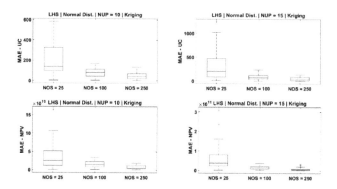

Figure 5: Effect of number of samples on the propagation of metric uncertainty into metamodels

Figure 5 illustrates the effect of number of samples on the goodness-of-fit of the generated metamodels. Clearly, the higher the number of samples the higher the accuracy of the resulting models is. However, increased NOS means additional computational burden. So, there is a trade-off between acceptable model accuracy and computational burden. The analysis summarized in Figure 5 helps to quantify that trade-off. Very similar results were obtained in the other cases not depicted here.

3. Conclusions

The increase in the overall metric uncertainty of the simulated process metrics of a conceptually designed bioprocess stops after a certain the number of uncertain design and operational parameters is reached. Therefore, it is an acceptable strategy to limit the focus of uncertainty analysis to a selected few uncertain parameters. However, the type of probability distribution selected to characterize the parametric uncertainty seems to be a critical factor. Hence, attention must be paid to select the appropriate pdf.
Gaussian-process based Kriging performs better for metamodeling under uncertainty compared to conventional low-order polynomials. The accuracy of the metamodels depend on number of samples used much more than sampling method.

Acknowledgements
This work was supported by The Scientific and Technological Research Council of Turkey (TUBITAK) by the project 217M526.

References

F. P. Bernardo, 2016, Model analysis and optimization under uncertainty using highly efficient integration techniques, in: Z. Kravanja and M. Bogataj (Eds.), ESCAPE 26, European Symposium on Computer Aided Process Engineering. Elsevier, Portoroz (Slovenia), pp. 2151-2156.
A. Bhosekar, M. Ierapetritou, 2018, Advances in surrogate based modeling, feasibility analysis, and optimization: A review, Computers and Chemical Engineering, 108, 250-267.
P. Cheali, A. Quaglia, K. V. Gernaey, G. Sin, 2014, Effect of market price uncertainties on the deisgn of optimal biorefinery systems – A systematic approach, Industrial & Engineering Chemistry Research, 53, 6021-6032.
C. L. Gargalo, P. Cheali, J. A. Posada, K. V. Gernaey, G. Sin, 2016, Economic risk assessment of early stage designs for glycerol valorization in bioreninery concepts, Industrial & Engineering Chemistry Research, 55, 6801-6814.
S. S. Garud, I. A. Karimi, G. P. E. Brownbridge, M. Kraft, 2018, Evaluating smart sampling for constructing multidimensional surrogate models, Computers and Chemical Engineering, 108, 276-288.
J. P. C. Kleijnen, 2017, Regression and Kriging metamodels with their experimental designs in simulation: A review, European Journal of Operational Research, 256, 1-16.
R. Morlaes-Rodrigues, A. S. Meyer, K. V. Gernaey, G. Sin, 2012, A framework for model-based optimization of bioprocesses under uncertainty: Lignocellulosic ethanol production case, Computers and Chemical Engineering, 42, 115-129.
N. A. Sayar, O. Pinar, D. Kazan, A. A. Sayar, 2019, Bioethanol production from Turkish hazelnut husk process design and economic evaluation, Waste and Biomass Valorization, 10(4), 909-923.

Sauro Pierucci, Flavio Manenti, Giulia Bozzano, Davide Manca (Eds.)
Proceedings of the 30th European Symposium on Computer Aided Process Engineering
(ESCAPE30), May 24-27, 2020, Milano, Italy. © 2020 Elsevier B.V. All rights reserved.
http://dx.doi.org/10.1016/B978-0-12-823377-1.50107-5

New set of Graphical Axes for Grassroots Design of Heat Exchanger Networks for Chemical Engineering Applications

Dina Kamel [a*], Mamdouh Gadalla [b], Fatma Ashour[c]

[a] British University in Egypt, 11837, Cairo, Egypt.
[b] Port Said University, Port Said, Egypt.
[c] Cairo University, Giza, Egypt.
Dina.ahmed@bue.edu.eg

Abstract

This paper presents a graphical technique for optimum design of heat exchanger networks (HENs) by applying the pinch analysis rules. The new contribution of this graphical approach is to include the driving force of temperatures and their variations throughout the design in the graphical representations. This would allow the consideration of both heat transfer area and energy during the design/analysis. The graphical approach is applied on a case study of low temperature distillation process.

Keywords: Pinch analysis, Heat exchanger network, Graphical approach, Driving force.

1. Introduction

The HEN is a group of heat exchangers connected for the maximization of heat integration in chemical plants by using the heating duties of process sources to heat the cold streams and on the same time the hot streams are being cooled, this process integration will reduce the use of external utilities for heating and cooling and consequently reduce the overall operating cost.

Several methods and approaches are present in literature for the design of heat exchanger networks. Klemeš et al. (2018) reviewed in their work the new directions of implementation of pinch technology through the previous years in different engineering applications, based on that study they suggested possible direction of development in each field.

Heat integration using pinch analysis is an organized method for designing of efficient thermal processes. It helps in the calculation of the minimum energy requirements and maximum possible heat integration by detecting any thermodynamic bottleneck, or the pinch point for heat integration (Alwi, et al., 2010). According to pinch analysis principles, transferring heat through the pinch temperatures will require more energy than the minimum required energy. Linnhoff and Hindmarsh (1983) provided the important steps to decrease the energy necessities. The minimum energy required (targets) for heating and cooling were either determined by the composite curves; graphically (Smith, 2005), or numerically by problem table algorithm (Linnhoff, et al., 1978).

Liu et al. (2013) applied the principle of mass and heat integration for introducing a systematic simultaneous technique for the design of mass and heat exchanger networks.

Anastasovski (2014) established a new methodology for designing HENs; this methodology combined both problem table algorithm and pinch design method. The methodology worked on dividing the problem to several enthalpy intervals; each interval is determined from the breaking points at composite curves. Liu et al. (2018) presented in their work a MINLP model for simultaneous integrated design for HENs and cooling

Zubairu et al. (2015) indicated that the composite curves, which were initially introduced by Hohmann (1971) as a graphical tool for identifying the energy targets along with the pinch temperatures, have been widely used and is considered as an incomparable method.

The new contribution of this graphical approach is that it provides a visual representation for each heat exchanger, position of inefficiencies, and temperature driving forces in each exchanger, to overcome any mistakes in the design, Moreover the new approach provides simple and applicable insights for efficient design with respect to the heat exchanger area.

2. Temperature- driving force (TDF) graphical approach

This graphical technique follows and applies the principles of pinch analysis. This graphical technique describes the heat recovery through employing two axes of temperatures. For a given heat exchanger, the driving force across each end are plotted on the Y-axis against the corresponding cold stream temperature on the X-axis as presented in Figure (1).

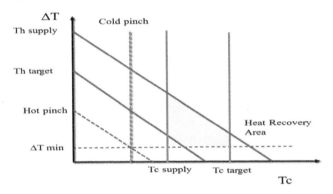

Figure (1): Key lines in the graphical representation

Figure (1) represents the driving forces in heat exchanger against the cold streams temperature that flow through these exchangers. At any given point in this graph both driving force across an exchanger; the corresponding cold temperatures can be identified. The basic characteristics of the new approach are as follows:

A given cold stream is represented as a vertical straight line at the value of the cold temperature on the X-axis, while the hot stream line is plotted as an inclined straight line that starts from the value of Th $=\Delta T$ on the Y- coordinate (Tc=zero) and ends at the value of Th= Tc on the X-coordinate (ΔT=zero) as shown Figure (1).

ΔT_{min} is represented as horizontal line starting at $\Delta T = \Delta T_{min}$.

The shaded area in Figure (1) represents the heat recovery area; the site of heat integration between the hot stream and the cold stream supply and target temperatures.

Each exchanger is plotted as a straight line (assuming constant heat capacities). The exchanger starts at the hot end driving force and ends at the cold end driving force.

The graph is divided into 5 regions according to the pinch analysis principals as shown in Figure (2):

- Region (1): exchangers matches integrate heat between hot streams below the pinch with cold streams below the pinch.
- Region (2): exchangers matches integrate heat between hot streams above the pinch with cold streams below the pinch
- Region (3): exchanger matches integrate heat between hot streams above the pinch with cold streams above the pinch
- Region (4): exchangers matches integrate heat between hot streams below the **ΔTmin line**
- Region (5): exchangers matches integrate heat below ΔT=0, thermodynamically infeasible.

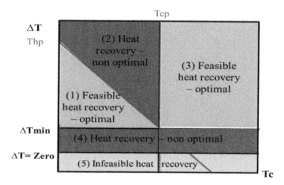

Figure (2): Feasible regions for heat integration

3. Graphical design of new HENs

As presented above in the literature, the pinch technology–based design methods were applied to design HENs according to energy matches and to then calculate the heat transfer area for the final heat exchanger network. In several design practices, the heat transfer area is a key issue in reaching an optimum design. The new TDF graphical method considers the temperature driving forces while designing HENs to obtain relatively optimum network with respect to energy targets, area and cost.

3.1 Procedure for graphical design

1.   The design of the network is divided into 2 sections; above and below the pinch.

2.   Above the pinch:

The first step is to determine the starting point for the 1st heat exchanger above the pinch, in general cases it exists at (T_{ht} , T_{cs}). In certain cases, the hot target temperature value is less than the hot pinch temperature value, so the starting point should be at the hot pinch temperature. Similarly, if the T_{cs} value is less than the T_{cp} value, start at the cold pinch temperature. For proper heat exchanger network design, heat integration should be fulfilled above the pinch by selecting the best exchanger matches.

3.   Below the pinch:

The steps are similar to the design above the pinch except that the starting point for the 1st heat exchanger is at (T_{hs} , T_{ct}).

The principals of heat integration are applied to recover heat from hot streams graphically.

4.   For the complete heat exchanger network design both algorithms are merged.

4. Case study: Low – temperature distillation process

The design of heat exchanger networks for low temperature applications is very challenging; it is very difficult to meet the minimum temperature difference while not crossing the pinch temperatures.

The minimum hot and cold utility requirements are 1.84 MW and 1.84 MW, respectively. The hot pinch temperature = -19°C and the cold pinch temperature = -24°C, assuming a minimum temperature difference of 5°C.

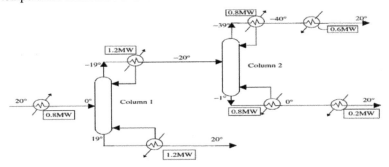

Figure (3): A low temperature distillation process (Smith, 2005)

The process has three hot streams and four cold streams, their temperatures and heat capacities are presented in Figure (3).

4.1 Graphical design of HEN

The first step in the graphical design of any HEN is plotting all the available hot and cold streams using the supply and target temperatures, and then representing graphically the key lines; hot pinch temperature line, cold pinch temperature line and ΔT_{min} line. At this point the design of the HEN is divided into two problems; above the pinch and below the pinch.

4.1.1   Graphical design below the pinch

Exchanger E1 is plotted in Figure (4) between the hot stream H2 and the cold stream C3, the starting point of this exchanger is at the intersection between the hot pinch line at -19°C and the cold pinch line at -24°C. The hot stream is only cooled from -19°C till -19.13°C, this minor change is due to the relatively high slope value as it nearly equal -1; at which the line concise with the hot stream. External cooling is used for cooling the unsatisfied hot streams.

4.1.2   Graphical design above the pinch

As presented in Figure (5), Exchanger E2 is plotted between H1 and C3, this exchanger will neither satisfy the hot stream nor satisfy the cold stream as it will intersect the ΔT_{min} line first, and here it come the advantage of this method even though through duty calculations the available duty of the hot stream can completely satisfy C3 to reach its target temperature at 20°C, this will lead to unfeasible design the minimum difference will be less than zero.

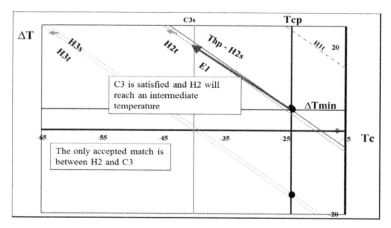

Figure (4): HEN design below the pinch

Similarly, Exchanger E3 is plotted between H1 and C2, the hot stream is completely satisfied, while the cold stream will reach an intermediate temperature of -0.315°C. External heating is required for heating the unsatisfied cold streams.

Figure (6) present a grid diagram of the HEN

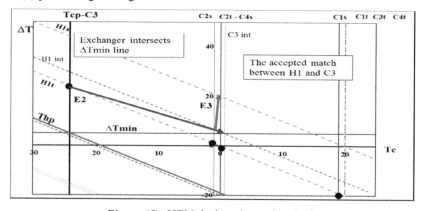

Figure (5): HEN design above the pinch

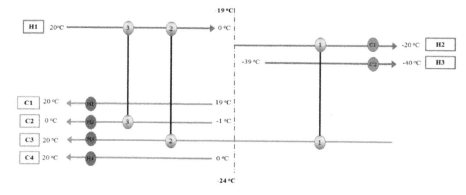

Figure (6): Grid diagram for HEN

The above design has been compared by a design generated by Aspen energy analyzer (V. 7.3) discussed above the disadvantages of the second design are: Exchanger 1 is crossing the pinch temperature, The design does not reach the hot and cold utility target requirements, and The design has more units which affects the total cost of the HEN.

Its only advantage that it has lower area of heat transfer, and even this advantage has minimum or zero effect as the total cost of the graphical approach design is lower than the total cost of the energy analyzer design by 7.9 %; this difference is due to the fact that the second design consumes more external utilities and has one more unit.

5. Conclusion

A new graphical approach was presented, which follows completely the pinch analysis principals.

The main merits of this approach are: its simplicity as each heat exchanger in the HEN can be represented by a straight line. Both the length and the slope of each exchanger line has a significant physical meaning. Other advantages are the visibility of the feasible regions for the heat integration.

The TDF approach provides a complete and systematic procedure for the grassroots design of HENs, the new approach is characterized by several advantaged, including: visual identification of the temperature driving force for each exchanger to avoid the presence of network pinch, visual and easy identification of possible and excluded matches regarding the driving force, visual and easy identification of optimum matches with respect to the area; as the exchanger approaches ΔT_{min} line, its area increases. Visualization in design especially for low temperature applications.

References

B. Zubairu, B. Highina and B. Gutti, "Minimizing hot and cold utility requirements for vegetable oil refinery plant using pinch Analysis," International journal of scientific engineering and technology, vol. 4, no. 5, pp. 298-301, 2015.

J. Klemeš, P. Varbanov, T. Walmsley and X. Jia, "New directions in the implementation of Pinch Methodology (PM)," Renewable and Sustainable Energy Reviews, vol. 98, pp. 439-468, 2018.

B. Linnhoff and E. Hindmarsh, "The pinch design method for heat exchanger networks," Chemical engineering science, vol. 38, no. 5, p. 745–763, 1983.

S. Alwi and Z. Manan, "STEP—A new graphical tool for simultaneous targeting and design of a heat exchanger network," chemical engineering journal, vol. 162, no. 1, pp. 106-121, 2010.

R. Smith, Chemical process design and integration, England: John Whiley & Sons Ltd, 2005.

B. Linnhoff and J. Flower, "Synthesis of heat exchanger networks: I. Systematic generation of energy optimal networks," Alche, vol. 24, no. 4, pp. 633-642, 1978.

A. Anastasovski, "Enthalpy Table Algorithm for design of Heat Exchanger Network as optimal solution in Pinch technology," Applied thermal engineering, vol. 73, no. 1, pp. 1113-1128, 2014.

F. Liu, J. Ma, X. Feng and Y. Wang, "Simultaneous integrated design for heat exchanger network and cooling water system," Applied Thermal Engineering, vol. 128, pp. 1510-1519, 2018.

E. Hohman, "Optimum networks of heat exchange," Ph.D. thesis ; University of Southern California, USA, 1971.

Aspen HYSYS, V7.3,Aspen technology inc, USA: University program, 2011.

Sauro Pierucci, Flavio Manenti, Giulia Bozzano, Davide Manca (Eds.)
Proceedings of the 30th European Symposium on Computer Aided Process Engineering
(ESCAPE30), May 24-27, 2020, Milano, Italy. © 2020 Elsevier B.V. All rights reserved.
http://dx.doi.org/10.1016/B978-0-12-823377-1.50108-7

A Novel Process for Dimethyl Ether Synthesis Using Inter-Stage Ceramic Membrane for Water Removal

Abdulrahman A. Al-Rabiah

Department of Chemical Engineering, College of Engineering, King Saud University, P. O. Box 800 , Riyadh 11421, Saudi Arabia

arabiah@ksu.edu.sa

Abstract

Dimethyl ether has received great interest since it is considered as an environmentally-friendly chemical and can be utilized in a wide range of applications. DME is mainly used as aerosol propellant and intermediate in oil industry. It is also used as clean fuel in power generation and diesel engines. DME is produced directly from synthesis gas and indirectly via methanol dehydration over commercial γ-Al_2O_3 pellets. The methanol dehydration process has a low conversion which is limited by the thermodynamic equilibrium leading to a large recycle stream and size equipment. In addition, the presence of water in the feed with methanol reduces the equilibrium conversion that can be attained. An inter-stage membrane for water removal can overcome the thermodynamic limitations related to the conventional process.

In this study, two adiabatic reactor stages with inter-stage hydrophilic ceramic membrane for water removal were considered for the synthesis of DME via methanol dehydration. A commercial conventional process was simulated using Aspen-Plus ™ for an annual plant capacity of 50,000 metric tons and a 99.5 wt. % purity of DME product. A modified process for DME synthesis using water-selective alumina-silica composite membrane was developed and simulated. A parametric study was conducted to show the effect of inlet temperature on the reactor conversion which can be increased to 93 % using the inter-stage membrane. The high temperature reactor effluent was used to preheat methanol feed. The modified process shows potentials to reduce both energy and equipment size which leads to a lower process cost for DME production.

Keywords: dimethyl ether, process synthesis, membrane, simulation.

1. Introduction

Dimethyl ether is an alternative clean fuel that can be used in diesel engines for electric power generation, and in domestic applications such as heating. DME is used primarily as an aerosol propellant (Turton et al., 2013). It can be produced from many sources, including natural gas, crude oil, coal and biomass. DME is produced directly from synthesis gas or indirectly via methanol dehydration. Most of the industrial DME processes are based on methanol dehydration over γ-alumina catalyst.

In commercial DME production from methanol, the conversion is thermodynamically limited to about 82 %, leading to large recycle of non-converted methanol. There are many attempts to use new technologies to improve the DME process. Most of suggested schemes are hindered by the limited conversion of methanol which requires costly downstream processing (Azizi et al., 2014). For example, Luyben (2017) investigated the use of a vaporizer, a cooled tubular reactor and an economizer in a conventional methanol dehydration process. The methanol conversion in the reactor under these operating conditions was increased only by 1.1 %. The increase in conversion results in a 12.8 % decrease in methanol recycle which shows the dominant effect of conversion on methanol recycle.

Membrane reactor has been suggested to enhance the conversion of methanol by removing water during the reaction. The ceramic membrane reactor was recently proposed to improve the performance of DME synthesis via dehydration of methanol (Lee, 2006). However, the conversion, when using the membrane reactor was improved by 6.2 % compared to the industrial reactor (Farsi, 2011).

In this study, an inter-stage membrane will be investigated to remove water between two reactor stages. There are many materials that can be used for water removal. Ceramics and polymers are the two main materials that are used for water separation. Currently, polymeric membranes are dominant in water treatment. However, their drawbacks, such as poor stability, easy fouling and short lifetime, are limiting their applications (He, 2019). Hydrophilic membranes such as zeolite, silica and alumina are suitable for water removal from organic mixtures at high temperatures. Lee et al. (2006) studied the separation of water from methanol and DME using alumina-silica composite membrane which provides high water selectivity.

The objective of this study is to determine the effects of using an inter-stage hydrophilic ceramic membrane on the conventional DME process. A hydrophilic ceramic (alumina-silica) membrane for water removal is proposed in this study to develop an intensified process for DME synthesis. A comparison with the conventional process will be illustrated.

2. Conventional Process

The synthesis of DME is via the catalytic dehydration of methanol over γ-alumina. The reaction is exothermic and reversible as shown:

$$2CH_3OH \leftrightarrow CH_3OCH_3 + H_2O \qquad \Delta H_{298K}^0 = -23.5 \, kJ/mol \qquad (1)$$

The reaction rate of the gas phase methanol dehydration, on a commercial γ-alumina catalyst, was precisely described by the following kinetic model (Berčič and Levec, 1993):

$$-r_m = \frac{k_s K_M^2 \left(C_M^2 - \frac{C_D C_W}{K_{eq}} \right)}{\left(1 + 2\sqrt{K_M C_M} + K_W C_W \right)^4} \qquad (2)$$

$$k_s = 5.35 \times 10^{13} e^{\frac{-17280}{T}} \quad , \quad kmol/(kg.h) \qquad (3)$$

$$K_M = 5.39 \times 10^{-4} e^{\frac{8487}{T}} \quad , \quad m^3/kmol \qquad (4)$$

$$K_W = 8.47 \times 10^{-2} e^{\frac{5070}{T}} \quad , \quad m^3/kmol \qquad (5)$$

The equilibrium constant K_{eq} is calculated (by Aspen Plus) from Gibbs free energies.

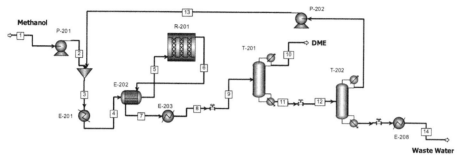

Figure 1. Dimethyl Ether Conventional Process Flow Diagram

The conventional industrial flowsheet based on DuPont process (Turton et al., 2013) is shown in Figure 1. The conventional process was rigorously simulated by Aspen Plus using UNIFAC thermodynamics model. The plant annual capacity is 50,000 tons of 99.5 wt. % DME product. The dehydration of methanol is a vapor-phase reaction conducted in an adiabatic reactor. The LHHW (Langmuir-Hinshelwood Hougen-Watson) kinetic model described in Eq. (2) was used to simulate the reactor and determine the conversion of methanol and the effluent yield. Figure 1 shows the base-case design that represents the industrial process. The liquid fresh methanol and recycle stream are first vaporized in E-201 and then preheated in a feed-effluent heat exchanger, E-202, before entering the reactor operating at 14.7 bar. The reactor effluent is then cooled in a cooler, E-203, and fed to the first distillation column operating at 10.3 bar (cooling water is used in the condenser), which produces a DME as distillate. The bottoms stream is separated in the second distillation column, which produces a water bottoms and a methanol distillate for recycle back to the feed vaporizer. The streams data calculated by Aspen Plus are shown in Table 1. The temperature profile and mole compositions of methanol and DME are shown in Figure 2. The calculated conversion of methanol is about % 81.8 which is in a good agreement with the industrial conversion using adiabatic fixed bed reactor. The maximum conversion is attained at an adiabatic temperature of 371.2 °C.

Table 1. Streams Data of Dimethyl Ether Conventional Process

Stream Number	1	2	3	4	5	6	7
Temperature (°C)	25.00	25.40	46.10	154.00	250.00	371.23	288.34
Pressure (bar)	1.10	15.50	15.50	15.10	14.70	13.90	13.80
Vapor Fraction	0.00	0.00	0.00	1.00	1.00	1.00	1.00
Mass Flows (t/h)	9.22	9.22	11.31	11.31	11.31	11.31	11.31
Mole Flows (kmol/h)	262.20	262.20	321.23	321.23	321.23	321.23	321.23
Component flowrates (kmol/h)							
DME	0.00	0.00	1.40	1.40	1.40	130.67	130.67
METHANOL	259.70	259.70	316.03	316.03	316.03	57.48	57.48
WATER	2.50	2.50	3.80	3.80	3.80	133.07	133.07
Stream Number	8	9	10	11	12	13	14
Temperature (°C)	100.00	90.53	45.75	152.98	140.02	120.72	50.00
Pressure (bar)	13.40	10.40	10.30	10.50	7.40	15.50	1.20
Vapor Fraction	0.16	0.22	0.00	0.00	0.04	0.00	0.00
Mass Flows (t/h)	11.31	11.31	6.58	4.72	4.72	2.09	2.64
Mole Flows (kmol/h)	321.23	321.22	129.80	191.42	191.42	59.03	132.39
Component flowrates (kmol/h)							
DME	130.67	130.67	129.27	1.40	1.40	1.40	0.00
METHANOL	57.48	57.48	0.53	56.95	56.95	56.33	0.62
WATER	133.07	133.07	0.00	133.07	133.07	1.30	131.77

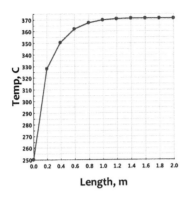

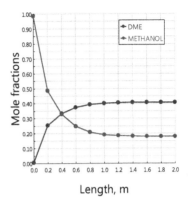

Figure 2. Temperature Profile and Mole Fractions of Methanol and DME along the Adiabatic Reactor Length

3. Membrane for Water Removal

A hydrophilic ceramic membrane is very suitable and selective for water removal from organic mixtures. Lee et al. (2006) developed a selective alumina-silica composite membrane for water removal from methanol and DME. The water-selective alumina-silica composite membrane is permeable to water with a permeability of 1.1440×10^{-7} mol m^{-2} s Pa^{-1} at a temperature of 250 °C. The water/methanol and water/DME selectivities are 8.4 and 62.9, respectively. Eq. 6 is used to calculate the membrane flux:

$$Q_i = \pi_i \left(P_i - P_i^m \right) \tag{6}$$

Where π_i, P_i and P_i^m are the membrane permeance, partial pressure at feed and partial pressure at permeant of component i, respectively. The water vapor which is generated via methanol dehydration in the first reactor stage is removed from the effluent before sending methanol and DME to the second reactor stage.

4. Modified Process

Figure 3 shows the flowsheet of modified process for DME production. The plant capacity and product purity of modified process are kept identical to the conventional process. The changes from the conventional process include the use of two identical reactor stages and an inter-stage alumina-silica composite membrane. The two fixed bed reactors are operated adiabatically using γ-alumina catalyst with an inlet feed temperature of 240 °C to the first stage reactor and 250 °C to the second stage reactor. Water is removed through the ceramic membrane which is located between the two reactor stages. Water (stream 9) is used to preheat the methanol feed (stream 3). The methanol feed is further preheated to 153 °C using the effluent of the first reactor stage (stream 6) which is cooled to 250 °C. Two additional heat exchangers (E201 and E202) are required to replace the preheater for heat integration. The methanol conversion of modified process was increased to 93 % which is improved by 13.7 % compared to the conventional industrial reactor. Table 2 shows the streams data of the modified process. A comparison between the modified process and the conventional process is shown in Table 3. There are significant improvements on the conventional process when the inter-stage membrane

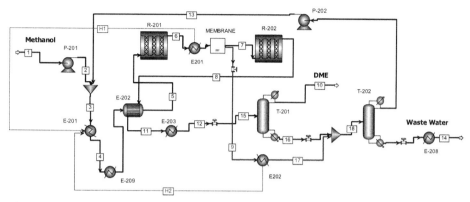

Figure 3. Dimethyl Ether Modified Process Flow Diagram

is used. The conversion of methanol was increased while the recycle was decreased. The major decrease is on the reboiler duty of first column (T-201) since water was separated via the membrane unit and then sent to the second column (T-202) for further purification. The effect of inlet temperature was investigated. The amount of unconverted methanol which is separated with water and unconverted methanol which exits the second reactor stage were calculated to optimize the inlet temperature, as shown in Figure 4. The highest conversion can be attained at feed temperature between 240 °C and 245 °C.

5. Conclusions

The industrial process for production DME was improved significantly when using an inter-stage hydrophilic alumina-silica membrane for water removal. The conversion was increased to 93 % with a decrease of about 59.7 % in methanol recycle stream. The process was heat integrated by preheating methanol feed using the two reactors effluents and the separated water in the membrane unit. The total hot and cold utilities were considerably decreased to 60.3 % and 69.5 %, respectively. The results proved that DME synthesis in the suggested inter-stage ceramic membrane is feasible and promising.

Table 2. Streams Data of Dimethyl Ether Modified Process

Stream Number	1	2	3	4	5	6	7
Temperature (°C)	25.00	25.40	28.50	153.28	240.00	361.20	250.00
Pressure (bar)	1.10	15.50	15.50	15.10	14.70	13.90	13.80
Vapor Fraction	0.00	0.00	0.00	0.55	1.00	1.00	1.00
Mass Flows (t/h)	9.22	9.22	10.09	10.09	10.09	10.09	7.45
Mole Flows (kmol/h)	262.20	262.20	286.01	286.01	286.01	286.01	160.36
Component flowrates (kmol/h)							
DME	0.00	0.00	3.26	3.26	3.26	117.32	115.47
METHANOL	259.70	259.70	278.95	278.95	278.95	50.82	44.78
WATER	2.50	2.50	3.81	3.81	3.81	117.87	0.12
Stream Number	8	9	10	11	12	13	14
Temperature (°C)	272.60	239.83	45.62	162.66	100.00	58.86	50.00
Pressure (bar)	13.00	3.10	10.30	12.90	12.80	15.50	1.20
Vapor Fraction	1.00	1.00	0.00	1.00	0.91	0.00	0.00
Mass Flows (t/h)	7.45	2.65	6.59	7.45	7.45	0.87	2.63
Mole Flows (kmol/h)	160.36	125.65	129.80	160.36	160.36	23.81	132.39
Component flowrates (kmol/h)							
DME	131.08	1.85	129.68	131.08	131.08	3.26	0.00
METHANOL	13.54	6.04	0.13	13.54	13.54	19.25	0.21
WATER	15.73	117.75	0.00	15.73	15.73	1.31	132.18

Table 3. Comparison of Conventional Process with Modified Process

Cases	Conventional Process	Modified Process	Comparison %
Methanol conversion %	81.8	93.0	+13.7
Methanol recycle, kmol/h	59.03	23.81	-59.7
Condenser duty of T-201, cal/s	217,197	213,162	-1.86
Reboiler duty of T-201, cal/s	167,118	2568	-98.46
Condenser duty of T-202, cal/s	344,221	164,847	- 52.1
Reboiler duty of T-202, cal/s	338,579	215,472	-36.4
Recycle pump (P-202) , hp	2.94	1.69	-42.5
Total heating utilities, cal/s	1,520,000	603,100	-60.3
Total cooling utilities, cal/s	2,206,000	671,900	-69.5

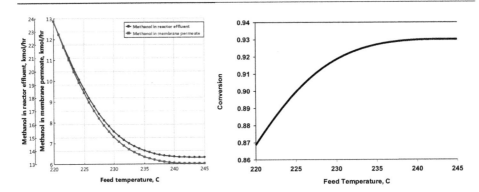

Figure 4. The Effect of Feed Temperature on Methanol Outlet Flowrates and Conversion

References

Azizi Z., Rezaeimanesh M., Tohidian T., Rahimpour M., 2014, Dimethyl ether: A review of technologies and production challenges, Chemical Engineering and Processing: Process Intensification, 82, 150-172.

Berčič G., Levec J., 1993, Catalytic Dehydration of Methanol to Dimethyl Ether. Kinetic Investigation and Reactor Simulation, Ind. Eng. Chem. Res.,32, 2478-2484.

Farsi M., Jahanmiri A., 2011, Enhancement of DME Production in an Optimized Membrane Isothermal Fixed-Bed Reactor, International Journal of Chemical Reactor Engineering, 9, 1-18.

He Z., Lyu Z., Gu Q., Zhang L., Wang J., 2019, Ceramic-based membranes for water and wastewater treatment, Colloids and Surfaces A, 578, 1-19.

Lee K., Youn M., Sea B., 2006, Preparation of hydrophilic ceramic membranes for a dehydration membrane reactor, Desalination, 191, 296-302.

Luyben W., 2017, Improving the conventional reactor/separation/recycle DME process, Computers and Chemical Engineering, 106, 17-22.

Turton R., Bailie R., Whiting W., Shaeiwitz J., Bhattacharyya D., 2013, Analysis, Synthesis, and Design of Chemical Processes, 4th edition, Prentice Hall, USA.

Sauro Pierucci, Flavio Manenti, Giulia Bozzano, Davide Manca (Eds.)
Proceedings of the 30th European Symposium on Computer Aided Process Engineering
(ESCAPE30), May 24-27, 2020, Milano, Italy. © 2020 Elsevier B.V. All rights reserved.
http://dx.doi.org/10.1016/B978-0-12-823377-1.50109-9

Computer-aided Solvent Mixture Design for the Crystallisation and Isolation of Mefenamic Acid

Suela Jonuzaj,[a] Oliver L. Watson,[a] Sara Ottoboni,[b] Chris J. Price,[b] Jan Sefcik,[b] Amparo Galindo,[a] George Jackson,[a] Claire S. Adjiman[a,*]

[a]Centre for Process Systems Engineering, Department of Chemical Engineering, Imperial College London, SW7 2AZ, UK
[b]Department of Chemical and Process Engineering, University of Strathclyde, G1 1XQ, Glasgow, UK
c.adjiman@imperial.ac.uk

Abstract

We present a systematic computer-aided methodology for the integrated design of solvent blends used in the purification (i.e., crystallisation and isolation) of pharmaceutical compounds. In particular, we investigate the design of optimal solvent mixtures for combined cooling and antisolvent crystallisation, taking into account interlinked design decisions across both crystallisation and isolation (washing) stages. Within the proposed approach, the optimal solvents, antisolvents, the best mixture composition and the optimal process temperatures are determined simultaneously. Furthermore, comprehensive design specifications for both crystallisation and isolation units, such as the miscibility of crystallisation and wash solvents, their environmental impact, and health and safety metrics, are investigated. The design method is applied to identifying potential high-performance solvent blends for the purification of mefenamic acid, while removing an impurity, chlorobenzoic acid, from the system.

Keywords: Crystallisation, isolation, CAM^{b}D, solvent blends, mefenamic acid.

1. Introduction

The importance of solvents in the manufacturing of pharmaceutical products has long been established and their presence is essential in many steps of the process, spanning synthesis, separation/purification and product formulation. Of particular interest are purification processes, where the extensive use of solvents in different process units can affect process efficiency, cost/environmental/safety performance, and final product quality. A comprehensive study on the green manufacturing of pharmaceuticals by Jiménez-González et al. (2011) and a life cycle assessment of pharmaceutical products by Ott et al. (2014) have shown that the choice of solvents is one of the key drivers to improving the sustainability of the manufacturing process. Currently, several pharmaceutical companies are using in-house solvent selection guides and workflows that have been developed based on heuristic approaches. Despite these tools, the development and manufacturing of a new medicine continues to require time-consuming and costly experimental investigations if a wide range of options is to be explored. Thus, more streamlined and systematic methods and workflows are required to enable the rapid exploration of numerous design options and to enhance innovation (Brown et al., 2018).

Computer-aided mixture/blend design (CAM^{b}D) (Gani, 2004) is a promising approach for identifying suitable solvent blends that meet predefined target properties and optimise a given performance measure. CAM^{b}D has often been used in the design of optimal solvent mixtures for crystallisation processes (Austin et al., 2016; Jonuzaj et al., 2016, 2018; Karunanithi, et al., 2006; Watson et al., 2019) in order to facilitate and improve the production of pharmaceuticals. Karunanithi et al. (2006) proposed a decomposition-based approach for the design of binary solvent and/or antisolvent mixtures used in the crystallisation of active pharmaceutical ingredients (APIs), where smaller molecular and mixture design subproblems were posed and solved. The design of solvent mixtures for crystallisation was also studied by Austin et al. (2016), where the mixture design problem with a fixed number of ingredients was decomposed into molecular and mole fraction optimisation formulations. Jonuzaj et al. (2016, 2018) presented a general CAM^{b}D formulation for the selection and design of solvent mixtures for separation processes, in which the number of ingredients in the blend, the identities of solvents and their mole fractions are optimised at the same time.

To date, most solvent mixture design approaches have been applied to optimise a single purification process unit with fixed operating conditions. Selecting optimal solvents for a specific unit (e.g., crystallisation), without consideration for the overall process, may impact negatively on the effectiveness of subsequent purification steps (e.g., washing), and thus deteriorate the efficiency of the overall process. Furthermore, by operating at fixed process conditions, such as temperature, the entire design space of possibilities is not fully explored. The latter issue has been addressed in the recent work by Watson et al. (2019) who proposed a solvent mixture design formulation for the coupled cooling and antisolvent crystallisation, with variable process temperature. In this work, we extend the approach and present a comprehensive methodology for the design of solvent mixtures that includes both the crystallisation and the isolation of pharmaceutical compounds. In our new integrated formulation, optimal mixtures of crystallisation solvents and antisolvents, their compositions, and the optimal process temperatures are determined simultaneously. To ensure the overall purification process is effective, mixture property constraints (such as the miscibility of crystallisation and washing solvent mixtures) are enforced for both crystallisation and isolation stages. The methodology is applied to the design of solvent blends for the purification of mefenamic acid (MA), with the aim to minimise solvent consumption, while ensuring a high crystal yield of MA is achieved, and avoiding the crystallisation of a given impurity (chlorobenzoic acid (CBA)). In addition, the crystallisation solvents are selected subject to health-and-safety constraints that are included within the optimisation formulation, and they are screened for miscibility with a wash solvent at optimal values of the composition.

2. Solvent mixture design for crystallisation and isolation processes

2.1. Problem definition

The proposed CAM^{b}D problem involves a comprehensive formulation for the design of optimal solvent mixtures for the cooling/antisolvent crystallisation and washing processes of pharmaceutical compounds. Mixtures of N_c components are designed and consist of an active pharmaceutical ingredient (API), a solid impurity, a crystallisation solvent and antisolvent pair, and a wash solvent. In order to develop the mathematical formulation, we define the sets $I = \{1, \dots, N_c - 1\}$ and $\tilde{I} = \{1, \dots, N_c\}$ for all components in the crystallisation and washing blends, respectively. The first two elements of sets I and $\tilde{I}$ consist of the API and its impurity (denoted by subset JJ), while the rest of the elements, denoted by subsets II and $\tilde{II}$, represent the solvent molecules ($I = JJ \cup II$; $\tilde{I} = JJ \cup \tilde{II}$). The set $S = \{1, \dots, N_s\}$ defines the lists of chemical compounds from which the optimal solvents are to be chosen. The crystallisation process consists of initial/heated (in) and final/cooled (f) states, denoted by the set $St = \{in, f\}$.

2.2. MINLP formulation of the integrated CAM^{b}D problem

The integrated formulation of the CAM^{b}D problem consists of an objective function (f) to be optimised, general constrains ($g, \tilde{g}$) that hold regardless of the discrete choices, and conditional constraints ($h, \tilde{h}$) that depend on the logic decisions (e.g., solvent identity), and are formulated using the big-M approach (Jonuzaj et at., 2016), as shown below:

$$\min_{x,p,y} \ f(x,p)$$
$$\text{s.t.} \ \ g_t(x,p) \leq 0, \ t \in St$$
$$\tilde{g}(x,p) \leq 0$$
$$h_{i,s,t}(x,p) \leq M_{i,s,t}(1-y_{i,s}), i \in I \ ; s \in S; \ t \in St$$
$$\tilde{h}_{i,s}(x,p) \leq \tilde{M}_{i,s}(1-y_{i,s}), i \in \tilde{I} \ ; s \in S$$
$$Ay \leq a$$
$$x \in [x^L, x^U] \subset \mathbb{R}^{Nc}; \ p \in [p^L, p^U] \subset \mathbb{R}^{m_p}; \ y \in \{0,1\}^q \qquad (P)$$

where x is a vector of mole fractions for the components in the crystallisation and wash blends, p is a vector of other continuous variables and y is a binary variable for assigning solvents from the set S to the solvent components in the mixture. The constraints g and h describe the initial/final states of the coupled cooling-antisolvent crystallisation, whereas $\tilde{g}$ and $\tilde{h}$ functions correspond to the washing process at ambient conditions.

3. Case study: solvent mixture design for purifying mefenamic acid

3.1. Problem description

Mefenamic acid (MA) is a nonsteroidal anti-inflammatory drug with analgesic properties. Its low solubility in common solvents requires identifying suitable solvents and solvent mixtures for the efficient purification of the drug. Specifically, we identify optimal solvent mixtures for the cooling and antisolvent crystallisation of MA with the objective to minimise solvent consumption (χ_s in (g solvents/g MA crystals)), while achieving high crystal yield of the API and avoiding crystallisation of CBA, an impurity. Here, the crystal yield of MA is set to be greater than or equal to a user-specified lower bound of 90 % (i.e., $\acute{Y}_{MA} \geq 90$ %), whereas the crystal yield of CBA is set to zero (i.e., $\acute{Y}_{CBA} = 0$). The initial amounts of MA and CBA in the crystallisation blend are set to be $n_{MA,in} = 1$ mol and $n_{CBA,in} = 0.2$ mol, respectively. Solvent use is bounded by a (heuristic) lower value of 3.5 (g total solvent/g MA crystals) to ensure that adequate amounts of solvents are present to facilitate processing. The optimal crystallisation blend at final (cooled) conditions goes through a filtration and washing (isolation) process. The solvent & antisolvent mixture present in the cake after filtration needs to be miscible with the wash solvent, so that the crystallisation solvents and the impurity are removed successfully from the system (Ottoboni, 2018). In this case study, n-heptane is chosen as the wash solvent and the miscibility of each crystallisation solvent with n-heptane is tested. It is noted that MA has very low solubility in n-heptane around ambient conditions ensuring that the solid API is not dissolved in the wash solvent. The optimal crystallisation solvents/antisolvents are selected from a list of 69 candidates. The design specifications and the main model equations (i.e., relations for calculating solvent consumption and crystal yields; solid-liquid equilibrium equation for calculating the solubilities of MA and CBA in the solvent mixtures; and the miscibility function to ensure that there is no phase split between the different pairs of solvent, antisolvent and wash solvent) are presented in Table 1. The liquid-phase activity coefficients, denoted by γ, are calculated with the UNIFAC model (Fredenslund et al., 1975). Superscript ^{i,j} indicates the binary mixture of components i and j considered, at the ratio of mole fractions found in the multicomponent mixture.

Table 1: Main problem equations and design specifications. See Table 2 and text for symbols.

Description	Main model equations and design specifications
Solvent use; crystal yield	$\chi_s \left[\dfrac{\text{g solvents}}{\text{g MA crystals}} \right] = \dfrac{\Sigma_{ii} m_{ii}}{m_{MA,\text{in}} - m_{MA,f}}$; $\acute{Y}_{jj} = \dfrac{n_{jj,\text{in}} - n_{jj,f}}{n_{jj,\text{in}}}$
Solubility; miscibility	$\ln x_{jj,t} + \ln \gamma_{jj,t} = \dfrac{\Delta H_{fus,jj}}{R} \left[\dfrac{1}{T_{m,jj}} - \dfrac{1}{T_t} \right]$; $\dfrac{\partial \ln \gamma_{i,t}^{i,j}}{\partial x_{i,t}^{i,j}} + \dfrac{1}{x_{i,t}^{i,j}} \geq 0$
Components in the mixture	1 API (MA), 1 impurity (CBA), 2 crystallisation solvents (s_1, s_2) and 1 wash solvent (s_w)
Fixed components in the blend	MA, CBA, s_w (n-heptane)
Designed solvents in the blend	s_1, s_2
Problem size	32,048 eqns.; 29,334 continuous and 360 discrete vars.

3.2. Results and discussion

The integrated formulation is implemented and solved in GAMS version 28.2.0, using SBB, a local branch & bound MINLP solver. The integrated MINLP model for the crystallisation and washing of MA can be found at *doi.org/10.5281/zenodo.3628753* and the results obtained are summarized in Table 2.

Table 2: Optimal solutions obtained when solving the integrated formulation of the case study. Fixed mixture ingredients (MA, CBA, s_w) and optimal solvents (s_1, s_2); solvent use (χ_s); % crystal yields of MA and CBA (% $\acute{Y}_{jj}$); composition ($x_{i,t}$) & mass ($m_{i,t}$) of mixture ingredients, and initial (T_{in}) & final (T_f) temperatures in the crystallisation unit; composition ($\tilde{x}_i$) and mass ($\tilde{m}_i$) of mixture ingredients in the wash solvent, after washing.

Components (i)	Crystallisation							Washing	
	χ_s (g/g)	% $\acute{Y}_{jj}$	$x_{i,\text{in}}$	$x_{i,f}$	$m_{i,\text{in}}$ (g)	$m_{i,f}$ (g)	T_{in} (K) T_f (K)	$\tilde{x}_i$	$\tilde{m}_i$ (g)
API: MA	3.5	97.2	0.108	0.003	241	7	380	0.001	0.02
Impurity: CBA		0	0.021	0.024	31	31	290	0.006	0.10
s_1: n-methylpyrrollidone			0.523	0.584	479	479		0.139	1.48
s_2: o-xylene			0.348	0.389	342	342		0.092	1.05
s_w: n-heptane								0.762	8.21
API: MA	3.5	94.5	0.073	0.004	241	13	364	0.001	0.06
Impurity: CBA		0	0.015	0.016	31	31	292	0.004	0.14
s_1: DMAC			0.401	0.431	477	477		0.113	2.18
s_2: formic acid			0.511	0.549	321	321		0.143	1.46
s_w: n-heptane								0.739	16.4
API: MA	3.5	90.0	0.119	0.011	241	24	362	0.002	0.06
Impurity: CBA		0	0.024	0.023	31	31	290	0.005	0.08
s_1: pyridine			0.663	0.642	440	440		0.142	1.18
s_2: 2,2,4-trimethylpentane			0.194	0.324	186	320		0.072	0.86
s_w: n-heptane								0.779	8.21

A ranked list of 10 optimal solutions is generated by including integer cuts in the MINLP formulation. The optimal value of solvent consumption obtained in all cases is at the lower bound. Three of the optimal solutions obtained are presented in Table 2. These solutions show large variations in the crystal yields and in the solvent blends used, demonstrating the benefits of the proposed approach, where many design decisions are optimised simultaneously. In the first two solutions, MA is crystallised by a cooling process (starting at 380 K or 364 K) and there is no addition of solvent between the initial and final states of the crystallisation. In the third solution a high crystal yield and a low solvent consumption are achieved by the combination of cooling and antisolvent crystallisation, where MA crystals are produced by increasing the amount of antisolvent, 2,2,4-trimethylpentane and reducing the process temperature from 362 K. Thanks to the constraints imposed in this model, the crystallisation solvent blends obtained with the integrated model are in a single liquid phase in both initial and final crystallisation stages, and both solvents used are miscible with n-heptane in the washing unit. In a non-integrated approach (without considering washing), several optimal blends obtained consist of solvents acetic acid and 1,2-propanediol, which are immiscible with n-heptane at the washing stage. Hence, the use of models that consider the purification process in an integrated fashion is essential to achieve a feasible design.

The list of optimal blends generated includes solvents that have high environmental and health impact, such as n-methylpyrrolidone, o-xylene & pyridine. To ensure that safe solvents are chosen, we extend the approach to use the GSK solvent selection guide (Henderson et al., 2011) and include constrains on the flammability, health and environmental impacts, and reactivity of each solvent in the optimisation model. A set of optimal blends is obtained with a multiobjective optimisation (MOO) formulation, where solvent use is

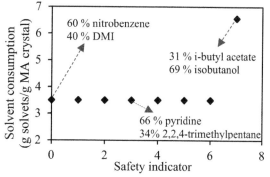

Figure 1: Pareto optimal solutions when solving the integrated crystallisation and washing process. Minimum solvent consumption for different safety indicator values.

minimised whereas the GSK safety indicator values are maximised. The set of Pareto optimum solutions given in Figure 1 is obtained using the ϵ-constrained method, in which solvent consumption is optimised and the safety indicators are constrained by a given lower bound. The generated Pareto set consists of blends with different solvents and compositions. As shown in Figure 1, there are several solutions that yield the same low solvent consumption but very different safety indicators. However, a safety indicator greater than 6 can only be achieved with a significant increase in solvent use. Thus, MOO provides a useful tool to make better design decisions, in conjunction with other key aspects related to solvent selection, such as stability of solid form and crystal morphology, that ensure downstream process feasibility.

4. Conclusions

In this work, a systematic methodology for the design of optimal solvent mixtures for integrated purification processes of pharmaceuticals has been presented. Within the proposed approach, the simultaneous optimisation of crystallisation and washing steps was explored, where optimal solvent mixtures were identified for the combined cooling and antisolvent crystallisation and their interaction with the wash solvent was investigated. The model was applied to the selection of optimal solvent mixtures for the purification of mefenamic acid. A range of design options were obtained, achieving both low solvent use and high crystal yield, while limiting impurities in the crystallisation. Further, the use of a comprehensive framework has been shown to lead to a wide range of more promising design options. This highlights the necessity of developing integrated approaches to solvent design for purification over sequential solvent selection workflows. Future work will focus on optimising the identity of the wash solvent and the overall crystal yield and solvent consumption across both purification stages, while taking into account critical factors such as the solid form stability and crystal morphology.

Acknowledgments: The authors gratefully acknowledge financial support from the EPSRC and the Future Continuous Manufacturing and Advanced Crystallisation Research Hub (Grant Ref: EP/P006965/1) for funding this work. The Molecular Systems Engineering Group also appreciated support from the EPSRC (grants GR/T17595, GR/N35991, EP/E016340, EP/J014958 and a Doctoral Prize to S.J.).

Data statement: Data underlying this article can be accessed and used under the Creative Commons Attribution license on Zenodo at *doi.org/10.5281/zenodo.3628753*.

References

N.D. Austin, A.P. Samudra, N.V. Sahinidis, D.W. Trahan, 2016. Mixture design using derivative-free optimization in the space of individual component properties. AIChE Journal 62, 1514-30.

C.J. Brown, T. McGlone, S. Yerdele, V. Srirambhatla, F. Mabbott, R. Gurung, M.L. Briuglia, B. Ahmed, H. Polyzois, J. McGinty, F. Perciballi, 2018. Enabling precision manufacturing of active pharmaceutical ingredients: workflow for seeded cooling continuous crystallisations. Molecular Systems Design & Engineering 3, 518-549.

A. Fredenslund, R.L. Jones, J.M. Prausnitz, 1975. Group-contribution estimation of activity coefficients in nonideal liquid mixtures. AIChE Journal 21, 1086–1099.

R. Gani, 2004. Chemical product design: challenges and opportunities. Computers & Chemical Engineering 28, 2441-2457.

R.K. Henderson, C. Jiménez-González, D.J.C. Constable, S.R. Alston, G.G.A. Inglis, G. Fisher, J. Sherwood, S.P. Binksa, A.D. Curzons, 2011. Expanding GSK's solvent selection guide - embedding sustainability into solvent selection starting at medicinal chemistry. Green Chemistry 13, 854-862.

C. Jimenez-Gonzalez, P. Poechlauer, Q.B. Broxterman, B-S. Yang, D. am Ende, J. Baird, C. Bertsch, R.E. Hannah, P. Dell'Orco, H. Noorman, S. Yee, R. Reintjens, A. Wells, V. Massonneau, J. Manley. 2011. Key green engineering research areas for sustainable manufacturing: A perspective from pharmaceutical and fine chemicals manufacturers. Organic Process Research & Development 15, 900-911.

S. Jonuzaj, P.T. Akula, P. Kleniati, C.S. Adjiman, 2016. The formulation of optimal mixtures with generalized disjunctive programming: A solvent design case study. AIChE Journal 62, 1616-33.

S. Jonuzaj, A. Gupta, C.S. Adjiman, 2018. The design of optimal mixtures from atom groups using generalized disjunctive programming. Computers & Chemical Engineering 116, 401-421.

AT. Karunanithi, L.E.K. Achenie, R. Gani, 2006. A computer-aided molecular design framework for crystallization solvent design. Chemical Engineering Science 61, 1247-60.

D. Ott, D. Kralisch, I. Denčić, V. Hessel, Y. Laribi, P. Perrichon, C. Berguerand, L. Kiwi-Minsker, P. Loeb, 2014. Life cycle analysis within pharmaceutical process optimization and intensification: Case study of an API production. ChemSusChem 7, 3521-3533.

S. Ottoboni, 2018. Developing strategies and equipment for continuous isolation of active pharmaceutical ingredients (APIs) by filtration, washing and drying. PhD Thesis, Chemical and Process Engineering, University of Strathclyde.

O.L. Watson, A. Galindo, G. Jackson, C.S. Adjiman, 2019. Computer-aided design of solvent blends for the cooling and anti-solvent crystallisation of ibuprofen. Computer Aided Chemical Engineering 46, 949-954.

Sauro Pierucci, Flavio Manenti, Giulia Bozzano, Davide Manca (Eds.)
Proceedings of the 30th European Symposium on Computer Aided Process Engineering
(ESCAPE30), May 24-27, 2020, Milano, Italy. © 2020 Elsevier B.V. All rights reserved.
http://dx.doi.org/10.1016/B978-0-12-823377-1.50110-5

Direct DME Synthesis from Syngas: a Technoeconomic Model-based Investigation

Andrea Bernardi[a,b], Yuchu Chen[b], David Chadwick[b] , Benoît Chachuat[a,b,*]

[a]Centre for Process Systems Engineering, Imperial College London, SW7 2AZ, UK
[a]Department of Chemical Engineering, Imperial College London, SW7 2AZ, UK
b.chachuat@imperial.ac.uk

Abstract

Dymethyl ether (DME) is of industrial interest since it is used as a precursor in many other chemical processes and it can be used as fuel in diesel engines. Nowadays, the main route to produce DME is a two-step process in which a methanol dehydration unit is connected to a methanol synthesis plant (indirect synthesis). Combining methanol synthesis and dehydration in a single reactor (direct synthesis) has attracted significant attention in recent years as it offers a theoretically higher syngas conversion per pass but leads to a more challenging downstream separation. The main contribution of this paper is a model-based comparison between an indirect DME process and two direct DME processes: a standard reactor/separation/recycle process and a once-through configuration where the unreacted syngas is used to co-produce electricity. The key-performance indicators in our analysis are the break-even price of DME, the carbon efficiency, and the energy return on energy invested. The results suggest that indirect and direct DME synthesis have similar performances both in economic terms, and in carbon and energy efficiencies terms.

Keywords: DME, process simulation, techno-economic analysis, carbon efficiency, energy efficiency

1. Introduction

Dimethyl ether (DME) is an important precursor for a large number of chemicals, including light olefins, acetic acid, and methyl acetate. It is also an interesting fuel alternative due to its high cetane number—which makes it ideal for diesel engines—and its similar vapor pressure as LPG—which makes it compatible with existing infrastructure for fuel transportation and storage. The traditional method of DME synthesis in the chemical industry is the indirect synthesis, a two-step process whereby syngas is first converted to methanol and the methanol is then dehydrated to DME in a separate reactor. The equilibrium limitation of methanol synthesis in the first step calls for large recycle loops in order to achieve high syngas conversion. Nevertheless, the indirect synthesis has the advantage of a well-developed catalytic system and the fact that DME has a much lower boiling point than water and methanol, so their separation is easy (Azizi et al., 2014).

The combination of methanol synthesis and methanol dehydration in a single reactor has generated a lot interest over the past decades. The main advantage of this direct synthesis is that methanol is consumed in the same reactor where it is produced, therefore shifting the equilibrium towards higher syngas conversion (Ng et al., 1999). Significant research has been devoted to the development of suitable catalysts for direct

DME synthesis (Sun et al., 2014), with a focus on catalyst stability and reactor technology (Mondal and Yadav, 2019). But there has been comparatively little research conducted on the techno-economic assessment of direct DME synthesis in a plantwide manner. The low boiling point of DME makes its separation from the unreacted syngas challenging, which may have a large impact on the overall process performance in turn. Other process configurations have been suggested for direct DME synthesis. In the once-through configuration for instance, the unreacted syngas is used to generate electricity, which may lower the capital and operating costs as a compressor is no longer needed for recycling the syngas (Narvaez et al., 2019). Trippe et al. (2013) compared direct DME synthesis and FT synthesis, using syngas from biomass gasification. However, in their study the DME reactor is followed by a gasoline-synthesis reactor without intermediate purification of the DME since they were interested in comparing gas-to-liquid technologies. They furthermore used equilibrium models (Gibbs reactor) of the DME and FT reactors to conduct the assessment. Hankin and Shah (2017) compared methanol and DME syntheses (both direct and indirect) using CO_2 and H_2 as feedstock focusing on the energy efficiency. They considered different layouts, including electrocatalytic cells (SOECs) and a separate water-gas-shift reactor prior to the reactor in order to adjust the $CO:CO_2:H_2$ ratio for each conversion technology, and they also used equilibrium models in their assessment. Detailed process simulations for indirect DME synthesis has also been carried out for process intensification purposes: Luyben (2017) proposed an optimized version of the conventional reactor/separation/recycle DME process, which compares favorably to intensified configurations, such as the DME process based on a reactive dividing-wall column developed by Kiss and David (2012).

The main purpose of this paper is to conduct a comparative assessment of direct and indirect DME synthesis from syngas, by accounting for different $H_2:CO$ feed ratios. The methodology applied for the assessment is described in the next section, followed by results and discussions, before concluding the paper.

2. Methodology

In Figure 1 the block flow diagrams of the different processes considered in this paper are presented. The indirect DME synthesis (i-DME) is a two step process, in which methanol synthesis and methanol dehydration occur in two separate reactors. In the direct synthesis (d-DME) the DME is produced from syngas in a single reactor using a bi-functional catalyst. Since the compressors to recycle the syngas contribute a significant part of the capital and operational expenditures, a once-through configuration (d-DME-OT) is also analyzed whereby the unreacted syngas is burned to produce electricity.

The analysis is conducted on the basis of a plant producing 100,000 tonnes of DME a year (273 kmol/h) at 99.5% purity. The influence of the syngas composition is analyzed by simulating each process for three different $H_2:CO$ inlet ratios (1, 1.5 and 2), with the molar fractions of CO_2, H_2O and N_2 kept constant at 0.03, 0.01 and 0.01 in all the scenarios. The syngas feed stream is assumed to be available at 25°C and 25 bar, and its flowrate is adjusted in order to meet the productivity requirements. Three key-performance indicators (KPIs) are used to assess and compare the DME production processes. The *break-even price* (BEP) indicator represents the lowest DME selling price for the process to remain economically feasible, here considering a process lifetime of 30 years and the price scenario of Europe 2018. The *carbon efficiency* (CE) indicator accounts for the fraction of carbon from the syngas that ends up in the DME. Lastly, the *energy return on energy investment* (EROEI) is the amount of energy in the products divided by the amount of energy provided to the process, considering chemical, thermal and electrical energy all together.

Process flowsheets for methanol synthesis and methanol dehydration (i-DME), and for direct DME synthesis with and without recycle of the unreacted syngas are simulated in Aspen HYSYS®. Heat integration is performed for all the process alternatives using Aspen Energy Analyzer to minimize the external heating and cooling utilities requirement. The techno-economic KPIs are computed using the information provided by the process simulator, which relies on mass and energy balances, thermodynamic properties and reaction kinetics. Specifically, the kinetic rate expressions are taken from the work of Van-Dal and Bouallou (2013), and Bercic and Levec (1993) for methanol and DME synthesis, respectively. In the following the three processes are described in more details.

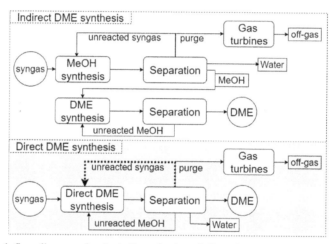

Figure 1: Block flow diagrams for the indirect (top), and direct DME process (bottom). In the direct DME synthesis the unreacted syngas (dotted line) is either recycled back to the reactor or used for electricity production.

Indirect DME synthesis. The i-DME plant is based on the work of Luyben (2010) for methanol synthesis and Luyben (2017) for methanol dehydration. The operating pressure of the methanol reactor is set to 75 bar, which is the upper bound for the kinetic model used, and the temperature is set to 250°C. The unreacted syngas is separated from the liquid products (methanol and water) using two consecutive flashes operating at different pressures. A distillation column then separates the methanol from the water. A small (2%) fraction of the unconverted syngas is purged and burned to produce electricity, while the rest is recycled back to the reactor. The electricity production unit is simulated as a syngas-fired gas turbine integrated with a steam turbine. The gas turbine cycle consists in a compressor to pressurize the air at 15 bar, a combustion chamber, and an expander. The hot flue-gas are then used to produce additional electricity with a Rankine cycle. The operating variable such as the pressure of the combustion chamber, and the parameters as the compressors and turbines efficiencies are taken from Narvaez et al. (2019). The methanol is fed at 250 °C to the DME reactor where it is dehydrated at 12 bar. The reactor is cooled to keep the internal temperature lower than 400 °C to avoid catalyst deactivation, and the outlet stream exits at 360°C. Two distillation columns are used to separate the products. DME is extracted from the top of the first column at the required purity, while methanol is separated from the water in the second column and recycled to the reactor. Since water is the only impurity present in the recycle stream, a purge stream is not necessary.

Direct dimethyl ether synthesis. In the direct DME process the syngas is fed to an isothermal reactor operated at 55 bar and 260°C. The outlet stream is a mixture containing the unreacted syngas, DME, methanol and water. Off the possible downstream separation strategies investigated we only report the one we found the most promising. The outlet stream is cooled to 35 °C and sent to a flash separator. The flashed gas contains most of the DME and is fed to an absorption column where a mixture of water and methanol is used as the absorbing agent. The gas stream leaving the absorption column has most of the unreacted syngas with traces of DME. In the d-DME configuration a small (2%) fraction is used to produce electricity while the rest is recycled to the reactor. In the d-DME-OT process all the unreacted syngas is burned to produce electricity with a combined gas and steam turbine. DME, methanol and water exit the absorption column in the liquid stream and are fed to a mixed distillation sequence. The first column separates water and methanol from the DME and gaseous impurities. Water and methanol are in part recycled to the absorption column and in part fed to a second distillation column for their separation. The top stream of the first column is fed to a third column operated at 10 bar where DME is obtained from the bottom at the required purity. A small (3%) fraction of DME is lost from the top of the column in order to maintain a temperature above -20°C in the condenser.

3. Results and discussion

The process simulation results are summarized in Figure 2 and Table 1. A first observation is that the H_2:CO ratio of the syngas has a very large effect on the carbon efficiency and to a lower extent on the economic performances and the energy efficiency. We also note that d-DME-OT is always a net producer of electricity while the other two processes either consume or produce electricity depending on the syngas composition.

Table 1: Syngas consumption and net electricity production for d-DME, d-DME-OT and i-DME, for the three syngas compositions considered.

H_2:CO	Syngas consumption [kmol/h]			Electricity production [MW]		
[-]	d-DME	d-DME-OT	i-DME	d-DME	d-DME-OT	i-DME
1.0	2060	2070	2390	2.1	6.5	16.0
1.5	1890	2450	1900	-1.6	19.0	2.4
2.0	1830	2690	1800	-1.5	28.0	-1.7

Economic performance. We start by noting that for a syngas with H_2:CO equal 1.5 and 2 the three processes present a similar economic performance. When the syngas has a lower hydrogen content the direct synthesis becomes significantly cheaper than the indirect process, because the latter requires a high recycle rate and a high excess of fresh syngas in the methanol synthesis section to meet the productivity requirements. An advantage of d-DME-OT is that it requires 2.5 to 4 times less cooling water than the other alternatives. It is interesting to note that at $H_2:CO = 1$ the once-through configuration has almost the same syngas consumption as the direct DME synthesis with recycle, which is due to the high CO conversion per pass (80%). We also note that, regardless of the high recycle rate in the indirect synthesis, the process is a net electricity producer since the purge is rich in CO and can therefore produce a large amount of electricity. The base case assumes an electricity price of 0.06 $/kWh, in addition an optimistic scenario with electricity price of 0.15 $/kWh, and a pessimistic scenario where no electricity is sold are represented. The processes that produce electricity benefit from an high electricity price and in particular the once-through configuration performs better for all the syngas compositions considered when the electricity price is 0.15 $/kWh. Finally, the direct DME synthesis with recycle is the least sensitive to both the electricity price and the syngas composition.

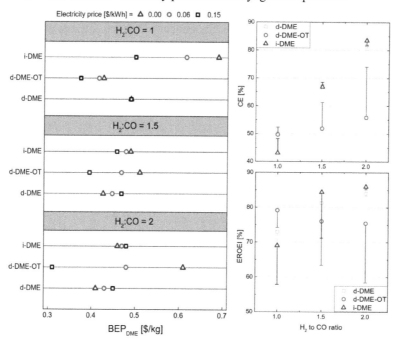

Figure 2: Comparison between d-DME, d-DME-OT and i-DME processes in terms of break-even price (left), carbon efficiency (top right), and energy efficiency (bottom right)

Carbon conversion efficiency. The d-DME-OT process has a low carbon efficiency, around 50% at $H_2:CO=1$ and increasing only slightly thereafter. The d-DME and i-DME processes also have a low CE between 40-50% at $H_2:CO = 1$ but show a significant increase thereafter, reaching a value of about 80% at $H_2:CO = 2$. The electricity produced/consumed by each process can be included in the CE by substracting/summing the carbon emission related to the production of the same amount of electricity, for instance from using natural gas. The whiskers in the plot represents the CE obtained considering a value of 380 kg-CO_2-eq/MWh for electricity produced from natural gas in a combined cycle (Turconi et al., 2013).

Energy efficiency. The three processes show a similar EROEI with an efficiency ranging between 75% and 85%. The bars represent the contribution of the produced electricity to the EROEI value. If the chemical energy of the DME (based on the LHV) is considered the only output of the system the i-DME for H_2:CO = 1 and the d-DME-OT for H_2:CO = 2 share the lowest EROEI value of about 60%, while the d-DME process is less affected and its efficiency remains in the range of 70-85%.

4. Conclusions

This paper has presented a systematic, model-based comparison between different DME production technologies. Our results show that the production of DME via direct synthesis presents a similar performance to the indirect synthesis both in economic terms and in carbon and energy efficiencies terms. The indirect synthesis performs worse than the direct synthesis if a H_2 lean syngas is used. It is also worth noting that the once-through configuration may be the best alternative from an economic point of view when the selling price for the electricity is high, but it has the lowest carbon efficiency and therefore the highest CO_2 emissions. Our current investigations aim at completing the sustainability assessment by looking at additional environmental impacts and including the syngas production step in the analysis.

Acknowledgements: This paper is based upon work supported by the Engineering and Physical Sciences Research Council (EPSRC) under Grant EP/P016650/1 "Flexible routes to liquid fuels from CO_2 by advanced catalysis and engineering".

References

Z. Azizi, M. Rezaeimanesh, T. Tohidian, M. R. Rahimpour, 2014. Dimethyl ether: A review of technologies and production challenges. Chemical Engineering and Processing: Process Intensification 82, 150–172.

G. Bercic, J. Levec, 1993. Catalytic dehydration of methanol to dimethyl ether – Kinetic investigation and reactor simulation. Industrial & Engineering Chemistry Research 32 (11), 2478–2484.

A. Hankin, N. Shah, 2017. Process exploration and assessment for the production of methanol and dimethyl ether from carbon dioxide and water. Sustainable Energy & Fuels 1 (7), 1541–1556.

A. A. Kiss, J.-P. S. David, 2012. Innovative dimethyl ether synthesis in a reactive dividing-wall column. Computers & Chemical Engineering 38, 74–81.

W. L. Luyben, 2010. Design and control of a methanol reactor/column process. Industrial & Engineering Chemistry Research 49 (13), 6150–6163.

W. L. Luyben, 2017. Improving the conventional reactor/separation/recycle dme process. Computers & Chemical Engineering 106, 17–22.

U. Mondal, G. D. Yadav, 2019. Perspective of dimethyl ether as fuel: Part ii- analysis of reactor systems and industrial processes. Journal of CO_2 Utilization (32), 321–338.

A. Narvaez, D. Chadwick, L. Kershenbaum, 2019. Performance of small-medium scale polygeneration systems for dimethyl ether and power production. Energy 188, 116058.

K. L. Ng, D. Chadwick, B. Toseland, 1999. Kinetics and modelling of dimethyl ether synthesis from synthesis gas. Chemical Engineering Science 54 (15-16), 3587–3592.

J. Sun, G. Yang, Y. Yoneyama, N. Tsubaki, 2014. Catalysis chemistry of dimethyl ether synthesis. ACS Catalysis 4 (10), 3346–3356.

F. Trippe, M. Fröhling, F. Schultmann, R. Stahl, E. Henrich, A. Dalai, 2013. Comprehensive techno-economic assessment of dimethyl ether (DME) synthesis and Fischer–Tropsch synthesis as alternative process steps within biomass-to-liquid production. Fuel Processing Technology 106, 577–586.

R. Turconi, A. Boldrin, T. Astrup, 2013. Life cycle assessment (lca) of electricity generation technologies: Overview, comparability and limitations. Renewable and sustainable energy reviews 28, 555–565.

E. S. Van-Dal, C. Bouallou, 2013. Design and simulation of a methanol production plant from CO2 hydrogenation. Journal of Cleaner Production 57, 38–45.

Sauro Pierucci, Flavio Manenti, Giulia Bozzano, Davide Manca (Eds.)
Proceedings of the 30th European Symposium on Computer Aided Process Engineering
(ESCAPE30), May 24-27, 2020, Milano, Italy. © 2020 Elsevier B.V. All rights reserved.
http://dx.doi.org/10.1016/B978-0-12-823377-1.50111-7

Microbial Pb(II) Precipitation: Kinetic Modelling of Pb(II) Removal and Microbial Growth

Carla Hörstmann, Hendrik G. Brink*, Evans M.N. Chirwa

Department of Chemical Engineering, Faculty of Engineering, Built Environment and Information Technology, University of Pretoria, Pretoria, South Africa
deon.brink@up.ac.za

Abstract

The study aimed to propose a preliminary kinetic model for Pb(II) bioremoval by an industrially obtained microbial consortium. The consortium has previously been shown to be extremely effective at precipitating Pb(II) from solution. For data generation, 100 mL batch reactors were set up anaerobically and spiked with either 80 ppm Pb(II) or 500 ppm Pb(II). Each of the concentrations contained either Standard LB broth or Simulated LB broth; Simulated LB broth contained double the amount of nutrients (yeast extract and tryptone) as Standard LB broth. Four datasets where thus used with notation, 80LB, 80Sim, 500LB and 500Sim. The study focused on the initial 33 h of experimentation with all four conditions. It was observed that most of the Pb(II) were removed within the first 3 h (± 50%) in all the reactors, in the absence of visual changes, followed by a slower rate of Pb(II) removal and dark precipitation forming. The Pb(II) removal was found to be independent of the amount of the microbial growth rate or nutrients present. A two-phase exponential decay model was proposed with rapid Pb(II) removal linked to an adsorption mechanism within the initial 3 h, followed by a slower Pb(II) precipitation mechanism. Microbial growth was found to be dependent on the concentration of Pb(II), nitrates, and available nutrients in the system. Growth in the samples in all the samples was modelled in one phase, namely a nitrate dependent exponential growth phase, modelled using Monod type kinetics. The nitrate dependent exponential growth phase was constructed using the Monod kinetic model in conjunction with a non-competitive Pb(II)-inhibition Michaelis–Menten term. The same maximum specific growth rate (28.2 d^{-1}) and Pb(II)-inhibition constant were determined for all fermentation conditions. These results suggest a detoxification mechanism via adsorption of Pb(II) onto biomass present in order to initiate growth, followed by the biological precipitation of the adsorbed Pb(II). The study presents the first model for microbial Pb(II) precipitation and provides a basis for the design of a continuous reaction setup required for future industrial application.

Keywords: Bioremediation, kinetic model, lead, anaerobic.

1. Introduction

Lead is a widely distributed and mobilized toxic heavy metal that accumulates in living organisms as well as the environment. The estimated maximum safe concentration of lead in drinking water is 0.01 ppm and the limit for causing serious harm to aquatic life is 0.0058 ppm (Duruibe et al., 2007). The major health effects are identified to be neurological, cardiovascular, renal, immunological, haematological, reproductive, and developmental (Substances Agency for toxic and disease registry, 2019). The recovery and not just removal of Pb(II) is of importance due to the continuing demand for and limited supply of raw lead reserves. It is estimated that there is roughly 17 years supply of lead available worldwide with an annual global consumption rate of about 5 million t/a (International Lead Association, 2019) and only a total of 83.3 x 10^6 t of reserve remaining (Statista, 2019).

Background on anaerobic respiration is required for this study as it is conducted with viable microbial biomass under anaerobic conditions. Anaerobic respiration is a metabolic process, during which microbes transfer electrons to terminal electron acceptors. It is essential when the bacteria require the removal of residual electrons to maintain the internal redox balance in the cell. Compounds such as nitrate or metals have been used in the past as electron acceptors for oxidizing NAD(P)H to NAD(P)+ (Kim et al, 2016).

The current research team have conducted various studies on Pb(II) removal using the same industrially obtained microbial consortia used in this specific study under anaerobic conditions. The bioremoval of Pb(II) has been demonstrated for the microbial consortium under investigation, with a dark grey precipitate observed when cultivated using Luria Bertani broth as growth substrate (Brink et al., 2018). The precipitate was identified as mostly PbS and a fractional amount of elemental Pb (Brink et al., 2019). No kinetic study has however been conducted on the mechanisms responsible and Pb(II) removal from solution and consequent precipitation by this consortium. The purpose of the study was to determine the effects of substrate levels and Pb(II) concentration on the kinetics of the microbial consortium.

2. Materials and Methods

2.1. Materials

The experiments were conducted anaerobically with 100 mL serum bottles. A lead stock solution was prepared using $Pb(NO_3)_2$ (Merck, Kennelworth, NJ). A rich growth media, standard Miller Luria Bertani Broth (Sigma Aldrich, St Louis, MO) was used, made to a final concentration of 25 mg/L or simulated LB broth which consists out of double the amount of nutrients and less NaCl. Metabolic activity (MA_{550}) measurements were conducted with 3-(4,5-dimethylthiazol-2-yl)-2,5-diphenyl tetrazolium bromide (MTT) and dimethyl sulfoxide (DMSO) at a wavelength of 550 nm (Sigma Aldrich, St Louis, MO). The nitrate levels were tested using nitrate testing kits (Merck, Darmstadt, Germany) and measured photometrically using the Spectroquant Nova 600 (Merck, Darmstadt, Germany).

2.2. Microbial culture

The Pb(II) resistant microbial consortium was collected from a borehole at an automotive-battery recycling plant in Gauteng, South Africa. The inoculum was prepared by adding 1 g of Pb(II) contaminated soil to a mixture of LB (Luria Bertani) broth and 80 ppm Pb(II) in a 100 mL serum bottle, which was then incubated anaerobically for 24 hours at 32 °C at a speed of 120 rpm. Glycerol was added to a final ratio of 20% v/v and stored at -77 °C cryogenically. The preculture was then prepared from the stored inoculum. It was prepared by inoculating one loop of stock culture to 100 mL anaerobic serum bottles containing LB broth spiked with either 80 ppm Pb(II) or 500 ppm Pb(II) depending on the subsequent experiment. The serum bottles were purged with nitrogen gas for 3 min and sealed to maintain anaerobic conditions, then incubated at 30°C and 120 rpm for a period of 3 days before inoculation of the experiments took place.

2.3. Experimental

The Pb(II) stock solution and simulated or standard LB broth were prepared and autoclaved separately, after which it was cooled to room temperature. The Pb(II) stock solution was added to the standard or simulated LB broth in a biological safety cabinet under sterile conditions. The serum bottles were inoculated with an inoculation loop from the abovementioned preculture. The batch reactors were purged with nitrogen gas for 3 min, sealed with a rubber stopper and clamped with a metal cap to ensure anaerobic conditions. The batch reactors were placed in a shaker incubator at a speed of 120 rpm and 35 °C for a period of 33 h. The experiments were conducted in triplicate.

2.4. Sampling

Samples were taken for a period of 33 h, every 3 h at 3h, 6h, 9h, 24h, 27h, 30h, 33h. The sealed serum bottles were shaken thoroughly before sampling. A hypodermic needle and sterile syringe were used to pierce the rubber stopper.

2.5. Analysis

The metabolic activity measurements are performed immediately after sampling. The metabolic activity of bacterial cells was quantified using MTT (Wang et al., 2010). Two sets of analyses were performed, one with biomass and the other without. The samples were filtered with 25 mm nylon syringe filters with 0.45 μm pores (Anatech), to represent the sample without biomass. The rest of the analysis was conducted by diluting the sample (with or without biomass) and adding the MTT solution and finally incubated for one hour at 35 °C. The samples were then dissolved in DMSO after incubation. The absorbance at 550 nm on a V spectrophotometer was measured and recorded as an indication of metabolic activity.

The residual aqueous Pb(II) was measured using an atomic absorption spectrometer (Perkin Elmer AAnalyst 400, Waltham, Massachusetts), with a Pb Lumina hollow cathode lamp. The supernatants of the samples stored at 5 °C were used, to avoid causing blockages on the instrument.

The samples used for nitrate testing were stored and measured at a later stage using nitrate testing kits (Merck, Darmstadt, Germany). The nitrate ions react with a form of benzoic acid in sulfuric acid to form a red nitro solution that is measured photometrically using the Spectroquant Nova 600 (Merck, Darmstadt, Germany).

3. Results and Discussion

3.1. Overall discussion

It was observed from the results that the most of the Pb(II) (approximately 50 %) was removed within the first 3 h. The rapid removal was then followed by a slower more gradual decrease. Metabolic activity lagged within the first 6 h, after which a dramatic increase in growth was observed. It was subsequently observed that the increase of growth was coupled with a sharp decrease in nitrate levels in all the reactors. From these findings, it was hypothesised that Pb(II) removal was not dependent on the amount of nutrients present. Growth may, however, are dependent on the initial rapid removal of Pb(II) as an initial detoxification mechanism to initialise growth.

3.2. Pb(II) Removal

Pb(II) removal in all the reactors followed a clear trend, with initial rapid Pb(II) removal followed by a slow gradual rate of removal. The Monod equation was proposed as appropriate model, with a few adjustments (Roestorff and Chirwa, 2018):

$$-\frac{dPb(II)}{dt} = \frac{k_m Pb(II)}{Pb(II) + K_c} \cdot \mu \qquad (1)$$

Which reduces to the first order rate expression (equation 2) for $K_c \gg Pb(II)$

$$-\frac{dPb(II)}{dt} = \frac{k_m}{K_c} Pb(II) \cdot \mu \tag{2}$$

It was observed that Pb(II) removal is not dependent on growth at any time in the system and that an adsorption mechanism might be responsible for rapid and slow Pb(II) removal. A global differential equation was proposed. The constant parameters τ and ϕ incorporated the fraction of Pb(II)-removal by each phase as well as the growth contribution to the mechanism.

$$-\frac{dPb(II)}{dt} = \tau \left(\frac{k_m}{K_c} Pb(II) \right)_{rapid} + \phi \left(\frac{k_m}{K_c} Pb(II) \right)_{slow} \tag{3}$$

The differential equation was solved and simplified with two constants α_{rapid} or α_{slow} equal to k_m/K_c for each phase, respectively.

$$Pb(II) = \tau \cdot \Delta Pb(II) e^{-\alpha_{rapid} \cdot t} + \phi \cdot \Delta Pb(II) e^{-\alpha_{slow} \cdot t} + c \tag{4}$$

The model was fitted on Aquasim (Reichert, 1994) to produce the following results for both the short and extended experiments.

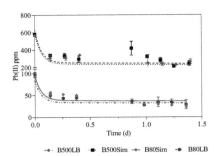

Figure 1: *Pb(II) concentration measurements with time, with the fitted kinetic model.*

Table 1: *Parameter estimation for Pb(II) removal*

Reactor	τ	α_{rapid} (d⁻¹)	ϕ	α_{slow} (d⁻¹)	c	R^2
B500Sim&LB B80Sim&LB	0.596	17.4	0.404	0.0436	0	0.966

3.3. Growth

It was observed that initial growth was directly dependent on the amount of nitrate available, while the concentration of aqeous Pb(II) had an inhibitory effect on growth. The differential mathematical relationship identified for the growth model (equation 5) was that of specific growth and non-competitive Pb inhibition (Birgin and Preisig, 2018) and was related to the rate of nitrate reduction $\left(\frac{dN}{dt} \right)$.

$$\frac{dX}{dt} = \mu_{apparent}X = \frac{\mu}{1+\frac{Pb(II)}{K_i}}X = \frac{\mu_{max}\left(\frac{N-N_{critical}}{k_s+(N-N_{critical})}\right)}{1+\frac{Pb(II)}{K_i}}X = Y_{XN}\frac{dN}{d_t} \qquad (5)$$

With $N_{critical}$ the critical amount of Nitrate needed in the system, μ_{max} the maximum specific growth rate (d^{-1}) and k_s the half-velocity constant. The constant K_i refers to the estimated inhibition constant due to Pb(II). Y_{XN} is the yield of biomass versus nitrates measured over time. The model was only proposed for the first day, as it was observed that an apparent second phase of growth appeared in samples containing double nutrients (B500Sim and B80Sim), but further investigations should be conducted into this hypothesis. The proposed growth models are presented in Figure 4, followed by the necessary parameter estimation in Table 4.

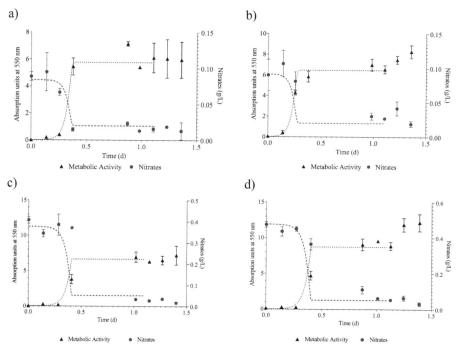

Figure 4: *a) B80LB, b) B80Sim, c) B500LB and d) B500Sim growth and nitrates with time.*

Table 4: *Estimated Nitrate dependent growth parameters.*

Reactor Type	μ_{max}	k_s	Y_{XN}	K_i	R^2
B500Sim&LB			0.0487		
B80Sim&LB	28.2	0.01	0.0110	498.8	0.966

It was observed in the data gathered above that the μ_{max} values were equal for all the reactors (28.2 d^{-1}). The biomass to nitrate yields was equal for both the 80 ppm (0.011) samples and the 500 ppm (0.049) samples respectively. The k_s and K_i constants were equal for all experiments, indicating non-competitive inhibition.

4. Conclusions

The amount of nutrients available does not promote Pb(II) bioremoval. The results indicate an adsorption mechanism for the initial rapid removal of available Pb(II) before precipitation. An anaerobic respiratory denitrification mechanism is suggested during the first phase of exponential growth when NO_3- is used as an alternative electron sink for oxidising NAD(P)H to NAD(P)+ to produce cellular energy by the microorganism. It is known from previous studies conducted by this team that the precipitate consists of mostly PbS and a small amount of Pb0 (which is higher in samples containing more Pb(II). It can be hypothesised that sulphur is released during denitrification with the enzyme nitrate reductase from cysteine and methionine present in the substrate during the first stage of growth, which in turns binds with Pb(II) to form PbS. When the nitrates are depleted and the second stage of growth might be initiated in the samples containing simulated LB broth, the remainder of available Pb(II) is used as an alternative electron sink for further anaerobic respiration to produce Pb0.

A kinetic model has been proposed for microbial Pb(II) removal and further studies should be conducted into applying this knowledge to develop a design for industrial application. The validation of the model will first be established by comparing the current model to more data gathered through experimentation. Further design and research can then be conducted into continuous industrial application.

References

Birgen C, Preisig HA, 2018, Dynamic Modeling of Butanol Production from Lignocellulosic Sugars. Comput Aided Chem Eng 43:1547–1552. doi: 10.1016/B978-0-444-64235-6.50270-9

Brink HG, Hörstmann C, Peens J, 2019, Microbial Pb(II)-precipitation: the influence of oxygen on Pb(II)-removal from aqueous environment and the resulting precipitate identity. Int J Environ Sci Technol. doi: 10.1007/s13762-019-02502-4

Brink HG, Mahlangu Z, 2018, Microbial Lead(II) precipitation: the influence of growth substrate, Chemical Engineering Transactions, 64, doi: 10.3303/CET1864074

Duruibe J O, Ogwuegbu M O C and Egwurugwu J N, 2007, Heavy metal pollution and human biotoxic effects, International Journal Physical Sciences, 2(5), 112–118. doi: 10.1016/j.proenv.2011.09.146.

International Lead Association, 2019, ILA - International Lead Association, 1–4.

Statista, 2019, Lead reserves worldwide as of 2018, by country (in million metric tons), 1–5.

Kim C, Ainala S K, Oh Y, Jeon B, Park S and Kim J R, 2016, Metabolic Flux Change in Klebsiella pneumoniae L17 by Anaerobic Respiration in Microbial Fuel Cell, 260, 250–260. doi: 10.1007/s12257-015-0777-6.

Reichert P, AQUASIM - A tool for simulation and data analysis of aquatic systems, Water Science Technology, 30(2), 21-30, 1994. http://wst.iwaponline.com/content/30/2/21(open access)

Roestorff M M and Chirwa E M N, 2018, Comparison of the Performance of Chlorococcum Ellipsoideum and Tetradesmus Obliquus as a Carbon Source for Reduction of Cr (VI) with Bacteria, Chemical Engineering Transactions, 70(VI), 463–468, doi: 10.3303/CET1870078.

Substances Agency for toxic and disease registry, 2019, Toxicological Profile for Lead.

Wang H, Cheng H, Wang F, Wei D and Wang X, 2010, An improved 3-(4,5-dimethylthiazol-2-yl)-2,5-diphenyl tetrazolium bromide (MTT) reduction assay for evaluating the viability of Escherichia coli cells, Journal of Microbiological Methods, 82(3), 330–333, doi: 10.1016/j.mimet.2010.06.014.

Sauro Pierucci, Flavio Manenti, Giulia Bozzano, Davide Manca (Eds.)
Proceedings of the 30th European Symposium on Computer Aided Process Engineering
(ESCAPE30), May 24-27, 2020, Milano, Italy. © 2020 Elsevier B.V. All rights reserved.
http://dx.doi.org/10.1016/B978-0-12-823377-1.50112-9

Optimization of a Cyclone Reactor for Biomass Hydropyrolysis through Global Sensitivity Analysis and Stochastic Optimization

Yris Gonzalez[a], Wilfredo Angulo[a], Dany De Cecchis[a], María Lucena[b], Santiago D. Salas[a]*

[a] *Escuela Superior Politécnica del Litoral, ESPOL, Facultad de Ciencias Naturales y Matemáticas, Campus Gustavo Galindo Km 30.5 Vía Perimetral, Guayaquil, Ecuador.*

[b] *Departamento de Ingeniería Química. Universidad Nacional Politécnica Antonio José de Sucre. Av. Corpahuaico con Av. La Salle. UNEXPO, Barquisimeto - 3001. Venezuela.*
sdsalas@espol.edu.ec

Abstract

This study investigates the use of global sensitivity analysis combined with stochastic optimization for improving the conversion of biomass in an inverted cyclone reactor. A validated mathematical model of the process permits to develop a model-centric framework that analyzes the most important process variables and design parameters, for later selecting the combination that achieves the highest biomass conversion rate.

The implemented global sensitivity analysis, which is a variation of the Sobol method, permits to identify the most influential variables in biomass conversion. Thereafter, the important process variables of the system are optimized respecting inequality and equality constraints towards the maximization of the conversion, providing an improved reactor setup. The proposed framework has the potential of evaluating different biomass conversion models that aim to transform biomass into value-added chemicals through different objective functions.

Keywords: Biomass hydropyrolysis, global sensitivity analysis, evolutionary optimization.

1. Introduction

Several processes have been proposed to produce fuels from lignocellulosic biomass. Hydropyrolysis is one of the most promising paths. This process characterizes by the rapid thermal degradation of organic material, under high heating rates in a hydrogen environment. The rapid heating decomposes the large molecules of biomass into smaller ones, which are released into the form of volatile compounds. The volatiles are then quickly cooled back producing biofuel. The key to maximize valuable biofuels is a short residence time for the volatiles (usually a few seconds), to prevent secondary cracking reactions (*Resend F.*, 2016).

In hydropyrolysis, the use of inverted cyclone reactors provides the advantage of short residence times and high efficiency in the separation of the solid, as well as that the feed does not require to be preheated to the high temperature demanded by the reaction. In a previous study, the simulation model of an inverted cyclone reactor for flash hydropyrolysis of biomass was developed from mass and energy balances, combined with the kinetics and fluid dynamics. The performance analysis applied to the model evaluated the conversion effect of two process variables while the other variables remained constant (*Galiasso et al.*, 2014).

In this work, a validated mathematical model permits to develop a framework that analyzes the most influential process variables and design parameters for later finding the process setting that achieve the highest conversion of the system. In this sense, initially the important variables are selected using a global sensitivity analysis based on the Sobol method (*Salas et al.*, 2017, 2019). Then, these important variables are optimized using a stochastic optimization algorithm based on evolutionary principles seeking to maximize the biomass conversion.

2. Background

2.1. System Description

The potential reactors for hydropyrolysis are a riser cyclone or a downer cyclone. They are transport reactors that could work satisfactorily for the thermal cracking of biomass. In both types of reactors, the residence time could be from a few to several seconds because the separation takes additional time. In this context, the inverted cyclone reactor appears to be ideal for carrying out these ultrafast chemical reactions coupled with separation (*Galiasso et al.*, 2011).

In the inverted cyclone reactor portrayed in Figure 1a, a solid at high temperature combined with biomass feed, which is mixed with hydrogen, moves spirally downflow inside the reactor. This fluid experiences a brief gas-solid contact at the inlet. Then, it is separated by centrifugal forces while it moves down the reactor in the so-called Zone 1. In the lower part of the cylindrical section, the gas and micro-particles disengage from the solid and move up spirally around the central pipe to leave the reactor, referred as the Zone 2. At the top, they are carried down again inside the internal pipe to leave by the side, identified as Zone 3. The zones location is depicted in Figure 1b.

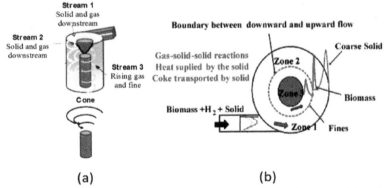

Figure 1. Schematic illustrating the trajectory of the three streams inside the reactor (a), and a view inside of the reactor from the top of the transversal cylindrical section (b).

2.2. Nonlinear model

The nonlinear model of the system was reported only for the Zone 1 of the reactor because in this region takes place the highest conversion (*Galiasso et al.*, 2014). The model is described by the gas phase mass balance of the reactive system; the mass balance of the solid phase (biomass); the energy balances for the gas phase and solid phase, which equations are, respectively,

$$\frac{dM_j}{dL_1} = \sum_{i=1}^{z} r_{ij}(T_{g1}) \frac{a_{t1}}{\frac{\dot{m}_s}{0.45\rho_s} + v_{o_1}} \tag{1}$$

$$\frac{dM_{Bio}}{dL_1} = \sum_{i=1}^{z} -r_{1Bio}(T_{g1}) \frac{a_{t1}}{\frac{\dot{m}_s}{0.45\rho_s} + v_{o_1}} \tag{2}$$

$$\frac{dT_{g1}}{dL_1} = \frac{Ua(T_S - T_{g1}) + \sum_{i=1}^{q} r_{ij}\left[-\Delta H_{Rx_{ij}}(T_{g1})\right]\frac{a_{t1}}{\frac{\dot{m}_s}{0.45\rho_s} + v_{o_1}}}{\sum_{j=i}^{n} M_j C_{p(T_{g1})_j}} \tag{3}$$

$$\frac{dT_S}{dL_1} = -\frac{Ua(T_S - T_{g1})}{M_S C_{ps(T_S)}} \tag{4}$$

where M_j is the flow rate of the compound j, L_l is the reactor spire length, a_{tl} is the cross-section area where solid-free gas stream in Zone 1, Tg is the solid-free gas phase temperature, $\Delta H_{Rx_{ij}}$ is the heat of reaction i for compound j, Ts is the solid phase temperature, U is the overall heat transfer coefficient, a is the heat exchange area per unit reactor length, and C_{pj} is the heat capacity of compound j. For a detailed model description and definition of variables and constants, please refer to *Galiasso et al.* (2014).

2.3. A global sensitivity analysis

A global sensitivity analysis (GSA) shows the importance of input variables along with an output of interest. A widely used variance-based GSA method is the Sobol method. A more computationally efficient Sobol approach is introduced by *Wu et al.* (2012). Here, the considered samples are augmented by averaging the evaluated points. In this study, the utilized approach is the one proposed by *Salas et al.* (2019), which is a robust computational implementation of the Sobol method. For more details about Sobol's GSA methods please refer to *Salas et al.* (2017, 2019) and *Fesanghary et al.* (2009).

The GSA algorithm calculates the first-order and the total sensitivity indices of all the input variables. The implemented GSA algorithm is shown in Figure 2. For this approach, it is defined that n_p is the number of input variables $\mathbf{z} = (z_1, ..., z_{np})$, or parameters considered by the GSA, of a function $G = g(\mathbf{z})$. Three matrices are considered for sampling, resampling, and reposition. Finally, for each variable z_n, it is obtained $\hat{S}_n$ and $\hat{S}_{Tn}$ as the first-order and the total sensitivity indices, respectively. The first-order index $\hat{S}_n$ indicates its sensitivity depending on the individual contribution of the variance whenever changing z_n in the function G. While the total index $\hat{S}_{Tn}$ incorporates the effect of all other variables when excluding the variable z_n. The indices $\hat{S}_n$ and $\hat{S}_{Tn}$ can be compared to evaluate whether a model is additive or not. Non-additive models hold the characteristic $\hat{S}_j < \hat{S}_{Tj}$, while additive models $\hat{S}_j = \hat{S}_{Tj}$. Additive models are those in which no interactions between evaluated parameters occur.

In this study, the GSA is performed analyzing the reactor conversion. The evaluated input variables, reported in Table 1, are those related to the process variables and the design parameters of the reactor.

The range of variation of these input variables has an uncertainty index of 5% from its average value reported in *Galiasso et al.* (2014). The length of the reactor spire was estimated from the validated model, and it shows that the highest conversion is reached almost at three meters, suggesting that three reactor zones are not required to evaluate the maximum biomass conversion.

Input: Given $np, nd \in \mathbb{R}$, $\bar{z} \in \mathbb{R}^{np}$, γ, $G = g(\mathbf{z})$.
Output: $\hat{S}_n$, and $\hat{S}_{T n}$, with $n = 1, \ldots, np$.

   Initialization:

1: Let generate $nd \times np$ matrices $M1$, $M2$ and $M3$ with rows varying randomly $\bar{z} \pm \gamma\%$

   Sampling & Resampling:

2: **for** $d \leftarrow 1$ **to** nd **do**
3:   $Y_d \leftarrow g(M1_{d,:})$ { $M1_{d,:}$ is the d-th row of matrix $M1$.}
4:   **if** (Y_d is not a feasible value) **then**
5:     **while** (Y_d is not a feasible value) **do**
6:       Use the first not used row r, to make $Y_r \leftarrow g(M3_{r,:})$
7:     **end while**
8:     $M1_{d,:} \leftarrow M3_{r,:}$
9:   **end if**

10:   $Y_{R d} \leftarrow g(M2_{d,:})$
11:   **if** ($Y_{R d}$ is not a feasible value) **then**
12:     **while** ($Y_{R d}$ is not a feasible value) **do**
13:       Use the first not used row r, to make $Y_{R d} \leftarrow g(M3_{r,:})$
14:     **end while**
15:     $M1_{d,:} \leftarrow M3_{r,:}$
16:   **end if**
17: **end for**

Output varying the input variables:

18: $\hat{f}_0 \leftarrow (\text{mean}(Y) + \text{mean}(Y_R))/2$
19: **for** $n \leftarrow 1$ **to** np **do**
20:   $N \leftarrow M2$; $[N]_{:,n} \leftarrow [M1]_{:,n}$
21:   $NT \leftarrow M1$; $[NT]_{:,n} \leftarrow [M2]_{:,n}$
22:   **for** $d \leftarrow 1$ **to** nd **do**
23:     $Y_{P d,n} \leftarrow g([N]_{d,:})$
24:     **if** ($Y_{P d,n}$ is not a feasible value) **then**
25:       $Y_{P d,n} \leftarrow \hat{f}_0$
26:     **end if**
27:     $Y_{RP d,n} \leftarrow g([NT]_{d,:})$
28:     **if** ($Y_{RP d,n}$ is not a feasible value) **then**
29:       $Y_{RP d,n} \leftarrow \hat{f}_0$
30:     **end if**
31:   **end for**
32: **end for**

Individual & global variances

33: $\widehat{V} = \sum_{d=1}^{nd}(Y_d^2 + Y_{R d}^2)/(2 \, nd) - \hat{f}_0^2$
34: $\Gamma_P^2 \leftarrow \sum_{d=1}^{nd}(Y_d \, Y_{R d} + Y_{P d,:} \, Y_{RP d,:})/(2 \, nd)$
35: $\widehat{V}_P = (Y_P^T Y + Y_{RP}^T Y_R)/(2 \, nd) - \Gamma_P^2$
36: $\widehat{V}_{-P} = (Y_{RP}^T Y + Y_P^T Y_R)/(2 \, nd) - \Gamma_P^2$
37: $\hat{S} = \widehat{V}_P./\widehat{V}$ {Where $./$ is the element-wise division}
38: $\hat{S}_T = 1 - \widehat{V}_{-P}./\widehat{V}$

Figure 2. GSA algorithm to calculate, in one run, the first-order and the total sensitivity indices for all the input variables.

Table 1. The range of values for the input variables of the uniflow reactor.

Input Variables	Description	Unit	Range		
H2Bi	Hydrogen/Biomass Relation	--	0.1	to	0.5
P	Pressure	MPa	0.1E-06	to	0.2E-06
Ts	Solid Temperature	K	880	to	1000
Tg	Gas Temperature	K	600	to	700
mso	Solid Flow	kg/s	0.02	to	0.03
D1	External Cylinder Diameter	m	0.0486	to	0.054
D2	Internal Cylinder Diameter	m	0.031	to	0.042
L	Reactor Spire Length	m	1	to	6

2.4. Stochastic Evolutionary Optimization

The evolutionary heuristic referenced as the differential evolution (DE) algorithm is employed for the optimization of the sensitive input variables (*Storn & Price*, 1997). The DE has demonstrated proficiency when it is compared with other heuristic algorithms (*Salas et al.*, 2017). It involves the evolution of a population of solutions by applying mutation, crossover, and selection as operators. The initial population follows a uniform distribution over the solution domain. Each solution vector resembles a target vector during a generation. For each target vector, the mutation operator generates a new vector by adding a weighted difference between two population vectors. These three vectors are selected randomly and must differ from the target. A scaling factor β controls the amplification of the differential variation between the second and the third randomly chosen vectors. In the crossover, a uniform arrangement builds trial vectors from values replicated from two different vectors. Finally, the vector which maximizes the objective function is the target for the next generation.

In this work, a crossover rate of 0.70 was selected, and β was randomly chosen between [0.2, 0.8]. A total of 25 generations with a population size of 20 generated sufficient simulations. The method runs 30 times to verify its consistency.

3. Results

From the GSA applied to the model, it is assessed the relative importance of each model variable. It is found that some input variables are rather insensitive. Thus, a simpler optimization problem can be formulated when the insensitive input variables are maintained constant. This model is then used to optimize the biomass conversion of the reactor. The results for the GSA are shown in Figure 3. The black horizontally striped bars on the left are the first-order sensitivity indices. The grey vertically striped bars on the right are the total sensitivity indices. Considering the first-order sensitivity index, four input variables affect significantly the conversion of the reactor. They are Ts, Tg, mso, and $D1$. On the other hand, it is observed from the total sensitivity index that all the parameters have some effect on its cooperation respecting the others. Although, similarly to the first-order indices, they show the same pattern of importance in terms of the reactor conversion.

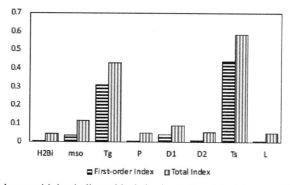

Figure 3. First-order sensitivity indices, black horizontally striped bars on the right; and total sensitivity indices, grey vertically striped bars on the left, for each of the input variables considered in the reactor conversion.

Therefore, Ts, Tg, mso, $D1$ were the decision variables considered in the optimization problem. These variables are reported in Table 2. The base case and optimal case for biomass conversion are depicted as a function of the spire length in Figure 4. The plot shows an improvement, and it suggests that it is possible to reach the highest conversion with certain operating conditions with less spire length. Additionally, from the 30 optimal set of values, the set with the lowest Tg was selected among all others for reducing the heat demand of the feed.

Table 2. The values of the input variables for the base and optimal cases.

Case	*mso*	*Tg*	*D1*	*Ts*
Base	0.025	650	0.0513	940
Optimal	0.030	669	0.0527	995

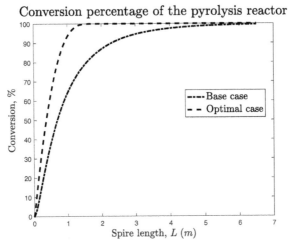

Figure 4. Conversion rate between the base case and the optimal case vs. the reactor spire length.

4. Conclusions

The global sensitivity analysis, in contrast with the previous evaluations; allows identifying new variables that affect significantly the conversion of the reactor. The main input variables that have a significant influence on the reactor conversion are, in priority order, the solid and gas temperature, solid mass, and external diameter. The optimization allows to reach an improvement of about one-third from the base case conversion. The obtained results highlight that the biomass hydropyrolysis is conditioned by its solid carrier, the gas phase and by the reactor geometry. The developed framework could be a potential tool for the study of other types of biomass and other objective functions.

References

Fesanghary M, Damangir E, Soleimani I. 2009. Design optimization of shell and tube heat exchangers using global sensitivity analysis and harmony search algorithm. *Applied Thermal Engineering*. 29, 1026-1031.

Galiasso R, Gonzalez Y, Lucena M. 2014. New inverted cyclone reactor for flash hydropyrolysis. *Catalyst Today*. 220, 186-197.

Galiasso, R., Freitez J., González, Y. y Rodríguez, J. 2011. Pyrolysis of cracked gasoline into olefins: I. design and construction of a cold model for circulating type reactor. *Ind. Eng. Chem. Res*. 50 (5), 2726-2735.

Resende F. 2016. Recent advances on fast hydropyrolysis of biomass. *Catalysis Today*. 269, Pages 148-155.

Salas, S. D., Brandão, A. L., Soares, J. B., & Romagnoli, J. A. 2019. Data-Driven Estimation of Significant Kinetic Parameters Applied to the Synthesis of Polyolefins. *Processes*. 7(5), 309.

Salas, S. D., Chebeir, J., Tronci, S., Baratti, R., & Romagnoli, J. A. 2018. Real-Time Nonlinear State Estimation in Polymerization Reactors for Smart Manufacturing. *In Computer Aided Chemical Engineering* (Vol. 43, pp. 1207-1212). *Elsevier*.

Salas, S. D., Geraili, A., & Romagnoli, J. A..2017. Optimization of renewable energy businesses under operational level uncertainties through extensive sensitivity analysis and stochastic global optimization. *Ind. Eng. Chem. Res*. 56(12), 3360-3372.

Storn, R., & Price, K..1997. Differential evolution–a simple and efficient heuristic for global optimization over continuous spaces. *Journal of Global Optimization*. 11(4), 341-359.

Wu, Q. L.; Cournede, P. H.; Mathieu, A. 2012. An efficient computational method for global sensitivity analysis and its application to tree growth modelling. *Reliability Engineering and System Safety*. 107, 35–43.

Sauro Pierucci, Flavio Manenti, Giulia Bozzano, Davide Manca (Eds.)
Proceedings of the 30ᵗʰ European Symposium on Computer Aided Process Engineering
(ESCAPE30), May 24-27, 2020, Milano, Italy. © 2020 Elsevier B.V. All rights reserved.
http://dx.doi.org/10.1016/B978-0-12-823377-1.50113-0

Dynamic Modeling for PHB Production Based on Linear MFA and Measurements from Batch Fermentation

Adriana C. Torres Ospina, Carlos A. M. Riascos*

Institute of Biotechnology, Universidad Nacional de Colombia, Av. Carrera 30 No. 45-03, Bogota 111321, Colombia
camartinezri@unal.edu.co

Abstract

Mathematical models of fermentative processes allow to predict their behaviour, both in steady state and in dynamic conditions, so they are a key tool in the improvement of these processes. The objective of this work is to develop a mathematical model that simulates the growth and production of polyhidroxybutirate (PHB) in a hyper-producing *Burkholderia cepacia* strain, considering metabolic changes that occur between the phases of feast & famine, and that allows the process optimization. To achieve this objective, it was necessary: i) to analyse the behaviour of the strain in batch fermentation, ii) to characterize the metabolism of the strain by linear metabolic flux analysis (MFA), iii) to adjust semi-empirical models for each phase, and iv) to validate the model with new experimental data. Results show that metabolic fluxes undergo significant changes during the batch process: metabolic pathways are adjusted to lead carbon, in a greater extent, towards growth in the feast phase, and towards PHB production in the famine phase. Fed batch fermentation for model validation employs pulses for adding carbon and nitrogen sources, separately. Feeding allows to extend the feast phase and obtain higher biomass concentrations. The developed model will allow to analyse new operational options and increase process productivity by mathematical programming. In other way, the proposed methodology, that considers results of MFA for model formulation, is a novel strategy to improve modelling.

Keywords: *B. cepacia*, linear MFA, feast & famine,

1. Introduction

Metabolic pathways involved in PHAs metabolism are complex and depend on the selected microorganism. Additionally, metabolic analysis for PHAs production must include reactions for polymer synthesis and hydrolysis, granules formation, as well as the connection of these pathways with central and peripheral ones (Fernández, 2012).

Vegetable oils have been studied as an alternative to traditional carbon sources, specifically for PHAs production at commercial scale. An advantage of using fatty acids is the higher yield, compared with sugars (Riascos et al., 2013), and as a complex carbon source, it is metabolized through several metabolic pathways. Experimental yields (Suriyamongkol et al., 2007) obtained for butiric acid (0.65-0.98 kg/kg) and glucose (0.32-0.48 kg/kg) confirm the advantage suggested from metabolic analysis.

A novel strategy to improve the prediction of mathematical models on fermentative processes is to include metabolic issues in the models. An example of applying metabolic information in modeling was presented by Nandong et al. (2008) who formulated a model for alcoholic fermentation; it relates specific rates for growing and production with metabolic fluxes, obtaining improvements in the prediction.

2. Methodology

The inclusion of information from MFA in the mathematical model of fermentative processes requires to connect extra- with intra-cellular information. Extra-cellular information allows to identify the stages that take place in the process, while intra-cellular information will show how the metabolism operates in each stage.

2.1. Behaviour Analysis of the Strain

Batch fermentations were performed to analyse the behaviour of the strain. These fermentations allow to identify the stages of the process and to define characteristic time instants for each stage. Measurements of viable cells as colony-forming units by mL (CFUs/mL) were key for this analysis. Batch fermentations were developed at the best conditions identified in a previous work: 20 g/L of fatty acids, 2.5 g/L of ammonium as nitrogen source, 2 vvm of air supply, pH = 6.5 (Mendez, 2016).

2.2. Metabolism Characterization

The metabolism was characterized by linear MFA and the measurement of specific rates for growth, PHB and CO_2 production, and carbon source consumption. Specific rates were useful to propose the phenomena that we must include in the model and as measured fluxes to solve the MFA without including cofactor balances (Gombert and Nielsen, 2013). The stoichiometric matrix for the metabolic analysis was based on genome of the parental strain *B. cenocepacia J2315* (Fang et al., 2011), and an analysis of biomass generation to create a stoichiometric equation.

2.3. Model Fitting and Validation

The fitting was developed by a cyclic procedure starting with a simple model, and then, adding mathematical elements to include observed phenomena and to improve the fitting. The differential equation system was solved by the ODE23 function, and parameters were estimated by minimizing residuals on concentrations with a genetic algorithm (GA function), both in MatLab programming environment. Data from long-time fermentation was employed for model fitting; whereas, data from fed-batch fermentation was employed for validation.

2.4. Specific Rates Estimation

Rates for biomass, product and fatty acids were estimated based on their definition, i.e. $\mu_P = dP/dt * 1/X$. Measurements of concentrations were performed in the following way: dry weight for total biomass, liquid chromatography (Aminex HPX-87H column) for PHB, and gas chromatography (Agilent 6890, with DB 23 column) for fatty acids, whereas the quantification of CO_2 rates employed measurements of CO_2 concentration and air supply, as well as the estimation of air molar volume (Torres, 2019).

3. Results and Analysis

3.1. Extra- and Intra-cellular Characterization

From the behaviour analysis, it was observed that in long-time batch fermentation the process goes through a short lag stage (0-4 h), an exponential growing stage (4-14 h), a stationary stage (14-54 h), and a death stage (54-96 h). With that observation 12, 24, 48 and 96 h were selected as characteristic instants of the main stages. Figure 1 shows the profile obtained for the CFU, and Table 1 shows the specific rates for the characteristic instants.

For the MFA, a stoichiometric matrix considering 59 reactions and 55 intracellular metabolites was built, and the measurement of four specific rates (Table 1) allowed to quantify the metabolic fluxes in the characteristic instants (Figure 2).

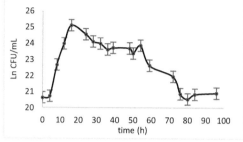

Figure 1. CFU profile in batch fermentation.

Table 1. Specific rates (g/g X h).

Time (h)	μ_X	μ_P	μ_S	μ_{CO2}
12	1.18	0.18	0.598	0.097
24	0.48	0.21	0.186	0.081
48	0.04	0.26	0.058	0.085
96	0.00	0.12	0.039	0.070

The rates of metabolic reactions at each instant evidence that fluxes in β-oxidation, depolymerisation, and tricarboxylic acid (TCA) pathways achieve their maxima values during the exponential growing stage (t = 12 h) which is consistent with a higher biomass production; in contrast, reactions of gluconeogenesis, phosphate pentoses, phaA (acetyl-coA generation as ending step of β-oxidation), and succinate production in TCA run at their highest values but in the inverse direction. This metabolic behaviour is due to the sugar unavailability and the necessity of generating biomass precursors. In the stationary stage (t = 24 h) it is observed that those reactions keep the direction but the rates are significantly reduced. Finally, at the end of the stationary stage (t = 48 h) and at the death stage (t = 96 h) most fluxes are almost zero. The MFA results confirm that the metabolism experiment strong changes during a batch process: at the beginning, with well-balanced carbon and nitrogen sources, the carbon is mainly driven to biomass production (87 %); whereas, during the stationary phase, with a reduced C/N ratio, the fraction of carbon driven to biomass goes from 70 % (t = 24 h) to 14 % (t = 48 h). It confirms that process goes from a feast phase to a famine phase.

3.2. Model Formulation and Fitting

The model considers that biomass is formed by two components: residual biomass (with the metabolic capacities) and the polymer. The initial formulation included limitations on growing and production by carbon source (Sc), carbon consumption for growing and production, and nitrogen consumption for growing and maintenance. The fitting of the initial model was non-satisfactory and it was observed that it is impossible to adjust simultaneously the behaviour at the starting and at the ending of the batch fermentation, confirming that a feast & famine approach is necessary.

$$\mu_X = \mu_{X\max} * \left(\frac{Sc}{K_{ScX} + Sc} \right)$$

$$\mu_P = \mu_{P\max} * \left(\frac{Sc}{K_{ScP} + Sc} \right)$$

$$\mu_{Sc} = -\left| \frac{1}{Y_{X/Sc}} * \mu_X \right| - \left| \frac{1}{Y_{P/Sc}} * \mu_P \right|$$

$$\mu_{Sn} = -\frac{1}{Y_{X/Sn}} * \mu_X - m_n$$

Initial Model

For the next cycle in the fitting procedure, a feast & famine approach was included (*CN chang*). It improved the fitting but an overestimation of the production in the beginning of the famine phase was observed (results not shown). Because of that, a term to consider adaptation (*Tadapt*) on the production period was included, and finally, limitation on growing by nitrogen was added. The fitting of the model is in Figure 3 and its parameters in Table 2.

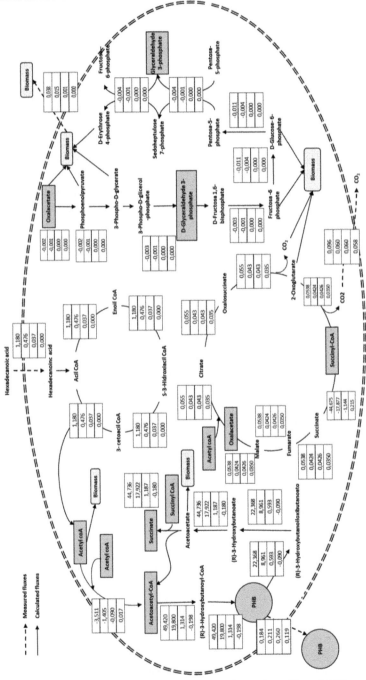

Figure 2. Metabolic network with quantified fluxes (mmol/mmol X h).

A key observation is that the transition from feast to famine was identified as happening at *Tchang* = 12.9 h, which strongly coincide with the end of the exponential stage. The carbon/nitrogen rate for this transition was 5.9 g/g and this value was selected as the mathematical criteria for switching between the models; additionally, the time for total adaptation of the metabolism (T_{adap}) was estimated as 14 h. The final model is as follows:

$$if \quad C/N > C/N_{chang} \quad \left| \begin{array}{l} \mu_X = \mu_{X\max} * \left(\dfrac{Sc}{K_{ScX} + Sc} \right) * \left(\dfrac{Sn}{K_{SnX} + Sn} \right) \\[3mm] \mu_P = \mu_{P\max} * \left(\dfrac{Sc}{K_{ScP} + Sc} \right) \end{array} \right.$$

Feast Phase

$$if \quad C/N = C/N_{chang} \qquad t_{chang} = t$$

Phase Change

$$if \quad C/N < C/N_{chang} \quad \left\{ \begin{array}{l} \mu_X = \mu_{X\max 2} * \left(\dfrac{Sc}{K_{ScX2} + Sc} \right) * \left(\dfrac{Sn}{K_{SnX2} + Sn} \right) \\[3mm] if \ t < t_{chang} + t_{adap} \quad \mu_P = \mu_{P\max 2} * \left(\dfrac{Sc}{K_{ScP2} + Sc} \right) * \left(\dfrac{t - t_{chang}}{t_{adap}} \right)^{\alpha} \\[3mm] if \ t > t_{chang} + t_{adap} \quad \mu_P = \mu_{P\max 2} * \left(\dfrac{Sc}{K_{ScP2} + Sc} \right) \end{array} \right.$$

Famine Phase

$$\mu_{Sc} = -\left[\dfrac{1}{Y_{X/Sc}} * \mu_X \right] - \left[\dfrac{1}{Y_{P/Sc}} * \mu_P \right]$$

$$\mu_{Sn} = -\dfrac{1}{Y_{X/Sn}} * \mu_X + m_n$$

Both Phases

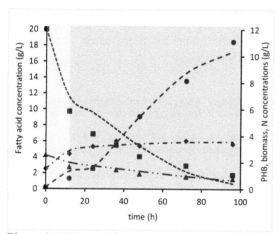

Table 2. Parameters of final model.

Parameter	unit	value
$\mu_{X\max}$	h^{-1}	0.059
K_{ScX}	g/L	4.68
K_{SnX}	g/L	0.048
$\mu_{P\max}$	h^{-1}	0.093
K_{ScP}	g/L	12.85
K_{SnX2}	g/L	3.998
C/N_{chang}	g/g	5.9
$\mu_{X\max 2}$	h^{-1}	0.040
$\mu_{P\max 2}$	h^{-1}	0.10
t_{adap}	h	14
$Y_{P/Sc}$	g PHB/g Sc	1.37
$Y_{X/Sc}$	g X/g Sc	0.18
$Y_{X/Sn}$	g X/g Sn	2.97
K_{ScP2}	g/L	6.50
K_{ScX2}	g/L	63.40
m_n	g Sn/g X h	0.005

Figure 3. Fitting of final model (in-silico). ■ fatty acid (....) , ▲ ammonium (-..-), ● PHB (---), ♦ biomass (-.-.).

3.3. Model Validation

A fed-batch fermentation with independent pulses of fatty acids and a 50 g/L ammonium solution was employed for model validation. Magnitude and time location of pulses were defined to extend the feast phase to 24 hours and increase biomass concentration to 5,8 g/L (residual Biomass). Measured and predicted concentrations are shown in Figure 4. It can be seen that the model generates a very good prediction for carbon (R^2 0,96) and nitrogen (R^2 0,94), while for biomass (R^2 0,94) and PHB (R^2 0,99) the prediction is satisfactory with overestimations at the end of the process.

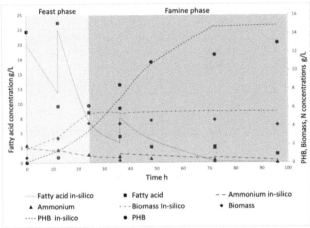

Figure 4. Profiles for model validation and optimization.

4. Conclusions

The strong change in the fraction of carbon driven to biomass production confirms that the metabolism experiments structural modifications; these modifications are consistent with a process with feast and famine phases. The C/N ratio is the key operational condition to move from feast to famine phase. The incorporation of an adaptation time during the change of phase generates an improving in the fitting, confirming that this change is not instantaneous. The satisfactory fitting for a fed-batch fermentation supports that the model is phenomenologically right.

References

K. Fang, H. Zhao, C. Sun, C.M.C. Lam, S. Chang, K. Zhang, J. Wang, 2011, Exploring the metabolic network of the epidemic pathogen *Burkholderia cenocepacia J2315* via genome-scale reconstruction. BMC Systems Biology, 5, 1, 83.

I. Fernández, 2012, Estudio del metabolismo de polihidroxialcanoatos en *Pseudomona putida*: implicaciones fisiológicas y aplicaciones en el desarrollo de bioplásticos funcionalizados. Ph.D. Thesis, Universidad Complutense de Madrid, España.

A.K. Gombert, J. Nielsen, 2003, Quantification of Metabolic Fluxes, Encyclopedia of Life Sciences, McMillan Publishers Ltda.

D.A. Méndez, 2016, Modelamiento matemático y optimización del proceso de producción de Polihidroxialcanoatos empleando la bacteria *Burkholderia cepacia B27* a partir de ácidos grasos, M.Sc. Thesis, Universidad Nacional de Colombia, Bogotá, Colombia.

J. Nandong, Y. Samyudia, M. Tadé, 2008, Multi-scale Framework for Modeling and Control of Fermentation Processes, IFAC Proceedings, 41, 2, 9673-9678.

C.A.M. Riascos, A.K. Gombert, L.F. Silva, M.K Taciro, J.G.C. Gomez, G.A.C. LeRoux, 2013, Metabolic pathways analysis in PHAs production by *Pseudomonas* with ^{13}C-labeling experiments, Computers Aided Chem. Eng., 32, 121-126.

P. Suriyamongkol, R. Weselake, S. Narine, M. Moloney, S. Sahah, Biotechnological approaches for the production of polyhydroxyalkanoates in microorganisms and plants: A Review, Biotechnological Advances, 25, 2 148-175.

A.C. Torres, 2019, Formulación de un modelo metabólicamente estructurado para optimizar la producción de Polihidroxialcanoatos (PHA) a partir de *Burkholderia cepacia*.Ph.D. Thesis, Universidad Nacional de Colombia, Bogotá, Colombia.

Sauro Pierucci, Flavio Manenti, Giulia Bozzano, Davide Manca (Eds.)
Proceedings of the 30th European Symposium on Computer Aided Process Engineering
(ESCAPE30), May 24-27, 2020, Milano, Italy. © 2020 Elsevier B.V. All rights reserved.
http://dx.doi.org/10.1016/B978-0-12-823377-1.50114-2

A Methodological Design Framework for Hybrid "Power-to-Methane" and "Power-to-Hydrogen" Supply Chains: application to Occitania Region, France

Eduardo Carrera Guilarte, Catherine Azzaro-Pantel

Laboratoire de Génie Chimique, Université Toulouse, CNRS, INPT, UPS, Toulouse, France
eduardo.carreraguilarte@toulouse-inp.fr

Abstract

This work presents a methodological design framework for hybrid Hydrogen and Methane Supply Chains (HMSC). The optimization approach of De-León Almaraz et al. (2012) has been extended to meet simultaneous demands for hydrogen and methane. The overall objective is to model and optimize HMSC in order to provide effective support for the study of deployment scenarios. The methodological framework is based on a multi-period mono-objective optimization formulation of the linear programming type in mixed variables (MILP). It is implemented in the GAMS environment and solved by using CPLEX 12. The objective to be minimized is the Total Annual Cost (TAC) of the HMSC over the entire period studied. The optimization variables involve the number and size of both production and storage units, the number of tanker truck and the flows of imported/exported hydrogen from one grid to another. The methodology is applied to the case study of Occitania (France). The costs of hydrogen and methane were obtained from the optimization strategy. The results show that hydrogen could be used as fuel for Fuel Cell Electric Vehicles (FCEV). However, synthetic methane could not be competitive without carbon tax implementation.
Keywords: Power-to-Gas, Hydrogen, Methane, MILP, Gams

1. Introduction

One response to the threat of climate change is to develop energy systems based on renewable energies (RES). However, the intermittent nature of renewable energy production remains a potential barrier to its increased penetration into the electricity mix. To meet this challenge, Power-to Gas systems (PtG) represent a promising alternative to valorize the overproduction of renewable electricity (mainly solar and wind) by transforming it into gas for different uses and, consequently, an option to decarbonize sectors such as transport and heat generation (Ademe, 2018). The scientific objective of this work is to develop a methodological framework for the deployment and design of PtG systems, involving the hybridization of hydrogen and methane supply chains: PtG implies the conversion of Power-to-Hydrogen, which can be subsequently used as an energy carrier or as a reactant for further compounds, i.e. methane. A CO_2 methanation reactor is considered here for producing synthetic methane due to the additional environmental benefit of the CO_2 reuse . It must be highlighted that if modelling and optimization of hydrogen supply chains started to gain some attention roughly ten years ago (the work developed in Almansoori and Shah (2009) can be viewed as a starting point), there is a lack of network modelling approaches considering their integration with other networks (Samsatli and Samsatli, 2019). Both pathways are therefore explored in this study, considering hydrogen both as an intermediate product to produce methane and as a final product for several market segments (industry, transport, buildings): via a methanation step, hydrogen can be converted with CO_2 to produce synthetic methane and water (Sabatier Reaction), which facilitates the use of the existing gas network (E&E consultant et al., 2014; Götz et al., 2016). Such process conversions have a typical efficiency of 65–75% for Power-to-Hydrogen (electrolysis) and 75% for hydrogen to methane (HHV) (Götz et al., 2016). This paper is divided into five sections following this introduction: section 2 presents the problem formulation; section 3 highlights the key points involved in the optimization model. The case study is the core of section 4 and some typical results are discussed in section 5. Finally, conclusions and possible future research directions are proposed in section 6.

2. Problem formulation

The contribution of this work is the development of a comprehensive optimization model, that can simultaneously determine the design and operation of hydrogen and methane value chains mainly based on renewable energies such that the Total Annual Cost (TAC) of the whole network is minimized. The problem formulation is based on the guidelines proposed by De-León Almaraz et al. (2012) for hydrogen network modelling with the following assumptions:

- The territory to be studied is divided into a set of grids.
- In each grid, production, transport and storage plants of hydrogen and methane can be installed.
- Two demands need to be satisfied, respectively for hydrogen and methane, only through Power-to-Gas systems.
- There is limited availability of primary energy and CO_2 sources.
- Transport may exist only between grids.
- A multi-period formulation is involved.

The decision variables considered are the following ones:

- Number, size, capacity, production rate and location of hydrogen and methane production and storage units.
- Number of transport units and flow of hydrogen transported between grids.
- Specification of the sources and quantity of electricity and CO_2 consumed.

So as to:

- Minimize TAC.

3. Model description

The methodological framework is based on Mixed Integer Liner Programming (MILP). The formulation aims to satisfy the demands of both energy vectors "i" (in this case, hydrogen and methane), considering the potentialities of each grid "g". The availability of energy source "e" and CO_2 "c", production type "p", storage option "s", transport option "l", for each period "t" are taken into account. The model involves a steady-state balance of mass/energy and possibilities of import of primary resources. The fundamental constraint is the resource balance, which considers all possible flows of each resource into or out of each zone (import, export, transportation). The model is solved through CPLEX 12, by using the GAMS environment, in an Intel Xeon E3-1505MV6, 3.00 GHz computer with 32 GB RAM. The superstructure of the HMSC is shown in Figure 1. Only the key points are discussed below.

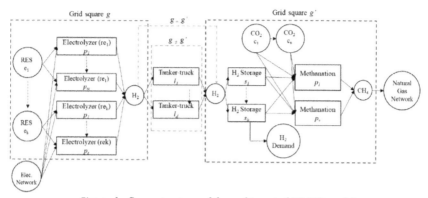

Figure 1. Superstructure of the multi-period HMSC model

3.1. Methanation facility capital cost

The methanation facility capital cost ($MFCC_t$, €/year) (see Eq. (1)) involves the Capital Cost for the installation of a methane plant ($MPCC_{pijt}$, €) as well as the Number of Facilities installed in each period (MIP_{pijgt}, year⁻¹).

$$MFCC_t = \sum_{pijg}{}' MPCC_{pijt} MIP_{pijgt} \quad \forall t \tag{1}$$

3.2. Methanation facility operational cost

Methanation facility operational cost ($MFOC_t$, €/year) is determined in Eq. (2), taking into account the operational and maintenance cost ($MMOC_{pij}$, €/kg-CH₄), the production rate of methane (MPR_{pigt}, kg-CH₄/year) and CO_2 cost (CO_2SC_t, €/year).

$$MFOC_t = \sum_{pijg}{}' MMOC_{pij} MPR_{pigt} + CO_2SC_t \quad \forall t \tag{2}$$

3.3. CO₂ source constraint

The CO_2 available amount ($CO_{2_{cgt}}$, kg-CO_2) to produce methane is calculated in Eq. (3), considering the availability of CO_2 sources on the territory (CO_2A_{cgt}, kg-CO_2/year), the imported CO_2 ($IPCO_2S_{cgt}$, kg-CO_2/year) and the consumed CO_2 during methane production ($SSF \sum_{pji} \delta_{cpj} MPR_{pijgt}$). In the last term, the amount of CO_2 needed to produce 1 kg of methane (δ_{cpj}, kg-CO_2/kg-CH₄) and a safety stock factor (SSF = 5%) for storing a small inventory of CO_2 are involved.

$$CO_{2_{cgt}} = CO_2A_{cgt} + IPCO_2S_{cgt} - SSF \sum_{pji} \delta_{cpj} MPR_{pijgt} \forall c, t, g; g \neq g' \tag{3}$$

3.4. CO₂ cost

The CO_2 cost (see Eq. (4)) depends on the total CO_2 consumption and the cost of each CO_2 source (UCO_2C_{ct} , €/kgCO₂) and is expressed as follows:

$$CO_2SC_t = \sum_{cg} UCO_2C_{ct} \times \left(IPCO_2S_{cgt} + \sum_{pji} \delta_{cpj} MPR_{pijgt} \right) \quad \forall t \tag{4}$$

3.5. Total annual cost

The Total Annual Cost (TAC_t , €/year, Eq. (5)) takes into account the investment ($MFCC_t$) and operating costs ($MFOC_t$) for methane production. A discount cost of hydrogen production ($HTAC_t$) is calculated according to (De-León Almaraz et al. (2012)) (with discount rate (r)) :

$$TAC_t = \left(\frac{MFCC_t + MFOC_t + HTAC_t}{(1+r)^t} \right) \quad \forall t \tag{5}$$

3.6. Objective function

The objective function to be minimized is expressed by Eq. (6) in which *TACtotal* represents the total cost of the HMSC over the entire period studied.

$$TACtotal = \sum_{t} TAC_t \tag{6}$$

3.7. Levelized Cost of Energy (LCOE)

Finally, the Levelized Cost of Energy ($LCOE_i$, €/MWh) is calculated in Eq. (7) for hydrogen and methane demands (E_{it} , MWh/year).

$$LCOE_i = \frac{\sum_t \dfrac{TAC_{it}}{(1+r)^t}}{\sum_t \dfrac{E_{it}}{(1+r)^t}} \quad \forall i \tag{7}$$

4. Case study

The Occitania region in the south of France that aims to become the first positive energy region in Europe by 2050 is taken as a case study. The territory is divided into 36 grids that correspond to the districts of this region. An average inter-district distance has been considered for transport purpose. Three renewable energy sources have been identified, that are solar, wind and hydro-power. Hydrogen is produced in the form of gas and cryogenic storage is assumed for hydrogen with gaseous transportation by tanker trucks. Synthetic methane is assumed to be produced from hydrogen in a catalytic methanation process (Collet et al., 2017; Götz et al., 2016). Medium sized electrolysers and catalyst reactors are taken into account. CO_2 sources stem from methanisation and gasification processes. Hydrogen demand was determined based on the expected use of fuel cell electric vehicles (FCEVs). The demand for renewable methane has been estimated from the scenarios developed by Ademe and Occitania Region (Ademe, 2018; E&E consultant et al., 2014). A three-year period is used in time discretization. The cost of electricity varies according to the source, which is a key parameter in the resulting cost of hydrogen.

5. Results and discussion

The optimal values of the decision variables and the associated costs that define the configuration of the future HMSC are shown in Table 1. This network uses tanker trucks to deliver H_2 to storage facilities. A decrease in the use of transport between grids is also observed as new hydrogen plants are installed. A high investment cost is due to the HMSC deployment in the first period. Although the involved costs progressively decrease until 2050, the LCOE of methane is yet too high to be competitive compared to natural gas cost of 45 €/MWh (ADEME, 2018). The LCOE of hydrogen reaches less than 130 €/MWh, which could be an interesting option for the transport sector (Hydrogen Europe, 2018). The HMSC configuration in 2050 can be visualised in Figure 2. The main source of electricity used is wind energy followed by solar energy. Yet, a part of the electricity is satisfied through electricity imported from the national electricity network (71.6% nuclear basis) in order to minimize costs. The main characteristics and computational effort of the solution found for the optimization model are summarized in Table 2.

Table 1. Optimization results of the hydrogen and methane supply chain

Year	2035	2038	2041	2044	2047	2050
H_2 Demand (GWh-H_2 per year)	38	54	70	86	102	117
CH_4 Demand (GWh-CH_4 per year)	98	235	438	783	1,237	1,845
Number of hydrogen production facilities	5	5	7	11	15	21
Number of hydrogen storage facilities	10	14	17	21	31	44
Number of methane production facilities	7	7	7	7	7	7
Number of transport units	9	8	5	2	2	3
TAC (M€/year)	87.69	13.38	18.24	26.42	34.62	40.45
CH_4 LCOE (€/MWh)			158			
H_2 LCOE (€/MWh)			112			
Objective function: TACtotal (M€)			**220.82**			

Figure 2. Network structure of hydrogen and methane supply chain distributed via tanker trucks in Occitania region

Table 2. Computational results for the optimization

Continuous variables	Binary Variables	Constraints	CPU (s)	GAP
44,684	23,328	338,462	5400	0.006

6. Conclusion and perspectives

In this paper, a general methodology for the design and deployment of a hybrid hydrogen and methane supply chain was developed and used for a base case study devoted to the Occitania region in France. The unit cost of hydrogen was obtained from the optimization strategy, using different parameters, for example the price of electricity. The results show that with electricity prices close to 31 €/MWh, FCEVs and synthetic methane could play an important role as energy vectors, even if their evolution will depend on the policy implemented, such as carbon tax.

The approach and results presented in this paper are useful for policy-makers as they provide insights and recommendations as to what technologies should be accelerated (hydrogen, synthetic methane) and where subsidies and other policy instruments should be applied to make the deployment of these supply chains viable. A more exhaustive methodological framework could be achieved by carrying out a multi-objective optimization, taking into account performance indicators (e.g. exergy and thermoeconomic costs) and environmental impacts (i.e. Global Warming Potential).

References

ADEME. (2018). Un mix de gaz 100 % renouvelable en 2050 ? Paris, France.

Almansoori, A., & Shah, N. (2009). Design and operation of a future hydrogen supply chain: Multi-period model. International Journal of Hydrogen Energy, 34(19), 7883–7897. https://doi.org/10.1016/j.ijhydene.2009.07.109

Collet, P., Flottes, E., Favre, A., Raynal, L., Pierre, H., Capela, S., & Peregrina, C. (2017). Techno-economic and Life Cycle Assessment of methane production via biogas upgrading and power to gas technology. Applied Energy, 192, 282–295. https://doi.org/10.1016/j.apenergy.2016.08.181

De-León Almaraz, S., Azzaro-Pantel, C., Montastruc, L., Pibouleau, L., & Senties, O. B. (2012). Design of a hydrogen supply chain using multiobjective optimisation. Computer Aided Chemical Engineering, 30, 292–296. https://doi.org/10.1016/B978-0-444-59519-5.50059-9

E&E consultant, HESPUL, & Solagro. (2014). Etude portant sur l'hydrogène et la méthanation comme procédé de valorisation de l'électricité excédentaire. Paris, France.

Götz, M., Lefebvre, J., Mörs, F., McDaniel Koch, A., Graf, F., Bajohr, S., Kolb, T. (2016). Renewable Power-to-Gas: A technological and economic review. Renewable Energy, 85, 1371–1390. https://doi.org/10.1016/j.renene.2015.07.066

Hydrogen Europe. (2018). Hydrogen, enabling a zero emission Europe. Brussels, Belgium

Samsatli, S., Samsatli, N. J. The role of renewable hydrogen and inter-seasonal storage in decarbonising heat – Comprehensive optimisation of future renewable energy value chains, Applied Energy, Volumes 233–234, 2019, Pages 854-893, ISSN 0306-2619, https://doi.org/10.1016/j.apenergy.2018.09.159.

Printed and bound by CPI Group (UK) Ltd, Croydon, CR0 4YY

03/10/2024

01040326-0010